THE APPLETON–CENTURY MATHEMATICS SERIES

Edited by Raymond W. Brink

ANALYTIC GEOMETRY
AND CALCULUS

THE APPLETON-CENTURY MATHEMATICS SERIES

Edited by Raymond W. Brink

Intermediate Algebra, Second Edition
by Raymond W. Brink

College Algebra, Second Edition
by Raymond W. Brink

Algebra—College Course, Second Edition
by Raymond W. Brink

A First Year of College Mathematics, Second Edition
by Raymond W. Brink

The Mathematics of Finance
by Franklin C. Smith

Plane Trigonometry, Third Edition
by Raymond W. Brink

Spherical Trigonometry
by Raymond W. Brink

Essentials of Analytic Geometry
by Raymond W. Brink

Analytic Geometry
by Edwin J. Purcell

Analytic Geometry, Revised Edition
by Raymond W. Brink

Analytic Geometry and Calculus
by Lloyd L. Smail

College Geometry
by Leslie H. Miller

Calculus
by Lloyd L. Smail

Solid Analytic Geometry
by John M. H. Olmsted

Intermediate Analysis
by John M. H. Olmsted

Introduction to the Laplace Transform
by Dio L. Holl, Clair G. Maple, and Bernard Vinograde

Analytic Geometry and Calculus

LLOYD L. SMAIL, Ph.D.

Professor of Mathematics
Lehigh University

New York

APPLETON–CENTURY–CROFTS, INC.

PRINTED IN THE UNITED STATES OF AMERICA

Preface

This book is intended for a combined course in analytic geometry and calculus. It is suitable both for liberal arts students and for students of engineering and science. It gives an integrated treatment of both analytic geometry and calculus, in which the fundamental ideas of calculus are introduced early. Sufficient analytic geometry is given at the beginning to serve as an adequate basis for the early parts of calculus, and additional topics of analytic geometry are presented later as the need for them in the development of the calculus arises. The important basic concepts and processes of calculus are given sufficiently early for use in science and engineering courses which use calculus methods. The treatment of the two subjects is unified, and yet they are not so "scrambled" as to be confusing to the student.

The calculus part of this book has been taken, with certain omissions and improvements, from the author's previous book on Calculus. The features which distinguished that book are preserved in the present work.

In order to assist the student to gain a real mastery of the subject, an effort has been made to give proper emphasis to the meaning of fundamental concepts, as well as to give sufficient drill in technique and applications. Greater attention than usual has been given to the careful formulation of fundamental definitions and to their display in separate italicized statements. All important theorems have also been given in separate italicized statements, and all important formulas have been stated in the form of theorems giving the conditions of validity and meaning of the symbols involved. The book also gives an improved derivation of a number of important formulas.

All important concepts, definitions, theorems and methods are illustrated by carefully selected concrete examples. A list of exercises is placed at the end of nearly every article, in order to make it easier for the instructor to make lesson assignments of any desired length. These exercise lists contain a well-balanced selection of problems, giving plenty of routine drill problems, exercises on theory, and

numerous applied problems of great variety.   Answers are given for
the odd-numbered exercises.   The earlier exercises in each list are
arranged in pairs of problems of comparable type and difficulty, so
that an instructor may assign an odd-numbered problem with answer
or a similar even-numbered problem without answer.   Special attention has been given to making the figures as instructive as possible.

After the basic ideas and methods of plane analytic geometry have
been given in the first three chapters, the fundamental conceptions
and processes of calculus are introduced.   The fundamental concepts
of the derivative and the definite integral are presented first by
analytical definition, as a limit of a certain type of quotient and as
a limit of a certain type of sum, respectively, and then are immediately illustrated by geometrical and physical interpretations.   Basic
geometrical and physical notions, such as area, volume, length, work,
liquid pressure, and moments of mass and of inertia, are defined directly as definite integrals.   The work on differentiation is at first
confined to algebraic functions.   After some simple applications of
derivatives and a discussion of differentials, chapters on the indefinite
integral and the definite integral, with applications to geometrical
and physical problems, are given before the differentiation of transcendental functions.   The essential properties of the circle and of
the conic sections are next discussed.   This is followed by the differentiation of the transcendental functions.   The topics of polar coördinates and parametric equations follow the chapter on transcendental
functions, so that calculus problems on this material may be treated
at this time.   The subject of solid analytic geometry immediately pre-
cedes the chapters on partial derivatives and multiple integrals, so
that it may be fresh in mind when using it in the calculus of functions
of several variables.

The fundamental theorem of integration, giving the relation between definite integrals and indefinite integrals, is proved analytically, without use of the derivative of the area under a curve found
on an intuitive basis, as is the usual custom.   The use of Duhamel's
theorem in setting up definite integral problems is replaced by use of
a much simpler theorem due to Bliss.   A clear distinction is made
between the concepts of multiple integrals and iterated integrals.
Improper integrals are treated in a separate chapter in order to
emphasize the distinction between this concept and that of proper
integrals.   One of the points at which the present treatment departs
from that of the author's *Calculus* is that the subject of expansion

of functions in power series by Taylor's theorem is given just after the chapter on infinite series. The formal derivation of the coefficients of these series, on the assumption of the possibility of such an expansion, is immediately followed by a derivation of Taylor's formula with a remainder, which is then applied to a discussion of the validity of a Taylor's series.

Certain articles and problems which may be omitted for a shorter course and whose omission will not disturb the continuity of the course are marked with a star. For a still shorter course, the last chapter on differential equations and parts of other chapters may be omitted.

The author acknowledges with gratitude the suggestions made by various colleagues. He expresses special appreciation to Professor R. W. Brink of the University of Minnesota for his very valuable suggestions and criticism of the work during its preparation.

L.L.S.

Contents

★ Sections marked with a ★ may be omitted.
(Section numbers of exercises are omitted in the Table of Contents)

CONTENTS

ANALYTIC GEOMETRY
AND CALCULUS

CHAPTER I

Rectangular Coördinates in the Plane

1. Introduction

Analytic geometry is essentially the study of geometric problems by use of algebraic (analytic) methods.

Elementary geometry had its beginnings with the ancient Greeks and most of its propositions were discovered by them. The first systematic treatment of this subject which we have was written by Euclid about 300 B.C.; our present textbooks of elementary geometry are merely modifications of this great work of Euclid. This development of geometry was attained by use of purely geometric methods and with almost no use of algebraic methods. Indeed, algebra was practically unknown to the ancient Greeks.

Elementary algebra originated among the ancient Hindus and was developed further by the Arabs of the earlier Middle Ages. The stage of development indicated by our present textbooks of elementary algebra was not reached historically until after the close of the Middle Ages. Thus, elementary geometry and elementary algebra developed historically as two separate branches of mathematics.

The development of geometry made little progress beyond the stage of the ancient Greeks until the seventeenth century, when algebra was first applied systematically to the treatment of geometric questions. In 1637 the French mathematician and philosopher René Descartes (1596–1650) published his great work *La Géométrie*, in which he showed how algebraic methods could be applied to the study of geometry. He thus became the recognized founder of analytic geometry. At about the same time, however, another French mathematician, Pierre Fermat (1601–1665), also discovered the idea of applying algebra to geometry systematically, but his work was not published and recognized until much later.

While analytic geometry deals with a much more extensive subject-matter than does elementary geometry, its especial value lies

1

in its *new method*, by which geometric properties of figures are treated systematically by means of algebraic processes.

The methods of solution of problems and proofs of theorems in elementary geometry involve a great many special and ingenious devices, and no general and uniform procedure is apparent. Analytic geometry, however, furnishes simple general procedures for the solution of problems and proofs of theorems, which greatly simplify the study of geometry. These new methods also enable us to solve in a simple manner many problems of geometry not considered by the ancient Greeks or problems very difficult of solution by the methods of elementary geometry. Thus, analytic geometry gives a new powerful tool for the study of old and new questions in geometry.

The essence of the new method of analytic geometry lies in its representation of points by sets of numbers and its representation of geometric figures by equations.

Calculus deals with the fundamental problem of finding the rate of change of a given function, with the inverse problem of finding a function when its rate of change is given, and with the applications of these ideas.

As a distinctly new mathematical method, calculus was founded in the seventeenth century by the English mathematician and scientist Sir Isaac Newton (1642–1727) and the German mathematician and philosopher Gottfried Wilhelm Leibnitz (1646–1716). Calculus originated in attempts to solve certain problems of geometry, such as finding the tangent to a curve, the length of an arc of a curve, the area bounded by one or more curves, the volume of a solid, and also in certain problems of mechanics, such as finding the velocity of a moving body, the work done by a force, and the center of mass of a body.

Calculus has numerous applications in many different fields. It is fundamental for the study of most further branches of mathematics, and it is extensively applied in the sciences and engineering.

2. Real Numbers

We shall assume familiarity with the system of *real numbers*, but we recall a few of the properties of these numbers.

There are two classes of real numbers, the rational numbers and the irrational numbers. A *rational number* is any number that is expressible as the ratio of one integer to another; any real number that cannot be so expressed is an *irrational number*. The rational numbers include the **positive integers** 1, 2, 3, etc., the **negative integers** -1, -2, -3, etc., the **integer zero** (0), and the **rational fractions** such as $\frac{1}{2}$, $\frac{2}{3}$, $\frac{8}{5}$, $-\frac{5}{6}$, $-\frac{11}{3}$, etc.

Any irrational number, such as $\sqrt{2}$, $\sqrt[3]{5}$, $-\frac{1}{2}\sqrt{3}$, π, etc., can be approximated to any desired degree of accuracy by rational numbers which are less than the given irrational number and also by rational numbers which are greater than the irrational number. Thus, the irrational number $\sqrt{2}$ is greater than the rational numbers 1, 1.4, 1.41, 1.414, 1.4142, etc., and is less than the rational numbers 2, 1.5, 1.42, 1.415, 1.4143, etc.

The **absolute value** of a real number a is defined as the number a itself when a is positive or zero and as the number $-a$ when a is negative. It is denoted by $|a|$. Thus, $|3| = 3$, and $|-5| = 5$.

3. Graphical Representation of Real Numbers

Lying at the foundation of analytic geometry is the geometric representation of real numbers.

On a horizontal straight line, which we call the **axis,** select any convenient point, which we call the **origin,** and denote it by O (Fig. 1).

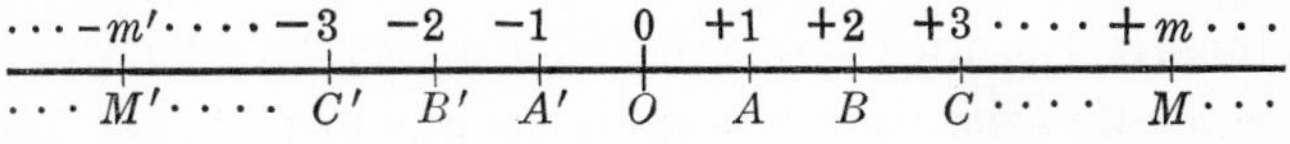

$$\cdots -m' \cdots -3 \quad -2 \quad -1 \quad 0 \quad +1 \quad +2 \quad +3 \cdots +m \cdots$$
$$\cdots M' \cdots \quad C' \quad B' \quad A' \quad O \quad A \quad B \quad C \cdots \quad M \cdots$$

Fig. 1

Select any convenient length such as that of the line-segment OA to use as the *unit of length*. We may choose either sense of direction on the axis as the positive sense; we agree to take as the *positive* sense the one to the *right*, and as the *negative* sense the one to the *left*. We proceed to represent the real numbers by points on this axis as follows.

We take the origin O to represent the number zero. Starting with O, let us lay off the unit segment OA successively to the right and to the left, locating the points A, B, C, etc., and A', B', C', etc. We then take the points A, B, C, etc., to represent the positive integers 1, 2, 3, etc., and the points A', B', C', etc., to represent the negative integers -1, -2, -3, etc. (Fig. 1).

The non-integral rational numbers may be represented by points between the points A, B, C, etc., and A', B', C', etc., at the proper proportional distances between them. Thus, the number $\frac{2}{3}$ is represented by a point two-thirds of the way from O to A, the number $-\frac{3}{2}$ is represented by a point half-way between A' and B', etc. (Fig. 2). In this way, we represent the rational numbers by points on the axis. We call these points *rational points*.

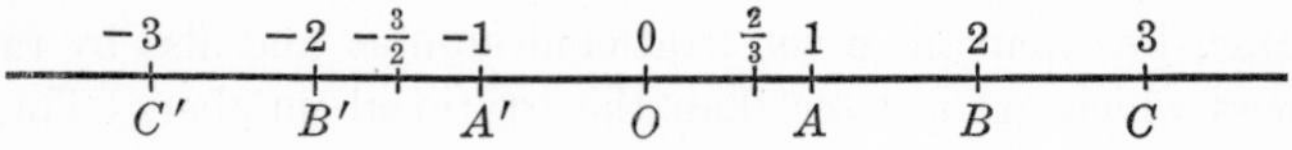

Fig. 2

It can be proved that on every segment of the axis there are points which do not correspond to any rational numbers; these points are called *irrational points* of the axis. We now assume, as a geometric axiom, that, if a is any irrational number, on the axis there is one and only one irrational point which lies to the right of all rational points corresponding to rational numbers less than a and to the left of all rational points corresponding to rational numbers greater than a. This irrational point is taken as the graphical representation of the irrational number a. For example, we assume that there is a single irrational point which lies to the right of the rational points representing the rational numbers 1, 1.4, 1.41, 1.414, 1.4142, etc., and to the left of those representing the rational numbers 2, 1.5, 1.42, 1.415, 1.4143, etc.; we say that this point represents the irrational number $\sqrt{2}$.

Now let P be any point on the axis such that the segment OP is commensurable with the unit segment OA; then it can be readily shown that there is a single rational number determined by OP, and we say that this rational number represents the point P. If P' is any point on the axis such that the segment OP' is incommensurable with the unit segment OA, by use of a geometric axiom concerning the continuity of a straight line, it can be shown that the segment OP' determines a single irrational number, and we say that this irrational number represents the point P'. Hence:

To any real number there corresponds a single point on the axis, and conversely, to any point of the axis there corresponds a single real number.

We have thus established a *one-to-one correspondence* between the set of all real numbers and the set of all points on the axis.

If any real number x is represented on the axis by the point P (Fig. 3), we call x the **coördinate** of the point P with respect to the axis of real numbers. In terms of the chosen unit-segment, the *distance* OP or the **length** OP is defined as $|x|$, the absolute value of x.

The relation of order (or inequality) between real numbers is shown graphically as follows: If $a < b$ (a is less than b), then the point representing a is to the left of the point representing b; if $a' > b'$ (a' is greater than b'), the point representing a' is to the right of the point representing b'.

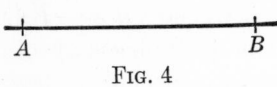

Fig. 3

It should be noted that a double inequality $a < b < c$ means that $a < b$ *and* $b < c$; also, that $|x| < r$ is equivalent to $-r < x < r$, when $r > 0$.

4. Directed Line-Segments; Directed Distances

A **line-segment** is the portion of a straight line bounded by two points of the line (Fig. 4). A line-segment bounded by two points A and B may be thought of as generated by the motion of a point from A to B or from B to A. In the first case, we denote the segment by $\overrightarrow{AB}$, in the second case by

Fig. 4

$\overrightarrow{BA}$. In the segment $\overrightarrow{AB}$, the point A is called the *initial point* and B the *terminal point* of the segment; in the segment $\overrightarrow{BA}$, the initial and terminal points are reversed. The two segments $\overrightarrow{AB}$ and $\overrightarrow{BA}$ have the same length and lie on the same straight line, but they are said to *differ in sense* or to *have opposite senses*.

Line-segments (such as $\overrightarrow{AB}$ and $\overrightarrow{BA}$) in which opposite senses are distinguished are called **directed line-segments**.

To distinguish between two directed line-segments, as $\overrightarrow{AB}$ and $\overrightarrow{BA}$, which have opposite senses but the same length and lie on the same straight line, we give them *opposite algebraic signs* $+$ and $-$. One of the two segments may be chosen arbitrarily to be the one with the positive sense; the one with the negative sense is then determined. We call each of these directed segments the *negative* of the other, and we write $\overrightarrow{BA} = -\overrightarrow{AB}$ and $\overrightarrow{AB} = -\overrightarrow{BA}$.

On a given straight *line* there are two opposite *senses*; when these are distinguished from each other, the line is called a **directed line**.

One of these senses may be indicated as positive and the other as negative; the positive sense is usually indicated by an arrow-head.

When a directed line-segment lies on a directed line, the positive sense of the segment must agree with the positive sense of the line.

Using the idea of representing opposite senses by plus and minus signs, we may generalize the notion of *distance* or *length* of a line-segment as follows:

The **directed distance** *from a point A to a point B or the* **directed length** *of the segment $\overrightarrow{AB}$ is defined as the real number whose absolute value is the same as the length of the line-segment AB and whose algebraic sign is the same as that of the directed line-segment $\overrightarrow{AB}$. It will be denoted by $\overline{AB}$.*

It is necessary to distinguish between the directed distance $\overline{AB}$ (from A to B) and the directed distance $\overline{BA}$ (from B to A). The one is the negative of the other, so that $\overline{BA} = -\overline{AB}$ and $\overline{AB} = -\overline{BA}$.

Now let us consider the relation between the three line-segments determined by any three points A, B and C on a straight line. There are six possible cases to be distinguished; see Fig. 5. We consider the directed distances $\overline{AB}$, $\overline{BC}$ and $\overline{AC}$.

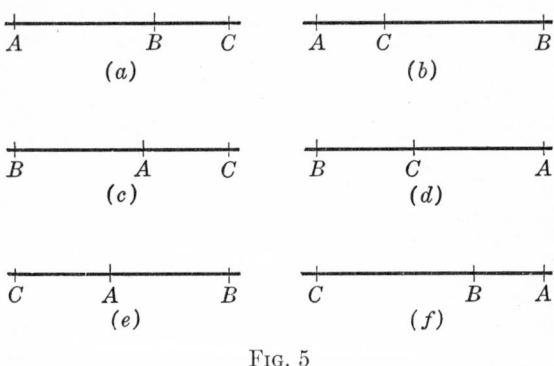

Fig. 5

In (a), $\overline{AB} + \overline{BC} = \overline{AC}$, directly, since all of the segments have the same sense.

In (b), we have $\overline{AB} + \overline{BC} = \overline{AB} - \overline{CB} = \overline{AC}$.

In (c), $\overline{AB} + \overline{BC} = -\overline{BA} + \overline{BC} = \overline{BC} - \overline{BA} = \overline{AC}$.

In (d), $\overline{AB} + \overline{BC} = -\overline{BA} + \overline{BC} = -(\overline{BA} - \overline{BC}) = -\overline{CA} = \overline{AC}$.

In (e), $\overline{AB} + \overline{BC} = \overline{AB} - \overline{CB} = -(\overline{CB} - \overline{AB}) = -\overline{CA} = \overline{AC}$.

In (f), $\overline{AB} + \overline{BC} = -\overline{BA} - \overline{CB} = -(\overline{CB} + \overline{BA}) = -\overline{CA} = \overline{AC}$.

In every case, we obtain the same result: $\overline{AB} + \overline{BC} = \overline{AC}$.   Hence, we have the following fundamental theorem:

If A, B and C are any three points on a straight line, in any order, then

(1) $$\overline{AB} + \overline{BC} = \overline{AC},$$

where $\overline{AB}$, $\overline{BC}$ and $\overline{AC}$ denote directed distances.

It is evident that formula (1) may be extended to the case of any number of points on a straight line, in any order, thus:

$$\overline{AB} + \overline{BC} + \overline{CD} + \overline{DE} + \overline{EF} = \overline{AF}.$$

We shall use the term *length* or *distance* (or undirected distance) without further qualification to mean the *positive* number defined in § 3.

5. Rectangular Coördinates of a Point in a Plane

The *coördinates* of a point are numbers which determine the position of the point with respect to some framework of reference.

One simple method of specifying the position of a point in a plane is to use its distances from two perpendicular lines in the plane.

Let $X'X$ and $Y'Y$ (Fig. 6) be two perpendicular straight lines, called the **X-axis** and **Y-axis**, respectively, and let their intersection be the point O, called the **origin.** The X-axis is usually drawn horizontally and the Y-axis vertically. These axes are called *rectangular axes*.

The axes $X'X$ and $Y'Y$ divide the plane into four **quadrants,**

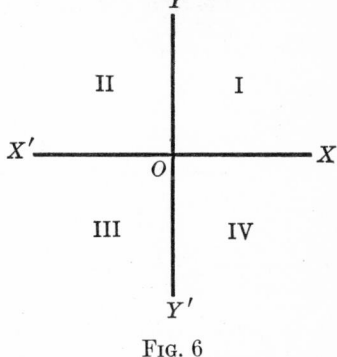

Fig. 6

which are numbered in the counter-clockwise direction from the upper right-hand one, as in Fig. 6.

We shall consider directed distances along or parallel to the X-axis as positive when they have the sense from left to right and negative when their sense is from right to left, and directed distances along or parallel to the Y-axis as positive when they have the sense from below upward and negative when their sense is from above downward.

Taking two rectangular axes $X'X$ and $Y'Y$ as reference lines, let P be any point in the plane of these axes. From P draw lines PM and PN perpendicular to the axes $X'X$ and $Y'Y$ respectively (Fig. 7). Then the position of P is determined by the directed distances $\overline{NP}$ and $\overline{MP}$, which may then be taken as coördinates of P. The coördinates $\overline{NP}$ and $\overline{MP}$ are named as follows:

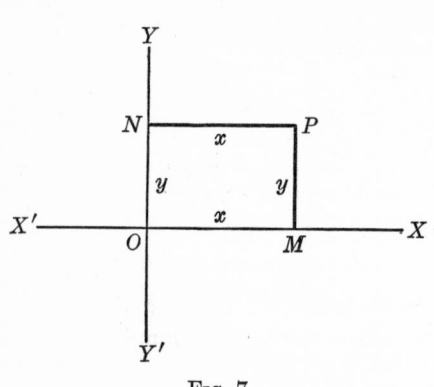

Fig. 7

*The directed distance $\overline{NP}$ of the point P from the Y-axis is called the **abscissa** of P, and the directed distance $\overline{MP}$ of the point P from the X-axis is called the **ordinate** of P.*

If a point is on the Y-axis, its abscissa is 0; *if the point is on the X-axis, its ordinate is* 0. The origin O then has the abscissa 0 and ordinate 0.

Together, the abscissa and ordinate of a point are called its ***rectangular coördinates.****

The abscissa of a point is usually denoted in general by x and the ordinate by y. A point whose abscissa is x and whose ordinate is y is usually denoted by the symbol (x, y), in which the abscissa x is always written first.

It should be noted that the abscissa and ordinate of a point P may be represented by the directed distances $\overline{OM}$ and $\overline{MP}$ respectively (Fig. 7). This is generally the way in which the rectangular coördinates are visualized in practice.

---

* Rectangular coördinates are sometimes called *rectangular Cartesian coördinates*, after the latinized form, Cartesius, of the name of Descartes, the founder of analytic geometry.

When a point in a plane is located by means of its coördinates, it is said to be *plotted*. The plotting of points in rectangular coördinates is much facilitated by the use of *rectangular-coördinate paper* (also called cross-section paper or squared paper), which is ruled into small squares (Fig. 8).

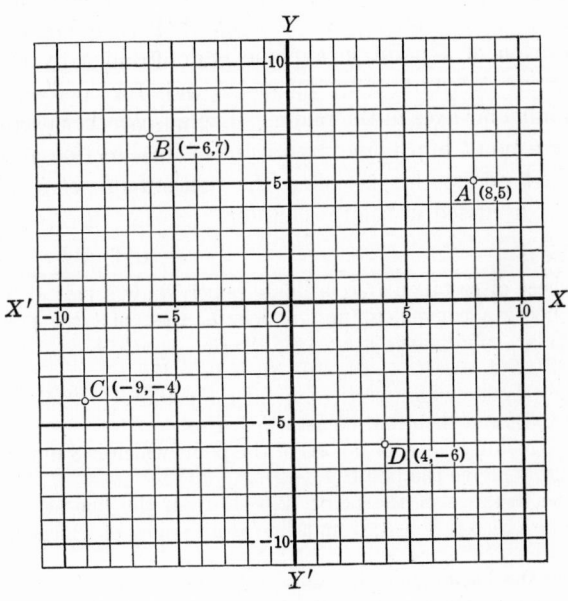

FIG. 8

EXAMPLE. Fig. 8 shows the points $A(8, 5)$, $B(-6, 7)$, $C(-9, -4)$ and $D(4, -6)$ plotted on rectangular coördinate paper.

The algebraic signs of the rectangular coördinates of points in the various quadrants are shown in the following table, which can be readily verified:

Quadrant	I	II	III	IV
Abscissa x	+	−	−	+
Ordinate y	+	+	−	−

It will be noted that the algebraic signs of the rectangular coördinates determine the quadrant in which the point lies, while the absolute values of the coördinates determine the position of the point in the quadrant.

The method of rectangular coördinates establishes a one-to-one correspondence between the points of a plane and the pairs of real numbers. That is, *to each pair of real numbers, there is a single point in the plane, and to each point of the plane, there is a single pair of real numbers.*

The position of a point in a plane is determined by the method of rectangular coördinates by means of its directed distances from two perpendicular axes in the plane. There is another useful method of locating a point in a plane, by means of its direction and distance from a fixed point; this is called the method of *polar coördinates*, and will be discussed in a later chapter.

6. Exercises

1. On a sheet of rectangular coördinate paper, draw a pair of rectangular axes, choose a convenient unit of length, then plot the points whose rectangular coördinates are: $A(2, 3)$, $B(1, 1)$. $C(-3, 2)$, $D(-2, -3)$, $E(3, -2)$, $F(4, 0)$, $G(-4, 0)$, $H(0, 3)$, $K(0, -4)$.
2. Plot the triangle whose vertices are at the points $A(-3, 5)$, $B(-3, -2)$ and $C(2, 3)$, and then find its area.
3. Find the rectangular coördinates of the point which is 3 units to the left and 4 units above the point $(1, -2)$.
4. Find the distance of the point $(2, -4)$ from the line at all points of which the abscissa is -3; from a line at all points of which the ordinate is 2.
5. Describe the location of all points: (*a*) whose abscissas have the value -2; (*b*) whose ordinates have the value 6.
6. Where does a point lie if: (*a*) both of its rectangular coördinates are positive; (*b*) both coördinates are negative; (*c*) its abscissa is positive and its ordinate is negative?
7. Where do all the points lie whose abscissas and ordinates are equal?
8. Where do all the points lie whose abscissas have the same absolute value as their ordinates but opposite signs?
9. A line-segment with one end at the point $(-3, 2)$ is bisected at the origin; what are the coördinates of the other end of the segment?
10. A square whose side is 6 has its diagonals lying along the coördinate axes; what are the coördinates of its vertices?
11. An isosceles triangle with altitude 8 has its base vertices at $(-2, -4)$ and $(4, -4)$; find the coördinates of its third vertex.
12. Three vertices of a rectangle are $(3, 4)$, $(3, -2)$ and $(-1, -2)$; find the coördinates of its fourth vertex.
13. What are the coördinates of the fourth vertex of a parallelogram which has three vertices at $(2, 1)$, $(5, 4)$ and $(4, 7)$?
14. If three vertices of a parallelogram are at $(0, 0)$, $(a, 0)$ and (b, c), what are the coördinates of the fourth vertex?

15. Find the distance from the origin: (*a*) to the point $(3, 4)$; (*b*) to the point $(-4, 5)$.

16. If A, B, C and D are any four points on a straight line, show that

$$\overline{AB} + \overline{BC} + \overline{CD} + \overline{DA} = 0,$$

where the symbols on the left denote directed distances.

7. Projections

*The **projection** of a point P on a straight line l is the point M which is the foot of the perpendicular from P to l.*

*The **projection** of a line-segment P_1P_2 on a straight line l is the line-segment M_1M_2, where M_1 and M_2 are the projections of the points P_1 and P_2 on l* (Fig. 9).

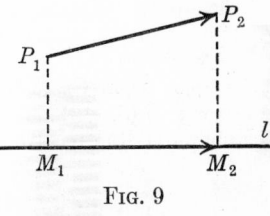

Let us investigate the projections of the segment $\overrightarrow{P_1P_2}$ on a set of rectangular coördinate axes. In Fig. 10, let M_1 and M_2 be the projections of P_1 and P_2 on the X-axis, and let N_1 and N_2 be their projec-

Fig. 9

tions on the Y-axis. Then $\overrightarrow{M_1M_2}$ and $\overrightarrow{N_1N_2}$ are the directed projec-

tions of the segment $\overrightarrow{P_1P_2}$ on the X- and Y-axes, respectively.

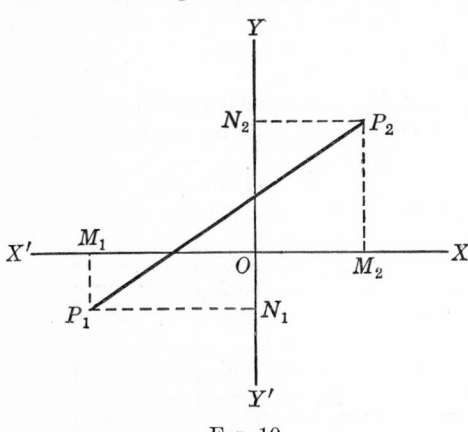

Whatever the positions of M_1 and M_2 on the X-axis, by formula (1) of § 4, we have

$$\overline{M_1M_2} = \overline{M_1O} + \overline{OM_2}$$
$$= -\overline{OM_1} + \overline{OM_2}.$$

Let the coördinates of P_1 and P_2 be (x_1, y_1) and (x_2, y_2), so that

$$\overline{OM_1} = x_1, \overline{OM_2} = x_2.$$

Therefore,

$$\overline{M_1M_2} = -x_1 + x_2$$
$$= x_2 - x_1.$$

Fig. 10

Similarly, we have

$$\overline{N_1N_2} = \overline{N_1O} + \overline{ON_2} = -\overline{ON_1} + \overline{ON_2} = -y_1 + y_2 = y_2 - y_1.$$

Therefore, the directed lengths of the projections of $\overrightarrow{P_1P_2}$ on the X- and Y-axes are $x_2 - x_1$ and $y_2 - y_1$ respectively. It is evident that these results hold whether P_1P_2 is parallel to one of the coördinate axes or is not; that is, they hold for *all* positions of P_1 and P_2. We may state the conclusion thus:

The directed lengths of the projections on the X-axis and on the Y-axis of the directed line-segment $\overrightarrow{P_1P_2}$ joining the points $P_1(x_1, y_1)$ and $P_2(x_2, y_2)$ are equal to $x_2 - x_1$ and $y_2 - y_1$ respectively.

8. Exercises

1. Find the directed lengths of the projections on the coördinate axes of each of the line-segments $\overrightarrow{P_1P_2}$, when P_1 and P_2 are respectively the points: (a) $(3, 2)$ and $(7, 5)$; (b) $(-3, 4)$ and $(4, -3)$; (c) $(-5, 2)$ and $(-2, 6)$; (d) $(3, -3)$ and $(7, 6)$.
2. Proceed as in Exercise 1 with: (a) $(2, 3)$ and $(6, 8)$; (b) $(-4, -2)$ and $(2, 3)$; (c) $(5, -3)$ and $(-2, 1)$; (d) $(3, 4)$ and $(-4, -5)$.
3. Show that the rectangular coördinates x and y of a point P may be regarded as the directed lengths of the projections of $\overrightarrow{OP}$ on the X- and Y-axes, respectively.
4. Plot the points $A(-3, 4)$, $B(2, 6)$, $C(7, 1)$ and $D(4, -3)$, draw the broken line $ABCD$ and the segment AD; then compare the sum of the directed lengths of the projections on the X-axis of the segments $\overrightarrow{AB}$, $\overrightarrow{BC}$ and $\overrightarrow{CD}$ with that of $\overrightarrow{AD}$. Does this result suggest a general theorem?

9. Distance Between Two Points

Many problems in geometry involve lengths of line-segments. In order to be able to apply the method of coördinates to such problems, we need a formula for *length* in terms of coördinates.

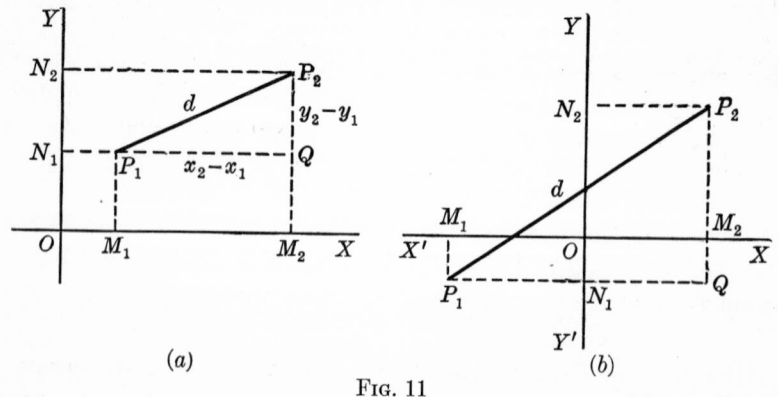

(a) (b)

Fig. 11

Let $P_1(x_1, y_1)$ and $P_2(x_2, y_2)$ be any two given points such that the line P_1P_2 is not parallel to either coördinate axis. Let their projections on the X-axis be M_1 and M_2 and on the Y-axis N_1 and N_2 (Fig. 11), and let Q be the intersection of N_1P_1 and M_2P_2. Denote the length P_1P_2 by d. In the right triangle P_1QP_2, by the Pythagorean theorem of geometry, we have

$$(a) \qquad (P_1P_2)^2 = (P_1Q)^2 + (QP_2)^2.$$

But by § 7, $\quad (P_1Q)^2 = (M_1M_2)^2 = (\overline{M_1M_2})^2 = (x_2 - x_1)^2,$ and $(QP_2)^2 = (N_1N_2)^2 = (\overline{N_1N_2})^2 = (y_2 - y_1)^2.$ Therefore,

$$d^2 = (P_1P_2)^2 = (x_2 - x_1)^2 + (y_2 - y_1)^2,$$

from which we get

$$(b) \qquad d = \sqrt{(x_2 - x_1)^2 + (y_2 - y_1)^2}.$$

This formula gives the undirected length P_1P_2 if we take, as indicated, the positive sign with the radical.*

If P_1 and P_2 are in such positions that the line P_1P_2 is parallel to the X-axis (Fig. 12 (a)), then $y_2 = y_1$, and, by § 7, we have

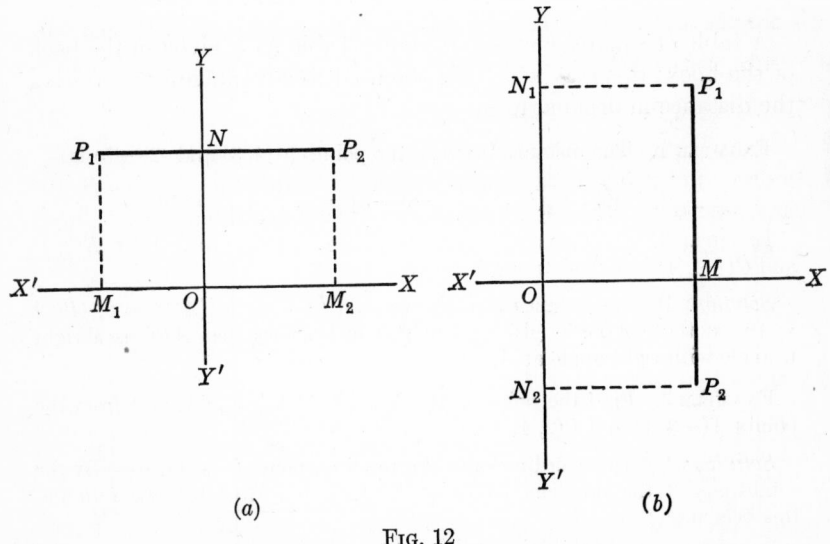

(a) (b)

Fig. 12

---

* Remember that the radical symbol $\sqrt{a}$ is *defined* to mean the *positive* square root of a when a is positive.

$\overline{P_1P_2} = \overline{M_1M_2} = x_2 - x_1$ for the directed distance. The undirected distance P_1P_2 is therefore given by

$$(c) \qquad\qquad d = P_1P_2 = |x_2 - x_1|.$$

This result is readily seen to be a special case of formula (b) when $y_2 - y_1 = 0$. Similarly, if P_1P_2 is parallel to the Y-axis (Fig. 12 (b)), then $x_2 = x_1$, and we have in this case,

$$(d) \qquad\qquad d = P_1P_2 = |y_2 - y_1|.$$

This is a special case of formula (b) when $x_2 - x_1 = 0$.

We have now found that, for all positions of the points P_1 and P_2, the distance P_1P_2 is given by formula (b); that is:

The distance d between the points $P_1(x_1, y_1)$ and $P_2(x_2, y_2)$ is given by the formula

$$(2) \qquad\qquad d = \sqrt{(x_2 - x_1)^2 + (y_2 - y_1)^2}.$$

Note the symmetry of this formula in the x's and y's.

Since $(x_2 - x_1)^2 = (x_1 - x_2)^2$ and $(y_2 - y_1)^2 = (y_1 - y_2)^2$, the distance formula may equally well be written

$$(e) \qquad\qquad d = \sqrt{(x_1 - x_2)^2 + (y_1 - y_2)^2}.$$

A table of squares and square roots (Table A) is given in the back of the book; this may sometimes be used to advantage in expressing the distance in decimal form.

EXAMPLE 1. The distance between the points $(-4, 3)$ and $(2, -5)$ is

$$d = \sqrt{[2 - (-4)]^2 + [-5 - 3]^2} = \sqrt{6^2 + 8^2} = 10.$$

EXAMPLE 2. Show that the triangle whose vertices are $A(1, 2)$, $B(3, 4)$ and $C(-1, 4)$ is a right triangle.

Solution: By the distance formula, we find $(AB)^2 = 8$, $(AC)^2 = 8$, $(BC)^2 = 16$, so that $(AB)^2 + (AC)^2 = (BC)^2$, which shows that ABC is a right triangle with right angle at A.

EXAMPLE 3. Find the point on the X-axis which is equidistant from the points $A(-3, 1)$ and $B(2, 4)$.

Solution: Let the coördinates of the required point P be $(x, 0)$. By the conditions of the problem, $(AP)^2 = (BP)^2$, and by the distance formula, this becomes

$$(x + 3)^2 + (-1)^2 = (x - 2)^2 + (-4)^2,$$

from which we find $x = 1$. Hence, the required point is $(1, 0)$.

10. Exercises

In most of the following problems a figure should be drawn with care.

1. State the distance formula (2) in words.
2. Write out the formula for the distance between the origin and the point (x, y).
3. Find the distance between each of the following pairs of points: (a) $(2, 3)$ and $(5, 7)$; (b) $(2, 5)$ and $(-3, -7)$; (c) $(-3, 2)$ and $(-1, -5)$.
4. Find the distance between each of the following pairs of points: (a) $(6, 8)$ and $(2, 5)$; (b) $(-4, -6)$ and $(4, 9)$; (c) $(3, -2)$ and $(-2, 4)$.
5. Find the distance between the points $(2, 3)$ and $(-3, 5)$, correct to 2 decimal places.
6. How far from the origin is the point $(4, 3)$? the point $(3, -2)$?
7. Find the lengths of the sides and the lengths of the diagonals of the quadrilateral whose vertices are $(3, 2)$, $(-2, 6)$, $(-5, -2)$ and $(2, -7)$.
8. Find the perimeter of the triangle whose vertices are $(2, 3)$, $(-2, 0)$ and $(1, -4)$.
9. Show that the triangle whose vertices are $(-1, 2)$, $(4, -3)$ and $(5, 3)$ is an isosceles triangle.
10. Show that the triangle whose vertices are $(2, 2)$, $(-2, -2)$ and $(2\sqrt{3}, -2\sqrt{3})$ is an equilateral triangle.
11. Show that the triangle whose vertices are $(-6, 2)$, $(5, -1)$ and $(4, 4)$ is a right triangle.
12. Show that the triangle with vertices at $(1, 8)$, $(3, 2)$ and $(9, 4)$ is an isosceles right triangle, and find its area.
13. Show that the points $(-4, -2)$, $(2, 0)$, $(8, 6)$ and $(2, 4)$ are the vertices of a parallelogram; also find the lengths of its diagonals.
14. Show that the points $(8, 5)$, $(-4, -11)$ and $(-6, 3)$ lie on a circle with center at $(2, -3)$; find its radius.
15. Show that the point $(-3, 11)$ lies on the perpendicular bisector of the line-segment joining the points $(-2, -1)$ and $(6, 3)$.
16. Find the coördinates of the point on the Y-axis which is equidistant from the points $(-3, -5)$ and $(2, 4)$.
17. Express by an equation the fact that the point $P(x, y)$ is always at a distance 4 from the point $(-1, 2)$. What can you say about the location of the point P?
18. Express by an equation the fact that the point $P(x, y)$ is always equidistant from the points $(-4, -1)$ and $(2, -5)$. What is the location of the point P?

11. Mid-Point of a Line-Segment

Let $P_1(x_1, y_1)$ and $P_2(x_2, y_2)$ be any two points, and let $P(x, y)$ denote the mid-point of the segment P_1P_2. Let M_1, M_2 and M be the projections on the X-axis of the points P_1, P_2 and P respectively, and let N_1, N_2 and N be the corresponding projections on the Y-axis (Fig. 13). Let Q and Q_2 be the intersections of P_1N_1 with MP

and M_2P_2 respectively. Since P is the mid-point of P_1P_2, it follows (from similar triangles) that M is the mid-point of M_1M_2. Now

$$\overline{OM} = \overline{OM_1} + \overline{M_1M} = \overline{OM_1} + \tfrac{1}{2}\,\overline{M_1M_2};$$

but $\overline{OM} = x,\ \overline{OM_1} = x_1,\ \overline{M_1M_2} = x_2 - x_1$

(by § 7), hence

$$x = \overline{OM} = x_1 + \tfrac{1}{2}(x_2 - x_1) = \tfrac{1}{2}(x_1 + x_2).$$

Similarly, we find

$$y = y_1 + \tfrac{1}{2}(y_2 - y_1) = \tfrac{1}{2}(y_1 + y_2).$$

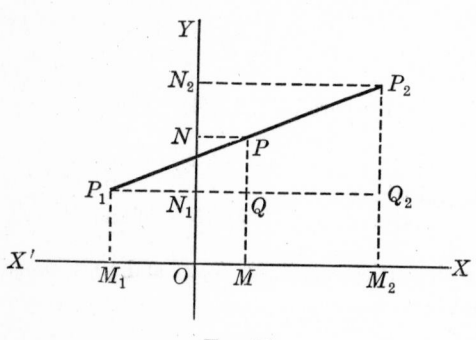

Fig. 13

In the above discussion, we have assumed implicitly that P_1P_2 is not parallel to either coördinate axis. It is readily seen that the above formulas also hold when P_1P_2 is parallel to one of the axes. Hence:

The coördinates of the mid-point P of the line-segment joining the points $P_1(x_1, y_1)$ and $P_2(x_2, y_2)$ are given by the formulas

(3) $$x = \tfrac{1}{2}\,(x_1 + x_2), \qquad y = \tfrac{1}{2}\,(y_1 + y_2).$$

Note the symmetry in the formulas (3): the second equation may be written down from the first by merely replacing each x by the corresponding y.

EXAMPLE 1. The coördinates of the mid-point of the segment joining the points $(-3, 5)$ and $(5, -1)$ are:

$$x = \tfrac{1}{2}[(-3) + 5] = 1,\ y = \tfrac{1}{2}[5 + (-1)] = 2.$$

EXAMPLE 2. Show that the mid-points of the diagonals of the quadrilateral whose vertices are $A(2, 1)$, $B(7, 1)$, $C(9, 3)$ and $D(4, 3)$ coincide.

Solution: The mid-point of the diagonal AC has the coördinates: $x = \tfrac{1}{2}(2 + 9) = \tfrac{11}{2}$, $y = \tfrac{1}{2}(1 + 3) = 2$; the mid-point of the diagonal BD has the coördinates: $x = \tfrac{1}{2}(7 + 4) = \tfrac{11}{2}$, $y = \tfrac{1}{2}(1 + 3) = 2$. Hence, the mid-points of the diagonals coincide, and the diagonals therefore bisect each other.

12. Exercises

1. State the mid-point formulas in words.
2. Prove the mid-point formulas by use of the distance formula (2).
3. Find the coördinates of the mid-points of the line-segments joining the following pairs of points: (*a*) (2, 1) and (4, 3); (*b*) (−2, 3) and (3, −5).
4. Find the coördinates of the mid-points of the sides of the triangle whose vertices are: $A(4, 5)$, $B(−6, 3)$ and $C(−4, −7)$.
5. The mid-point of a line-segment is (−1, 2); one end of the segment is (−5, −3). Find the coördinates of the other end of the segment.
6. Do the diagonals of the quadrilateral whose vertices are $A(−1, 3)$, $B(4, 6)$, $C(3, −2)$ and $D(−2, −1)$ bisect each other?
7. Find the lengths of the medians of the triangle whose vertices are $A(−5, 2)$, $B(2, 3)$ and $C(4, −5)$. (A *median* of a triangle is a line-segment joining any vertex of the triangle to the mid-point of the opposite side.)
8. Find the center and radius of the circle having the segment from (−4, −2) to (2, 4) as a diameter.
9. Draw the quadrilateral whose vertices are $A(5, 7)$, $B(−3, 4)$, $C(−6, −9)$ and $D(7, −4)$. Find the coördinates of the mid-points of the line-segments joining the mid-points of opposite sides and also of the mid-point of the segment joining the mid-points of the diagonals. Compare results. Do these suggest a general theorem?
10. Derive the mid-point formulas (3) by equating the directed lengths of the projections of P_1P and PP_2 on the coördinate axes and solving the resulting equations for x and y. [*Hint.* $x_1 − x = x − x_2$.]
11. Prove that a point P which divides the line-segment from $P_1(x_1, y_1)$ to $P_2(x_2, y_2)$ in the ratio $\overline{P_1P}/\overline{P_1P_2} = r$ has coördinates given by
$$x = x_1 + r(x_2 − x_1), \qquad y = y_1 + r(y_2 − y_1).$$
[*Hint.* Use method similar to that used in the derivation of the mid-point formulas.]
12. Write out formulas for the coördinates of the points of trisection of a line-segment P_1P_2, by taking $r = \frac{1}{3}$ and $r = \frac{2}{3}$ in Exercise 11 and simplifying.
13. Find the coördinates of the point which is three-fourths of the way from the point (2, 3) to the point (6, −5). (Use Exercise 11.)
14. Show that the medians of the triangle whose vertices are $(7, 2)$, $(−1, 4)$ and $(3, −6)$ meet in a common point which is two-thirds of the way from each vertex to the opposite side. [*Hint.* Find the coördinates of each point which is two-thirds of the way from each vertex to the middle point of the opposite side. Use result of Exercise 12.]

13. Applications to Analytic Proofs of Geometric Theorems

By means of the formulas already derived, many geometric theorems may be proved very easily. In such analytic proofs, the algebraic details may often be greatly simplified by a suitable choice of the coördinate axes with reference to the given figure. In general, the axes should be placed after the geometric figure is drawn.

EXAMPLE 1. Prove analytically that: the diagonals of any rectangle are equal in length and bisect each other.

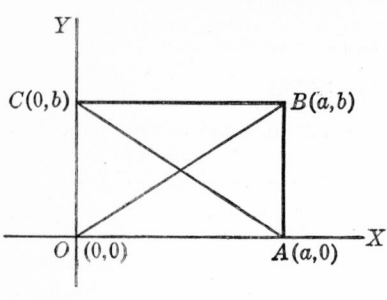

FIG. 14

Solution: Draw any rectangle, and let the lengths of its sides be denoted by a and b. Place the coördinate axes as indicated in Fig. 14, with two adjacent sides of the rectangle along the X- and Y-axes. Then the coördinates of the four vertices of the rectangle are $(0, 0)$, $(a, 0)$, (a, b) and $(0, b)$. By the distance formula,

$$OB = \sqrt{a^2 + b^2} \quad \text{and}$$
$$AC = \sqrt{a^2 + (-b)^2} = \sqrt{a^2 + b^2},$$

which shows that the diagonals are equal in length. By the mid-point formulas, the coördinates of the mid-point of OB are $x = \frac{1}{2} a$, $y = \frac{1}{2} b$, and the coördinates of the mid-point of AC are $x = \frac{1}{2} a$, $y = \frac{1}{2} b$, which shows that the two mid-points coincide and that therefore the diagonals bisect each other.

Since general letters a and b were used to denote the dimensions of the rectangle, and since the proposition evidently does not depend on the position of the axes, the proof of the theorem given above holds for all rectangles.

EXAMPLE 2. Prove analytically that: the line-segments joining the mid-points of opposite sides of any quadrilateral and the line-segment joining the mid-points of the diagonals of the quadrilateral bisect each other.

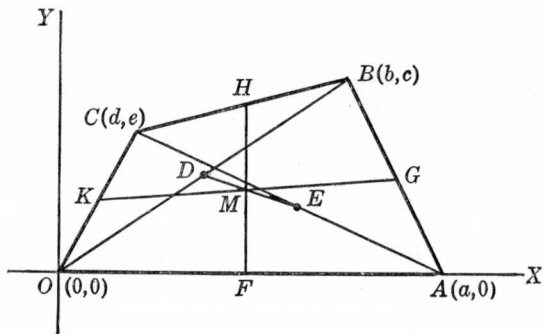

FIG. 15

Solution: Draw any quadrilateral $OABC$ and place the coördinate axes as shown in Fig. 15, denoting the vertices of the quadrilateral by $(0, 0)$, $(a, 0)$, (b, c) and (d, e), so that the figure may represent *any* quadrilateral. Then the coördinates of the mid-points of the sides are:

$$F[\tfrac{1}{2}\,a,\,0], \qquad G[\tfrac{1}{2}(a+b),\,\tfrac{1}{2}\,c], \qquad H[\tfrac{1}{2}(b+d),\,\tfrac{1}{2}(c+e)], \qquad K[\tfrac{1}{2}\,d,\,\tfrac{1}{2}\,e].$$

The coördinates of the mid-points of the diagonals are:

$$D[\tfrac{1}{2}\,b,\,\tfrac{1}{2}\,c], \qquad E[\tfrac{1}{2}(a+d),\,\tfrac{1}{2}\,e].$$

Then the coördinates of the mid-point of FH are:

(a) $\quad x = \tfrac{1}{2}[\tfrac{1}{2}\,a + \tfrac{1}{2}(b+d)] = \tfrac{1}{4}(a+b+d), \quad y = \tfrac{1}{2}[\tfrac{1}{2}(c+e)] = \tfrac{1}{4}(c+e).$

The coördinates of the mid-point of GK are:

(b) $\quad x = \tfrac{1}{2}[\tfrac{1}{2}(a+b) + \tfrac{1}{2}\,d] = \tfrac{1}{4}(a+b+d), \quad y = \tfrac{1}{2}[\tfrac{1}{2}\,c + \tfrac{1}{2}\,e] = \tfrac{1}{4}(c+e).$

The coördinates of the mid-point of DE are:

(c) $\quad x = \tfrac{1}{2}[\tfrac{1}{2}\,b + \tfrac{1}{2}(a+d)] = \tfrac{1}{4}(a+b+d), \quad y = \tfrac{1}{2}[\tfrac{1}{2}\,c + \tfrac{1}{2}\,e] = \tfrac{1}{4}(c+e).$

Comparison of the sets of coördinates (a), (b) and (c) shows that the mid-points of FH, GK and DE coincide, which proves the proposition. This proof applies to any quadrilateral since the letters a, b, c, d, e may represent any real numbers.

EXAMPLE 3. Prove analytically that: in any triangle, the sum of the squares of two sides is equal to twice the square of half the third side plus twice the square of the median to that side.

Solution: Place the triangle as in Fig. 16. If we denote the coördinates of A by $(2\,a,\,0)$ and of B by $(b,\,c)$, this will represent any triangle. (The abscissa of A was denoted by $2\,a$ to avoid fractions later.) The coördinates of the mid-point C of OA are $(a,\,0)$. BC is a median of the triangle. To prove the proposition, we must show that

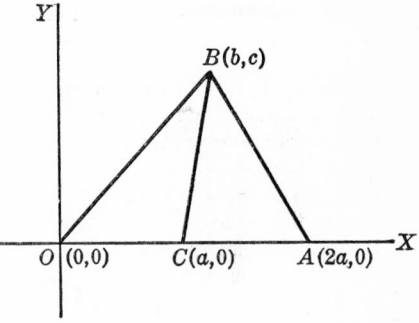

Fig. 16

(d) $$(OB)^2 + (BA)^2 = 2(OC)^2 + 2(BC)^2.$$

By the distance formula, we have

(e) $$\begin{aligned}(OB)^2 + (BA)^2 &= [b^2 + c^2] + [(2\,a - b)^2 + (-c)^2]\\ &= 2\,b^2 + 2\,c^2 + 4\,a^2 - 4\,ab,\end{aligned}$$

(f) $$\begin{aligned}2(OC)^2 + 2(BC)^2 &= 2[a^2] + 2[(a - b)^2 + (-c)^2]\\ &= 2\,b^2 + 2\,c^2 + 4\,a^2 - 4\,ab.\end{aligned}$$

Comparing these two results, we see that the relation (d) is satisfied, from which our theorem follows.

When giving analytical proofs of geometrical theorems, the figure and proof must be for general rather than special cases.

14. Exercises

Prove analytically that:

1. The mid-point of the hypotenuse of any right triangle is equidistant from the three vertices.
2. The diagonals of any parallelogram bisect each other.
3. The line-segments joining the mid-points of opposite sides of any quadrilateral bisect each other.
4. The line-segments joining the mid-points of the successive sides of any rectangle form a rhombus.
5. Two of the medians of an isosceles triangle are equal.
6. If two medians of a triangle are equal, the triangle is isosceles.
7. The line-segment joining the mid-points of two sides of any triangle is equal in length to half the third side.
8. The line-segment joining the mid-points of the two non-parallel sides of any trapezoid is equal in length to half the sum of the parallel sides. [*Hint.* Take the vertices of the trapezoid as $(0, 0)$, $(a, 0)$, (b, c), (d, c) to express the fact that the figure is a trapezoid.]
9. The diagonals of an isosceles trapezoid (i.e., one in which the two non-parallel sides are equal) are equal.
10. If the diagonals of a parallelogram are equal, the figure is a rectangle.
11. The line-segments joining the consecutive mid-points of the sides of any quadrilateral form a parallelogram.
12. The medians of any triangle meet in a single point which is two-thirds of the way from each vertex to the opposite side. [*Hint.* See § 12, Exercises 12, 14.]
13. The sum of the squares of the sides of any parallelogram is equal to the sum of the squares of the diagonals.
14. In any triangle, the square of a side opposite an acute angle is equal to the sum of the squares of the other two sides minus twice the product of one of these sides by the projection of the other upon it.
15. In any triangle, the sum of the squares of the medians is equal to three-fourths the sum of the squares of the sides.

15. Slope of a Straight Line

The direction of a straight line may be indicated by the angle that it makes with a reference line, such as the X-axis.

*The **inclination** of a straight line not parallel to the X-axis is defined as the least angle α measured counter-clockwise from the positive X-axis to the line; the **inclination** of a line parallel to the X-axis is defined to be $0°$.* The inclination is a positive angle less than $180°$, or is $0°$.

EXAMPLE 1. In Fig. 17, the inclination of the line l_1 is $\alpha = 30°$, and the inclination of the line l_2 is $\alpha = 135°$.

For many purposes the direction of a line is more conveniently expressed by the *tangent* of the angle of inclination.

*The **slope** of a straight line is defined as the tangent of its inclination α.*   It is generally denoted by m; then

(a) $m = \tan \alpha.$

It follows from the definition of slope that a line parallel to the X-axis has the slope 0, since its inclination is 0°. It also follows that *a line parallel to the Y-axis has no slope,* since

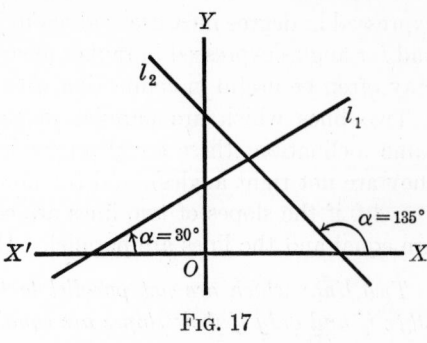

Fig. 17

its inclination is 90° and tan 90° does not exist.   But a line whose inclination is nearly 90° has a slope which is numerically very large.

The slope of a line measures the *steepness* of the line; the greater the numerical value of the slope, the steeper is the line.   The steepness of a road or hillside is often given by its slope expressed as a percentage and called its *grade*.   For example, a grade of 4% means a slope of 0.04, i.e., a rise of 4 feet in 100 feet horizontal advance.

If a line rises from left to right (Fig. 18 (*a*)), its inclination is an acute angle, the tangent is positive and hence the slope is positive; and conversely.   If the line falls from left to right (Fig. 18 (*b*)), its inclination is an obtuse angle, the tangent is negative and hence the slope is negative; and conversely.   The slope of a line may be any real number, positive or negative, or zero.

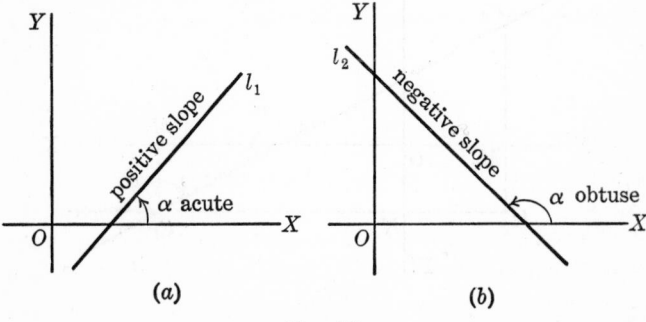

Fig. 18

EXAMPLE 2. In Fig. 18, the slope of the line l_1 is tan $30° = \frac{1}{3}\sqrt{3}$, and the slope of the line l_2 is tan $135° = -1$.

A small table of values of the trigonometric functions for angles expressed in degree measure is given in Table B (in back of the book), and for angles expressed in radian measure in Table C. Such a table may often be useful in connection with slope problems.

Two lines which are parallel to each other evidently have the same inclination; these equal angles have equal tangents (provided they are not right angles), and therefore the slopes are equal. Conversely, if the slopes of two lines are equal, the angles of inclination are equal and the lines are parallel. Hence:

Two lines which are not parallel to the Y-axis are parallel to each other if and only if their slopes are equal.

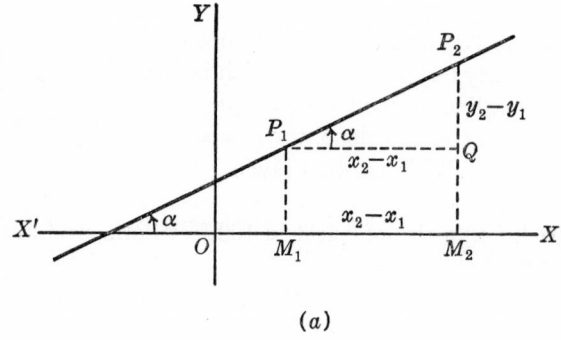

(a)

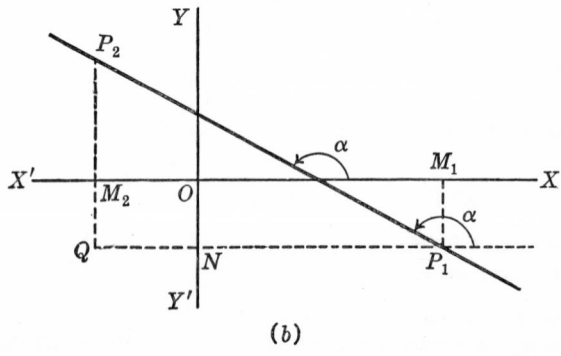

(b)

FIG. 19

16. Slope of a Line Through Two Given Points

For expressing directions in analytic geometry it is necessary to have a formula giving the slope of a line in terms of the coördinates of two points on it.

Let $P_1(x_1, y_1)$ and $P_2(x_2, y_2)$ be two given points such that P_1P_2 is not parallel to either coördinate axis. Let α be the inclination of P_1P_2, and let $m = \tan \alpha$ be its slope (Fig. 19). Draw P_1M_1 and P_2M_2 perpendicular to the X-axis and P_1Q perpendicular to P_2M_2. Then $\overline{P_1Q} = x_2 - x_1$ and $\overline{QP_2} = y_2 - y_1$. By definition of the tangent of an angle in trigonometry, we have $\tan \alpha = \overline{QP_2}/\overline{P_1Q}$, so that

$$(a) \qquad m = \frac{y_2 - y_1}{x_2 - x_1}.$$

If P_1P_2 is parallel to the X-axis, its slope is 0; but in this case, $y_2 = y_1$, and formula (a) still holds.

If P_1P_2 is parallel to the Y-axis, it has no slope, so formula (a) does not hold since m does not exist; since $x_2 = x_1$ in this case, the right-hand side would have a zero denominator, which is not permissible.

Hence:

The slope of the line joining the points $P_1(x_1, y_1)$ and $P_2(x_2, y_2)$ is given by the formula

$$(4) \qquad m = \frac{y_2 - y_1}{x_2 - x_1},$$

provided the line P_1P_2 is not parallel to the Y-axis.

Since $y_2 - y_1 = -(y_1 - y_2)$ and $x_2 - x_1 = -(x_1 - x_2)$, the slope formula may also be written $m = (y_1 - y_2)/(x_1 - x_2)$.

EXAMPLE 1. Find the slope of the line joining the points $(2, -3)$ and $(-3, 4)$; also find the inclination of this line.

Solution: By formula (4), the slope is

$$m = \frac{4 - (-3)}{-3 - 2} = -\frac{7}{5},$$

and the inclination is the angle between $0°$ and $180°$ whose tangent is $-\frac{7}{5}$, or $\alpha = 125\frac{1}{2}°$ approximately.

EXAMPLE 2. Find the coördinates of the fourth vertex D of a parallelogram $ABCD$, of which three vertices are $A(-4, 1)$, $B(-5, -4)$ and $C(1, -2)$ (Fig. 20).

Solution: Let the coördinates of the point D be (x, y). Then, by the slope formula (4), we find:

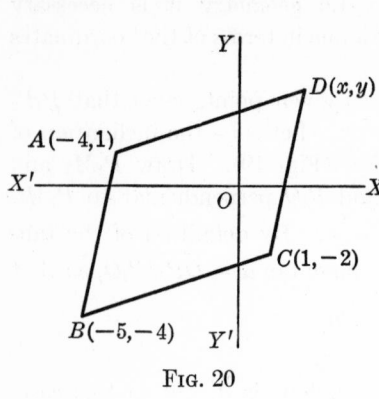

$$\text{slope } AD = \frac{y - 1}{x + 4}$$

and

$$\text{slope } BC = \frac{1}{3}.$$

Equating these slopes since AD and BC are parallel, we obtain an equation with two unknowns:

$$(b) \qquad \frac{y - 1}{x + 4} = \frac{1}{3}$$

or

$$x - 3y = -7.$$

Similarly, equating the slopes of CD and AB, we obtain the equation

Fig. 20

$$(c) \qquad \frac{y + 2}{x - 1} = \frac{5}{1} \qquad \text{or} \qquad 5x - y = 7.$$

Solving these two linear equations for x and y, we find $x = 2$, $y = 3$. Hence, the required coördinates of the vertex D are $(2, 3)$.

17. Exercises

1. Express the slope formula (4) in words.
2. Show that the slope of a line may be represented as the change (positive or negative) in the ordinate for an increase of 1 unit in the abscissa, as a point moves along the line.
3. Find the slopes of lines which have the following inclinations: (a) $45°$; (b) $120°$; (c) $35°$; (d) $155°$.
4. Find the slopes of lines which have the following inclinations: (a) $60°$; (b) $150°$; (c) $75°$; (d) $105°$.
5. Find the inclinations of lines which have the following slopes: (a) $\frac{1}{3}\sqrt{3}$; (b) $-\sqrt{3}$; (c) 2; (d) -0.8.
6. Find the inclinations of lines which have the following slopes: (a) 1; (b) $-\frac{1}{3}\sqrt{3}$; (c) $\frac{1}{2}$; (d) -1.4.
7. Find the slopes of the line-segments joining the following pairs of points: (a) $(3, 1)$ and $(7, 5)$; (b) $(-3, 2)$ and $(5, 1)$; (c) $(-2, -3)$ and $(4, 4)$.
8. Find the slopes of the sides of the triangle whose vertices are $A(-4, 1)$, $B(-1, -3)$ and $C(3, 5)$.
9. Show how to construct a line: (a) through the point $(2, 1)$ with a slope $\frac{3}{5}$; (b) through $(0, 2)$ with a slope $-\frac{2}{5}$.
10. Show that the line joining the points $A(-2, -4)$ and $B(3, 3)$ is parallel to the line joining the points $C(1, -2)$ and $D(6, 5)$.
11. Show that the points $(-2, -1)$, $(1, 0)$, $(4, 3)$ and $(1, 2)$ are the vertices of a parallelogram, by two methods.

12. Three vertices of a parallelogram are, in order, $A(8, 6)$, $B(2, 5)$ and $C(4, -2)$. Find the coördinates of the fourth vertex D.

13. The center of a circle of radius 5 is at the point $(2, 3)$. Find the coördinates of the ends of the diameter whose slope is $\frac{3}{4}$.

14. Show, by use of slopes, that the figure obtained by joining mid-points of consecutive sides of the quadrilateral $A(3, 4)$, $B(-3, 2)$, $C(-4, -5)$ and $D(5, -3)$ is a parallelogram.

18. Condition of Perpendicularity of Two Lines

Let l_1 and l_2 be any two lines perpendicular to each other but not parallel to either coördinate axis (Fig. 21), with inclinations α_1 and α_2

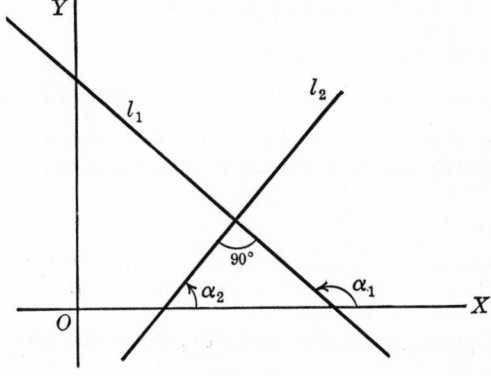

FIG. 21

and slopes m_1 and m_2 respectively; suppose that α_1 is the larger of the two angles of inclination. By elementary geometry, $\alpha_1 = 90° + \alpha_2$, and then by trigonometry,

$$(a) \qquad m_1 = \tan \alpha_1 = \tan(90° + \alpha_2) = -\cot \alpha_2 = -\frac{1}{\tan \alpha_2} = -\frac{1}{m_2}.$$

This relation $m_1 = -\dfrac{1}{m_2}$ may also be written $m_2 = -\dfrac{1}{m_1}$ or $m_1 m_2 = -1$.

Conversely, if l_1 and l_2 are two lines whose slopes m_1 and m_2 satisfy the relation $m_1 = -1/m_2$, it follows that

$$(b) \qquad \tan \alpha_1 = -\frac{1}{\tan \alpha_2} = -\cot \alpha_2.$$

By trigonometry, the angles α_1 and α_2 differ by $90°$, since the inclination is never greater than $180°$ (by definition), and therefore the lines l_1 and l_2 are perpendicular to each other.

If either of the given lines were parallel to the Y-axis, it would have no slope, and the relation $m_1 = -1/m_2$ could not hold.

Hence:

Two lines with slopes m_1 and m_2 are perpendicular if and only if their slopes are negative reciprocals of each other, that is, if

$$(5) \quad m_1 = -\frac{1}{m_2}, \quad or \quad m_2 = -\frac{1}{m_1}, \quad or \quad m_1 m_2 = -1,$$

provided neither slope is 0.

EXAMPLE. Show that the triangle whose vertices are $A(-4, 3)$, $B(-1, -8)$ and $C(2, 1)$ is a right triangle.

Solution: By the slope formula (4),

slope $AC = m_1 = -\frac{1}{3}$,   slope $BC = m_2 = 3$,   slope $AB = m_3 = -\frac{11}{3}$.

Since m_1 is the negative reciprocal of m_2, it follows that AC is perpendicular to BC, so that ABC is a right triangle with right angle at C.

19. Exercises

1. If the slope of a line is $\frac{1}{2}$, what is the slope of any line perpendicular to it?
2. Find the slope of a line which is perpendicular to a line whose slope is $-\frac{3}{4}$.
3. Find the slope of a line perpendicular to the line through the points $(3, 7)$ and $(-4, -2)$.
4. Find the slope of the perpendicular bisector of the line-segment joining the points $(-2, -1)$ and $(6, 3)$.
5. Show that the line-segment joining the points $(4, 1)$ and $(2, -3)$ is perpendicular to the line-segment joining the points $(-4, 0)$ and $(-8, 2)$.
6. Find the slopes of the sides and also the slopes of the altitudes of the triangle whose vertices are $A(3, 2)$, $B(4, -1)$ and $C(-1, -3)$.
7. Show, in two ways, that the points $A(-1, 1)$, $B(5, -2)$ and $C(-2, -1)$ are the vertices of a right triangle.
8. Show, in two ways, that the triangle whose vertices are $(1, -6)$, $(8, 8)$ and $(-7, -2)$ is a right triangle.

★ 20. Further Applications to Analytic Proofs of Geometric Theorems

EXAMPLE 1. Prove analytically that: the line-segments joining the consecutive mid-points of the sides of any quadrilateral form a parallelogram.

Solution: Place the quadrilateral as in Fig. 22 and denote the vertices by $(0, 0)$, $(2\,a, 0)$, $(2\,b, 2\,c)$ and $(2\,d, 2\,e)$; this represents *any* quadrilateral. The mid-points of the sides of the quadrilateral have the coördinates:

$$E(a, 0), \quad F(a + b, c), \quad G(b + d, c + e), \quad D(d, e).$$

The slopes of DE and of FG are:

$$(a) \qquad m_1 = \frac{e}{d-a}, \qquad m_2 = \frac{(c+e)-c}{(b+d)-(a+b)} = \frac{e}{d-a};$$

then $m_1 = m_2$, and therefore DE and FG are parallel. Similarly, the slopes of EF and of DG are:

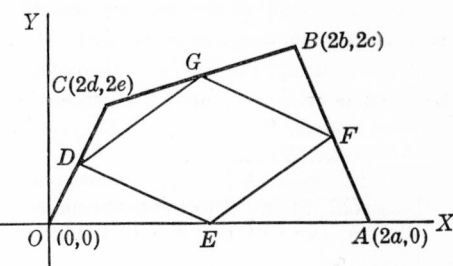

Fig. 22

$$(b) \qquad m_3 = \frac{c}{b},$$

$$m_4 = \frac{(c+e)-e}{(b+d)-d} = \frac{c}{b};$$

since $m_3 = m_4$, it follows that EF and DG are parallel. Since the opposite sides are parallel, the figure is a parallelogram.

EXAMPLE 2. Prove analytically that: the diagonals of a rhombus are perpendicular to each other.

Solution: A rhombus is a parallelogram all of whose sides are equal. Place the rhombus relative to the axes as in Fig. 23. If the coördinates of A and C are denoted by $(a, 0)$ and (b, c), then the ordinate of B is c, since $EB = DC = c$, and the abscissa of B is $a + b$, since $AE = OD = b$; this expresses the fact that the figure is a parallelogram. To express the fact that the figure is a rhombus, we must use the additional condition that $OC = OA$, so that

$$(OC)^2 = (OA)^2$$
$$= (OD)^2 + (DC)^2, \text{ or}$$

$$(c) \qquad a^2 = b^2 + c^2.$$

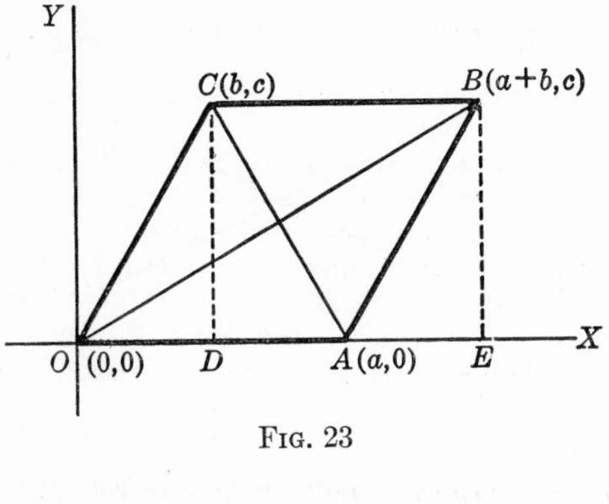

Fig. 23

By the slope formula, the slopes of the diagonals OB and CA are, respectively:

$$m_1 = \frac{c}{b+a}, \qquad m_2 = \frac{c}{b-a}.$$

Then

$$(d) \qquad m_1 \cdot m_2 = \frac{c}{b+a} \cdot \frac{c}{b-a} = \frac{c^2}{b^2-a^2}.$$

But since $a^2 = b^2 + c^2$, by (c), we have $b^2 - a^2 = -c^2$, so that (d) becomes: $m_1 m_2 = \dfrac{c^2}{-c^2} = -1$, which, by the perpendicularity condition, shows that the diagonals are perpendicular to each other.

★ 21. Exercises

Prove analytically the following theorems:

1. The diagonals of a square are perpendicular to each other.
2. The line-segment joining the mid-points of two sides of a triangle is parallel to the third side.
3. The line-segment joining the mid-points of the non-parallel sides of a trapezoid is parallel to the bases (parallel sides).
4. The line-segment dividing two sides of a triangle in the same ratio is parallel to the third side.
5. The line-segments joining consecutive mid-points of the sides of a rectangle form a rhombus.
6. If the diagonals of a parallelogram are perpendicular to each other, the figure is a rhombus.
7. The line-segment from a vertex of a parallelogram to the mid-point of one of the opposite sides trisects the opposite diagonal. (See § 12, Exercise 12.)

22. Angle Between Two Lines Whose Slopes Are Given

*The **angle from a line l_1 to a line l_2** is defined as the smallest positive (counter-clockwise) angle through which l_1 must be rotated in order to*

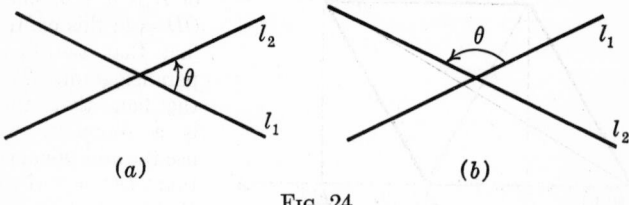

(a) (b)

Fig. 24

make it coincide with l_2 (Fig. 24). This angle is less than 180°. For this angle, the expression: *the angle which l_2 makes with l_1*, is frequently used.

Since the direction of a line is so frequently given by its slope, it is desirable to have a formula for the angle between lines in terms of their slopes. Let l_1 and l_2 be two lines neither of which is parallel to the Y-axis and which are not perpendicular to each other; let their inclinations be α_1 and α_2, and their slopes m_1 and m_2, respectively. Let ϕ be the angle from l_1 to l_2. There are two cases to consider:

case I, in which $\alpha_2 > \alpha_1$, and case II, in which $\alpha_1 > \alpha_2$ (Fig. 25).

In case I, $\alpha_2 > \alpha_1$ (Fig. 25 (a)), we have, by elementary geometry,
$\alpha_2 = \alpha_1 + \phi$ or $\phi = \alpha_2 - \alpha_1$,
then $\tan \phi = \tan (\alpha_2 - \alpha_1)$.
In case II, $\alpha_1 > \alpha_2$ (Fig. 25 (b)), we have

$$\alpha_1 = \alpha_2 + (180° - \phi) \text{ or}$$
$$\phi = 180° + (\alpha_2 - \alpha_1),$$

then $\tan \phi$

$$= \tan [180° + (\alpha_2 - \alpha_1)]$$
$$= \tan (\alpha_2 - \alpha_1).$$

In either case, by trigonometry, we get

$$\tan \phi = \tan (\alpha_2 - \alpha_1)$$
$$= \frac{\tan \alpha_2 - \tan \alpha_1}{1 + \tan \alpha_2 \tan \alpha_1}$$
$$= \frac{m_2 - m_1}{1 + m_1 m_2}.$$

Hence:

The angle ϕ from a line l_1 with slope m_1 to a line l_2 with slope m_2 is given by the formula:

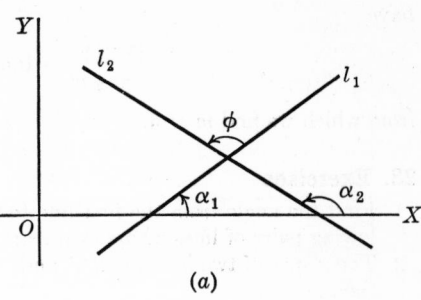

(a)

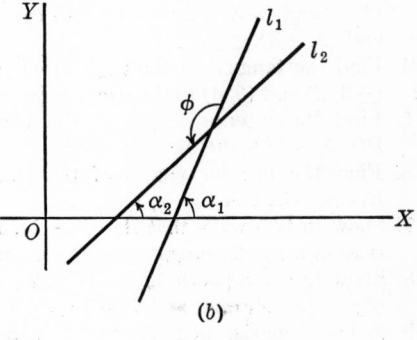

(b)

Fig. 25

(6)
$$\tan \phi = \frac{m_2 - m_1}{1 + m_1 m_2},$$

provided neither line is parallel to the Y-axis and that the given lines are not perpendicular to each other.

EXAMPLE 1. Find the angle A of the triangle whose vertices are $A(4, 3)$, $B(-4, -2)$ and $C(2, 0)$.

Solution: Let m_1, m_2 and m_3 denote the slopes of AB, BC and CA respectively. By the slope formula (4), we find

$$m_1 = \frac{-2 - 3}{-4 - 4} = \frac{5}{8}, \qquad m_2 = \frac{0 - (-2)}{2 - (-4)} = \frac{1}{3}, \qquad m_3 = \frac{3 - 0}{4 - 2} = \frac{3}{2}.$$

Then by formula (6), we get

$$\tan A = \frac{m_3 - m_1}{1 + m_1 m_3} = \frac{\frac{3}{2} - \frac{5}{8}}{1 + \frac{3}{2} \cdot \frac{5}{8}} = \frac{14}{31} = 0.452, \quad \therefore A = 24° \text{ approximately.}$$

EXAMPLE 2. If a line l_1 has the slope $\frac{1}{2}$, find the slope of a line l which makes an angle of 45° with l_1.

Solution: Let m be the required slope of the line l. By formula (6), we have

$$\frac{m - \frac{1}{2}}{1 + \frac{1}{2} m} = \tan 45° = 1,$$

from which we find $m = 3$.

23. Exercises

1. Find the angle from the first line to the second line for each of the following pairs of lines whose slopes are: (a) 2, $\frac{1}{2}$; (b) $\frac{1}{3}$, -2; (c) $-\frac{2}{3}$, $\frac{3}{4}$.
2. The slopes of two lines are 2.65 and -0.58; find the acute angle between them.
3. Find the tangent of the angle that the line-segment joining the points $(4, 3)$ and $(-3, -2)$ makes with the segment joining the points $(-5, 2)$ and $(2, -3)$.
4. Find the tangent of the angle from the line-segment joining the points $(-3, 2)$ and $(5, 4)$ to the segment joining the points $(-2, 5)$ and $(4, -3)$.
5. Find the interior angles of the triangle whose vertices are $A(3, 4)$, $B(-5, -1)$ and $C(6, -3)$.
6. Find the interior angles of the triangle whose vertices are $A(4, 1)$, $B(-4, -3)$ and $C(-2, 3)$.
7. Show in two ways that $A(-7, -1)$, $B(6, 5)$ and $C(1, -5)$ are the vertices of a right triangle, and find its acute angles.
8. Show that the points $(2, 1)$, $(-1, 2)$, $(-3, 4)$ and $(0, 3)$ are the vertices of a parallelogram, and find the angles between its diagonals.
9. A line l makes an angle of 45° with the line through $(-4, -1)$ and $(2, 3)$; find the slope of l.
10. Find the slope of a line which makes an angle of 60° with a line whose slope is 2.

24. Variables and Constants

In many mathematical problems we discuss properties of *any one* of a class of things, without specifying a particular one of them.

For example, the area of *any* triangle is always equal to half the product of its base by its altitude; the speed of *any* falling body (in a vacuum) is always proportional to the time of falling. We often say, for example, in elementary geometry, let P be *any* point on the line, or let ABC be *any* triangle, or let C be *any* circle.

*A symbol which represents **any one** of a given set of numbers or set of elements of any kind, in a given problem or discussion, is called a **variable**. The numbers or elements of the set are called **values** of the variable; the set of numbers or elements is called the **range** of the variable.*

A symbol which represents only one particular number or element, in a given problem or discussion, is called a **constant.**

EXAMPLE 1. In the expression πr^2, which gives the area of any circle of radius r, the letter r may represent any positive number, and it is therefore a variable, but the symbol π always denotes the same number, 3.1416 approximately, and therefore it is a constant.

Constants may be classified for convenience into two classes: absolute or numerical constants, and arbitrary constants. An *absolute constant* is one which represents the same number or element in all problems and in all discussions, as for example, 5 or $\sqrt{2}$ or π. An *arbitrary constant* is one which represents one particular number or element in a given problem or discussion, but which in another situation may represent another number or element.

Variables are usually denoted by the later letters of the alphabet, and constants by the earlier letters, although in applied problems a letter is often used which suggests the quantity (variable or constant) which it represents.

When the letters x, y or x', y' are used for rectangular coördinates, it will generally be supposed that they represent variables. When subscripts are used with these letters, as x_1, y_1, it will generally be assumed that these coördinates are arbitrary constants, so that the point (x_1, y_1) is an arbitrary fixed point.

An additional illustration of variables and constants is given by the following example.

EXAMPLE 2. The formula $s = \frac{1}{2} gt^2$ gives the distance s that a body will fall in a vacuum from rest in time t. The letters s and t denote variables. The letter g denotes the acceleration of gravity, which is ordinarily taken as a constant whose numerical value is approximately 32.2 when s is expressed in feet and t is expressed in seconds; g is then an absolute constant.

25. Equations and Loci

In the early part of this chapter, by means of rectangular coördinates, we have seen that a correspondence is set up between points and pairs of numbers (the coördinates). We shall now show that it is possible to set up a correspondence between certain geometric figures and equations involving variables.

If we have given an equation involving two variables x and y, this equation is satisfied by certain pairs of values of x and y but not by all pairs. If we interpret these pairs of values of x and y which satisfy the equation as rectangular coördinates of points, the corresponding points form a geometrical figure which can be taken as a graphical representation of the equation. We are thus led to the following important concept:

*The **locus** (or **graph**) of a given equation in two variables representing coördinates in a plane is the geometric figure consisting of all those points in the plane, and only those points, whose coördinates satisfy the equation.* *

The locus of an equation in two variables is usually a curve or straight line, but not always.

EXAMPLE 1. The locus of the equation $y = x$ is evidently the straight line through the origin with an inclination of 45°, since each point on this line is equidistant from both coördinate axes, and therefore the abscissa and ordinate x and y of each point of this line are equal numerically and are of like sign.

EXAMPLE 2. The locus of the equation $x^2 + y^2 = 25$ is the circle with center at the origin and radius 5, since the expression $x^2 + y^2$ gives the square of the distance of any point $P(x, y)$ from the origin (by the distance formula).

We may obtain a preliminary idea of the meaning of the locus or graph of an equation as follows. From the given equation we may find as many pairs of values of the variables as we please which satisfy the equation, by assigning values to one of the variables and then calculating from the equation a corresponding value or values of the other variable. To each such pair of numbers there corresponds a point, having these numbers as rectangular coördinates. The set of all such points constitutes the locus.

EXAMPLE 3. Consider the equation $y = x^2$. If we take $x = 1$, we find $y = 1$; if we take $x = 2$, we find $y = 4$; if $x = 3$, we get $y = 9$, etc.; if $x = -1$, then $y = 1$; if $x = -2$, then $y = 4$, etc. We may thus obtain the following table of related values of x and y from the given equation:

x	0	1	2	3	4	-1	-2	-3	-4
y	0	1	4	9	16	1	4	9	16

* The word *locus* is used in elementary geometry to mean the set of all points which satisfy a given geometric condition. It is often convenient to think of the locus as the path traced out by a point which moves in such a way as always to satisfy the given condition. Thus, the locus of a point in a plane which is equally distant from two fixed points in the plane is the line which is the perpendicular bisector of the line-segment joining the given points.

If we plot these pairs of corresponding values as rectangular coördinates, we obtain the set of points shown by the black dots in Fig. 26. Drawing a smooth line through these points, we have the curve of Fig. 26, which is the graph or locus of the equation $y = x^2$.

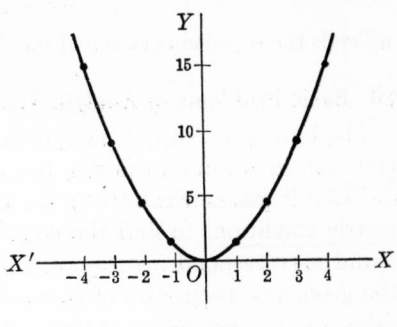

Fig. 26

Having discussed briefly the concept of the *locus of a given equation*, we now turn to a brief consideration of the converse idea of the *equation of a given locus*. Suppose that we have a locus or geometric figure which is defined by means of a given geometric condition. If we determine the position of a point on the locus by means of coördinates, the condition which defines the locus may often be expressed by an equation involving the variable coördinates of any point of the locus. We are thus led to the following important concept:

*An **equation of a given locus** is an equation which is satisfied by the coördinates of every point on the locus and by the coördinates of no other points.*

EXAMPLE 4. The equation of the circle whose center is at $(1, 2)$ and whose radius is 4 is

$$(a) \qquad (x - 1)^2 + (y - 2)^2 = 16,$$

since the square of the distance from any point (x, y) on the circle to the center $(1, 2)$ is $(x - 1)^2 + (y - 2)^2$, by the distance formula, and this must be equal to the square of the radius 4.*

EXAMPLE 5. Let it be required to find the equation of the perpendicular bisector of the line-segment joining the points $A(-4, 2)$ and $B(6, 4)$. Let $P(x, y)$ be *any* point on the given locus, then $PA = PB$. By the distance formula,

$$PA = \sqrt{(x + 4)^2 + (y - 2)^2}, \qquad PB = \sqrt{(x - 6)^2 + (y - 4)^2}.$$

Then

$$\sqrt{(x + 4)^2 + (y - 2)^2} = \sqrt{(x - 6)^2 + (y - 4)^2}.$$

* Strictly speaking, the equation (a) should be called *an* equation, instead of *the* equation, of the circle, since this equation (a) can be written in other equivalent forms. For convenience, we shall speak of any equivalent simplified form of an equation of a locus as *the* equation of the given locus.

If we simplify this equation by squaring both sides, expanding the squares of the binomials and collecting like terms, the equation reduces to

$$5x + y = 8,$$

which is the required equation of the locus.

26. Basic Problems of Analytic Geometry

The basic problems of analytic geometry are: (1) having given an equation in several variables, to find the locus of the equation and describe it geometrically; (2) having given a locus satisfying a geometric condition, to find the equation of the locus; and (3) having found a correspondence between loci and equations, to investigate the geometric properties of the loci by use of their equations, or by using the geometric properties of the loci, to shed light on the analytical relations among the variables of their equations.

The definition of the locus of an equation and of the equation of a locus is so important that we formulate it again in another form:

Fundamental principle of analytic geometry: If a point lies on a locus, the coördinates of the point satisfy the equation of the locus; and conversely, if the coördinates of a point satisfy an equation, the point lies on the locus of the equation.

CHAPTER II

Straight Lines

27. Equation of a Straight Line

A straight line may be determined geometrically in several ways, as for example: by two points, or by one point and a direction.

We may derive the equation of a straight line satisfying given conditions. There are different *forms* of the equation of a straight line, corresponding to various sets of conditions which determine the line. These various forms are called *standard forms* of the equation of a line.

We now proceed to derive, discuss and apply the various standard forms of the equation of a straight line. In this chapter and generally hereafter we shall use the word *line* to mean *straight line*.

28. Line Parallel to a Coördinate Axis

The *X-intercept* and the *Y-intercept* of a line are defined as the directed distances from the origin to the points where the line meets the X-axis and the Y-axis, respectively.

If a line is parallel to the Y-axis and has the X-intercept a

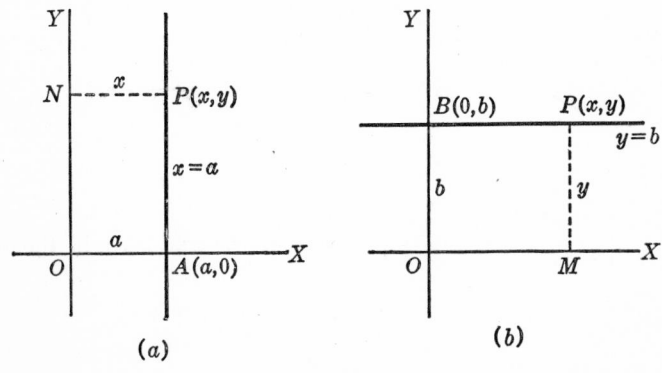

FIG. 27

(Fig. 27 (a)), it follows at once that the abscissa of any point on this line is $x = a$; and conversely, that any point with abscissa $x = a$ lies on the given line. Hence, the equation of any line parallel to the Y-axis is of the form $x = a$. In a similar way, it can be seen that the equation of a line parallel to the X-axis with the Y-intercept b (Fig. 27 (b)) is $y = b$. Therefore:

The equation of a line parallel to the Y-axis is

(1) $$x = a,$$

where a is the X-intercept of the line; and the equation of a line parallel to the X-axis is

(2) $$y = b,$$

where b is the Y-intercept of the line.

29. Point-Slope Form of the Equation of a Line

One of the simplest ways in which a line is determined and which gives rise to one of the most useful standard equations of a line is that in which the slope of the line and the coördinates of a fixed point on the line are given.

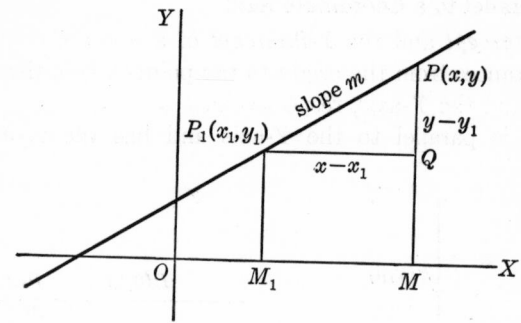

FIG. 28

Let $P_1(x_1, y_1)$ be a given fixed point on a line and let m be the given slope of the line. Let $P(x, y)$ be *any* point, other than P_1, on the given line (Fig. 28). By the slope formula, the slope of P_1P is

(a) $$\frac{y - y_1}{x - x_1} = m.$$

Clearing of fractions, we obtain

$$(b) \qquad\qquad y - y_1 = m(x - x_1).$$

That is, the coördinates (x, y) of any point on the line, other than P_1, satisfy the equation (b). The coördinates (x_1, y_1) of P_1 obviously satisfy (b). Hence, equation (b) holds for all points on the given line.

Conversely, if the coördinates (x, y) of any point P, other than P_1, satisfy equation (b), they also satisfy (a), so that P lies on the straight line through P_1 with slope m. Therefore, (b) is the equation of the given line. Hence:

The equation of a straight line with given slope m and passing through the given fixed point (x_1, y_1) is

$$(3) \qquad\qquad y - y_1 = m(x - x_1).$$

This is called the ***point-slope form*** of the equation of a straight line.

EXAMPLE 1. The equation of the line through the point $(2, -4)$ with slope 3 is

$$y - (-4) = 3(x - 2) \qquad \text{or} \qquad y + 4 = 3(x - 2).$$

This equation may also be written in the form $3x - y - 10 = 0$.

EXAMPLE 2. Find the equation of the perpendicular bisector of the line-segment joining the points $A(3, -1)$ and $B(-5, -3)$.

Solution: The coördinates of the mid-point of AB are $(-1, -2)$. The slope of AB is $\dfrac{-3 - (-1)}{-5 - 3} = \dfrac{1}{4}$; then the slope of any line perpendicular to AB is the negative reciprocal $m = -4$. The required line passes through the point $(-1, -2)$ and has the slope -4, hence its equation is

$$y - (-2) = -4[x - (-1)], \qquad \text{or} \qquad y + 2 = -4(x + 1), \qquad \text{or}$$
$$4x + y + 6 = 0.$$

The point-slope form *fails* for a line parallel to the Y-axis, since such a line has no slope; but in this case, the equation of the line is of the form $x = a$. For a line parallel to the X-axis, the point-slope form reduces to $y - y_1 = 0$, which is of the form $y = b$.

30. Slope-Intercept Form of the Equation of a Line

A special case of the point-slope form of the equation of a straight line, which is sufficiently useful to be treated separately, is that in which the line is determined by its slope and its Y-intercept.

Let a given line have the Y-intercept b and the slope m. Then the point $B(0, b)$ lies on the line (Fig. 29).   In the point-slope equation (3) of § 29, we may then take the coördinates (x_1, y_1) of the fixed point as $(0, b)$, which gives

$$y - b = m(x - 0) \qquad \text{or} \qquad y = mx + b.$$

Hence:

The equation of a straight line with slope m and Y-intercept b is

(4) $y = mx + b.$

This is called the ***slope-intercept form*** of the equation of a line.

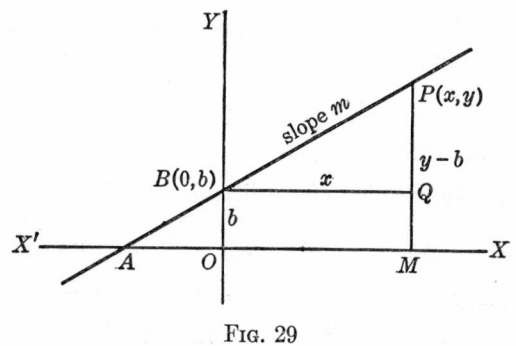

FIG. 29

EXAMPLE 1.   The equation of the line with slope $\frac{2}{3}$ and Y-intercept 4 is

$$y = \tfrac{2}{3} x + 4.$$

It should be noted that the equation of any line through the origin, except the Y-axis, is of the form

(a) $y = mx,$

since $b = 0$ for such a line.

The slope-intercept form of the equation *fails* for a line parallel to the Y-axis, since such a line has no slope and has no Y-intercept; in this case we use the form $x = a$ (§ 28).   For a line parallel to the X-axis, the slope m is 0, and the slope-intercept form becomes $y = b$, which agrees with the result in § 28.

31. Exercises

1. Write the equation of the line through the point $(3, -4)$ which is: (a) perpendicular to the X-axis; (b) perpendicular to the Y-axis.
2. What is the equation of the line which is: (a) parallel to the X-axis and 3 units above it; (b) parallel to the Y-axis and 2 units to the left of it?

3. Find the equation of each of the following lines: (a) through the point (4, 3) with slope 2; (b) through the point $(-2, 4)$ with slope $-\frac{3}{2}$; (c) through (0, 4) with slope -3; (d) through $(-2, -1)$ with inclination $135°$.

4. Find the equation of each of the following lines: (a) through the point $(4, -5)$ with slope $\frac{1}{2}$; (b) through the point $(-3, 4)$ with slope $-\frac{2}{3}$; (c) through $(-2, 0)$ with slope -2; (d) through $(5, -3)$ with inclination $60°$.

5. Find the equation of each of the following lines: (a) with slope 3 and Y-intercept 2; (b) with slope $-\frac{1}{2}$ and Y-intercept 5; (c) with slope -4 and Y-intercept -4; (d) with inclination $135°$ and Y-intercept $\frac{3}{2}$.

6. Find the equation of each of the following lines: (a) with slope 2 and Y-intercept $\frac{5}{3}$; (b) with slope -4 and Y-intercept 2; (c) with slope $-\frac{3}{4}$ and Y-intercept -3; (d) with inclination $120°$ and Y-intercept 1.

7. Find the equation of the line with Y-intercept 4, which is parallel to the line through the points $(2, 3)$ and $(-1, 5)$.

8. Find the equation of the line with Y-intercept -2, which is perpendicular to the line through the points $(5, -2)$ and $(3, 2)$.

9. Find the equation of the line through $(-3, 5)$ which is perpendicular to the line-segment joining the points $(-4, 1)$ and $(6, -3)$.

10. Find the equation of the line passing through $(2, 6)$ which is parallel to the line-segment joining the points $(-5, -3)$ and $(1, 4)$.

11. Find the equation of the line with slope 2 and X-intercept -3.

12. Derive the equation of the line with slope m and X-intercept a.

13. Describe the locus of each of the following equations:
    (a) $y - 4 = 2(x - 1)$;   (b) $y + 1 = -3(x - 2)$;
    (c) $y = 5(x - 4)$;   (d) $y = -2x + 7$.

14. Draw the lines whose equations are:
    (a) $y - 2 = 2(x - 3)$;   (b) $y + 3 = \frac{1}{2}(x + 2)$;
    (c) $y = -\frac{2}{3}(x - 5)$;   (d) $y = -2x + 1$.

15. Find the equation of the perpendicular bisector of the line-segment joining the points $(2, 5)$ and $(-4, 1)$.

16. The vertices of a triangle are $A(-4, 2)$, $B(6, 6)$ and $C(-3, -4)$. Find the equations of the perpendiculars from the vertices to the opposite sides of the triangle (the altitudes of the triangle).

32. Line Through Two Given Points

A straight line is determined by two given points. The equation of such a line may be obtained by use of the point-slope form and the slope formula for a line joining two given points.

EXAMPLE. Find the equation of the line through the points $A(4, 1)$ and $B(-2, 3)$.

Solution: By the slope formula,

$$\text{slope } AB = \frac{3 - 1}{-2 - 4} = -\frac{1}{3}.$$

By the point-slope form of the equation of a line, using A as the point P_1, we have

$$y - 1 = -\tfrac{1}{3}(x - 4) \qquad \text{or} \qquad x + 3y - 7 = 0.$$

We could equally well have taken the point B as P_1; then we get

$$y - 3 = -\tfrac{1}{3}(x + 2) \qquad \text{or} \qquad x + 3y - 7 = 0.$$

33. Intercept Form of the Equation of a Line

Let the X- and Y-intercepts of a given line be a and b respectively. Then the points $A(a, 0)$ and $B(0, b)$ are points on the line (Fig. 30).

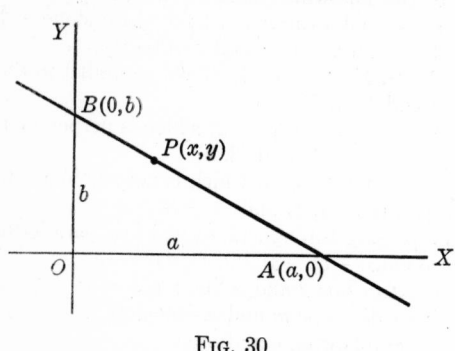

By the method of § 32 for finding the equation of a line through two points, we find that the equation of the line through A and B is

$$y - b = -\frac{b}{a} \cdot x,$$

or

$$\frac{x}{a} + \frac{y}{b} = 1.$$

Fig. 30

Hence:

The equation of the line whose X- and Y-intercepts are a and b respectively is

(5)
$$\frac{x}{a} + \frac{y}{b} = 1,$$

provided a and b are not zero.

This is called the **intercept form** of the equation of a line. It *fails* for lines parallel to either coördinate axis and for lines through the origin.

EXAMPLE. The line whose X- and Y-intercepts are 3 and -2 has the equation

$$\frac{x}{3} + \frac{y}{-2} = 1, \qquad \text{or} \qquad \frac{x}{3} - \frac{y}{2} = 1.$$

34. Exercises

1. Find the equation of each of the following lines:
   (a) through the points $(4, -2)$ and $(-2, 6)$;
   (b) through the points $(3, 2)$ and $(1, -4)$.

2. Find the equation of each of the following lines:
   (*a*) through the points $(5, 3)$ and $(1, 7)$;
   (*b*) through the points $(6, -3)$ and $(-1, 4)$.
3. Find the equations of the sides of the triangle whose vertices are $(-2, 1)$, $(3, 5)$ and $(1, -4)$.
4. The vertices of a triangle are at $(-3, 5)$, $(5, 7)$ and $(-1, -3)$; find the equations of its sides.
5. Find the equation of the line whose Y-intercept is 4 and which passes through the point $(-2, -5)$.
6. Find the equation of the line with X-intercept -3 and which passes through the point $(5, 4)$.
7. Find the ordinate of a point if its abscissa is 4 and if it lies on the line through $(3, -5)$ and $(-1, 7)$.
8. Find the equations of the medians of the triangle whose vertices are $A(-2, 1)$, $B(4, 5)$ and $C(2, -3)$.
9. Find the equations of the lines whose intercepts are:
   (*a*) $a = 4$ and $b = 3$;　　　(*b*) $a = 3$ and $b = -4$.
10. Find the equations of the lines whose intercepts are:
    (*a*) $a = 3$ and $b = 1$;　　　(*b*) $a = -5$ and $b = -1$.
11. Draw the lines whose equations are:

   (*a*) $\dfrac{x}{5} + \dfrac{y}{3} = 1$;　　　　　　(*b*) $\dfrac{x}{4} - \dfrac{y}{2} = 1$.

12. Draw the locus of each of the following equations:

   (*a*) $\dfrac{x}{4} + \dfrac{y}{3} = 1$;　　　　　　(*b*) $\dfrac{x}{2} - \dfrac{y}{5} = 1$.

35. The General Equation of the First Degree

Any equation of the first degree in the variables x and y can be written in the general form

(*a*)
$$Ax + By + C = 0,$$

where A, B and C are constants, and A and B are not both zero.

Consider *any* straight line. Every line in the XY-plane which is not parallel to the Y-axis has an equation of the form $y = mx + b$, as was shown in § 30. Every line which is parallel to the Y-axis has an equation of the form $x = a$, as was seen in § 28. Both of these equations are of the first degree in x and y. Hence, we have the important theorem:

Every straight line in the XY-plane has an equation of the first degree, in one or both variables x, y.

Now let us examine the converse of this result. Consider the general equation $Ax + By + C = 0$ of the first degree. There are two cases to be treated, according as $B \neq 0$ or $B = 0$.

If $B \neq 0$, we can solve the given equation for y in terms of x and get

$$(b) \qquad y = -\frac{A}{B}x - \frac{C}{B}.$$

This equation is of the form $y = mx + b$; therefore it is the equation of a line with the slope $m = -A/B$ and Y-intercept $b = -C/B$.

If $B = 0$, then $A \neq 0$, and the given equation becomes $Ax + C = 0$, and by dividing by A, we get

$$(c) \qquad x = -\frac{C}{A}.$$

This equation is of the form $x = a$, and therefore it is the equation of a line parallel to the Y-axis with the X-intercept $a = -C/A$.

Hence, in both cases, $Ax + By + C = 0$ is the equation of a straight line. It is called the **general form** of the equation of a line. We have therefore proved the converse of the preceding theorem, namely:

The locus of any equation of the first degree in x and y is a straight line.

Since every equation of the first degree in x and y has a straight line graph, an equation of the first degree in any number of variables is often called a *linear equation*.

An important use of the slope-intercept form of the equation of a line is in finding the slope of a line when its equation is given in some other form. If the given equation in the form $Ax + By + C = 0$ is solved for y in terms of x to reduce it to the form $y = mx + b$, then the coefficient of x is the slope.

EXAMPLE 1. To find the slope of the line $8x - 2y + 5 = 0$, we solve the equation for y and get $y = 4x + \frac{5}{2}$, so that the slope is 4.

In plotting a straight line from its equation, one of the easiest ways is to find its intercepts on the axes (if it has any) and locate the corresponding points on the axes. The X-intercept is found by putting $y = 0$ in the equation and solving for x; similarly for the Y-intercept, we put $x = 0$ and solve for y.

EXAMPLE 2. To plot the graph of the equation $2x - 3y - 12 = 0$, we find that if $y = 0$, then $x = 6$, and if $x = 0$, then $y = -4$. If we plot the intercept-points $(6, 0)$ and $(0, -4)$, we may draw the line through them, and this line is the required graph.

We shall find it convenient to use the expression:

$$\text{the line } Ax + By + C = 0,$$

to mean:

$$\text{the line whose equation is } Ax + By + C = 0.$$

36. Points of Intersection of Lines

It is evident from the fundamental principle of § 26 that if two lines intersect in a point, the coördinates of the point of intersection must satisfy the equation of each line. Hence, to find the point of intersection of two lines, we solve the equations of the lines simultaneously for x and y.

EXAMPLE. Find the point of intersection of the lines $2x - y = 1$ and $3x + 4y = 18$.

Solution: By solving the equations simultaneously, we find $x = 2$ and $y = 3$. Therefore, the lines intersect at the point $(2, 3)$.

37. Exercises

1. Reduce each of the following equations of lines to the slope-intercept form:
   - (a) $3x - 6y = 12$;
   - (b) $x + y - 8 = 0$;
   - (c) $x + 2y - 6 = 0$;
   - (d) $5x - 2y = 7$.

2. Proceed as in Exercise 1 with:
   - (a) $2x - y = 3$;
   - (b) $3x + 3y - 5 = 0$;
   - (c) $3x + 5y + 2 = 0$;
   - (d) $x - 4y = 9$.

3. Find the slope and both intercepts of each of the lines whose equations are:
   - (a) $2x - y + 6 = 0$;
   - (b) $x + y - 4 = 0$;
   - (c) $3x + 4y - 24 = 0$;
   - (d) $5x + 7y + 8 = 0$.

4. Proceed as in Exercise 3 with:
   - (a) $5x - y - 10 = 0$;
   - (b) $3x + y - 5 = 0$;
   - (c) $2x - 3y - 7 = 0$;
   - (d) $4x + 4y - 9 = 0$.

5. Plot the lines whose equations are:
   - (a) $2x - y - 4 = 0$;
   - (b) $x + 3y - 7 = 0$.

6. Plot the lines whose equations are:
   - (a) $x + y - 5 = 0$;
   - (b) $3x - 4y - 12 = 0$.

7. Find the equation of the line through the point $(2, 3)$ and parallel to the line $3x - 5y + 7 = 0$.

8. Find the equation of the line through the point $(4, 0)$ and perpendicular to the line $4x + 5y + 10 = 0$.

9. Find the equation of the line perpendicular to the line $2x - 3y + 4 = 0$ and passing through the origin.

10. Find the equation of the line which is parallel to the line $x + 3y - 7 = 0$ and which has the X-intercept 5.

11. Which of the following lines are parallel and which are perpendicular:
    (a) $2x + 4y - 7 = 0$;   (b) $x - 2y + 5 = 0$;
    (c) $4x + 2y + 9 = 0$;   (d) $2x - y - 4 = 0$;
    (e) $3x - 6y - 11 = 0$?

12. Reduce each of the following equations of lines to the intercept form:
    (a) $3x - 6y - 12 = 0$;   (b) $x + y - 8 = 0$;
    (c) $x + 2y - 6 = 0$;   (d) $5x - 2y - 7 = 0$.

13. Find the equation of the line whose intercepts are twice those of the line $2x - 3y - 6 = 0$.

14. Find the coördinates of the point of intersection of the lines

$$2x - 5y + 9 = 0, \quad 4x + y + 7 = 0.$$

15. Find the point of intersection of the line $3x + 5y = 7$ with the line through the points $(-3, -1)$ and $(7, 3)$.

16. Find the coördinates of the vertices of the triangle whose sides are on the lines

$$3x + 4y - 17 = 0, \quad 4x - 3y + 9 = 0 \text{ and } 5x - 12y - 19 = 0.$$

17. Find the equation of the line with slope 2 and passing through the intersection of the lines $x + 3y = 0$ and $4x - y = 13$.

18. Show that the three medians of the triangle whose vertices are $A(-2, 1)$, $B(4, 5)$ and $C(2, -3)$ intersect in a single point.

19. Show that the three altitudes of the triangle whose vertices are $A(-4, 2)$, $B(6, 6)$ and $C(-3, -4)$ intersect in a single point.

20. Find the coördinates of the center of the circle passing through the points $A(5, 3)$, $B(-3, 7)$ and $C(1, -5)$. [*Hint.* Find the point of intersection of the perpendicular bisectors of AB and BC.]

21. Find the angle between the lines whose equations are $2x + 3y - 7 = 0$ and $3x - 5y - 2 = 0$.

22. Find the equations of the two lines through $(3, -4)$ making an angle of $45°$ with the line $6x - 3y + 5 = 0$.

23. Prove that the angle between the lines $A_1x + B_1y + C_1 = 0$ and $A_2x + B_2y + C_2 = 0$ is given by

$$\tan \phi = \frac{A_1B_2 - A_2B_1}{A_1A_2 + B_1B_2}.$$

24. Prove analytically that the locus of a point equidistant from two given points is the perpendicular bisector of the line segment joining the given points. [*Hint.* Take the given points as $(0, 0)$ and $(2a, 0)$.]

25. Prove that the locus of a point whose distances from two given perpendicular lines have a constant ratio is a straight line.

26. Prove analytically that in a trapezoid the diagonals and the line drawn through the mid-points of the parallel sides intersect in a single point.

27. Prove analytically that the perpendiculars from the vertices of a triangle to the opposite sides intersect in a single point.

28. Prove analytically that the medians of any triangle intersect in a single point.

38. Distance from a Line to a Point

Let $P_1(x_1, y_1)$ be a given point and let l be a given line not parallel to the Y-axis and not passing through P_1. We wish to derive a formula for the directed distance from the line l to the point P_1. We shall agree to consider the distance *from* a line *to* a point positive if the point is above the line and negative if the point is below the line.

In Fig. 31, draw the line l' through the given point P_1 parallel to

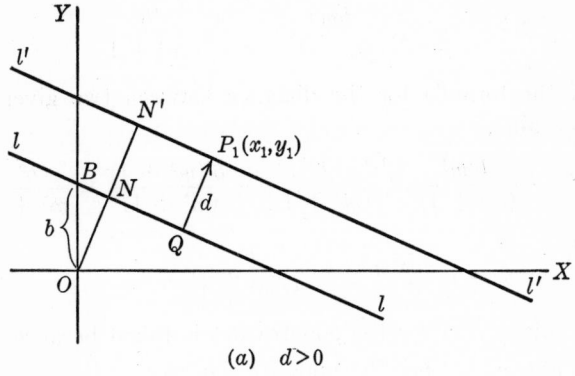

(a) $d > 0$

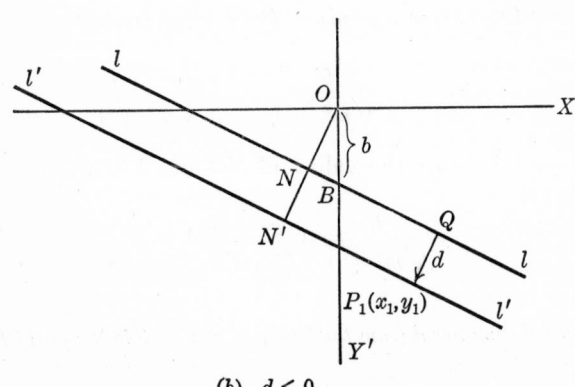

(b) $d < 0$

Fig. 31

the given line l, and through the origin O draw ONN' perpendicular to l and to l'. By the fundamental theorem for directed line segments (§ 4), the directed distance d from l to P_1 is given by

$$(a) \qquad d = \overline{NN'} = \overline{NO} + \overline{ON'} = \overline{NO} - \overline{N'O}.$$

The equation of the line l may be written in the form $y = mx + b$. Since the line ON is perpendicular to l, its slope is $-\dfrac{1}{m}$, and since it passes through the origin, its equation is $y = \left(-\dfrac{1}{m}\right)x$. If we solve this equation simultaneously with $y = mx + b$, we find that the co-ordinates of N are

$$(b) \qquad N: \qquad x = -\frac{bm}{m^2 + 1}, \qquad y = \frac{b}{m^2 + 1}.$$

By use of the formula for the distance between two given points (§ 9), we obtain

$$(NO)^2 = \frac{b^2 m^2}{(m^2 + 1)^2} + \frac{b^2}{(m^2 + 1)^2} = \frac{b^2(m^2 + 1)}{(m^2 + 1)^2} = \frac{b^2}{m^2 + 1}.$$

Then

$$(c) \qquad \overline{NO} = -\frac{b}{\sqrt{m^2 + 1}},$$

where the minus sign for the square root is taken because, by the agreement above, $\overline{NO}$ has the opposite sign to $b = \overline{OB}$.

We may obtain the distance $\overline{N'O}$ from l' to O from formula (c) by replacing b by the Y-intercept b' of l'. The equation of the line l' is $y - y_1 = m(x - x_1)$ or $y = mx + (y_1 - mx_1)$, so that $b' = y_1 - mx_1$. Therefore,

$$(d) \qquad \overline{N'O} = -\frac{b'}{\sqrt{m^2 + 1}} = -\frac{y_1 - mx_1}{\sqrt{m^2 + 1}}.$$

If we now substitute the values of $\overline{NO}$ and $\overline{N'O}$ from (c) and (d) in (a), we get

$$d = \overline{NN'} = -\frac{b}{\sqrt{m^2 + 1}} + \frac{y_1 - mx_1}{\sqrt{m^2 + 1}} = \frac{y_1 - mx_1 - b}{\sqrt{m^2 + 1}}.$$

Hence:

The directed distance d from the line $y = mx + b$ to the point $P_1(x_1, y_1)$ is given by

$$(6) \qquad d = \frac{y_1 - mx_1 - b}{\sqrt{m^2 + 1}}.$$

This directed distance is positive if P_1 is above the given line and negative if P_1 is below the line.

If the equation of the given line is not in the form $y = mx + b$, it should first be reduced to this form by solving for y in terms of x, and then formula (6) can be applied.

If a given line is parallel to the Y-axis, its equation is of the form $x = a$; the directed distance from this line to the point (x_1, y_1) is evidently $d = x_1 - a$.

EXAMPLE. Find the distance from the line $3x - 4y - 14 = 0$ to the point $(6, -4)$.

Solution: The slope-intercept form of the equation of the given line is $y = \frac{3}{4}x - \frac{7}{2}$, so that $m = \frac{3}{4}$, $b = -\frac{7}{2}$. By formula (6), we find

$$d = \frac{-4 - \frac{3}{4}(6) + \frac{7}{2}}{\sqrt{1 + \frac{9}{16}}} = -4.$$

The negative sign of the result indicates that the given point is below the line.

39. Exercises

1. Find the distance from the given line to the given point:
   (a) $3x + 4y - 25 = 0$, $(6, 8)$; (b) $2x - 3y = 5$, $(-3, -2)$.
2. Find the distance from the given line to the given point:
   (a) $5x - 12y - 39 = 0$, $(8, -1)$; (b) $3x + 5y + 12 = 0$, $(-2, 3)$.
3. Find the distance between the parallel lines
   $$3x + 4y = 5 \text{ and } 6x + 8y = -15.$$
   [*Hint.* Use the coördinates of some point on one of the lines.]
4. Find the distance of the point $(-2, 6)$ from the line whose slope is 2 and which passes through the point $(2, 1)$.
5. A circle whose center is at $(2, 3)$ is tangent to the line $7x + 24y = 11$. Find the radius of the circle.
6. Find the lengths of the altitudes of the triangle whose sides lie on the lines $2x - y = 0$, $4x - 3y + 8 = 0$ and $5y - 12x = 8$.
7. Find the area of the triangle whose sides lie on the lines $3x + y + 1 = 0$, $x + 4y - 7 = 0$ and $2y - 5x + 13 = 0$. [*Hint.* Find the length of one side and the altitude on that side.]
8. Find the equation of the line parallel to $5x - 12y = 17$ and tangent to the circle with center at $(4, -3)$ and radius 5.
9. Find the equation of the locus of a point which lies at a distance from the line $15x + 8y - 34 = 0$ equal to 4. (Two solutions.)

★ 40. Systems of Lines

The equation of a straight line contains *two essential constants.* Thus, in the standard forms $y = mx + b$, or $\frac{x}{a} + \frac{y}{b} = 1$, there are the two constants m and b, or a and b; they cannot be reduced in number. The general linear form $Ax + By + C = 0$ contains three constants A, B and C, but they are not all essential. For, since A and B cannot both be zero, we may divide by one of them, say A, and get

$x + \dfrac{B}{A} y + \dfrac{C}{A} = 0$ or $x + B'y + C' = 0$, where $B' = B/A$ and $C' = C/A$, in which case there are the two essential constants B' and C'.

This algebraic result corresponds to the geometric fact that in general a line is determined by two independent geometric conditions. The position of the line relative to the coördinate axes depends on the essential constants in its equation.

The set of all the lines which satisfy one geometric condition is said to form a *system of lines* (or family of lines). For example, all the lines passing through a given point form a system of lines. If in one of the standard forms of the equation of a line we assign a particular value to one of the essential constants, we obtain a linear equation involving one arbitrary constant. This corresponds to imposing one geometric condition; hence the resulting equation represents a system of lines. The arbitrary constant in the equation of the system of lines is called the *parameter* of the system. In general, for each value of the parameter there is one line of the system, and for each line of the system there is one value of the parameter, although there may be certain particular lines that do not correspond to any value of the parameter.

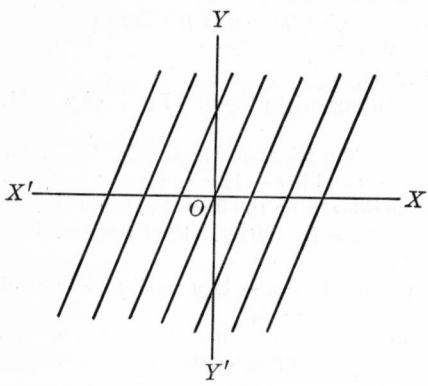

Fig. 32

EXAMPLE 1. If in the slope-intercept form of equation, $y = mx + b$, we impose the condition that the slope of the line be always equal to 2, we obtain the equation

(a) $y = 2x + b$,

which represents the system of all parallel lines having a slope of 2 (Fig. 32), but with varying Y-intercept b. The parameter of this system is b.

EXAMPLE 2. If in the equation $y = mx + b$, we put $b = 3$, we get the equation

(b) $$y = mx + 3,$$

which represents the system of all lines passing through the point $(0, 3)$, with varying slope m (Fig. 33). The parameter in this case is m. (The Y-axis belongs to the system of lines passing through $(0, 3)$ but it does not correspond to any value of m since the Y-axis has no slope.)

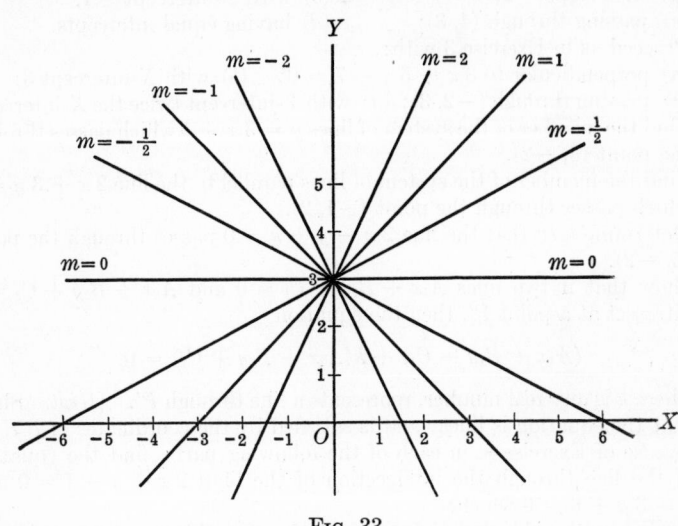

FIG. 33

EXAMPLE 3. The equation

(c) $$y - 2 = m(x + 3)$$

represents the system of lines through the fixed point $(-3, 2)$ with varying slopes. The parameter is m.

★ 41. Exercises

1. For each of the following equations draw four lines of the system of lines, state the parameter, and state a geometric property common to all the lines of each system:

(a) $y = 3x + b$; (b) $y = mx - 2$;

(c) $x = a$; (d) $y - 2 = m(x - 3)$;

(e) $\dfrac{x}{3} + \dfrac{y}{b} = 1$; (f) $y = kx$;

(g) $y + 3 - kx = 4k$; (h) $3x + ky + 2k = 0$.

2. Proceed as in Exercise 1 with:

(a) $y = -2x + k$; (b) $y = mx + 3$;

(c) $y = b$; (d) $y - 3 = k(x + 4)$;

$(e)\ \dfrac{x}{a} - \dfrac{y}{2} = 1;$ $(f)\ x = ky;$

$(g)\ kx + y + 2\,k = 0;$ $(h)\ ky - 5 = 2\,x.$

3. Find the equation of the system of lines satisfying each of the following conditions, and draw four lines of each system:
   (a) with slope -2; (b) with Y-intercept -4;
   (c) passing through $(4, 3)$; (d) having equal intercepts.

4. Proceed as in Exercise 3 with:
   (a) perpendicular to $3\,x + 5\,y - 7 = 0$; (b) with X-intercept 3;
   (c) passing through $(-2, 3)$; (d) with Y-intercept twice the X-intercept.

5. Find the member of the system of lines $y = 3\,x + b$ which passes through the point $(3, -2)$.

6. Find the member of the system of lines parallel to the line $2\,x + 3\,y = 0$ which passes through the point $(-1, 2)$.

7. Determine k so that the line $2\,x - y + k = 0$ passes through the point $(5, -2)$.

8. Show that if two lines $A_1x + B_1y + C_1 = 0$ and $A_2x + B_2y + C_2 = 0$ intersect at a point P', then the equation

$$(A_1x + B_1y + C_1) + k(A_2x + B_2y + C_2) = 0,$$

where k is any real number, represents a line through P'. [*Hint.* Show that the equation is linear and is satisfied by the coördinates of P'.]

9. By use of Exercise 8, in each of the following parts, find the equation of the line through the intersection of the lines $2\,x + y - 4 = 0$ and $x - 3\,y + 6 = 0$ which:
   (a) passes through the origin; (b) has the Y-intercept 3;
   (c) has the slope 2; (d) is parallel to the Y-axis.

10. By use of Exercise 8, in each of the following parts, find the equation of the line through the intersection of the lines $x - 3\,y + 7 = 0$ and $3\,x + 2\,y - 4 = 0$ which:
    (a) passes through the point $(3, -1)$; (b) is parallel to the X-axis;
    (c) has the X-intercept -4; (d) is perpendicular to $x + 2\,y = 6$.

CHAPTER III

Equations of Curves

---

42. Locus of an Equation and Equation of a Locus

At the end of Chapter I we saw that by means of rectangular coördinates it is often possible to associate with a given curve an equation which can be used to represent it analytically, and, conversely, to associate with a given equation a geometrical representation. We shall now consider these important concepts in more detail.

It should be recalled that the *locus of a given equation* in rectangular coördinates x and y is the set of all points whose coördinates satisfy the equation and only such points; this is usually a curve or line. Also, the *equation of a given locus* is an equation which is satisfied by the coördinates of all points on the locus and by only such coördinates.

43. Plotting the Locus of an Equation in Rectangular Coördinates

An equation in two variables is in general satisfied by an unlimited number of pairs of values; it is therefore impossible, in general, to plot *all* the points of the locus of a given equation. We can usually, however, approximate the locus by finding a limited number of points whose coördinates satisfy the equation and joining them by a smooth curve. This process is called *plotting the locus or graph of the equation*.

The detailed procedure in constructing, by point-by-point plotting, the graph of a given equation in rectangular coördinates x and y may be described thus:

(1) Solve the equation for y in terms of x, or for x in terms of y if this is simpler.

(2) Assign convenient values to x and calculate the corresponding values of y (or the reverse, if x has been found in terms of y), and arrange these pairs of corresponding values in a table, in order of increasing values of x (or of y).

(3) Plot the points corresponding to the tabulated values of x and y, and draw one or more smooth curves through these points,

being careful to avoid drawing the graph through points where it has breaks or other irregularities.

This gives an approximation to the graph; a better approximation can be obtained by plotting more points.

EXAMPLE 1. Plot the graph of the equation $y = x^2 - 2x - 5$.

Solution: From the given equation, we calculate the following table of corresponding values of x and y:

x	-3	-2	-1	0	1	2	3	4	5
y	10	3	-2	-5	-6	-5	-2	3	10

Plotting the pairs of values of x and y in this table, we get the set of points marked as black dots in Fig. 34. Drawing a smooth line through these points gives the curve shown in Fig. 34. This curve is the graph of the given equation.

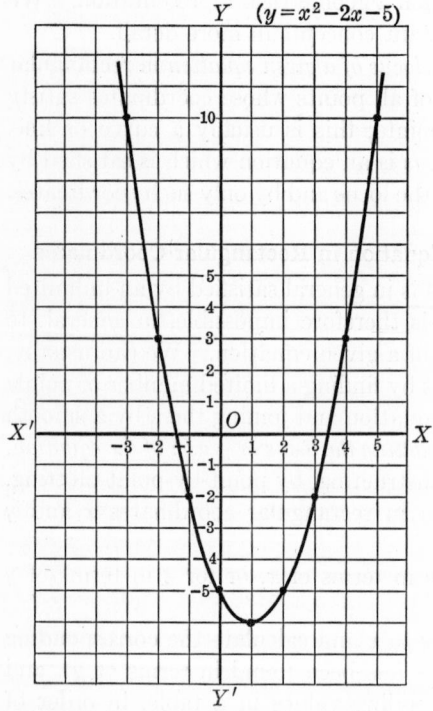

EXAMPLE 2. Plot the graph of the equation

$$y^2 - y = x + 2.$$

Solution: We may easily solve the given equation for x in terms of y, obtaining $x = y^2 - y - 2$; to obtain y in terms of x would require the solution of a quadratic equation. The student should assign values to y and calculate the corresponding values of x from the equation

$$x = y^2 - y - 2,$$

plot the resulting pairs of values, and draw the graph of the equation.

EXAMPLE 3. Plot the graph of the equation

$$y = x^3 - 3x^2 - 4x + 10.$$

FIG. 34

Solution: From the given equation we calculate the following table of corresponding values of x and y:

x	-3	-2	-1	0	1	2	3	4	5
y	-32	-2	10	10	4	-2	-2	10	40

Plotting these pairs of values and drawing a smooth curve through the corresponding points, we obtain the graph shown in Fig. 35.

EXAMPLE 4. Plot the graph of the equation

$$x^2 + y^2 = 25.$$

Solution: If we solve the given equation for y in terms of x, we obtain

(a) $y = \pm\sqrt{25 - x^2}.$

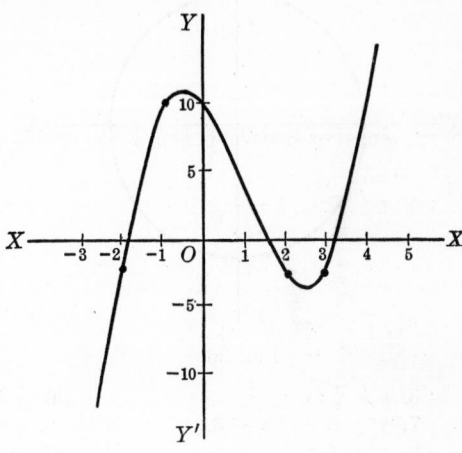

For each value of x between -5 and 5, there are two values of y, giving two corresponding points of the graph; thus, for $x = 3$ or $x = -3$, we get $y = \pm4$, and for $x = 2$ or $x = -2$, we get $y = \pm\sqrt{21} = \pm4.6$ approximately. When $x = \pm5$,

FIG. 35

we have $y = 0$. When x is greater than 5 or less than -5, the expression $25 - x^2$ is negative and y is imaginary; in this case, no corresponding point exists on the curve, since we can plot only real numbers as rectangular coördinates. We may thus calculate the following table of corresponding values of x and y:

x	$x < -5$	-5	-4	-3	-2	-1	0	1	2	3	4	5	$x > 5$
y	imag.	0	±3	±4	±4.6	±4.9	±5	±4.9	±4.6	±4	±3	0	imag.

When we plot these pairs of values and draw a smooth curve through the resulting points, we obtain the graph shown in Fig. 36.

When plotting the graph of a given equation, one should extend the table of corresponding values of the variables far enough so that a good idea of the shape of the graph can be obtained from the points plotted. If the points which have been plotted do not indicate clearly the form of the graph, additional intermediate values should be calculated and plotted.

Some equations in x and y are not satisfied by any real values of x and y (as, for example, $x^2 + y^2 + 1 = 0$); such an equation has no graph. Some equations are satisfied by only one pair of real values of x and y (as, for example, $x^2 + y^2 = 0$); in this case, the graph consists of a single point. In general, the graph of a given equation consists of an unlimited number of points, forming a curve.*

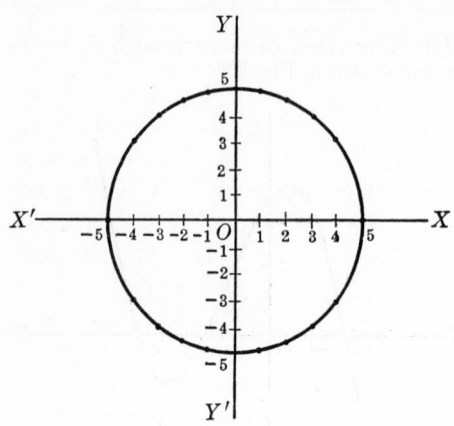

FIG. 36

44. Exercises

Plot the graph of each of the following equations:

1. $3x + 2y - 12 = 0$.
2. $2x - 3y = 0$.
3. $2x - 3y - 3 = 0$.
4. $3x - y + 2 = 0$.
5. $y = \frac{1}{2} x^2$.
6. $y = -2x^2$.
7. $y = x^2 - 2x - 3$.
8. $y = 2x - x^2$.
9. $y^2 = 4x$.
10. $x^2 + 4y - 5 = 0$.
11. $y^2 - x + 2y - 3 = 0$.
12. $2y^2 - 4y - x + 6 = 0$.
13. $y = x^3$.
14. $y = x^3 - 6x$.
15. $y = x^3 - 7x^2 + 4x + 12$.
16. $y = x^3 - x^2 - 5$.
17. $x^2 + y^2 = 16$.
18. $2x^2 + y^2 = 4$.
19. $4x^2 + 9y^2 = 36$.
20. $x^2 - y^2 = 9$.
21. $x^2 + y^2 + 8x = 0$.
22. $x^2 + y^2 - 4y = 5$.
23. $xy = 4$.
24. $x^2y = 4$.
25. $y^2 = x^3$.
26. $y^3 = 8x^2$.

27. Plot the graphs of the equations $y = x^2 + x - 2$, $y = x^2 + x$ and $y = x^2 + x + 2$ on the same axes, and compare the results.
28. Plot the graphs of the equations $y = x^2$, $y = 2x^2$ and $y = \frac{1}{2} x^2$ on the same axes, and compare the results.
29. An open box is to be made from a sheet of cardboard 12 inches square by cutting equal squares from the four corners and bending up the sides. Express the volume y in terms of the side x of the square cut out. Then plot the graph of this equation. From the graph, estimate as closely as possible the value of x for which the volume is a maximum.
30. A uniform beam of length l, fixed at one end, supports a weight at the other end. The deflection y of the beam at a distance x from the fixed end is given by the equation $y = k(\frac{1}{2} lx^2 - \frac{1}{6} x^3)$, where k is a constant.

---

* In analytic geometry, the term *curve* is generally used to include a straight line as a special case.

Plot a curve to show the deflection of any point of a beam 10 feet long which is deflected 1 foot at the free end.

45. Discussion of the Equation of a Locus

Plotting the graph of an equation point-by-point, as described in § 43, is frequently laborious and difficult, and may often give very inadequate information about the precise form of the curve. By an algebraic examination of the given equation of the locus, certain properties of the curve may be discovered which make it possible to sketch the curve by plotting only a few well-chosen points and making use of these properties of the graph. This examination of the equation is called the *discussion of the equation of the locus*. The simplest properties of a locus that may be studied by such a discussion of its equation are the *intercepts, symmetry, extent* and horizontal and vertical *asymptotes*.

Intercepts: The points that can be located on the locus of an equation most easily are the points where the locus cuts or meets the coordinate axes. The **X-intercepts** of a locus are the abscissas of the points where the locus meets the X-axis; the **Y-intercepts** are the ordinates of the points where the locus meets the Y-axis. The intercepts of a locus are therefore the directed distances from the origin to the points at which the locus crosses or meets the coördinate axes.

Evidently, *to find the X-intercepts, we set $y = 0$ in the equation of the locus and then solve the resulting equation for x; to find the Y-intercepts, we set $x = 0$ and solve the resulting equation for y.*

EXAMPLE 1. Find the intercepts of the graph of $y = 1 - x^2$.

Solution: If we put $y = 0$, we find $x^2 = 1$ and $x = \pm 1$; if we put $x = 0$, we find $y = 1$. Hence, the X-intercepts of the locus are 1 and -1, and the Y-intercept is 1.

Symmetry: Two points are said to be *symmetric with respect to a given line* if this line is the perpendicular bisector of the line segment joining the points. Two points are said to be *symmetric with respect to a given point* if this point is the mid-point of the line segment joining the points.

A *locus* is said to be **symmetric with respect to a given line** if each point of the locus has its symmetric point, with respect to the given line, also on the locus. The given line is then called *an axis of symmetry* of the locus.

A *locus* is said to be **symmetric with respect to a given point** if each point of the locus has its symmetric point, with respect to the given point, also on the locus. The given point is then called a *center of symmetry* of the locus.

Thus, the curve in Fig. 37 (*a*) is symmetric with respect to the line *l*, and the curve of Fig. 37 (*b*) is symmetric with respect to the point *O*.

It is evident that a curve is symmetric with respect to the *X*-axis if, for each point (x, y) on the curve, the point $(x, -y)$ is also on the curve. Similarly, a curve is symmetric with respect to the *Y*-axis if for each point (x, y) on the curve, the point $(-x, y)$ is also on the

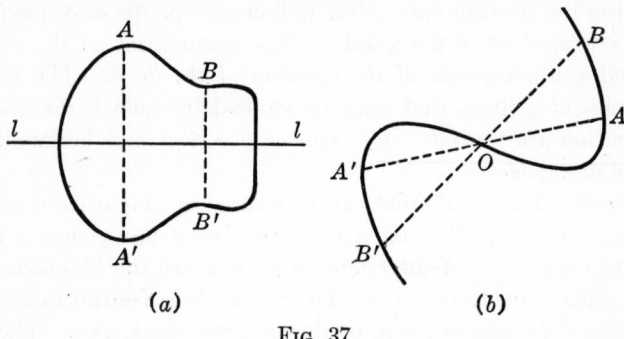

(*a*)   (*b*)

FIG. 37

curve. Also, a curve is symmetric with respect to the origin if for each point (x, y) on the curve the point $(-x, -y)$ is also on the curve. It follows that the symmetry of a locus with respect to the coördinate axes and the origin may be determined by inspection of its equation by means of the following test:

A locus is symmetric with respect to the X-axis if its equation remains equivalent when y is replaced by $-y$; it is symmetric with respect to the Y-axis if its equation remains equivalent when x is replaced by $-x$. It is symmetric with respect to the origin if its equation remains equivalent when x is replaced by $-x$ and y is replaced by $-y$.

EXAMPLE 2. (*a*) The locus of the equation $y^2 = 4x$ is symmetric with respect to the *X*-axis, since $(-y)^2 = 4x$ reduces to $y^2 = 4x$. It is not symmetric with respect to the *Y*-axis, since $y^2 = 4(-x)$ does not reduce to $y^2 = 4x$.

(*b*) The locus of $xy = 4$ is symmetric with respect to the origin, since $(-x)(-y) = 4$ reduces to $xy = 4$. It is not symmetric with respect to either coördinate axis, since $x(-y) = 4$ and $(-x)y = 4$ are not equivalent to $xy = 4$.

(*c*) The locus of $4x^2 + 9y^2 = 36$ is symmetric with respect to the *X*-axis, the *Y*-axis and the origin.

A knowledge of symmetry of the locus of an equation is very helpful in drawing the locus.

It is possible that a curve may have an axis of symmetry other than one of the coördinate axes and a center of symmetry other than the origin.

Extent: Imaginary values of rectangular coördinates cannot be plotted. It follows that, in plotting the locus of an equation, values of x or y which make the other coördinate imaginary must be excluded. Since division by zero is not permissible, values of x or y which give a zero divisor must also be excluded.

If the equation of a given locus is solved for each variable x and y in terms of the other, we may usually determine whether any values of either variable make the other imaginary or give a zero divisor. This may give *excluded regions* of the plane, and may give an idea of the horizontal or vertical extent of the locus.

EXAMPLE 3. Examine the equation $y^2 = 4x - 4$ for extent of its locus.

Solution: If we solve the given equation for y in terms of x and for x in terms of y, we get

(a) $$y = \pm 2\sqrt{x-1},$$

(b) $$x = \tfrac{1}{4}(y^2 + 4).$$

From (a) we see that y is imaginary when $x - 1$ is negative or $x < 1$, and from (b) we see that x is real for all real values of y. Hence, the region to the left of the line $x = 1$ must be excluded; the locus extends without bound to the right of the line $x = 1$ and also without bound above and below to the right of the line $x = 1$.

Horizontal and vertical asymptotes: Sometimes the graph of an equation has one or more straight lines related to it in such a way that the curve approaches the line or lines.

EXAMPLE 4. Consider the graph of the equation $xy + x - 2y = 6$. If we solve this equation for y in terms of x, we get

(c) $$y = \frac{6 - x}{x - 2}.$$

There is a point of the graph for each value of x except for $x = 2$. When $x = 2$, the denominator of the fraction in (c) is zero and the fraction is undefined, and the equation gives no value of y. Suppose that x is greater than 2 but close to 2. Then the denominator of the fraction is small and positive, and the fraction itself is a large positive number. As x approaches 2 from the right, y increases, and y is greater than an arbitrarily large positive number for all values of x that are sufficiently close to 2. In terms of the graphic representation, we may express this behavior by saying that the graph rises indefinitely upward as it approaches the line $x = 2$ from the right. This is shown in Fig. 38. We say that the line $x = 2$ is a *vertical asymptote* to the curve, or that the curve *approaches* the line $x = 2$ *asymptotically* upward from the right.

Now suppose that x is slightly less than 2; then the fraction in (c) is negative but is numerically large. As x approaches 2 from the left, y increases numerically through negative values, and the absolute value of y is greater than an arbitrarily large positive number for all values of x that are sufficiently close to 2. We may then say that the graph falls indefinitely down-

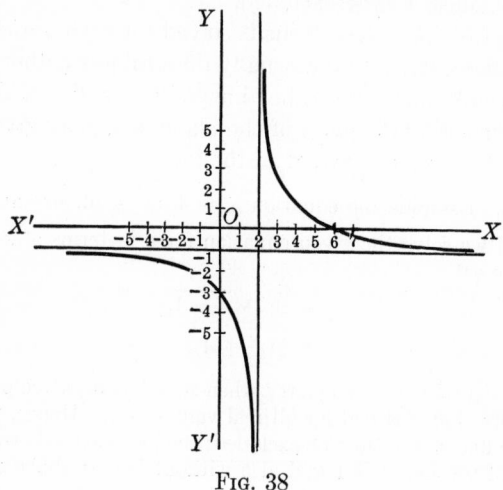

Fɪɢ. 38

ward as it approaches the line $x = 2$ from the left (see Fig. 38). We say that the curve *approaches* the line $x = 2$ *asymptotically* downward from the left.

If we solve the given equation for x in terms of y, we obtain

$$(d) \qquad\qquad x = \frac{2y + 6}{y + 1}.$$

Reasoning as before, we see that as y approaches -1 from above, x is positive and is greater than an arbitrarily large positive number for all values of y that are sufficiently near -1. We may then say that the graph extends indefinitely to the right as we approach the line $y = -1$ from above. The line $y = -1$ is said to be a *horizontal asymptote* to the curve; the curve approaches the line $y = -1$ asymptotically to the right from above. (Fig. 38.) Similarly, we may see that the curve approaches the line $y = -1$ asymptotically to the left from below, as y takes values less than -1 but nearer to -1.

In general, if the equation of any curve is such that the ordinate y is numerically greater than an arbitrarily large positive number for all values of x sufficiently near a value $x = a$, we say that the line $x = a$ is a *vertical asymptote* to the curve. A *horizontal asymptote* is defined similarly.*

When a curve has one or more vertical or horizontal asymptotes, the location of these asymptotes is of great help in drawing the graph.

46. Exercises

1. Find the X- and Y-intercepts of the graph of each of the following equations:
   (a) $y^2 = 4x - 8$;   (b) $4x^2 + 9y^2 = 36$;
   (c) $x^2 - y^2 = 4$;   (d) $y = (x - 1)(x + 2)$.

2. Proceed as in Exercise 1 with:
   (a) $x^2 = 2y + 4$;   (b) $x^2 + y^2 = 9$;
   (c) $9x^2 - 16y^2 = 144$;   (d) $x^2 = 8y + 2x$.

3. Does the graph of $xy = 4$ have X- and Y-intercepts?

4. Does the graph of $x^2y = 1$ have X- and Y-intercepts?

5. Determine whether the graph of each of the following equations has symmetry with respect to either coördinate axis or with respect to the origin:
   (a) $y^2 = 8x$;   (b) $4x^2 + 9y^2 = 36$;
   (c) $x^2y = 4$;   (d) $y = x^3$.

6. Proceed as in Exercise 5 with:
   (a) $x^2 = y - 1$;   (b) $9x^2 - 4y^2 = 36$;
   (c) $x^2 + y^2 - 4x = 12$;   (d) $y^2 = x^3$.

7. If $P_1(x_1, y_1)$ is any point, show that its symmetric point with respect to the line which bisects the first and third quadrants is (y_1, x_1).

8. Show how to test a curve for symmetry with respect to the line which bisects the second and fourth quadrants.

9. Determine the horizontal and vertical extent of the graph of each of the following equations:
   (a) $x^2 = -9y$;   (b) $x^2 + y^2 = 25$;
   (c) $x^2 + 4y^2 = 36$;   (d) $x^2 - y^2 = 4$.

10. Proceed as in Exercise 9 with:
    (a) $y^2 = x^3$;   (b) $x^2 + y^2 - 4x = 0$;
    (c) $9x^2 + 25y^2 = 225$;   (d) $4x^2 - 9y^2 = 36$.

11. Determine any horizontal or vertical asymptotes, for the graph of each of the following equations:
    (a) $xy = 4$;   (b) $xy - 2y = 12$;
    (c) $xy - 2x + 3y = 12$;   (d) $y(1 + x^2) = 1$.

---

* Curves sometimes have *oblique asymptotes*, which are defined in a somewhat similar way.

(e) $y = \dfrac{x^2}{x^2 - 25}$; $\qquad$ (f) $y = \dfrac{1 - x^2}{(x - 2)(x + 3)}$.

12. Proceed as in Exercise 11 with:

$\quad$ (a) $2\,xy = -9$; $\qquad\qquad$ (b) $xy + 4\,x = 8$;

$\quad$ (c) $xy^2 = x - y$; $\qquad\qquad$ (d) $y(x^2 - 4) = 8$.

47. Curve Sketching

In order to sketch the curve representing a given equation in rectangular coördinates, the equation should first be examined for symmetry, intercepts, extent and asymptotes. This information should be noted down on the figure. Then a few well-placed points should be plotted to supplement the above information.

EXAMPLE 1. Discuss and sketch the graph of $9\,x^2 + 25\,y^2 = 225$.

Solution: The curve is symmetric with respect to both coördinate axes and with respect to the origin. If $y = 0$, we get $x = \pm 5$, and if $x = 0$, we get $y = \pm 3$. The intercepts are then $x = \pm 5$, $y = \pm 3$; this gives the points A, B, C and D in Fig. 39. Solving the given equation for x and for y, we have

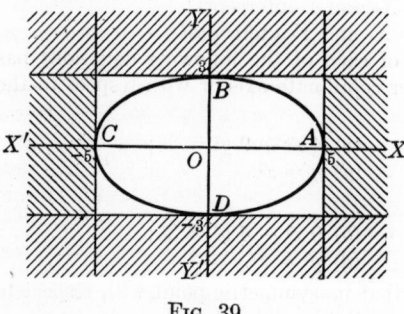

$$y = \pm\tfrac{3}{5}\sqrt{25 - x^2},$$
$$x = \pm\tfrac{5}{3}\sqrt{9 - y^2}.$$

If $x > 5$ or $x < -5$, the value of y is imaginary; hence, the regions to the right of the line $x = 5$ and to the left of the line $x = -5$ must be excluded. If

FIG. 39

$y > 3$ or $y < -3$, the value of x is imaginary; hence, the regions above the line $y = 3$ and below the line $y = -3$ must be excluded. The curve therefore lies within a rectangle. Plotting the points for $x = 3$ and $x = 4$, and making use of the symmetry, we obtain the curve shown in Fig. 39.

EXAMPLE 2. Discuss and sketch the locus of $x^2 - y^2 = 4$.

Solution: This graph is symmetric with respect to both coördinate axes and with respect to the origin. When $y = 0$, we have $x = \pm 2$; these are the X-intercepts. When $x = 0$, we get $y^2 = -4$, so that y is imaginary, and the curve has no Y-intercept. From the given equation we find

$$y = \pm\sqrt{x^2 - 4}, \qquad x = \pm\sqrt{y^2 + 4}.$$

From the first of these equations we see that y is imaginary when $x^2 < 4$, or $-2 < x < 2$; hence, we must exclude the vertical strip between the lines $x = -2$ and $x = 2$. The second equation above shows that x is real for all real values of y, so that the curve has unlimited vertical extent.   Plotting the points corresponding to $x = 3, 4, 5$, and making use of the above information, we obtain the graph shown in Fig. 40.   It consists of two distinct pieces, called branches.

EXAMPLE 3. Discuss and sketch the graph of $y = \dfrac{1}{x^2 - 1}$.

Solution: This curve is symmetric with respect to the Y-axis, but not with respect to the X-axis or origin.   From the given equation we see that y cannot be 0 for any value of x. If we solve the given equation for x in terms of y, we obtain

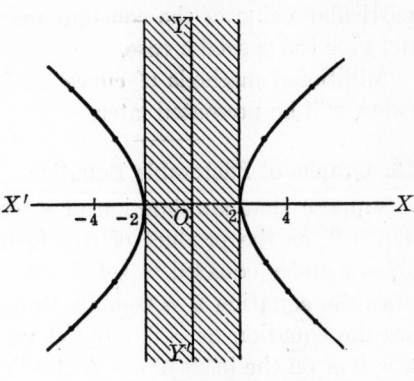

FIG. 40

$$(a) \qquad x^2 = \frac{y + 1}{y};$$

from this equation we find that $x = 0$ when $y = -1$.   Hence, the curve has no X-intercept but has the Y-intercept -1.   The given equation shows that the graph has unlimited extent in the x-direction.   Equation (a) shows that x is imaginary when y is between -1 and 0, so that the region between the X-axis and the line $y = -1$ is an excluded region.   When $x > 1$, y is positive; when x approaches 1 through values greater than 1, y increases

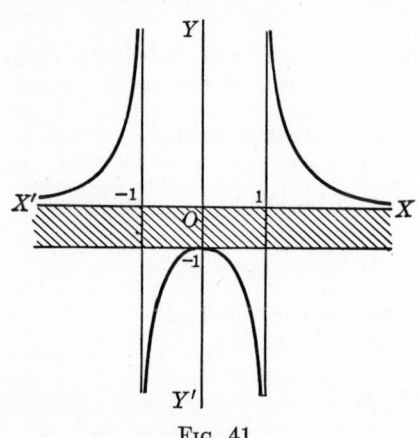

FIG. 41

through positive values and is arbitrarily large for all values of x greater than 1 which are sufficiently close to 1.   Therefore, the graph approaches the vertical asymptote $x = 1$ upward from the right.   Similarly, when x is less than 1 but approaching 1, y is negative but is arbitrarily large in absolute value for all values of x less than 1 which are sufficiently close to 1.   Hence, the graph approaches the line $x = 1$ asymptotically downward from the left.   The given equation shows that y is positive when $x > 1$ and is arbitrarily near 0 for all values of x which are sufficiently large; therefore, the graph approaches the X-axis (the line $y = 0$) as an asymptote from above to the right.   The symmetry with respect to the Y-axis (or similar reasoning to that above) shows that the curve has the vertical asymptote $x = -1$ and the X-axis as a horizontal asymptote.   The resulting graph is shown in Fig. 41.

When examining an equation of a locus which involves an arbitrary constant, one should *discuss* it without substituting a particular value for the constant, but for *plotting* the graph, any convenient particular value of the constant may be used provided that it does not give too special a case.

Additional methods of curve tracing, by use of processes of calculus, will be presented later.

48. Graphs of Factorable Equations

Suppose that an equation of a locus can be written in the form $u \cdot v = 0$, as the product of two factors involving one or both variables x and y equated to zero. Any pair of values (x, y) which satisfies the equation $u = 0$ or the equation $v = 0$ evidently also satisfies the equation $uv = 0$. It follows that any point on the locus of $u = 0$ or on the locus of $v = 0$ also lies on the locus of $uv = 0$. Conversely, any point on the locus of $uv = 0$ also lies either on the locus of $u = 0$ or on the locus of $v = 0$ or on both, because if $uv = 0$, then either $u = 0$ or $v = 0$ or both. Hence:

If the equation of a locus can be expressed as the product of two or more factors equated to zero, each factor involving the variable coördinates, its locus consists of the loci of the equations obtained by putting each factor equal to zero separately.

EXAMPLE. (a) The graph of the equation $y^2 - x^2 = 0$ consists of the loci of the equations $y - x = 0$ and $y + x = 0$, that is, of the lines $y = x$ and $y = -x$.

(b) The equation $xy^2 + y^2 - 4x^2 - 4x = 0$ can be written
$$(x + 1)(y^2 - 4x) = 0$$
by factoring. Its locus therefore consists of the line $x = -1$ and the curve $y^2 = 4x$.

49. Exercises

1. Discuss and sketch the graphs of the following equations:

    (a) $y = 1 - x^2$;   (b) $y = x^2 - 4x$;
    (c) $x^2 + y^2 = 16$;   (d) $4x^2 + y^2 = 16$;
    (e) $4x^2 - 25y^2 = 100$;   (f) $x^2 - 6x - y + 3 = 0$;
    (g) $x^2 + 9y^2 - 4x = 0$;   (h) $xy = -4$.

2. Discuss and sketch the graphs of the following equations:

    (a) $y = x^2 - 4$;   (b) $y^2 + x - 2 = 0$;
    (c) $y^2 = x^2 + 1$;   (d) $4x^2 + 25y^2 = 100$;
    (e) $y^2 + 4x - 2y + 5 = 0$;   (f) $x^2 + 8y - x = 0$;
    (g) $y = x^2 + 2x - 4$;   (h) $x^2y = 4$.

3. Discuss and sketch the graphs of the following equations:

   (a) $y = x^3$;   (b) $y^2 = x^3$;   (c) $y^3 = x^2$.

4. Discuss and sketch the graphs of the following equations:

   (a) $3y = 3x - x^3$;   (b) $4y = x^4 - 4x^2$.

5. Discuss and sketch the graphs of the following equations:

   (a) $y(x^2 + 1) = 1$;   (b) $y(x^2 - x) = 4$;

   (c) $x = y(x - 1)^2$;   (d) $xy - 4y = 16$.

6. Discuss and sketch the graphs of the following equations:

   (a) $x(y^2 + 4) = 12$;   (b) $(x - 2)^2 y = 8$;

   (c) $xy + 4x = 12$;   (d) $xy^2 - 16x = 16$.

7. Discuss and sketch the graphs of the following equations:

   (a) $x^2 + y^2 = a^2$;   (b) $b^2x^2 + a^2y^2 = a^2b^2$;

   (c) $y^2 = 4ax$;   (d) $b^2x^2 - a^2y^2 = a^2b^2$.

8. Discuss the graphs of the equations:

   (a) $y^2 + 4x^2 = 0$;   (b) $x^2 + y^2 + 4 = 0$.

9. Draw the graphs of the following equations:

   (a) $xy - 4x = 0$;   (b) $x^2 - 2xy = 0$;

   (c) $x^2 - 2xy - 3y^2 = 0$;   (d) $x^2 - 16 = 0$.

10. Draw the graphs of the following equations:

   (a) $9x^2 - 4y^2 = 0$;   (b) $3x^2 + 7xy + 2y^2 = 0$;

   (c) $xy + 3x - 2y - 6 = 0$;   (d) $2x^2 + 3x = 0$.

50. Graphs of Certain Important Equations of the Second Degree

Graphs of equations of the second degree will be met frequently in the course of this book, and it will be helpful if at this point their form can be quickly recognized at sight. These curves will be studied systematically later (Chapter XII), but in the meantime the following facts should be noted; they will be proved later.

(1) The graph of an equation of the form

(a)
$$x^2 + y^2 = R^2$$

is a **circle** with center at the origin and radius R.

(2) The graph of an equation of the form

(b)
$$Ax^2 + By^2 = C,$$

where A, B and C are positive and $A \neq B$, is an **ellipse,** which is an oval-shaped curve, symmetric about both axes and the origin (see Fig. 39).

(3) The graph of an equation of the form

(c)
$$Ax^2 - By^2 = C \qquad \text{or} \qquad -Ax^2 + By^2 = C,$$

where A, B and C are positive, is a **hyperbola,** which is an open curve with two distinct portions (called branches), symmetric about both axes and the origin (see Fig. 40).

(4) The graph of an equation of the form

(d) $y = Ax^2 + Bx + C$ or $x = Ay^2 + By + C$,

where $A \neq 0$ and B and C are any real numbers, is a **parabola,** which is an open curve with one portion only, which has a vertical axis of symmetry for the first equation and a horizontal axis of symmetry for the second equation (see Fig. 34).

(5) The graph of an equation of the form

(e) $xy = C$,

where C is a constant, is a **hyperbola** asymptotic to the X- and Y-axes.

51. Intersection of Curves

It follows from the definition of the locus of an equation that the coördinates of a point of intersection of two loci satisfy both equations of the loci, and conversely that a pair of real solutions of two equations represents the coördinates of a point common to the loci of the equations. Therefore, *the coördinates of the points of intersection of two curves whose equations are given may be obtained by solving the equations as simultaneous equations and taking all pairs of real solutions.* If the equations have no real solutions, the corresponding curves do not intersect.

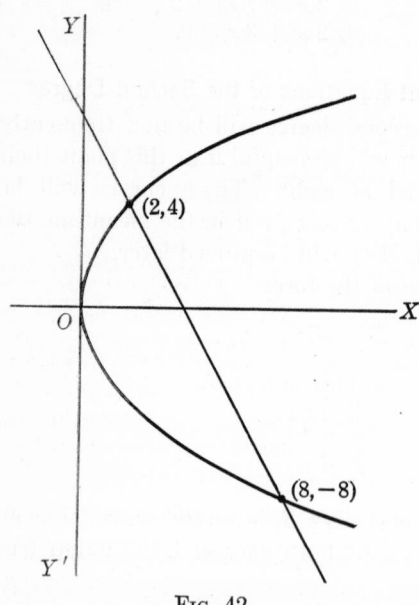

FIG. 42

EXAMPLE 1. Find the points of intersection of the loci of $2x + y = 8$ and $y^2 = 8x$.

Solution: From the first equation we get $y = 8 - 2x$; substituting this value of y in the second equation, we have

$$64 - 32x + 4x^2 = 8x \quad \text{or} \quad x^2 - 10x + 16 = 0.$$

By factoring we find the roots of the last equation to be $x = 2$ and $x = 8$. From the first given equation, when $x = 2$ we get $y = 4$, and when $x = 8$, we get $y = -8$. Hence, the required points of intersection are $(2, 4)$ and $(8, -8)$. (See Fig. 42.) The first locus is a straight line and the second is a parabola.

EXAMPLE 2. Find the points of intersection of the curves whose equations are $y^2 = 6\,x$ and $x^2 + y^2 = 16$.

Solution: If we substitute the value of y^2 from the first equation into the second equation, we get $x^2 + 6\,x = 16$, whose roots are $x = 2$ and $x = -8$. When $x = 2$, we find from $y^2 = 6\,x$ that $y = \pm\sqrt{12} = \pm 2\sqrt{3}$. But when $x = -8$, the equation $y^2 = 6\,x$ gives $y^2 = -48$, so that y is then imaginary. Hence, the only points of intersection of the given curves are $(2, 2\sqrt{3})$ and $(2, -2\sqrt{3})$. (See Fig. 43.) The first curve is a parabola and the second is a circle.

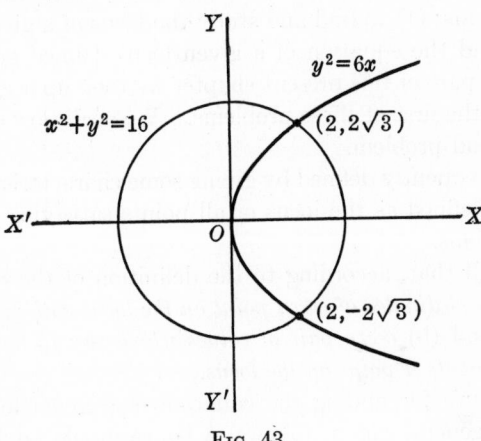

FIG. 43

52. Exercises

1. Sketch the graph of the equation $x^2 + y^2 = R^2$ when $R = 5$.
2. Sketch the graphs of the equation $Ax^2 + By^2 = C$ when:

    (a) $A = 16, B = 9, C = 144$;   (b) $A = 4, B = 16, C = 64$.

3. Sketch the graphs of the equation $Ax^2 - By^2 = C$ when:

    (a) $A = 25, B = 9, C = 225$;   (b) $A = 9, B = 16, C = -144$.

4. Sketch the graphs of:

    (a) the equation $y = Ax^2 + Bx + C$ when $A = -1, B = 2, C = -3$;
    (b) the equation $x = Ay^2 + By + C$ when $A = 1, B = -4, C = 0$.

5. Find the coördinates of the points of intersection of the graphs of the following pairs of equations:

    (a) $2\,x - y = 4, x + y = 2$;   (b) $y^2 = 2\,x, y = 2\,x$;
    (c) $x^2 - y^2 = 4, 3\,x - y = 6$;   (d) $x^2 + y^2 = 25, x^2 + 4\,y^2 = 73$;
    (e) $y^2 = 4\,x, x^2 = 4\,y$;   (f) $y = x^3, y = x$.

6. Proceed as in Exercise 5 with:

    (a) $2x - y = 5$, $x + 3y = 6$;   (b) $x^2 + y^2 = 25$, $x + 2y = 2$;
    (c) $4x^2 + y^2 = 5$, $y + 2 = x$;   (d) $x^2 + y^2 = 16$, $x^2 - y^2 = 9$;
    (e) $x^2 + y^2 = 5$, $xy = 2$;   (f) $y^2 = 2x$, $4y = x^3$.

7. Show that the loci of $y^2 - 2x = 0$ and $y = 3x + 2$ do not intersect.

8. Show that the loci of $4x^2 + 9y^2 = 36$ and $4x^2 + 4y^2 = 9$ do not intersect.

9. Find the length of the common chord of the curves $y = 4x - x^2$ and $y = x^2 - 6x$.

10. Find the length of the line joining the points of intersection of the curves $y^2 = 15x$ and $x^2 + y^2 = 100$.

53. Derivation of the Equation of a Locus

At the end of the first chapter we considered briefly the two fundamental problems: (1) to find and study the locus of a given equation, and (2) to find the equation of a given locus defined geometrically. In the earlier part of this present chapter we took up a more detailed discussion of the first of these problems. We shall now discuss more fully the second problem.

A locus is frequently defined by giving some characteristic property, that is, it is defined as the locus of all points satisfying certain geometric conditions.

Let us recall that, according to the definition of the *equation of a locus*: (a) *the coördinates of every point on the locus satisfy the equation of the locus*, and (b) *every pair of values which satisfy the equation of the locus represents a point on the locus*.

The procedure for finding the equation of a given locus may be outlined in a general way as follows: A figure should be drawn showing the given data for a typical point P of the locus; this point P should not be placed in a special position but should be placed in a general position. If a coördinate system is not given in the problem, a set of coördinate axes should be taken in a convenient position; these axes may frequently be chosen in such a special way that the later algebraic expressions are in simplest form. Denote the coördinates of the typical point P of the locus by (x, y). Then express the given conditions defining the locus by an equation in terms of geometrical quantities involving the point P. This equation should next be expressed in terms of the coördinates x, y of the typical point P, and then simplified algebraically. To prove that this simplified equation is the required equation of the given locus, it is necessary to show that any point whose coördinates satisfy the equation lies on the locus. In this case, this simplified equation is the required result.

In order to prove that any point whose coördinates satisfy the equation of the locus lies on the locus, it is usually sufficient to show that the preceding derivation can be reversed by retracing the steps and leading back to the original conditions which define the locus.

EXAMPLE 1. Find the equation of the locus of points equidistant from the points $A(4, 1)$ and $B(-2, 4)$.

Solution: Let $P(x, y)$ be *any* point on the locus; then, for any position of P on the locus, we must have

$$(a) \qquad\qquad PA = PB.$$

By the fundamental distance formula, equation (a) can be expressed in terms of the coördinates x and y of P by

$$(b) \qquad\qquad \sqrt{(x-4)^2 + (y-1)^2} = \sqrt{(x+2)^2 + (y-4)^2}.$$

Simplifying this equation by squaring both sides, cancelling terms in x^2 and y^2, and collecting other terms, we obtain

$$(c) \qquad\qquad 4x - 2y + 1 = 0.$$

It can readily be seen that if (x, y) represents any pair of real numbers satisfying equation (c), then we can retrace the preceding steps and arrive at the equation (a) which defines the locus. Hence, equation (c) is the required equation of the given locus in simplified form. The locus is evidently the perpendicular bisector of the segment AB.

EXAMPLE 2. Find the equation of the locus of all points at a distance 5 from the point $C(2, 3)$.

Solution: The locus is evidently the circle with center at $C(2, 3)$ and radius 5. Let $P(x, y)$ be any point on the locus; then by the definition of the locus,

$$(d) \qquad\qquad PC = 5.$$

By use of the distance formula, this becomes

$$(e) \qquad\qquad \sqrt{(x-2)^2 + (y-3)^2} = 5,$$

or

$$(f) \qquad\qquad (x-2)^2 + (y-3)^2 = 25.$$

Since any pair of real values (x, y) which satisfy equation (f) will also satisfy equation (e), it follows that any point whose coördinates satisfy (f) lies on the locus. This equation (f) may be taken as the required equation of the locus. An equivalent alternative form of the equation may be obtained by expanding the binomial squares and collecting terms; this gives

$$(g) \qquad\qquad x^2 + y^2 - 4x - 6y - 12 = 0.$$

EXAMPLE 3. Derive the equation of the locus of a point P which moves so that the sum o its distances from the points $A(4, 0)$ and $B(-4, 0)$ is always equal to 10.

Solution: The definition of the locus may be written

(h)
$$PA + PB = 10.$$

Using the distance formula, this equation becomes

$$\sqrt{(x-4)^2 + y^2} + \sqrt{(x+4)^2 + y^2} = 10.$$

To simplify this, transpose the second term, square and simplify; we get

$$5\sqrt{(x+4)^2 + y^2} = 25 + 4\,x.$$

Squaring again and simplifying, we obtain

(i)
$$9\,x^2 + 25\,y^2 = 225.$$

These steps may be reversed to go from (i) to (h), showing that any pair of real values (x, y) will be the coördinates of a point on the locus. Therefore, equation (i) is the required equation of the locus.

EXAMPLE 4. If $A(-2, 3)$ and $B(6, 5)$ are given points, find the locus of the point $P(x, y)$ which moves so that the slope of PA is always 2 less than the slope of PB.

Solution: By definition of the locus,

(j)
$$\text{slope } PA = \text{slope } PB - 2.$$

By the slope formula,

(k)
$$\frac{y-3}{x+2} = \frac{y-5}{x-6} - 2.$$

When simplified, this equation reduces to

(l)
$$x^2 - 3\,x - 4\,y + 2 = 0,$$

which is the required equation of the locus, since the above steps can be reversed.

54. Exercises

1. Find the equation of the straight line parallel to the Y-axis which is:
   (a) 5 units to the right of it; (b) 3 units to the left of it.
2. Find the equation of the straight line parallel to the X-axis which is:
   (a) 4 units above it; (b) 2 units below it.
3. Find the equation of the locus of all points which are equidistant from the points $(-3, 4)$ and $(5, -2)$.
4. Find the equation of the perpendicular bisector of the line segment joining the points $(-4, -2)$ and $(5, 3)$.
5. A point moves so that it is always at a distance of 4 units from the point $(3, 2)$. Find the equation of the locus of the point.

6. What is the equation of the circle with center at $(-4, 5)$ and radius 6?

7. Find the equation of the locus of a point which moves so that the sum of its distances from the points $(0, 3)$ and $(0, -3)$ is always equal to 10.

8. Find the equation of the locus of a point which moves so that the sum of its distances from the points $(1, 2)$ and $(-1, 2)$ is always equal to 4.

9. A point moves so that the difference of its distances from the points $(5, 0)$ and $(-5, 0)$ is always equal to 8. Find the equation of its locus.

10. Find the equation of the locus of a point which moves so that the difference of its distances from $(0, -4)$ and $(0, 4)$ is equal to 6.

11. A point moves so that its distance from the point $(6, 4)$ is twice its distance from the origin. Find the equation of the locus of this point.

12. Find the equation of the locus of a point moving so that its distance from the point $(1, 2)$ is equal to its distance from the Y-axis.

13. Find the equation of the locus of a point which moves so that its distance from the point $(0, 5)$ is twice its distance from the X-axis.

14. Find the equation of the locus of all points equidistant from the point $(-3, 5)$ and the line $x = 3$.

15. A variable point P moves so that the slope of PA is half the slope of BP, where A is the point $(4, 1)$ and B is the point $(-3, -4)$. Find the equation of the locus of P.

16. Find the equation of the locus of a point which moves so that the product of its distances from $(4, 0)$ and $(-4, 0)$ is always equal to 16.

17. Find the equation of the locus of a point which moves so that the ratio of its distances from $(0, 5)$ and $(0, 3)$ is equal to 2.

18. Find the equation of the locus of a point which moves so that its distance from the Y-axis is equal to the square of its distance from the point $(4, 0)$.

19. If $A(4, -1)$ and $B(-2, 3)$ are given points, find the equation of the locus of the point P which moves so that angle APB is always equal to $45°$.

20. Find the equation of the locus of a point which moves so that the ratio of its distances from two fixed points is constant.

CHAPTER IV

Functions and Limits

55. Functions of One Variable

In many mathematical investigations we deal with *related variables.*

*If two variables are so related that to each value of one variable in a given range there corresponds one value, or more than one value, of the second variable, then the second variable is called a **function** of the first variable in that range.*

EXAMPLE 1. If $y = 4 - x^2$, the variables x and y are related by this equation so that to each value of x a corresponding value of y is determined and can be calculated from the equation. Therefore, y is a function of x.

The first variable is also called the **independent variable,** and the second related variable or function is called the **dependent variable.** When a functional relation is given, it is generally possible to choose arbitrarily either one of the related variables as the *independent variable.* In any particular problem, we choose as the independent variable that variable which seems the more natural choice, or which makes the later work simpler.

Any algebraic expression, or in general any mathematical expression, containing a symbol, as x, denoting a variable, is evidently a function of that variable.

EXAMPLE 2. The expressions $3x + 2$, $x^2 + x + 1$, $4/x$, $\sqrt{x^2 + 1}$, 2^x, $\log x$, $\sin x$ and $\arctan x$ are functions of x.

The formulas of geometry and the laws of physical science afford numerous simple examples of functions, often expressed by verbal statements.

EXAMPLE 3. (*a*) The volume of a cone with fixed base is a function of its altitude. (*b*) The period of oscillation of a pendulum is a function of its length. (*c*) The solubility of a substance is generally a function of its temperature.

A function which has only one value for each given value of the independent variable is called a *single-valued function.* A function which has more than one value, in general, for each given value of the independent variable is called a *multiple-valued function.*

EXAMPLE 4. The function $y = x^2 - 2x$ is a single-valued function, but the function y defined by $y^2 = x$ for $x > 0$ (that is, $y = \pm\sqrt{x}$) is a double-valued function.

Functional relationships may be determined in various ways, as for example: (1) by a formula or analytic representation; (2) by a verbal statement; (3) by a table giving corresponding values of the variables; and (4) by a graph or geometric figure.

It is sometimes convenient to *restrict the range* of the independent variable for some particular reason.

EXAMPLE 5. If $y = \sqrt{1 - x^2}$ and we wish to deal only with *real values,* we must restrict x to the interval $-1 \leqq x \leqq 1$.

As is shown in algebra, *division by zero is never permissible.* If, for some value of the independent variable, the definition of a function apparently requires division by zero, the function must be regarded as *undefined* for that value of the variable. Thus, the function $2/(x - 1)$ is undefined for $x = 1$, but is defined for all other values of x.

A function need not be represented by the same expression or formula for all values of the independent variable in its range. Cases sometimes occur in which the function is represented by different expressions in different portions of the range of the variable.

EXAMPLE 6. A function y is defined by:

$$\begin{cases} y = 1 + x & \text{when} & -1 \leqq x \leqq 0, \\ y = 1 - x & \text{when} & 0 \leqq x \leqq 1, \end{cases}$$

in the range $(-1, 1)$, because for each value of the variable x in this interval a value of y is determined by this definition.

56. Functional Notation

We frequently need to discuss properties of functions without specifying any particular function, and so it becomes desirable to be able to express symbolically the fact that one variable is a function of another without assigning the particular form of the functional relation.

If a variable, as y, is a function of an independent variable, as x, this fact is often denoted in general by such symbols as $y = f(x)$ or $y = F(x)$ or $y = \phi(x)$, etc.

An important feature of this functional notation is the following:

If $f(x)$ denotes a given function of x, the result of substituting in the function any particular value a for the variable x is indicated by $f(a)$; that is:

$f(a)$ denotes the value of $f(x)$ when x has the value a.

EXAMPLE 1. If $f(x) = x^2 - x + 1$, then
$$f(2) = 2^2 - 2 + 1 = 3; f(-3) = (-3)^2 - (-3) + 1 = 13;$$
$$f(a) = a^2 - a + 1; f(x + 2) = (x + 2)^2 - (x + 2) + 1 = x^2 + 3x + 3;$$
$$f(x + h) - f(x) = [(x + h)^2 - (x + h) + 1] - [x^2 - x + 1]$$
$$= 2xh + h^2 - h.$$

EXAMPLE 2. If $F(x) = \log x$, show that $F(xy) = F(x) + F(y)$.

Solution: $F(xy) = \log (xy) = \log x + \log y = F(x) + F(y)$.

57. Exercises

1. If $f(x) = x^2 - 2x + 3$, find $f(1)$, $f(2)$, $f(0)$, $f(-2)$, $f(2t)$, $f(1 + h)$, $f(2 + h) - f(2), f(a + h) - f(a)$.

2. If $F(x) = \dfrac{x + 1}{x}$, find $F(2)$, $F(-3)$, $F(-1)$, $F(y)$, $F(a - 1)$, $F(a + h) - F(a)$. Is $F(x)$ defined for $x = -1$ or for $x = 0$?

3. If $g(x) = x^3 - 6x^2 + 11x - 10$, show that $g(1) = g(2) = g(3)$.

4. If $f(x) = \cos x + \sin x$, find $f(0), f(\frac{1}{2}\pi), f(\pi), f(\frac{1}{4}\pi), f(x + \pi), f(-x)$.

5. If $\phi(x) = \log x$, find $\phi(1)$, $\phi(2a)$, $\phi(x/y)$, $\phi(x^n)$.

6. Show that if $F(x) = a^x$, then $F(x - y) = F(x)/F(y)$.

7. Write out and simplify $\dfrac{f(a + h) - f(a)}{h}$ when:

   (a) $f(x) = x^2$;   (b) $f(x) = x + \dfrac{1}{x}$.

8. Write out and simplify $\dfrac{f(a + h) - f(a)}{h}$ when:

   (a) $f(x) = x^3$;   (b) $f(x) = x^2 - \dfrac{2}{x}$.

9. If $f(x) = x^2 - 1$ and $F(u) = u^{\frac{1}{2}}$, express $F[f(x)]$ in terms of x.

10. If $y = f(x) = \dfrac{1 - x}{1 + x}$, show that $x = f(y)$. [*Hint.* Solve the given equation for x in terms of y.]

58. Setting Up Functions

When a functional definition is not expressed directly by a formula, as for example when it is given by a verbal statement, it frequently becomes necessary to express the function by a *formula* in mathematical symbols.

EXAMPLE 1. Express the volume of a right circular cylinder inscribed in a sphere of radius 6 as a function of its altitude.

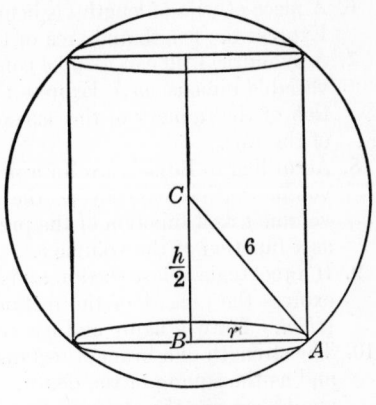

Solution: Let h be the altitude and r the radius of the base of the cylinder (Fig. 44). From the figure, we have $r^2 = 6^2 - (\frac{1}{2} h)^2$; the volume is therefore

$$V = \pi r^2 h = \pi h(36 - \tfrac{1}{4} h^2)$$
$$= 36 \pi h - \tfrac{1}{4} \pi h^3.$$

FIG. 44

EXAMPLE 2. The stiffness of a rectangular beam varies as the product of the breadth and the cube of the depth. Express the stiffness of the beam that can be cut from a cylindrical log as a function of its breadth.

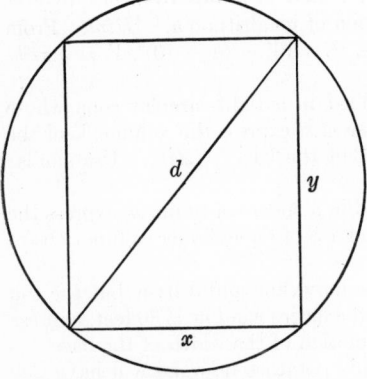

Solution: Let d be the diameter of a circular cross-section of the log, and let x be the breadth and y the depth of the beam (Fig. 45). Then the stiffness of the beam is $S = kxy^3$, where k is a constant. From the figure, we see that $y^2 = d^2 - x^2$, so that $y = (d^2 - x^2)^{\frac{1}{2}}$, and hence

$$S = kx(d^2 - x^2)^{\frac{3}{2}}.$$

FIG. 45

59. Exercises

Express the following functional relations by means of algebraic formulas:

1. The hypotenuse of a right triangle is 5; express one side y as a function of the other side x.
2. Express the altitude h and area A of an equilateral triangle as functions of its side s.
3. Express the length l of any chord of a circle of radius 10 as a function of the perpendicular distance d of the chord from the center of the circle.
4. If the radius r of a circle is increased by an amount x, express the corresponding increase y of the area as a function of x.

5. An open box is to be made from a sheet of cardboard 12 inches square, by cutting equal squares from the four corners and bending up the sides. If x is the length of the side of the square cut out, express the volume V of the box as a function of x.

6. A piece of wire of length l is bent into the form of a rectangle of width x. Express the length and area of the rectangle as functions of x.

7. A cylindrical tin can is to be constructed with given volume V, but with variable dimensions. Express the amount A of tin required as a function of the radius r of the base of the cylinder (neglecting the thickness of the tin).

8. According to Boyle's law for a perfect gas, at a constant temperature the volume varies inversely as the pressure. Using this law, express the volume v as a function of the pressure p, and also express the pressure p as a function of the volume v.

9. If a rectangle is inscribed in an isosceles triangle of base b and altitude h, express the area A of the rectangle as a function of one of its sides x. [*Hint.* Draw a figure and use similar triangles.]

10. The strength of a beam of rectangular cross-section varies as the breadth and as the square of the depth. If the breadth is denoted by b (a constant), express the strength S as a function of the depth y.

11. A rectangle is inscribed in a circle of radius r; express the area A of the rectangle as a function of the acute angle α between its diagonals.

12. Express the volume of a right circular cylinder as a function of its altitude if the radius of the base is always half the altitude.

13. A right circular cone is inscribed in a sphere of radius 10 inches; express the volume V of the cone as a function of its altitude h. [*Hint.* From a figure, if r is the radius of the base, $r^2 = 10^2 - (h - 10)^2$, $V = \frac{1}{3} \pi r^2 h$; eliminate r.]

14. If a right circular cylinder is inscribed in a right circular cone whose altitude is h and whose radius of base is r, express the volume V of the cylinder as a function of the radius R of the base. [*Hint.* Use similar triangles.]

15. If a right circular cylinder is inscribed in a sphere of radius a, express the volume V and also the total surface area S of the cylinder as functions of the radius r of the base.

16. A Norman window has vertical sides and a horizontal base, but the top is a semi-circle. If the perimeter of the entire window is 30 feet, express the area of the entire window as a function of the width of the base.

17. A farmer estimates that if he digs his potatoes now, he will have 200 bushels worth $2 per bushel; but if he waits, the crop will grow 40 bushels per week, while the price will drop 20 cents per bushel per week. Express the total selling price of the crop at the end of x weeks as a function of x.

18. A trough of rectangular cross-section is to be made from a long rectangular sheet of tin 24 inches wide, by bending up the edges. Express the cross-sectional area of the trough in terms of its depth x.

60. Functions of Several Variables

Mathematical problems often give rise to variables which depend on more than one other variable.

*If one variable is so related to several other variables that to each set of values of the last mentioned variables in their respective ranges there corresponds one value (or more than one value) of the first variable, then the first variable is said to be a **function** of the other variables.*

The first variable (function) is often called the *dependent variable* and the other variables the *independent variables.*

EXAMPLE 1. (*a*) The volume of a right circular cylinder depends on its radius of base and altitude thus: $V = \pi r^2 h$, therefore V is a function of the independent variables r and h. (*b*) The pressure of a gas is a function of the volume and of the temperature. (*c*) The expression $u = x^2 + xy + y^2$ is a function of the independent variables x and y.

A function of two variables, as x and y, may be represented in general by such symbols as $f(x, y)$, $F(x, y)$, etc.; similar notation is used for functions of three or more variables.

61. Exercises

1. Express the area of a triangle as a function of its base b and altitude h.
2. Express the volume and lateral area of a right circular cone as functions of the altitude h and the radius of base r.
3. A water-tank is in the form of a hemisphere surmounted by a cylinder, whose radius of base is the same as the radius of the hemisphere. Express the volume and total surface area of the tank as functions of the radius r of the hemisphere and the height h of the cylinder.
4. The heat H generated in an electric circuit by a current is proportional to the square of the current i and to the resistance R of the circuit. Express the heat H as a function of i and R.
5. If $f(x, y) = x^2 - xy + y^2$, find $f(1, 1), f(2, -1), f(a, b), f(m, 1), f(2\,u, 2\,v), f(x, x)$.
6. If $F(x, y) = \dfrac{2\,x - y}{x + 2\,y}$, find $F(2, 1), F(1, 2), F(3, 0), F(p, q), F(2\,r, s)$.

62. Graphic Representation of Functions

One of the clearest ways of exhibiting the character of a function is to give it a graphic representation.

*The **graph of a function** of one variable is the figure consisting of the totality of all points whose coördinates are corresponding values of the independent variable and of the function.*

In constructing the graph in rectangular coördinates, it is customary to plot values of the independent variable as abscissas and values of the function as ordinates.

If the functional relation is given by an *equation* connecting the independent and dependent variables, it is evident that the *graph of the function* is the same as the *locus of the equation* which defines the function.

EXAMPLE. Consider the graph of the function $y = x^3 - 3x^2 - 4x + 10$. If we plot the locus of the equation which defines the given functional rela-

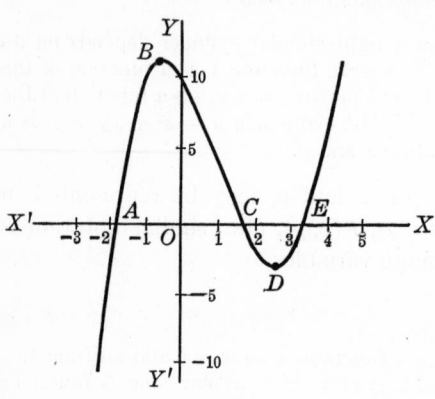

tion by the methods of §§ 43, 47, we obtain the curve shown in Fig. 46. The graph shows that the function has a maximum value at the point B (which is higher than all neighboring points), a minimum value at the point D (which is lower than all neighboring points), that the function has the value zero at the points A, C and E, and is increasing to the left of point B, is decreasing from B to D and is increasing to the right of D.

FIG. 46

As we have seen in the preceding example, a graph of a function exhibits to advantage many properties of a function. Thus, it may show where the function is positive and where negative, where it is equal to zero, where it is increasing and where decreasing, where it attains a maximum or minimum value, etc.

The graphic representation of a function of two variables requires figures in three-dimensional space; it will be discussed later in the chapter on solid analytic geometry. It will be found there that in general the graphs are surfaces.

63. Exercises

1. Draw the graph of each of the following functions:

(a) $y = 4 - 2x$;
(b) $y = x^2 - 4x$;

(c) $y = x^3 - 4x$;
(d) $y = \dfrac{2}{(x-1)^2}$.

2. Draw the graph of each of the following functions:

(a) $y = 2x - 3$;
(b) $y = x^2 - 4x + 3$;

(c) $y = x^3 - 2\,x^2$; 　　　　　　　(d) $y = \dfrac{x-1}{x^2-4}$.

3. Draw the graph of the function y defined by each of the following equations:

   (a) $x^2 + y^2 = 25$; 　　　　　(b) $x^2 - y^2 = 16$;
   (c) $4\,x^2 + 9\,y^2 = 36$; 　　　　(d) $y^2 = x^3$.

4. Draw the graph of the function y defined by each of the following equations:

   (a) $x^2 + y^2 - 2\,x = 0$; 　　　(b) $x^2 + 4\,y^2 = 4$;
   (c) $4\,x^2 - 9\,y^2 = 36$; 　　　　(d) $y^3 = x^2$.

5. Draw the graph of each of the following functions:

   (a) $y = \pm\sqrt{9 - x^2}$; 　　　　(b) $y = \sqrt{9 - x^2}$.

6. Draw the graph of the function defined by:

$$\begin{cases} y = 1 & \text{when} & -2 \leqq x < 0, \\ y = x & \text{when} & 0 \leqq x \leqq 2. \end{cases}$$

7. In the curve whose equation is $y = f(x)$, show that the ordinate of the point whose abscissa is a is $f(a)$.

8. In the curve whose equation is $y = f(x)$, show that the Y-intercept of the curve is the value of $f(0)$.

9. What is the graphical characteristic of a single-valued function? Of a multiple-valued function?

10. In the graph of the function $f(x)$, what is the geometric meaning of the expression

$$\frac{f(a + h) - f(a)}{h}?$$

64. Increments of Functions

Since calculus is concerned with the rates of change of functions, it is desirable to have a brief convenient way of expressing *changes* in variables and functions.

*An **increment** of a variable x is the difference between two values of the variable, and may be thought of as a change in value of the variable.* It is denoted by the symbol Δx, read: "delta x" (in which Δ is not a multiplier of x but is part of a compound symbol). Similarly, an increment of any other variable y is denoted by Δy.

If $y = f(x)$, and if x is given an increment Δx, then y receives a *corresponding* increment Δy. This increment Δy will in general depend on both x and Δx. Since $y + \Delta y = f(x + \Delta x)$, we have

(a) 　　　　　　　$\Delta y = f(x + \Delta x) - f(x).$

EXAMPLE 1. For the function $y = x^2$, calculate the increment Δy of the function: (a) when x changes from 2 to 2.1, and (b) when x changes from 2 to $2 + \Delta x$.

Solution: (a) When $x = 2$ we have $y = 2^2 = 4$, and when $x = 2.1$ we have $y = 2.1^2 = 4.41$; therefore, when x has the increment $\Delta x = 0.1$, the function has the corresponding increment $\Delta y = 0.41$.

(b) When $x = 2$ we have $y = 4$, and when $x = 2 + \Delta x$ we have

$$y = (2 + \Delta x)^2 = 4 + 4(\Delta x) + (\Delta x)^2,$$

hence corresponding to the increment Δx we have

$$\Delta y = [4 + 4(\Delta x) + (\Delta x)^2] - 4 = 4(\Delta x) + (\Delta x)^2.$$

EXAMPLE 2. Find the increment of the function $y = x^2 - 2x + 5$ when x is given an increment Δx, starting with the initial value $x = x_1$.

Solution: If y_1 is the value of y corresponding to $x = x_1$, then

(b) $$y_1 = x_1^2 - 2x_1 + 5;$$

the new values of x and y are $x_1 + \Delta x$ and $y_1 + \Delta y$. Therefore

(c) $$y_1 + \Delta y = (x_1 + \Delta x)^2 - 2(x_1 + \Delta x) + 5$$
$$= x_1^2 + 2x_1(\Delta x) + (\Delta x)^2 - 2x_1 - 2(\Delta x) + 5.$$

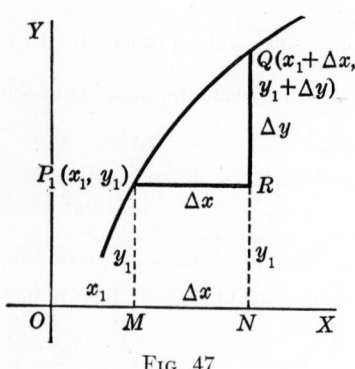

FIG. 47

Subtracting (b) from (c), we get

(d) $\Delta y = 2x_1(\Delta x) + (\Delta x)^2 - 2(\Delta x)$

as the required increment of the function.

A graphical representation of the related increments of a variable and function is helpful. In Fig. 47, the curve represents a given function $y = f(x)$. Let x_1 be any given initial value of x, and let $P_1(x_1, y_1)$ be the corresponding point of the curve. If we take a neighboring point Q on the curve, then in going from P_1 to Q, the corresponding increments of x and y are: $\Delta x = \overline{MN} = \overline{P_1R}$ and $\Delta y = \overline{RQ}$; the coördinates of Q are $(x_1 + \Delta x, y_1 + \Delta y)$.

65. Exercises

1. If $y = x^2 - 2x$, find: (a) Δy when $x = 3$ and $\Delta x = 0.1$; (b) Δy in terms of x and Δx in general.

2. If $y = \dfrac{2x + 1}{x}$, find: (a) Δy when $x = 2$ and $\Delta x = 0.02$; (b) Δy in terms of x and Δx in general.

3. If $y = x^2 - x$, calculate and tabulate the values of the ratio $\Delta y/\Delta x$ when x starts at the value $x = 2$ and takes the successive increments $\Delta x = 1$, 0.1, 0.01, 0.001, 0.0001, 0.00001.

4. If $y = 4x - x^2$, calculate and tabulate the values of the ratio $\Delta y/\Delta x$ when x starts at the value $x = 1$ and takes the successive increments $\Delta x = 1$, 0.1, 0.01, 0.001, 0.0001, 0.00001.

In Exercises 5–12, find Δy and also $\Delta y/\Delta x$ in terms of x and Δx for each of the given functions:

5. $y = 1 + x + x^2$.　　　　　　6. $y = 4 - x^2$.

7. $y = x^3 - x$.　　　　　　　8. $y = 3 - x + 2x^2$.

9. $y = \dfrac{2}{x + 1}$.　　　　　　10. $y = 6x^2 - x^3$.

11. $y = x^4$.　　　　　　　　12. $y = 1/x^2$.

66. Limits

One of the most fundamental concepts of calculus is that of a *limit*.

The idea of a limit has already been met in elementary geometry and algebra. In geometry, the area of a circle is defined and determined as the common limit of the areas of a set of inscribed and circumscribed regular polygons as the number of sides increases beyond all bounds. Similarly, the circumference of a circle is obtained as the limit of the perimeters of a set of polygons. In algebra, the "sum" of an infinite geometric progression is defined and calculated as the limit of the sum of the first n terms of the progression as n increases beyond all bounds. It will be seen later that the basic calculus concepts are defined as limits of certain types of expressions.

67. Limit of a Function

Consider a function $f(x)$, and let the independent variable x take values near a given constant a; then the function $f(x)$ takes a corresponding set of values. It may happen that when x is close to a, the corresponding values of $f(x)$ are close to some constant L. Moreover, it may be that the values of $f(x)$ can be made to differ from L by *as little as we please* by taking values of x that are *sufficiently close* to a, and this may be true for *all such values* of x (except, perhaps, for $x = a$ itself). Under these conditions, we say that $f(x)$ *approaches the limit L as x approaches a*. In this concept of limit, we are not interested in the value of $f(x)$ when x is equal to a, but rather in the values of $f(x)$ when the values of x are close to a but different from a. This idea of a limit may be defined more concisely as follows:

*A function $f(x)$ is said to **approach a limit L as x approaches a** if the difference between $f(x)$ and L is numerically less than an arbitrarily small positive number for all values of x in the range of definition that are sufficiently close to a and for which $x \neq a$.* We indicate this by the notation:

$$\lim_{x \to a} f(x) = L \qquad \text{or} \qquad f(x) \to L \text{ as } x \to a.$$

EXAMPLE 1. Consider the values of the function $f(x) = 2x + 5$ for values of x near 0. The difference between $f(x)$ and the number 5 can evidently be made numerically less than any preassigned small positive number for all values of x (different from 0) that are sufficiently near 0. Hence, $\lim_{x \to 0} f(x) = 5$.

EXAMPLE 2. If $F(x) = x^2 + x + 1$, we have $\lim_{x \to 2} F(x) = 7$, since we can make the difference between $F(x)$ and the value 7 arbitrarily small in absolute value for all values of x sufficiently close to 2 (but different from 2).

The notation $\lim_{x \to a^+} f(x)$ is used when we consider only values of x greater than a and $\lim_{x \to a^-} f(x)$ when we consider only values of x less than a. $\lim_{x \to a} f(x)$ does not exist if $\lim_{x \to a^+} f(x) \neq \lim_{x \to a^-} f(x)$. An example of this is in § 74, Example 3 (Fig. 49).

68. Variables and Functions That Become Infinite

Another type of limit of a function involves the idea of taking large values of the independent variable.

*If the difference between a function $f(x)$ and a constant L is less in absolute value than an arbitrarily small positive number for all positive values of x that are sufficiently large, then we say that $f(x)$ **approaches L as a limit when x becomes positively infinite**.* We indicate this by the notation:

$$f(x) \to L \text{ as } x \to +\infty \qquad \text{or} \qquad \lim_{x \to +\infty} f(x) = L.^*$$

EXAMPLE 1. Consider the function $f(x) = 1 - \dfrac{1}{x}$ for large values of x. When x increases through positive values, $1/x$ decreases and $f(x)$ takes values near 1. We can make $f(x)$ and 1 differ numerically by an arbitrarily small amount for all sufficiently large values of x; hence, $f(x) \to 1$ as $x \to +\infty$.

* The symbol "∞," generally read "infinity," which occurs in this notation, *is not a number*, but is merely part of a symbol indicating a mode of limiting behavior; this symbol ∞ has no meaning when standing alone.

Similarly, we may define the limit

$$f(x) \to L' \quad \text{as} \quad x \to -\infty \qquad \text{or} \qquad \lim_{x \to -\infty} f(x) = L',$$

which is read: "$f(x)$ approaches L' as a limit when x becomes negatively infinite," by using numerically large negative values of x.

Still another type of limiting behavior of a function is given by the following definition:

If a function $f(x)$ is greater than an arbitrarily large positive number for all values of x that are sufficiently near a constant a and for which $x \neq a$, then we say that $f(x)$ becomes positively infinite as x approaches a. We indicate this by the notation:

$$f(x) \to +\infty \quad \text{as} \quad x \to a.^*$$

EXAMPLE 2. In the function $f(x) = \dfrac{1}{(x-2)^2}$, when x is close to 2 (but different from 2), the value of $f(x)$ is large. By taking x sufficiently near 2 but not equal to 2, we can make $f(x)$ as large as we please. Therefore, by the definition above, we have $f(x) \to +\infty$ as $x \to 2$.

Similarly, we define the notation: $f(x) \to -\infty$ as $x \to a$.

Finally, we may have a type of limiting behavior given by the following definition:

If a function $f(x)$ is greater than an arbitrarily large positive number for all positive values of x that are sufficiently large, then we say that $f(x)$ becomes positively infinite as x becomes positively infinite. We indicate this by the notation:

$$f(x) \to +\infty \quad \text{as} \quad x \to +\infty.$$

In a way readily suggested by the preceding definitions, we may define what is meant by the notations: $f(x) \to +\infty$ as $x \to -\infty$, $f(x) \to -\infty$ as $x \to +\infty$, and $f(x) \to -\infty$ as $x \to -\infty$.

It is often convenient to write $\lim\limits_{x \to \infty} f(x)$ to mean *either* $\lim\limits_{x \to +\infty} f(x)$ or $\lim\limits_{x \to -\infty} f(x)$.

An *infinitesimal* is defined as a function which has the limit 0.

* This is frequently written: $\lim\limits_{x \to a} f(x) = +\infty$.

That is, a function $f(x)$ is an **infinitesimal** as $x \to a$ if $\lim\limits_{x \to a} f(x) = 0$; a similar definition applies if $\lim\limits_{x \to \infty} f(x) = 0$.*

69. Exercises

Evaluate each of the limits in Exercises 1–8:

1. $\lim\limits_{x \to 3} (x^2 + 1)$.

2. $\lim\limits_{x \to 1} (4 - x^2)$.

3. $\lim\limits_{x \to 2} \left(\dfrac{x + 2}{x} \right)$.

4. $\lim\limits_{x \to -2} \left(4 - \dfrac{1}{x^2} \right)$.

5. $\lim\limits_{x \to +\infty} \left(\dfrac{2}{x^2 + 4} \right)$.

6. $\lim\limits_{x \to +\infty} \left(1 + \dfrac{2}{x^2} \right)$.

7. $\lim\limits_{x \to -\infty} \left(\dfrac{3}{x^3} \right)$.

8. $\lim\limits_{x \to -\infty} \left(1 - \dfrac{1}{x^3 + 1} \right)$.

Discuss the behavior of each of the functions in Exercises 9–12:

9. $f(x) = 2 + \dfrac{1}{x^4}$ as $x \to 0$.

10. $f(x) = 3 - \dfrac{4}{(x + 1)^2}$ as $x \to -1$.

11. $f(x) = \dfrac{3}{(x - 4)^4}$ as $x \to 4$.

12. $f(x) = x + \dfrac{1}{x^2}$ as $x \to 0$.

13. Formulate in detail the definition of: $\lim\limits_{x \to -\infty} f(x) = L'$.

14. Formulate in detail the definition of: $f(x) \to -\infty$ as $x \to a$.

15. State exactly in words what is meant by each of the limiting processes mentioned near the end of § 68.

70. Operations with Limits

The following limit theorems give rules for operating with limits; for proofs of them we must refer to more advanced works.†

Let u and v be any functions of x which possess limits as x approaches some value a or as $x \to +\infty$ or as $x \to -\infty$. Then:

I. *The limit of the algebraic sum of two functions is equal to the algebraic sum of their limits:*

(1) $\lim (u + v) = \lim u + \lim v$.

This rule also applies to the sum of any finite number of functions.

II. *The limit of the product of two functions is equal to the product of their limits:*

---

* According to this definition, a constant is never an infinitesimal, no matter how small this constant may be. This differs essentially from the non-mathematical use of the term, where it is often employed to mean merely a *very small* quantity.

† See, for example, Sokolnikoff, *Advanced Calculus*, § 9.

(2) $$\lim (u \cdot v) = \lim u \cdot \lim v.$$

This rule also applies to the product of any finite number of functions.

III. *The limit of the quotient of two functions is equal to the quotient of their limits, provided that the limit of the divisor is not zero:*

(3) $$\lim \left(\frac{u}{v}\right) = \frac{\lim u}{\lim v}, \qquad \text{if } \lim v \neq 0.$$

By use of rule II applied to the product of any number of equal factors, we obtain the result:

IV. *The limit of the n-th power of any function is equal to the n-th power of the limit of the function:*

(4) $$\lim (u^n) = (\lim u)^n,$$

where n is any constant positive integral exponent.

By use of this result, it can be shown that:

V. *The limit of the principal n-th root of a positive function is equal to the principal n-th root of the limit of that function:*

(5) $$\lim (\sqrt[n]{u}) = \sqrt[n]{\lim u}.$$

EXAMPLE 1. $\lim\limits_{x \to 2} (x^3 - 3x + 5) = \lim\limits_{x \to 2} (x^3) - \lim\limits_{x \to 2} (3x) + \lim\limits_{x \to 2} (5)$
$$= (\lim\limits_{x \to 2} x)^3 - 3(\lim\limits_{x \to 2} x) + 5 = 2^3 - 3(2) + 5 = 7$$

EXAMPLE 2. $\lim\limits_{x \to 2} \left(\dfrac{x^2 \sqrt{x+2}}{x^2+1}\right) = \dfrac{\lim\limits_{x \to 2} (x^2) \cdot \sqrt{\lim\limits_{x \to 2} (x+2)}}{\lim\limits_{x \to 2} (x^2+1)} = \dfrac{2^2 \cdot \sqrt{4}}{4+1} = \dfrac{8}{5}.$

71. Exercises

Evaluate each of the limits in Exercises 1–16:

1. $\lim\limits_{x \to 1} (x^2 - 2x + 3).$

2. $\lim\limits_{x \to 0} (2x^2 - x + 4).$

3. $\lim\limits_{x \to 2} \left(x + \dfrac{1}{x}\right).$

4. $\lim\limits_{x \to 3} \left(x^2 - \dfrac{1}{x}\right).$

5. $\lim\limits_{x \to 0} \left(\dfrac{x-1}{x+1}\right).$

6. $\lim\limits_{x \to 0} \left(\dfrac{x}{x+2}\right).$

7. $\lim\limits_{x \to 0} \left(\dfrac{x^2+9}{(x-2)^2}\right).$

8. $\lim\limits_{x \to -1} \left(\dfrac{x^2+1}{x^2+x+1}\right).$

9. $\lim\limits_{x \to 1} \left(x^2 + 1 - \dfrac{1}{x-2}\right).$

10. $\lim\limits_{x \to 1} \left(2 - \dfrac{x-1}{x^2}\right).$

11. $\lim\limits_{x \to 0} (x - 2 + \sqrt{x + 4})$.

12. $\lim\limits_{x \to 2} (4x - \sqrt{x^2 - 4})$.

13. $\lim\limits_{x \to +\infty} \left(\dfrac{2}{x^2 + 1} \right)$.

14. $\lim\limits_{x \to +\infty} \left(4 - \dfrac{2}{x + 1} \right)$.

15. $\lim\limits_{x \to -\infty} (1 + 2^x)$.

16. $\lim\limits_{x \to +\infty} \left(\dfrac{2}{3^x} \right)$.

Discuss the limiting behavior of each of the functions in Exercises 17–20:

17. $y = 1 + \dfrac{1}{x^2}$ as $x \to 0$.

18. $F(x) = \dfrac{x^2 + 1}{(x^2 - 4)^2}$ as $x \to -2$.

19. $f(x) = x - \dfrac{10}{(x - 2)^2}$ as $x \to 2$.

20. $y = 2x - \dfrac{1}{x^2}$ as $x \to 0$.

21. Show that if $P(x) = c_0 x^n + c_1 x^{n-1} + \cdots + c_{n-1} x + c_n$ is any polynomial in x, then

$$\lim_{x \to a} P(x) = P(a).$$

22. If $P(x)$ and $Q(x)$ are any two polynomials in x, and if a is not a root of the equation $Q(x) = 0$, show that:

$$\lim_{x \to a} \frac{P(x)}{Q(x)} = \frac{P(a)}{Q(a)}.$$

23. Prove that if $0 < r < 1$, then $r^n \to 0$ as $n \to +\infty$ (through positive integral values). [*Hint.* Let $r = 1/(1 + p)$, where $p > 0$; by the binomial theorem,

$$r^n = \frac{1}{(1 + p)^n} = \frac{1}{1 + np + \dfrac{n(n - 1)}{2} p^2 + \cdots + p^n} < \frac{1}{np}. \Big]$$

24. Prove that if $r > 1$, then $r^n \to +\infty$ as $n \to +\infty$ (through positive integral values). [*Hint.* Let $r = 1 + p$, where $p > 0$; by the binomial theorem,

$$r^n = (1 + p)^n = 1 + np + \frac{n(n - 1)}{2} p^2 + \cdots + p^n > np. \Big]$$

72. Indeterminate Forms

In applying the theorem on the limit of a quotient ($\S$ 70, III), it may happen that the quotient of the limits takes the meaningless form "0/0," generally called an "indeterminate form." But the original quotient may still approach a "determinate" limit, if a different procedure is used.

EXAMPLE 1. If $f(x) = \dfrac{x^2 - 4}{x - 2}$, and if we apply theorem III of $\S$ 70 to find $\lim\limits_{x \to 2} f(x)$, we get the indeterminate form 0/0. But if $x \neq 2$, we can divide by

$x - 2$ and obtain

$$f(x) = \frac{x^2 - 4}{x - 2} = x + 2.$$

As pointed out in § 67, in considering the limit of $f(x)$ as x approaches 2, we are not interested in the value of $f(x)$ at $x = 2$ itself but only in other neighboring values. Therefore, for these values, $f(x) = x + 2$, and we have

$$\lim_{x \to 2} f(x) = \lim_{x \to 2} (x + 2) = 4.$$

Thus, even though $f(x)$ is *undefined* at $x = 2$, it has a *limit* 4 when $x \to 2$.

Limits of functions which take indeterminate forms of the preceding type lie at the basis of the discussions of the next chapter; the following example is typical.

EXAMPLE 2. Consider the function $F(h) = \dfrac{(2 + h)^2 - 4}{h}$. If we try to find $\lim\limits_{h \to 0} F(h)$ by means of theorem III of § 70, we obtain the indeterminate form $0/0$. But if $h \neq 0$, we can simplify the numerator and then divide numerator and denominator by h and get

$$F(h) = \frac{4 + 4\,h + h^2 - 4}{h} = \frac{4\,h + h^2}{h} = 4 + h.$$

Therefore, $\lim\limits_{h \to 0} F(h) = 4$.

73. Exercises

Evaluate each of the limits in Exercises 1–8:

1. $\lim\limits_{x \to 3} \left(\dfrac{x^2 - 9}{x - 3} \right).$

2. $\lim\limits_{x \to 1} \left(\dfrac{x - 1}{x^2 - 1} \right).$

3. $\lim\limits_{x \to 1} \left(\dfrac{x^2 - x}{x^2 - 1} \right).$

4. $\lim\limits_{x \to -4} \left(\dfrac{x^3 - 16\,x}{x + 4} \right).$

5. $\lim\limits_{x \to 2} \left(\dfrac{x^3 - 8}{x - 2} \right).$

6. $\lim\limits_{x \to 2} \left(\dfrac{x^2 - 5\,x + 6}{x^2 - x - 2} \right).$

7. $\lim\limits_{x \to 0} \left(\dfrac{x^3 - x^2}{x^2 + 3\,x} \right).$

8. $\lim\limits_{x \to 1} \left(\dfrac{1}{2\,x^2 + x - 3} - \dfrac{1}{3\,x^2 - x - 2} \right).$

9. Evaluate:

   (a) $\lim\limits_{h \to 0} \dfrac{(1 + h)^2 - 1}{h};$

   (b) $\lim\limits_{k \to 0} \dfrac{(x + k)^3 - x^3}{k}.$

10. If $f(x) = x^2 + 2\,x$, show that:

$$\lim_{h \to 0} \frac{f(x + h) - f(x)}{h} = 2\,x + 2.$$

74. Continuity of Functions

In the definition of $\lim_{x \to a} f(x)$, nothing is said about the value of $f(x)$ for $x = a$; this limit depends only on the values of $f(x)$ in the neighborhood of $x = a$ but not on the value of $f(x)$ at $x = a$. That is, $\lim_{x \to a} f(x)$ may or may not be equal to $f(a)$. The case where this limit exists and the value $f(a)$ exists and is equal to the limit, is of special importance.

*A function $f(x)$ which is defined at all points in the neighborhood of a point $x = a$ is said to be **continuous for $x = a$** if the following three conditions are satisfied: (a) $f(a)$ exists, (b) $\lim_{x \to a} f(x)$ exists, and (c) $\lim_{x \to a} f(x) = f(a)$.*

*A function is said to be **continuous in an interval** if it is continuous at every point of the interval.*

EXAMPLE 1. For the function $f(x) = x^2$, we have $\lim_{x \to 3} f(x) = 9$, and $f(3) = 9$, therefore this function is continuous at $x = 3$. Since $\lim_{x \to a} f(x) = a^2 = f(a)$ for any value a, the function is continuous for all values of x.

*A function which is not continuous at a point $x = a$ is said to be **discontinuous** there.*

The principal type of discontinuity met in ordinary elementary work is that in which the *function becomes infinite* when x approaches some particular value a. In this case, $\lim_{x \to a} f(x)$ does not exist, and of course condition (c) of the definition of continuity cannot be satisfied.

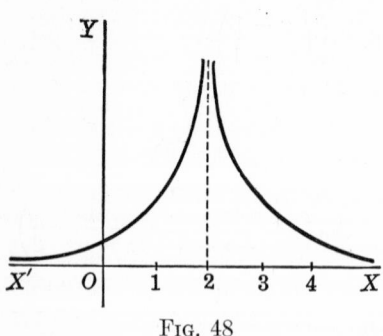

Fig. 48

EXAMPLE 2. The function $f(x) = \dfrac{1}{(x - 2)^2}$, whose graph is shown in Fig. 48, has an infinite discontinuity at $x = 2$, since

$$f(x) \to +\infty \text{ as } x \to 2$$

and $f(2)$ is undefined and does not exist. This function is continuous for all other values than $x = 2$.

The case of a *finite discontinuity* is much less important for elementary work than that of an infinite discontinuity. The following examples illustrate types that sometimes occur.

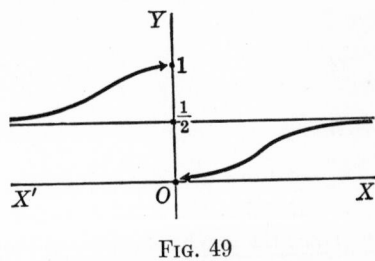

EXAMPLE 3. The function $f(x) = \dfrac{1}{1 + 2^{\frac{1}{x}}}$, whose graph is shown in Fig. 49, has a finite discontinuity or "jump" at $x = 0$, since $\lim\limits_{x \to 0} f(x)$ does not exist, but it is continuous elsewhere.

FIG. 49

EXAMPLE 4. Another example of a function with a finite discontinuity is the function $f(x)$ defined by:

$$\begin{cases} f(x) = 1 & \text{when} & 0 < x < 1, \\ f(x) = -1 & \text{when} & -1 < x < 0, \end{cases}$$

which has a finite discontinuity at $x = 0$. (Draw a graph.)

If $y = f(x)$ is continuous at $x = a$, then $f(x) \to f(a)$ as $x \to a$, or $f(x) - f(a) \to 0$ as $x - a \to 0$. In increment notation,

$$\Delta y = f(x) - f(a) \to 0 \quad \text{as} \quad \Delta x = x - a \to 0.$$

Hence, *if y is a continuous function of x, then $\Delta y \to 0$ when $\Delta x \to 0$.*

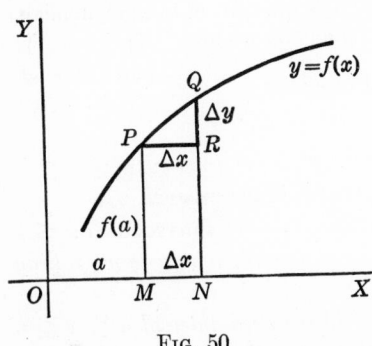

Interpreting this graphically, in Fig. 50, this means that when $y = f(x)$ is a continuous function of x at $x = a$, in the graph of the function, a sufficiently small change $\Delta x = \overline{PR}$ in the abscissa produces an arbitrarily small change $\Delta y = \overline{RQ}$ in the ordinate.

A result of great practical importance which follows at once from the definition of continuity of a function is that if we are required to find $\lim\limits_{x \to a} f(x)$ *when $f(x)$ is continuous at $x = a$*, we may do so by finding $f(a)$, i.e., by substituting a in place of x in $f(x)$.

FIG. 50

75. Exercises

Find the discontinuities of each of the functions in Exercises 1–8:

1. $\dfrac{x+1}{x-1}$.

2. $\dfrac{x^2+1}{x^2}$.

3. $\dfrac{2\,x}{1-x^2}$.

4. $\dfrac{x+1}{(x-1)(x+3)}$.

5. $\dfrac{x}{x^2+2\,x-3}$.

6. $\dfrac{2\,x-1}{x(x^2+1)}$.

7. $\dfrac{x^2-5\,x+4}{x^2-7\,x+6}$.

8. $\dfrac{x-1}{x^2-1}$.

9. Draw the graphs of each of the following functions, and discuss the continuity and discontinuity of the functions:

    (a) $f(x) = \dfrac{1}{x(x-2)}$;

    (b) $f(x) = \dfrac{4\,x}{4-x^2}$.

10. Discuss the behavior of the function $y = 10^{\frac{1}{x}}$ as $x \to 0$. Is this function continuous at $x = 0$?

11. Graph and discuss the continuity of the function defined by:

$$\begin{cases} f(x) = \pi + x & \text{when} & 0 < x < \pi, \\ f(x) = \pi - x & \text{when} & -\pi < x < 0, \\ f(0) = 0. \end{cases}$$

12. Prove that: the sum, difference, product or quotient of two continuous functions is a continuous function, provided that no zero denominator occurs in the case of a quotient. [*Hint.* Use § 70.]

13. Prove that a polynomial in x is continuous for all values of x. [*Hint.* See § 71, Exercise 21.]

14. Prove that a rational algebraic function (a quotient of two polynomials) is continuous except where a zero denominator occurs.

76. Some Properties of Continuous Functions

It is proved in more advanced works* that:

I. *If a function $f(x)$ is continuous in a closed interval $a \leqq x \leqq b$, then $f(x)$ has a greatest value and a least value in the interval.*

II. *A function $f(x)$ which is continuous in a closed interval $a \leqq x \leqq b$ cannot pass from one value to another in the interval without taking every intermediate value at least once.*

III. *If a function $f(x)$ is continuous in a closed interval $a \leqq x \leqq b$ and if $f(a)$ and $f(b)$ are opposite in sign, then there exists at least one value $x = c$ in the interval such that $f(c) = 0$.*

Exercise. Draw appropriate figures to illustrate the above theorems geometrically.

* See, for example, Fine, *Calculus*, § 18.

CHAPTER V

Derivatives

77. The Derivative of a Function

We shall now define analytically a certain fundamental concept, called the *derivative* of a function, and then, as an indication of its usefulness, we shall present several particular interpretations.

Let $y = f(x)$ be any function of an independent variable x. Let x_1 be a fixed initial value of x, and y_1 the corresponding value of the function y. Let x be given an arbitrary increment Δx, starting with x_1; then y receives a corresponding increment Δy, starting at y_1. The new values of x and y are $x_1 + \Delta x$ and $y_1 + \Delta y$. From the functional relation $y = f(x)$, we may calculate Δy in terms of x_1 and Δx (as was shown in § 64). We then form the ratio $\Delta y/\Delta x$ of these increments. If we keep x_1 fixed and treat Δx as a variable, this ratio may approach a limit as Δx approaches zero. This limit is so important that we give it a name and study its properties.

When the limit of the ratio $\Delta y/\Delta x$ as Δx approaches zero exists, it is called the **derivative** *of the function $y = f(x)$ with respect to x for the value $x = x_1$.*

EXAMPLE 1. Find the derivative of the function $y = x^2$ for the value $x = 3$.

Solution: Corresponding to the initial value $x_1 = 3$, we find the initial value of the function $y_1 = 3^2 = 9$. If we give x an increment Δx, the function takes the corresponding increment Δy, and the new values of x and y are $3 + \Delta x$ and $9 + \Delta y$. By the functional relation, we have

(a) $$9 + \Delta y = (3 + \Delta x)^2 = 9 + 6(\Delta x) + (\Delta x)^2,$$

from which we get

(b) $$\Delta y = 6(\Delta x) + (\Delta x)^2,$$

and

(c) $$\frac{\Delta y}{\Delta x} = 6 + \Delta x.$$

Therefore, the required value of the derivative is

(d) $$\lim_{\Delta x \to 0} \left(\frac{\Delta y}{\Delta x} \right) = 6.$$

EXAMPLE 2. Find the derivative of the function $y = x^3 - 3x$ for $x = x_1$.

Solution: If y_1 is the value of y corresponding to $x = x_1$, and Δx and Δy are corresponding increments of x and y, then

(e) $\qquad y_1 = x_1^3 - 3x_1,$

(f) $\qquad y_1 + \Delta y = (x_1 + \Delta x)^3 - 3(x_1 + \Delta x)$
$$= x_1^3 + 3x_1^2(\Delta x) + 3x_1(\Delta x)^2 + (\Delta x)^3 - 3x_1 - 3(\Delta x).$$

Subtracting (e) from (f), we get

(g) $\qquad \Delta y = 3x_1^2(\Delta x) + 3x_1(\Delta x)^2 + (\Delta x)^3 - 3(\Delta x);$

then

(h) $\qquad \dfrac{\Delta y}{\Delta x} = 3x_1^2 + 3x_1(\Delta x) + (\Delta x)^2 - 3.$

Holding x_1 fixed, and using the limit theorems of § 70, we obtain for the derivative at $x = x_1$ the result:

(i) $$\lim_{\Delta x \to 0} \left(\frac{\Delta y}{\Delta x} \right) = 3x_1^2 - 3.$$

If we denote the fixed initial value of the independent variable by x instead of x_1, then the derivative will be expressed in terms of x instead of x_1; we may therefore regard the derivative of a given function of x as another associated function of x.

Alternative notations for the derivative of a function $y = f(x)$ with respect to x are:

$$D_x y, \qquad \text{or} \qquad D_x f(x), \qquad \text{or} \qquad f'(x), \qquad \text{or} \qquad y'.^*$$

To indicate the value of the derivative of $y = f(x)$ for some particular value of x, as $x = x_1$, we may write: $f'(x_1)$, or y_1', or $D_x y|_{x=x_1}$.

The process of finding the derivative of a function is called **differentiation.** If, for a given value of the variable x, the derivative of a function $f(x)$ exists, the function is said to be **differentiable** for that value of x. We may consider the symbol $D_x y$ for the derivative as indicating that the operation of differentiation, denoted by D_x, is to be performed on the function y with respect to the independent variable x.

---

* Another notation, $\dfrac{dy}{dx}$, will be introduced later (§ 141).

The definition of a derivative may be stated thus:

*The **derivative** of a function is the limit of the ratio of the increment of the function to the corresponding increment of the independent variable, when the latter increment approaches zero.*

(1)

$$If\ y = f(x),\ then$$
$$D_x y = f'(x) = \lim_{\Delta x \to 0} \left(\frac{\Delta y}{\Delta x} \right).$$

Since $\Delta y = f(x + \Delta x) - f(x)$, we may also write:

(j)
$$f'(x) = \lim_{\Delta x \to 0} \frac{f(x + \Delta x) - f(x)}{\Delta x}.$$

EXAMPLE 3. Find the derivative of $y = 1/x$.

Solution: Since $y = 1/x$,

$$y + \Delta y = \frac{1}{x + \Delta x},$$

$$\Delta y = \frac{1}{x + \Delta x} - \frac{1}{x} = -\frac{\Delta x}{x(x + \Delta x)},$$

$$\frac{\Delta y}{\Delta x} = \frac{-1}{x(x + \Delta x)}.$$

$$\therefore D_x y = \lim_{\Delta x \to 0} \left(\frac{\Delta y}{\Delta x} \right) = -\frac{1}{x^2}.$$

Since $f'(x) = \lim_{\Delta x \to 0} (\Delta y / \Delta x)$ when $y = f(x)$, it follows from the definition of a limit (§67) that we may write

$$\frac{\Delta y}{\Delta x} = f'(x) + \epsilon, \quad \text{where} \quad \epsilon \to 0 \quad \text{as} \quad \Delta x \to 0,$$

or

(k)
$$\Delta y = f'(x) \cdot \Delta x + \epsilon \cdot \Delta x.$$

From this relation we see that $\Delta y \to 0$ and $y + \Delta y \to y$ when $\Delta x \to 0$. Therefore, y is a continuous function of x. Hence:

*If a function $f(x)$ is differentiable for all values of x in a given interval, it is continuous in that interval.**

* It is possible for a function $f(x)$ to be continuous in an interval and yet not be differentiable for any value of x in that interval. Such functions are not met in elementary calculus.

78. Exercises

Find the derivative of each of the functions in Exercises 1–8:

1. $y = x^2 - 4x + 5$.   2. $y = 2x - x^2$.

3. $y = x^3 - 2x + 1$.   4. $y = 6x - x^3$.

5. $u = \dfrac{x}{x+1}$.   6. $v = \dfrac{z+4}{2z}$.

7. $w = \dfrac{z+1}{z-1}$.   8. $s = t + \dfrac{1}{t}$.

Find the value of each of the following derivatives, for the indicated value of the variable:

9. $D_x(x^3 - 2x^2 + x)$ when $x = 2$.   10. $D_r(r^2 + 3r - 7)$ when $r = -2$.

11. $f'(2)$ when $f(x) = 2x^2 - \dfrac{1}{x^2}$.   12. $F'(-2)$ when $F(t) = \dfrac{t+1}{t^2}$.

13. Find the derivative of each of the following functions: (a) x^2; (b) x^3; (c) x^4; (d) x^5. From these results can you predict the derivative of x^8, and also the derivative of x^n?

14. Find the derivative of $y = \sqrt{x}$ when $x \neq 0$; also show that $y = \sqrt{x}$ has no derivative when $x = 0$. [*Hint.* In the expression

$$\frac{\Delta y}{\Delta x} = \frac{\sqrt{x + \Delta x} - \sqrt{x}}{\Delta x},$$

multiply the numerator and denominator by $\sqrt{x + \Delta x} + \sqrt{x}$, simplify and then take the limit.]

79. Geometric Interpretation of the Derivative: Slope of the Tangent to a Curve

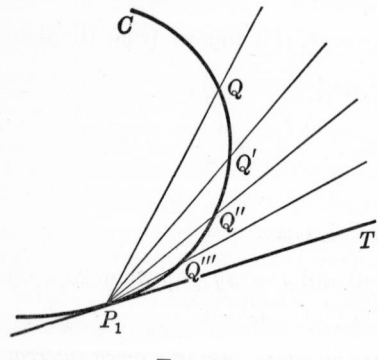

FIG. 51

One of the fundamental problems which historically gave rise to the development of differential calculus was that of finding the *slope of the tangent to a curve.*

Let us examine this problem. It is necessary first to define what is meant by a tangent to any curve at a given point on it. Consider any fixed point P_1 on a given curve (Fig. 51), and let Q be a variable neighboring point on the curve, and let P_1Q be the corresponding secant. Let Q vary its position on the curve and approach P_1 along the curve; the secant P_1Q will rotate about the point P_1, and P_1Q may approach a limiting position P_1T. Then:

The **tangent** to a curve at a point P_1 is defined as the limiting position P_1T (if such exists) of a secant P_1Q as the point Q approaches P_1 along the curve.

Let the curve in Fig. 52 be the graph of the function $y = f(x)$, where $f(x)$ is a differentiable function. Let $P_1(x_1, y_1)$ be a fixed point on the curve, and let Q be a neighboring point on the curve. If the

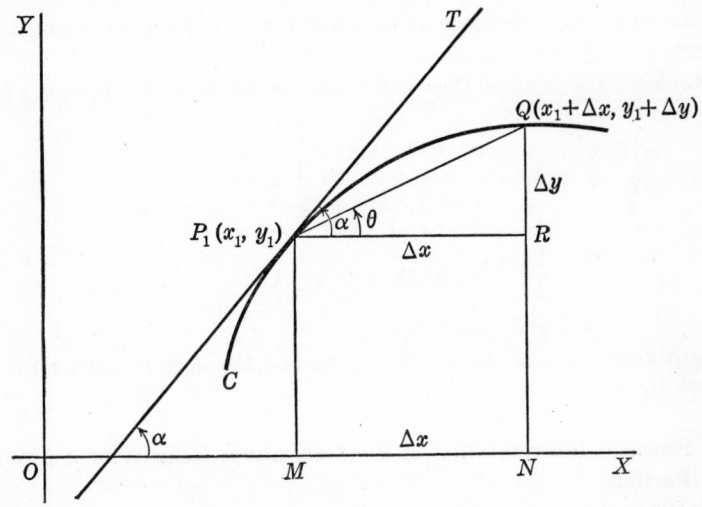

FIG. 52

coördinates of Q differ from those of P_1 by $\overline{P_1R} = \Delta x$ and $\overline{RQ} = \Delta y$, then the coördinates of Q are $(x_1 + \Delta x, y_1 + \Delta y)$. Now

$$(a) \qquad \text{slope of secant } P_1Q = \tan \theta = \frac{\overline{RQ}}{\overline{P_1R}} = \frac{\Delta y}{\Delta x},$$

where θ is the angle of inclination RP_1Q. By the preceding definition of tangent line, from equation (a) we obtain:

$$(b) \qquad \textit{slope of tangent } P_1T = \tan \alpha = \lim_{\Delta x \to 0} \left(\frac{\Delta y}{\Delta x} \right),$$

where α is the inclination of the tangent.

But by definition of the derivative,

$$(c) \qquad \lim_{\Delta x \to 0} (\Delta y / \Delta x) = D_x y|_{x=x_1} = f'(x_1).$$

Hence:

The slope of the tangent to a curve whose equation is $y = f(x)$, at a point of tangency (x_1, y_1), is given by the value of the derivative of the function $f(x)$ with respect to x at $x = x_1$:

(2)   *slope of tangent* $= f'(x_1) = D_x y\big|_{x=x_1}.$

The slope of the tangent to a curve is sometimes called the *slope of the curve* at the point of tangency.

EXAMPLE. Find the slope of the curve $y = x^2 - 4x$ at the point where $x = 4$.

Solution: The required slope is the value of the derivative $D_x y$ for $x = 4$, which is found as follows:

$$\begin{aligned}
y &= x^2 - 4x, \\
y + \Delta y &= (x + \Delta x)^2 - 4(x + \Delta x) \\
&= x^2 + 2x(\Delta x) + (\Delta x)^2 - 4x - 4(\Delta x), \\
\Delta y &= 2x(\Delta x) + (\Delta x)^2 - 4(\Delta x), \\
\frac{\Delta y}{\Delta x} &= 2x + \Delta x - 4. \\
\therefore f'(x) &= 2x - 4.
\end{aligned}$$

Substituting $x = 4$ in this derivative, we find the slope $m = 4$ for the required tangent line.

80. Physical Interpretation of the Derivative: Velocity of a Moving Particle

Another type of problem which played an important part in the early development of differential calculus was that of finding the *velocity of a moving body* at a given instant, in any kind of motion.

Let us examine this problem. As before, it is necessary to begin by *defining* velocity. Consider a particle moving along a straight line path, and let t denote the time measured from some fixed instant, and let s denote the distance of the particle from some fixed origin on the line, considered positive or negative according to the direction from the origin. Suppose that the distance is given in terms of the time by a function $s = f(t)$; this equation will be called the *law of motion*. At a certain time t_1, let the particle be at a point P_1 at a directed distance s_1 from the origin O (Fig. 53), and suppose that dur-

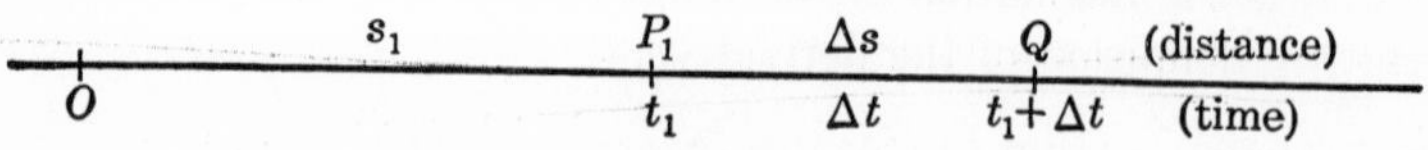

FIG. 53

ing the following time-interval Δt the particle moves a distance Δs from P_1 to Q.

If the ratio $\Delta s/\Delta t$ is constant, so that equal distances are traversed in equal intervals of time, the motion is called *uniform*, and the ratio is called the *velocity* at any instant.

If, however, the motion is not uniform, the ratio $\Delta s/\Delta t$ varies, as Δt varies, and we can no longer take this ratio as the velocity at an instant. Instead, we define this ratio as the **average velocity** of the particle *during the time-interval Δt:*

$$(a) \qquad\qquad \text{average velocity} = \frac{\Delta s}{\Delta t}.$$

If we now let the time-interval Δt become smaller, this average velocity $\Delta s/\Delta t$ may approach a limit as Δt approaches zero. We have the following definition:

*The **velocity** of a particle at a given instant t_1 (sometimes called the instantaneous velocity) is defined as the limit of the average velocity $\Delta s/\Delta t$ of the particle during a time-interval Δt starting at t_1, as this time-interval approaches zero:*

$$(b) \qquad\qquad \textbf{\textit{instantaneous velocity}} = \lim_{\Delta t \to 0}\left(\frac{\Delta s}{\Delta t}\right).$$

But the limit of the ratio of the increments $\Delta s/\Delta t$ as $\Delta t \to 0$ is, by definition, the derivative $f'(t_1)$ or $D_t s|_{t=t_1}$. Hence:

The velocity of a particle moving in a straight line according to the law of motion $s = f(t)$, where s is the directed distance from a fixed origin and t is the time, at an instant t_1, is given by the value of the derivative of s with respect to t for $t = t_1$:

$$(3) \qquad\qquad \textbf{\textit{velocity }} v = f'(t_1) = D_t s \mid_{t=t_1}.$$

EXAMPLE. Find the velocity of a rectilinear motion given by the equation $s = 16\,t^2 - 48\,t + 80$ at the instant when $t = 2$.

Solution: $s = 16\,t^2 - 48\,t + 80,$

$$\begin{aligned}
s + \Delta s &= 16(t + \Delta t)^2 - 48(t + \Delta t) + 80 \\
&= 16\,t^2 + 32\,t(\Delta t) + 16(\Delta t)^2 - 48\,t - 48(\Delta t) + 80, \\
\Delta s &= 32\,t(\Delta t) + 16(\Delta t)^2 - 48(\Delta t);
\end{aligned}$$

$$\frac{\Delta s}{\Delta t} = 32\,t + 16(\Delta t) - 48,$$

$$\therefore v = D_t s = 32\,t - 48.$$

When $t = 2$, we find the velocity is $v = 16$.

The term *speed* is frequently used to mean the magnitude (absolute value) of the velocity.

81. Exercises

1. Find the slope of the tangent to the curve $y = 2x - x^2$ at the point where $x = 1$, and also at the point (x_1, y_1).
2. Find the inclination α of the tangent to the curve $y = x^2 - 3x + 4$ at the point $(2, 2)$. [*Hint.* $\tan \alpha = f'(x_1)$.]
3. Find the slope of the tangent to the curve $y = x^3 - 3x^2 + 2x$ at each of the points where it crosses the X-axis.
4. Find the point on the curve $y = x^2 - 2x$ at which the tangent makes an angle of $45°$ with the X-axis.
5. Find the velocity of the particle in straight line motion whose equation of motion is $s = t^2 - t$, at the time $t = 2$, and also at the time $t = t_1$.
6. For a body rising vertically, the height at time t was $s = 120t - 16t^2$. Find the velocity at any time t; also find when the velocity was 0.

82. Interpretation of the Sign of the Derivative

Consider a function $y = f(x)$ at a value $x = x_1$ and let $y_1 = f(x_1)$. We then define the function as increasing or decreasing as follows:

*A function $f(x)$ is said to be **increasing** for a value x_1 of x if $f(x)$ is differentiable at $x = x_1$ and if the derivative $f'(x_1)$ is positive, and it is said to be **decreasing** at $x = x_1$ if the derivative $f'(x_1)$ is negative.*

We may interpret this notion graphically in this way: Suppose that $f'(x_1)$ is positive. When $|\Delta x|$ is sufficiently small, the quotient $\Delta y/\Delta x$ is positive, since its limit $f'(x_1)$ is positive. Then Δy and Δx have the same sign for sufficiently small values of $|\Delta x|$, not zero. If Δx is positive, it follows that Δy is positive and $y_1 + \Delta y$ is greater than y_1; if Δx is negative, $y_1 + \Delta y$ is less than y_1. Graphically, this means that when the slope is positive, if we go from left to right, the graph of $f(x)$ is *rising* at the point where $x = x_1$ (Fig. 54).

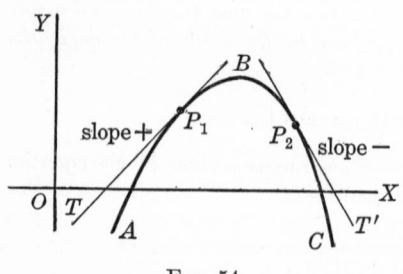

Fig. 54

Similarly, if $f'(x_1)$ is negative, then Δy and Δx have opposite signs for sufficiently small values of $|\Delta x|$, not zero. In this case, the graph of $f(x)$ is *falling* at the point where $x = x_1$, when the slope is negative (Fig. 54).

83. Rate of Change of a Varying Quantity

Let p and q denote the measures of two related varying physical quantities, so that we may regard q as a function of p. Form the ratio $\Delta q/\Delta p$ of corresponding changes in these quantities. If this ratio has the same value for all values of Δp, this ratio is called the *rate of change* of q with respect to p, and q is said to *change uniformly* with respect to p. But if the ratio $\Delta q/\Delta p$ is not constant as Δp changes, q does not change uniformly, and $\Delta q/\Delta p$ is then called the *average rate of change* of q with respect to p *over the interval* Δp.

If the ratio $\Delta q/\Delta p$ approaches a limit when Δp approaches zero, then this limit is defined to be the **instantaneous rate of change** *of q with respect to p.*

From the definition of derivative, it follows that:

The rate of change of a variable quantity q with respect to a related variable quantity p is given by the derivative $D_p q$ of the function q with respect to the independent variable p.

Of special importance is the *time-rate of change $D_t q$* of a varying quantity q. Thus, the velocity of a particle is the time-rate of change of its distance from a fixed origin.

It is a common practice to extend this notion of rate of change of a variable quantity to the case of any function, and to use the expression *"rate of change of a function"* as equivalent to the derivative of the function.

84. Exercises

1. Prove that the rate of change of the area of a circle with respect to the radius is equal to the circumference.
2. Prove that the rate of change of the volume of a sphere with respect to the radius is equal to the surface area.
3. The pressure of the atmosphere decreases as the distance from the earth's surface increases, and the rate of change of pressure with respect to height is proportional to the pressure. Express this law in the form of an equation in terms of calculus symbols.
4. Under certain conditions, an electric current dies out at a rate (with respect to time) that is proportional to the current remaining. Express this in the form of an equation in terms of calculus symbols.

5. The intensity of illumination I on a surface is inversely proportional to the square of the distance r from the surface to the source of light. If the intensity is 1000 units when the distance is 1 foot, find the rate of change of the intensity with respect to the distance, when the distance is 10 feet.

CHAPTER VI

Differentiation of Algebraic Functions

85. Algebraic Functions

A *polynomial function* of x is a function which is expressible in the form

$$(a) \qquad a_0x^n + a_1x^{n-1} + \cdots + a_{n-1}x + a_n,$$

where a_0, a_1, $\cdots$, a_{n-1}, a_n are constants, $a_0 \neq 0$, and n is a positive integer or 0, which is called the *degree* of the function.

A *rational function* is a function which is either a polynomial function or expressible as a quotient of two polynomial functions.

EXAMPLE 1. The expressions $x^2 - 2x + 3$ and $x^3 - \frac{5}{2}x + \frac{2}{3}$ are polynomial functions, of the second and third degree respectively. The expressions $\dfrac{x^2 - x + 1}{x^2 + x + 1}$ and $2x - 1 + \dfrac{x}{x^2 + 1}$ are rational functions.

A function $y = f(x)$ is called an *algebraic function* if y is a root of an equation of the form

$$(b) \qquad P_0(x) \cdot y^n + P_1(x) \cdot y^{n-1} + \cdots + P_{n-1}(x) \cdot y + P_n(x) = 0,$$

where $P_0(x)$, $P_1(x)$, $\cdots$, $P_n(x)$ are given polynomial functions of x and n is a positive integer.

Polynomial functions and rational functions are special types of algebraic functions.

EXAMPLE 2. The equation $xy^2 - 2y + 3x = 0$ defines y as an algebraic function of x, which may also be expressed (by use of the quadratic formula of algebra) in the form $y = \dfrac{1 \pm \sqrt{1 - 3x^2}}{x}$.

An algebraic function which is not a rational function is called an *irrational function*.

EXAMPLE 3. The expressions $\sqrt{x - 4}$, $x + \sqrt[3]{2 + x}$ and $\dfrac{2x}{\sqrt{4 - x^2}}$ are irrational functions.

A function which is not an algebraic function is called a *transcendental function.*

86. Rules and Formulas of Differentiation

Differentiation by use of the increment method based on the definition of the derivative may become very laborious. To simplify this work, we shall now derive some formulas for finding derivatives of certain standard types of functions. In this chapter, we obtain such formulas for algebraic functions; in a later chapter, we shall obtain formulas for certain transcendental functions.

It will be assumed, usually without explicit statement each time, that all functions considered are differentiable and therefore continuous except for certain isolated values of the independent variable. It should be recalled that if $y = f(x)$ is a continuous function, then $\Delta y \to 0$ when $\Delta x \to 0$ (§ 74). From this, it appears that the determination of the derivative $\lim_{\Delta x \to 0} (\Delta y / \Delta x)$ will involve the problem of indeterminate forms (§ 72). In finding derivatives, we avoid the indeterminate form $0/0$ by changing the form of the quotient before taking the limit.

87. Derivative of a Constant

Let $y = c$, a constant. Then for any increment Δx of the independent variable, y remains unchanged, so that $\Delta y = 0$, and

$$(a) \qquad\qquad \frac{\Delta y}{\Delta x} = 0.$$

Therefore, $D_x y = \lim_{\Delta x \to 0} \left(\frac{\Delta y}{\Delta x} \right) = 0,$ or $D_x c = 0.$ Hence:

The derivative of a constant is zero:

$$(1) \qquad\qquad D_x(c) = 0.$$

This result is evident at once from the fact that the slope of the line $y = c$ is zero (using the geometric interpretation of the derivative).

88. Derivative of the Independent Variable

Let $y = x$; then if x takes an increment Δx, the corresponding increment of y is obviously $\Delta y = \Delta x$, so that

$$(a) \qquad\qquad \frac{\Delta y}{\Delta x} = 1.$$

Therefore, $D_x y = \lim\limits_{\Delta x \to 0} \left(\dfrac{\Delta y}{\Delta x}\right) = 1$, or $D_x(x) = 1$. Hence:

The derivative of the independent variable is 1:

(2) $D_x(x) = 1.$

This result accords with the fact that the slope of the line $y = x$ is 1.

89. Derivative of a Power of the Independent Variable

Consider the function $y = x^n$, where n is a positive integer. If x is given an increment Δx, then y receives a corresponding increment Δy, and we have

$$y + \Delta y = (x + \Delta x)^n.$$

Applying the binomial theorem, we get

$$y + \Delta y = x^n + nx^{n-1}(\Delta x) + \frac{n(n-1)}{2} x^{n-2}(\Delta x)^2 + \cdots + (\Delta x)^n,$$

$$\Delta y = nx^{n-1}(\Delta x) + \frac{n(n-1)}{2} x^{n-2}(\Delta x)^2 + \cdots + (\Delta x)^n,$$

(a) $\dfrac{\Delta y}{\Delta x} = nx^{n-1} + \dfrac{n(n-1)}{2} x^{n-2}(\Delta x) + \cdots + (\Delta x)^{n-1}.$

Each of the last $(n - 1)$ terms of (a) contains Δx as a factor; therefore, if we use the limit theorems I, II and IV of § 70, we obtain from (a):

(b) $D_x y = \lim\limits_{\Delta x \to 0} \left(\dfrac{\Delta y}{\Delta x}\right) = nx^{n-1}.$

This derivation of formula (b) applies only in case the exponent n is a positive integer. However, it will be shown in § 99 that this formula holds without change when n is a negative integer or a rational fraction. We may therefore state the following rule, generally called the *power rule*:

The derivative of a power of the independent variable with a constant rational exponent is equal to the exponent times the variable with an exponent equal to the original exponent diminished by 1:

(3) $D_x(x^n) = nx^{n-1}.$

EXAMPLE. $D_x(x^2) = 2x$, $D_x(x^3) = 3x^2$, $D_x(x^4) = 4x^3$, etc.

90. Derivative of a Constant Times a Function

Let $y = c \cdot u$, where c is a constant and u is a function of x. When x is given an increment Δx, then u receives a corresponding increment Δu, and thence y receives a corresponding increment Δy. Then

$$y + \Delta y = c(u + \Delta u) = cu + c(\Delta u).$$

Subtracting $y = cu$ gives $\Delta y = c(\Delta u)$, and

$$(a) \qquad \frac{\Delta y}{\Delta x} = c \cdot \frac{\Delta u}{\Delta x}.$$

Therefore, by use of theorem II of § 70, we get

$$D_x y = \lim_{\Delta x \to 0} \left(c \cdot \frac{\Delta u}{\Delta x} \right) = c \cdot \lim_{\Delta x \to 0} \left(\frac{\Delta u}{\Delta x} \right) = c \cdot D_x u.$$

Hence:

The derivative of a constant times a function is equal to the constant times the derivative of the function:

(4) $\qquad\qquad D_x(c \cdot u) = c \cdot D_x u.$

EXAMPLE. $D_x(5 \, x^4) = 5 \cdot D_x(x^4) = 5(4 \, x^3) = 20 \, x^3.$

As a special case, when $c = -1$, we have:

$$(b) \qquad\qquad D_x(-u) = -D_x u.$$

91. Derivative of a Sum of Functions

Let $y = u + v$, where u and v are functions of x. For any increment Δx, the functions u and v take corresponding increments Δu and Δv, and we have

$$y + \Delta y = (u + \Delta u) + (v + \Delta v), \text{ and } \Delta y = \Delta u + \Delta v.$$

Then

$$(a) \qquad \frac{\Delta y}{\Delta x} = \frac{\Delta u}{\Delta x} + \frac{\Delta v}{\Delta x}.$$

From (a), by use of theorem I of § 70, we get

$$D_x y = \lim_{\Delta x \to 0} \left(\frac{\Delta u}{\Delta x} \right) + \lim_{\Delta x \to 0} \left(\frac{\Delta v}{\Delta x} \right),$$

or

$$(b) \qquad\qquad D_x(u + v) = D_x u + D_x v.$$

Since $u - v = u + (-v)$, and since $D_x(-v) = -D_x v$ (§ 90), we have

$$(c) \qquad D_x(u - v) = D_x u + D_x(-v) = D_x u - D_x v.$$

For the sum of three or more functions, a formula similar to (b) would evidently be obtained.

Therefore:

The derivative of the algebraic sum of a finite number of functions is equal to the algebraic sum of their derivatives:

$$(5) \qquad D_x(u + v + w) = D_x u + D_x v + D_x w.$$

EXAMPLE. $D_x(x^3 - 5x^2 + 4) = D_x(x^3) - D_x(5x^2) + D_x(4)$
$$= 3x^2 - 5(2x) + 0 = 3x^2 - 10x.$$

92. Exercises

In Exercises 1–12, find the derivative of each of the given functions:

1. $y = 4x^5$.
2. $y = \frac{1}{2}x^4$.
3. $y = 4x - x^2$.
4. $y = x^3 + x^2 - x$.
5. $y = 3x^4 - 2x^3$.
6. $y = 2x^4 - 3x^3 + x^2 - 4x + 5$.
7. $y = \frac{1}{3}x^3 - \frac{1}{2}x^2 - x + \sqrt{2}$.
8. $y = 4x^5 - \frac{2}{3}x^3 - 1$.
9. $s = t^3 - 4t^2 + 5$.
10. $u = 1 + x - \frac{1}{2}x^2 + x^3 - \frac{1}{4}x^4$.
11. $w = 3z + \frac{1}{3}z^3$.
12. $s = 1 + 2t + 3t^2$.

In Exercises 13–16, find the value of the derivative of each of the given functions, for the given value of the independent variable:

13. $y = x^2 + 2x$, $x = 1$.
14. $y = 4x^3 - 3x^2 + x - 5$, $x = 2$.
15. $u = 2z^3 + 5z^2 - z$, $z = -3$.
16. $f(t) = t^4 - 4t^3 + 12$, $t = -1$.

Find the derivative of each of the following functions, by multiplying out each product before differentiating:

17. $y = 5x^2(4 - x)$.
18. $y = x^3(x^2 + 2)$.
19. $u = (z - 1)(z + 2)$.
20. $s = (2t - 3)(t^2 + 2)$.

21. Find the slope of each of the following curves:

   (a) $y = x^2 - 3x$, at $x = 4$;   (b) $y = \frac{1}{3}x^3 - \frac{3}{2}x^2 + x + 1$, at $x = 0$.

22. Find the coördinates of the points on each of the following curves at which the tangent is parallel to the X-axis:

   (a) $y = 2x - x^2$;   (b) $y = x^3 - 3x$.

23. Find the velocity of a particle in rectilinear motion for each of the following laws of motion:

   (a) $s = t^2 - 4t + 2$;   (b) $s = 64t - 16t^2$.

24. A bullet was fired straight upward, its height (in feet) after t seconds being $s = 1600t - 16t^2$. (a) How fast did it start up? (b) What was its greatest height? (c) When did it strike the ground and with what speed?

25. The distance d (feet) required for stopping an automobile under normal conditions varies as the square of the velocity v (miles per hour). If $d = 18$ when $v = 20$, find how fast d increases with respect to v at $v = 20$, and also at $v = 60$.

26. If a soap bubble expands, always remaining spherical, find the rate of change of the volume with respect to the radius.

93. Derivative of a Product of Functions

Let $y = u \cdot v$, where u and v are functions of x. If x is given an increment Δx, then

$$y + \Delta y = (u + \Delta u)(v + \Delta v)$$
$$= uv + u \cdot \Delta v + v \cdot \Delta u + \Delta u \cdot \Delta v.$$

Subtracting $y = uv$, we get

$$\Delta y = u \cdot \Delta v + v \cdot \Delta u + \Delta u \cdot \Delta v,$$

(a)
$$\frac{\Delta y}{\Delta x} = u \frac{\Delta v}{\Delta x} + v \frac{\Delta u}{\Delta x} + \Delta u \frac{\Delta v}{\Delta x}.$$

Using the fact that $\Delta u \to 0$ as $\Delta x \to 0$, and making use of the limit theorems I and II of § 70, from (a) we obtain $D_x y = u \cdot D_x v + v \cdot D_x u$. Therefore:

The derivative of the product of two functions is equal to the first function times the derivative of the second plus the second function times the derivative of the first:

(6)
$$D_x(u \cdot v) = u \cdot D_x v + v \cdot D_x u.$$

The derivative of the product of more than two factors can be found by successive applications of this rule.

EXAMPLE. Differentiate $y = (2x + 3)(x^2 - 1)$.

Solution: $D_x y = (2x + 3) \cdot D_x(x^2 - 1) + (x^2 - 1) \cdot D_x(2x + 3)$
$= (2x + 3) \cdot 2x + (x^2 - 1) \cdot 2 = 6x^2 + 6x - 2.$

94. Derivative of a Quotient of Functions

Let $y = u/v$, where u and v are functions of x. When x changes by an increment Δx, we have

$$y + \Delta y = \frac{u + \Delta u}{v + \Delta v};$$

subtracting $y = u/v$, we get

$$\Delta y = \frac{u + \Delta u}{v + \Delta v} - \frac{u}{v} = \frac{uv + v \cdot \Delta u - uv - u \cdot \Delta v}{(v + \Delta v) \cdot v} = \frac{v \cdot \Delta u - u \cdot \Delta v}{(v + \Delta v) \cdot v},$$

$$(a) \qquad \frac{\Delta y}{\Delta x} = \frac{v\dfrac{\Delta u}{\Delta x} - u\dfrac{\Delta v}{\Delta x}}{v^2 + v\cdot\Delta v}.$$

From this, since $\Delta v \to 0$ as $\Delta x \to 0$, by using theorems I, II and III of § 70, we obtain

$$D_x y = \frac{v\cdot D_x u - u\cdot D_x v}{v^2}.$$

Hence:

The derivative of the quotient of two functions is equal to the denominator times the derivative of the numerator minus the numerator times the derivative of the denominator, all divided by the square of the denominator:

$$(7) \qquad D_x\left(\frac{u}{v}\right) = \frac{v\cdot D_x u - u\cdot D_x v}{v^2}.$$

EXAMPLE 1. Differentiate $y = \dfrac{x^3 + 1}{x^2 - 2\,x}$.

Solution:
$$
\begin{aligned}
D_x y &= \frac{(x^2 - 2\,x)\cdot D_x(x^3 + 1) - (x^3 + 1)\cdot D_x(x^2 - 2\,x)}{(x^2 - 2\,x)^2} \\[2mm]
&= \frac{(x^2 - 2\,x)\cdot 3\,x^2 - (x^3 + 1)\cdot(2\,x - 2)}{(x^2 - 2\,x)^2} \\[2mm]
&= \frac{x^4 - 4\,x^3 - 2\,x + 2}{(x^2 - 2\,x)^2}.
\end{aligned}
$$

The derivative of $1/u$, where u is a given function of x, is needed so often that it is desirable to write out a special formula for it, although it is a special case of the quotient formula (7). By use of formula (7), we have

$$D_x\left(\frac{1}{u}\right) = \frac{u\cdot D_x 1 - 1\cdot D_x u}{u^2} = \frac{-D_x u}{u^2};$$

hence:

$$(8) \qquad D_x\left(\frac{1}{u}\right) = -\frac{1}{u^2}\cdot D_x u.$$

EXAMPLE 2. (a) $D_x(1/x) = -1/x^2$;
(b) $D_x(1/x^2) = -(1/x^4)\cdot 2\,x = -2/x^3$.

EXAMPLE 3. Differentiate $y = \dfrac{1}{x^2 + 1}$.

Solution: $D_x y = -\dfrac{1}{(x^2 + 1)^2}\cdot 2\,x = -\dfrac{2\,x}{(x^2 + 1)^2}.$

95. Exercises

In Exercises 1–8, differentiate by use of the product rule, and then check by multiplying out before differentiating:

1. $y = (x + 1)(x^2 + 2).$ 2. $y = (x^2 - 1)(x^3 + 1).$
3. $u = (r - 3)(r^2 + 1).$ 4. $s = t^2(t^3 - 1).$
5. $f(x) = x(a + x)(a - x).$ 6. $q = (at^2 + b)(ct^2 + d).$
7. $y = (x - 1)(x - 2)(x - 3).$ 8. $w = z^2(z + 1)(z - 2).$

In Exercises 9–16, differentiate by the quotient rule:

9. $y = \dfrac{x + 1}{x - 1}.$ 10. $y = \dfrac{2\,x}{x - 2}.$

11. $s = \dfrac{t + 1}{t^2 + 1}.$ 12. $w = \dfrac{z^3 - z}{z + 1}.$

13. $w = \dfrac{1 - z + z^2}{1 + z + z^2}.$ 14. $f(x) = \dfrac{x^2 + 1}{x + 1}.$

15. $u = 3\,r + \dfrac{r}{r + 1}.$ 16. $q = \dfrac{p^3 - 1}{p^2}.$

Find the value of the derivative of each of the following functions:

17. $y = (2x - 1)(x^2 - 4),$ at $x = 1.$ 18. $u = (z + 2)(z^2 - z + 1),$ at $z = 2.$

19. $y = \dfrac{x + 2}{2 - x},$ at $x = 1.$ 20. $u = \dfrac{t}{t^2 + a^2},$ at $t = a.$

21. Find the slope of the curve $y = (x^2 + 1)(x + 4)$ at $x = 1.$

22. Find the slope of the curve $y = \dfrac{2\,x}{x - 1}$ at the point $(2, 4).$

23. Find the velocity at any time t in the straight line motion given by

$$s = \frac{t - 1}{t + 1}.$$

24. Prove that: $\dfrac{D_x(uv)}{uv} = \dfrac{D_x u}{u} + \dfrac{D_x v}{v}.$

96. Composite Functions

In order to be able to differentiate certain types of functions, $y = f(x)$, it is frequently found convenient to express y as a function of an auxiliary variable u, where u is a function of x.

EXAMPLE. Suppose that we wish to find the derivative of $y = \sqrt{x^2 + 1}$ with respect to x; none of the previous rules apply. But we may express this function by: $u = x^2 + 1$ and $y = \sqrt{u}$. Here y is represented as a function of u, and u is represented as a function of x.

For the general case, if y is a function of u, $y = \phi(u)$, and if u is a function of x, $u = F(x)$, then y is a function of x through the intermediary of u, and we call y a *function of a function*, or a **composite function:** $y = \phi[F(x)] = f(x)$.

97. Derivative of a Composite Function

Let $y = \phi(u)$ and $u = F(x)$.   Let x be given an increment Δx, then u receives a corresponding increment Δu, and thence y receives an increment Δy.   Then we may write the algebraic identity:

$$(a) \qquad \frac{\Delta y}{\Delta x} = \frac{\Delta y}{\Delta u} \cdot \frac{\Delta u}{\Delta x},$$

provided $\Delta u \neq 0$.   Since $\Delta u \to 0$ as $\Delta x \to 0$, we have

$$(b) \qquad D_x y = \lim_{\Delta x \to 0} \left(\frac{\Delta y}{\Delta x} \right) = \lim_{\Delta u \to 0} \left(\frac{\Delta y}{\Delta u} \right) \cdot \lim_{\Delta x \to 0} \left(\frac{\Delta u}{\Delta x} \right) = D_u y \cdot D_x u.$$

It is proved in more advanced works* that even if $\Delta u = 0$ for arbitrarily small values of Δx, the formula (b) still holds.   Hence:

If y is a function of u, and if u is a function of x, then:

$$(9) \qquad \qquad D_x y = D_u y \cdot D_x u.$$

EXAMPLE 1.   Find $D_x y$ if $y = u^2 + 2u$ and $u = x^3 + 3x^2 + 5$.

Solution: $D_u y = 2u + 2$ and $D_x u = 3x^2 + 6x$, then
$$D_x y = (2u + 2)(3x^2 + 6x) = 6x(x + 2)(u + 1).$$

EXAMPLE 2.   Find $D_x y$ if $y = (x^2 + 1)^4$.

Solution: Put $u = x^2 + 1$ and $y = u^4$, then $y = (x^2 + 1)^4$.
Now $D_u y = 4u^3$ and $D_x u = 2x$, therefore $D_x y = 4u^3 \cdot 2x = 8x(x^2 + 1)^3$.

98. Exercises

1. Find $D_x y$ from:

(a) $y = v^2 + 4$, $v = \dfrac{1}{x}$;   (b) $y = \dfrac{1 - z}{z}$, $z = \dfrac{1 - x}{1 + x}$.

2. For a body falling from rest (in a vacuum), $s = \frac{1}{2} g t^2$, $v = gt$.   Find $D_s v$ without solving the given equations for v in terms of s.

3. The resistance R (ohms) of an electric wire 100 meters long varies with the radius x (centimeters) according to the formula $R = 0.0048/x^2$; and x varies with the absolute temperature T thus: $x = 0.1991 + 0.0000037T$. How fast does R change with T, per degree, at $T = 300°$?   (Do not eliminate x from the given equations.)

* See, for example, Franklin, *Treatise on Advanced Calculus*, § 65.

99. Derivative of a Power of a Function

The power rule of § 89: $D_x(x^n) = nx^{n-1}$, may now be extended to the case of a power of a function of x, and also proved for any rational exponent.

Let $y = u^n$, where u is a function of x. Consider first the case where n is a positive integer. Then $D_u y = nu^{n-1}$ (by the power rule of § 89), and $D_x y = D_u y \cdot D_x u$ (by the composite function rule of § 97). Therefore, $D_x y = nu^{n-1} D_x u$, or

$$(a) \qquad D_x(u^n) = nu^{n-1} D_x u.$$

Next consider the case where n is a positive fraction. Let $n = p/q$, where p and q are positive integers prime to each other, and consider only values of x for which $u^{\frac{p}{q}}$ has real values. From $y = u^n = u^{\frac{p}{q}}$, we have $y^q = u^p$. We may regard y^q and u^p as two different forms of a new function of x, as $v = y^q = u^p$. Differentiating v with respect to x by the power rule just established for the case in which the exponent is a positive integer, we have

$$D_x v = qy^{q-1} D_x y \qquad \text{and} \qquad D_x v = pu^{p-1} D_x u.$$

Therefore,

$$qy^{q-1} D_x y = pu^{p-1} D_x u.$$

Then

$$D_x y = \frac{pu^{p-1}}{qy^{q-1}} D_x u = \frac{p}{q} \cdot \frac{u^{p-1}}{(u^{\frac{p}{q}})^{q-1}} D_x u$$

$$= \frac{p}{q} \cdot \frac{u^{p-1}}{u^{p-\frac{p}{q}}} D_x u = \frac{p}{q} \cdot u^{\frac{p}{q}-1} \cdot D_x u,$$

or

$$(b) \qquad D_x(u^{\frac{p}{q}}) = \left(\frac{p}{q}\right) u^{\left(\frac{p}{q}\right)-1} D_x u.$$

Finally, consider the case where n is a negative rational number. Let $n = -m$, where m is a positive integer or a positive fraction.

$$D_x y = D_x(u^{-m}) = D_x\left(\frac{1}{u^m}\right) = -\frac{1}{u^{2m}} \cdot D_x(u^m) = -\frac{1}{u^{2m}}(mu^{m-1} D_x u),$$

or

$$(c) \qquad D_x(u^{-m}) = (-m)u^{(-m)-1} \cdot D_x u.$$

From formulas (a), (b) and (c), it follows that:

The general power rule:

(10)
$$D_x(u^n) = nu^{n-1} \cdot D_x u$$

holds when the exponent n is any rational number, and u is a function of x.[*]

Care should be taken, in applying formula (10), to avoid the common mistake of forgetting the factor $D_x u$ at the end of the formula.

As a special case of the general rule above, when $u = x$, we have the formula:

(11)
$$D_x(x^n) = nx^{n-1},$$

when n is any rational number.

EXAMPLE 1. (a) $D_x(\sqrt{x}) = D_x(x^{\frac{1}{2}}) = \frac{1}{2} x^{-\frac{1}{2}} = \dfrac{1}{2\sqrt{x}}$;

(b) $D_x\left(\dfrac{1}{x^3}\right) = D_x(x^{-3}) = -3 x^{-4} = -\dfrac{3}{x^4}.$

EXAMPLE 2. $D_x(x^2 + x + 1)^5 = 5(x^2 + x + 1)^4 \cdot D_x(x^2 + x + 1)$
$$= 5(x^2 + x + 1)^4 \cdot (2x + 1),$$
by use of formula (10).

EXAMPLE 3. $D_x\sqrt{1 - x^2} = D_x(1 - x^2)^{\frac{1}{2}} = \frac{1}{2}(1 - x^2)^{-\frac{1}{2}} \cdot D_x(1 - x^2)$

$$= \tfrac{1}{2}(1 - x^2)^{-\frac{1}{2}} \cdot (-2x) = -\dfrac{x}{\sqrt{1 - x^2}}.$$

EXAMPLE 4. If $y = (x^2 + 1)\sqrt{x^2 - 4}$, find $D_x y$.

Solution: By use of the product rule of § 93, and the general power rule (10), we get

$$\begin{aligned}
D_x y &= (x^2 + 1) \cdot D_x(x^2 - 4)^{\frac{1}{2}} + (x^2 - 4)^{\frac{1}{2}} \cdot D_x(x^2 + 1) \\
&= (x^2 + 1) \cdot \tfrac{1}{2}(x^2 - 4)^{-\frac{1}{2}} \cdot 2x + (x^2 - 4)^{\frac{1}{2}} \cdot 2x \\
&= x(x^2 - 4)^{-\frac{1}{2}}[(x^2 + 1) + 2(x^2 - 4)] \\
&= \dfrac{x(3x^2 - 7)}{\sqrt{x^2 - 4}}.
\end{aligned}$$

100. Exercises

1. Differentiate: (a) $\sqrt[3]{x}$; (b) $x^{\frac{5}{2}}$; (c) $\sqrt[3]{x^4}$; (d) $x^2\sqrt{x}$; (e) x^{-2}; (f) $1/x^5$; (g) $1/\sqrt{x}$; (h) $x^{1.4}$.

2. Differentiate: (a) $x^{\frac{3}{2}}$; (b) $\sqrt[5]{x^2}$; (c) $x\sqrt[3]{x}$; (d) x^{-4}; (e) $4/x^6$; (f) $1/\sqrt[3]{x}$; (g) $2 x^{-1.2}$; (h) $3/x^{0.4}$.

---

[*] It will be proved in § 283 that this formula also holds for any real value of n.

In Exercises 3–18, differentiate each of the given functions:

3. $y = 2x^{-1} - 3x^{-2}$.

4. $y = \dfrac{1}{x} + \dfrac{1}{x^2}$.

5. $f(x) = 3x - \dfrac{2}{x^2}$.

6. $y = x\sqrt{x} - \dfrac{2}{x^3}$.

7. $F(x) = \sqrt{x} + \dfrac{1}{\sqrt{x}}$.

8. $w = \dfrac{\sqrt{z}}{1 + z^2}$.

9. $\phi(t) = (t + 1)\sqrt{t}$.

10. $f(x) = \dfrac{x + 1}{x^3} - \dfrac{2}{\sqrt[3]{x}}$.

11. $y = (x^2 + 1)^5$.

12. $y = (x^3 - 2)^4$.

13. $y = \dfrac{1}{(x^2 + 4)^3}$.

14. $y = \dfrac{2}{(1 - x^2)^2}$.

15. $w = \sqrt{z^2 + 9}$.

16. $f(x) = \sqrt{a^2 - x^2}$.

17. $\phi(t) = \dfrac{1}{\sqrt{t^2 - 1}}$.

18. $u = (1 + 2z)^{\frac{3}{2}}$.

Find the value of $D_x y$ for each of the functions in Exercises 19–22:

19. $y = (x^2 + 4)^5$, for $x = 1$.

20. $y = (4x^2 + 9)^3$, for $x = -2$.

21. $y = \sqrt{x^2 - 16}$, for $x = 5$.

22. $y = \dfrac{2}{\sqrt{x - 1}}$, for $x = 5$.

Differentiate by use of the product rule:

23. $y = \dfrac{x}{\sqrt{1 - x}}$.

24. $y = \dfrac{x}{\sqrt{a^2 + x^2}}$.

In Exercises 25–34, differentiate each of the given functions:

25. $y = (x + 1)\sqrt{1 - x}$.

26. $s = \sqrt{t^2 - 2t}$.

27. $f(x) = x^2\sqrt{x^4 + 1}$.

28. $y = (a^2 + x^2)\sqrt{a^2 - x^2}$.

29. $s = \dfrac{t^3}{(1 + t^2)^3}$.

30. $y = 6x\sqrt{x - 2} - 4(x - 2)^{\frac{3}{2}}$.

31. $u = \dfrac{x}{\sqrt{1 + x^2}}$.

32. $F(z) = \dfrac{z}{\sqrt{4 - z^2}}$.

33. $v = \dfrac{a}{z}\sqrt{a^2 - z^2}$.

34. $v = y^2\sqrt{2y - 3}$.

35. Find the slope of the curve $y = \sqrt{a^2 - x^2}$ at the point where $x = a/2$.

36. Draw the graph of $y = x^{\frac{2}{3}}$, and investigate the behavior of the tangent to the curve as $x \to 0$.

37. The lowest flying speed V (feet per second) for a certain airplane varies as the square root of the wing loading w (pounds per square foot). If $V = 57$ when $w = 9$, find the rate of change of V with respect to w.

38. The pressure p of 1 pound of saturated steam in terms of its volume v (cubic feet) is given by the formula $p = 478.2/v^{1.064}$. Find the rate of change of pressure with respect to volume when $v = 200$.

101. Explicit and Implicit Functions

Consider an equation involving two variables x and y. If we choose x as the independent variable and assign a value to it, then a value (or set of values) of the variable y is determined by the equation, and y is defined as a function of x. If the equation expresses y directly in terms of x, the function so defined is called an **explicit function**. But if the equation must be solved for y in order to express y directly in terms of x, then y is said to be defined *implicitly* as a function of x, or y is called an **implicit function** of x.

EXAMPLE. The equation $y = 4 - x^2$ defines y as an explicit function of x; but the equation $x^2 + y^2 = 25$ defines y as an implicit function of x.

Sometimes an equation defining an implicit function can be solved to give an explicit function form. Thus, the equation $x^2 + y^2 = 25$ defining y as an implicit function of x can be solved for y, giving the explicit function form $y = \pm\sqrt{25 - x^2}$.

Sometimes it is not possible to solve the equation expressing an implicit function relation to obtain the explicit form, as for example in the case of the equation $y^5 - xy^2 + 4x - 3 = 0$, which cannot be solved for y in terms of x in algebraic form.

When a function is given in implicit function form, it is *not always desirable* to change it to explicit form, even when this can be done readily.

102. Differentiation of Implicit Functions

The derivative of an implicit function may be found directly from the implicit functional relation without the necessity of solving for the explicit functional form, by the following procedure:

When y is defined as an implicit function of x by an equation $F(x, y) = 0$, the derivative of y with respect to x may be found by differentiating the equation $F(x, y) = 0$ term by term with respect to x, regarding y as a function of x, and then solving the resulting equation for the derivative $D_x y$.

EXAMPLE 1. Find $D_x y$ if $x^2 + xy + y^2 = 1$.

Solution: Differentiating each term with respect to x, we get

$$D_x(x^2) + D_x(xy) + D_x(y^2) = 0;$$

by use of the general power rule and the product rule, this becomes

$$2x + (x \cdot D_x y + y) + 2y \cdot D_x y = 0.$$

Then
$$(x + 2 y) \cdot D_x y = -2 x - y = -(2 x + y),$$
from which we find
$$D_x y = -\frac{2 x + y}{x + 2 y}.$$

EXAMPLE 2. Find the slope of the tangent to the circle
$$x^2 + y^2 - 4 x + 2 y - 20 = 0$$
at the point $(6, 2)$.

Solution: Denote the derivative of y with respect to x, for brevity, by y'. Then
$$2 x + 2 yy' - 4 + 2 y' = 0;$$
substitute $x = 6$, $y = 2$ in this, obtaining $12 + 4 y' - 4 + 2 y' = 0$. Solving for y', we find $m = y' = -\frac{4}{3}$ for the required slope.

103. Exercises

Find $D_x y$ in terms of x and y from the equations in Exercises 1–14:

1. $2 x - y = 3$.
2. $4 x^2 + y^2 = 12$.
3. $xy = 4$.
4. $x^2 y = 8$.
5. $x^2 - y^2 = a^2$.
6. $x^2 + y^2 - 6 y = 0$.
7. $4 xy + y^2 = 8$.
8. $(x - 1)^2 + (y - 2)^2 = 16$.
9. $x^2 - xy - 3 y^2 = 0$.
10. $y^2 = x^3 - x^2$.
11. $x^{\frac{1}{2}} + y^{\frac{1}{2}} = a^{\frac{1}{2}}$.
12. $x^2 - 2 xy + y^2 - x - 1 = 0$.
13. $xy^2 - x^2 + y = 0$.
14. $x^2 y^2 = 2(x^2 + y^2)$.

Find the value of $D_x y$ from:

15. $x^2 y = 1$, for $x = 1$.
16. $xy = 4$, for $x = 1$.
17. $4 xy^2 + y^2 = 9$, for $y = 1$.
18. $x^2 - 2 xy + 2 y^2 = 17$, for $x = 3$.

Find the slope of each of the following curves:

19. $x^2 + y^2 = 25$, at $(3, 4)$.
20. $y^2 = x^3$, at $(1, 1)$.
21. $y^2(2 a - x) = x^3$, at (a, a).
22. $x^2 + xy = 2$, at $(2, -1)$.

23. Prove that there is no point on the parabola $y^2 = 4 ax$ at which the tangent is parallel to the X-axis.

24. Show that the slope of the tangent at any point (x, y) of the curve $x^{\frac{2}{3}} + y^{\frac{2}{3}} = a^{\frac{2}{3}}$ is $-\sqrt[3]{y/x}$.

104. Inverse Functions

We have already seen (§ 55) that in a functional relation between two variables, either variable may be regarded as a function of the other.

If y is a function of x, expressed by $y = f(x)$, then x is in general a function of y, which may be indicated by $x = h(y)$. These functions $y = f(x)$ and $x = h(y)$ are called *inverse functions;* each one is the *inverse* of the other.

A more precise statement is the following: It can be proved *
that, if in an x-interval (a, b) a function $y = f(x)$ is single-valued,
continuous and steadily increasing (or decreasing), then in the corresponding y-interval $(f(a), f(b))$, x is a single-valued, continuous and
steadily increasing (or decreasing) function of y, say $x = h(y)$. Then
$x = h(y)$ is called the **inverse** of the given function $y = f(x)$, in the
interval $(f(a), f(b))$.

In simple cases, the inverse function may be obtained by solving
the equation $y = f(x)$ for x in terms of y.

EXAMPLE. If y is defined as a function of x by the equation $y = 2x - 1$,
then by solving this equation for x in terms of y, we find $x = \frac{1}{2}(y + 1)$; this
latter is the inverse function of the former.

Important examples of pairs of inverse functions are: (1) the square
and square root functions $y = x^2$ and $x = \sqrt{y}$; (2) the trigonometric
and inverse trigonometric functions, as $y = \sin x$ and $x = \text{Arc} \sin y$
(or $\text{Sin}^{-1} y$); and (3) the exponential and logarithmic functions
$y = a^x$ and $x = \log_a y$.

105. Derivative of an Inverse Function

Let $y = f(x)$ be a single-valued function having a derivative $f'(x)$
which is different from 0 at $x = x_1$. Then, by the theorem at the
end of § 77, $f(x)$ is continuous at $x = x_1$, and by § 82, $f(x)$ is an increasing or decreasing function in the neighborhood of $x = x_1$. Hence,
by § 104, $y = f(x)$ has an inverse $x = h(y)$ in the neighborhood of
$y = y_1$, where $y_1 = f(x_1)$, which is single-valued, continuous and
increasing or decreasing in that neighborhood.

In the inverse function $x = h(y)$, let us give y an increment Δy,
different from 0, starting at $y = y_1$; then x will receive a corresponding
increment Δx which cannot be 0, since $h(y)$ is an increasing or decreasing function in the neighborhood of $y = y_1$. Also, we have $\Delta x \to 0$
when $\Delta y \to 0$, since $x = h(y)$ is continuous at $y = y_1$. We may then
write the identity

$$(a) \qquad \frac{\Delta x}{\Delta y} = \frac{1}{\frac{\Delta y}{\Delta x}}.$$

Then

$$(b) \qquad h'(y_1) = \lim_{\Delta y \to 0} \left(\frac{\Delta x}{\Delta y} \right) = \lim_{\Delta x \to 0} \frac{1}{\left(\frac{\Delta y}{\Delta x} \right)} = \frac{1}{\lim_{\Delta x \to 0} \left(\frac{\Delta y}{\Delta x} \right)} = \frac{1}{f'(x_1)}.$$

* See, for example, Fine, *Calculus*, § 52.

This shows that the inverse function $h(y)$ has a derivative at $y = y_1$, which is related to the derivative of $f(x)$ by the relation $h'(y) = 1/f'(x)$. Since $f'(x) = D_x y$ and $h'(y) = D_y x$, we have the theorem:

If $y = f(x)$ is a single-valued function which has a derivative which is not 0 in a given interval, then the inverse function $x = h(y)$ exists and has a derivative, and

$$(12) \hspace{3cm} D_y x = \frac{1}{D_x y}.$$

EXAMPLE.   Find $D_y x$ when $y = x^2 - 4x$.

Solution: $D_x y = 2x - 4$, therefore $D_y x = \dfrac{1}{2x - 4}$.

106. Exercises

Find the inverse of each of the following functions:

1. $y = ax + b$.

2. $y = x^2 - 4x + 2$.

3. $y = \sqrt{a^2 - x^2}$.

4. $y = \dfrac{x + 1}{x}$.

Find $D_y x$ in terms of x from:

5. $y = 4 - x^2$.

6. $y = x^3 - x + 2$.

7. $y = \dfrac{x - 1}{x + 1}$.

8. $y = (x - 2)\sqrt{x}$.

107. Higher Derivatives

The derivative of a function $y = f(x)$ is itself a function of x which can in general be differentiated with respect to x.

*If $y = f(x)$, the derivative of its derivative is called the **second derivative** of $y = f(x)$, and it is denoted by*

$$D_x^2 y, \hspace{1cm} \text{or} \hspace{1cm} f''(x), \hspace{1cm} \text{or} \hspace{1cm} y''.$$

*Similarly, the derivative of the second derivative is called the **third derivative** of $y = f(x)$, and it is denoted by*

$$D_x^3 y, \hspace{1cm} \text{or} \hspace{1cm} f'''(x), \hspace{1cm} \text{or} \hspace{1cm} y''';$$

*and so on for derivatives of any order. For the **n-th derivative**, we write*

$$D_x^n y, \hspace{1cm} \text{or} \hspace{1cm} f^{(n)}(x), \hspace{1cm} \text{or} \hspace{1cm} y^{(n)}.$$

These higher derivatives are sometimes called *successive derivatives*.

EXAMPLE 1. If $y = x^3 - 3x^2 + 2x - 5 = f(x)$, then

$$D_x y = 3x^2 - 6x + 2 = f'(x) = y',$$
$$D_x^2 y = 6x - 6 \qquad = f''(x) = y'',$$
$$D_x^3 y = 6 \qquad\qquad = f'''(x) = y''',$$
$$D_x^4 y = 0 \qquad\qquad = f^{(4)}(x) = y^{(4)}.$$

EXAMPLE 2. If $y = (1 - x^2)^{\frac{1}{2}}$, then

$$y' = \tfrac{1}{2}(1 - x^2)^{-\frac{1}{2}} \cdot (-2x) = -x(1 - x^2)^{-\frac{1}{2}},$$
$$y'' = -x(-\tfrac{1}{2})(1 - x^2)^{-\frac{3}{2}}(-2x) - (1 - x^2)^{-\frac{1}{2}}$$
$$= -(1 - x^2)^{-\frac{3}{2}}[x^2 + 1 - x^2] = -(1 - x^2)^{-\frac{3}{2}},$$
$$y''' = -(-\tfrac{3}{2})(1 - x^2)^{-\frac{5}{2}}(-2x) = -3x(1 - x^2)^{-\frac{5}{2}}.$$

In some cases, it is possible to obtain an expression for the n-th derivative, where n is any positive integer, by writing out enough of the first few derivatives so that the general rule of formation can be inferred. This is not always possible.

EXAMPLE 3. If $y = \dfrac{1}{1 + x} = (1 + x)^{-1}$, then

$$D_x y = (-1)(1 + x)^{-2} = -\frac{1}{(1 + x)^2},$$

$$D_x^2 y = (-1)(-2)(1 + x)^{-3} = \frac{2!}{(1 + x)^3},$$

$$D_x^3 y = 2!\,(-3)(1 + x)^{-4} = -\frac{3!}{(1 + x)^4},$$

$$\cdots \cdots \cdots \cdots \cdots$$

$$\therefore\ D_x^n y = (-3!)(-4)\cdots(-n)(1 + x)^{-n-1} = (-1)^n n!(1 + x)^{-(n+1)}$$
$$= (-1)^n \cdot \frac{n!}{(1 + x)^{n+1}}.$$

108. Exercises

In Exercises 1–8, find all the successive derivatives of each of the given functions:

1. $y = x^2 - 3x + 4.$
2. $y = 3x - x^3.$
3. $y = x^3 + 2x^2 - 5x + 3.$
4. $y = x^4 - 5x^3 + 2x - 4.$
5. $f(x) = x^4 - 3x^3 + 6x.$
6. $u = (z^2 + 1)(z^3 - 1).$
7. $s = t(t^2 - 1)^2.$
8. $s = t(t - 1)^3.$

In Exercises 9–16, find the second derivative of each of the given functions:

9. $y = \dfrac{1}{\sqrt{x}}.$
10. $y = \dfrac{1 - x}{1 + x}.$
11. $y = \dfrac{(1 - x)^2}{x}.$
12. $F(x) = \dfrac{x^2}{x + 1}.$

13. $f(x) = \sqrt{x^2 + a^2}$.

14. $v = \sqrt{2t - t^2}$.

15. $w = (a^2 - z^2)^{\frac{3}{2}}$.

16. $u = \dfrac{x}{\sqrt{1 - x^2}}$.

In Exercises 17–24, find the first few successive derivatives of each of the given functions, and thence infer a formula for the n-th derivative:

17. $y = 1/x$.

18. $y = 2/x^3$.

19. $y = \sqrt{x}$.

20. $y = x^{\frac{2}{3}}$.

21. $u = \dfrac{z - 1}{z}$.

22. $y = \sqrt{1 + x}$.

23. $s = \dfrac{1}{\sqrt{1 + t}}$.

24. $s = \dfrac{t^2}{t - 1}$.

25. Find: (a) $D_x^p(x^n)$ when $p < n$; (b) $D_x^n(x^n)$; (c) $D_x^q(x^n)$ when $q > n$.

26. Prove that, if u and v are functions of x:
$$D_x^2(u + v) = D_x^2 u + D_x^2 v, \qquad D_x^3(u + v) = D_x^3 u + D_x^3 v,$$
$$D_x^n(u + v) = D_x^n u + D_x^n v.$$

27. If $D_x y = p$, show that:

(a) $D_x^2 y = p \cdot D_y p$;

(b) $D_x^3 y = p^2 \cdot D_y^2 p + p(D_y p)^2$.

109. Successive Differentiation of Implicit Functions

EXAMPLE 1. If $y^2 = 4ax$, find $D_x^2 y$.

Solution: Denote the first and second derivatives of y with respect to x by y' and y'' for brevity. Differentiating the given equation with respect to x term by term gives $2yy' = 4a$ or

(a) $$yy' = 2a.$$

Differentiating both sides of (a) again with respect to x, we get

(b) $$yy'' + y' \cdot y' = 0.$$

Solving (a) for y' gives

(c) $$y' = \frac{2a}{y};$$

substituting this value of y' in (b) gives

$$yy'' + \frac{4a^2}{y^2} = 0,$$

from which

$$y'' = D_x^2 y = -\frac{4a^2}{y^3}.$$

EXAMPLE 2. If $x^2 + y^2 = a^2$, find y''.

Solution: Differentiating both sides of the given equation twice with respect to x term by term, we obtain

(d)
$$2x + 2yy' = 0,$$

(e)
$$2 + 2yy'' + 2y'y' = 0.$$

Solving (d) for y' and substituting it in (e) gives

$$1 + yy'' + \frac{x^2}{y^2} = 0.$$

Then

$$yy'' = -1 - \frac{x^2}{y^2} = -\frac{x^2 + y^2}{y^2} = -\frac{a^2}{y^2},$$

$$y'' = -\frac{a^2}{y^3}.$$

110. Exercises

Find $D_x^2 y$ from Exercises 1–8:

1. $x^2 - y^2 = a^2$.   2. $x^2 y = a^3$.
3. $xy = a$.   4. $xy + y^2 = 4$.
5. $x^2 - xy + y^2 = 1$.   6. $y^3 = x^2$.
7. $y^2 = x^3$.   8. $y^2 + 2y = x^2$.

Find the values of $D_x y$ and $D_x^2 y$ from Exercises 9–12:

9. $x^2 + 4y^2 = 25$, when $x = 3$, $y = 2$.
10. $x^2 - xy + y^2 = 7$, when $x = 2$, $y = -1$.
11. $x^2 - xy = 16$, when $x = 1$.
12. $xy = x + y$, when $x = 3$.
13. If $x^2 + y^2 = a^2$, find $D_x^3 y$.
14. If $p \cdot v^n = c$ (constant), show that: $D_v^2 p = n(n + 1) \cdot \dfrac{p}{v^2}$.

111. Miscellaneous Exercises on Rules of Differentiation

Differentiate each of the following functions:

1. $y = (ax + b)^n$.   2. $y = \sqrt{2px}$.

3. $y = x\sqrt{1 - x}$.   4. $y = \dfrac{1}{\sqrt{x^2 + 1}}$.

5. $f(x) = \dfrac{x^2}{x + 1}$.   6. $F(z) = \dfrac{2}{\sqrt{z}}$.

7. $u = \dfrac{r}{a^2\sqrt{a^2 - r^2}}$.   8. $s = \dfrac{t^3}{t - 2}$.

9. $y = (x^2 + 4)^{\frac{3}{2}}$.   10. $y = x(a^2 + x^2)\sqrt{a^2 - x^2}$.
11. $y = 3x^{-2} + 2x^{-1} + 1$.   12. $w = (z^2 + 1)^{\frac{5}{2}}$.

13. $u = \dfrac{1}{z^2 + 1}$.   14. $s = (t - 1)^{\frac{5}{2}}$.

15. $f(x) = \dfrac{x^2}{\sqrt{x^2 - 1}}$.

16. $\phi(x) = \dfrac{\sqrt{x + 1}}{x}$.

17. $q = \dfrac{\sqrt{p^2 - 1}}{a^2 p}$.

18. $r = \left(x + \sqrt{x^2 - 1}\right)^n$.

19. $y = x^2(a^2 + x^2)^{\frac{3}{2}}$.

20. $z = \dfrac{\sqrt{2\,ax - x^2}}{x}$.

21. $y = \sqrt{x + 2}$.

22. $y = \sqrt{x} + \sqrt[3]{x}$.

23. $u = \dfrac{y}{\sqrt{y^2 + 9}}$.

24. $w = \dfrac{v - 1}{v^2 + 1}$.

25. $f(x) = \sqrt{1 - x^2}$.

26. $F(x) = \dfrac{2}{(a^2 - x^2)^{\frac{3}{2}}}$.

27. $w = \dfrac{1}{1 - z + z^2}$.

28. $r = (t - 1)\sqrt{t^2 + 1}$.

29. $y = (1 - x^3)^{\frac{1}{2}}$.

30. $\phi(x) = \dfrac{(x^2 - a^2)^{\frac{3}{2}}}{x^3}$.

31. $v = (1 + u)^{\frac{3}{2}}$.

32. $y = x\sqrt{3 - x}$.

33. $f(x) = \dfrac{x^2}{(x - 1)^2}$.

34. $g(x) = x^2\sqrt{2\,ax - x^2}$.

35. $u = (a^{\frac{1}{2}} - x^{\frac{1}{2}})^2$.

36. $v = (2\,r - 1)^{\frac{5}{2}}$.

CHAPTER VII

Some Applications of Derivatives

112. Tangents and Normals to Plane Curves

We recall, from § 79, that the slope m of the *tangent* at any point (x_1, y_1) of a curve whose equation is $y = f(x)$ is equal to the value of the derivative $f'(x_1)$.

By § 29, the equation of a straight line with slope m through the point (x_1, y_1) is

(a) $$y - y_1 = m(x - x_1).$$

The equation of a tangent to a curve can therefore be found by combining the two preceding results.

A *normal* to a curve is a straight line which is perpendicular to a tangent at the point of tangency. By § 18, its slope is therefore the negative reciprocal of the slope of the tangent.

EXAMPLE 1. Find the equations of the tangent and normal to the curve $y = x^2 - x + 3$ at the point $(2, 5)$.

Solution: If $f(x) = x^2 - x + 3$, then $f'(x) = 2x - 1$; therefore, the slope of the tangent is $m = f'(2) = 3$. Hence, the equation of the tangent is

$$y - 5 = 3(x - 2) \qquad \text{or} \qquad 3x - y - 1 = 0.$$

The slope of the normal is $-\dfrac{1}{m} = -\dfrac{1}{3}$; hence, the equation of the normal is

$$y - 5 = -\tfrac{1}{3}(x - 2) \qquad \text{or} \qquad x + 3y - 17 = 0.$$

EXAMPLE 2. Find the equation of the tangent to the parabola $y^2 = 2px$ at the point (x_1, y_1).

Solution: Differentiating the equation of the curve with respect to x, we have

$$2yy' = 2p \qquad \text{or} \qquad y' = p/y;$$

the slope of the tangent at (x_1, y_1) is therefore $m = p/y_1$. The equation of the tangent is then

$$y - y_1 = \frac{p}{y_1}(x - x_1)$$

or

$$y_1 y - y_1{}^2 = px - px_1.$$

Rearranging terms and using $y_1{}^2 = 2\,px_1$, we get

$$y_1 y = px - px_1 + 2\,px_1 = p(x + x_1).$$

The required equation of the tangent is therefore

$$y_1 y = p(x + x_1).$$

The form of this equation should be compared with that of the equation of the curve.

The *angle between two curves* is defined as the angle between the tangents to the curves at the point of intersection.

By § 22, the angle ϕ between two lines whose slopes are m_1 and m_2 is given by:

$$(b) \qquad\qquad \tan \phi = \frac{m_1 - m_2}{1 + m_1 m_2}.$$

If the lines are perpendicular, their slopes m_1 and m_2 are negative reciprocals:

$$(c) \qquad\qquad m_2 = -\frac{1}{m_1} \qquad \text{or} \qquad m_1 m_2 = -1.$$

Two curves are said to *intersect orthogonally* when they intersect at right angles.

EXAMPLE 3. Find the angle of intersection of the circle $x^2 + y^2 = 8$ and the parabola $x^2 = 2\,y$.

Solution: By solving the equations of the curves simultaneously, we find two points of intersection $(2, 2)$ and $(-2, 2)$. By symmetry, it is evident that the angle of intersection is the same at both of these points; let us therefore find the angle of intersection at $(2, 2)$. From the equation of the circle, we find $2\,x + 2\,yy' = 0$ and $y' = -x/y$; hence, the slope of the tangent to the circle at $(2, 2)$ is $m_1 = -\frac{2}{2} = -1$. For the parabola, $2\,x = 2\,y'$ and $y' = x$; therefore, the slope of the tangent to the parabola at $(2, 2)$ is $m_2 = 2$. Then, by formula (b),

$$\tan \phi = \frac{(-1) - 2}{1 + (-1)2} = \frac{-3}{-1} = 3, \qquad \therefore \ \phi = \text{Arc tan } 3.$$

EXAMPLE 4. Show that the parabola $y^2 = 4\,x$ and the ellipse $2\,x^2 + y^2 = 6$ intersect orthogonally.

Solution: For the parabola, $2\,yy' = 4$ and $y' = 2/y$; for the ellipse, $4\,x + 2\,yy' = 0$ and $y' = -2\,x/y$. Let $P_1(x_1, y_1)$ be the point of intersection of the two curves in the first quadrant; then the slopes of the tangents to the curves at P_1 are: $m_1 = 2/y_1$ and $m_2 = -2\,x_1/y_1$. Then

$m_1m_2 = -4\,x_1/y_1^2$. But since P_1 is on the parabola, we have $y_1^2 = 4\,x_1$. From this we get $m_1m_2 = -1$, which shows that the tangents are perpendicular to each other. The two curves are therefore orthogonal to each other at P_1. By symmetry, the tangents at the other point of intersection are also perpendicular to each other.

113. Exercises

In Exercises 1–12, find the equations of the tangent and normal to each of the given curves at the point indicated:

1. $y = x^2 - 4\,x + 3$, at $(3, 0)$.   2. $y = x^2 - 5\,x + 4$, at $(-1, 10)$.
3. $y = x^3 - 12\,x + 7$, at $(1, -4)$.   4. $y = x^4 - 3\,x^2 + 1$, at $(2, 5)$.

5. $y = \dfrac{1}{\sqrt{x}}$, at $(4, \tfrac{1}{2})$.   6. $y = \dfrac{8}{x^2 + 1}$, at $(1, 4)$.

7. $y^2 = 8\,x$, at $(1, 2\sqrt{2})$.   8. $x^2 - y^2 = 16$, at $(5, 3)$.
9. $x^2 + y^2 - 10\,x = 0$, at $(8, -4)$.   10. $4\,x^2 + 9\,y^2 = 25$, at $(2, -1)$.
11. $x^2 + xy + y^2 = 1$, at $(0, 1)$.   12. $x^2y + y = 4$, at $(1, 2)$.

Prove that the equation of the tangent at (x_1, y_1) to each of the following curves is as indicated:

13. Circle $x^2 + y^2 = a^2$: tangent $x_1x + y_1y = a^2$.
14. Ellipse $b^2x^2 + a^2y^2 = a^2b^2$: tangent $b^2x_1x + a^2y_1y = a^2b^2$.
15. Hyperbola $b^2x^2 - a^2y^2 = a^2b^2$: tangent $b^2x_1x - a^2y_1y = a^2b^2$.
16. Hyperbola $2\,xy = a^2$: tangent $x_1y + xy_1 = a^2$.

Find the angle of intersection of each of the following pairs of curves:

17. $2\,y = x^2 - 4,\ 8\,y = 4 - x^2$.   18. $y^2 = 6\,x,\ x^2 + y^2 = 16$.
19. $x^2 + y^2 = 25,\ xy = 12$.   20. $y^2 = x,\ x^2 - y^2 = 6$.

21. Find the equations of the tangents to the curve $y = x^3 - x^2$ which cut the X-axis at an angle of $45°$.
22. Find the equations of the tangents to the curve $y = x^3 - 12\,x$ which are perpendicular to the line $x + 36\,y + 5 = 0$.
23. Find the tangent of the angle of intersection of the parabolas $y^2 = 2\,px$ and $x^2 = 2\,py$ at their points of intersection.
24. Show that the ellipse $4\,x^2 + 9\,y^2 = 72$ and the hyperbola $x^2 - y^2 = 5$ intersect at right angles.
25. Show that any hyperbola of the form $x^2 - y^2 = c$ cuts any hyperbola of the form $xy = c'$ orthogonally.
26. Show that the parabolas $x^2 = 4(y + 1)$ and $x^2 = -16(y - 4)$ intersect at right angles.
27. Show that the equation of the tangent to a curve $y = f(x)$ at the point (x_1, y_1) may be written:

$$y - y_1 = f'(x_1)(x - x_1),$$

and that of the corresponding normal:

$$y - y_1 = -\frac{1}{f'(x_1)}\,(x - x_1).$$

★ 114. Multiple Roots of Polynomial Equations

According to the factor theorem of algebra, if $x = a$ is a *root* of the polynomial equation $P(x) = 0$, then $x - a$ is a *factor* of $P(x)$, and conversely.

*If the polynomial $P(x)$ contains as a factor $(x - a)^r$, where $r \geqq 1$, and no higher power of $x - a$, then $x = a$ is called a **root of order r** of the equation $P(x) = 0$. If $r = 1$, then $x = a$ is called a **simple root**, and if $r > 1$ it is called a **multiple root**.*

EXAMPLE 1. For the equation $x^3 - 3x + 2 = 0$, $x = 1$ is a double root (root of order 2), since $x^3 - 3x + 2 = (x-1)^2(x+2)$.

We shall now derive a test for multiple roots, by use of the derivative. Let $x = a$ be a root of the polynomial equation $P(x) = 0$ of order r; then, by definition,

$$(a) \qquad P(x) = (x - a)^r Q(x),$$

where $Q(x)$ is a polynomial which does not contain $x - a$ as a factor. By the rule for the derivative of a product, we have

$$(b) \qquad \begin{aligned} P'(x) &= r(x - a)^{r-1}Q(x) + (x - a)^r Q'(x) \\ &= (x - a)^{r-1}[rQ(x) + (x - a)Q'(x)]. \end{aligned}$$

If $x - a$ occurs only once as a factor of $P(x)$, it follows from (b) that it is not a factor of $P'(x)$, since then $r - 1 = 0$. But if $r > 1$, (b) shows that if $x - a$ occurs exactly r times in $P(x)$, then it occurs exactly $r - 1$ times in $P'(x)$, since $Q(a) \neq 0$. Hence, any root of $P(x) = 0$ of order r is a root of $P'(x) = 0$ of order $r - 1$.

Conversely, any factor $x - a$ which is common to $P(x)$ and $P'(x)$ must, by (b), appear in $P(x)$ to a degree one higher than in $P'(x)$. Therefore:

If a is a simple root of the polynomial equation $P(x) = 0$, then a is not a root of the equation $P'(x) = 0$; but if a is a root of order $r > 1$ of $P(x) = 0$, then a is a root of order $r - 1$ of $P'(x) = 0$. Conversely, if a is a root of $P'(x) = 0$ of order $r - 1$ and is also a root of $P(x) = 0$, then a is a root of $P(x) = 0$ of order r.

Hence, to find the multiple roots of a polynomial equation $P(x) = 0$, find the roots of $P'(x) = 0$, if possible, and substitute them in $P(x) = 0$. Any root of $P'(x) = 0$ of order k that satisfies $P(x) = 0$ is a root of $P(x) = 0$ of order $k + 1$.

EXAMPLE 2. Test the equation $x^3 - x^2 - 8x + 12 = 0$ for multiple roots.

Solution: If $P(x) = x^3 - x^2 - 8x + 12$, then $P'(x) = 3x^2 - 2x - 8$. The roots of $3x^2 - 2x - 8 = 0$ are $x = 2$ and $x = -\frac{4}{3}$. By substitution in $P(x)$, we find that $x = 2$ satisfies the equation $P(x) = 0$, but $x = -\frac{4}{3}$ does not. Hence, $x = 2$ is a double root of the given equation.

★ 115. Exercises

In Exercises 1–8, find the multiple roots of each of the given equations:

1. $x^3 - 3x^2 + 4 = 0$.
2. $x^3 - 2x^2 - 15x + 36 = 0$.
3. $x^3 - x^2 - 5x - 3 = 0$.
4. $4x^3 - 8x^2 - 3x + 9 = 0$.
5. $4x^3 + 16x^2 + 21x + 9 = 0$.
6. $x^4 - 6x^3 + 9x^2 + 4x - 12 = 0$.
7. $x^4 + 2x^3 - 3x^2 - 4x + 4 = 0$.
8. $4x^4 - 12x^3 + x^2 + 12x + 4 = 0$.

9. Show that the equation $x^5 - 10x^2 + 15x - 6 = 0$ has a triple root.
10. Prove that the condition that the cubic equation $x^3 - qx + r = 0$ should have a double root is $4q^3 = 27r^2$.
11. Prove that if $x = a$ is a multiple root of order r of the polynomial equation $P(x) = 0$, then $P'(x)$, $P''(x)$, $\cdots$, $P^{(r-1)}(x)$ vanish simultaneously at $x = a$.
12. Find any multiple roots of the equation $x^4 + 5x^3 + 6x^2 - 4x - 8 = 0$. (Use Exercise 11).

116. Acceleration in Rectilinear Motion

Suppose that a particle P is moving along a straight line path so that its distance s from a fixed origin is related to the time t by an equation $s = f(t)$. We have already seen (in § 80) that the *velocity v* of the particle P is defined as the time-rate of change of the distance s, that is, as the value of the derivative $v = D_t s$.

*The **acceleration**, a, of the particle P is defined as the time-rate of change of the velocity v; that is, $a = D_t v$.* Since $v = D_t s$, we have $a = D_t^2 s$.

EXAMPLE 1. Find the velocity and acceleration at time t for the rectilinear motion for which $s = t^3 - 2t^2 + 6t - 5$.

Solution: $v = D_t s = 3t^2 - 4t + 6$, $a = D_t v = 6t - 4$.

EXAMPLE 2. In a certain rectilinear motion, $t = ks^2$ (k constant); show that the acceleration varies as the cube of the velocity.

Solution: Differentiating both sides of the equation $t = ks^2$ with respect to t, we get

$$(a) \qquad 1 = 2ks \cdot D_t s = 2ks \cdot v,$$

and differentiating again with respect to t, we have

$$(b) \qquad 0 = 2ks \cdot D_t v + 2kv \cdot D_t s = 2ksa + 2kv^2.$$

From (b), we find $a = -v^2/s$; but from (a), $1/s = 2\,kv$. Therefore, $a = -2\,kv^3$, which shows that a varies as v^3.

117. Exercises

In Exercises 1–8, find the velocity and acceleration at any time t of a particle in straight line motion for each of the given laws of motion:

1. $s = t^2 - 4\,t + 2$.

2. $s = 64\,t - 16\,t^2$.

3. $s = \frac{1}{3}\,t^3 - \frac{1}{2}\,t^2 + t - 2$.

4. $s = 24 + 6\,t - t^3$.

5. $s = \dfrac{t-1}{t+1}$.

6. $s = t - \dfrac{4}{t}$.

7. $s = t\sqrt{1+t}$.

8. $s = 2\sqrt{1+t^2}$.

9. If a particle moves in a straight line according to the law
$$s = t^3 - 6\,t^2 + 9\,t - 5,$$
find the acceleration when the velocity is 0.

10. Show that for a body falling in a vacuum, whose equation of motion is $s = -\frac{1}{2}\,gt^2 + v_0 t + s_0$, where g, v_0 and s_0 are constants, the acceleration is constant.

11. Show that in rectilinear motion: $a = v \cdot D_s v$.

12. If a particle moves in a straight line path so that $v^2 = 2\,gs$ (g constant), show that the acceleration is constant.

118. Exercises

1. If a line rotates in a plane through an angle θ in time t, the time-rate of change of θ is called the *angular velocity* ω of the rotating line. The time-rate of change of the angular velocity ω is called the *angular acceleration* α of the rotating line.

   A wheel turns through an angle θ in time t, where $\theta = 112\,t - 16\,t^2$. Find: (a) the angular velocity and the angular acceleration at the end of 2 seconds; (b) the initial angular velocity.

2. If a metal rod of unit length at some standard temperature, say 0° C., is heated to a temperature T and expands a length x, the temperature-rate of change of x is called the *coefficient of linear expansion* of the rod at temperature T.

   If the expansion is given by $x = aT + bT^2$ (a and b constant), find the coefficient of expansion.

3. If in a chemical reaction, x is the amount of a substance transformed in time t, the time-rate of change of x is called the *rate of reaction* at time t.

   If x is the number of gram molecules of a substance A transformed by a reaction with another substance B in time t, experiment shows that
$$\frac{x}{a-x} = akt,$$
where a and k are constants. Show that the rate of reaction is $k(a-x)^2$.

4. If Q is the quantity of heat required to raise the temperature of unit mass of a substance from a standard temperature, say 0° C., to a temperature

T, the temperature-rate of change of Q is called the *specific heat* of the substance at temperature T.

It is found by experiment that the quantity of heat Q required to raise the temperature of 1 gram of water from $0°$ C. to $T°$ C. (between $0°$ and $200°$) is

$$Q = T + 2 \cdot 10^{-5}T^2 + 3 \cdot 10^{-7}T^3.$$

Find the specific heat of water at any temperature T, and also at $T = 35°$ C.

5. The electrical resistance R of a wire varies inversely as the square of the diameter d. If $R = 20$ when $d = 5$, find the rate of change of R with respect to d at $d = 5$.

6. The intensity of light I needed to produce x units of a certain chemical in the retina of the eye is

$$I = \frac{kx^2}{a - x},$$

where a and k are constants. Find the rate of change of I with respect to x.

7. The quantity of sugar present in a certain chemical reaction t minutes after starting was

$$Q = \frac{c}{1 + kt},$$

where c and k are constants. Show that the rate of decrease of Q with respect to t was always k/c times Q^2.

8. In studying the physiology of the blood, the formula

$$S = \frac{kx^n}{1 + kx^n},$$

where k and n are constants, has been used. Find the rate of change of S with respect to x.

119. Related Rates

If a relation between two quantities which vary with the time is known and is expressed by an equation, the time-rate of change of one of them can be expressed in terms of the time-rate of change of the other by differentiating the given equation term by term with respect to the time.

EXAMPLE 1. Grain flowing from a spout at a rate of 1500 cubic inches per minute forms a conical pile on a level floor, the angle at the vertex of the cone being $120°$. At a certain instant the diameter of the base of the cone is 10 feet. Find the rate of increase of the diameter at this instant.

Solution: Let r, h and V denote the radius of base, altitude and volume of the cone at any time t (Fig. 55). Then $V = \frac{1}{3}\pi r^2 h$; but $h/r = \tan 30°$, so that $h = \frac{1}{3}\sqrt{3}\, r$, and

(a) $$V = \tfrac{1}{9}\,\pi\sqrt{3}\,r^3.$$

Differentiation of both sides of (a) with respect to t gives

(b) $$D_t V = \tfrac{1}{9}\,\pi\sqrt{3}\cdot 3\,r^2 D_t r = \tfrac{1}{3}\,\pi\sqrt{3}\,r^2 D_t r.$$

But when the diameter is 10 feet, $r = 5$ feet $= 60$ inches, and $D_t V = 1500$ cubic inches per minute. Substituting these values in (b), we have

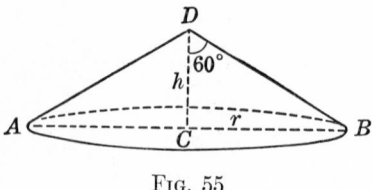

Fig. 55

$$1500 = \tfrac{1}{3}\,\pi\sqrt{3}\cdot 3600 D_t r,$$

then $D_t r = \dfrac{5}{4\,\pi\sqrt{3}} = 0.23$ inches per minute.

Since the diameter is twice the radius, the required rate of increase of the diameter is $\dfrac{5}{2\,\pi\sqrt{3}} = 0.46$ inches per minute.

Notice that the particular value $r = 60$ is not to be substituted until after the general relation $V = \tfrac{1}{9}\,\pi\sqrt{3}\,r^3$ has been differentiated with respect to t.

EXAMPLE 2. At noon a vessel is sailing due north at the uniform rate of 15 miles per hour. Another vessel, 30 miles due north of the first vessel, is sailing due east at the uniform rate of 20 miles per hour. At what rate is the distance between the vessels changing at the end of 1 hour?

Solution: In Fig. 56, let A and B be the positions of the two vessels at noon, with $AB = 30$. Let S_1 and S_2 be the corresponding positions of the vessels at any later time t; and let $x = AS_1$ be the distance in miles that the first vessel has sailed in t hours and $y = BS_2$ the distance in miles that the second vessel has sailed in t hours. Then $z = S_1S_2$ is the number of miles between the vessels at that time. We have given: $D_t x = 15$, $D_t y = 20$. Now at any time t,

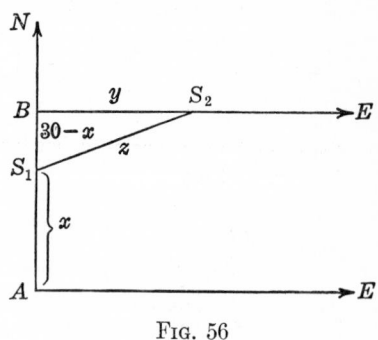

Fig. 56

(c) $$z^2 = (30 - x)^2 + y^2$$

from triangle S_1BS_2. Then

$$2\,z D_t z = 2(30 - x)(-1)D_t x + 2\,y D_t y,$$

or

(d) $$z D_t z = -(30 - x)D_t x + y D_t y.$$

This gives a relation between the rates of z, x and y at any time t. Now let $t = 1$, then $x = 15$, $y = 20$; from (c) we find $z = 25$ when $t = 1$. Substituting $z = 25$, $x = 15$, $y = 20$, $D_t x = 15$ and $D_t y = 20$ in (d), we get

$$25 D_t z = -15 \times 15 + 20 \times 20 = 175, \qquad D_t z = 7.$$

Hence, at the end of 1 hour the vessels are separating at the rate of 7 miles per hour.

120. Exercises

1. Sand is being poured on the ground, forming a conical pile with its altitude equal to one-fourth of the diameter of the base. If the sand is falling at the rate of 8 cubic feet per second, how fast is the altitude increasing when it is 4 feet?

2. If water is flowing into a vertical cylindrical tank of diameter 10 feet at the rate of 20 cubic feet per minute, show that the surface of the water is rising at a uniform rate, and find its rate of rise.

3. A cistern is in the shape of a cone 12 feet deep and 6 feet in diameter at the top, into which 10 cubic feet of water are pouring each minute. If at the time the water is 8 feet deep, it is observed to be rising 6 inches per minute, how much water is leaking away?

4. A conical funnel 6 inches in diameter and 6 inches deep is filled with liquid which runs out at the rate of 2 cubic inches per minute. How fast is the surface falling when the depth of the liquid is 4 inches?

5. A solution is filtering through a conical filter 18 inches deep and 12 inches across the top into a cylindrical vessel whose diameter is 10 inches. When the depth of the solution in the filter is 12 inches, its level is falling at the rate of 1 inch per minute. At what rate is its level in the cylinder then rising?

6. The cross-section of a trough 10 feet long is an equilateral triangle. If water flows in at the rate of 10 cubic feet per second, find the rate at which the depth is increasing when the water is 18 inches deep.

7. A man 6 feet tall walks at the rate of 240 feet per minute toward a street light which is 12 feet above the ground. At what rate is the tip of his shadow moving?

8. A man is approaching a wall 120 feet high at the rate of 3 feet per second. At what rate is his distance from the top of the wall changing when he is 60 feet from the wall?

9. A square plate of metal is expanding under the action of heat, and its side is increasing at the uniform rate of 0.1 inch per hour. What is the rate of increase of the area of the plate at the moment when the side is 16 inches long?

10. In an expanding circular plate, what is the value of the radius when the area is increasing twice as fast as the radius?

11. Gas is escaping from a spherical balloon at the rate of 1 cubic foot per minute. How fast is the radius of the balloon decreasing, and how fast is the surface shrinking when the radius is 10 feet?

12. A spherical shell of ice surrounds a spherical iron ball concentric with it. The radius of the iron ball is 3 inches. If the ice is melting at the rate of

25 cubic inches per minute, at what rate is the thickness of the icy shell decreasing when it is 2 inches thick?

13. A ship leaves port at 10 A.M., sailing west at the rate of 9 miles per hour. Another ship leaves the same port at 11 A.M., sailing south at the rate of 12 miles per hour. How fast are they separating at noon?

14. An airplane leaves a field at 10 A.M. and flies westward at 120 miles per hour. Another airplane leaves the same field at 11 A.M. and flies northward at 150 miles per hour. How fast are the airplanes separating at noon?

15. A boy flies a kite which is 200 feet high and there are 250 feet of string out. If the wind carries the kite horizontally directly away from the boy, and if the string is paid out at the rate of 30 feet per second, how fast is the kite moving, on the assumption that the string has no sag?

16. An airplane is flying horizontally at an altitude of 3000 feet and at a speed of 100 miles per hour. An observer on the ground is in the vertical plane through the line of flight. At what rate is the plane approaching the observer when it is at a distance of 4000 feet from him?

17. A man standing on a wharf 24 feet above the water is pulling in a rope attached to a boat at the rate of 4 feet per second. How fast is the boat approaching the wharf when there are 32 feet of rope out?

18. A ship is moving at the rate of 600 feet per minute. A man in the stern, 20 feet above the water, is pulling in a rope attached to a rowboat at the rate of 200 feet per minute. At what rate is the rowboat moving through the water when there are 52 feet of rope out?

19. A light is at the top of a pole 60 feet high. From a point on the ground 25 feet from the base of the pole a ball is tossed upward with an initial velocity of 40 feet per second. At what rate is the shadow of the ball moving along the ground 1 second later? [*Hint.* The height of the ball above the ground at the end of t seconds is $h = 40\,t - 16\,t^2$.]

20. A balloon leaves the ground at a point 90 feet from an observer and rises at the uniform rate of 12 feet per second. How fast is the balloon receding from the observer at the end of 10 seconds?

21. A weight is attached to one end of an 85 foot rope passing over a small pulley 45 feet above the ground. A man whose hand is 5 feet above the ground grasps the other end of the rope and walks away at the rate of 5 feet per second. How fast is the weight rising when the man is 9 feet from the point directly below the pulley?

22. A man is walking at the rate of 6 feet per second across a bridge 40 feet above the water, and a man in a rowboat is rowing, immediately below the man on the bridge, at right angles to the bridge and at the rate of 4 feet per second. How rapidly are the men separating at the end of 10 seconds?

121. Increasing and Decreasing Functions

In § 82 the following definition was given: *If $f'(x_1)$ is positive, then $f(x)$ is increasing at $x = x_1$, and if $f'(x_1)$ is negative, then $f(x)$ is decreasing at $x = x_1$, as x increases in either case.*

It follows that, if the derivative $f'(x)$ is positive throughout an interval, then $f(x)$ is increasing over this interval, and if $f'(x)$ is negative throughout an interval, then $f(x)$ is decreasing over this interval.

If $f'(x_1) = 0$, the function $f(x)$ is neither increasing nor decreasing at $x = x_1$. In this case, we say that $f(x)$ is **stationary** at $x = x_1$. Thus, $y = x^3$ is stationary at $x = 0$, although x^3 increases as x increases *through $x = 0$.*

EXAMPLE 1. Find where the function $y = x^3 - 3x^2 - 24x + 8$ is increasing and where it is decreasing.

Solution: We find:

$$D_x y = 3x^2 - 6x - 24 = 3(x + 2)(x - 4).$$

If $x < -2$, both factors above are negative, and $D_x y$ is therefore positive; if $-2 < x < 4$, the first factor is positive but the second factor is negative, and $D_x y$ is negative; and if $x > 4$, both factors are positive, and $D_x y$ is positive. By the preceding theorem, it follows that y increases for $x < -2$, decreases for $-2 < x < 4$, and again increases for $x > 4$. At $x = -2$ and at $x = 4$, we have $D_x y = 0$; therefore the function y is stationary at these points.

EXAMPLE 2. Discuss the motion of a particle P which moves in a straight line so that at the end of t seconds its distance s (in feet) from an origin O is given by $s = t^3 - 9t^2 + 15t + 12$.

Solution: We find for the velocity

$$v = D_t s = 3t^2 - 18t + 15 = 3(t - 1)(t - 5).$$

Analyzing this derivative as was done in the previous example, we find that: if $0 < t < 1$, v is positive; if $1 < t < 5$, v is negative; and if $t > 5$, v is positive. Hence, P first moves forward (to the right) for 1 second, then backward for 4 seconds and then forward again.

122. Exercises

1. Determine whether the curve $y = x^2 - 3x + 1$ is rising or falling when:
   (a) $x = 1$; (b) $x = 2$.
2. Show that the curve $xy = 1$ is falling at all of its points.

In Exercises 3–6, find where each of the given functions is increasing and where it is decreasing:

3. $y = x^2 - 8x + 6$.
4. $f(x) = x^2(x - 1)^2$.
5. $y = x^3 - 12x$.
6. $F(x) = x^4 + 4x^2 - 5$.

7. Show that the curve $y = x^3 - 3x + 2$ is falling when x lies between -1 and 1, and is rising when x is greater than 1 or less than -1.
8. Show that the function $2x^3 - 3x^2 + 6x - 5$ always increases with x.

9. Show that the curve $y = \dfrac{x}{x + 1}$ is always rising, when defined.

10. Show that the curve $y = \dfrac{x+1}{x}$ is always falling, when defined.

Discuss the direction of motion of a particle moving in a straight line for each of the following laws of motion:

11. $s = t^2 - 6t + 7$. 　　　　12. $s = 8t - t^2$.

13. $s = t^4 - 2t^2$. 　　　　　13. 14. $s = t^3 - 2t^2 - 4t + 8$.

123. Smooth Functions

*A function $f(x)$ is called a **smooth function** if both $f(x)$ and its derivative $f'(x)$ are continuous.* The graph of a smooth function is called a *smooth curve;* such a curve is not only continuous and unbroken but also has a continuously turning tangent.

EXAMPLE. (*a*) The graph of the function $y = 1 - x^2$ is a smooth curve throughout its entire extent (Fig. 57 (*a*)), since y and its derivative $y' = -2x$ are everywhere continuous.

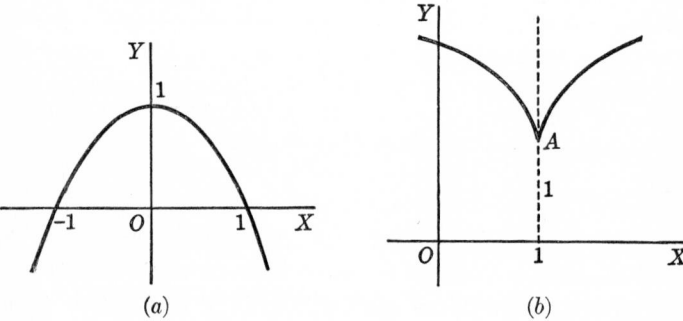

(*a*)　　　　　　　　　　(*b*)

FIG. 57

(*b*) The graph of the function $y = (x - 1)^{\frac{2}{3}} + 1$ (Fig. 57 (*b*)) is not a smooth curve at $x = 1$, since its derivative

$$y' = \tfrac{2}{3}(x - 1)^{-\frac{1}{3}} = \frac{2}{3\sqrt[3]{x - 1}}$$

is discontinuous (becomes infinite) at $x = 1$.

124. Maxima and Minima of Functions of One Variable

*A **maximum value** of a function is defined as a value of the function that is greater than any value of the function immediately preceding or following.*

*A **minimum value** of a function is defined as a value of the function that is less than any value of the function immediately preceding or following.*

If we consider the graph of a function $f(x)$ (Fig. 58), corresponding to a maximum value of the function $f(x)$, the curve has a *maximum point* (as at A and D) which is higher than all neighboring points of the curve, and where the curve ceases to rise and begins to fall. Corresponding to a minimum value of the function $f(x)$, the curve

has a *minimum point* (as at B and E) which is lower than all neighboring points of the curve, where the curve ceases to fall and begins to rise.

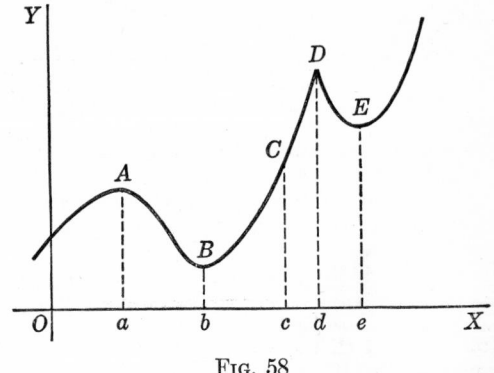

FIG. 58

Maximum and minimum values of a function (or maximum and minimum points of a curve) are together called the **extreme values** (or **extreme points**), or merely the **extremes.**

A maximum value of a function, as defined above, is not necessarily the greatest possible value, nor is a minimum value necessarily the least value. For example, in Fig. 58, points C, D and E are higher than the maximum point A. It may even happen that a minimum is greater than a maximum, as is illustrated in Fig. 58 at points A and E.

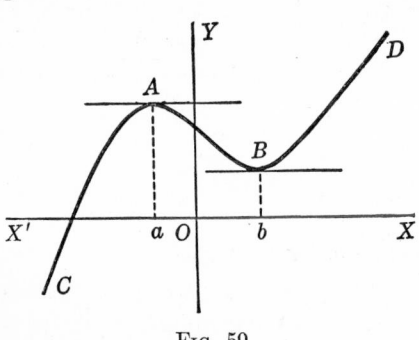

FIG. 59

To emphasize this fact, a maximum value as defined above is often called a *relative maximum*, and similarly, a minimum is called a *relative minimum*.

125. Critical Values for a Function

Let the curve in Fig. 59 be a smooth curve with a maximum point at A and a minimum point at B. It is evident geometrically that at either extreme point A or B, the tangent is horizontal and the slope is zero. Such extreme points are called *turning points* of the curve. If $y = f(x)$

is the equation of the curve, the slope of the curve is given by the derivative $f'(x)$; therefore, at the maximum and minimum points A and B, we have $f'(x) = 0$. This geometric result leads to the conclusion:

If a differentiable function $f(x)$ has a relative maximum or a relative minimum at $x = a$, then $f'(a) = 0$.

This theorem may be proved analytically as follows: Suppose that $f(x)$ has a maximum at $x = a$. By definition of relative maximum, we have

$$(a) \qquad f(a + \Delta x) - f(a) < 0$$

for all values of Δx, positive or negative but different from zero, which are numerically sufficiently small. Form the difference-quotient

$$\frac{f(a + \Delta x) - f(a)}{\Delta x};$$

the limit of this quotient when $\Delta x \to 0$ through positive values or through negative values is, by definition, the value of the derivative $f'(a)$. Since the numerator of this difference-quotient is negative, by (a), we have

$$(b) \qquad \frac{f(a + \Delta x) - f(a)}{\Delta x} < 0 \text{ for } \Delta x > 0,$$

$$(c) \qquad \frac{f(a + \Delta x) - f(a)}{\Delta x} > 0 \text{ for } \Delta x < 0.$$

If we now take the limit in (b) as $\Delta x \to 0$ through positive values, we get $f'(a) \leqq 0$, and if we take the limit in (c) as $\Delta x \to 0$ through negative values, we get $f'(a) \geqq 0$. Since these two limits must be equal, it follows that $f'(a) = 0$. Similarly we may treat the case where $f(x)$ has a minimum at $x = a$.

Values of the independent variable for which $f'(x) = 0$ are called **critical values** *for the function $f(x)$; and corresponding points on the graph of $f(x)$ are called* **critical points** *of the curve.*

If a smooth function $f(x)$ has any maxima or minima, the corresponding values of x are evidently included among the critical values.

It is important to note that: *a smooth function $f(x)$ may have a critical value at $x = a$ and yet not have a maximum or a minimum there.* In other words, the condition that $f'(a) = 0$ is *necessary* but not *sufficient* for $f(x)$ to have an extreme value at $x = a$.

This is illustrated by the example $f(x) = x^3$. Here $f'(x) = 3x^2$ and $f'(0) = 0$, so that $x = 0$ is a critical value.   But $f(0) = 0$ is not an extreme value, since $f(x) < 0$ when $x < 0$ and $f(x) > 0$ when $x > 0$.   (Fig. 60.)

126. First Derivative Test for Maxima and Minima

There are several useful tests for determining whether the critical values of a smooth function give maximum values or minimum values or neither. One of these, which may be called the *first derivative test*, may be derived as follows:

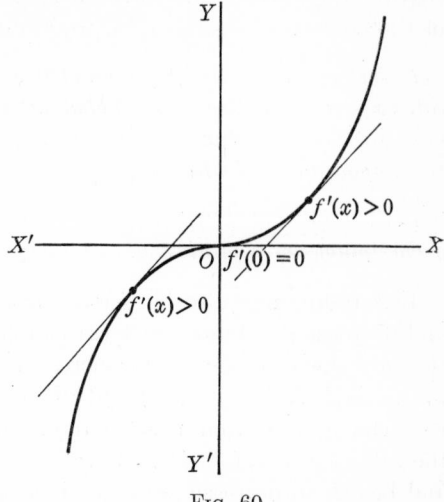

Fig. 60

Consider a smooth curve having a maximum point and a minimum point, such as that in Fig. 61.   It is geometrically evident that, as we pass from left to right through a maximum point (such as B), the slope changes from a positive value (as at A) through 0 (as at B) to a negative value (as at C); and similarly, as we pass

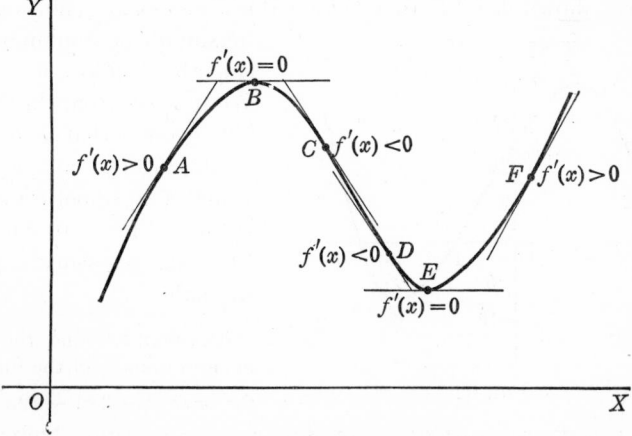

Fig. 61

through a minimum point (such as E), the slope changes from negative (as at D) through 0 (as at E) to positive (as at F). Remembering that the slope of the tangent to a curve is represented by the derivative of the corresponding function, we are led to the following theorem:

If $f(x)$ is a smooth function, and if as x increases through a critical value $x = a$, the derivative **$f'(x)$ changes sign from positive to negative,** *then $f(a)$ is a* **maximum** *value of the function; but if* **$f'(x)$ changes sign from negative to positive,** *then $f(a)$ is a* **minimum** *value of the function.*

If $f'(x)$ does not change sign as x passes through a, then $f(a)$ is neither a maximum nor a minimum.

This result may also be derived from the theorem on increasing and decreasing functions in § 121 as follows: If $f'(x)$ is positive for a certain value of x, then $f(x)$ is increasing there, and if $f'(x)$ is negative for a certain value of x, then $f(x)$ is decreasing there. Therefore, if $f'(x)$ changes sign from positive to negative when x increases through the value $x = a$, it follows that at $x = a$ the function ceases to increase and begins to decrease, and $f(a)$ is a maximum of $f(x)$. But since $f'(x)$ is continuous, it can only change sign from $+$ to $-$ by taking the value 0 when $x = a$ (by § 76, III). Similarly, if $f'(x)$ changes from negative to positive when x increases through a, it follows that at $x = a$ the function $f(x)$ changes from decreasing to increasing, and $f(a)$ is a minimum of $f(x)$, and as before, $f'(x)$ can only change sign from $-$ to $+$ by passing through 0 at $x = a$.

It was shown in § 125 that $f'(a) = 0$ is a necessary condition for a maximum or minimum of a smooth function at $x = a$. We now see from the preceding theorem that a *sufficient* condition for an extreme value of a smooth function is that $f'(a) = 0$ *and* that $f'(x)$ changes sign as x passes through a.

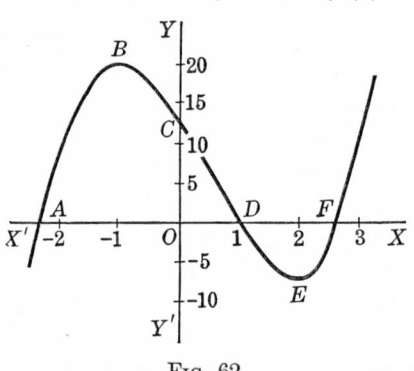

Fig. 62

EXAMPLE 1. Find the maxima and minima of the function

$$f(x) = 2x^3 - 3x^2 - 12x + 13.$$

Solution: We first find $f'(x) = 6x^2 - 6x - 12 = 6(x - 2)(x + 1)$. Putting $f'(x) = 0$ and solving for x gives the critical values $x = 2$ and

$x = -1$. If $-1 < x < 2$, the factor $x - 2$ is negative and the factor $x + 1$ is positive; therefore the product of these factors is negative and $f'(x)$ is negative. If $x > 2$, we see in the same way from the factored form of $f'(x)$ that $f'(x)$ is positive. Hence, in passing through $x = 2$ from left to right, $f'(x)$ changes sign from $-$ to $+$, and the function has a minimum at $x = 2$ (see Fig. 62). If $x < -1$, we find similarly that $f'(x)$ is positive and if $-1 < x < 2$, we find that $f'(x)$ is negative; hence, $f'(x)$ changes from $+$ to $-$, and $f(x)$ has a maximum at $x = -1$ (see Fig. 62).

To find the extreme values of the function, we must substitute the critical values in the original function. Thus, when $x = 2$, we find $f(x) = -7$, and when $x = -1$, we find $f(x) = 20$. The required results are therefore: $f(x)$ has a maximum value 20 at $x = -1$ and a minimum value -7 at $x = 2$.

EXAMPLE 2. Find the maxima and minima of the function

$$f(x) = 3\,x^4 - 4\,x^3.$$

Solution: Since

$$f'(x) = 12\,x^2(x - 1),$$

the critical values are $x = 0$ and $x = 1$. Let us first examine the critical value $x = 1$. If $x < 1$, then $f'(x) < 0$, and if $x > 1$, then $f'(x) > 0$; hence, the given function has a minimum value at $x = 1$. If

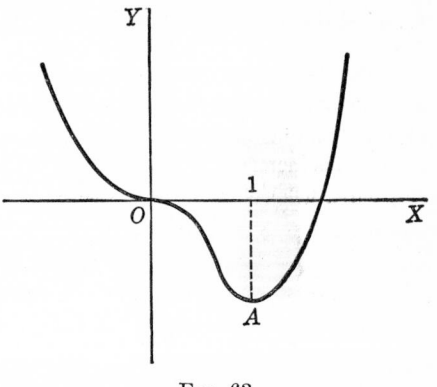

FIG. 63

$x < 0$, we have $f'(x) < 0$, but if $0 < x < 1$, then $f'(x) < 0$; hence, since $f'(x)$ does not change sign in passing through $x = 0$, $f(x)$ does not have a maximum nor a minimum at the critical value $x = 0$.   (See Fig. 63.)

The first derivative test for extreme values may be summarized as follows: To find the maximum and minimum values of a smooth function $f(x)$, we first solve the equation $f'(x) = 0$ to find all of its real roots (critical values); then for each such root a we find whether or not $f'(x)$ changes sign as x increases through a. Then:

> *Maximum:* $f'(a) = 0$, $f'(x)$ *changes from $+$ to $-$*;
> *minimum:* $f'(a) = 0$, $f'(x)$ *changes from $-$ to $+$*.

127. Exercises

In Exercises 1–16, find the maxima and minima of each of the given functions:

1. $y = x^3 - 6\,x^2 + 9\,x + 1$.
2. $y = x^3 - 3\,x^2 - 9\,x$.
3. $y = x^3 - x^2 - 5\,x + 5$.
4. $y = 2\,x^3 - 9\,x^2 + 12\,x - 3$.

5. $f(x) = x^3 - 12\,x.$

6. $F(x) = 4 + 2\,x^2 - x^3.$

7. $F(x) = x^4 - 4\,x^3 + 16.$

8. $g(x) = x^4 - 2\,x^3 - 2\,x^2 + 1.$

9. $y = \dfrac{2\,x}{1 + x^2}.$

10. $y = \dfrac{1 - x + x^2}{1 + x + x^2}.$

11. $y = \dfrac{x - 2}{x^2 - 2\,x + 4}.$

12. $y = \dfrac{(3 - x)^3}{3 - 2\,x}.$

13. $F(x) = \dfrac{x}{\sqrt{x^2 + 1}}.$

14. $f(x) = x\sqrt{1 - x^2}.$

15. $u = \dfrac{x}{(1 + x^2)^{\frac{3}{2}}}.$

16. $v = \dfrac{x^2 - 2}{\sqrt{4 - x^2}}.$

17. Find the maximum or minimum slope of the curve
$$y = x^3 - 8\,x^2 - x + 16.$$

18. Find where the slope of the curve $y = 18\,x^2 - x^4$ is a maximum; also find where the slope of the curve is increasing most rapidly.

19. Find the inclination of the curve $y = 3\,x^3 - x^4$ at the point where the slope is increasing most rapidly.

20. Show that the parabola $y^2 = 2\,px$ has no maximum or minimum points.

21. Show that the function $y = \dfrac{1}{1 - x}$ has no maximum or minimum.

22. Show that the function $y = x + \dfrac{1}{x}$ has a maximum and a minimum, but that the maximum is less than the minimum.

23. Find two numbers whose sum is 36 and whose product is as large as possible.

24. Find two numbers whose product is 64 and such that the sum of their squares is a minimum.

25. The number of articles which a manufacturer can sell monthly at a price of x dollars is $y = 180 - 5\,x$, and the cost of them to him is $C = 600 + 4\,y$ dollars. What price x will give him a maximum profit?

128. Concavity of Curves

A smooth curve is said to be **concave upward** *at a point if the tangent to the curve turns counter-clockwise (that is, if the slope increases) as the point of tangency goes through the point from left to right; it is* **concave downward** *if the tangent turns clockwise (that is, if the slope decreases).*

A simple test for determining the direction of concavity may be derived as follows: Suppose that at a given point $P_1(x_1, y_1)$ of a curve $y = f(x)$, the second derivative $f''(x_1)$ is positive. Since $f''(x)$ is the derivative of $f'(x)$, it follows from § 121 that $f'(x)$ is increasing at $x = x_1$. Consequently, the slope is increasing at P_1, the tangent is turning counter-clockwise, and the curve is concave upward at P_1.

Similarly, if $f''(x_1)$ is negative, then $f'(x)$ is decreasing at P_1, the tangent is turning clockwise, and the curve is concave downward at P_1. If $f''(x_1) = 0$, and if $f''(x)$ is positive in the neighborhood of x_1 except at x_1, then the tangent turns counter-clockwise as the point of tangency goes through x_1, and the curve is concave upward at P_1. Similarly, if $f''(x_1) = 0$ and if $f''(x)$ is negative in the neighborhood of x_1 except at x_1, the curve is concave downward at P_1. Hence:

The graph of a function $f(x)$ is concave upward at a point x_1 if $f''(x_1) > 0$ and concave downward at x_1 if $f''(x_1) < 0$. If $f''(x_1) = 0$, the graph is concave upward at x_1 if $f''(x) > 0$ in the neighborhood of x_1 (except at x_1), and is concave downward at x_1 if $f''(x) < 0$ in the neighborhood of x_1 (except at x_1).

Where the curve is concave upward, the curve lies above the tangent, and where the curve is concave downward, the curve lies below the tangent.

EXAMPLE 1.   Determine where the curve $6\,y = 2\,x^3 - 12\,x^2 + 18\,x + 14$ is concave upward and where it is concave downward.

Solution: We have $6\,y' = 6\,x^2 - 24\,x + 18$, $6\,y'' = 12\,x - 24$, and

$$(a) \qquad y'' = 2(x - 2).$$

It is evident from (a) that y'' is positive when $x > 2$, y'' is negative when $x < 2$, and $y'' = 0$ when $x = 2$. It follows that the curve is concave upward when $x > 2$ and is concave downward when $x < 2$ (Fig. 64).

EXAMPLE 2.   For the curve $y = x^4$, we have $y' = 4\,x^3$, $y'' = 12\,x^2$. When $x = 0$, we have $y'' = 0$, but for all other values of x, y'' is positive. Hence, the graph of $y = x^4$ is concave upward everywhere.

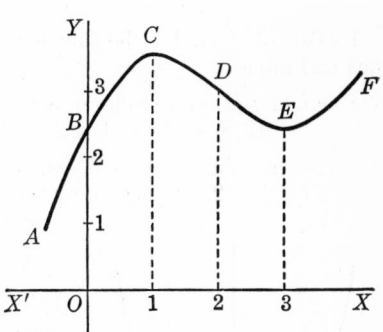

FIG. 64

129. Exercises

In Exercises 1–8, test each of the given curves for direction of concavity:

1. $y = x^3 - 2\,x^2 + 5$.
2. $y = x^3 - 3\,x + 3$.
3. $y = x^4 - 4\,x^3 + 6\,x^2 + 12\,x$.
4. $y = 2\,x^3 - 3\,x^2 - 6\,x + 1$.
5. $y = x^4 - 2\,x^2$.
6. $y = x^3 - \frac{6}{5}\,x^5$.
7. $y = x^4 - 4\,x^3 - 18\,x^2 + 12\,x - 9$.
8. $y = x^4 - 6\,x^2 + 4\,x - 1$.
9. Test the curve $x^2y - 4\,x + 3\,y = 0$ for direction of concavity.

10. When is the curve $y = ax^2 + bx + c$ concave upward and when is it concave downward?

11. Show analytically that the ellipse $b^2x^2 + a^2y^2 = a^2b^2$ is always concave toward the X-axis.

130. Second Derivative Test for Maxima and Minima

From the preceding results about concavity of curves (§ 128), there follows another very convenient test for extreme values of a function.

It is evident geometrically that a critical point where the curve is concave upward is a minimum point, and that a critical point where the curve is concave downward is a maximum point. Hence, from the theorem of § 128 it follows at once that:

If $x = a$ is a critical value for $f(x)$ such that $f''(a)$ is negative, then $f(x)$ has a relative maximum at $x = a$; and if $x = a$ is a critical value for $f(x)$ such that $f''(a)$ is positive, then $f(x)$ has a relative minimum at $x = a$:

Maximum at $x = a$ if $f'(a) = 0$,   and $f''(a) < 0$;
minimum at $x = a$ if $f'(a) = 0$,   and $f''(a) > 0$.

EXAMPLE. Examine the function $f(x) = \frac{1}{3} x^3 - 2 x^2 + 3 x + 1$ for maxima and minima.

Solution: $f'(x) = x^2 - 4 x + 3 = (x - 1)(x - 3)$,
       $f''(x) = 2 x - 4 = 2(x - 2)$.

The critical values are $x = 1$ and $x = 3$. For $x = 1, f''(x) = -2$, and for $x = 3, f''(x) = 2$. Hence, the given function has a maximum at $x = 1$ and a minimum at $x = 3$.

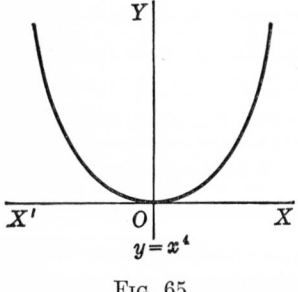

$y = x^4$

FIG. 65

At a critical value $x = a$ it may happen that the second derivative $f''(a)$ is zero as well as the first derivative $f'(a)$. In this case, the preceding theorem fails to apply; the critical value may give a maximum value or a minimum value, or it may give neither, as is illustrated by the following two examples:

(1) For the function $f(x) = x^3$, we have $f'(x) = 3 x^2$, giving the critical value $x = 0$; $f''(x) = 6 x$, which becomes 0 for $x = 0$. But we saw in § 125 that at $x = 0$ this function has neither a maximum nor a minimum.

(2) For the function $f(x) = x^4$, we have $f'(x) = 4\,x^3$, giving the critical value $x = 0$; $f''(x) = 12\,x^2$, which becomes 0 for $x = 0$. But if we let x increase through 0, the first derivative changes sign from $-$ to $+$, so that the given function has a minimum at $x = 0$ (see Fig. 65).

It follows from the preceding discussion that the second derivative test for maxima and minima is less general than the first derivative test (§ 126). In many cases, however, the second derivative test is more convenient.

131. Exercises

In Exercises 1–12, find the maxima and minima of each of the given functions:

1. $y = x^3 - 3\,x$.
2. $y = x^3 + 6\,x$.
3. $2\,y = 2\,x^3 - 3\,x^2 - 12\,x + 6$.
4. $y = x^4 - 2\,x^3 + 2\,x - 1$.
5. $y = \dfrac{x^2}{1 + x^2}$.
6. $y = \dfrac{1}{x} + \dfrac{1}{1 - x}$.
7. $f(x) = x^2\sqrt{1 - x^2}$.
8. $f(x) = (x + 1)^{\frac{2}{3}}(x - 4)^2$.
9. $y = \dfrac{\sqrt{x}}{1 + x}$.
10. $y = \dfrac{x}{(1 + x^2)^{\frac{3}{2}}}$.
11. $xy = x^2 + x + 1$.
12. $xy - x^2 + y = 0$.
13. Show that the function $f(x) = 4\,x^3 - 18\,x^2 + 27\,x - 7$ has no maxima or minima.
14. Show that the maximum and minimum points on the cubic curve $y = x^3 - ax + b$ (when they exist) are at equal distances from the Y-axis.
15. What number exceeds its square by the greatest amount?
16. The velocity of a body in rectilinear motion was: $v = 20\,t^3 - t^4$. When was the acceleration increasing most rapidly? How rapidly?
17. In a certain beam problem, the formula

$$M = \frac{wx}{2\,l^2}\,(l^2 - 4\,x^2)$$

occurs. If w and l are constant, for what value of x is M a maximum?
18. Prove that the function

$$S = m_1(x - x_1)^2 + m_2(x - x_2)^2 + \cdots + m_n(x - x_n)^2,$$

where $m_1, m_2, \cdots, m_n$ and $x_1, x_2, \cdots, x_n$ are positive constants, is a minimum when

$$x = \frac{m_1x_1 + m_2x_2 + \cdots + m_nx_n}{m_1 + m_2 + \cdots + m_n}.$$

(This occurs in the theory of least squares, in the theory of errors and statistics.)

132. Applied Problems in Maxima and Minima

Practical problems frequently occur in which it is necessary to find a maximum or minimum value of a function. A general method of attacking such problems may be briefly summarized as follows: Analyze carefully the statement of the problem. Determine the variable quantity y which is to be a maximum or minimum. In some cases, it may be possible to express the quantity y as a function of a single independent variable x. In other cases, y may be expressed most easily in terms of two or more variables; the conditions of the problem should furnish enough relations between these variables so that all but one may be eliminated, and y may then be expressed in terms of a single variable x. In any case, to the resulting function of a single variable, we may apply either of the preceding methods for finding maxima and minima. In most such problems, it is evident from the nature of the problem whether a critical value gives a maximum or a minimum, and there is then no need to test the critical values.

EXAMPLE 1. A man in a rowboat 3 miles from the nearest point A of a straight shore wishes to reach in the shortest time a place on the shore 5 miles from A. If he can run 5 miles per hour but row only 4 miles per hour, at what place must he land?

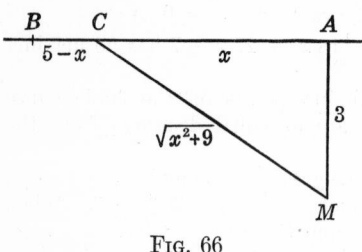

FIG. 66

Solution: In Fig. 66, the man rows from M to C and then runs from C to B. If $AC = x$, then $CB = 5 - x$ and $MC = \sqrt{x^2 + 9}$. The time required to go from M to B is then

$$t = \frac{\sqrt{x^2 + 9}}{4} + \frac{5 - x}{5}.$$

We wish to find the value of x for which t is a minimum. We find

$$D_x t = \tfrac{1}{4} \cdot \tfrac{1}{2}(x^2 + 9)^{-\frac{1}{2}} \cdot 2\,x - \tfrac{1}{5} = \frac{x}{4\sqrt{x^2 + 9}} - \frac{1}{5}.$$

If we put $D_x t = 0$ and solve for x, we find $x = 4$. Hence, the man should land 4 miles from A and 1 mile from B.

EXAMPLE 2. The strength of a rectangular beam is proportional to the width and the square of the depth. Find the dimensions of the cross-section of the strongest beam that can be cut from a circular cylindrical log of diameter 12 inches.

Solution: In Fig. 67, let $x = AB$ be the width and $y = BC$ be the depth of the beam; $AC = 12$ is a diameter of the circle. Then

(a)
$$x^2 + y^2 = 144.$$

The strength S of the beam is given by

(b)
$$S = kxy^2,$$

where k is a constant of proportionality. Substituting from (a) the value of y into (b), we have

(c) $S = kx(144 - x^2) = k(144\,x - x^3).$

We wish to find the value of x which makes S a maximum. Since

$$D_xS = k(144 - 3\,x^2),$$

if we put $D_xS = 0$ to find the critical values, we have $144 - 3\,x^2 = 0$, from which

$$x = \pm 4\sqrt{3}.$$

Since x is the width of the beam, we take the positive value $x = 4\sqrt{3}$. From (a) we then find $y = 4\sqrt{6}$. The required dimensions of the beam are therefore: width $4\sqrt{3}$, depth $4\sqrt{6}$.

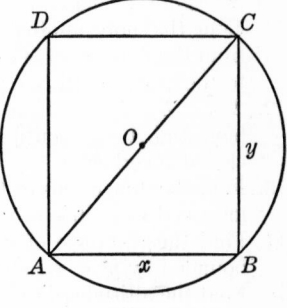

Fig. 67

133. Exercises

1. A rectangular box is to be made from a piece of cardboard 24 inches long and 9 inches wide by cutting out a square from each corner and turning up the sides. Find the volume of the largest box that can be so constructed.

2. A sheet of paper for a poster contains 12 square feet. The margins at top and bottom are 4 inches and on the sides 3 inches. What are the dimensions of the printed area if it is to be a maximum?

3. An open cylindrical can is to contain $125\,\pi$ cubic inches. What dimensions will require the least material?

4. A V-shaped trough of maximum capacity is to be made by bending down the middle a piece of tin 20 inches wide. Find the width of the trough at the top.

5. It is required to fence three sides of a rectangular plot of ground of area 1210 square yards. Find the dimensions of the plot in order that the least length of fence will be required.

6. Find the dimensions of the most economical shape for a pan with a square bottom and vertical sides, if it is to hold 4 cubic feet.

7. A farmer estimates that if he digs his potatoes now he will have 120 bushels worth $1 per bushel, but if he waits, the crop will grow 20 bushels per week while the price will drop 10¢ per bushel per week. When should he dig them to get the largest cash return?

8. A telephone company finds that there is a net profit of $15 per instrument if an exchange has 1000 subscribers or less. If there are over 1000 subscribers, the profits per instrument decrease 1¢ for each subscriber

over that number. How many subscribers would give the maximum net profit?

9. A long sheet of tin 25 inches wide is to be made into a gutter, by turning up strips vertically along the two sides. How many inches should be turned up at each side to secure the greatest carrying capacity?

10. A right prism, the base of which is an equilateral triangle, has a volume of 2 cubic feet. Find the edge of the base for minimum total surface.

11. A vessel is anchored 3 miles off shore. Opposite a point 5 miles farther along the shore, another vessel is anchored 9 miles off the shore. A boat from the first vessel is to land a passenger on the shore and then proceed to the other vessel. What is the shortest course of the boat?

12. A ship B is 75 miles due east of a ship A. If B sails west at 12 miles per hour and A sails south at 9 miles per hour, find when the ships will be closest together.

13. Find the dimensions of the rectangle of maximum perimeter that can be inscribed in a circle of radius 4.

14. Find the rectangle of greatest area inscribed in the parabolic segment bounded by $y^2 = 8x$ and $x = 4$.

15. Find the altitude of the right circular cylinder of maximum volume that can be inscribed in a sphere of radius a.

16. Find the altitude of the right circular cylinder of maximum curved surface that can be inscribed in a sphere of radius a.

17. A cylindrical tin boiler, open at the top, has a copper bottom. If sheet copper is five times as expensive as tin, per unit area, find the most economical proportions (for a given volume).

18. A box with a lid, on a square base, is to be made of sheet metal, the thickness of the base to be double that of the sides and lid. Find the dimensions for least weight of a box of capacity 2 cubic feet.

19. A rectangular sheet of metal 16 inches wide is to be bent into an open channel whose section is a trapezoid with the sides inclined at $120°$ to the base. Find the dimensions of the channel so that it may allow the greatest possible flow of water.

20. The space within a mile race-track consists of a rectangle with a semicircle at each end. To make the area of the rectangle as large as possible, how much of the mile should be given to the straight sides and how much to the curved ends?

134. Implicit Function Method in Applied Maximum and Minimum Problems

When the function that is to be made a maximum or minimum is expressed as a function of two variables which are related by a given equation, instead of eliminating one of the variables by use of the given relation, it is frequently better not to do this but to carry along both functional relations and use the method of implicit function differentiation, as illustrated by the following examples. If we wish to find *relative dimensions* instead of absolute dimensions, this method is usually better.

EXAMPLE 1. A cylindrical tin tomato can is to be made to contain 1 quart. Find the relative dimensions so that the least amount of tin shall be used.

Solution: Let r and h denote the radius of base and the altitude of the cylinder (Fig. 68). Then, if r and h are expressed in proper units,

(a) $$\pi r^2 h = 1,$$

(b) $$2\pi rh + 2\pi r^2 = S \text{ (total surface)}.$$

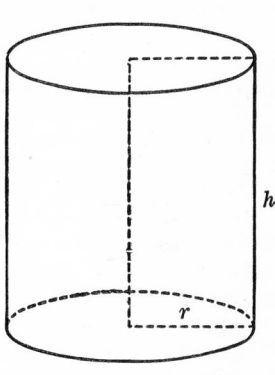

Let r be regarded as the independent variable and consider h a function of r, defined by equation (a). Differentiate (a) and (b) with respect to r; denoting $D_r h$ by h', we get:

(c) $\pi r^2 h' + 2\pi rh = 0$ or $rh' + 2h = 0,$

(d) $\quad 2\pi rh' + 2\pi h + 4\pi r = 0$
  or $rh' + h + 2r = 0.$

The right hand side of (d) is 0, since S is to be a minimum. We eliminate h' from (c) and (d) by subtraction, obtaining $h - 2r = 0$ or $h = 2r$. Hence, for minimum total surface S, we must have: altitude = diameter of base.

FIG. 68

EXAMPLE 2. The stiffness of a rectangular beam varies as its width and as the cube of its depth. Find the relative dimensions of the stiffest beam that can be cut from a circular cylindrical log of given diameter (Fig. 69).

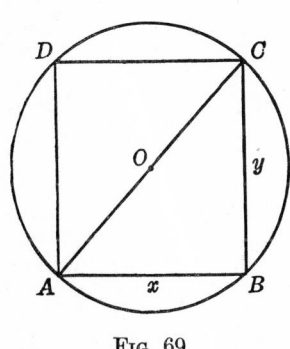

FIG. 69

Solution: Let x denote the width and y the depth of the cross-section of the beam, and let a be the diameter of the log. We have

(e) $$x^2 + y^2 = a^2,$$

(f) $$S = kxy^3,$$

where S is the stiffness and k and a are constant. We wish to make S a maximum. Regarding x as the independent variable and y as a function of x (defined by (e)), and differentiating equations (e) and (f) with respect to x, we obtain

(g) $$2x + 2yy' = 0,$$

(h) $$D_x S = ky^3 + 3kxy^2 y' = 0.$$

Eliminating y' from these two equations, we find $y^2 = 3x^2$, or $y = x\sqrt{3}$, which gives the required relative dimensions.

EXAMPLE 3. Find the relative dimensions of the right circular cone of maximum volume inscribed in a sphere of radius a.

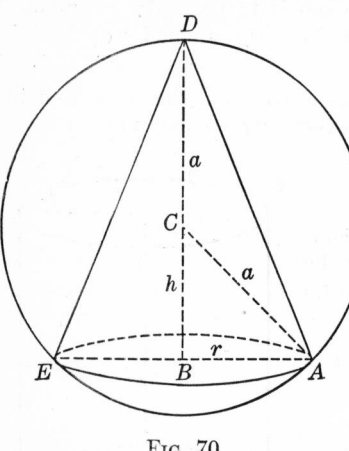

FIG. 70

Solution: From Fig. 70, we have

(i) $h^2 + r^2 = a^2$,

(j) $V = \frac{1}{3}\pi r^2(h + a)$.

Let r be the independent variable and consider h to be a function of r. Differentiating both equations (i) and (j) with respect to r, we obtain

(k) $2hh' + 2r = 0$,

(l) $\frac{1}{3}\pi r^2 h' + \frac{1}{3}\pi h \cdot 2r + \frac{1}{3}\pi a \cdot 2r = 0$.

Eliminating h' from these two equations, we find $r^2 = 2h(a + h)$.

135. Exercises

1. Find the relative dimensions of the largest rectangle that can be cut from a semicircle whose radius is a.

2. Show that the rectangle of given perimeter with shortest diagonal is a square.

3. Show that the rectangle of least perimeter for a given area is a square.

4. Find the relative dimensions of the rectangle of maximum perimeter that can be inscribed in a given circle.

5. Find the relative dimensions of the right circular cylinder of maximum volume for a given total surface.

6. Find the relative dimensions of the right circular cylinder of minimum total surface area for a given volume.

7. A rectangular box with square base and open at the top is to be made out of a given amount of material. If no allowance is made for thickness of material or waste in construction, what are the relative dimensions of the largest box that can be made?

8. A cylindrical cistern is to be constructed with open top and of a given capacity. Find the ratio of the diameter to the depth of the cistern of minimum total surface (side and bottom).

9. What are the most economical proportions for an open cylindrical water tank, if the cost of the side per square foot is two-thirds the cost of the bottom per square foot?

10. A silo of given volume is to be made in the form of a cylinder surmounted by a hemisphere. Find the relative dimensions if the total cost of the floor, wall and roof, all made of the same material, is to be the least.

11. Find the right circular cylinder of greatest volume that can be inscribed in a given right circular cone.

12. For a right circular cylinder inscribed in a given right circular cone, find the relative dimensions for the maximum curved surface of the cylinder.

13. A Norman window has the form of a rectangle surmounted by a semi-circle. If the perimeter is 30 feet, find the relative dimensions so that the greatest amount of light may be admitted.

14. Show that the largest rectangle that can be inscribed in the segment of the parabola $y^2 = 2\,px$ bounded by the line $x = a$ has a horizontal dimension equal to $\frac{2}{3}\,a$.

15. An open bin, with square base and vertical sides, is to hold a given volume of wheat. What must be its relative dimensions in order that as little material as possible may be needed to construct it, the thickness of the material being disregarded?

16. An open trough of given volume and minimum surface is to be made in the form of a half-cylinder. Find the ratio of the diameter of the semi-circular ends to the length of the trough.

17. Find the altitude of the largest cylinder that can be inscribed in a sphere of radius a.

18. Find the right circular cylinder of greatest curved surface that can be inscribed in a sphere of radius a.

19. Find the relative dimensions of the conical tent of given volume that requires the least material.

20. A right circular cone of maximum volume is inscribed in a given right circular cone, the vertex of the one being at the center of the base of the other. Show that the altitude of the inscribed cone is one-third the altitude of the other.

21. If the strength of a rectangular beam is proportional to its width and the square of its depth, find the dimensions of the beam of maximum strength that can be cut from a log which is an elliptic cylinder whose cross-section is an ellipse with the equation $9\,x^2 + 4\,y^2 = 36$.

22. An oil can is made in the shape of a cylinder surmounted by a cone. If the radius of the base of the cone is three-fourths its altitude, find the most economical proportions.

23. Find the shape of the cone of maximum curved surface inscribed in a given sphere.

24. Find the shape of the cone of maximum volume inscribed in a given sphere.

★ 136. Other Types of Maxima and Minima

Some relative maxima and minima of a function $f(x)$ may occur at points where $f'(x) \neq 0$. This may happen if $f(x)$ is defined and continuous at a point where the derivative $f'(x)$ is discontinuous. Fig. 71 (a) shows the graph of such a function having a vertical tangent at $x = a$. In this case $f'(x)$ has an infinite discontinuity at $x = a$, and $|f'(x)| \to +\infty$ as $x \to a$. In Fig. 71 (b) there are two distinct tangents to the curve at $x = a$, and $f'(x)$ has a finite discontinuity there. In both cases, $f'(x)$ changes sign from $+$ to $-$ as x increases through a, and A is a maximum point of the curve.

It can be seen graphically that if $f(x)$ is continuous at $x = a$ and if $f'(x)$ is discontinuous at a, and if $f'(x)$ changes sign from $+$ to $-$ as x increases through a, then $f(a)$ is a maximum value of $f(x)$; and

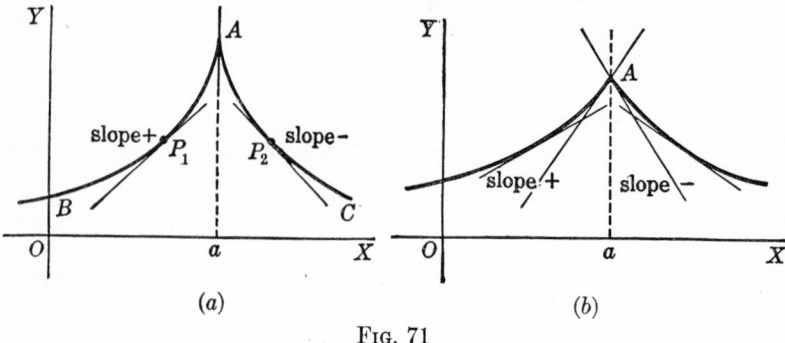

Fig. 71

similarly, if $f'(x)$ changes sign from $-$ to $+$, then $f(a)$ is a minimum value of $f(x)$.

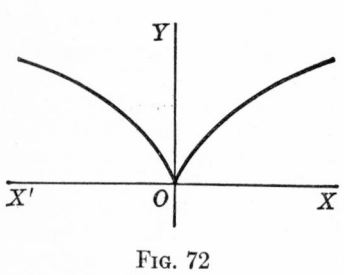

Fig. 72

EXAMPLE 1. If $f(x) = x^{\frac{2}{3}}$, then $f'(x) = \frac{2}{3}x^{-\frac{1}{3}} = \frac{2}{3\sqrt[3]{x}}$, and $|f'(x)| \to + \infty$ as $x \to 0$. As x increases through 0, $f'(x)$ changes sign from $-$ to $+$, therefore $f(x)$ has a minimum value $f(0) = 0$ at $x = 0$. The graph of this function (Fig. 72) has a sharp change in direction at the origin, with a vertical tangent there. The origin is a minimum point of the curve.

The **greatest** or **least value** of a function **in an interval** may not be a relative maximum or minimum, but may occur at one end of the interval, without having the derivative equal to 0 there.

EXAMPLE 2. The preceding statement is illustrated by the function $f(x) = x^2 - 2x$ for the interval (2, 4). The graph (Fig. 73) of this function indicates that the least value of $f(x)$ in the interval (2, 4) is at the end point $x = 2$ for which $f(2) = 0$, and the greatest value is at the end point $x = 4$ for which $f(4) = 8$; at neither of these points $x = 2$ or $x = 4$ does the derivative $f'(x) = 2(x - 1)$ equal 0. The critical point $x = 1$ gives a relative minimum of $f(x)$ but this point is outside the given interval.

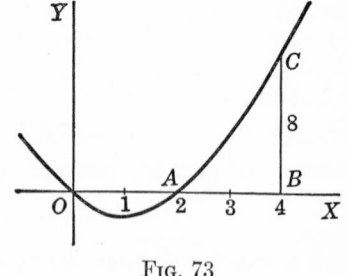

Fig. 73

Exercise 1. Examine the following functions for maxima and minima:

(a) $f(x) = (1 - x)^{\frac{2}{3}}(2 + x)^{\frac{1}{3}}$;   (b) $f(x) = (x - 1)^{\frac{1}{3}}(x + 1)^{\frac{2}{3}}$.

Exercise 2. Find the greatest and least values of the function $f(x) = 2x^3 + 3x^2 - 12x - 4$ in the interval $(-3, 3)$, including the end points of the interval.

137. Points of Inflection of a Curve

Closely associated with maximum and minimum points of a curve are certain points called *points of inflection*.

*A point on a smooth curve at which the curve changes from concave upward to concave downward or vice versa is called a **point of inflection**.* Thus, in Fig. 74, C is a point of inflection.

Since the tangent to a curve always lies opposite the concave side of the curve, it follows that at a point of inflection the tangent crosses the curve.

Let $f(x)$ be a function with a continuous second derivative. Suppose that as x increases through the value a, $f''(x)$ changes sign from $+$ to $-$. By § 128, the curve changes from concave upward to concave downward at $x = a$, hence by definition the curve has a point of inflection at $x = a$. Similarly, if $f''(x)$ changes sign from $-$ to $+$ as x increases through a, the curve changes from concave downward to concave upward, and again the curve has a point of

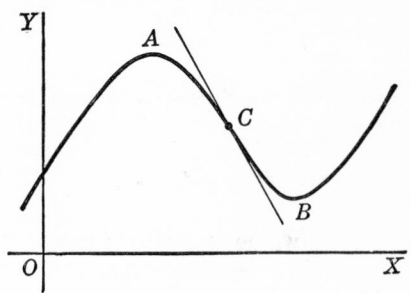

Fig. 74

inflection at $x = a$. Moreover, if $x = a$ is a point of inflection, the direction of concavity is reversed and $f''(x)$ changes sign as x increases through a. Since $f''(x)$ is continuous, by hypothesis, it becomes equal to 0 wherever it changes sign. Therefore, points of inflection can occur only for values of x for which $f''(x) = 0$. Hence:

I. *If $f(x)$ is a function with a continuous second derivative, and if, as x increases through the value a, $f''(x)$ changes sign, then the graph of $f(x)$ has a point of inflection at $x = a$. In this case, $f''(a) = 0$. Also, if $f''(x)$ is continuous, at a point of inflection $x = a$, $f''(x)$ changes sign, and we have $f''(a) = 0$.*

EXAMPLE. Test the curve $y = f(x) = \frac{1}{3} x^3 - 2 x^2 + 3 x + 1$ for points of inflection.

Solution: $f'(x) = x^2 - 4 x + 3$, $f''(x) = 2(x - 2)$. If $f''(x) = 0$, then $x = 2$. As x increases through the value 2, $f''(x)$ evidently changes sign from $-$ to $+$, showing that the curve has a point of inflection at $x = 2$.

For the type of function $f(x)$ that we have been considering, we have seen that the condition $f''(a) = 0$ is a *necessary* condition for a point of inflection at $x = a$. It is not, however, a *sufficient* condition. This is shown by the example: $f(x) = x^4$, for which $f''(x) = 12 x^2$ and $f''(0) = 0$. The point $x = 0$ is not a point of inflection, for as x increases through 0, $f''(x)$ does not change sign, as required by the preceding theorem. In fact, this function has a minimum point at $x = 0$ (§ 130).

Let $f(x)$ be a function with a continuous second derivative. Suppose that at a value $x = a$ we have $f''(a) = 0$ and $f'''(a) \neq 0$. Then, by § 121, $f''(x)$ is either an increasing or a decreasing function at $x = a$. Therefore, since $f''(a) = 0$, it follows that $f''(x)$ either increases from negative to positive or decreases from positive to negative as x increases through a. Consequently the graph of $f(x)$ has a point of inflection at $x = a$. Hence:

II. *If $f(x)$ is a function with a continuous second derivative, and if $f''(a) = 0$ and $f'''(a) \neq 0$, then the graph of $f(x)$ has a point of inflection at $x = a$.*

138. Exercises

In Exercises 1–12, find the maximum and minimum points and the points of inflection of each of the given curves:

1. $y = \frac{1}{2} x^4 - 3 x^2$.
2. $y = x^3 - 6 x^2$.
3. $y = x^3(x - 2)$.
4. $3 y = x^4 - 6 x^2$.
5. $y = x^3 - 3 x^2 - 9 x + 5$.
6. $y = \frac{1}{4} x^4 + \frac{1}{3} x^3 - 3 x^2 + 2$.
7. $y = (x^2 - 1)^2$.
8. $y = 3 x - x^3$.
9. $y = \dfrac{1}{x^2 + 4}$.
10. $y = \dfrac{2 x}{x^2 - 1}$.
11. $y = \dfrac{x}{\sqrt{x^2 + 1}}$.
12. $y = x\sqrt{1 - x^2}$.

13. Show that at a point of inflection of a curve, the slope is either a maximum or a minimum.

14. Prove that every cubic curve whose equation is of the form

$$y = ax^3 + bx^2 + cx + d$$

has one point of inflection, and that the curve is symmetrical with respect to that point.

15. If a uniform beam of length l is supported at both ends by being embedded firmly at both ends, a uniform load produces the deflection

$$y = k(x^4 - 2\,lx^3 + l^2x^2).$$

Find the maximum deflection, and also find the position of the points of inflection of the deflection curve.

139. Curve Tracing

In Chapter III, it was shown how the graph of a given equation or function may be traced by plotting points whose coördinates are calculated from the given equation, and by discussing the equation to determine the intercepts, symmetry, extent, horizontal or vertical asymptotes, etc.

By finding the first two or three derivatives and determining the maximum and minimum points, points of inflection and regions of concavity, we may supplement the preceding information greatly.

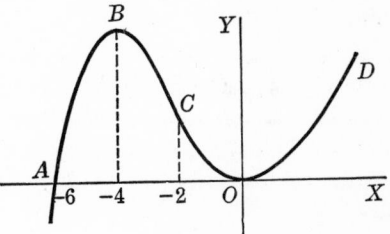

FIG. 75

Example. Trace the curve $y = x^3 + 6\,x^2$.

Solution: If $y = 0$, then $x = 0$ or -6.

$$y' = 3\,x^2 + 12\,x = 3\,x(x + 4); \text{ if } y' = 0, \text{ then } x = 0 \text{ or } -4;$$
$$y'' = 6\,x + 12 = 6(x + 2); \text{ if } y'' = 0, \text{ then } x = -2;$$
$$y''' = 6.$$

Hence, the curve cuts the X-axis at $x = 0$ and $x = -6$, it has a minimum point at $x = 0$ and a maximum point at $x = -4$, and a point of inflection at $x = -2$. The curve is shown in Fig. 75.

140. Exercises

Discuss and trace the following curves:

1. $y = \frac{1}{12}\,x^3 - x.$
2. $y = 3\,x + x^2.$
3. $2\,y = 3\,x - x^3.$
4. $6\,y = 4\,x - x^4.$
5. $y = x^5 - x.$
6. $y = x^5 - x^2.$
7. $y = x^2(x^2 - 4).$
8. $y = \dfrac{2\,x^2}{x^2 + 4}.$
9. $y = x + \dfrac{4}{x}.$
10. $y = x + \dfrac{4}{x^2}.$
11. $y = x^2 + \dfrac{4}{x}.$
12. $y = \dfrac{8\,a^3}{x^2 + 4\,a^2}.$

13. $3x = y^2 + 2y - 5$.

14. $xy = -8$.

15. $xy + y - x = 0$.

16. $x^2y + y - x^2 = 0$.

17. $x^2 + xy + y^2 = 4$.

18. $x^2 + 3xy + y^2 = 4$.

19. $x^2 + xy + y^2 + 3y = 0$.

20. $y^2 = x^2(x^2 - 16)$.

21. $xy^2 + y^2 - x = 0$.

22. $y^2 = (4 - x)(3 - x)(2 - x)$.

23. $x^2 + 2xy + y^2 + 3x - 3y = 0$.

24. $3x^2 - 10xy + 10y^2 = 2$.

CHAPTER VIII

Differentials

141. Differentials

Let $y = f(x)$ be a differentiable function of x. By the definition of a derivative,

$$\lim_{\Delta x \to 0} \left(\frac{\Delta y}{\Delta x} \right) = f'(x).$$

By the definition of a limit, this may be written

$$\frac{\Delta y}{\Delta x} = f'(x) + \epsilon,$$

where $\epsilon \to 0$ when $\Delta x \to 0$. This gives the following important result:

If $y = f(x)$ is a differentiable function, the increment of the function corresponding to a given increment Δx of the independent variable is given by:

(1) $\qquad \Delta y = f'(x) \cdot \Delta x + \epsilon \cdot \Delta x, \qquad$ *where $\epsilon \to 0$ when $\Delta x \to 0$.*

EXAMPLE 1. If $y = x^3$, then

$$\Delta y = 3 \, x^2(\Delta x) + 3 \, x(\Delta x)^2 + (\Delta x)^3 = 3 \, x^2(\Delta x) + [3 \, x(\Delta x) + (\Delta x)^2]\Delta x.$$
In this case, therefore, $\epsilon = 3 \, x(\Delta x) + (\Delta x)^2$.

Formula (1) expresses the increment Δy as a function of the two *independent* variables x and Δx. If we momentarily hold x constant and allow Δx to vary, the formula gives a decomposition of the increment Δy into two parts: the first of these is a constant times Δx, and the second is a product of Δx by a variable ϵ which approaches 0 when $\Delta x \to 0$. If Δx is sufficiently small, the second term is considerably smaller numerically than the first term (unless $f'(x) = 0$). The smaller Δx is taken, the more will the first term predominate over the second term. Because of its importance, we give a special name and notation to this term $f'(x) \cdot \Delta x$, as follows:

When $y = f(x)$, *the product* $f'(x) \cdot \Delta x$ *is called the **differential** of* y, *and is denoted by* **dy:**

(2) $$dy = f'(x) \cdot \Delta x,$$

where Δx *is an arbitrary increment of* x.

That is, *the **differential of a function** is defined as its derivative multiplied by an increment of the independent variable.*

EXAMPLE 2. If $y = x^3$, then $dy = 3\,x^2 \cdot \Delta x$ (see Example 1).

For convenience, *we define the **differential dx** of the **independent variable** x as equal to its increment Δx:*

(3) $$dx = \Delta x,$$

which is consistent with (2) when $y = f(x) = x$.

It should be noted that the value of dy depends upon the values of the independent variables x and Δx; also that the differential of the *function* is *not* in general equal to its increment.

It follows from the definition of dx that we may write the defining equation (2) in the form:

(4) $$dy = f'(x)\, dx.$$

If we divide both members of equation (4) by dx, we get

(5) $$\frac{dy}{dx} = f'(x) = D_x y.$$

This gives us an expression for the derivative as a *quotient*, and also gives us a new *notation* $\dfrac{dy}{dx}$ for the derivative, which is the notation most widely used, and which will be used extensively hereafter in this book.   Its advantage is that it may be treated as a fraction.

The geometric interpretation of the differential dy is of interest and importance.   In Fig. 76, let $P(x, y)$ and $Q(x + \Delta x, y + \Delta y)$ be two neighboring points on the graph of $y = f(x)$, let PT be the tangent at P; then

$$\overline{PR} = \Delta x = dx, \ \overline{RQ} = \Delta y, \ \overline{RS} = \Delta x \tan RPT = f'(x) \cdot \Delta x = dy,$$
and
$$\overline{SQ} = \overline{RQ} - \overline{RS} = \Delta y - dy = \epsilon \cdot \Delta x.$$

Hence, *the increment Δy is represented graphically by the segment $\overline{RQ}$ from the horizontal line through P to the curve, while the differential dy is represented by the segment $\overline{RS}$ from the horizontal to the tangent.*

Since the difference $\Delta y - dy = \epsilon \cdot \Delta x$, and since $\epsilon \to 0$ as $\Delta x \to 0$, it is evident that dy is a good approximation to Δy for sufficiently small values of Δx.

It follows from the definition of the differential of a function that:

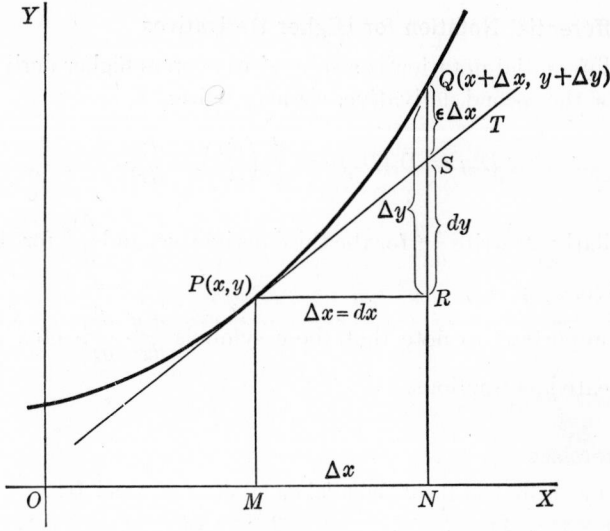

FIG. 76

All the fundamental formulas for derivatives of special types of functions become differential formulas when we multiply through by the differential of the independent variable.

EXAMPLE 3. $d(x^3) = 3\,x^2\,dx$, $d(\sqrt{x}) = \frac{1}{2}\,x^{-\frac{1}{2}}\,dx$, $d(xy) = x\,dy + y\,dx$, etc.

An important property of differentials is the following: Let $y = F(u)$ and $u = \phi(x)$, then by § 97,

$$\frac{dy}{dx} = D_x y = D_u y \cdot D_x u = F'(u) \cdot \frac{du}{dx},$$

$$\frac{dy}{dx} \cdot dx = F'(u) \cdot \frac{du}{dx} \cdot dx = F'(u) \cdot du,$$

since $\dfrac{du}{dx} \cdot dx = du$. Therefore,

(a) $$dy = F'(u) \cdot du.$$

It follows that:

The differential of a function of a variable (whether this latter variable is an independent variable or a dependent variable), is equal to the derivative of the function with respect to that variable multiplied by the differential of that variable.

142. Differential Notation for Higher Derivatives

The differential notation is also used to express higher derivatives. Thus, for the second derivative, we may write:

$$D_x^2 y = D_x(D_x y) = \frac{d}{dx}\left(\frac{dy}{dx}\right) = \frac{d^2 y}{dx^2},$$

and similarly we write $\dfrac{d^3 y}{dx^3}$ for the third derivative, and $\dfrac{d^n y}{dx^n}$ for the n-th derivative.

It is important to note that these symbols $\dfrac{d^2 y}{dx^2}$, $\dfrac{d^3 y}{dx^3}$, etc., are *not* to be treated as fractions.

143. Exercises

In Exercises 1–10, find the differential dy in terms of x and dx:

1. $y = x^3 + 3x.$
2. $y = 2x - x^4.$
3. $y = \dfrac{x - 1}{x + 1}.$
4. $y = \dfrac{x + 1}{x}.$
5. $y = \sqrt{1 + x^2}.$
6. $y = \sqrt{1 - 2x}.$
7. $y = (x + 1)\sqrt{x}.$
8. $y = x\sqrt{1 - x^2}.$
9. $y = \dfrac{\sqrt{x^2 - 1}}{x}.$
10. $y = \dfrac{1 + x}{\sqrt{x}}.$

11. Write in differential notation all the differentiation rules of Chapter VI.
12. Show that:

   (a) $x^2\, dy + 2xy\, dx = d(x^2 y)$;   (b) $\dfrac{y\, dx - x\, dy}{y^2} = d\left(\dfrac{x}{y}\right).$

13. If $y = x^2 - 2x$, find $\Delta y - dy$ in terms of x and Δx.
14. If $y = 4x - x^3$, find $\Delta y - dy$ in terms of x and Δx.
15. When each side of a square increases by an amount Δs, show that the area increases by the amount $\Delta A = 2s \cdot \Delta s + (\Delta s)^2$. Make a diagram to exhibit these two terms geometrically. What is dA?
16. When each edge of a cube increases by an amount Δe, show that the volume increases by the amount $\Delta V = 3e^2 \cdot \Delta e + 3e(\Delta e)^2 + (\Delta e)^3$. Make a diagram to interpret these three terms geometrically. What is dV?

144. Approximation of Increments by Differentials

From the discussion in § 141, it follows that:

The differential dy of a function $y = f(x)$ may be used as an approximation to the increment Δy:

(6)
$$\Delta y \approx dy,$$

provided Δx is sufficiently small in numerical value.

The differential of a function is more easily calculated, in general, than the increment. Therefore, the differential is frequently used in calculations of approximate values of increments of functions, and in deriving approximate formulas.

EXAMPLE 1. If $y = \sqrt{9 + x^2}$, and if x increases from $x = 4$ to $x = 4.05$, find the approximate change in y.

Solution: The problem is to find an approximate value of Δy when $x = 4$ and $\Delta x = 0.05$. Since

$$dy = \tfrac{1}{2}(9 + x^2)^{-\frac{1}{2}} \cdot 2\, x\, dx = \frac{x\, dx}{\sqrt{9 + x^2}},$$

we have $dy = \tfrac{4}{5}\, dx = \tfrac{4}{5}(0.05) = 0.04$. Using $\Delta y \approx dy$, we find that the required approximate value of Δy is 0.04.

EXAMPLE 2. Approximately what change would be necessary in the radius of a spherical balloon in order to increase the volume by 10 cubic feet, if the radius is 20 feet?

Solution: We have $V = \tfrac{4}{3} \pi r^3$, $r = 20$, $\Delta V = 10$; then $dV \approx 10$. Since

$$dV = \tfrac{4}{3} \pi \cdot 3\, r^2\, dr = 4\, \pi r^2\, dr,$$

we have $10 = 4\, \pi \cdot 20^2 \cdot dr$, from which $dr = \dfrac{10}{1600\, \pi} = \dfrac{1}{160\, \pi} \approx 0.00199$. Hence, the required change in r is approximately 0.002 feet.

EXAMPLE 3. Find an approximate formula for the area of a narrow circular ring, of inner radius r and thickness dr.

Solution: $A = \pi r^2$, $dA = 2\, \pi r\, dr$, hence $\Delta A \approx 2\, \pi r\, dr$.

145. Approximation of Small Errors by Differentials

An important use of differentials is to find the *error* or degree of uncertainty in numerical results calculated from given data, resulting from errors in the data. We may interpret a *small error* in the calculated value of a function as an *increment* of the function corresponding to the error of measurement, which may be regarded as an increment of the independent variable. Hence, we can approximate the error of the function by means of its differential.

EXAMPLE 1. If the radius of a sphere is measured as 3 inches with a possible error of measurement of 0.002 inch, find the maximum error in the calculated volume.

Solution: $V = \frac{4}{3}\pi r^3$, $dV = \frac{4}{3}\pi \cdot 3\, r^2\, dr = 4\,\pi r^2\, dr$. When $r = 3$ and $dr = 0.002$, we find $dV = 36\,\pi(0.002) = 0.072\,\pi = 0.226$ approximately. The maximum numerical error in the volume of the sphere is therefore approximately 0.226 cubic inch.

The *relative error* of a measured quantity y is the ratio of the error Δy to the quantity y itself:

(a) $$\text{relative error} = \frac{\Delta y}{y} \approx \frac{dy}{y}.$$

The *percentage error* is 100 times the relative error.

EXAMPLE 2. Show that the relative error in the volume of a sphere due to an error in measuring the radius, is approximately three times the relative error in the measurement of the radius.

Solution: $V = \frac{4}{3}\pi r^3$, $dV = 4\,\pi r^2\, dr$; then

$$\frac{dV}{V} = \frac{4\,\pi r^2\, dr}{\frac{4}{3}\pi r^3} = 3 \cdot \frac{dr}{r}.$$

Now $\dfrac{dr}{r}$ is the relative error in the radius and $\dfrac{dV}{V}$ is approximately the relative error in the volume, hence the stated result follows.

146. Exercises

1. What is the exact change in value of $y = x^2$ when x changes from 20 to 20.1? What is the approximate change in y found by use of differentials?
2. Find the approximate change in the value of $y = x^3 - 3\,x$ when x changes from 2 to 2.05 by use of differentials.
3. The radius of a soap bubble increases from 1.5 inches to 1.515 inches. Calculate the approximate increase in the area of the surface.
4. What is the approximate change in the volume and surface-area of a ball-bearing if it wears down from a radius of 5 mm. to one of 4.98 mm.?
5. The maximum deflection D of a beam varies as the cube of the length l. If $D = 0.4$ when $l = 10$, find approximately how much larger D is for $l = 12.08$ than for $l = 12$.
6. For a gas at constant temperature, the pressure p and the volume v are related by the formula $pv = c$ (constant). If $v = 50$ cubic inches when $p = 28$ pounds per square inch, find approximately the change in p when v increases from 50 cubic inches to 50.5 cubic inches.
7. A given quantity of material is to be cast into the form of a cylinder of

height 8 inches and radius 2 inches. If the radius is made $\frac{1}{32}$ of an inch too large, what will be the approximate change in height?

8. For the flow of a liquid through a fine tube, $V = \dfrac{\pi p r^4}{8\, l\eta}$. If l varies and p, r and η remain constant, find the approximate change in V due to a small change in l.

9. If A is the area of a circle of radius r, show that ΔA is the area of a circular ring of inner radius r and width dr, and that dA is the product of the inner circumference of the ring by its width.

10. Find an approximate formula for the volume of a thin spherical shell of inner radius r and thickness dr.

11. Show that the volume of a thin cylindrical shell is approximately equal to the area of its inner surface times its thickness.

12. The attraction between two magnetic poles is inversely proportional to the square of the distance between them: $F = k/r^2$ (k constant). If the distance is slightly increased, how is the attraction affected?

13. The side of a square is 8 inches with a possible error of 0.01 inch. Find the maximum possible error in the area of the square.

14. The edge of a cube was measured as 20 inches, but, to the nearest hundredth of an inch, was really 19.98 inches. About how much was the calculated volume in error?

15. The velocity v (feet per second) attained by a body that has fallen from rest a distance h (feet) is given by $v = \sqrt{64.4 h}$. Find the error in v due to a small error dh in measuring h.

16. If an aviator flew around the world at the equator keeping always one mile above the surface of the earth, how many more miles would he travel than a person who went around the world staying on the surface of the earth?

17. If the radius of a circle is measured and its area calculated by using the result, show that an error of 1% in the measurement of the radius will lead to an error of about 2% in the area.

18. The volume of a sphere is to be found with an error of less than 2%. How accurately must the diameter be measured?

147. Use of Differentials in Implicit Functions

In finding derivatives from implicit functions, it is sometimes convenient to use differentials.

EXAMPLE. Find $\dfrac{dy}{dx}$ and $\dfrac{d^2y}{dx^2}$ from $x^2 + xy + y^2 = 3$.

Solution: $2\, x\, dx + (x\, dy + y\, dx) + 2\, y\, dy = 0$, or

$$(x + 2\, y)\, dy = -(2\, x + y)\, dx,$$

(a) $$\therefore \frac{dy}{dx} = -\frac{2\, x + y}{x + 2\, y} = y'.$$

$$dy' = -\frac{(x + 2\, y)(2\, dx + dy) - (2\, x + y)(dx + 2\, dy)}{(x + 2\, y)^2}$$

$$= -\frac{3\,y\,dx - 3\,x\,dy}{(x + 2\,y)^2},$$

$$\frac{d^2y}{dx^2} = \frac{dy'}{dx} = -\frac{3\,y - 3\,x\,\dfrac{dy}{dx}}{(x + 2\,y)^2} = -\frac{3\,y + 3\,x\,\dfrac{2\,x + y}{x + 2\,y}}{(x + 2\,y)^2}$$

$$= -6\,\frac{x^2 + xy + y^2}{(x + 2\,y)^3} = -\frac{18}{(x + 2\,y)^3}.$$

148. Exercises

In Exercises 1–4, find dy in terms of x, y and dx:

1. $y^2 = 8\,x.$
2. $x^2y = a^3.$
3. $x^2 + y^2 - 2\,x = 0.$
4. $xy - x^2 - 4\,y = 0.$

In Exercises 5–12, find $\dfrac{dy}{dx}$ and $\dfrac{d^2y}{dx^2}$ in terms of x and y:

5. $x^2 - xy + 2\,y^2 = 1.$
6. $x^2 - 3\,xy + 4\,y^2 = 6.$
7. $b^2x^2 + a^2y^2 = a^2b^2.$
8. $b^2x^2 - a^2y^2 = a^2b^2.$
9. $x^2y + xy^2 = 1.$
10. $y^2 - 4\,xy = 2.$
11. $x^{\frac{1}{2}} + y^{\frac{1}{2}} = a^{\frac{1}{2}}.$
12. $x^{\frac{2}{3}} + y^{\frac{2}{3}} = a^{\frac{2}{3}}.$

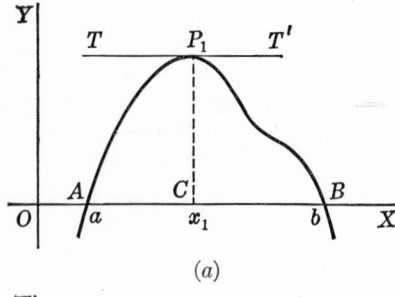

(a)

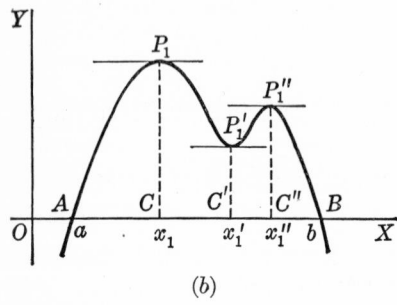

(b)

Fig. 77

149. Rolle's Theorem

Let the curve in Fig. 77 be the graph of a continuous function $f(x)$, which cuts the X-axis at two points A and B, where $x = a$ and $x = b$ respectively, so that $f(a) = f(b) = 0$; suppose also that $f(x)$ has a derivative at each point between A and B. Then it is geometrically evident that between A and B there must be at least one point P_1 at which the tangent to the curve is parallel to the X-axis. If x_1 is the abscissa of P_1, then $a < x_1 < b$ and $f'(x_1) = 0$. This leads to the following important theorem, called *Rolle's theorem:*

If $f(x)$ is a continuous function in the closed interval $a \leqq x \leqq b$, and if it has a derivative $f'(x)$ at each point within the open interval *a < x < b, and if, moreover, f(a) = f(b) = 0, then there exists at least one point x_1 such that a < x_1 < b for which the derivative f'(x_1) is zero.*

Fig. 77 (*b*) shows that there may be cases where there are two or more values $x = x_1$ for which $f'(x_1) = 0$. In any case, there is always at least one such value $x = x_1$.

If $f(x)$ does not have a derivative at every interior point of the interval $a < x < b$, even though it be continuous in that interval, and vanishes at $x = a$ and $x = b$, Rolle's theorem may fail to apply, as is illustrated in Fig. 78 (*a*) and (*b*). In these cases, we cannot say that a value $x = x_1$ exists where the tangent is parallel to the X-axis.

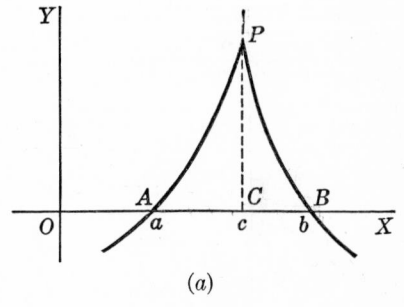

(a)

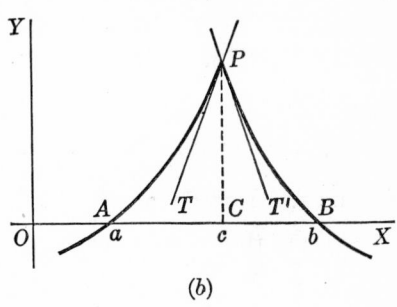

(b)

Fig. 78

An analytical proof of Rolle's theorem is the following: If $f(x)$ has the constant value 0, the theorem is obviously true. If $f(x)$ is not always 0, it must take values different from 0. Since $f(x)$ is assumed to be continuous, it must have a maximum value M and a minimum value m in the interval $a \leq x \leq b$, by § 76, I. At least one of the values M, m must be different from 0, and it must be attained at an interior point x_1 of the interval. But if a differentiable function has a maximum or minimum value at a point x_1, its derivative must vanish there (§ 125). Hence, $f'(x_1) = 0$ at some point x_1 of the interval $a < x < b$.

150. Mean-Value Theorem for Derivatives

A generalization of Rolle's theorem, which is known as the *mean-value theorem* (or law of the mean) *for derivatives*, may be obtained as follows:

Let the curve in Fig. 79 be the graph of a continuous function $f(x)$, and let A and B be two points on it for which $x = a$ and $x = b$ respectively, and suppose that this curve has a tangent at each point between A and B. Draw the chord AB. Then it is geometrically evident that between A and B on the curve there must be at least one point P_1 at which the tangent is parallel to the chord. If x_1 is the

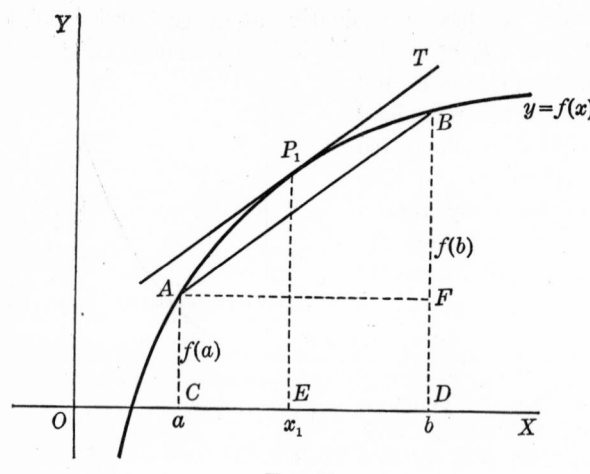

FIG. 79

abscissa of P_1, then $a < x_1 < b$. Since the ordinates of A and B are $f(a)$ and $f(b)$ respectively, the slope of the chord AB is $\dfrac{f(b) - f(a)}{b - a}$. The slope of the tangent is $f'(x_1)$. Hence,

$$\frac{f(b) - f(a)}{b - a} = f'(x_1).$$

Therefore, we have the following ***mean-value theorem:***

I. *If $f(x)$ is continuous in the closed interval $a \leqq x \leqq b$, and if it has a derivative $f'(x)$ at each point within the open interval $a < x < b$, then there exists at least one value x_1 of x for which $a < x_1 < b$ such that:*

(7) $$f(b) - f(a) = (b - a) f'(x_1).$$

As in the case of Rolle's theorem, there may exist more than one such point P_1. Also, if the derivative does not exist at some point of the interval, the theorem may not apply.

An analytical proof of this mean-value theorem, based on Rolle's theorem, is the following: Form the auxiliary function

(a)
$$F(x) = f(x) - f(a) - (x - a)\frac{f(b) - f(a)}{b - a}.$$

We have at once: $F(a) = 0$ and $F(b) = 0$; also

(b)
$$F'(x) = f'(x) - \frac{f(b) - f(a)}{b - a}.$$

We may now apply Rolle's theorem to $F(x)$, since the conditions of that theorem are satisfied by the function $F(x)$. There must therefore exist at least one number x_1 between a and b such that $F'(x_1) = 0$, hence

(c)
$$f'(x_1) - \frac{f(b) - f(a)}{b - a} = 0,$$

from which the mean-value formula (7) follows at once.

Put $b = a + h$, so that $b - a = h$; then formula (7) may be written in the form:

(d) $\qquad f(a + h) - f(a) = hf'(x_1),$ $\qquad$ *where x_1 is between a and $a + h$.*

Any number between a and $a + h$ can be expressed in the form $a + \theta h$, where θ is some number between 0 and 1. Then another form of the mean-value theorem is:

(e) $\qquad f(a + h) = f(a) + hf'(a + \theta h),$ $\qquad$ *where $0 < \theta < 1$.*

An application of the mean-value theorem is given in the proof of the following theorem (which will be of importance in Chapter IX):

II. *If $f(x)$ satisfies the conditions of theorem* I, *and if $f'(x) = 0$ throughout the interval (a, b), then $f(x)$ is constant throughout this interval.*

For, if x is any number in (a, b), by the mean-value theorem, we have

(f) $\qquad f(x) - f(a) = f'(x_1)(x - a),$ $\qquad a < x_1 < x.$

But by hypothesis, $f'(x_1) = 0$. Then from (f) it follows that $f(x) - f(a) = 0$ for any value of x in (a, b), hence $f(x)$ has the constant value $f(a)$ everywhere in the interval (a, b).

Exercise. Apply the mean-value theorem to the function $f(x) = x^2$ for the interval (a, b), and find x_1.

151. Newton's Method for Solving Equations

A method generally called *Newton's method* will enable us to find, to any desired degree of accuracy, the real roots of many equations, polynomial or transcendental.

Let $y = f(x)$ be any given smooth function, and let its graph be given by the curve in Fig. 80.   Suppose that we wish to find the real roots of the equation $f(x) = 0$.   Graphically, this means that we are

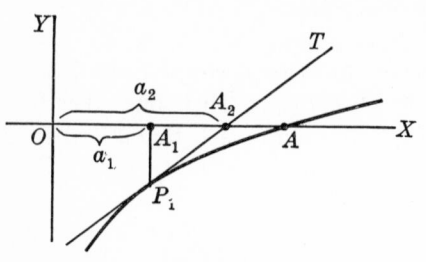

to find the X-intercepts of the curve, that is, the points of intersection of the curve with the X-axis.

Suppose that, from a graph or from tables or by trial calculations, we have found that the equation $f(x) = 0$ has a real root in the neighborhood of the value $x = a_1$.   Draw the tangent P_1T to the curve

FIG. 80

$y = f(x)$ at the point P_1 where $x = a_1$, and let A_2 be the point where this tangent intersects the X-axis.   Then, in general, if $x = a_1$ is a fair first approximation to the required root of the given equation $f(x) = 0$, the X-intercept $a_2 = \overline{OA_2}$ of the tangent will give a better or second approximation to the root.   Graphically, this is the essence of Newton's method of solving equations.

We may derive a formula for calculating the approximation a_2 as follows: The coördinates of P_1 are $(a_1, f(a_1))$, and the slope of the tangent at P_1 is $f'(a_1)$.   Therefore the equation of the tangent at P_1 is:

$$y - f(a_1) = f'(a_1)(x - a_1).$$

Putting $y = 0$ in this equation and solving for x, in order to find the intersection of the tangent with the X-axis, we obtain

$$x = a_2 = a_1 - \frac{f(a_1)}{f'(a_1)}.$$

Hence:

If $x = a_1$ is a sufficiently close first approximation to a real root of the equation $f(x) = 0$, then the formula

(8) $$a_2 = a_1 - \frac{f(a_1)}{f'(a_1)}$$

gives a closer second approximation to the root.

We may now use a_2 in formula (8) in place of a_1, and get a third and probably closer approximation to the required root of the equation; the process may be repeated as often as required to give the desired degree of accuracy.

EXAMPLE. Find the real positive root of the equation $x^3 - 2x - 5 = 0$ by Newton's method, correct to 3 decimal places.

Solution: Let $f(x) = x^3 - 2x - 5$; we find $f(2) = -1$ and $f(3) = 16$, which indicates that the given equation has a root between 2 and 3, and considerably nearer 2 than 3; therefore we take $a_1 = 2$ and apply Newton's formula. Then $f(a_1) = f(2) = -1$. Since $f'(x) = 3x^2 - 2$, we have $f'(a_1) = f'(2) = 10$. By formula (8),

$$(a) \qquad a_2 = 2 - \frac{(-1)}{10} = 2.1.$$

Now apply formula (8) again, with $a_1 = 2.1$. We find $f(2.1) = 0.061$ and $f'(2.1) = 11.23$, and

$$(b) \qquad a_3 = 2.1 - \frac{0.061}{11.23} = 2.1 - 0.0054 = 2.0946.$$

Correct to 3 decimal places, the required root is 2.095.

The use of Newton's method in solving transcendental equations will be discussed in § 301.

152. Exercises

Solve the following problems by use of Newton's method.

In each of the equations of Exercises 1–8, find the irrational root indicated, correct to 3 decimal places:

1. $x^3 + 3x - 5 = 0$, root between 1 and 2.
2. $x^3 - 4x + 2 = 0$, root between 1 and 2.
3. $2x^3 + 3x^2 - 4x - 10 = 0$, root between 1 and 2.
4. $x^3 - x^2 - 2x + 1 = 0$, root between 0 and 1.
5. $x^3 - 6x - 12 = 0$, root between 3 and 4.
6. $3x^3 + 5x - 40 = 0$, root between 2 and 3.
7. $x^4 - 2x^3 + 21x - 23 = 0$, root between 1 and 2.
8. $x^4 - x^3 + x - 2 = 0$, root between 1 and 2.
9. Calculate the value of $\sqrt[3]{2}$, correct to 4 decimal places, by use of Newton's method.
10. Calculate the value of $\sqrt[5]{10}$, correct to 4 decimal places, by use of Newton's method.
11. The volume of a spherical segment is given by $V = \frac{1}{3}\pi h^2(3r - h)$, where r is the radius of the sphere and h is the height of the segment. If $r = 4$ feet and $V = 12$ cubic feet, find the value of h correct to 2 decimal places.
12. A solid wooden sphere of diameter d and specific gravity S sinks in water to a depth h, which is determined by the equation $2x^3 - 3x^2 + S = 0$, where $x = h/d$. Find h for a maple ball of diameter 6 inches for which $S = 0.786$.

CHAPTER IX

Indefinite Integrals

153. Integration

In a great variety of problems, the derivative of a function is given and it is required to find the function.

EXAMPLE 1. Find the curve for which the tangent at any point has a slope equal to twice the abscissa of that point.

Solution: Since the slope of the tangent to a curve $y = f(x)$ is equal to the derivative $D_x y$, we have

(a)
$$D_x y = 2 x$$

for all values of x. But $D_x(x^2) = 2 x$, hence a curve which has the required property is $y = x^2$. Also, any member of the system of curves $y = x^2 + C$ (where C is any constant) will have the property, since

$$D_x(x^2 + C) = D_x(x^2) + 0 = 2 x.$$

The process by which a function is found when its derivative is given is called **integration.** It follows that *integration is the* **inverse** *of differentiation.*

If $f(x)$ is a given function and if $F(x)$ is a function whose derivative is $f(x)$, so that $F'(x) = f(x)$, then $F(x)$ is called **an integral** *of $f(x)$.*

We often use the differential terminology and notation, and we say that if $F(x)$ has $f(x)\, dx$ for its differential, then $F(x)$ is an integral of $f(x)\, dx$.

It can be shown that if $f(x)$ is single-valued and continuous on a closed interval, such an integral $F(x)$ always exists in the interval.

EXAMPLE 2. (a) x^3 is an integral of $3 x^2$, since $D_x(x^3) = 3 x^2$; $x^3 + C$ (where C is any constant) is also an integral of $3 x^2$.

(b) x^4 is an integral of $4 x^3\, dx$, since $d(x^4) = 4 x^3\, dx$, and so also is $x^4 + C$.

154. The Indefinite Integral

An integral of a function $f(x)$ was defined in § 153 as a function $F(x)$ such that $F'(x) = f(x)$. A more specific concept is introduced by the following theorem:

If $F(x)$ is any particular integral of $f(x)$, the most general integral of $f(x)$ is of the form $F(x) + C$, where C is an arbitrary constant.

This theorem may be proved as follows:

(1) Any function of the form $F(x) + C$ is an integral of $f(x)$, since

$$D_x[F(x) + C] = F'(x) + 0 = f(x).$$

(2) Any integral of $f(x)$ is of the form $F(x) + C$. For, let $G(x)$ be any other integral of $f(x)$, so that $G'(x) = f(x)$. Then

$$D_x[G(x) - F(x)] = G'(x) - F'(x) = f(x) - f(x) = 0.$$

By theorem II of § 150, if the derivative of a function is always zero, the function must be constant; therefore $G(x) - F(x) = C$ or $G(x) = F(x) + C$.

*The most general integral of a function $f(x)$ is called **the indefinite integral** of $f(x)$, and it is denoted by the symbol*

$$\int f(x)\,dx,$$

so that

(1)
$$\int f(x)\,dx = F(x) + C,$$

where $F(x)$ is any function such that $D_x F(x) = f(x)$.

*The function $f(x)$ is called the **integrand,** and the process or operation of finding the integral is called **integration.***

The symbol $\int$ is called the **integral sign.** The symbol $\int f(x)\,dx$ is read: "the integral of $f(x)$ with respect to x" or "the integral of $f(x)\,dx$."

EXAMPLE. The indefinite integral $\int x^2\,dx$ is equal to $\frac{1}{3} x^3 + C$, since $D_x(\frac{1}{3} x^3) = x^2$.

*The constant C in $\int f(x)\,dx = F(x) + C$ is called the **constant of integration.*** It is an arbitrary constant; that is, it may have any value.

In order to determine the constant of integration in any given problem, additional information besides the value of the derivative must be furnished. This will be discussed in detail later.

The function whose derivative is given is not completely determined, since it contains an arbitrary constant of integration; it is for this reason that the general integral $\int f(x)\, dx$ is called the *indefinite integral*. An indefinite integral is sometimes called an *anti-derivative* of the given integrand, since it is an inverse of a derivative.

From the definition of an integral, we may write:

(a)
$$\int f'(x)\, dx = f(x) + C;$$

(b)
$$D_x \int f(x)\, dx = f(x) \quad \text{or} \quad d \int f(x)\, dx = f(x)\, dx.$$

To *check* any integration, we need merely to differentiate the result; the derivative of the result must be the integrand.

Exercise. What is the value of:

(a) $\int 5\, x^4\, dx$; (b) $\int x^4\, dx$; (c) $\int (x^2 - x + 1)\, dx$; (d) $\int x^{\frac{1}{2}}\, dx$?

155. Some Fundamental Rules of Integration

The following rules are justified by the fact that the derivative of the right-hand member of each formula is equal to the integrand in the left-hand member.

I. *The integral of the algebraic sum of two functions is equal to the algebraic sum of the integrals of the functions:*

(2)
$$\int (u + v)\, dx = \int u\, dx + \int v\, dx,$$

where u and v are functions of x. A similar rule and formula holds for the sum of three or more functions, finite in number.

II. *The integral of a constant times a function is equal to the constant times the integral of the function:*

(3)
$$\int ku\, dx = k \int u\, dx,$$

where k is a given constant, and u is a function of x.

By this rule, a constant factor may be moved from one side of the integral sign to the other, but a variable factor cannot be moved in this way.

III. *If n is any constant exponent, positive or negative, integral or fractional, except -1, the integral of u^n is obtained by increasing the exponent of u by 1 and then dividing by the new exponent:*

$$(4) \qquad \int u^n \, du = \frac{u^{n+1}}{n+1} + C, \qquad \text{if } n \neq -1.$$

This is called the *power rule* for integration.

EXAMPLE 1. (a) $\int x^4 \, dx = \frac{1}{5} x^5 + C;$

(b) $\int x^{-3} \, dx = \frac{x^{-2}}{-2} + C = -\frac{1}{2 x^2} + C;$

(c) $\int \sqrt{y} \, dy = \int y^{\frac{1}{2}} \, dy = \frac{y^{\frac{3}{2}}}{\frac{3}{2}} + C = \frac{2}{3} y^{\frac{3}{2}} + C;$

(d) $\int \frac{dv}{\sqrt{v}} = \int v^{-\frac{1}{2}} \, dv = \frac{v^{\frac{1}{2}}}{\frac{1}{2}} + C = 2\sqrt{v} + C.$

EXAMPLE 2. $\int \left(x^3 + 3x - 2 + \frac{5}{x^5} \right) dx$

$$= \int x^3 \, dx + \int 3x \, dx - \int 2 \, dx + \int 5 x^{-5} \, dx$$

$$= \int x^3 \, dx + 3 \int x \, dx - 2 \int dx + 5 \int x^{-5} \, dx$$

$$= \frac{1}{4} x^4 + 3 \cdot \frac{1}{2} x^2 - 2x + 5 \cdot \frac{x^{-4}}{-4} + C$$

$$= \frac{1}{4} x^4 + \frac{3}{2} x^2 - 2x - \frac{5}{4 x^4} + C.$$

EXAMPLE 3. $\int y^3 (1 + y)^2 \, dy = \int (y^3 + 2 y^4 + y^5) \, dy$

$$= \frac{1}{4} y^4 + \frac{2}{5} y^5 + \frac{1}{6} y^6 + C.$$

EXAMPLE 4. $\int \frac{v^3 - 2v + 1}{v^3} \, dv = \int \left(1 - \frac{2}{v^2} + \frac{1}{v^3} \right) dv$

$$= \int (1 - 2 v^{-2} + v^{-3}) \, dv = v + \frac{2}{v} - \frac{1}{2 v^2} + C.$$

156. Exercises

In each of the following exercises, check the answer by differentiation. Evaluate each of the integrals in Exercises 1–20:

1. $\int x^5 \, dx.$

2. $\int x^8 \, dx.$

3. $\int y^{-4}\,dy.$

4. $\int z^{-6}\,dz.$

5. $\int v^{\frac{2}{3}}\,dv.$

6. $\int y^{\frac{3}{4}}\,dy.$

7. $\int x^{-\frac{3}{2}}\,dx.$

8. $\int t^{-\frac{5}{4}}\,dt.$

9. $\int \sqrt[3]{t}\,dt.$

10. $\int (8\,x^3 - 6\,x^2 + 4\,x - 1)\,dx.$

11. $\int \dfrac{dz}{\sqrt[5]{z}}.$

12. $\int \left(\dfrac{9}{y^4} - \dfrac{8}{y^3}\right)\,dy.$

13. $\int (6\,x^2 + 6\,x - 2)\,dx.$

14. $\int \sqrt{z}(1 - z^2)\,dz.$

15. $\int \left(2\,y - \dfrac{3}{y^2}\right)\,dy.$

16. $\int \dfrac{1 + x}{x^3}\,dx.$

17. $\int (2\sqrt[3]{y} - \sqrt{y})\,dy.$

18. $\int \left(t^4 - \dfrac{1}{t^4} + \sqrt[4]{t}\right)\,dt.$

19. $\int \dfrac{1 + u}{\sqrt{u}}\,du.$

20. $\int (1 - x^2)^3\,dx.$

Integrate each of the following:

21. $\dfrac{dy}{dx} = x\sqrt{x}.$

22. $\dfrac{dy}{dx} = (x + 1)(x - 2).$

23. $D_t s = t(t^2 - 1)^2.$

24. $D_z y = (1 + \sqrt{z})^2.$

25. $du = \dfrac{(x^2 - 2)^2}{x^2}\,dx.$

26. $dv = \dfrac{(t^2 - 1)^2}{\sqrt{t}}\,dt.$

27. $dz = \dfrac{(1 + v)^2}{v^{\frac{3}{2}}}\,dv.$

28. $ds = (1 + \sqrt[3]{t})^3\,dt.$

29. Find $\int p\,dv$ when $p \cdot v^\gamma = k$, where γ and k are constants.

30. Find $\int y^2\,dx$ when $x^2 + y^2 = a^2$ (a constant).

157. Change of Variable of Integration

Many integrals can be evaluated most easily by making a change of the variable of integration. In an integral of the form $\int f(x)\,dx$, we can often express the integrand $f(x)$ as a simpler function of a variable u, where u is some suitable function of x. The integral can then be expressed as an integral having u as its variable of integration in accordance with the following theorem:

If u is a function of x, then

(5)
$$\int \phi(u) \cdot \frac{du}{dx} \cdot dx = \int \phi(u)\, du;$$

that is, we may replace $\dfrac{du}{dx} \cdot dx$ under the integral sign by du, and vice versa.

For, if $\phi(u)$ is a function of u and u is a function of x, then by the definition of an integral, we have

(a)
$$\frac{d}{dx} \int \left[\phi(u) \cdot \frac{du}{dx} \right] dx = \phi(u) \cdot \frac{du}{dx}.$$

By the rule for the derivative of a composite function (§ 97),

(b)
$$\frac{d}{dx} \int \phi(u)\, du = \left[\frac{d}{du} \int \phi(u)\, du \right] \frac{du}{dx} = \phi(u) \cdot \frac{du}{dx}.$$

Therefore, $\int \phi(u)\, du$ and $\int \phi(u) \cdot \dfrac{du}{dx} \cdot dx$ differ at most by a constant, since their derivatives are equal; formula (5) is therefore proved.

EXAMPLE 1.   Consider the integral $\int 2\, x(x^2 + 1)^3\, dx$.   If we put $x^2 + 1 = u$ and $\phi(u) = u^3 = (x^2 + 1)^3$, then $\dfrac{du}{dx} = 2\, x$ or $2\, x\, dx = du$.   By (5),

$$\int 2\, x(x^2 + 1)^3\, dx = \int (x^2 + 1)^3 \cdot 2\, x \cdot dx = \int u^3 \cdot \frac{du}{dx} \cdot dx$$
$$= \int u^3\, du = \tfrac{1}{4}\, u^4 + C = \tfrac{1}{4}(x^2 + 1)^4 + C.$$

EXAMPLE 2.   Evaluate $\int x\sqrt{1 + x^2}\, dx$.

Solution: Let $1 + x^2 = u$, so that $2\, x\, dx = du$.   Then we may write

$$\int x\sqrt{1 + x^2}\, dx = \tfrac{1}{2} \int (1 + x^2)^{\frac{1}{2}}(2\, x\, dx) = \tfrac{1}{2} \int u^{\frac{1}{2}}\, du$$
$$= \tfrac{1}{2} \cdot \frac{u^{\frac{3}{2}}}{\frac{3}{2}} + C = \tfrac{1}{3}(1 + x^2)^{\frac{3}{2}} + C.$$

After solving some problems, as in the preceding examples, by change of variable, the student should try to dispense with the actual writing down of the new variable, as illustrated in the following example:

EXAMPLE 3. $\displaystyle \int \frac{6\, x\, dx}{\sqrt{x^2 + 4}} = 3 \int (x^2 + 4)^{-\frac{1}{2}}(2\, x\, dx)$

$$= 3 \int (x^2 + 4)^{-\frac{1}{2}} d(x^2 + 4) = 3 \cdot \frac{(x^2 + 4)^{\frac{1}{2}}}{\frac{1}{2}} + C = 6\sqrt{x^2 + 4} + C.$$

158. Exercises

Evaluate each of the integrals in Exercises 1–16:

1. $\int (x^2 + 1)^2 2\, x\, dx.$

2. $\int (1 + x^3)^2 3\, x^2\, dx.$

3. $\int \sqrt{x - 2}\, dx.$

4. $\int (1 - x)^{\frac{3}{2}}\, dx.$

5. $\int \dfrac{dx}{\sqrt{1 - x}}.$

6. $\int 3\, y\sqrt{y^2 + a^2}\, dy.$

7. $\int y\sqrt{y^2 - 4}\, dy.$

8. $\int \dfrac{6\, t\, dt}{\sqrt{1 - 2\, t^2}}.$

9. $\int \dfrac{z\, dz}{\sqrt{z^2 + 1}}.$

10. $\int \dfrac{v\, dv}{(a^2 - v^2)^2}.$

11. $\int v^2 (v^3 + a^3)^{\frac{1}{2}}\, dv.$

12. $\int \dfrac{z^2\, dz}{\sqrt{z^3 + 2}}.$

13. $\int \dfrac{t + 1}{\sqrt{t^2 + 2\, t}}\, dt.$

14. $\int (x^2 - 2\, x)^{\frac{3}{2}} (x - 1)\, dx.$

15. $\int (1 + \sqrt{x})^9 \cdot \dfrac{dx}{2\sqrt{x}}.$

16. $\int \dfrac{y^2 - 1}{(y^3 - 3\, y)^2}\, dy.$

Integrate each of the following:

17. $\dfrac{dy}{dx} = x\sqrt{x^2 - 1}.$

18. $\dfrac{dy}{dx} = \dfrac{1}{\sqrt{x + 1}}.$

19. $\dfrac{du}{dy} = \dfrac{y}{(y^2 + 1)^3}.$

20. $F'(z) = 5\, z\sqrt{2\, z^2 - 1}.$

21. $f'(t) = \dfrac{t}{\sqrt{t^2 - 9}}.$

22. $D_t s = t^2 \sqrt{2\, t^3 + 1}.$

23. $dy = \sqrt{1 + 4\, x}\, dx.$

24. $dv = \dfrac{u^3\, du}{\sqrt{u^4 - 1}}.$

25. Evaluate $\int x(1 + x^2)^2\, dx$ in two different ways, and reconcile the answers.

26. Show that $\int 3(x + 1)^2\, dx$ may be written in either of the forms $x^3 + 3\, x^2 + 3\, x + C$ or $(x + 1)^3 + C'.$

159. Integrals Involving Roots of Linear Functions

Certain expressions involving a root of a linear expression may be integrated by substituting a new variable for the radical.

Example 1. Evaluate $\int \dfrac{x+2}{\sqrt{x+1}}\,dx$.

Solution: Put $\sqrt{x+1} = v$. Then $x + 1 = v^2$, $x + 2 = v^2 + 1$, $dx = 2\,v\,dv$, and the integral becomes

$$\int \frac{v^2+1}{v}\cdot 2\,v\,dv = 2\int (v^2+1)\,dv = 2(\tfrac{1}{3}\,v^3 + v) + C.$$

In this result, we must replace v by its original meaning $\sqrt{x+1}$, and we have

$$\int \frac{x+2}{\sqrt{x+1}}\,dx = \tfrac{2}{3}(\sqrt{x+1})^3 + 2\sqrt{x+1} + C = \tfrac{2}{3}(x+1)^{\frac{3}{2}} + 2(x+1)^{\frac{1}{2}} + C.$$

This answer may be written in another form, sometimes more convenient, thus:

$$\tfrac{2}{3}(x+1)^{\frac{1}{2}}[(x+1)+3] + C = \tfrac{2}{3}(x+4)\sqrt{x+1} + C.$$

Example 2. Find $\int (x-2)\sqrt[3]{2\,x+1}\,dx$.

Solution: Put $\sqrt[3]{2\,x+1} = v$. Then $2\,x+1 = v^3$, $x = \tfrac{1}{2}(v^3-1)$, $x - 2 = \tfrac{1}{2}(v^3-5)$, $dx = \tfrac{3}{2}\,v^2\,dv$, and the integral becomes

$$\int \tfrac{1}{2}(v^3-5)\,v\cdot\tfrac{3}{2}\,v^2\,dv = \tfrac{3}{4}\int (v^6 - 5\,v^3)\,dv = \tfrac{3}{4}(\tfrac{1}{7}\,v^7 - \tfrac{5}{4}\,v^4) + C.$$

In terms of the original variable x, the integral is then

$$\tfrac{3}{28}(\sqrt[3]{2\,x+1})^7 - \tfrac{15}{16}(\sqrt[3]{2\,x+1})^4 + C = \tfrac{3}{28}(2\,x+1)^{\frac{7}{3}} - \tfrac{15}{16}(2\,x+1)^{\frac{4}{3}} + C.$$

This result may also be written

$$\tfrac{3}{112}(2\,x+1)^{\frac{4}{3}}[4(2\,x+1)-35] + C = \tfrac{3}{112}(8\,x-31)(2\,x+1)^{\frac{4}{3}} + C.$$

160. Exercises

Evaluate each of the following integrals:

1. $\int \dfrac{x^2\,dx}{\sqrt{x+1}}$.

2. $\int x\sqrt{3-x}\,dx$.

3. $\int \dfrac{z\,dz}{\sqrt{z+3}}$.

4. $\int \dfrac{y^2\,dy}{\sqrt{1-y}}$.

5. $\int \dfrac{3\,x\,dx}{\sqrt{2\,x+3}}$.

6. $\int \dfrac{z^2\,dz}{(4\,z+1)^{\frac{5}{2}}}$.

7. $\int x^2\sqrt{1+x}\,dx$.

8. $\int x(ax+b)^{\frac{1}{2}}\,dx$.

9. $\int x\sqrt[3]{8-x}\,dx$.

10. $\int \dfrac{x\,dx}{\sqrt[4]{2\,x+3}}$.

11. $\int x(x-4)^{\frac{2}{3}}\,dx$.

12. $\int \dfrac{t\,dt}{\sqrt[4]{t-1}}$.

161. Determination of the Constant of Integration by Means of Given Conditions

If the derivative of an unknown function is given, the function is determined (by integration) except for an arbitrary additive constant of integration. If, however, a pair of corresponding values of the independent variable and of the function is given also, then the constant of integration is determined.

EXAMPLE. Find the function y when $\dfrac{dy}{dx} = 2\,x + 1$, if it is also known that $y = 3$ when $x = 2$.

Solution: From $\dfrac{dy}{dx} = 2\,x + 1$, we find by integration:

$$y = \int (2\,x + 1)\,dx = x^2 + x + C.$$

This relation between x and y must be satisfied by $x = 2$, $y = 3$; substituting these values, we have $3 = 4 + 2 + C$, from which $C = -3$. Therefore, $y = x^2 + x - 3$.

Examples of the determination of a constant of integration by use of given conditions are met in a great variety of problems in mathematics and its applications. A few typical illustrations will be treated in the following sections; further examples will be met in later chapters.

162. Exercises

In Exercises 1–4, find y in terms of x:

1. $\dfrac{dy}{dx} = 3\,x^2 - 2\,x + 1,$ $y = 5$ when $x = 1$.

2. $D_x y = \dfrac{2}{x^2},$ $y = 5$ when $x = 2$.

3. $dy = \sqrt{2\,x - 1}\,dx,$ $y = -1$ when $x = \frac{1}{2}$.

4. $dy = \dfrac{x}{\sqrt{x^2 + 1}}\,dx,$ $y = 2$ when $x = 0$.

5. The rate of change of y with respect to x is $6\,x^2$, and $y = 6$ when $x = 3$; find y when $x = 4$.

6. If the rate of change of y with respect to x is $0.6\,x - 0.3\,x^2$, find y as a function of x if its value is 1.5 when $x = 0$.

163. Geometric Applications of Indefinite Integrals

EXAMPLE 1. Find the curves whose slope at any point (x, y) is equal to $2\,x - 4$; also find that one of these curves which passes through the point $(3, 1)$.

Solution: The slope is given by dy/dx, which in this case is equal to $2x - 4$; integrating, we obtain

(a) $$y = x^2 - 4x + C.$$

This equation represents a system or family of parabolas, shown in Fig. 81 for various values of C. To find the particular curve of the family which passes through the given point $(3, 1)$, we substitute $y = 1$ and $x = 3$ in (a), and we find

$$1 = 9 - 12 + C \text{ or } C = 4.$$

Hence, the required curve has the equation $y = x^2 - 4x + 4$.

EXAMPLE 2. Find the curve whose slope at the point (x, y) is $-x/y$, and which passes through the point $(0, a)$.

Solution: We must find y from

(b) $$\frac{dy}{dx} = -\frac{x}{y}.$$

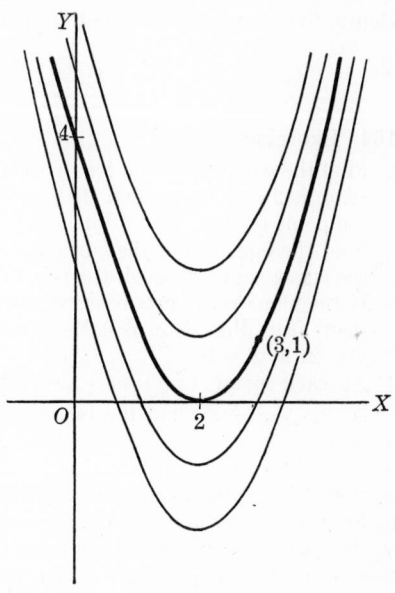

We cannot integrate this directly to obtain y as a function of x, but we may use the device of *separating variables*, by writing equation (b) in the differential form:

(c) $$y\,dy = -x\,dx,$$

and then integrating each side of this equation separately. We obtain:

FIG. 81

(d) $$\tfrac{1}{2}y^2 = -\tfrac{1}{2}x^2 + C.$$

Since the point $(0, a)$ is on this curve, we have $\tfrac{1}{2}a^2 = C$, and then equation (d) may be written

(e) $$x^2 + y^2 = a^2.$$

EXAMPLE 3. Find the equation of the curve at every point (x, y) of which $y'' = 6/x^3$ and which passes through the point $(1, 1)$ with an inclination of $135°$.

Solution: The integral of the second derivative y'' is the first derivative y'; therefore integration of $y'' = 6x^{-3}$ gives

(f) $$y' = -3x^{-2} + C.$$

At the point where $x = 1$, the slope of the tangent is $y' = \tan 135° = -1$; substitution of $x = 1$, $y' = -1$ in (f) gives $-1 = -3 + C$. Hence, $C = 2$, and

(g) $$y' = -3\,x^{-2} + 2.$$

Integrating (g), we get

(h) $$y = \frac{3}{x} + 2\,x + C'.$$

Since the required curve is to pass through the point $(1, 1)$, equation (h) must be satisfied by $x = 1$, $y = 1$; this gives $1 = 3 + 2 + C'$, and $C' = -4$. Hence, the required curve has the equation

(i) $$y = \frac{3}{x} + 2\,x - 4.$$

164. Exercises

1. Find the equation of the family of curves for which the slope at the point (x, y) is $2\,x - 1$; also find that one of these curves which passes through the point $(1, 1)$.
2. Find the equation of the curve whose slope at any point (x, y) is $3\,x^2$, if the curve passes through the point $(2, 6)$.
3. If the slope of a certain suspension cable at any horizontal distance x (feet) from the center is $0.008\,x$, find the height y (feet) at any point, if $y = 24$ at $x = 0$.
4. At each point (x, y) of a certain curve, the slope of the tangent is $-x/\sqrt{a^2 - x^2}$; find the equation of the curve if the point $(0, a)$ lies on it.
5. Find the equation of the curve through the point $(0, 2)$ which has the slope $3\,x^2/y$ at the point (x, y).
6. Find the equation of the curve whose slope at any point (x, y) is $6\,x^2 y^3$, if the curve passes through the point $(1, \frac{1}{2})$.
7. Find the equation of the curve at every point (x, y) of which $y'' = 15\sqrt{x}$ and which passes through the point $(4, 0)$ with an inclination of $45°$.
8. Find the equation of the curve for which $y'' = 2\,x$, if the curve is tangent to the line $2\,x - y - 3 = 0$ at the point $(1, -1)$.

165. Physical Applications of Indefinite Integrals

EXAMPLE 1. A certain particle moves in a straight line with the velocity $v = 2\,t - 3$ at any time t. If the displacement is $s = 4$ at time $t = 2$, find a formula for the displacement s at any time t.

Solution: Since the velocity in any rectilinear motion is given by $v = \dfrac{ds}{dt}$ (§ 80), we have

(a) $$\frac{ds}{dt} = 2\,t - 3.$$

Integrating, we get $s = t^2 - 3\,t + C$. From the given conditions, $s = 4$ when $t = 2$; hence, $4 = 4 - 6 + C$, or $C = 6$. The required displacement formula is then

(b) $$s = t^2 - 3\,t + 6.$$

EXAMPLE 2. A particle moves along a straight line with acceleration given by $a = 6\,t$, where t is the time. If the velocity is $v = 16$ when $t = 0$, and if the displacement is $s = 12$ when $t = 0$, find the velocity and displacement at any time t.

Solution: The acceleration in any rectilinear motion is given by $a = \dfrac{dv}{dt}$ (§ 116); hence in this case,

$$(c) \qquad \frac{dv}{dt} = 6\,t.$$

Integration gives $v = 3\,t^2 + C_1$; putting $v = 16$ and $t = 0$, we get $C_1 = 16$; then $v = \dfrac{ds}{dt} = 3\,t^2 + 16$. Integrating this, we have $s = t^3 + 16\,t + C_2$. Putting $s = 12$ and $t = 0$, we find $C_2 = 12$. Therefore, the displacement at any time t is

$$(d) \qquad s = t^3 + 16\,t + 12.$$

EXAMPLE 3. A ball was thrown upward from a window 80 feet above the ground, with an initial velocity of 64 feet per second. Express the height of the ball above the ground after t seconds. When was the ball highest, and how high was it then? When did it reach the ground, and with what velocity?

Solution: Let y be the height of the ball above the ground at time t, considered as positive when measured upward. If we neglect air resistance, the only force acting on the ball is that of gravity, which produces a constant acceleration vertically downward of g feet per second per second; we shall take $g = 32$. The differential equation of motion of the ball is then:

$$(e) \qquad \frac{dv}{dt} = -g = -32.$$

Integrating, we get

$$(f) \qquad v = -32\,t + C_1.$$

Taking $t = 0$ as the time of initial projection, we have $v = 64$ when $t = 0$; substituting these values in (f), we find $C_1 = 64$. Hence, the velocity at any time t is given by

$$(g) \qquad v = -32\,t + 64.$$

Integrating (g) in the form $\dfrac{dy}{dt} = -32\,t + 64$, we obtain

$$(h) \qquad y = -16\,t^2 + 64\,t + C_2.$$

But $y = 80$ when $t = 0$, so that $C_2 = 80$. Hence, the height above the ground at any time t is

$$(i) \qquad y = -16\,t^2 + 64\,t + 80.$$

To find when the ball was highest, we put $v = 0$ in equation (g) and solve for t; we then have $0 = -32\,t + 64$, from which we get $t = 2$ seconds. Its height at that time is obtained by putting $t = 2$ in (i), which gives $y = 144$ feet. The ball reached the ground when $y = 0$; putting $y = 0$ in equation (i) and solving for t, we find $t = 5$ seconds. To find the velocity of the ball when it reaches the ground, we substitute this value of t in (g), and get $v = -96$ feet per second.

166. Exercises

1. A particle is moving in a straight line. Its displacement s on the line is increasing at the rate $10\,t$, where t is the time. Express s as a function of t, if $s = 8$ when $t = 1$.

2. If a certain wheel turns through an angle θ (radians) in time t (seconds), determined by the equation $\dfrac{d\theta}{dt} = 50 - 0.3\,t$, express θ in terms of t, if $\theta = 5$ when $t = 1$. Also find the total number of revolutions of the wheel in 30 seconds from the instant at which $t = 0$.

3. A particle moves in a straight line with an acceleration $a = 12\,t$. When $t = 0$, its displacement and velocity are $s = 30$ and $v = 16$. Find its velocity and displacement at any time t.

4. A particle moves in a straight line with an acceleration $a = 6\,t$. When $t = 1$ and $t = 2$, its displacements are 10 and 80. Find its velocity and displacement at any time t, and also at $t = 3$.

5. A ball is thrown vertically upward from the ground with a velocity of 120 feet per second. How high will it rise; and how long will it take the ball to reach its greatest height?

6. A body falls from rest from a balloon 1000 feet above the ground. How far will the body fall during the first 5 seconds? How long will it take the body to reach the ground? With what velocity will it strike the ground?

7. A man in an elevator going up at a rate of 32 feet per second dropped out of the car a pencil which fell to the bottom of the shaft. If the man was 240 feet from the bottom of the shaft at the instant when the pencil was dropped, how long a time was required for the pencil to reach the bottom?

8. A stone was thrown straight down from a stationary balloon 16,000 feet high, with an initial velocity of 32 feet per second. Find its height above the ground after t seconds. When did it strike the ground?

9. A balloon was ascending with a velocity of 20 miles per hour. A stone dropped from the balloon reached the ground in 6 seconds. Find the height of the balloon when the stone was dropped.

10. Show that for a body falling from rest from a height s_0 to a height s, the velocity is given by $v^2 = 2\,g(s_0 - s)$.
$$\left[Hint. \quad a = \frac{dv}{dt} = \frac{dv}{ds} \cdot \frac{ds}{dt} = v\,\frac{dv}{ds} = -g. \right]$$

11. At a temperature $T°$ (C), the resistance of a copper wire is R ohms, where $\dfrac{dR}{dT} = 0.00428\,R_0$, and R_0 is the resistance at $0°$ (C). Find an expression for R at any temperature T, and then find the resistance at $107°$ (C) of a copper wire for which $R_0 = 3.5$ ohms.

12. An equation met in the study of digestion is $\dfrac{dx}{dt} = \dfrac{kFq}{2\,x}$, where k, F and q are constants. Solve for x in terms of t, if $x = X$ at $t = 0$.

CHAPTER X

Definite Integrals

167. The Definite Integral

In § 77 we defined a fundamental limit-form, the derivative, which occupies a basic position in calculus. We shall now consider a second fundamental limit-form which occurs in a large number of important types of problems in mathematics and its applications. As before, we first define analytically this limit-form in general terms, and then give several particular illustrations and applications of it, to be followed a little later by numerous other interpretations and applications of the concept.

Throughout this chapter, unless a contrary statement is made, when we speak of an interval (a, b), we shall mean the *closed* interval where $a \leqq x \leqq b$.

Let $y = f(x)$ be a single-valued function which is continuous in the interval (a, b). Divide this interval (a, b) into n sub-intervals by $n - 1$ division points $x_1, x_2, x_3, \cdots, x_{n-1}$ (Fig. 82), where $a < x_1 < x_2 < \cdots < x_{n-1} < b$. For convenience of notation later, let $x_0 = a$ and $x_n = b$.

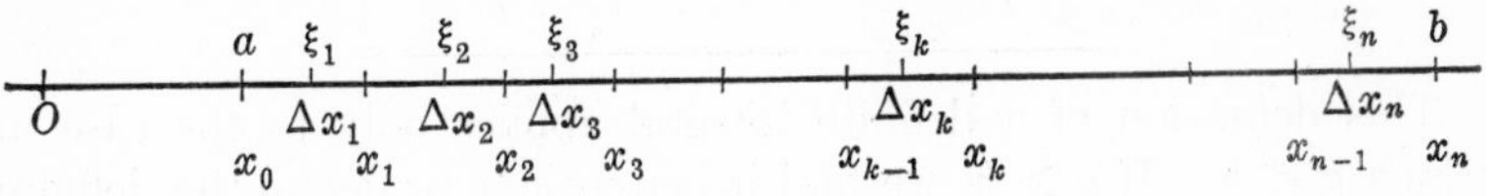

FIG. 82

Let ξ_k denote any point in or at an end of the k-th sub-interval (x_{k-1}, x_k), where k is any one of the numbers $1, 2, 3, \cdots, n$, so that $x_{k-1} \leqq \xi_k \leqq x_k$ for each value of k from 1 to n (see Fig. 82). Let Δx_k denote the length of the k-th sub-interval, so that $\Delta x_k = x_k - x_{k-1}$. It will also be convenient to refer to the k-th sub-interval itself as Δx_k. Suppose that δ is the length of the longest sub-interval, so that $\Delta x_k \leqq \delta$ for every value of k. We shall use this symbol δ

with this same meaning throughout the later applications of definite integrals.

Now form the sum

$$(a) \qquad S_n = f(\xi_1)\Delta x_1 + f(\xi_2)\Delta x_2 + \cdots + f(\xi_n)\Delta x_n.$$

This sum may be more briefly denoted by the summation notation:

$$(b) \qquad S_n = \sum_{k=1}^{n} f(\xi_k)\Delta x_k,$$

which means that, in the expression $f(\xi_k)\Delta x_k$, the index k is to be given successively the values 1, 2, 3, $\cdots$, n, and the results added. This sum S_n depends on the number n, on the choice of the division points x_k and the choice of the points ξ_k, and of course on the function $f(x)$.

Let n increase, and suppose that the mode of subdivision of the interval (a, b) into sub-intervals is such that $\delta \to 0$ as $n \to \infty$. We now formulate the following fundamental definition:

If $\lim\limits_{\delta \to 0} S_n$ *exists and if this limit is the same for all modes of subdivision of the interval* (a, b), *and for all choices of the points* ξ_k, *this limit is called the* **definite integral** *of* **f(x)** *from* a *to* b, *and is denoted by the symbol*

$$\int_a^b f(x)\, dx.$$

$$(1) \qquad \boxed{\int_a^b f(x)\, dx = \lim_{\delta \to 0} \sum_{k=1}^{n} f(\xi_k)\Delta x_k.}$$

This definition of a definite integral applies only to the case in which $a < b$. If $a > b$, we find it convenient to define the definite integral of $f(x)$ from a to b by:

$$(2) \qquad \int_a^b f(x)\, dx = -\int_b^a f(x)\, dx \qquad (a > b).$$

Also for later convenience we define:

$$(3) \qquad \int_a^a f(x)\, dx = 0.$$

In the definite integral $\int_a^b f(x)\, dx$, *the function* $f(x)$ *is called the integrand,* and a and b are called the **lower limit** and the **upper limit,** *respectively, of the integral. Each term of the sum* $S_n = \sum_{k=1}^{n} f(\xi_k)\Delta x_k$ *is called an* **element** *of the integral* $\int_a^b f(x)\,dx.$

When the limit of S_n exists, we say that $f(x)$ is **integrable** over the interval (a, b). A very important theorem which is proved in more advanced works* states that:

A function that is single-valued and continuous in the interval (a, b) is integrable there; that is, if $f(x)$ is continuous in (a, b), $\int_a^b f(x)\,dx$ exists.

It is only in exceptional cases that the value of a definite integral can be obtained readily from its definition as a limit of a sum. In the following example we give a specimen of this direct evaluation in order to illustrate more concretely just what this fundamental concept means. Better methods of evaluating definite integrals will be discussed later.

EXAMPLE. Evaluate the definite integral $\int_0^b x^2\,dx$, where $b > 0$.

Solution: Since the manner of choosing the sub-intervals Δx_k is arbitrary, when we wish to do so we may choose them equal and denote their common length by Δx. In the present example, for convenience, let us divide the interval $(0, b)$ into n equal sub-intervals of length $\Delta x = b/n$ by the points x_1, $x_2, \cdots, x_{n-1}$, with $x_0 = 0$ and $x_n = b$; then $\delta = \dfrac{b}{n}$. Let us take each ξ_k at the right hand end of the corresponding sub-interval, so that $\xi_k = x_k = k(\Delta x)$. (Fig. 83).

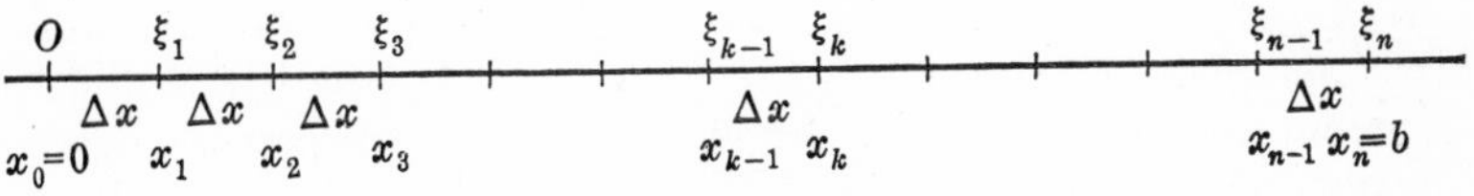

FIG. 83

Then the sum S_n is

$$S_n = \sum_{k=1}^{n} \xi_k{}^2 \cdot \Delta x_k = \sum_{k=1}^{n} (k \cdot \Delta x)^2 \cdot \Delta x = \sum_{k=1}^{n} k^2 (\Delta x)^3$$

(c)
$$= (\Delta x)^3 + 2^2(\Delta x)^3 + 3^2(\Delta x)^3 + \cdots + n^2(\Delta x)^3$$
$$= (\Delta x)^3 \left[1^2 + 2^2 + 3^2 + \cdots + n^2 \right].$$

* See, for example, Fine, *Calculus*, page 138, or Franklin, *Treatise on Advanced Calculus*, page 195.

But by algebra it may easily be shown that:

(d) $\qquad 1^2 + 2^2 + 3^2 + \cdots + n^2 = \frac{1}{6} n(n + 1)(2n + 1).$

Putting this result in (c) and using $\Delta x = b/n$, we get

$(e) \qquad S_n = \frac{1}{6}(\Delta x)^3 \cdot n(n + 1)(2n + 1) = \frac{1}{6}\frac{b^3}{n^3} \cdot n(n + 1)(2n + 1)$

$$= \frac{1}{6} b^3 \left(1 + \frac{1}{n}\right)\left(2 + \frac{1}{n}\right).$$

From (e) we get $\lim_{\delta \to 0} S_n = \frac{1}{3} b^3$, since $\frac{1}{n} \to 0$ as $n \to \infty$. Hence, the required value of the definite integral is

$(f) \qquad\qquad\qquad \int_0^b x^2 \, dx = \frac{1}{3} b^3.$

168. Exercises

1. Evaluate $\int_0^b x \, dx$ by use of its definition as a limit of a sum. [*Hint.* Use the formula of algebra for the sum of an arithmetic progression:
$$1 + 2 + 3 + \cdots + n = \frac{1}{2} n(n + 1).]$$

2. Evaluate $\int_0^b x^3 \, dx$ by use of its definition as a limit of a sum. [*Hint.* By algebra, $1^3 + 2^3 + 3^3 + \cdots + n^3 = \frac{1}{4} n^2(n + 1)^2.$]

169. A Geometrical Interpretation of a Definite Integral: Area Under a Curve

One of the fundamental problems which gave rise to the development of integral calculus was that of finding the *area* of a figure.

In elementary geometry, methods are developed for finding areas of *rectilinear figures*. The area of a rectangle is first shown by simple direct methods to be equal to the product of its length and width, and from this, by the simple methods of geometry, the areas of figures bounded by straight line segments are obtained. But these methods cannot be applied directly to figures bounded wholly or in part by curved lines. The area of a circle is determined in geometry by treating it as the common limit of a set of regular inscribed and circumscribed polygons as the number of their sides is indefinitely increased. To find areas of *curvilinear figures* in general, we must use the *method of limits*.

Let $f(x)$ be a single-valued function which is continuous in an interval (a, b). and let us suppose that $f(x)$ is never negative in (a, b).

Let CD (Fig. 84) be the arc of the graph of $f(x)$, where C and D are the points on the curve whose abscissas are a and b. This arc does not extend below the X-axis. Let R denote the region bounded by this arc CD, the lines $x = a$ and $x = b$, and the X-axis. We wish to *define* what is meant by the *area* of the region R, and to find a method for *calculating* this area.

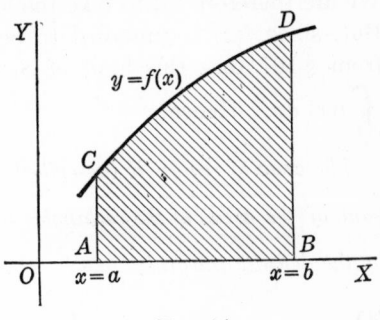

Fig. 84

As in § 167, divide the interval (a, b) into n sub-intervals Δx_k $(k = 1, 2, 3, \cdots, n)$, and on each sub-interval Δx_k select an arbitrary point ξ_k. On each sub-interval Δx_k as base, construct a rectangle with altitude $f(\xi_k)$, as shown in Fig. 85. The sum of the areas of these rectangles is represented by

$$(a) \qquad S_n = \sum_{k=1}^{n} f(\xi_k)\Delta x_k.$$

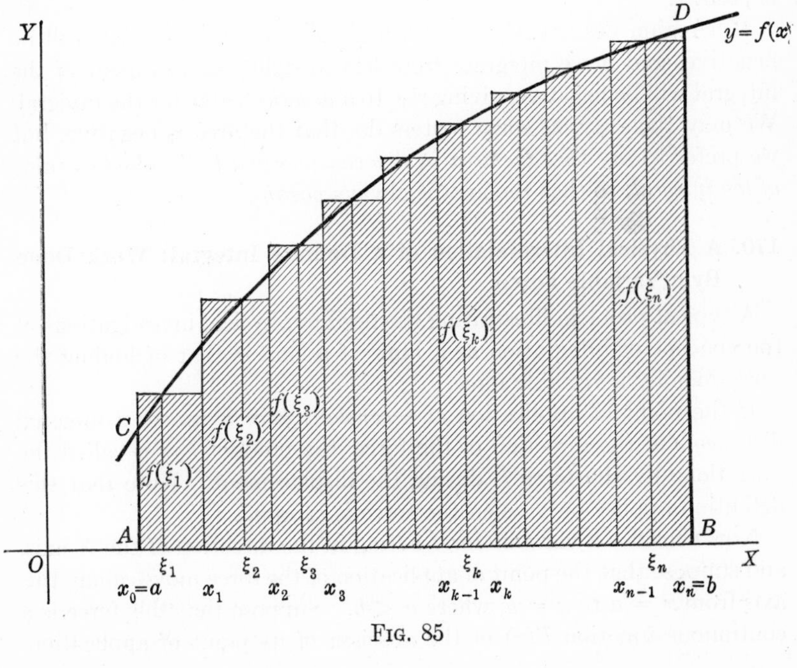

Fig. 85

These rectangles partially cover the region R; and it is intuitively evident that if we increase the number n of rectangles, the new set of rectangles will more and more completely cover the region R. We are therefore led to take the limit of S_n as $\delta \to 0$, where $\Delta x_k \leqq \delta$. But, since $f(x)$ is supposed to be a continuous function, it follows from § 167 that this limit of S_n exists and is the definite integral $\int_a^b f(x)\,dx$. Hence:

*The **area** of region R (described above) is defined to be the limit of the sum of the areas of the rectangles $S_n = \sum_{k=1}^{n} f(\xi_k)\Delta x_k$; therefore it is given by the definite integral:*

$$(4) \qquad \text{area under curve} = \int_a^b f(x)\,dx.$$

Since $f(x)$ has been assumed to be positive (or zero) throughout the interval (a, b), and since each Δx_k is positive (when $a < b$), each term of the sum S_n is positive, and therefore the limit (4) is positive. Thus, if a region lies entirely *above* the X-axis, the area defined above is *positive*.

If a region lies entirely *below* the X-axis, the ordinate $f(x)$ will be negative, and if we integrate from left to right, each element of the integral will be negative, giving rise to a *negative* value for the integral. We may then say, as some writers do, that the area is negative, but we prefer to say that *the area in this case is equal to the absolute value of the integral*, so that the area is always *positive*.

170. A Physical Interpretation of a Definite Integral: Work Done By a Variable Force

A typical problem illustrating the need in physical investigations of the concept of integration as a limit of a sum is that of finding the *work* done by a variable force.

If the point of application of a *constant force* F moves a directed distance s in the direction of the force, the product $F \cdot s$ is called the *work* done by the force F during the displacement. Note that this definition applies only when the force is *constant*.

Now consider a variable force acting in the direction of the X-axis, and suppose that the point of application of the force moves along this axis from $x = a$ to $x = b$, where $a < b$. Suppose that this force is a continuous function $F(x)$ of the abscissa of its point of application.

We must seek a *definition* of what is to be understood by the *work* done by this variable force. As in § 167, divide the interval (a, b) into n sub-intervals Δx_k (where $\Delta x_k \leqq \delta$) by the points x_k $(k = 1, 2, \cdots, n - 1)$, and let ξ_k be any point in the sub-interval Δx_k (Fig. 86).

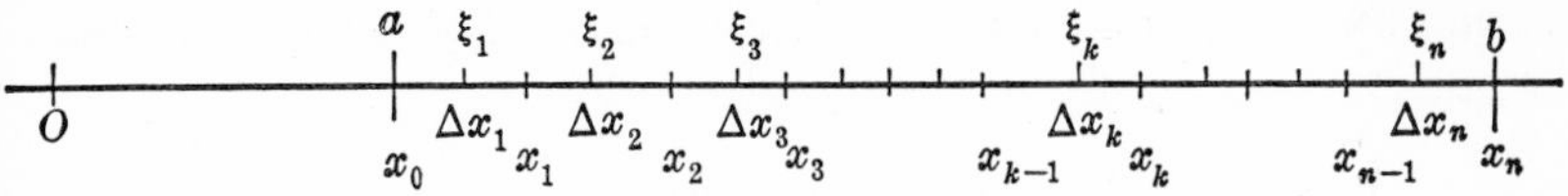

Fig. 86

If we multiply each distance Δx_k by the force $F(\xi_k)$ at the point ξ_k in that sub-interval Δx_k, we obtain the work done during the displacement by a force $F(\xi_k)$ which is assumed constant throughout that displacement. The sum

$$(a) \qquad S_n = \sum_{k=1}^{n} F(\xi_k)\Delta x_k$$

is the total work done by the set of assumed constant forces. If we let the number of sub-divisions increase, and suppose that $\delta \to 0$ as $n \to \infty$, the difference between the set of values of the actual force $F(x)$ and the set of assumed constant forces will diminish, and we are naturally led to take the limit of S_n as the *definition* of the work done by the actual variable force. By the definition of a definite integral, the limit of S_n as $\delta \to 0$ is $\int_a^b F(x)\, dx$. Hence:

*If a continuous force $F(x)$ acts along the X-axis, and if the point of application of this force is displaced along this axis from a position $x = a$ to a position $x = b$, the **work** done by the force $F(x)$ during this displacement is defined by:*

$$(5) \qquad W = \int_a^b F(x)\, dx.$$

171. Properties of Definite Integrals

The following properties of the definite integral follow readily from the definition in § 167.

If c is any point in the interval (a, b), we can break up the sum $\sum f(\xi_k)\Delta x_k$ for the interval (a, b) into two corresponding sums for the intervals (a, c) and (c, b), and in the limit we obtain:

$$(6) \qquad \int_a^b f(x)\, dx = \int_a^c f(x)\, dx + \int_c^b f(x)\, dx.$$

If c is any point outside the interval (a, b), we can easily prove that this formula still holds, by use of the definition (2) of § 167.

Since $\sum_{k=1}^n \Delta x_k = b - a$, if K is any constant we have

$$\int_a^b K\, dx = \lim_{\delta \to 0} \sum_{k=1}^n K \cdot \Delta x_k = \lim_{\delta \to 0} K \sum_{k=1}^n \Delta x_k = K(b - a); \text{ hence:}$$

$$(7) \qquad \int_a^b K\, dx = K(b - a).$$

By a similar argument, we may show that, if K is any constant:

$$(8) \qquad \int_a^b K f(x)\, dx = K \int_a^b f(x)\, dx.$$

It follows at once from the definition of a definite integral that:

$$(9) \qquad \int_a^b (u + v)\, dx = \int_a^b u\, dx + \int_a^b v\, dx,$$

where u and v are continuous functions of x in the interval (a, b). A similar formula holds for any finite number of continuous functions.

If we examine the definition of a definite integral, we see that the *value* of $\int_a^b f(x)\, dx$ depends only on the values of the integrand $f(x)$ and on the limits a and b, but does not depend on the symbol that is used to denote the independent variable. Hence, *we may use any letter to denote the variable of integration in the definite integral,* thus:

$$(10) \qquad \int_a^b f(x)\, dx = \int_a^b f(t)\, dt = \int_a^b f(z)\, dz.$$

172. Fundamental Theorem of Integral Calculus

Let $f(x)$ be continuous in an interval (a, b). Let $F(x)$ be any function whose derivative is $f(x)$, so that $F'(x) = f(x)$; then $F(x)$ is a particular integral of $f(x)$. By § 153, we know that such an integral $F(x)$ exists. Let $x_1, x_2, \cdots, x_{n-1}$ be any sub-division points which divide the interval (a, b) into sub-intervals Δx_k, as in § 167. The function $F(x)$ is continuous in (a, b), since it has a derivative, $f(x)$, there (§ 77). We may then apply the mean-value theorem for derivatives (§ 150) to the function $F(x)$ for each of the sub-intervals Δx_k; this gives:

(a) $$F(x_k) - F(x_{k-1}) = F'(\xi_k)(x_k - x_{k-1}) = f(\xi_k)\Delta x_k$$

for $k = 1, 2, \cdots, n$, where $\xi_1, \xi_2, \cdots, \xi_n$ are properly chosen points such that $x_{k-1} < \xi_k < x_k$. Taking $k = 1, 2, \cdots, n$ successively in (a), we have

$$\begin{aligned}
F(x_1) - F(a) &= f(\xi_1)\Delta x_1, & (a < \xi_1 < x_1), \\
F(x_2) - F(x_1) &= f(\xi_2)\Delta x_2, & (x_1 < \xi_2 < x_2), \\
F(x_3) - F(x_2) &= f(\xi_3)\Delta x_3, & (x_2 < \xi_3 < x_3),
\end{aligned}$$

$$F(b) - F(x_{n-1}) = f(\xi_n)\Delta x_n, \qquad (x_{n-1} < \xi_n < b).$$

Adding these equations, and noting that terms on the left cancel in pairs, except for $-F(a)$ and $F(b)$, we get

(b) $$F(b) - F(a) = \sum_{k=1}^{n} f(\xi_k)\Delta x_k.$$

If we take the points $\xi_1, \xi_2, \cdots, \xi_n$ as the points in the sub-intervals $\Delta x_1, \Delta x_2, \cdots, \Delta x_n$ at which we form the values of the function $f(x)$ in formulating the definition of the definite integral, as in § 167, and if we remember that according to the existence theorem in § 167 the value of the limit which defines the definite integral is independent of the choice of the points ξ_k, we have

$$\lim_{\delta \to 0} \sum_{k=1}^{n} f(\xi_k)\Delta x_k = \int_a^b f(x)\,dx.$$

From (b) we now obtain

(c) $$F(b) - F(a) = \int_a^b f(x)\,dx.$$

Hence:

If $f(x)$ is continuous in the interval (a, b), and if $F(x)$ is any particular integral of $f(x)$, the value of the definite integral $\int_a^b f(x)\,dx$ is given by;

(11) $$\boxed{\int_a^b f(x)\,dx = F(b) - F(a).}$$

This result is often called the **fundamental theorem of integral calculus**. It connects the two fundamental concepts of the indefinite integral and the definite integral.

It is found very convenient to use the symbol $F(x)\Big|_a^b$ to mean: $F(b) - F(a)$.

EXAMPLE. Evaluate $\int_a^b x^2\, dx$.

Solution: We have the indefinite integral

$$\int x^2\, dx = \tfrac{1}{3}\, x^3 + C.$$

Hence,

$$\int_a^b x^2\, dx = (\tfrac{1}{3}\, x^3 + C)\Big|_a^b = (\tfrac{1}{3}\, b^3 + C) - (\tfrac{1}{3}\, a^3 + C) = \tfrac{1}{3}(b^3 - a^3).$$

(Compare this result with that in the Example in § 167.)

173. Evaluation of Definite Integrals

To evaluate a given definite integral, we use the fundamental theorem of § 172:

$$(a) \qquad \int_a^b f(x)\, dx = F(b) - F(a), \qquad \text{where } F'(x) = f(x).$$

That is, we first find a particular integral $F(x)$, and then subtract the value of $F(x)$ at the lower limit a from its value at the upper limit b.

EXAMPLE 1. Find $\int_1^3 (x^2 - 1)\, dx$.

Solution: The indefinite integral is

$$\int (x^2 - 1)\, dx = \tfrac{1}{3}\, x^3 - x + C;$$

then

$$\int_1^3 (x^2 - 1)\, dx = (\tfrac{1}{3}\, x^3 - x + C)\Big|_1^3 = (9 - 3 + C) - (\tfrac{1}{3} - 1 + C) = \frac{20}{3}.$$

It will be noticed that the constant of integration C can always be taken as 0 to form the particular integral $F(x)$; if any other value is used for C, it will cancel out in the expression $F(b) - F(a)$.

EXAMPLE 2. Find $\int_0^3 \dfrac{5\, x\, dx}{\sqrt{1 + x^2}}$.

Solution: By the method of § 157, we find

$$\int \frac{5\, x\, dx}{\sqrt{1 + x^2}} = \frac{5}{2} \int (1 + x^2)^{-\frac{1}{2}}(2\, x\, dx) = 5(1 + x^2)^{\frac{1}{2}} + C;$$

therefore

$$\int_0^3 \frac{5\,x\,dx}{\sqrt{1+x^2}} = 5\sqrt{1+x^2}\,\Big|_0^3 = 5\sqrt{10} - 5 = 5(\sqrt{10} - 1).$$

174. Exercises

Evaluate each of the integrals in Exercises 1–16:

1. $\displaystyle\int_1^3 3\,x^2\,dx.$

2. $\displaystyle\int_0^2 5\,x^4\,dx.$

3. $\displaystyle\int_0^3 (x^2 - 5\,x + 2)\,dx.$

4. $\displaystyle\int_0^3 (y^3 - 4\,y + 5)\,dy.$

5. $\displaystyle\int_2^3 y(y^2 - 4)^2\,dy.$

6. $\displaystyle\int_{-2}^2 (z - 1)^3\,dz.$

7. $\displaystyle\int_{-1}^1 \sqrt{1 - z}\,dz.$

8. $\displaystyle\int_1^5 \frac{dt}{\sqrt{2\,t - 1}}.$

9. $\displaystyle\int_0^1 3\,t(t^2 + 1)^5\,dt.$

10. $\displaystyle\int_0^1 (1 - \sqrt{v})^2\,dv.$

11. $\displaystyle\int_{-1}^1 x\sqrt{3 - 2\,x^2}\,dx.$

12. $\displaystyle\int_0^a 3\,x(x^2 + a^2)^{\frac{1}{2}}\,dx.$

13. $\displaystyle\int_1^4 \frac{v + 1}{\sqrt{v}}\,dv.$

14. $\displaystyle\int_1^4 \frac{u^2 - 1}{2\,u^{\frac{3}{2}}}\,du.$

15. $\displaystyle\int_0^a \frac{x\,dx}{(a^2 + x^2)^{\frac{3}{2}}}.$

16. $\displaystyle\int_0^3 \frac{x\,dx}{\sqrt{x^2 + 16}}.$

In Exercises 17–24, find the value, correct to 3 decimal places, of each of the given integrals:

17. $\displaystyle\int_1^2 \sqrt{3\,x + 2}\,dx.$

18. $\displaystyle\int_0^4 \frac{dx}{\sqrt{x + 1}}.$

19. $\displaystyle\int_1^2 \frac{dt}{\sqrt{4\,t - 1}}.$

20. $\displaystyle\int_0^2 \sqrt{2\,z + 5}\,dz.$

21. $\displaystyle\int_1^3 \frac{x\,dx}{\sqrt{3 + x^2}}.$

22. $\displaystyle\int_2^4 \frac{3\,y\,dy}{\sqrt{y^2 - 1}}.$

23. $\displaystyle\int_0^2 5\,z(z^2 + 1)^{\frac{3}{2}}\,dz.$

24. $\displaystyle\int_0^2 \frac{u\,du}{\sqrt{9 - u^2}}.$

The following integrals occur in certain science and engineering problems; evaluate them:

25. $\displaystyle\int_0^L \frac{1}{EI}\,(-\tfrac{1}{2}\,wx^2)(-x)\,dx.$

26. $\displaystyle\int_{R_1}^{R_2} \frac{2\,\pi w V_1^2 r^2\,dr}{R_1^2}.$

27. $\displaystyle\int_H^h \frac{A y^{-\frac{1}{2}}\,dy}{a\sqrt{2\,g}}.$

28. $\displaystyle\int_r^0 \frac{\pi}{a\sqrt{2\,g}}\,(2\,ry^{\frac{1}{2}} - y^{\frac{3}{2}})\,dy.$

175. Change of Variable in Definite Integrals

To evaluate a definite integral $\int_a^b f(x)\,dx$, it is frequently necessary to make a substitution $x = \phi(t)$.

Let t_1 and t_2 be the values of t such that $\phi(t_1) = a$ and $\phi(t_2) = b$. Suppose that as t changes continuously from t_1 to t_2, x increases continuously or decreases continuously from a to b. Then it can be proved* that:

$$(12) \qquad \int_a^b f(x)\,dx = \int_{t_1}^{t_2} f[\phi(t)] \cdot \phi'(t)\,dt.$$

Since $dx = \phi'(t)\,dt$ when $x = \phi(t)$, formula (12) shows that if the change of variable $x = \phi(t)$ is made in a definite integral, the resulting integral may be obtained by substituting for x and dx in the original integral the values $x = \phi(t)$ and $dx = \phi'(t)\,dt$, and replacing the original limits of integration by the corresponding values of t.

EXAMPLE 1. Evaluate $\int_2^{10} \dfrac{x\,dx}{\sqrt{x-1}}$.

Solution: Put $\sqrt{x-1} = u$, then $x - 1 = u^2$, $x = 1 + u^2$, $dx = 2\,u\,du$. When $x = 2$, we have $u = 1$, and when $x = 10$, then $u = 3$. By formula (12), we have

$$\int_2^{10} \frac{x\,dx}{\sqrt{x-1}} = \int_1^3 \frac{(1+u^2)2\,u\,du}{u} = 2\int_1^3 (1+u^2)\,du$$

$$= 2(u + \tfrac{1}{3}\,u^3)\Big|_1^3 = \frac{64}{3}.$$

Definite integrals often occur in the form $\int_a^b y\,dx$, where x and y are connected by a functional relation, either explicit or implicit. The integral may then be evaluated by taking either variable x or y as the variable of integration.

EXAMPLE 2. Evaluate $\int_{x=1}^{x=4} y\,dx$ when $2\,x + 3\,y = 6$.

Solution: Taking x as the variable of integration, we have $y = \tfrac{1}{3}(6 - 2\,x)$; then

$$\int_{x=1}^{x=4} y\,dx = \tfrac{1}{3}\int_{x=1}^{x=4} (6 - 2\,x)\,dx = \tfrac{1}{3}(6\,x - x^2)\Big|_1^4 = 1.$$

If we take y as the variable of integration, we have $x = \tfrac{3}{2}(2 - y)$; then

* See, for example, Fine, Calculus, page 148.

$dx = -\frac{3}{2} dy$. When $x = 1$, we have $y = \frac{4}{3}$, and when $x = 4$, we have $y = -\frac{2}{3}$. Then

$$\int_{x=1}^{x=4} y \, dx = \int_{y=\frac{4}{3}}^{y=-\frac{2}{3}} y(-\tfrac{3}{2} dy) = -\tfrac{3}{2} \cdot \tfrac{1}{2} \, y^2 \Big|_{\frac{4}{3}}^{-\frac{2}{3}} = 1.$$

176. Exercises

In Exercises 1–4, evaluate each of the given integrals:

1. $\displaystyle\int_1^6 \frac{x \, dx}{\sqrt{3+x}}.$ 2. $\displaystyle\int_5^{10} \frac{x+1}{\sqrt{x-1}} \, dx.$

3. $\displaystyle\int_0^{-5} \frac{y+2}{\sqrt{4-y}} \, dy.$ 4. $\displaystyle\int_1^{13} \frac{t^2 \, dt}{\sqrt{2 \, t - 1}}.$

Find the value, correct to three decimal places, of each of the integrals in Exercises 5–8:

5. $\displaystyle\int_0^2 \frac{x+1}{\sqrt{4-x}} \, dx.$ 6. $\displaystyle\int_5^{10} x\sqrt{x-3} \, dx.$

7. $\displaystyle\int_0^3 3 \, x^2\sqrt{5-x} \, dx.$ 8. $\displaystyle\int_0^3 \frac{x^2 \, dx}{\sqrt{x+2}}.$

Evaluate each of the integrals in Exercises 9–12 in two different ways:

9. $\displaystyle\int_{x=0}^{x=4} y\,dx$, when $3x+4y = 12$.   10. $\displaystyle\int_{y=5}^{y=31} x \, dy$, when $y = x^2 + 4$.

11. $\displaystyle\int_{x=1}^{x=4} y\,dx$, when $y^2 = 4x\,(y > 0)$.   12. $\displaystyle\int_{x=0}^{x=13} y^2 \, dx$, when $y^3 = 2 \, x + 1$.

177. Bliss' Theorem

Let $f(x)$ and $g(x)$ be functions which are singled-valued and continuous in an interval (a, b). Let the interval (a, b) be divided into n subintervals by the points $x_1, x_2, \cdots, x_{n-1}$, as in § 167, let $x_0 = a$ and $x_n = b$, and let $\Delta x_k = x_k - x_{k-1}$. Let ξ_k and ξ_k' be arbitrary points in or at an end of the sub-interval (x_{k-1}, x_k) for $k = 1, 2, \cdots, n$. Then form the sum $\sum_{k=1}^{n} f(\xi_k)g(\xi_k')\Delta x_k$. Let n increase, and suppose that $\delta \to 0$ as $n \to \infty$, where δ is the length of the longest sub-interval Δx_k. It can be proved* that:

If $f(x)$ and $g(x)$ are single-valued and continuous in (a, b), then

$$(13) \qquad \lim_{\delta \to 0} \sum_{k=1}^{n} f(\xi_k)g(\xi_k')\Delta x_k = \int_a^b f(x) \, g(x) \, dx,$$

---

* See Bliss, G. A., "A Substitute for Duhamel's Theorem," *Annals of Mathematics*, vol. 16 (1914–15), pages 45–49, and Fine, *Calculus*, § 145.

where ξ_k and ξ'_k are any points of the sub-interval (x_{k-1}, x_k). This will be called **Bliss' theorem.**

This theorem will be used in numerous applications later.

178. Derivative of a Definite Integral

Let $f(x)$ be continuous in an interval (a, b), and consider the definite integral $\int_a^x f(t)\, dt$, where x is in the interval (a, b). If the upper limit x is variable, this integral is a function of x; let us write $\int_a^x f(t)\, dt = \phi(x)$. By the fundamental theorem of § 172, we know that

$$\phi(x) = \int_a^x f(t)\, dt = F(x) - F(a),$$

where $F(x)$ is a function having the derivative $f(x)$. Therefore,

$$D_x\phi(x) = D_x[F(x) - F(a)] = D_xF(x) = f(x).$$

Hence:

(14) $$D_x\left[\int_a^x f(t)\, dt\right] = f(x);$$

that is, *the derivative with respect to x of the definite integral from a to x is the value of the integrand at x.*

179. Mean-Value Theorem for Integrals

Let the curve CD (Fig. 87) represent the function $y = f(x)$, and consider the area $ABDC$ bounded by this curve, the X-axis and the

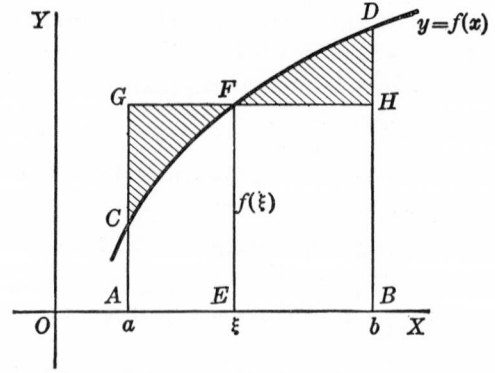

Fig. 87

ordinates $x = a$ and $x = b$. If this curve is continuous, it is geometrically evident that a mean ordinate $x = \xi$ can be drawn, with $a < \xi < b$, such that the area of the rectangle $ABHG$, with base AB and altitude $EF = f(\xi)$, will be equal to the area $ABDC$ under the curve. Since the area under the curve is given by $\int_a^b f(x)\,dx$, and since the area of the rectangle $ABHG$ is $f(\xi)(b - a)$, we arrive at the following *mean-value theorem for integrals:*

If $f(x)$ is continuous in an interval (a, b), then there exists a number ξ such that:

$$(15) \qquad \int_a^b f(x)\,dx = f(\xi)(b - a), \qquad \text{where} \qquad a < \xi < b.$$

This theorem may be proved analytically as follows: Let $F(x)$ be any particular integral of $f(x)$, so that $F'(x) = f(x)$ in the interval $a \leq x \leq b$. Then, by the Fundamental Theorem,

$$(a) \qquad \int_a^b f(x)\,dx = F(b) - F(a).$$

Since $F'(x) = f(x)$, $F(x)$ is differentiable and therefore continuous and satisfies the conditions for the mean-value theorem for derivatives (§ 150); therefore, there exists a value ξ such that $a < \xi < b$, and

$$(b) \qquad F(b) - F(a) = F'(\xi)(b - a) = f(\xi)(b - a).$$

Formula (15) then follows from (a) and (b).

180. Exercises

1. Prove that: $\int_a^x f'(t)\,dt = f(x) - f(a)$.

2. Show that the mean-value theorem of § 179 may be written in the form:

$$\int_a^{a+h} f(x)\,dx = hf(a + \theta h), \qquad 0 < \theta < 1.$$

3. Prove that if $f(x)$ is an even function, that is, if $f(-x) \equiv f(x)$, then

$$\int_{-a}^a f(x)\,dx = 2 \int_0^a f(x)\,dx;$$

and that if $f(x)$ is an odd function, that is, if $f(-x) \equiv -f(x)$, then

$$\int_{-a}^a f(x)\,dx = 0.$$

4. Show that

$$\int_0^a f(x)\, dx = \int_0^a f(a-x)\, dx,$$

by use of the substitution $x = a - t$.

5. Show that, if $f(a - x) \equiv f(x)$, then

$$\int_0^a f(x)\, dx = 2 \int_0^{\frac{a}{2}} f(x)\, dx.$$

[Hint. $\int_0^a f(x)\, dx = \int_0^{\frac{a}{2}} f(x)\, dx + \int_{\frac{a}{2}}^a f(x)\, dx.$]

CHAPTER XI

Some Applications of Definite Integrals

181. Plane Area: Rectangular Coördinates

We have already defined what is meant by the area under a curve (§ 169), and we found that the area is given by a definite integral. We may restate the result as follows:

I. *The area of the region bounded by the curve $y = f(x)$, the X-axis and the lines $x = a$ and $x = b$ is given by:*

$$(1) \qquad A = \int_a^b y \, dx = \int_a^b f(x) \, dx,$$

if $f(x)$ is positive throughout the interval (a, b); and the area is given by the negative of the above integral if $f(x)$ is negative throughout the interval (a, b).

Using the notation of § 169, this formula may be written:

$$(a) \qquad A = \int_a^b f(x) \, dx = \lim_{\delta \to 0} \sum_{k=1}^n f(\xi_k) \Delta x_k = \lim_{\delta \to 0} \sum_{k=1}^n y_k \Delta x_k,$$

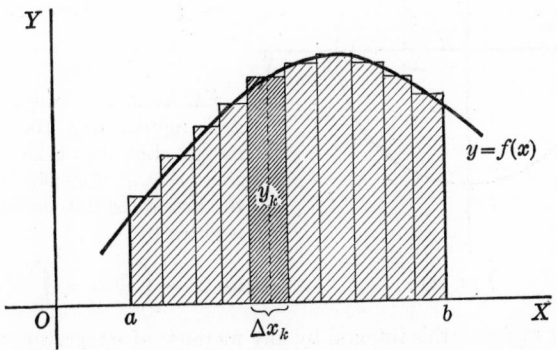

Fig. 88

193

where $y_k = f(\xi_k)$. The *element of area* in this case is $y_k \cdot \Delta x_k$, which is represented by the area of a rectangle, as indicated in Fig. 88. The area A is then written down as the limit of a sum of areas of rectangles:

$$A = \lim_{\delta \to 0} \sum_{k=1}^{n} y_k \Delta x_k = \int_a^b y \, dx.$$

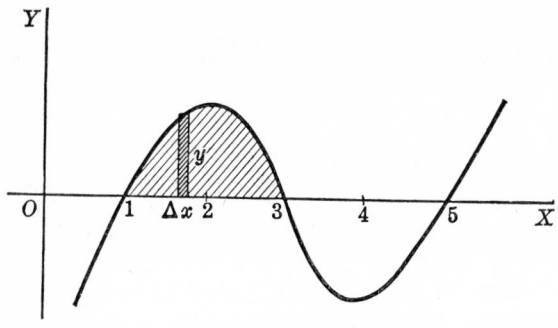

Fig. 89

EXAMPLE 1. Find the finite area above the X-axis and under the curve $y = x^3 - 9x^2 + 23x - 15$.

Solution: The given curve is shown in Fig. 89. It crosses the X-axis at $x = 1$, $x = 3$ and $x = 5$, and the required area is that of the shaded region, between $x = 1$ and $x = 3$. This area is

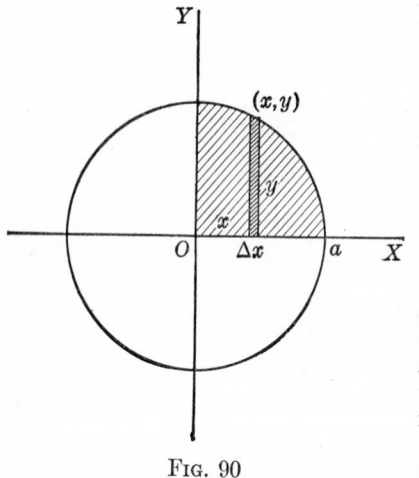

Fig. 90

$$A = \int_1^3 y \, dx$$
$$= \int_1^3 (x^3 - 9x^2 + 23x - 15) \, dx$$
$$= 4.$$

EXAMPLE 2. Consider the integral representing the area of a circle. Let us take the circle $x^2 + y^2 = a^2$ (Fig. 90); the area in the first quadrant under the circle is given by

$$(b) \quad A = \int_0^a y \, dx = \int_0^a \sqrt{a^2 - x^2} \, dx.$$

We cannot evaluate this integral by any methods of integration which have been discussed so far in this book. However, by using the known area of a circle from elementary geometry, we have $A = \frac{1}{4} \pi a^2$. Equating these two values of A, we obtain the very useful result:

$$(2) \qquad \int_0^a \sqrt{a^2 - x^2} \, dx = \frac{1}{4} \pi a^2.$$

We shall have occasion to use this formula a number of times in this chapter.

EXAMPLE 3. Find the area of the ellipse whose equation is
$$b^2x^2 + a^2y^2 = a^2b^2.$$

Solution: Taking the portion of the curve in the first quadrant, we have $y = \dfrac{b}{a} \sqrt{a^2 - x^2}$. The area of the ellipse in the first quadrant is

$$(c) \qquad A = \int_0^a y \, dx = \frac{b}{a} \int_0^a \sqrt{a^2 - x^2} \, dx.$$

The value of this integral may be taken from formula (2) of Example 2, and we have

$$A = \frac{b}{a} \cdot \frac{1}{4} \pi a^2 = \frac{1}{4} \pi ab.$$

The area of the entire ellipse, by symmetry, is $4 A$; therefore,

$$(d) \qquad \qquad \textbf{\textit{area of ellipse}} = \boldsymbol{\pi ab}.$$

This result is of frequent use.

Evidently, by interchanging the X- and Y-axes in theorem I, we have: the area of the region bounded by the curve $x = g(y)$, the Y-axis and the lines $y = c$ and $y = d$ is given by:

$$(e) \quad A = \lim_{\delta \to 0} \sum_{k=1}^n x_k \Delta y_k$$
$$= \int_c^d x \, dy = \int_c^d g(y) \, dy,$$

if $g(y)$ is positive throughout the interval (c, d); and the area is given by the negative of the above integral if $g(y)$ is negative throughout the interval (c, d).

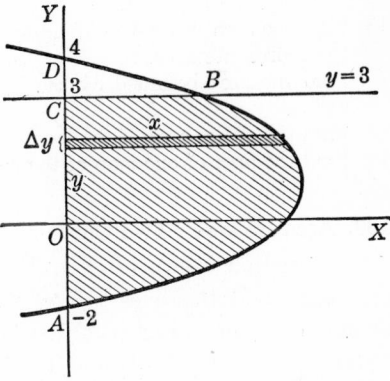

FIG. 91

EXAMPLE 4. Find   the   area bounded by the curve $x = 8 + 2y - y^2$, the Y-axis and the line $y = 3$, and below $y = 3$ (Fig. 91).

Solution: The given curve cuts the Y-axis at $y = 4$ and at $y = -2$. The required area is that of the shaded region ABC in the figure; this region extends from $y = -2$ to $y = 3$. Hence,

$$A = \int_{-2}^{3} x \, dy = \int_{-2}^{3} (8 + 2\,y - y^2) \, dy = \frac{100}{3}.$$

182. Exercises

In each of the following problems, draw a figure carefully, and shade the region whose area is to be found; also draw an appropriate rectangular element of area. In Exercises 1–4, find the area bounded by each of the given curves and the X-axis:

1. $y = 2\,x - x^2$.   2. $y = 4 - x^2$.
3. $y = x - x^3$ (in first quadrant).   4. $y = (x - 2)(x - 3)^2$.
5. Find by integration the area of the triangle bounded by the X-axis, and the lines $y = 2\,x$ and $x = 4$. Verify the result by elementary geometry.
6. Find the area bounded by the curve $y = x^3 - 3\,x + 3$, the X-axis, and the maximum and minimum ordinates of the curve.
7. Find the area bounded by the curve $x^2 + 4\,x - y + 4 = 0$ and the coördinate axes.
8. Find the area under the curve $y = 9 - x^2$ and above the X-axis, in two different ways.

In Exercises 9–12, find the area bounded by each of the given curves and the Y-axis:

9. $x = 2 + y - y^2$.   10. $x = 4\,y - y^2$.
11. $y^2 + 4\,x = 4\,y$.   12. $y^2 = 8 - 4\,x$.
13. Find the area bounded by $y^2 = 2\,x$, the Y-axis, and $y = 1$ and $y = 3$.
14. Find the area bounded by the parabola $y = 3\,x^2$, the Y-axis, and the lines $y = 2$ and $y = 4$.
15. Find the area in the first quadrant bounded by $y^2 + 2\,x - 2\,y = 3$ and the coördinate axes.
16. Find the area bounded by the curve $x^{\frac{1}{2}} + y^{\frac{1}{2}} = a^{\frac{1}{2}}$ and the coördinate axes.
17. Find the entire area of the loop of the curve $y^2 = 4\,x^2 - x^3$.
18. Find the area of one loop of the curve $y^2 = x^2(a^2 - x^2)$.

183. Area Between Two Curves

Suppose that we wish to find the area between the curves $y_1 = f(x)$, $y_2 = g(x)$, and the lines $x = a$ and $x = b$ (Fig. 92), and that, for definiteness, the curve $y_1 = f(x)$ lies below the curve $y_2 = g(x)$ but above the X-axis throughout (a, b). Then the required area is the difference between the areas under the two curves, or

$$A = \int_{a}^{b} y_2 \, dx - \int_{a}^{b} y_1 \, dx = \int_{a}^{b} (y_2 - y_1) \, dx.$$

Hence:

The area of the region bounded by the curves $y_1 = f(x)$, $y_2 = g(x)$, and the lines $x = a$ and $x = b$ (as described above) is given by:

(3)
$$A = \int_a^b (y_2 - y_1)\, dx = \int_a^b [g(x) - f(x)]\, dx.$$

This result may be visualized as a limit of a sum of areas of rectangles extending between the curves. Thus, in Fig. 92, an elemen-

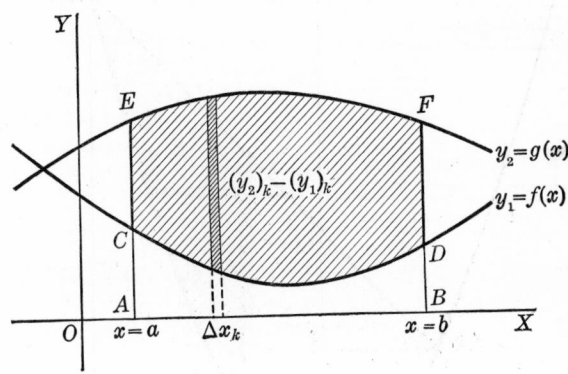

FIG. 92

tary rectangle is shown with length $(y_2)_k - (y_1)_k$ and width Δx_k, so that the limit of the sum of the areas of such rectangles gives

$$A = \lim_{\delta \to 0} \sum_{k=1}^{n} [(y_2)_k - (y_1)_k]\Delta x_k = \int_a^b (y_2 - y_1)\, dx,$$

which is the same as formula (3).

EXAMPLE. Find the area bounded by the parabola $2y = x^2$ and the line $y = x + 4$.

Solution: The required area is that of the shaded region in Fig. 93. The curve and the line intersect at $A(-2, 2)$ and $B(4, 8)$. Let us divide the given region into *vertical* strips and draw corresponding elementary rectangles, of width Δx_k and length $(y_2)_k - (y_1)_k$. We take $y_1 = \frac{1}{2} x^2$ and $y_2 = x + 4$; then $(y_2)_k - (y_1)_k = x_k + 4 - \frac{1}{2} x_k^2$. The required area is

$$A = \lim_{\delta \to 0} \sum_{k=1}^{n} (x_k + 4 - \tfrac{1}{2} x_k^2)\Delta x_k = \int_{-2}^{4} (x + 4 - \tfrac{1}{2} x^2)\, dx = 18.$$

If we had divided the given region into *horizontal* strips, it may be seen from Fig. 93 that for the region above the line AC the horizontal rectangles would extend from the straight line to the parabola, while for the region below the line AC the rectangles would extend from the curve to the curve. In this case, the required area would be expressed by the sum of two different integrals. The method of taking vertical strips is therefore the simpler method.

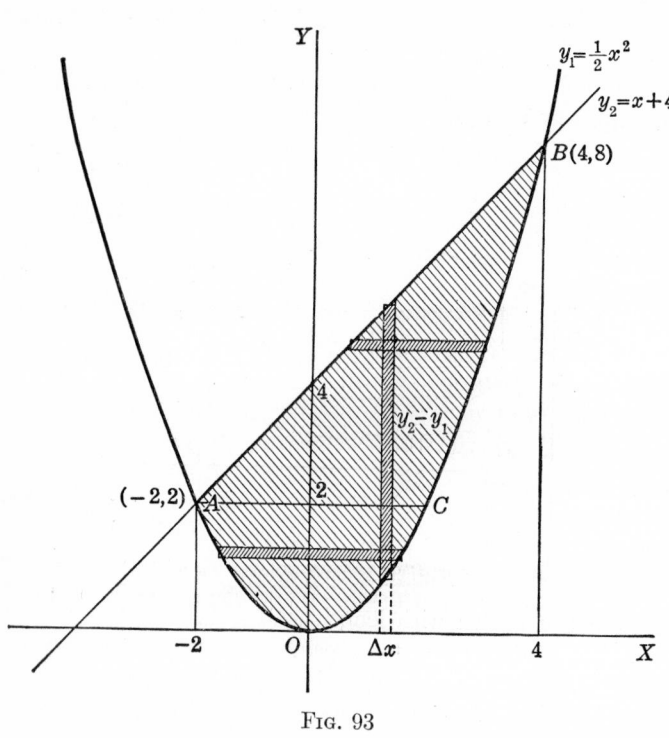

Fig. 93

184. Exercises

In each of the following problems, draw a figure carefully, and shade the region whose area is to be found; also draw an appropriate rectangular element of area.

In Exercises 1–10, find the area bounded by each of the given pairs of curves and lines:

1. $y = x^3$, $y = x$ (first quadrant).   2. $y^3 = 8x$, $y = 2x$.
3. $y^2 = 2(2 - x)$, $y = 2 - x$.   4. $y^2 = 4x$, $2x - y = 4$.
5. $x = 4y - y^2$, $y = x$.   6. $y = x - x^3$,
    $y = \frac{7}{16}x$ (in first quadrant).
7. $y = x^2$, $y = x^3$.   8. $y^2 = 4x$, $x^2 = 4y$.
9. $y = x^2$, $y = 4 - x^2$.   10. $y^2 = 4x$, $x = 12 + 2y - y^2$.

11. Find the area cut off from the parabola $y = 6 + x - x^2$ by the chord joining the points $(-1, 4)$ and $(3, 0)$.

12. Find the area bounded by the curve $x^2 y = a^3$, the lines $x = 2a$, $y = 2a$ and the coördinate axes.

13. Find the area bounded by $y = x^2$, $y = x$ and $y = 2x$.

14. Indicate a region for which the integral $\int_2^5 (x^2 - 2x)\, dx$ represents the area.

185. Volumes of Solids

Let us now consider the problem of defining and calculating the volume of a given solid.

Suppose that the solid has the property that it is possible to find an axis, which we shall take as the X-axis, such that the area of any plane section of the solid which is perpendicular to this axis can be expressed as a function $A(x)$ of its distance x from some origin on this axis. Let the solid extend from $x = a$ to $x = b$. Divide the interval (a, b) into sub-intervals Δx_k $(k = 1, 2, \cdots, n)$ as in § 167. Cut the given solid into thin slices by planes perpendicular to the X-axis at the points of subdivision. As element of volume, to approximate a typical slice, we take a prism or cylinder whose altitude is Δx_k and whose base is of area $A(\xi_k)$, where ξ_k is any point in the k-th sub-interval Δx_k. The volume of the k-th cylinder or prism is $A(\xi_k)\,\Delta x_k$.

We then *define* the **volume** of the given solid as the limit of the sum of the volumes of these prisms or cylinders, so that by definition:

$$(a) \qquad\qquad V = \lim_{\delta \to 0}\ \sum_{k=1}^{n} A(\xi_k)\Delta x_k.$$

By the definition of a definite integral, we then have:

The volume of a solid whose cross-sectional area perpendicular to the X-axis at a point x is $A(x)$ is given by:

$$(4) \qquad\qquad V = \int_a^b A(x)\, dx,$$

where a and b are the extreme values of x for the solid.

We shall apply this formula for volume to various special cases in the following articles.

186. Volumes of Solids of Revolution by Cylindrical Disks

A **solid of revolution** is a solid which is generated by revolving a plane region about an axis in its plane. Every section of such a solid by a plane perpendicular to its axis of revolution is a circle or a circular ring with its center on this axis. Thus, a right circular cone is generated by revolving a right triangle about one of its legs, and a sphere is generated by revolving a semicircle about its diameter.

Let a solid of revolution be generated by revolving about the X-axis the region in the XY-plane bounded by the arc CD of the plane curve

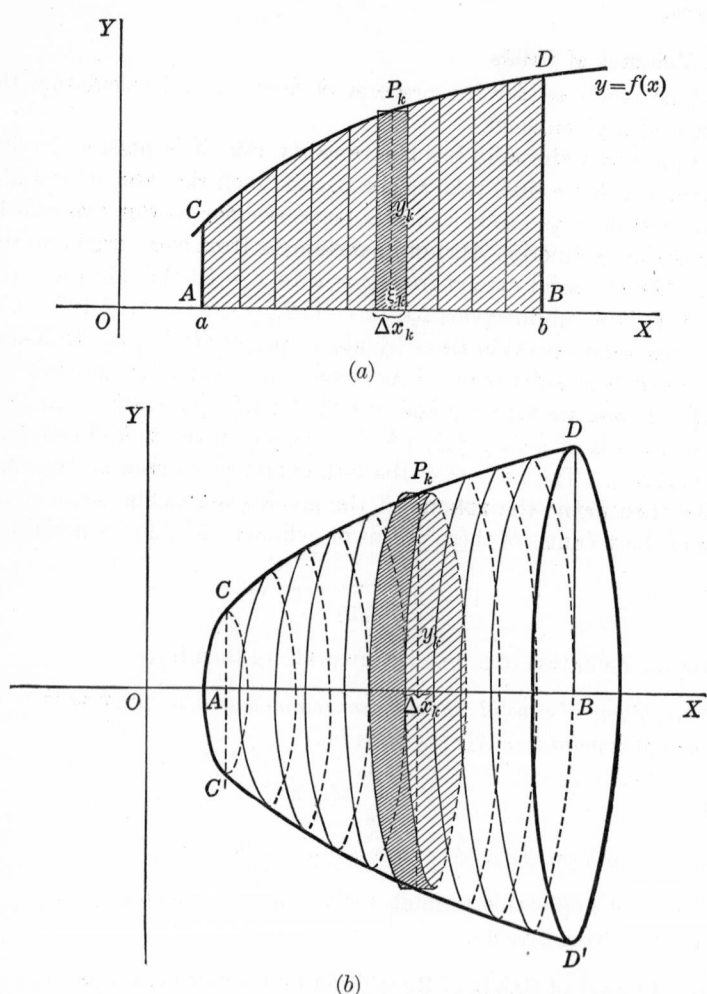

(a)

(b)

Fig. 94

$y = f(x)$, the X-axis and the lines $x = a$ and $x = b$ (Fig. 94).   The cross-sectional area of this solid at a point x is evidently that of a circle, $A(x) = \pi y^2$.   The *element of volume* is in this case a *cylindrical disk*, whose thickness is Δx_k and whose base is of area πy_k^2, where $y_k = f(\xi_k)$.   The definition of § 185 then becomes

$$(a) \qquad V = \lim_{\delta \to 0} \sum_{k=1}^{n} \pi y_k^2 \Delta x_k.$$

The theorem of § 185 for this special case may be stated:

The volume of the solid of revolution generated by revolving about the X-axis the region bounded by the curve $y = f(x)$, the X-axis and the lines $x = a$ and $x = b$ is given by:

$$(5) \quad V = \pi \int_a^b y^2 \, dx.$$

In applying this formula, it should be kept in mind that we are evaluating the *limit of a sum of volumes of cylindrical disks*.

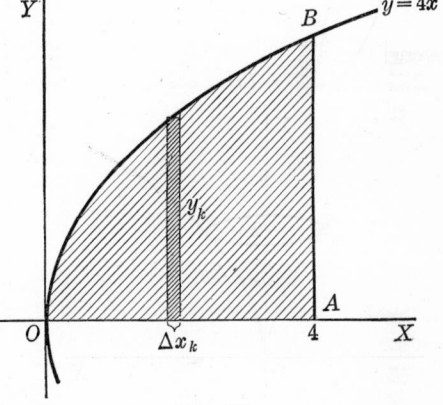

Fig. 95

EXAMPLE 1. Find the volume of the solid generated by revolving about the X-axis the region bounded by the parabola $y^2 = 4\,x$, the X-axis and the lines $x = 0$ and $x = 4$.   (Fig. 95).

Solution: $V = \pi \displaystyle\int_0^4 y^2 \, dx = \pi \int_0^4 4\,x \, dx = 32\,\pi.$

In a similar way, by interchanging the X- and Y-axes, we see that: the volume of the solid generated by revolving about the Y-axis the region bounded by the curve $x = g(y)$, the Y-axis and the lines $y = c$ and $y = d$ is given by

$$(b) \qquad V = \pi \int_c^d x^2 \, dy.$$

EXAMPLE 2. Find the volume of the solid generated by revolving about the Y-axis the region bounded by the parabola $y^2 = 4x$, the Y-axis and the line $y = 2$ (Fig. 96).

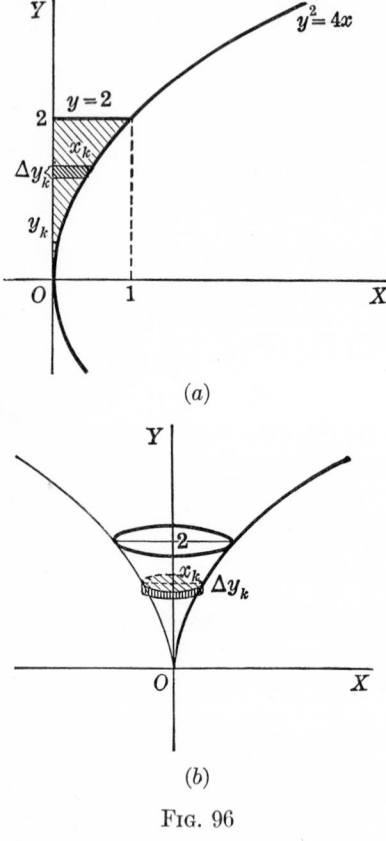

(a)

(b)

FIG. 96

Solution: $V = \pi \int_0^2 x^2 \, dy$

$$= \pi \int_0^2 \tfrac{1}{16} y^4 \, dy = \tfrac{2}{5}\pi.$$

When a region partially bounded by a straight line, not one of the coördinate axes, is revolved about this line as an axis, the volume of the resulting solid cannot be found *directly* by formula (5) or (b). But a similar method can be employed, still using cylindrical disks.

EXAMPLE 3. Find the volume of the solid generated by revolving about the line $y = 2$ the smaller region bounded by the curve $y^2 = 4x$ and the lines $y = 2$ and $x = 4$ (Fig. 97, page 203).

Solution: The region to be revolved is the region ABC, shaded in Fig. 97. Divide the segment AB into n parts Δx_k, and on each such part construct a rectangle of altitude $y_k - 2$ and base Δx_k, where y_k is the ordinate of the curve for some point in the sub-interval Δx_k. When revolved about the line $y = 2$, each such rectangle generates a cylindrical disk of radius $y_k - 2$ and thickness Δx_k. The required volume is then

$$V = \lim_{\delta \to 0} \sum_{k=1}^{n} \pi (y_k - 2)^2 \Delta x_k = \pi \int_1^4 (y - 2)^2 \, dx$$

$$= \pi \int_1^4 (y^2 - 4y + 4) \, dx = \pi \int_1^4 (4x - 8\sqrt{x} + 4) \, dx = \tfrac{14}{3}\pi.$$

187. Exercises

In each of the following problems, draw a figure carefully, and indicate the volume to be found; also draw an element of volume.

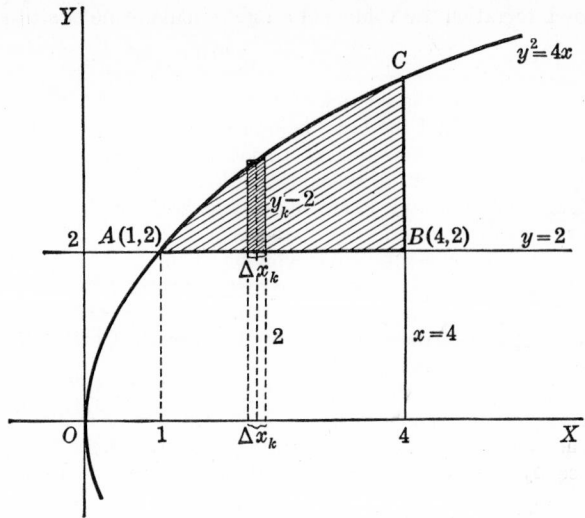

Fig. 97

In Exercises 1–4, find the volume of the solid generated by revolving about the X-axis the region bounded by each of the given sets of curves and lines:

1. $y = 1 - x^2$, $\quad y = 0$.
2. $y = 2x - x^2$, $\quad y = 0$.
3. $4x + y^2 - 16 = 0$, $\quad x = 0$.
4. $x^{\frac{1}{2}} + y^{\frac{1}{2}} = a^{\frac{1}{2}}$, $\quad x = 0$, $\quad y = 0$.

In Exercises 5–8, find the volume of the solid generated by revolving about the Y-axis the region bounded by each of the given sets of curves and lines:

5. $2y + x^2 = 4$, $\quad y = 0$.
6. $y^2 = 4ax$, $\quad x = 0$, $\quad y = 2a$.
7. $x^2 - y^2 = a^2$, $\quad y = 0$, $\quad y = a$.
8. $x^{\frac{2}{3}} + y^{\frac{2}{3}} = a^{\frac{2}{3}}$, $\quad x = 0$, $\quad y = 0$, in first quadrant.

9. Find the volume of the solid of revolution generated by revolving about the X-axis the region bounded by $y^2 = 4ax$ and $x = h$. Show that the result is one-half the volume of the cylinder having the same base and altitude.

10. Find the volume of the solid generated by revolving about the Y-axis the region bounded by $y^2 = 4ax$, $y = b$ and the Y-axis. Show that the result is one-fifth the volume of the cylinder having the same base and altitude.

11. Find the volume of a sphere of radius a, considered as generated by revolving a semicircle about its diameter. [*Hint.* Use the circle $x^2 + y^2 = a^2$.]

12. Find the volumes of the solids obtained by revolving the curve $\dfrac{x^2}{a^2} + \dfrac{y^2}{b^2} = 1$ about the X-axis and about the Y-axis.

13. Find by integration the volume of a right circular cone of altitude h and radius of base r.   [*Hint.*   Use the straight line $y = \dfrac{r}{h} \cdot x$].

14. Find by integration the volume of a frustum of a right circular cone of altitude h, the radii of the bases being r and R.

15. Find a formula for the volume of a spherical segment (of one base) of thickness t, if the radius of the sphere is R.

16. The oil in a spherical tank 40 feet in diameter is 15 feet deep.   How much oil does the tank contain?

17. Find the volume generated by revolving about the X-axis the region under the hyperbola $xy = a^2$ in the first quadrant between $x = a$ and $x = 2\,a$.

18. Find the volume of the solid generated by revolving about the X-axis the loop of the curve $y^2 = x^2(3 - x)$.

19. Find the volume generated by revolving about the line $x = 4$ the smaller region bounded by the curve $y^2 = 4\,x$ and the lines $y = 2$ and $x = 4$.

20. Find the volume generated by revolving about the line $x = 3$, the region bounded by the line $x - 2\,y + 2 = 0$, the X-axis, the Y-axis and the line $x = 3$.

188. Volumes of Solids of Revolution by Cylindrical Washers

Sometimes we need to find the volume of a *hollow* solid generated by revolving about an axis a plane region not bounded by the axis

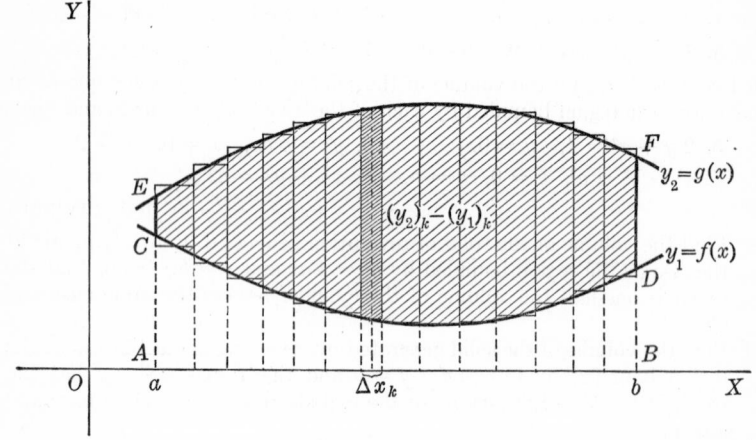

Fig. 98

of revolution.   Suppose, for example, we take the region $CDFE$, shaded in Fig. 98, bounded by the curves $y_1 = f(x)$, $y_2 = g(x)$, and the lines $x = a$ and $x = b$, and revolve it about the X-axis.   We assume, for simplicity, that arc EF is above arc CD throughout the interval (a, b), and that both are above the X-axis throughout (a, b).

The volume of the solid of revolution described above may be regarded as the difference between the volume generated by revolving about the X-axis the area $ABFE$ and the volume generated by revolving the area $ABDC$. By formula (5) of § 186, this volume is

$$(a) \qquad V = \pi \int_a^b y_2{}^2 \, dx - \pi \int_a^b y_1{}^2 \, dx = \pi \int_a^b (y_2{}^2 - y_1{}^2) \, dx.$$

Hence:

The volume of the solid generated by revolving about the X-axis the region bounded by the curves $y_1 = f(x)$, $y_2 = g(x)$ and the lines $x = a$ and $x = b$ (as described above) is given by:

$$(6) \qquad V = \pi \int_a^b (y_2{}^2 - y_1{}^2) \, dx.$$

This result may be visualized as the limit of a sum of volumes of "washer-shaped" elements.

EXAMPLE. Find the volume of the solid generated by revolving about the X-axis the region bounded by the curves $y = x^2$ and $y = 2 - x^2$.

Solution: In Fig. 99, the shaded region is to be revolved about the X-axis. The curves intersect at $(1, 1)$ and $(-1, 1)$. The required volume is therefore

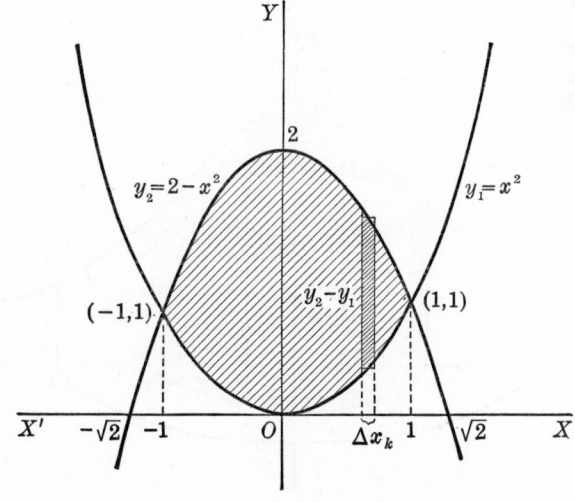

FIG. 99

$$V = \pi \int_{-1}^{1} [(2 - x^2)^2 - (x^2)^2] \, dx = \pi \int_{-1}^{1} (4 - 4\,x^2) \, dx = \tfrac{16}{3}\pi.$$

In a similar way, we may find the volume of the solid generated by revolving about the Y-axis a region between two curves. If a solid is generated by revolving a plane region between two curves about some other axis than one of the coördinate axes, a similar procedure may be used to find its volume.

189. Exercises

In each of the following problems, draw a figure carefully, and indicate the volume to be found.

In Exercises 1–4, find the volume generated by revolving about the X-axis the region bounded by:

1. $y^2 = 4\,x, \quad 2\,y = x.$ 2. $y^2 = 4\,x, \quad x^2 + y^2 = 5\,x.$
3. $y = x^2, \quad y^2 = x.$ 4. $y = 4\,x - x^2, \quad 2\,y = 4\,x - x^2.$

In Exercises 5–8, find the volume generated by revolving about the Y-axis the region bounded by:

5. $y = x^2, \quad y = 0, \quad x = 2.$ 6. $x^2 + y^2 = 4\,x, \quad y = x.$
7. $x^2 - y^2 = a^2, y = 0, x = 2\,a.$ 8. $y = 4\,x - x^2, y = 0.$

190. Volumes of Solids of Revolution by Cylindrical Shells

Instead of finding volumes of solids of revolution by use of cylindrical disks or washers, it is frequently more convenient to use *cylindrical shells*. In this case, the volume element is in the form of a thin hollow

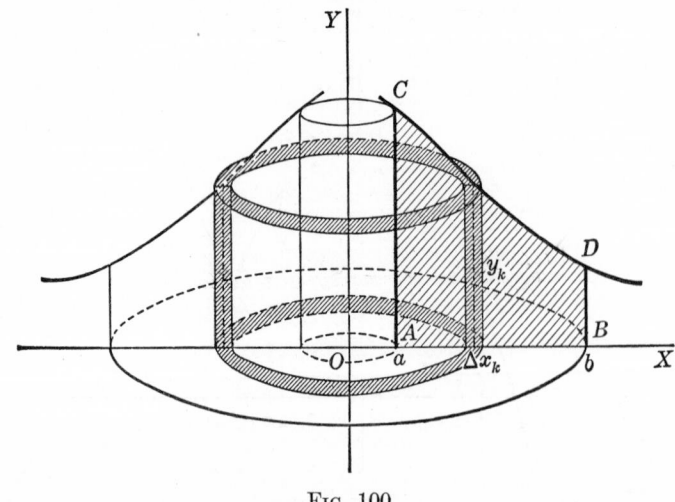

Fig. 100

circular cylinder generated by revolving a rectangle about a line parallel to one of its sides.

Suppose that the region $ABDC$ in Fig. 100, bounded by an arc CD of a curve $y = f(x)$, the X-axis and the lines $x = a$ and $x = b$, is to be revolved about the Y-axis to generate a solid of revolution. Divide the region $ABDC$ into vertical strips parallel to the axis of revolution, and draw approximating rectangles. If we take a rectangle of base Δx_k and altitude $y'_k = f(x'_k)$, where x'_k denotes the mid-point of the base Δx_k, then the volume of the cylindrical shell generated by revolving this rectangle about the Y-axis is $(2\,\pi x'_k)y'_k\Delta x_k$.* It can be shown without difficulty that as $n \to \infty$ and $\delta \to 0$, the sum of the volumes of the cylindrical shells approaches as a limit the volume of the solid of revolution as defined in § 185; that is,

$$(a) \qquad\qquad V = \lim_{\delta \to 0} \sum_{k=1}^{n} 2\,\pi x'_k y'_k \Delta x_k.$$

Therefore we have:

The volume of the solid generated by revolving about the Y-axis the region bounded by the curve $y = f(x)$, the X-axis and the lines $x = a$ and $x = b$ is given by:

$$(7) \quad V = 2\pi \int_a^b xy\,dx.$$

A similar formula may be developed for the case when a region is revolved about the X-axis, or about some line parallel to one of the coördinate axes.

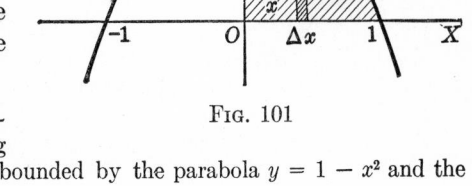

Fig. 101

EXAMPLE 1. Find the volume generated by revolving about the Y-axis the region bounded by the parabola $y = 1 - x^2$ and the coördinate axes (Fig. 101).

Solution: $V = 2\,\pi \int_0^1 xy\,dx = 2\,\pi \int_0^1 x(1 - x^2)\,dx = \tfrac{1}{2}\,\pi.$

EXAMPLE 2. The circle $x^2 + y^2 = 9$ and the parabola $x^2 = 8\,y$ are revolved about the Y-axis to generate surfaces of revolution. Find the volume of the smaller solid bounded by these surfaces.

* The volume of a cylindrical shell is equal to the mean circumference of the base times the altitude times the thickness of the shell. This result is readily obtained by subtracting the volumes of two concentric cylinders.

Solution: By solving together the equations of the two curves, we find that they intersect at the points $(\pm 2\sqrt{2}, 1)$ (Fig. 102). The length of a rectangular element extending between the parabola and the circle is $l = \sqrt{9 - x^2} - \frac{1}{8} x^2$. Therefore,

$$V = 2\pi \int_0^{2\sqrt{2}} x(\sqrt{9 - x^2} - \tfrac{1}{8} x^2)\, dx = \tfrac{40}{3}\pi.$$

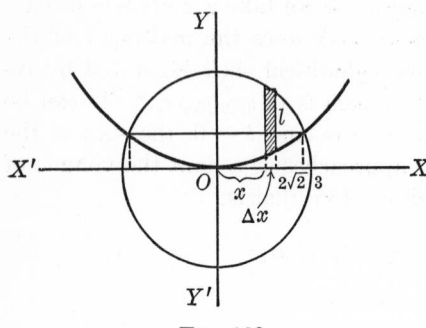

Fig. 102

191. Exercises

Solve each of the following problems by use of cylindrical shells. Draw a figure carefully in each case.

1. Find the volume of the solid generated by revolving about the Y-axis the region bounded by the parabola $y = 2x - x^2$ and the X-axis.

2. Find the volume of the solid generated by revolving about the Y-axis the region bounded by the hyperbola $xy = 4$, the X-axis and the lines $x = 2$ and $x = 4$.

3. Find the volume of a sphere of radius a.

4. The segment of the parabola $y^2 = 2\,px$ cut off by the line $x = h$ is revolved about the X-axis; find the volume of the solid generated.

5. The segment of the parabola $hy^2 = 4\,a^2x$ cut off by the line $x = h$ is revolved about the X-axis to form a solid of revolution. A hole of radius a is bored through the solid along the X-axis. Find the volume cut out.

6. What volume is obtained by use of the formula $V = 2\pi \int_c^d yx\, dy$, where $x = g(y)$?

7. The circle $x^2 + y^2 = 8$ and the line $y = x$ are revolved about the Y-axis to generate a sphere and a cone. Find the volume of the smaller solid bounded by the sphere and the cone.

8. The circle $x^2 + y^2 = 6$ and the parabola $y = x^2$ are revolved about the Y-axis to form a sphere and a paraboloid. Find the volume of the smaller solid bounded by these two surfaces.

192. Volumes of Solids of Known Cross-Section

It is frequently necessary to calculate volumes of solids whose boundaries are not surfaces of revolution. In this case, the methods of cylindrical disks or washers or cylindrical shells will not be applicable, but the general method of parallel slicing in § 185 may often be used. The basic formula for this method is:

(a)
$$V = \int_a^b A(x)\, dx,$$

where $A(x)$ is the cross-sectional area of the solid at a distance x from a fixed point.

EXAMPLE. The base of the solid shown in Fig. 103 is a circle of radius 5 inches, and each section of the solid by a plane perpendicular to a fixed diameter AB is an isosceles triangle with altitude 6 inches. Find the volume of the solid.

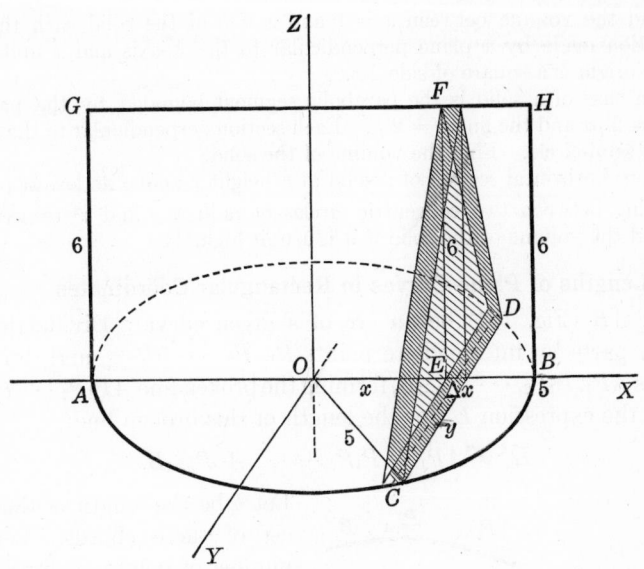

FIG. 103

Solution: Let CDF be a section of the solid perpendicular to AB at a distance x from the center O. Since $EC = \sqrt{25 - x^2}$ and $EF = 6$, the cross-sectional area CDF is $A(x) = 6\sqrt{25 - x^2}$. Then the volume of the right-hand half of the solid is

$$V = \int_0^5 A(x)\, dx = 6\int_0^5 \sqrt{25 - x^2}\, dx = \tfrac{75}{2}\,\pi,$$

which we obtain from the value of the integral $\int_0^a \sqrt{a^2 - x^2}\, dx$ in § 181, Example 2. The required volume of the entire solid is therefore $75\,\pi$.

193. Exercises

Draw a figure carefully for each of the following problems.

1. The cross-section of a loudspeaker horn perpendicular to its axis at a distance x from its end is a circle of radius $0.1\,x^2$. Find the volume of the part of the horn from the pointed end to a section 3 units distant from that end.

2. Every horizontal section of a steeple x feet from its top is a square whose side is $0.4\,x$ feet in length. Find the volume of the steeple if its height is 30 feet.

3. Find the volume, by integration, of a right pyramid of altitude h with square base of side a.

4. Find the volume between $x = 1$ and $x = 5$ of the solid such that the section made by a plane perpendicular to the X-axis and x units from the origin is a square of side $2\,x$.

5. The base of a solid is the parabolic segment bounded by the parabola $y^2 = 2\,px$ and the line $x = 2\,p$. Each section perpendicular to the X-axis is a semi-circle. Find the volume of the solid.

6. Every horizontal section of a solid at a height x above its lowest point is a ring between two concentric circles of radii $\sqrt{x}$ and x^2 respectively. Find the volume of the solid if it is 1 unit high.

194. Lengths of Plane Curves in Rectangular Coördinates

Let AB (Fig. 104) be an arc of a given curve. Divide this arc into n parts by intermediate points $P_1, P_2, \cdots, P_{n-1}$, and draw the chords $AP_1, P_1P_2, \cdots, P_{n-1}B$, forming the broken line $AP_1P_2 \cdots P_{n-1}B$. Form the expression L_n for the length of this broken line:

(a) $$L_n = AP_1 + P_1P_2 + \cdots + P_{n-1}B.$$

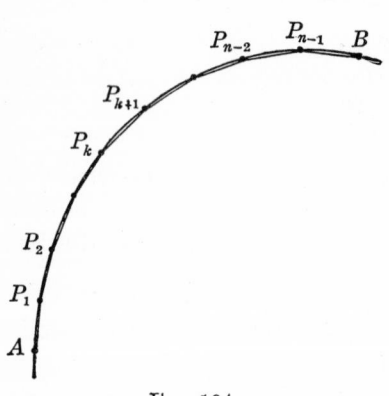

Let δ be the length of the longest of these chords. Let the number of points of division be increased in such a way that $\delta \to 0$ as $n \to \infty$.

If $\lim\limits_{\delta \to 0} L_n$ *exists and is independent of the choice of the points* $P_1, P_2, \cdots, P_{n-1},$ *the arc AB is said to be **rectifiable**, and this limit is defined to be the length of the arc.*

FIG. 104

Let us now derive a formula for calculating the arc length of a given curve. Let $y = f(x)$ be the equation of a smooth curve, so that $f(x)$ and $f'(x)$ are continuous functions of x in the x-interval (a, b)

corresponding to the arc AB. Suppose that the arc AB is divided into n parts as described above (Fig. 105), and let arc PQ be the k-th sub-arc, and let $MN = \Delta x_k$ be its projection on the X-axis. Let us assume that we go along the curve to the right, so that every Δx_k

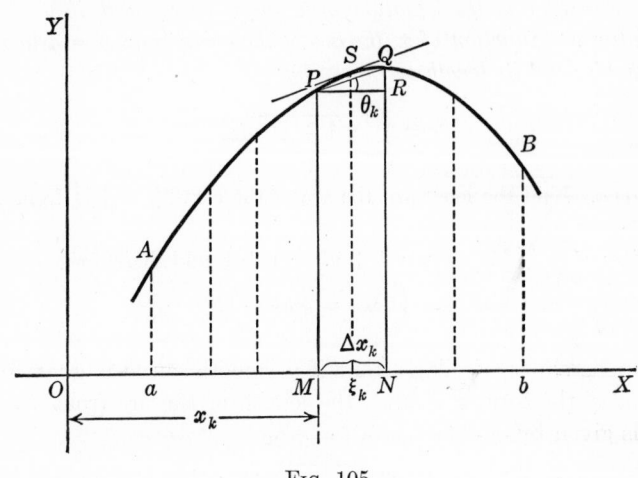

FIG. 105

is positive. If θ_k is the angle which the chord PQ makes with the X-axis, then

(b) chord $PQ = PR \, |\sec \theta_k| = \Delta x_k \, |\sec \theta_k| = \sqrt{1 + \tan^2 \theta_k} \cdot \Delta x_k.$

By the mean-value theorem for derivatives (§ 150), there is a point S on the arc PQ at which the slope of the tangent is equal to the slope of the chord PQ. If ξ_k is the abscissa of S, we then have

(c) $$\tan \theta_k = f'(\xi_k),$$

and therefore

(d) $$\text{chord } PQ = \sqrt{1 + [f'(\xi_k)]^2} \cdot \Delta x_k.$$

The total length L_n of the broken line $AP_1P_2 \cdots P_{n-1}B$ is then

(e) $$L_n = \sum_{k=1}^{n} \sqrt{1 + [f'(\xi_k)]^2} \cdot \Delta x_k.$$

Since $\sqrt{1 + [f'(x)]^2}$ is continuous, we know (from § 167) that as $n \to \infty$ and $\delta \to 0$, the limit of $\sum_{k=1}^{n} \sqrt{1 + [f'(\xi_k)]^2} \cdot \Delta x_k$ exists, and is equal to $\int_a^b \sqrt{1 + [f'(x)]^2}\, dx$.   Therefore, $\lim_{\delta \to 0} L_n$ exists, and by definition is equal to the required length of the arc AB. The formula for the length is easier to write if we put y' in place of $f'(x)$. Hence:

I. *If $y = f(x)$ is the equation of a given curve, and if $y' = f'(x)$ is a continuous function of x, the arc of the curve from $x = a$ to $x = b$ is rectifiable, and its length s is given by:*

$$(8) \qquad\qquad s = \int_a^b \sqrt{1 + y'^2}\, dx.$$

EXAMPLE. Find the length of the arc of the curve $y = \frac{2}{3} x^{\frac{3}{2}}$ from $x = 3$ to $x = 8$.

Solution: $y' = \frac{2}{3} \cdot \frac{3}{2} x^{\frac{1}{2}} = \sqrt{x}$, $1 + y'^2 = 1 + x$, and therefore

$$s = \int_3^8 \sqrt{1 + x}\, dx = \tfrac{38}{3}.$$

It can be shown similarly that if a smooth curve is given by an equation of the form $x = g(y)$, the length of the arc from $y = c$ to $y = d$ is given by

$$(f) \qquad\qquad s = \int_c^d \sqrt{1 + \left(\frac{dx}{dy}\right)^2}\, dy.$$

Now consider an arc PQ of the curve $y = f(x)$, the abscissa of P being x and that of Q being $x + \Delta x$. By the preceding theorem,

$$(g) \qquad\qquad \text{arc } PQ = \int_x^{x + \Delta x} \sqrt{1 + [f'(x)]^2}\, dx.$$

By the mean-value theorem for integrals (§ 179),

$$(h) \qquad\qquad \text{arc } PQ = \sqrt{1 + [f'(\eta)]^2} \cdot \Delta x,$$

where η is a value between x and $x + \Delta x$. As in (d),

$$(i) \qquad\qquad \text{chord } PQ = \sqrt{1 + [f'(\xi)]^2} \cdot \Delta x,$$

where ξ is a properly chosen value between x and $x + \Delta x$. Then

$$\frac{\text{arc } PQ}{\text{chord } PQ} = \frac{\sqrt{1 + [f'(\eta)]^2}}{\sqrt{1 + [f'(\xi)]^2}}.$$

It is evident that η and ξ approach the same limiting value x as $\Delta x \to 0$, and therefore that the above ratio has the limit 1 as $\Delta x \to 0$. Also, chord $PQ \to 0$ as $\Delta x \to 0$. Hence:

II. *For a smooth curve, the ratio of the length of an arc to the length of its chord has the limit 1 when the length of the chord approaches zero.*

195. Differential of Arc in Rectangular Coördinates

Let $P_0(x_0, y_0)$ be a fixed point and $P(x, y)$ a variable point on a smooth curve $y = f(x)$, and let s denote the length of the arc P_0P. Let us assume that we go along the curve to the right, so that s increases to the right. By § 194,

(a)
$$s = \int_{x_0}^{x} \sqrt{1 + y'^2}\, dx.$$

From this, by § 178, we obtain

(b)
$$\frac{ds}{dx} = \sqrt{1 + y'^2}.$$

Hence:

The differential of arc ds for a smooth curve $y = f(x)$ is given by:

(9)
$$ds = \sqrt{1 + y'^2}\, dx.$$

Squaring both sides of (9), we have

$$(ds)^2 = \left[1 + \left(\frac{dy}{dx}\right)^2\right](dx)^2,$$

or

(10)
$$(ds)^2 = (dx)^2 + (dy)^2.$$

196. Exercises

1. Find the length of the upper half of the curve $9\,y^2 = 4\,x^3$ from $x = 0$ to $x = 3$, by use of formula (8).
2. Find the entire length of the curve $x^{\frac{2}{3}} + y^{\frac{2}{3}} = a^{\frac{2}{3}}$, by use of formula (8).
3. Find the length of the curve $y = x^{\frac{2}{3}}$ from $x = 0$ to $x = 8$, by use of formula (f) of § 194.
4. Find the length of the curve $(x + 1)^2 = 4\,y^3$ from $y = 0$ to $y = 1$, by use of formula (f) of § 194.
5. Find the length of the loop of the curve $9\,y^2 = x(x - 3)^2$. (See § 417.)
6. Find the length of the curve $y = \dfrac{x^3}{6} + \dfrac{1}{2\,x}$ from $x = 1$ to $x = 3$.
7. Find ds in terms of x and dx for the curve $y = x^2$.
8. Find ds in terms of x and dx for the curve $y = \sqrt{1 - x^2}$.
9. Find ds in terms of x, y and dx for the curve $x^2 + y^2 = a^2$.

197. Work Done by a Variable Force

In § 170, we discussed the problem of finding the work done by a variable force. We may restate the result of that discussion as follows:

If a continuous force $F(x)$ acts in a constant direction and if its point of application moves in the direction of the force from a position $x = a$ to a position $x = b$, where x is the directed distance on the line of action of the force measured from some fixed origin on the line, then the work done by the force during this displacement is given by:

$$(11) \qquad W = \int_a^b F(x) \, dx.$$

EXAMPLE 1. If a particle free to move on the X-axis is attracted toward the origin by a force of magnitude equal to kx^2 (k constant), find the work done when the particle moves from the position $x = 4$ to the position $x = 2$.

Solution: Since the attraction is in the negative direction on the X-axis, we take $F(x) = -kx^2$; then

$$W = \int_4^2 F(x) \, dx = -\int_4^2 kx^2 \, dx = k \int_2^4 x^2 \, dx = \tfrac{56}{3} k.$$

EXAMPLE 2. A spring whose natural length is 15 inches requires a force of 8 pounds to stretch it 1 inch. Find the work necessary to stretch the spring from a length of 16 inches to a length of 18 inches.

Solution: By Hooke's law, the force $F(x)$ required to stretch the spring x inches is $F(x) = kx$. Since $F(x) = 8$ when $x = 1$, we have $k = 8$, so that in this case $F(x) = 8\,x$. The required work is then

$$W = 8 \int_1^3 x \, dx$$
$$= 32 \text{ inch-pounds}$$
$$= 2\tfrac{2}{3} \text{ foot-pounds.}$$

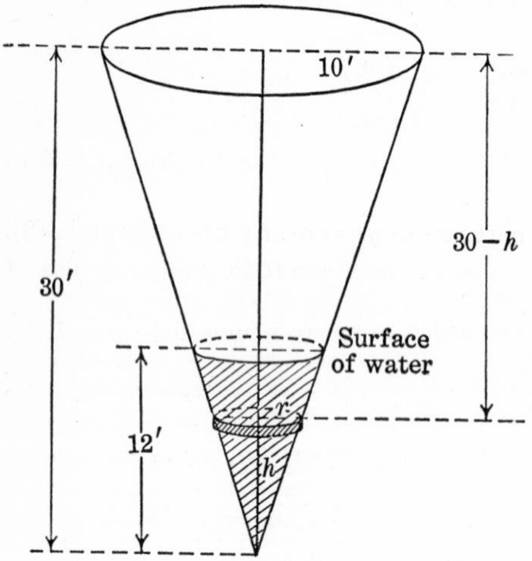

EXAMPLE 3. A conical tank with circular cross-section has its axis vertical and the vertex at the bottom; the radius of the top is 10 feet and the altitude is 30 feet, and water is 12 feet deep in it. Find the work required to pump the water out over the top. (Fig. 106.)

FIG. 106

Solution: Let us consider the water to be divided into n layers by horizontal planes, and let us approximate these layers by thin cylindrical disks (as in finding volumes by the method of § 186). If such a typical disk is at a distance h_k above the vertex and is of thickness Δh_k and of radius r_k, then the weight of this disk is $w \cdot \pi r_k^2 \Delta h_k$, where $w = 62.5$ (approximately) is the weight of 1 cubic foot of water, and r_k and h_k are expressed in feet. From similar triangles in the figure, we have

$$(a) \qquad \frac{r_k}{h_k} = \frac{10}{30} \qquad \text{or} \qquad r_k = \tfrac{1}{3} h_k.$$

The weight of the disk is then $\frac{1}{9} \pi w h_k^2 \Delta h_k$. In pumping out the water over the top, this typical layer (disk) is raised a distance $30 - h_k$ feet. Hence, the required work is

$$W = \tfrac{1}{9} \pi w \int_0^{12} h^2 (30 - h) \, dh = 1344 \, \pi w = 84,000 \, \pi \text{ foot-pounds.}$$

EXAMPLE 4. Two cubic feet of gas at a pressure of 100 pounds per square inch expands to a volume of 3 cubic feet. Find the work done if the relation between the pressure and volume is $pv^{1.4} = c$ (constant).

Solution: Substituting the corresponding values $p = 14,400$ (pounds per square foot) and $v = 2$ (cubic feet) in the formula $pv^{1.4} = c$, we find $c = 38,002$. Then $p = 38,002 \, v^{-1.4}$. The work done by an expanding gas depends only on the volume and not on the shape of the container. We can therefore suppose that the gas is in a cylinder and expands against a piston head of cross-sectional area A. If the gas expands an amount Δv, the piston moves a distance $\Delta v / A$ (feet); the force on the piston head is pA. By an argument similar to that used previously in work problems, we have

$$W = \int_{v_1}^{v_2} (pA) \cdot \frac{dv}{A} = \int_{v_1}^{v_2} p \, dv,$$

where v_1 and v_2 are the limiting volumes. In our present problem,

$$W = \int_2^3 p \, dv = 38,002 \int_2^3 v^{-1.4} \, dv = 10,781 \text{ foot-pounds (approximately).}$$

198. Exercises

1. A spiral spring stretches 1.2 inches under a load of 5 pounds. The natural length of the spring is 1 foot. Find the work done in stretching it from a length of 15 inches to a length of 20 inches.

2. Find the work done in compressing a spring of natural length 10 inches to a length of 7 inches, if a force of 500 pounds is required to compress it to a length of 9 inches.

3. In a spring whose natural length is 20 inches, is the work necessary to stretch it from 21 inches to 22 inches the same as that required to stretch it from 22 inches to 23 inches?

4. For a certain spring, 200 foot-pounds of work are required to stretch it from a length of 21 inches to a length of 23 inches, while 300 foot-pounds of work are needed to stretch it from 22 inches to a length of 24 inches. Find the natural length of the spring.

5. A cylindrical cistern of diameter 6 feet and depth 10 feet is full of water. Find the work required to pump the water out over the top.

6. A cylindrical tank 8 feet in diameter and 16 feet deep is half full of water. Find the work required to pump the water out over the top.

7. Calculate the work done in pumping the water out of a cylindrical tank of base radius 4 feet and altitude 10 feet if the pipe through which the water is pumped rises to a height of 10 feet above the tank.

8. A conical tank 12 feet deep is filled with a liquid weighing 80 pounds per cubic foot; the top of the tank is a circle 8 feet in diameter. Find the work done in pumping it out over the top.

9. Find the work done in pumping the water from a hemispherical cistern 12 feet in diameter if the water is 4 feet deep and is delivered to a height of 2 feet above the top of the cistern.

10. A water tank is in the form of a hemisphere 24 feet in diameter surmounted by a cylinder of the same diameter and 10 feet high. Find the work done in pumping it out over the top when the tank is filled within 2 feet of the top.

11. The pressure of 1 pound of steam is 130 pounds per square inch and the volume is 3.44 cubic feet. Find the work done by the steam in expanding to double its volume according to the law $pv^{1.14} = c$.

12. The pressure and volume of a certain gas obey the law $pv^{1.2} = 120$ (in inch-pound units). Find the work done when the gas expands from $v = 2.4$ to $v = 4.6$ cubic inches.

13. By Coulomb's law, a positive charge m of electricity repels a unit positive charge at the distance x with the force m/x^2. What is the work done when the unit charge is carried from $x = 2a$ to $x = a$?

14. A uniform 500-pound chain 50 feet long hangs from a windlass. How much work is required to wind it up?

15. In raising a leaky bucket from the bottom of a well 25 feet deep, one-fourth of the water is lost. If the bucket weighs 3.5 pounds, the water in the bucket at the start weighs 22 pounds and the amount which has leaked out is assumed proportional to the displacement, find the work done in raising the bucket.

199. Liquid Pressure

It is shown in physics that at any point within a liquid at rest the pressure is the same in all directions. It is also shown that at any point within the liquid *the pressure is proportional to the depth below the surface of the liquid*, and is, in fact, equal to the weight of a column of the liquid having unit cross-section and a height equal to the depth at the point. Thus, if w is the weight of one cubic unit of the liquid and h is the depth, the pressure, or force per unit area, is

(a) $$p = wh.$$

For water, we may take $w = 62.5$ pounds per cubic foot, approximately. Since pressure is force per unit area, it follows that the force on an area A, all points of which have the same depth and therefore the same pressure p, is equal to pA.

Now let us consider the problem of finding the force on one side of a flat surface S (Fig. 107) exerted by a liquid in which it is submerged vertically. Let the submerged area be divided into n strips parallel to the surface of the liquid, and draw approximating rectangles for all these strips.

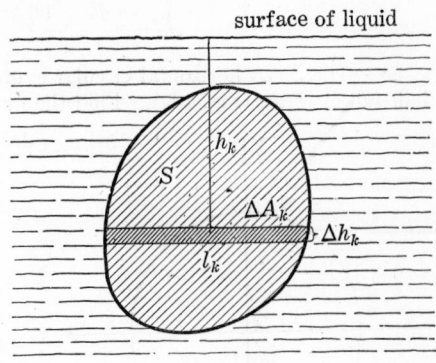

Let ΔA_k denote the area of a typical rectangle, let h_k be the vertical distance from the surface of the liquid to any point in ΔA_k, let Δh_k be the width (in the vertical direction) of the rectangle, and let l_k be the length of the rectangle. If p_k is the pressure at depth h_k, and if all points in the rectangle ΔA_k were at exactly the same depth h_k, the force exerted

Fig. 107

by the liquid on the rectangle ΔA_k would be

$$p_k \Delta A_k = w h_k \Delta A_k = w h_k l_k \Delta h_k.$$

It is therefore natural to form the sum $\sum_{k=1}^{n} w h_k l_k \Delta h_k$, and then take as the *definition* of the force on the entire surface S the limit of this sum as $\delta \to 0$. This limit is $\int_a^b whl\, dh$, where a and b are the extreme values of h for the surface S. In order to evaluate this integral, it is necessary to express the length l in terms of h for the boundary of S. Hence:

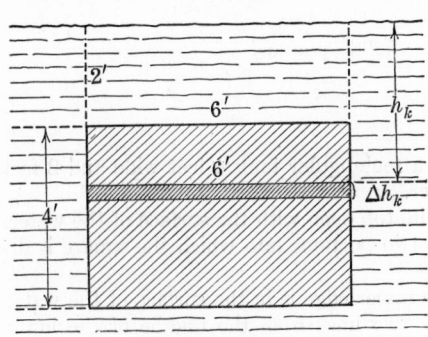

The force exerted by the liquid on the surface S is given by:

$$(12) \quad F = w \int_a^b lh\, dh,$$

where l is the width of S at depth h.

Fig. 108

EXAMPLE 1. A vertical floodgate in the form of a rectangle 6 feet long and 4 feet deep has its upper edge 2 feet below the surface of the water. Find the force which it must withstand. (Fig. 108.)

Solution: A typical rectangular strip of the floodgate surface has length $l_k = 6$, vertical width Δh_k and depth h_k, and to cover the gate h varies from 2 to 6. The required force is then

$$F = w \int_2^6 6\, h\, dh = 96\, w = 6000 \text{ pounds.}$$

EXAMPLE 2. A horizontal circular cylindrical tank of diameter 10 feet is half-full of water (Fig. 109). Find the force on one end.

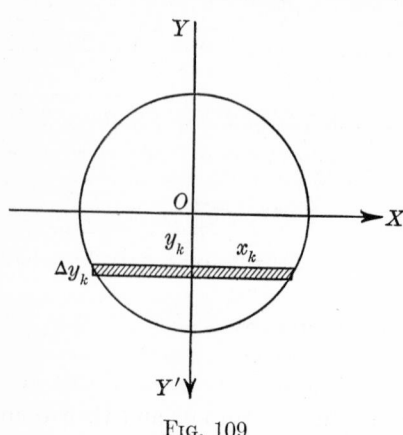

FIG. 109

Solution: If we take a set of rectangular axes as shown in Fig. 109, with the origin at the center of the circular end of the tank, with the positive Y-axis directed downward, the equation of the circle is $x^2 + y^2 = 25$. Let us take a horizontal rectangular element of area with ordinate y_k, width Δy_k and length $2\, x_k$. The force on this element is $w\, y_k\, (2\, x_k \cdot \Delta y_k)$, where

$$x_k = \sqrt{25 - y_k^2}.$$

The required force is then

$$F = w \int_0^5 2\, y\sqrt{25 - y^2}\, dy.$$

This integral may be evaluated by use of the power law, thus:

$$F = -w \int_0^5 (25 - y^2)^{\frac{1}{2}}(-2\, y\, dy) = -w \cdot \tfrac{2}{3}(25 - y^2)^{\frac{3}{2}}\Big|_0^5$$

$$= \frac{250}{3}\, w = 5208\tfrac{1}{3} \text{ pounds.}$$

200. Exercises

1. Find the force on one end of a rectangular tank 4 feet wide and 2 feet deep if the tank is full of water.

2. A floodgate 8 feet square has its top even with the surface of the water. Find the force on each of the two portions into which the square is divided by one of its diagonals.

3. A rectangular floodgate whose upper edge is in the surface of the water is divided into three parts by two lines from the middle of the lower edge to the extremities of the upper edge. Show that the parts sustain equal forces.

4. A rectangular gate 10 feet broad and 6 feet deep has its upper edge in the surface of the water; how far must it be sunk to double the force?

5. Find the force on one face of a square of side 4 feet if one diagonal is vertical and has its upper end in the surface of the water.

6. Find the force on the face of a vertical floodgate in the shape of an isosceles triangle whose base is 6 feet and whose altitude is 4 feet, if its base is in the surface of the water. [*Hint.* Use similar triangles to find the length of a horizontal strip.]

7. The ends of a trough are equilateral triangles of side 3 feet; find the force on one end, if the trough is full of water.

8. A vertical masonry dam in the form of an isosceles trapezoid is 200 feet long at the surface of the water, 150 feet long at the bottom and 60 feet high. What force must it withstand? Express the result in tons. [*Hint.* Use similar triangles.]

9. A horizontal circular cylindrical tank 8 feet in diameter is half-full of oil weighing 60 pounds per cubic foot. Find the force on one end.

10. A semi-circular gate of radius 6 feet is submerged in water with its diameter horizontal and at a depth of 10 feet, and with the semi-circular arc below the diameter. Find the force on the gate. [*Hint.* For the integration, use the power law and also formula (2) of § 181.]

201. Centroid of a Plane Area

The concept of the centroid of a plane area and of a solid plays an important part in mechanics.

In mechanics, if a mass m is at the distance d from an axis, the product md is called the *moment of the mass with respect to the axis*. By analogy with this, the following discussion is based on the idea that the moment of an *elementary area* with respect to an axis may be taken as the product of the area by the distance from the axis of some point in the area.

Consider a given region A in the XY-plane (Fig. 110) bounded above and below by smooth curves. Let us divide the region A into n strips by lines parallel to the Y-axis, and draw the approximating rectangles as in finding areas. Let the typical rectangle have the width Δx_k and length $h(\xi_k)$, where ξ_k is the abscissa of the midpoint of the sub-interval Δx_k, and let δ be the length of the longest sub-interval Δx_k. The area of this rectangle is $\Delta A_k = h(\xi_k)\Delta x_k$. Now form the product $\xi_k \cdot \Delta A_k$ of the area of the rectangle by the distance ξ_k from the Y-axis; then take the sum $\sum_{k=1}^{n} \xi_k \Delta A_k = \sum_{k=1}^{n} \xi_k h(\xi_k)\Delta x_k$ of all such products over the region A. This sum has a limit as $\delta \to 0$ which is the definite integral $\int_a^b x\, h(x)\, dx$, where a and b are the extreme values of x for the region A. We then have the following definition:

The expression

$$(13) \qquad M_y = \lim_{\delta \to 0} \sum_{k=1}^{n} \xi_k\, \Delta A_k = \int_a^b x\, h(x)\, dx$$

*is called the **first moment of the area A with respect to the Y-axis.***

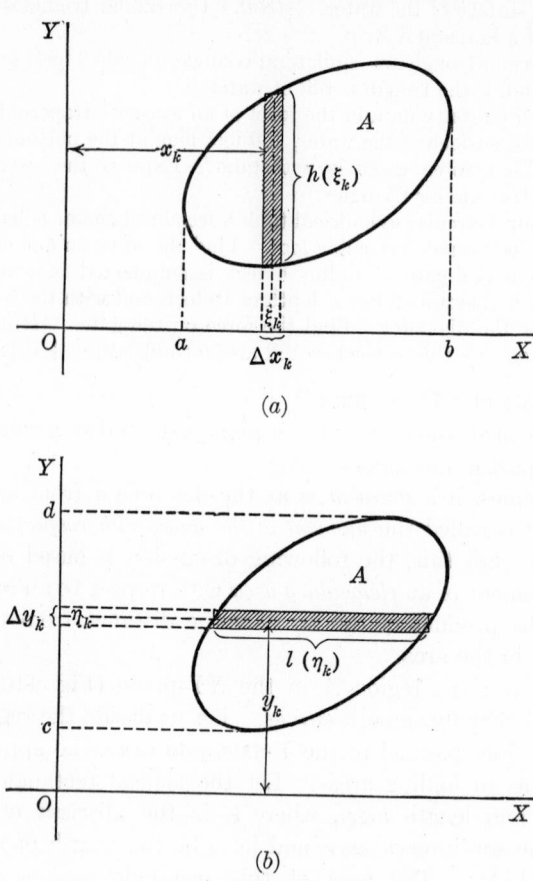

(a)

(b)

Fig. 110

In the integral (13), $h(x)$ must be expressed in terms of x from the equation or equations of the boundary of the region A.

In a similar way, we define the first moment of the area A with respect to the X-axis. We divide the region A into n strips by lines parallel to the X-axis and draw approximating rectangles. If the typical rectangle has a width Δy_k and length $l(\eta_k)$, where η_k is the ordinate of the mid-point of the sub-interval Δy_k, the area of the rectangle is $\Delta A_k = l(\eta_k)\Delta y_k$. We then form the sum

$\sum_{k=1}^{n} \eta_k \Delta A_k = \sum_{k=1}^{n} \eta_k l(\eta_k) \Delta y_k$, and take the limit as $\delta \to 0$, where δ is the length of the longest Δy_k. This limit is $\int_c^d y \, l(y) \, dy$, where c and d are the extreme values of y for the region A.

*We define the **first moment of the area A with respect to the X-axis** as:*

$$(14) \qquad M_x = \lim_{\delta \to 0} \sum_{k=1}^{n} \eta_k \, \Delta A_k = \int_c^d y \, l(y) \, dy.$$

The *area* of the region A is given by either of the expressions:

$$(15) \qquad A = \int_a^b h(x) \, dx = \int_c^d l(y) \, dy.$$

The centroid of the given region is now *defined* as follows:

The point $(\bar{x}, \bar{y})$ whose coördinates satisfy the relations

$$(16) \qquad A \, \bar{x} = M_y, \qquad A \, \bar{y} = M_x$$

*is called the **centroid** of the plane area A.**

The coördinates of the centroid of the area A are therefore given by:

$$(a) \qquad \bar{x} = \frac{\int_a^b x \, h(x) \, dx}{\int_a^b h(x) \, dx}, \qquad \bar{y} = \frac{\int_c^d y \, l(y) \, dy}{\int_c^d l(y) \, dy}.$$

It is shown in mechanics that the centroid of an area may be given a physical interpretation as follows: Let a piece of stiff flat cardboard be cut in form and size of the given region. If placed horizontally, the cardboard will balance if supported on a needle point at the centroid of the lower face.

EXAMPLE. Find the coördinates of the centroid of the region bounded by the curves $y^2 = x$ and $y = x^3$ (Fig. 111).

Solution: If we use strips parallel to the Y-axis as in Fig. 111 (a), the length $h(x)$ of the typical rectangle is the difference of the ordinates for the two curves for a given value of x, so that $h(x) = \sqrt{x} - x^3$. The curves intersect at the point $(1, 1)$. Then

---

* The centroid of a plane area is also sometimes called the *center of gravity*.

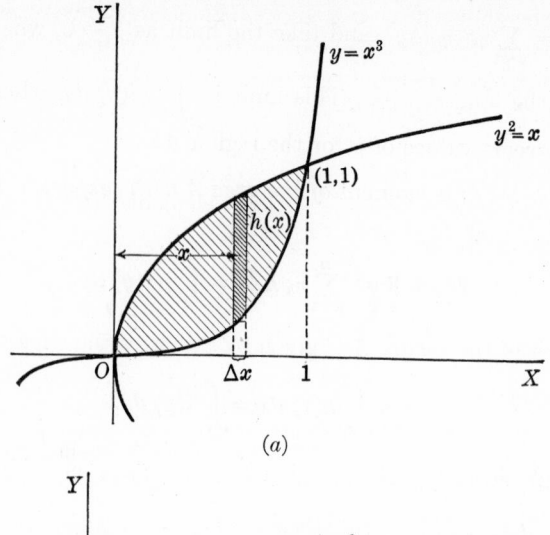

(a)

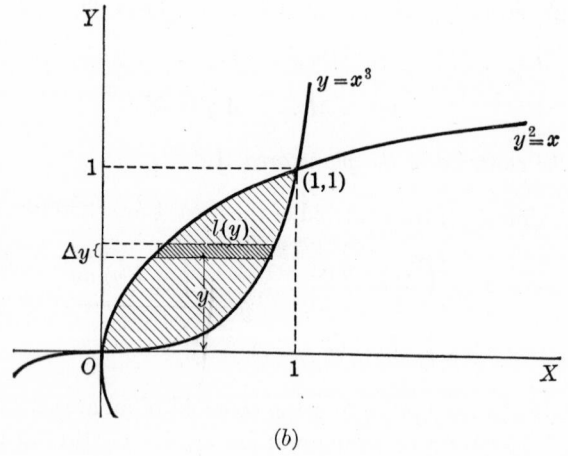

(b)

Fig. 111

$$M_y = \int_0^1 x(\sqrt{x} - x^3)\, dx = \tfrac{1}{5}, \qquad A = \int_0^1 (\sqrt{x} - x^3)\, dx = \tfrac{5}{12},$$

hence $\bar{x} = \tfrac{1}{5} \cdot \tfrac{12}{5} = \tfrac{12}{25}$.

Using strips parallel to the X-axis as in Fig. 111 (*b*), we have $l(y) = y^{\frac{1}{3}} - y^2$. Then

$$M_x = \int_0^1 y(y^{\frac{1}{3}} - y^2)\, dy = \tfrac{5}{28}, \qquad A = \tfrac{5}{12},$$

hence $\bar{y} = \tfrac{5}{28} \cdot \tfrac{12}{5} = \tfrac{3}{7}$. The centroid of the given region is therefore the point $(\tfrac{12}{25}, \tfrac{3}{7})$.

It can be shown that if a given region is symmetric with respect to any line in its plane, its centroid lies on this line. It follows that if the region has a center of symmetry, this point must be the centroid.

It is frequently desirable to find both moments M_x and M_y by using the same rectangular element for both calculations. It will be shown later (§ 529) that if the given region has the X-axis as one boundary and if we use a rectangular element parallel to the Y-axis, the moments M_y and M_x are given by

$$(b) \qquad M_y = \int_a^b xy\,dx, \qquad M_x = \tfrac{1}{2}\int_a^b y^2\,dx.$$

202. Exercises

Find the coördinates of the centroid of each of the regions described below.

1. The region bounded by the curve $y^2 = 4x$ and the line $x = 4$.
2. The region bounded by the curve $x^2 = 9y$ and the line $y = 2$.
3. The region bounded by a semi-circle of radius a and its diameter.
4. The region in the first quadrant bounded by the circle $x^2 + y^2 = a^2$.
5. The region in the first quadrant bounded by the ellipse $b^2x^2 + a^2y^2 = a^2b^2$.
6. The region of the loop of the curve $y^2 = 4x^2 - x^3$.
7. The region bounded by $y^2 = x$ and $x = 0$ and $y = 2$.
8. The region bounded by $x^2 + y^2 = a^2$, $x = a$ and $y = a$.
9. The smaller of the regions bounded by $x^2 + y^2 = 4$ and $y = 2 - x$.
10. The region between $y = 4 - x^2$ and $y = 4 - 2x$.
11. The region between the parabolas $y^2 = 4x + 4$ and $y^2 = -2x + 4$.
12. The region bounded by $y^2 = 4x$ and $2x - y = 4$.

203. Centroid of a Solid of Revolution

Suppose that the plane region $ABDC$ (Fig. 112), bounded by the curve $y = f(x)$, the X-axis and the lines $x = a$ and $x = b$, is revolved about the X-axis to generate a solid of revolution. We *define* the *centroid* of this solid as follows. Divide the interval (a, b) into n sub-intervals Δx_k, divide the solid into slices by planes perpendicular to the X-axis at the points of division, and construct the approximating cylindrical disks and denote the volume of the k-th disk by ΔV_k. Let the radius of the k-th disk be $y_k = f(\xi_k)$, then the volume of the disk is $\Delta V_k = \pi y_k^2 \Delta x_k$. Now form the product $\xi_k \cdot \Delta V_k$ of the volume of the typical disk by the distance ξ_k from the origin, and then take the sum $\sum_{k=1}^{n} \xi_k \Delta V_k = \sum_{k=1}^{n} \xi_k \cdot \pi y_k^2 \Delta x_k$ of all such products over the solid V.

As usual, let δ be the length of the longest Δx_k. The preceding sum

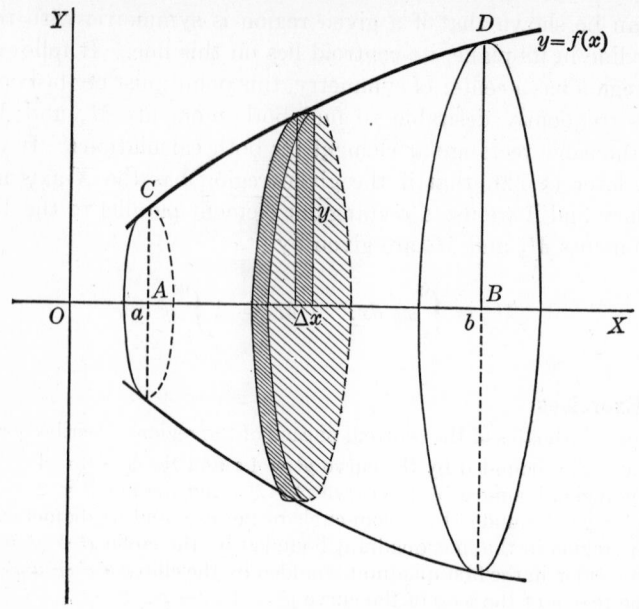

FIG. 112

has a limit as $\delta \rightarrow 0$ which is the definite integral $\int_a^b x \cdot \pi y^2 \, dx$.   We then have the following definition:

The expression

$$(17) \qquad M = \lim_{\delta \rightarrow 0} \sum_{k=1}^{n} \xi_k \cdot \Delta V_k = \pi \int_a^b xy^2 \, dx$$

*is called the **first moment of the solid of revolution with respect to a plane perpendicular to the X-axis through the origin.***

The *volume* of the solid is given by

$$(18) \qquad V = \pi \int_a^b y^2 \, dx.$$

*The **centroid** of the given solid of revolution is defined as the point on the X-axis whose abscissa is*

$$(19) \qquad \bar{x} = \frac{M}{V} = \frac{\int_a^b xy^2 \, dx}{\int_a^b y^2 \, dx}.$$

EXAMPLE. Locate the centroid of the solid hemisphere of radius a.

Solution: The hemisphere may be considered as generated by taking the circle of radius a with center at the origin and whose equation is $x^2 + y^2 = a^2$ and revolving about the X-axis the portion of this circle in the first quadrant. Since $y^2 = a^2 - x^2$ for this circle, we have

$$M = \pi \int_0^a xy^2 \, dx = \pi \int_0^a x(a^2 - x^2) \, dx = \tfrac{1}{4}\pi a^4,$$

$$V = \pi \int_0^a y^2 \, dx = \pi \int_0^a (a^2 - x^2) \, dx = \tfrac{2}{3}\pi a^3,$$

$$\therefore \ \bar{x} = \frac{\tfrac{1}{4}\pi a^4}{\tfrac{2}{3}\pi a^3} = \tfrac{3}{8}\,a.$$

The centroid therefore lies on the axis of symmetry of the hemisphere, at a distance $\tfrac{3}{8}\,a$ from the center.

204. Exercises

1. Find the coördinates of the centroid of a right circular cone of altitude h and radius of base a.
2. The radii of the upper and lower bases of a frustum of a cone of revolution are, respectively, 3 inches and 6 inches, and the altitude is 8 inches. Locate its centroid.
3. Locate the centroid of the solid generated by revolving about the X-axis the region bounded by the parabola $y^2 = 4\,ax$ and the line $x = 2\,a$.
4. Find the centroid of a spherical segment of one base with height h of a sphere of radius a.
5. Locate the centroid of the solid formed by revolving about the X-axis that part of the area of the ellipse $b^2x^2 + a^2y^2 = a^2b^2$ which lies in the first quadrant.
6. Find the centroid of the solid generated by revolving about the X-axis the region in the first quadrant bounded by the curve $b^2x^2 - a^2y^2 = a^2b^2$, the X-axis and the line $x = 2\,a$.
7. The region bounded by the curve $y = 1/x^2$, and the lines $y = 0$, $x = 1$ and $x = 2$ is revolved about the X-axis. Find the centroid of the solid generated.
8. The first quadrant region bounded by the curve $x^{\frac{2}{3}} + y^{\frac{2}{3}} = a^{\frac{2}{3}}$ and the coördinate axes is revolved about the X-axis. Locate the centroid of the solid formed.
9. Find the centroid of the solid formed by revolving about the Y-axis the region in the first quadrant bounded by the parabola $y^2 = 4\,ax$ and the lines $y = 0$ and $x = a$.
10. Find the centroid of the solid generated by revolving about the Y-axis the region in the first quadrant bounded by the hyperbola $x^2 - y^2 = a^2$, the X-axis and the line $x = 2\,a$.
11. The region bounded by the curve $y = x^2$, the X-axis and the line $x = 1$ is revolved about the line $x = 1$; find the centroid of the solid generated.

12. The region bounded by $x = y^3$, $y = 2$ and $x = 0$ is revolved about the line $y = 2$; find the centroid of the solid formed.

205. Second Moment of a Plane Area

Another important concept of mechanics which is similar to the first moment is that of the second moment or moment of inertia of a plane area or of a solid. The second moment differs essentially from the first moment in using the second power of a distance instead of the first power (which accounts for the names).

Consider the region A of Fig. 110 which was used in § 201. As before, let us take the vertical rectangular element of area ΔA_k of width Δx_k and height $h(\xi_k)$, and let δ be the length of the longest Δx_k. Form the product $\xi_k^2 \cdot \Delta A_k$, using the *square* of the abscissa ξ_k, and form the sum $\sum_{k=1}^{n} \xi_k^2 \Delta A_k = \sum_{k=1}^{n} \xi_k^2 h(\xi_k) \Delta x_k$ of all such products over the region A. This sum has a limit as $\delta \to 0$ which is the definite integral $\int_a^b x^2 \, h(x) \, dx$, where a and b are the extreme values of x for the region A.

The expression

$$(20) \qquad I_y = \lim_{\delta \to 0} \sum_{k=1}^{n} \xi_k^2 \Delta A_k = \int_a^b x^2 \, h(x) \, dx$$

*is called the **second moment** (or moment of inertia) **of the area A with respect to the Y-axis.***

In a similar way, *we define the **second moment** (or moment of inertia) **of the area A with respect to the X-axis as***

$$(21) \qquad I_x = \lim_{\delta \to 0} \sum_{k=1}^{n} \eta_k^2 \Delta A_k = \int_c^d y^2 \, l(y) \, dy,$$

where $l(y)$ is the length of a horizontal rectangular element of area, and c and d are the extreme values of y for the region A.

EXAMPLE 1. Find the second moment with respect to both axes of the region in the first quadrant bounded by the curve $y = 4 - x^2$ and the coördinate axes (Fig. 113).

Solution: For the vertical element of area (Fig. 113 (a)), $h(x) = y$, so that

$$I_v = \int_0^2 x^2 y \, dx = \int_0^2 x^2(4 - x^2) \, dx = \tfrac{64}{15}.$$

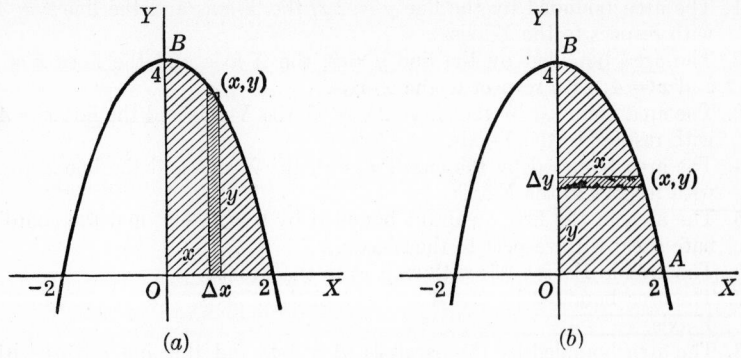

Fig. 113

For the horizontal element of area (Fig. 113 (b)), $l(y) = x$, therefore

$$I_x = \int_0^4 y^2 x \, dy = \int_0^4 y^2 (4 - y)^{\frac{1}{2}} \, dy = \tfrac{2\,0\,4\,8}{1\,0\,5}.$$

It is possible to find both moments I_x and I_y by use of the same rectangular element of area. It will be shown later (§ 530) that for a plane region having the X-axis as one boundary the moment I_x is given by

(a) $$I_x = \tfrac{1}{3} \int_a^b y^3 \, dx.$$

If A is the area of the given region and if I is its second moment with respect to an axis, the positive number R such that $R^2 A = I$ is called the *radius of gyration of the area with respect to the given axis*. If the entire area were thought of as concentrated at the distance R from the axis, its moment of inertia would be still equal to the actual moment I.

EXAMPLE 2. Find the radius of gyration of the area of Example 1 with respect to the Y-axis.

Solution: The area of the region in Example 1 is

$$A = \int_0^2 y \, dx = \int_0^2 (4 - x^2) \, dx = \tfrac{16}{3}.$$

By Example 1, $I_y = \dfrac{64}{15}$; then $R_y{}^2 = \dfrac{I_y}{A} = \dfrac{64}{15} \cdot \dfrac{3}{16} = \dfrac{4}{5}$, and $R_y = \dfrac{2}{5}\sqrt{5}$.

206. Exercises

In each of the following problems, find the second moment and the radius of gyration of the given area with respect to the axis indicated.

1. The area bounded by the line $y = 2x$, the X-axis and the line $x = 4$: with respect to the Y-axis.
2. The area bounded by the line $y = x$, the X-axis and the lines $x = 1$ and $x = 4$: with respect to the Y-axis.
3. The area bounded by the curve $2y = x^2$, the X-axis and the line $x = 4$: with respect to the Y-axis.
4. The area bounded by the curve $y = x^3$, the X-axis and the line $x = 2$: with respect to the Y-axis.
5. The area in the first quadrant bounded by $y = 1 - x^2$ and the coördinate axes: with respect to the X-axis.
6. The area in Exercise 5: with respect to the Y-axis.
7. The area bounded by $y = 4x - x^2$ and the X-axis: with respect to the Y-axis.
8. The area bounded by the parabola $y^2 = 4ax$ and the line $x = a$: with respect to the Y-axis.
9. The area between $y^2 = 4x$ and $y = x$: with respect to the X-axis.
10. The area between $y = x^2$ and $y = 2x$: with respect to the Y-axis.
11. The area bounded by $y^2 = 4x$ and $x = 4$: with respect to the line $x = 4$.
12. The area bounded by the parabola $y^2 = 4x$ and the line $x + y = 3$: with respect to the X-axis.
13. Find the second moment of the area of Exercise 1 with respect to the X-axis, by use of formula (a) of § 205.
14. Find the second moment of the area of Exercise 3 with respect to the X-axis, by use of formula (a) of § 205.

207. Second Moment or Moment of Inertia of a Solid of Revolution

Let the plane region $ABDC$ of Fig. 114, bounded by the curve $y = f(x)$, the X-axis and the lines $x = a$ and $x = b$, be revolved about

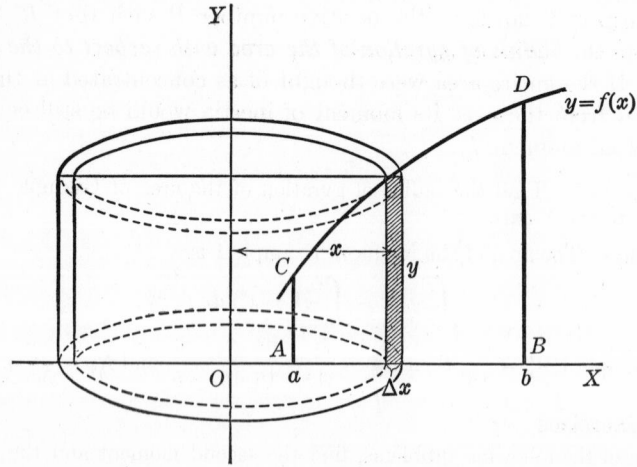

Fig. 114

the Y-axis, to generate a solid of revolution. Divide the solid into elementary cylindrical shells, of which a typical one has thickness Δx_k, radius ξ_k, height $y_k = f(\xi_k)$ and volume $\Delta V_k = 2\,\pi\xi_k y_k \Delta x_k$. Form the product $\xi_k^2 \cdot \Delta V_k$, using the square of the distance ξ_k, and form the sum $\sum_{k=1}^{n} \xi_k^2 \Delta V_k = \sum_{k=1}^{n} \xi_k^2 \cdot 2\,\pi\xi_k y_k \Delta x_k = \sum_{k=1}^{n} 2\,\pi\xi_k^3 y_k \Delta x_k$. If δ is the length of the longest Δx_k, this sum has as limit when $\delta \to 0$ the definite integral $\int_a^b 2\,\pi x^3 y\,dx$.

We define the **second moment** *or* **moment of inertia** *of the solid of revolution* **with respect to its axis of revolution** *as*

$$(22) \qquad I = \lim_{\delta \to 0}\ \sum_{k=1}^{n} \xi_k^2 \Delta V_k = 2\pi \int_a^b x^3 y\,dx.$$

The **radius of gyration** of the solid of revolution **with respect to its axis of revolution** is defined as the positive number R such that $R^2 \cdot V = I$, where V is the volume of the solid.

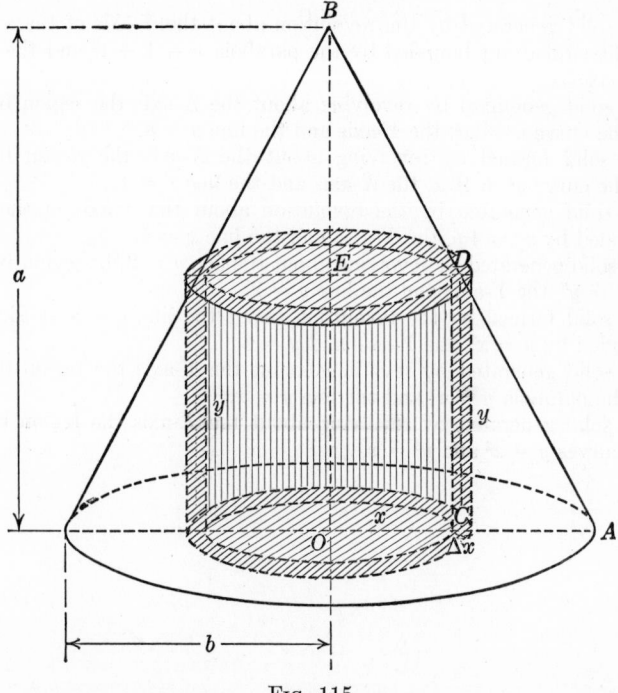

F<small>IG</small>. 115

EXAMPLE. Find the moment of inertia of a right circular cone of altitude a and radius of base b with respect to its axis; also find its radius of gyration with respect to its axis.

Solution: Place the cone as in Fig. 115, with its axis along the Y-axis, and the center of its base at the origin. The lateral surface of the cone may be thought of as generated by revolving the line AB (in the XY-plane) about the Y-axis. The equation of the line AB is $y = \dfrac{a}{b}(b - x)$. (This relation between x and y could also be obtained from the figure by use of similar triangles). By definition,

$$I = 2\pi \cdot \frac{a}{b} \int_a^b x^3(b - x)\, dx = \frac{1}{10}\pi a b^4.$$

The volume V of the cone is $\frac{1}{3}\pi b^2 a$; the radius of gyration R is determined by $R^2 V = I$, or $R^2 = \dfrac{\frac{1}{10}\pi a b^4}{\frac{1}{3}\pi a b^2} = \dfrac{3}{10}b^2$, whence $R = \dfrac{1}{10}\sqrt{30}\, b$.

208. Exercises

In each of the following problems, find the moment of inertia and the radius of gyration of the given solid of revolution with respect to the axis of revolution.

1. The solid generated by the revolution about the Y-axis of the region in the first quadrant bounded by the parabola $y = 1 - x^2$ and the coördinate axes.

2. The solid generated by revolving about the X-axis the region bounded by the curve $y^2 = x^3$, the Y-axis and the line $y = 8$.

3. The solid formed by revolving about the X-axis the region bounded by the curve $y^2 = 16\,x$, the X-axis and the line $x = 4$.

4. The solid generated by the revolution about the X-axis of the region bounded by $x^2 = 4\,y$, the X-axis and the line $x = 4$.

5. The solid generated by revolving about the line $y = 2$ the region bounded by $x = y^3$, the Y-axis and the line $y = 2$.

6. The solid formed by the revolution about the line $y = 8$ of the region bounded by $y = x^3$, the Y-axis and $y = 8$.

7. The solid generated by revolving about the Y-axis the region bounded by the parabola $y = x^2$ and the line $y = x$.

8. The solid generated by revolving about the X-axis the region between the curves $y = x^2$ and $y^2 = x$.

CHAPTER XII

Circles, Parabolas, Ellipses and Hyperbolas

209. Standard Form of the Equation of a Circle

In order to be able to study the circle by the method of analytic geometry, we need the equation of the circle as a locus. Let $P(x, y)$ be *any* point on the circle with center at $C(h, k)$ and radius r (Fig. 116).

By definition, $CP = r$ or $(CP)^2 = r^2$. Writing out the expression for $(CP)^2$ by the distance formula, we have

(a) $(x - h)^2 + (y - k)^2 = r^2$.

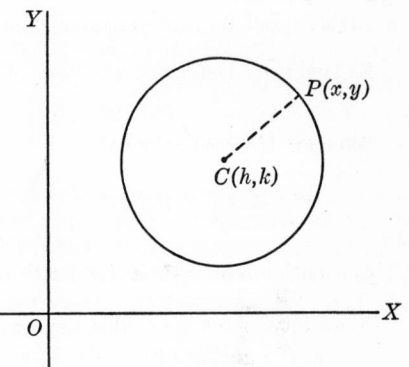

The coördinates x, y of any point P on the circle therefore satisfy equation (a). Conversely, if the coördinates of any point $P(x, y)$ satisfy the equation (a), then $CP = r$; the point P therefore lies on the circle with center C and radius r. Hence:

Fig. 116

The equation of the circle whose center is at (h, k) and whose radius is r is:

(1) $$(x - h)^2 + (y - k)^2 = r^2.$$

This is called the **standard equation** of a circle.

An important special case occurs when the center is at the origin, in which case $h = 0$ and $k = 0$; this gives the equation

(b) $$x^2 + y^2 = r^2.$$

EXAMPLE. The circle with center at $(2, -3)$ and radius 4 has the equation

$$(x - 2)^2 + (y + 3)^2 = 16, \quad \text{or} \quad x^2 + y^2 - 4x + 6y - 3 = 0.$$

210. General Form of the Equation of a Circle

If we expand the standard form $(x - h)^2 + (y - k)^2 = r^2$ of a circle, we obtain

(a) $$x^2 + y^2 - 2\,hx - 2\,ky + h^2 + k^2 - r^2 = 0.$$

This is of the form

(b) $$x^2 + y^2 + Dx + Ey + F = 0,$$

where $D = -2\,h$, $E = -2\,k$, $F = h^2 + k^2 - r^2$. Hence:

The equation of any circle can be written in the form

(2) $$x^2 + y^2 + Dx + Ey + F = 0.$$

This is often called the **general form** *of the equation of a circle.*

The question arises: does every equation of the form (2) represent a circle? Let us first consider a particular case.

EXAMPLE 1. Determine the locus of the equation

$$x^2 + y^2 - 8\,x + 6\,y - 11 = 0.$$

Solution: If we complete the squares of the terms in x and of those in y, we get

$$(x^2 - 8\,x + 16) + (y^2 + 6\,y + 9) = 11 + 16 + 9 = 36,$$

or $$(x - 4)^2 + (y + 3)^2 = 6^2.$$

This equation represents a circle with center at $(4, -3)$ and radius 6.

Now let us consider the general case. We complete squares in equation (2) and obtain

(c) $$(x + \tfrac{1}{2}\,D)^2 + (y + \tfrac{1}{2}\,E)^2 = \tfrac{1}{4}(D^2 + E^2 - 4\,F).$$

By comparison with the standard form (1), we see that:

The equation (2) represents a circle with center at $(-\tfrac{1}{2}\,D, -\tfrac{1}{2}\,E)$ and radius $\tfrac{1}{2}\sqrt{D^2 + E^2 - 4\,F}$, provided $D^2 + E^2 - 4\,F$ is positive.

However, if $D^2 + E^2 - 4\,F = 0$, equation (c) and therefore (2) is satisfied by the coördinates of only one point $(-\tfrac{1}{2}\,D, -\tfrac{1}{2}\,E)$; in this case, the equation (2) is sometimes said to represent a point-circle, at $(-\tfrac{1}{2}\,D, -\tfrac{1}{2}\,E)$. If $D^2 + E^2 - 4\,F$ is negative, equation (c) or (2) is not satisfied by the coördinates of any point, since the left-hand side is always positive or zero; in this case, equation (2) has no locus.

It should be noted that the equation of any circle is an equation of the second degree in x and y.

211. Exercises

1. Write the equation of each of the following circles:
   (a) center $(0, 0)$, radius 5;   (b) center $(4, 2)$, radius 6;
   (c) center $(5, -2)$, radius 4;   (d) center $(-6, -3)$, radius 1.

2. Write the equation of each of the following circles:
   (a) center $(2, 3)$, radius 2;   (b) center $(0, 0)$, radius 4;
   (c) center $(1, -3)$, radius 5;   (d) center $(-2, -5)$, radius 8.

3. Find the equation of the circle whose center is at the origin and which passes through the point $(-2, 3)$.

4. Find the equation of the circle whose center is at $(2, 1)$ and which passes through the point $(5, -4)$.

5. Find the equation of the circle of radius 5 which touches the X-axis at the origin.

6. Find the equation of the circle with center at $(4, 5)$ which is tangent to the X-axis.

7. Find the equation of the circle having the line-segment from $(-3, 4)$ to $(1, -2)$ as a diameter.

8. The points $(6, 3)$ and $(-2, 1)$ are ends of a diameter of a circle; find the equation of the circle.

9. Reduce each of the following equations to the standard form of the equation of a circle, and find the coördinates of the center and the radius of the circle:
   (a) $x^2 + y^2 - 8x + 10y + 5 = 0$; (b) $x^2 + y^2 + 16x + 30y = 0$;
   (c) $x^2 + y^2 - 6x - 7 = 0$;   (d) $3x^2 + 3y^2 + 4x - 10y - 7 = 0$.

10. Find the center and radius of each of the circles whose equations are:
    (a) $x^2 + y^2 + 4x - 6y - 12 = 0$; (b) $x^2 + y^2 - 2x - 8y = 0$;
    (c) $x^2 + y^2 + 10y + 9 = 0$;   (d) $8x^2 + 8y^2 + 12x - 28y - 3 = 0$.

11. Discuss the locus of each of the following equations:
    (a) $x^2 + y^2 - 2x + 2y + 2 = 0$; (b) $x^2 + y^2 + 10x - 2y + 42 = 0$.

12. Discuss the locus of each of the following equations:
    (a) $x^2 + y^2 - 6x + 12y + 49 = 0$; (b) $x^2 + y^2 - 10x + 25 = 0$.

13. Find the coördinates of the points at which each of the coördinate axes is cut by the circle $x^2 + y^2 - 4x - 6y + 3 = 0$.

14. Show that the circle $x^2 + y^2 - 8x + 4y + 4 = 0$ touches the Y-axis and cuts the X-axis in two distinct points.

15. Find the coördinates of the points of intersection of the line $x - y - 1 = 0$ and the circle $x^2 + y^2 - x - 3y = 0$.

16. Find the points of intersection of the circles $x^2 + y^2 - 7x - 2y + 7 = 0$ and $3x^2 + 3y^2 - 7x + y = 0$.

17. Find the equations of the tangent and normal to each of the following circles at the point indicated:

(a) $x^2 + y^2 = 25$, at $(-4, 3)$;

(b) $x^2 + y^2 - 6x + 4y - 4 = 0$, at $(2, 2)$.

18. Proceed as in Exercise 17 with:

(a) $x^2 + y^2 = 169$, at $(5, -12)$;

(b) $(x - 2)^2 + (y - 3)^2 = 5$, at $(4, 4)$.

19. Show that the line $3x + 4y + 25 = 0$ is tangent to the circle $x^2 + y^2 = 25$, and find the coördinates of the point of tangency.

20. Find the equations of the tangents to the circle $x^2 + y^2 = 16$ which are perpendicular to the line $x + 2y = 2$.

21. Find the angles of intersection of the line $x - 2y - 8 = 0$ and the circle $x^2 + y^2 - 12y - 64 = 0$.

22. Show that the circles

$$x^2 + y^2 + 2x - 4y = 0 \text{ and } x^2 + y^2 - 4x - 6y + 8 = 0$$

intersect orthogonally (i.e., at right angles).

212. Circles Satisfying Three Conditions

The equation of a circle contains three arbitrary constants, h, k and r in the standard form, and D, E and F in the general form. We can therefore make a circle satisfy certain given geometrical conditions; and since there are three independent constants, we may in general impose three conditions on the circle. For example, a circle may be determined by three given points (not in the same straight line), or by being made to pass through two given points and have its center on a given line.

EXAMPLE 1. Find the equation of the circle which passes through the three points $(0, 3)$, $(-4, 3)$ and $(-3, 4)$.

Solution: Let the equation of the circle be assumed to be of the form $x^2 + y^2 + Dx + Ey + F = 0$. Since each of the given points is to lie on this circle, their coördinates must satisfy this equation. Then we have

$$(a) \quad \begin{cases} 9 + 3E + F = 0 \\ 16 + 9 - 4D + 3E + F = 0 \\ 9 + 16 - 3D + 4E + F = 0 \end{cases} \text{ or } \begin{cases} 3E + F = -9 \\ -4D + 3E + F = -25 \\ -3D + 4E + F = -25. \end{cases}$$

Solving these equations for D, E and F, we find $D = 4$, $E = -4$ and $F = 3$. Then the required equation is $x^2 + y^2 + 4x - 4y + 3 = 0$.

EXAMPLE 2. Find the equation of the circle which goes through the point $(-5, 3)$, is tangent to the X-axis, and has its center on the line $x + y = 1$.

Solution: Let the equation of the circle be $(x - h)^2 + (y - k)^2 = r^2$. Since the circle touches the X-axis, we have

$$(b) \qquad\qquad\qquad k = r.$$

Since the center (h, k) lies on the line $x + y = 1$, we have

$$(c) \qquad\qquad\qquad h + k = 1.$$

Using the fact that the point $(-5, 3)$ lies on the circle, we get

(d) $$(-5 - h)^2 + (3 - k)^2 = r^2.$$

We need to solve equations (b), (c) and (d) for the unknowns h, k and r. From (c), we have $k = 1 - h$; from (b), $r = k = 1 - h$. Substituting these values of k and r in terms of h in (d), we obtain

(e) $$h^2 + 16\,h + 28 = 0,$$

from which we find $h = -2$ or -14. For $h = -2$, we get $k = 3$, $r = 3$; and for $h = -14$, we get $k = 15$, $r = 15$. Therefore, there are two solutions of the problem; the required equation of the circle is either

$$(x + 2)^2 + (y - 3)^2 = 9 \qquad \text{or} \qquad (x + 14)^2 + (y - 15)^2 = 225.$$

213. Exercises

1. Find the equation of the circle through each of the following sets of points:
   (a) $(3, -2)$, $(-1, -4)$, $(2, -5)$; (b) $(-2, -2)$, $(4, 6)$, $(-4, 2)$;
   (c) $(3, 1)$, $(6, 0)$, $(-1, -7)$.

2. Find the equation of the circle through each of the following sets of points:
   (a) $(3, 1)$, $(2, 2)$, $(-5, -5)$; (b) $(0, 0)$, $(3, 1)$, $(-2, -4)$;
   (c) $(2, 8)$, $(7, 3)$, $(5, 7)$.

3. Find the equation of the circle satisfying the following conditions:
   (a) center at $(4, -3)$, passing through the point $(1, 2)$;
   (b) passing through $(1, 5)$ and $(4, 6)$, center on the line $x - y - 4 = 0$;
   (c) passing through the points $(-3, 0)$ and $(5, 6)$, with radius $5\sqrt{2}$;
   (d) tangent to the line $3\,x + 2\,y = 16$, passing through $(1, 0)$ and $(-3, 6)$.

4. Find the equation of the circle satisfying the following conditions:
   (a) center at $(-2, 3)$, passing through the origin;
   (b) passing through $(-2, 0)$ and $(3, 5)$, with radius 4;
   (c) center on the line $2\,x - 3\,y = 20$, passing through $(-4, -2)$ and $(6, 4)$;
   (d) through the points $(1, -3)$ and $(2, -2)$, tangent to the line $3\,x - 4\,y - 15 = 0$.

5. Find the equation of the circle satisfying the following conditions:
   (a) center at $(-1, 4)$, tangent to $5\,x + 12\,y + 9 = 0$;
   (b) tangent to both axes, with radius 5 (in the first quadrant);
   (c) tangent to $3\,x + 2\,y + 7 = 0$ at $(-1, -2)$, center on the line $8\,x - 5\,y + 5 = 0$;
   (d) concentric with the circle $x^2 + y^2 - 3\,x - 7\,y + 2 = 0$, passing through $(5, 8)$.

6. Find the equation of the circle satisfying the following conditions:
   (a) tangent to the X-axis, radius 6, center on the line $x = 4$;
   (b) tangent to both axes, passing through $(-4, -3)$;
   (c) center on the Y-axis, passing through $(3, -1)$ and $(3, 7)$;
   (d) concentric with $x^2 + y^2 - 10\,x + 4\,y - 20 = 0$, tangent to $x + 2\,y + 9 = 0$.

7. Find the equation of the circle with center on the line $y = 5x$, tangent to the X-axis and passing through the point $(4, 1)$.

★ 214. Systems of Circles

When the general equation of a circle contains an arbitrary constant, we obtain a **system** (or family) **of circles;** the constant is called the **parameter** of the system.

EXAMPLE 1.   The equation $x^2 + y^2 = r^2$ represents the system of concentric circles with center at the origin and with different radii r.

EXAMPLE 2.   Consider the system of circles represented by the equation $x^2 + y^2 - 2ax = 0$, where a is a parameter.   If we transform this to the equivalent form $(x - a)^2 + y^2 = a^2$ by completing the square, we see that it represents the set of all circles with centers on the X-axis and passing through the origin (Fig. 117).   Similarly we may see that the equation $x^2 + y^2 - 2by = 0$ represents the system of all circles with centers on the Y-axis and passing through the origin.

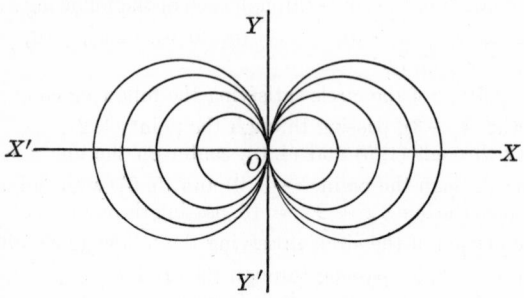

Fig. 117

EXAMPLE 3.   Find the equation of the system of circles that pass through the points $(2, 0)$ and $(-2, 0)$.

Solution: From symmetry it is evident that the center of each such circle is on the Y-axis.   Taking the coördinates of its center as $(0, k)$ and its radius as r, we can write its equation as $x^2 + (y - k)^2 = r^2$.   If this is to be satisfied by the coördinates $(2, 0)$ or $(-2, 0)$, we have $4 + k^2 = r^2$.   Therefore, the required equation is

$$x^2 + y^2 - 2ky + k^2 = 4 + k^2, \qquad \text{or} \qquad x^2 + y^2 - 2ky = 4.$$

★ 215. Exercises

1. Describe the system of circles represented by each of the following equations, where p is the variable parameter, and draw four circles of each system:

  (a) $(x - 3)^2 + (y - 2)^2 = p^2$;   (b) $(x - p)^2 + (y - 2)^2 = 9$;
  (c) $x^2 + y^2 + px - 4y = 0$;   (d) $x^2 + y^2 - 2px - 2py + p^2 = 0$.

2. Describe the system of circles represented by each of the following equations, where p is the variable parameter, and draw four circles of each system:

(a) $x^2 + y^2 = p^2 + 4$;   (b) $(x - 3)^2 + (y - p)^2 = 16$;
(c) $x^2 + y^2 + 2x + py = 0$;   (d) $x^2 + y^2 + px + py = 0$.

3. Find the equation of each of the following systems of circles:

(a) center at $(-2, 3)$;
(b) center on the line $y = 2x$, through the origin.

4. Find the equation of each of the following systems of circles:

(a) tangent to the lines $y = \pm 4$;
(b) center on $y = 3x$, tangent to the Y-axis.

5. Find the equation of the system of circles passing through the points $(3, 0)$ and $(-3, 0)$. Draw five circles of this system.

6. Describe the system of circles represented by $x^2 + y^2 + ax + by = 0$, where a and b are independent parameters.

7. Prove that each circle of the system $x^2 + y^2 + Dx = 0$ intersects each circle of the system $x^2 + y^2 + Ey = 0$ orthogonally.

★ 216. Analytical Proofs and Locus Problems Involving Circles

EXAMPLE 1. Prove analytically that an angle inscribed in a semicircle is a right angle.

Solution: Let the circle be placed with its center at the origin (Fig. 118), and let its radius be a. Let $P(x, y)$ be any point on the circle, and join it to the points $A(a, 0)$ and $A'(-a, 0)$.

Then the theorem will be proved if we show that PA is perpendicular to PA'. The equation of the circle is

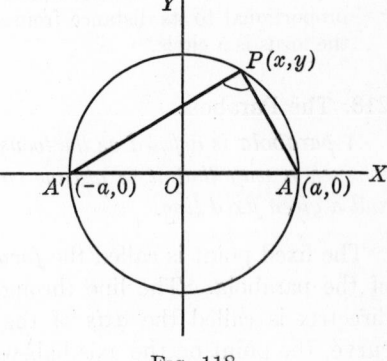

(a) $$x^2 + y^2 = a^2.$$

The slope of PA is $m_1 = \dfrac{y}{x - a}$ and the slope of PA' is

$$m_2 = \frac{y}{x + a}; \text{ then}$$

$$m_1 m_2 = \frac{y^2}{x^2 - a^2} = -1,$$

FIG. 118

since $y^2 = a^2 - x^2$ from (a).

Hence, PA is perpendicular to PA', since the product of their slopes is -1.

EXAMPLE 2. Find the equation of the locus of a point which moves so that the sum of the squares of its distances from the points $(3, 2)$ and $(-4, -1)$ is always equal to 14.

Solution: Let $P(x, y)$ be any point on the locus. Then

$$[(x - 3)^2 + (y - 2)^2] + [(x + 4)^2 + (y + 1)^2] = 14;$$

when simplified, this reduces to $x^2 + y^2 + x - y + 8 = 0$. The locus is therefore a circle with center at $(-\frac{1}{2}, \frac{1}{2})$ and radius $\frac{1}{2}\sqrt{122}$.

★ 217. Exercises

1. Prove analytically, without the use of slopes, that any angle inscribed in a semicircle is a right angle. [*Hint.* Use § 9.]
2. Prove analytically that all angles inscribed in the same segment of a circle are equal. [*Hint.* Let the ends of the segment be (a, b) and $(-a, b)$; prove that the tangent of the inscribed angle is constant.]
3. Prove analytically that a radius of a circle perpendicular to a chord bisects the chord.
4. Prove analytically that the line from the center of a circle bisecting a chord is perpendicular to it.
5. Prove analytically that the sum of the squares of the distances of any point on a circle from the ends of any diameter is a constant.
6. Prove analytically that a straight line cannot cut a circle in more than two points.
7. Find the equation of the locus of a point which moves so that the sum of the squares of its distances from $(3, 0)$ and $(-3, 0)$ is always 68.
8. A point moves so that its distances from $(3, 4)$ and $(-2, -3)$ are always in the ratio 2 to 3. Find the equation of the locus of this point.
9. A point moves so that its distance from the Y-axis is always four times the square of its distance from the point $(-2, 3)$. Find the equation of the locus of this point.
10. A point moves so that the square of its distance from a fixed point is proportional to its distance from a fixed line. Prove analytically that the locus is a circle.

218. The Parabola

*A **parabola** is defined as the locus of a point which moves in a plane in such a way that it is always equidistant from a given fixed point and a given fixed line.*

The fixed point is called the ***focus,*** and the fixed line the ***directrix*** of the parabola. The line through the focus perpendicular to the directrix is called the ***axis*** of the parabola. By definition of the curve, the point on the axis half-way between the focus and the directrix lies on the locus; it is called the ***vertex*** of the parabola.

219. Standard Form of the Equation of a Parabola

In Fig. 119, let F be the focus and DD' the directrix of a parabola. The figure shows the case where the focus is to the right and not to the left of the directrix. Let A be the point of intersection of the directrix and the axis of the parabola. To take care of both cases just mentioned at the same time, we shall denote the *directed distance* $\overline{AF}$ *from* the directrix *to* the focus by p, so that p is positive when F is to the right of DD' and p is negative when F is to the left of DD'. The following results apply equally to both cases.

To derive the equation of the parabola, we take the axis of the curve as the X-axis and the vertex as the origin (Fig. 119). This location of the axes gives the simplest form of the equation. Since the vertex is midway between the focus and the directrix, the coördinates of the focus F are $(\tfrac{1}{2} p, 0)$, and the equation of the directrix DD' is $x = -\tfrac{1}{2} p$.

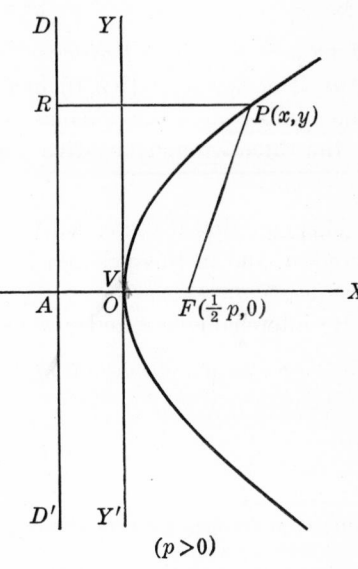

$(p > 0)$

Fig. 119

Let $P(x, y)$ be any point on the parabola, and let R be the foot of the perpendicular from P to DD'. The coördinates of R are $(-\tfrac{1}{2} p, y)$. By the definition of the parabola,

(a) $$FP = RP,$$
or $$(FP)^2 = (RP)^2.$$

By the distance formula,

$$(FP)^2 = (x - \tfrac{1}{2} p)^2 + (y - 0)^2, \qquad (RP)^2 = (x + \tfrac{1}{2} p)^2.$$

Equation (a) then becomes

(b) $$(x - \tfrac{1}{2} p)^2 + y^2 = (x + \tfrac{1}{2} p)^2,$$

which reduces to

(c) $$y^2 = 2 px.$$

Therefore, the coördinates of any point on the parabola satisfy the equation (c).

Conversely, if P is any point whose coördinates satisfy the equation (c), by adding $(x - \tfrac{1}{2} p)^2$ to both members of (c) and simplifying, we obtain (b) and (a). Therefore, $FP = RP$, and the point P lies on the parabola. Hence:

If the vertex is at the origin and the focus is on the X-axis, the equation of a parabola is

$$(3) \qquad\qquad y^2 = 2\,px,$$

where p is the directed distance from the directrix to the focus. The focus is at the point $(\frac{1}{2}\,p, 0)$ *and the directrix is the line* $x = -\frac{1}{2}\,p$. The number p is to be taken as positive when the focus is to the right of the directrix and negative when the focus is to the left of the directrix.

This equation (3) is called the **standard form** *of the equation of a parabola,* and in this position the parabola is said to be in *standard position.*

By interchanging x and y, we see that:

If the vertex of a parabola is at the origin and the focus is on the Y-axis, its equation is

$$(4) \qquad\qquad x^2 = 2\,py,$$

where p is the directed distance from the directrix to the focus. The focus is at $(0, \frac{1}{2}\,p)$ *and the directrix is* $y = -\frac{1}{2}\,p$.

The student should draw the figures when $p > 0$ and when $p < 0$.

220. Discussion of the Parabola

To obtain some properties of the parabola, we discuss the equation

$$(a) \qquad\qquad y^2 = 2\,px$$

by the methods of § 45. We consider the case where p is positive.

(1) *Symmetry:* The curve is symmetric with respect to the X-axis, the axis of the parabola, but is not symmetric with respect to the Y-axis nor to the origin.

(2) *Intercepts:* If $x = 0$, then $y = 0$, and conversely; therefore the curve meets either axis only at the vertex.

(3) *Extent:* Since $y = \pm\sqrt{2\,px}$ and $p > 0$, when $x > 0$, y is real and double-valued. If $x < 0$, y is imaginary; no part of the curve lies to the left of the vertex. Moreover, $y \to \pm\infty$ as $x \to +\infty$, so that the vertical width of the curve increases indefinitely as x increases.

The chord of the parabola through the focus, parallel to the directrix and terminated by the curve, is called the *latus rectum*. If we put $x = \frac{1}{2}p$ (for the focus) in the equation of the curve, we get $y^2 = 2p(\frac{1}{2}p) = p^2$, or $y = \pm p$. Hence, *the length of the latus rectum is equal to* $2p$. This gives a measure of the spread of the parabola; it is sometimes called the focal width.

EXAMPLE 1. Locate the vertex, axis, focus and directrix of the parabola $y^2 = 8x$.

Solution: The given equation is in the standard form (3), with $p = 4$; hence, the vertex is at the origin, its axis is the X-axis, its focus is at $(2, 0)$ and its directrix is $x = -2$.

EXAMPLE 2. Find the equation of the parabola having its vertex at the origin, its axis along the X-axis, and passing through the point $(-6, 4)$.

Solution: Since the parabola is in standard position, its equation has the form $y^2 = 2px$. The coördinates $(-6, 4)$ of the given point must satisfy the equation $y^2 = 2px$; then $16 = -12p$ or $2p = -\frac{8}{3}$. Therefore, the equation of the parabola is $y^2 = -\frac{8}{3}x$.

221. Exercises

1. Draw each of the parabolas whose equations are given below, and find the coördinates of the focus, the equation of the directrix and the length of the latus rectum in each case:
   - (a) $y^2 = 4x$;
   - (b) $y^2 = -12x$;
   - (c) $x^2 = 8y$;
   - (d) $x^2 = -16y$;
   - (e) $4y^2 - 3x = 0$;
   - (f) $4x^2 + 5y = 0$.

2. Proceed as in Exercise 1 with each of the following equations:
   - (a) $y^2 = 6x$;
   - (b) $y^2 = -2x$;
   - (c) $x^2 = 18y$;
   - (d) $x^2 = -14y$;
   - (e) $9y^2 + 4x = 0$;
   - (f) $2x^2 - 7y = 0$.

3. Find the equation of each parabola satisfying the following conditions:
   - (a) directrix $x = -4$, focus $(4, 0)$;
   - (b) directrix $x = 6$, focus $(-6, 0)$;
   - (c) vertex $(0, 0)$, focus $(8, 0)$;
   - (d) directrix $y = 5$, focus $(0, -5)$;
   - (e) vertex at origin, axis along X-axis, passing through the point $(4, 6)$;
   - (f) axis along Y-axis, open downward, length of latus rectum 12.

4. Find the equation of each parabola satisfying the following conditions:
   - (a) directrix $x = 8$, focus $(-8, 0)$;
   - (b) vertex $(0, 0)$, focus $(3, 0)$;
   - (c) vertex $(0, 0)$, directrix $y + 6 = 0$;
   - (d) focus $(0, -7)$, directrix $y = 7$;
   - (e) vertex at origin, axis along Y-axis, passing through the point $(-2, 4)$;
   - (f) axis along X-axis, open to left, length of latus rectum 9, vertex at 0.

5. The *focal radius* of a point on a parabola is defined as its distance from the focus. Show that the focal radius of a point (x_1, y_1) on the parabola $y^2 = 2px$ is equal to $|x_1 + \frac{1}{2}p|$.

6. Find the focal radii of the points on the parabola $y^2 = 12x$ for which:
   - (a) $x = 3$; (b) $y = 4$. (See Exercise 5.)

7. Prove that the lines drawn from the ends of the latus rectum of a parabola to the point of intersection of its axis and its directrix are perpendicular to each other.

8. Show that for all parabolas the lines from the vertex to the ends of the latus rectum include a constant angle. What is this angle?

9. Find the locus of the mid-points of all ordinates of the parabola $y^2 = 2\,px$.

10. Find the locus of the mid-points of all focal radii of the parabola $y^2 = 2\,px$.

11. By use of the *definition* of a parabola, find the equation of each parabola satisfying the following conditions, and sketch each curve: (*a*) directrix $x = -2$, focus $(4, 2)$; (*b*) directrix $x = 0$, vertex $(6, -2)$; (*c*) vertex $(0, -2)$, focus $(0, 6)$; (*d*) focus $(-2, 2)$, directrix $y = -4$.

12. Find the equation of the parabola with focus at the point $(4, 2)$ and directrix $3\,x - 4\,y = 15$. [*Hint.* Use the definition of a parabola, and also use § 38.]

13. The ends of the base of a triangle are the points $(a, 0)$ and $(-a, 0)$. Find the locus of the opposite vertex, if the ratio of the length of the base to that of the altitude is equal to the slope of the median to the base.

14. Find the equations of the tangent and the normal to each of the following parabolas at the point indicated:
    (*a*) $y^2 = 8\,x$, $(2, 4)$;   (*b*) $y + 2\,x^2 = 0$, $(2, -8)$.

15. Find the equation of the tangent to the parabola $y^2 = 6\,x$ which is perpendicular to the line $2\,x - y + 4 = 0$.

16. Prove that the tangents to a parabola at the ends of the latus rectum are perpendicular to each other and that they intersect on the directrix.

17. Prove that the equation of the tangent to the parabola $y^2 = 2\,px$ with given slope m is $y = mx + \dfrac{p}{2\,m}$.

18. Prove that any tangent to a parabola meets the directrix and the latus rectum extended in points which are equidistant from the focus. [*Hint.* Use Exercise 17.]

19. Find the angles at which the parabolas $y^2 = 2\,px$ and $x^2 = 2\,py$ intersect.

20. Find the dimensions of the largest rectangle which can be inscribed in the segment of the parabola $y^2 = 4\,x$ cut off by the line $x = 4$.

21. Prove that for any point (x_1, y_1) on the parabola $y^2 = 2\,px$, the segment of the tangent between the point of tangency and the X-axis has a projection upon the X-axis equal to $2\,x_1$. Using this result, derive a geometric construction for drawing a tangent to any parabola at any given point on it.

22. Prove that for any point on the parabola $y^2 = 2\,px$, the segment of the normal between the point of tangency and the X-axis has a projection upon the X-axis equal to p.

222. The Reflection Property of the Parabola

In Fig. 120, $P_1(x_1, y_1)$ is any point on the parabola $y^2 = 2\,px$, and TP_1 is the tangent to the curve at P_1. By differentiation in the equation of the curve, we find that the slope of the tangent at P_1 is

$m = p/y_1$. The equation of the tangent is then

$$(a) \qquad\qquad y - y_1 = \frac{p}{y_1}\,(x - x_1).$$

If we put $y = 0$ in this equation and solve for x, we find the abscissa of the point T to be $x = -x_1$. Since $OF = \frac{1}{2}\,p$, we have $TF = TO + OF = x_1 + \frac{1}{2}\,p$. By definition of a parabola, $FP_1 = RP_1 = AO + OM = \frac{1}{2}\,p + x_1$. Therefore, $TF = FP_1$; it follows that angle $FP_1T =$ angle $FTP_1 =$ angle QP_1T'. Hence, *the tangent to the parabola makes equal angles with the focal radius to the point of tangency and with the*

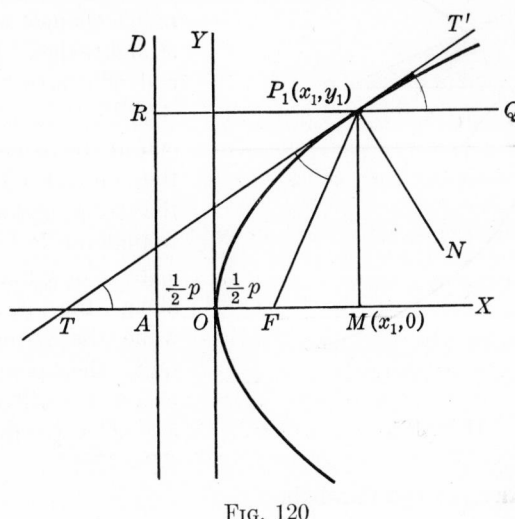

Fig. 120

line through the point of tangency parallel to the axis of the parabola.

According to the principles of optics, a ray of light striking a reflecting surface is reflected in such a direction that the incident ray and the reflected ray make equal angles with the normal to the surface and therefore equal angles with the tangent. A parabolic reflector is made by revolving a parabola about its axis. If the parabola of Fig. 120 is part of such a surface, and if a ray of light FP_1 issues from the focus F, it will be reflected along P_1Q parallel to the X-axis; therefore, all rays from F will be reflected in a bundle of parallel rays, forming a concentrated beam of light, as in a search-light. On the other hand, parallel rays (parallel to the axis) will all be reflected to the focus, giving a concentrated image; this is used in reflecting astronomical telescopes.

223. Construction of a Parabola

If the focus F and the directrix DD' of a parabola are given, the curve may be drawn by use of the following construction, based on the definition of the parabola. In Fig. 121, place a straight-edge along the directrix DD' and place one leg of a draftsman's triangle against the straight-edge. Fasten one end of a string of length AB at B and the other end at the focus F. With the point of a pencil pull the string tight against the triangle at P. If the triangle is now made to slide along the straight-edge while the string is held taut, the point of the pencil at P will describe an arc of a parabola, since $FP = PA$.

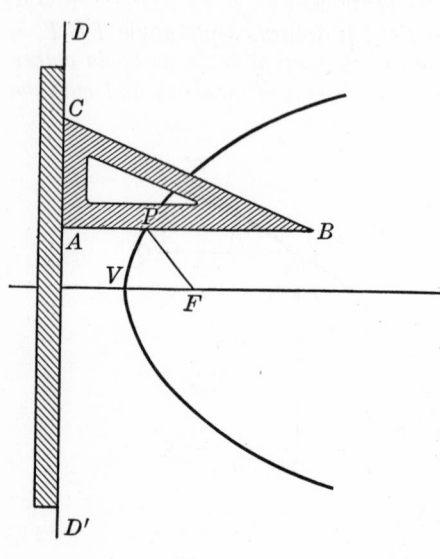

Fig. 121

224. Applications of the Parabola

The parabola has numerous applications in scientific and engineering work. A few of these will be mentioned here without proof.

If the resistance of the air were neglected, the path of a projectile would be (in general) an arc of a parabola.

The cables of a suspension bridge whose total weight is uniformly distributed along the bridge are parabolic in form.

Certain bridges involve parabolic arches.

A parabolic surface formed by rotating an arc of a parabola about its axis may be used as a reflecting surface for light or heat. If rays of light parallel to the axis meet the polished concave surface of such a reflector, they are reflected so as to pass through the focus. Reflecting telescopes used in astronomical work are based on this principle; faint rays of light from the distant stars are reflected from the mirror of the telescope to the focus and concentrated there, and the image there may be viewed with an eye piece. On the other hand, if a source of light is placed at the focus, the rays of light are reflected from the parabolic surface parallel to the axis in a concentrated beam. This is the principle on which is based the construction of searchlights and headlights of automobiles and locomotives. This property of the parabola was proved in § 222.

If a cylindrical container partly filled with water is rotated about its axis, a longitudinal section of the free surface of the water is parabolic.

Paths of comets about the sun are sometimes approximated by parabolas.

225. Exercises

1. Find the equation of the parabola with vertex at the origin and axis of symmetry along the X-axis, if it passes through the point (h, r).

2. A parabolic arch has a span of 120 feet and a height of 25 feet. Choose suitable rectangular axes and find the equation of the parabola. Then calculate the height of the arch at points 10 feet, 20 feet and 40 feet from the center.

3. If a parabolic reflector has a diameter of 8 inches and is 6 inches deep, how far from the vertex of the parabola should a light be placed so that the rays may be reflected parallel to the axis?

4. Suppose that a ray of light from the focus strikes the parabola $y^2 = 4x$ at the point $(9, 6)$. Draw a figure and draw the reflected ray, and find the equation of the line of the ray.

5. Show that the area of a parabolic segment cut off by a chord perpendicular to the axis of the parabola is equal to two-thirds of the area of the circumscribed rectangle. (§ 181)

6. The segment of the parabola of Exercise 1 cut off by the line $x = h$ is revolved about the X-axis. Find the volume of the solid of revolution which is generated. (§ 186)

7. The segment of the parabola $y^2 = 4ax$ which is cut off by the latus rectum is revolved about the directrix. Find the volume of the solid generated. (§ 188)

8. Show that if the segment of a parabola cut off by a line perpendicular to its axis is revolved about this line, the volume generated is $\frac{8}{15}$ of that of the circumscribed cylinder. (§ 188)

9. A trough 10 feet long with a vertical parabolic cross-section 4 feet deep and 4 feet across the top is filled with water. Find the work done in pumping out the trough. (§ 197)

10. A plate in the form of a parabolic segment cut off by a chord perpendicular to the axis is immersed vertically in water. The vertex is at the surface and the axis is vertical. It is 20 feet deep and 12 feet broad. Find the force on one face of the segment in tons. (§ 199).

226. The Ellipse

*An **ellipse** is defined as the locus of a point which moves in a plane in such a way that the sum of its distances from two fixed points is a constant which is greater than the distance between the fixed points.*

Each of the fixed points is called a **focus** of the ellipse; together, they are called the *foci*. The straight line through the foci is called the **principal axis** of the ellipse. The point midway between foci is called the **center** of the ellipse.

227. Standard Form of the Equation of an Ellipse

The simplest form of the equation of an ellipse is obtained by taking the X-axis through the foci and the origin midway between the foci. In Fig. 122, let F and F' be the foci and let $FF' = 2\,c$; then the co-

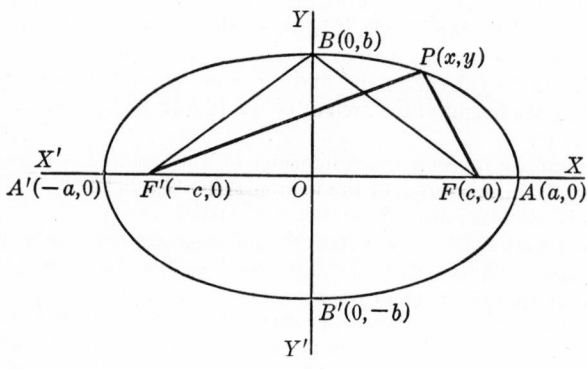

Fɪɢ. 122

ordinates of F are $(c, 0)$ and those of F' are $(-c, 0)$. Let $P(x, y)$ be any point on the ellipse.

By the definition of the ellipse,

(a) $$FP + F'P = 2\,a.$$

By use of the distance formula, this becomes

$$\sqrt{(x - c)^2 + y^2} + \sqrt{(x + c)^2 + y^2} = 2\,a.$$

If we transpose the second radical, square both sides and simplify, we have

$$a\sqrt{(x + c)^2 + y^2} = a^2 + cx.$$

If we square both sides again and simplify, we obtain

$$(b) \qquad (a^2 - c^2)x^2 + a^2y^2 = a^2(a^2 - c^2).$$

But $a > c$, so that $a^2 - c^2$ is positive; we shall denote this positive number by b^2. Substituting this value for $a^2 - c^2$ in equation (b), we get

$$(c) \qquad b^2x^2 + a^2y^2 = a^2b^2.$$

Dividing by a^2b^2, we have

$$(d) \qquad \frac{x^2}{a^2} + \frac{y^2}{b^2} = 1.$$

This equation is satisfied by the coördinates of any point on the ellipse. It can be shown conversely that if the equation (d) is satisfied by the coördinates of any point $P(x, y)$, then the point P lies on the ellipse. Hence, (d) is the required equation of the ellipse. Therefore:

If the foci are on the X-axis and the origin is midway between the foci, the equation of an ellipse is

$$(5) \qquad \frac{x^2}{a^2} + \frac{y^2}{b^2} = 1,$$

where $2a$ is the sum of the distances of any point of the ellipse from the foci, and b is defined by

$$(6) \qquad b^2 = a^2 - c^2,$$

where $2c$ is the distance between the foci.

Equation (5) is called the **standard form** of the equation of an ellipse, and in this position the ellipse is said to be in *standard position*.

If the foci of an ellipse are on the Y-axis, with coördinates $F(0, c)$ and $F'(0, -c)$, if $FP + F'P = 2a$ and if $b = \sqrt{a^2 - c^2}$, then the equation of the ellipse is, by symmetry,

$$(7) \qquad \frac{x^2}{b^2} + \frac{y^2}{a^2} = 1.$$

It should be noted that if we put $b = a$ in the equation of an ellipse, the equation becomes $x^2 + y^2 = a^2$, which is the equation of a circle. Therefore, we may regard a circle as a limiting form of an ellipse when the foci coincide (at the center).

228. Discussion of the Ellipse

An algebraic discussion of the standard equation of the ellipse:

(a)
$$\frac{x^2}{a^2} + \frac{y^2}{b^2} = 1,$$

will give some idea of the nature of the ellipse.

(1) *Symmetry:* By inspection of equation (a), it is evident that the curve is symmetric with respect to the X-axis and the Y-axis and therefore with respect to the origin.

(2) *Intercepts:* If $x = 0$, then $y = \pm b$, and if $y = 0$, then $x = \pm a$. This gives four points where the curve cuts the axes: the points $A(a, 0)$, $A'(-a, 0)$, $B(0, b)$, $B'(0, -b)$ (Fig. 122). The points A and A' are called the **vertices** of the ellipse.

(3) *Extent:* If we solve equation (a) for y and for x, we get

(b)
$$y = \pm \frac{b}{a} \sqrt{a^2 - x^2}, \qquad x = \pm \frac{a}{b} \sqrt{b^2 - y^2}.$$

The first of these equations shows that if x is numerically greater than a, then y is imaginary, and such values of x must be excluded. Similarly, from the second equation it follows that if y is numerically greater than b, then x is imaginary, and such values of y must be excluded. Hence, the ellipse does not extend outside the rectangle formed by the lines $x = \pm a$, $y = \pm b$. (See Fig. 122.)

The segment AA' between the vertices is called the **major axis** of the ellipse; its length is obviously $2\,a$. The segment BB', on the Y-axis, is called the **minor axis;** it is of length $2\,b$. The intersection of these two axes, O, is the *center* of the ellipse. The numbers a and b are the lengths of the *semi-major axis* and the *semi-minor axis*.

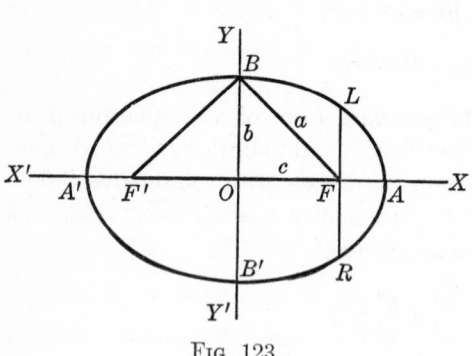

Fig. 123

By the definition of the ellipse, the sum of the distances BF and BF' is $2\,a$ (Fig. 123); since $BF = BF'$, it follows that $BF = a$. The important relation

(c) $$a^2 = b^2 + c^2$$

connecting the constants a, b, c can now be visualized in the triangle OBF of Fig. 123.

The chord of the ellipse through either focus perpendicular to the major axis AA' and terminated by the curve is called the *latus rectum*. Its length is twice the ordinate through a focus of the ellipse. This ordinate is obtained by putting $x = c$ or $x = -c$ in the first of equations (b); by use of equation (c), we find

$$y = \pm \frac{b}{a} \sqrt{a^2 - c^2} = \pm \frac{b^2}{a}.$$

Hence, the length of the latus rectum is $2\, b^2/a$.

The ratio c/a is called the **eccentricity** of the ellipse and it is denoted by e:

(8) $$e = \frac{c}{a}.$$

Since $c < a$, *the eccentricity of an ellipse is always less than* 1. If e is very small, then c is small compared with a, and since $c^2 = a^2 - b^2$, it follows that the difference between a and b is small compared with a; therefore, the foci are close together and the major and minor axes are nearly equal, so that the ellipse is very nearly circular. As e increases, the ellipse becomes less nearly circular and more flattened. If e is very near 1, c is nearly equal to a, and since $b^2 = a^2 - c^2$, it follows that b is very small compared to a; therefore, the ellipse is very narrow and elongated. Hence, it appears that the *shape* of the ellipse is determined by its eccentricity. It is sometimes said that a circle is a special case of an ellipse when the eccentricity is 0.

EXAMPLE 1. Find the vertices, foci, lengths of semi-axes and eccentricity of the ellipse whose equation is $9\,x^2 + 25\,y^2 = 225$.

Solution: The given equation may be written in the form

(d) $$\frac{x^2}{25} + \frac{y^2}{9} = 1.$$

Then the semi-axes are $a = 5$, $b = 3$ and $c = \sqrt{a^2 - b^2} = 4$. Hence, the vertices are $(\pm 5, 0)$, the foci are $(\pm 4, 0)$, and the eccentricity is $e = 4/5$.

EXAMPLE 2. If the vertices of an ellipse are $(\pm 8, 0)$ and the eccentricity is $e = \frac{1}{2}$, find the equation of the ellipse and locate its foci.

Solution: The ellipse is in standard position with center at the origin and foci on the X-axis. We have $a = 8$ and $e = \frac{1}{2}$; since $e = \dfrac{c}{a}$, we have $\dfrac{1}{2} = \dfrac{c}{8}$;

whence $c = 4$, and then $b^2 = a^2 - c^2 = 64 - 16 = 48$. The equation of the ellipse is therefore

(e)
$$\frac{x^2}{64} + \frac{y^2}{48} = 1.$$

The foci are at $(\pm 4, 0)$, since $c = 4$.

229. Exercises

1. Find the lengths of the semi-axes, the coördinates of the vertices and the foci, and the eccentricity of each of the following ellipses, and sketch each curve:

    (a) $4\,x^2 + 9\,y^2 = 36$; (b) $9\,x^2 + 16\,y^2 = 144$;
    (c) $25\,x^2 + 9\,y^2 = 225$; (d) $9\,x^2 + 4\,y^2 = 4$.

2. Proceed as in Exercise 1 with:

    (a) $25\,x^2 + 49\,y^2 = 1225$; (b) $9\,x^2 + 36\,y^2 = 324$;
    (c) $25\,x^2 + 4\,y^2 = 100$; (d) $4\,x^2 + 3\,y^2 = 12$.

3. Find the equation of each ellipse satisfying the following data, and sketch each curve:

    (a) foci $(\pm 3, 0)$, one vertex at $(5, 0)$;
    (b) foci $(\pm 5, 0)$, minor axis 4;
    (c) vertices $(0, \pm 6)$, semi-minor axis 3;
    (d) foci $(\pm 4, 0)$, eccentricity $2/3$.

4. Proceed as in Exercise 3 with the following data:

    (a) foci $(\pm 2, 0)$, major axis 8;
    (b) foci $(\pm 3, 0)$, semi-minor axis $\sqrt{3}$;
    (c) vertices $(0, \pm 5)$, ends of minor axis $(\pm 3, 0)$;
    (d) vertices $(\pm 10, 0)$, eccentricity $2/5$.

5. Find the equation of each ellipse with center at the origin and satisfying the following data:

    (a) one end of minor axis $(0, 4)$, distance between foci 6;
    (b) major axis 6, latus rectum 4, foci on the X-axis;
    (c) one vertex $(0, -4)$, eccentricity $1/3$;
    (d) vertex $(-3, 0)$, passing through $(2, 1)$;
    (e) focus $(0, 6)$, latus rectum 10.

6. Proceed as in Exercise 5 with the following data:

    (a) one vertex $(6, 0)$, minor axis 6;
    (b) semi-major axis 10, distance between foci 12, foci on X-axis;
    (c) minor axis 12, latus rectum $18/5$, foci on X-axis;
    (d) one end of minor axis $(0, 2)$, passing through $(2, 1)$;
    (e) eccentricity $1/4$, latus rectum 3, foci on Y-axis.

7. Find the equation of the ellipse with center at the origin, with its major axis on one of the coördinate axes, and passing through the two points:

    (a) $(2, 2)$ and $(4, 1)$; (b) $(-3, 2)$ and $(2, -4)$.

8. Find the coördinates of the points of intersection of each of the following pairs of curves, and sketch the curves:

    (a) $4\,x^2 + 9\,y^2 = 40$, $y^2 = 4\,x$; (b) $2\,x^2 + y^2 = 41$, $x^2 + y^2 = 25$.

9. Prove that if P is any point on the ellipse $b^2x^2 + a^2y^2 = a^2b^2$ and if A and A' are its vertices, the product of the slopes of PA and PA' is $-b^2/a^2$.

10. By use of the *definition* of an ellipse, find the equation of the ellipse whose foci are at $(6, 3)$ and $(-2, 3)$, and whose major axis is 10.

11. Find the equation of the locus of a point which moves so that its distance from the line $x = 8$ is twice its distance from the point $(2, 0)$. What is the locus?

12. Find the equation of the locus of the mid-points of ordinates of points of the circle $x^2 + y^2 = a^2$. What is the locus? [*Hint*. Let $P'(x', y')$ be any point on the circle, then $x'^2 + y'^2 = a^2$. The coördinates (x, y) of the mid-point of the ordinate of P' are $x = x'$, $y = \frac{1}{2} y'$.]

13. Find the equations of the tangent and normal to the ellipse $4 x^2 + y^2 = 8$ at the point $(1, 2)$.

14. Show that the line $8 x + 9 y - 25 = 0$ is tangent to the ellipse $4 x^2 + 9 y^2 = 25$.

15. Find the angles of intersection of the ellipses $4 x^2 + 9 y^2 = 36$ and $9 x^2 + 4 y^2 = 36$.

16. Find the angles of intersection of the curves $4 x^2 + y^2 = 8$ and $y^2 = 4 x$.

17. Show that the slope of the ellipse $b^2x^2 + a^2y^2 = a^2b^2$ at an end of a latus rectum is numerically equal to the eccentricity.

18. Find the area of the largest rectangle that can be inscribed in the ellipse $b^2x^2 + a^2y^2 = a^2b^2$.

19. Prove that the equations of the tangents with given slope m to the ellipse $b^2x^2 + a^2y^2 = a^2b^2$ are $y = mx \pm \sqrt{a^2m^2 + b^2}$.

20. Prove that the product of the perpendicular distances from the foci of an ellipse to any tangent line is a constant. [*Hint*. Use Exercise 19 and § 38.]

21. Prove that the tangent to the ellipse $b^2x^2 + a^2y^2 = a^2b^2$ at any point (x_1, y_1) on it and the tangent to the circle $x^2 + y^2 = a^2$ at the point on it whose abscissa is x_1 intersect the X-axis at the same point.

22. Prove that the normal to an ellipse at any point bisects the angle between the focal radii drawn to the point of tangency. (The focal radii of a point on the ellipse are the line segments from the foci to the point.) [*Hint*. Find the slope of the normal and the slopes of the focal radii, and use § 22.]

23. Show how to construct the tangent to an ellipse at any given point on it by use of Exercise 21, and also by use of Exercise 22.

230. Construction of an Ellipse

If the foci and the major axis of an ellipse are given, the curve may be drawn by the following construction, based on the definition of the ellipse: Let $2 a$ be the length of the major axis and $2 c$ the distance between the foci. Place two pins at the foci F and F' (Fig. 124) at a distance $2 c$ apart, and fasten the ends of a string of length $2 a$ to these pins. If we now pull the string taut by a pencil point and then move the pencil so as to keep the string taut, the pencil point will describe an ellipse, with the given values of a and c. A modification of this method which works more smoothly is to loop a string of total length $2\,a + 2\,c$ over the pins, pull the string taut by a pencil point and then move the pencil as before.

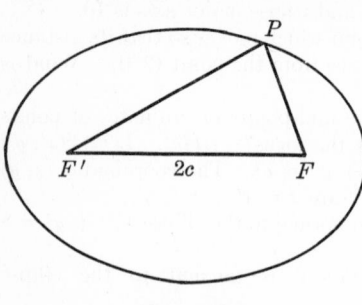

Fig. 124

231. Applications of the Ellipse

The ellipse has many applications in science and engineering. A few of these are:

The planets revolve about the sun in elliptical orbits with the sun at one focus. Some comets also move about the sun in elliptical orbits.

Semi-elliptical arches are often used in stone and concrete bridges, and in architecture.

In machinery, elliptical gears are used when variable rates of motion are needed.

Springs, such as automobile springs, are often elliptical or semi-elliptical in form.

The ellipse has a reflecting property (§ 229, Exercise 22), which is the explanation of the so-called "whispering galleries."

232. Exercises

1. The orbit of the earth is an ellipse with the sun at one focus. If the semi-major axis is taken as 92 million miles and the eccentricity as 1/60, find the greatest and least distances of the earth from the sun.
2. An arch in the form of half an ellipse is 40 feet wide and 15 feet high at the center. Find the height of the arch at intervals of 10 feet along its width.
3. The arch of a bridge is a semi-ellipse with major axis horizontal. The span is 30 feet and the top of the arch is 10 feet above the major axis. The roadway is horizontal and is 2 feet above the top of the arch. Find at five-foot intervals along the roadway the vertical distance from the roadway to the arch.
4. The Colosseum at Rome is in the form of an ellipse 615 feet long and 510 feet wide. Find the equation of the ellipse and the position of the foci.

233. The Hyperbola

*A **hyperbola** is defined as the locus of a point which moves in a plane in such a way that the difference of its distances from two fixed points is a constant.*

Each of the fixed points is called a *focus* of the hyperbola. The line through the foci is called the *principal axis* of the curve. The point half-way between the foci is called the *center* of the hyperbola.

234. Standard Form of the Equation of a Hyperbola

To obtain the simplest form of the equation of a hyperbola, we take the X-axis through the foci and the origin midway between the foci. In Fig. 125, let F and F' be the foci and $FF' = 2\,c$; then the

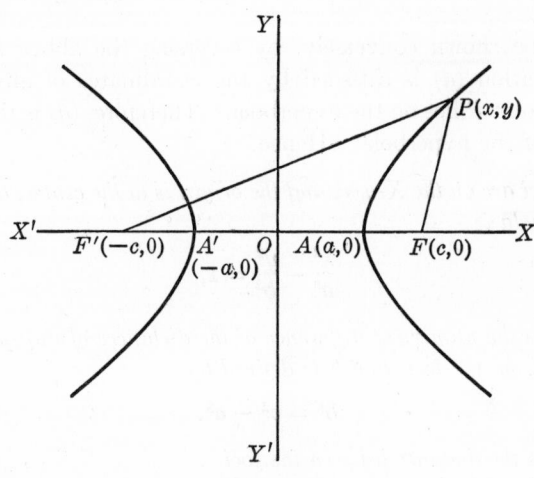

FIG. 125

coördinates of F and F' are $(c, 0)$ and $(-c, 0)$ respectively. Let $P(x, y)$ be any point on the hyperbola.

By the definition of the hyperbola,

(a) $$F'P - FP = \pm 2\,a.$$

By application of the distance formula, this becomes

$$\sqrt{(x + c)^2 + y^2} - \sqrt{(x - c)^2 + y^2} = \pm 2\,a.$$

If we transpose the second radical, square both sides and simplify, we obtain

$$cx - a = \pm a\sqrt{(x - c)^2 + y^2}.$$

Squaring both sides again and simplifying, we have

(b) $$(c^2 - a^2)x^2 - a^2 y^2 = a^2(c^2 - a^2).$$

But $a < c$, so that $c^2 - a^2$ is positive; we denote this positive number by b^2. Equation (b) then becomes

$$(c) \qquad\qquad b^2x^2 - a^2y^2 = a^2b^2.$$

Dividing by a^2b^2, we get

$$(d) \qquad\qquad \frac{x^2}{a^2} - \frac{y^2}{b^2} = 1.$$

This equation is satisfied by the coördinates of any point on the hyperbola.

It can be shown conversely, by reversing the above steps, that if the equation (d) is satisfied by the coördinates of any point P, then the point P lies on the hyperbola. Therefore, (d) is the required equation of the hyperbola. Hence:

If the foci are on the X-axis and the origin is at the center, the equation of a hyperbola is

$$(9) \qquad\qquad \frac{x^2}{a^2} - \frac{y^2}{b^2} = 1,$$

where $2\,a$ is the numerical difference of the distances of any point on the hyperbola from the foci, and b is defined by

$$(10) \qquad\qquad b^2 = c^2 - a^2,$$

where $2\,c$ is the distance between the foci.

Equation (9) is called the **standard form** of the equation of a hyperbola, and in this position the hyperbola is said to be in *standard position*.

If the foci of a hyperbola are on the Y-axis, with coördinates $F(0, c)$ and $F'(0, -c)$, if $FP - F'P = \pm 2\,a$ and if $b = \sqrt{c^2 - a^2}$, then the equation of the hyperbola is evidently

$$(11) \qquad\qquad \frac{y^2}{a^2} - \frac{x^2}{b^2} = 1.$$

235. Discussion of the Hyperbola

We shall now give an algebraic discussion of the standard equation of the hyperbola:

$$(a) \qquad\qquad \frac{x^2}{a^2} - \frac{y^2}{b^2} = 1,$$

to obtain some information about the nature of the curve.

(1) *Symmetry:* Inspection of the equation (a) shows that the hyperbola is symmetric with respect to the X-axis and the Y-axis and therefore with respect to the origin.

(2) *Intercepts:* If we put $y = 0$, we get $x = \pm a$; but if $x = 0$, we have $y^2 = -b^2$, so that y is pure imaginary. There are therefore two points $A(a, 0)$ and $A'(-a, 0)$ where the curve cuts the X-axis, but the curve does not cut the Y-axis. The points A and A' are called the **vertices** of the hyperbola.

(3) *Extent:* By solving equation (a) for y and for x, we get

$$(b) \qquad y = \pm \frac{b}{a} \sqrt{x^2 - a^2}, \qquad x = \pm \frac{a}{b} \sqrt{y^2 + b^2}.$$

The first equation shows that if x is numerically less than a, then y is imaginary, so that we must exclude the region between $x = a$ and $x = -a$. From the second equation we see that x is real for all real values of y, so that there are no excluded values of y. The curve consists of two disconnected pieces, called *branches*.

The segment AA' between the vertices is called the **transverse axis** of the hyperbola; it is of length $2\,a$. Although the hyperbola does not cut the Y-axis, the segment between the points $B(0, b)$ and $B'(0, -b)$ is called the **conjugate axis,** for a reason to be given presently; it is of length $2\,b$. The origin O, which is a center of symmetry of the curve, is the *center* of the hyperbola. The numbers a and b are the lengths of the *semi-transverse axis* and the *semi-conjugate axis*.

The chord of the hyperbola through either focus perpendicular to the transverse axis and terminated by the curve is called the *latus rectum.* The ordinate through a focus is found by putting $x = c$ or $x = -c$ in the first of equations (b); we obtain

$$y = \pm \frac{b}{a} \sqrt{c^2 - a^2} = \pm \frac{b^2}{a},$$

since $c^2 - a^2 = b^2$. Hence, the length of the latus rectum is $2\,b^2/a$.

The ratio c/a is called the **eccentricity** of the hyperbola and it is denoted by e:

$$(12) \qquad\qquad e = \frac{c}{a}.$$

Since $c > a$, the eccentricity of a hyperbola is always greater than 1. The shape of the hyperbola is determined by its eccentricity; this will be discussed later (§ 236).

EXAMPLE. Find the vertices, foci, lengths of semi-axes and eccentricity of the hyperbola whose equation is $9\,x^2 - 16\,y^2 = 144$.

Solution: If we write the given equation in the form

$$(c) \qquad \frac{x^2}{16} - \frac{y^2}{9} = 1,$$

we see that the semi-axes are $a = 4$, $b = 3$, and $c = \sqrt{a^2 + b^2} = 5$. Therefore, the vertices are at $(\pm 4, 0)$, the foci are at $(\pm 5, 0)$, and the eccentricity is $e = c/a = 5/4$.

236. Asymptotes of a Hyperbola

If we solve the equation $b^2x^2 - a^2y^2 = a^2b^2$ of the hyperbola for y in terms of x, we get

$$(a) \qquad y = \pm \frac{b}{a} \sqrt{x^2 - a^2} = \pm \frac{bx}{a} \sqrt{1 - \frac{a^2}{x^2}}.$$

When x is large in comparison with a, the value of the expression $\sqrt{1 - \dfrac{a^2}{x^2}}$ is near 1, so that the ordinate y for the hyperbola is approximately equal to $\pm bx/a$. This leads us to infer that the hyperbola approaches closer and closer to the straight lines whose equations are $y = \pm bx/a$ when the tracing point recedes further and further from the center.

In the general discussion of curves in Chapter III, we met the concept of an *asymptote* to a curve, which was defined as follows: When a straight line is related to a curve in such a way that as a variable

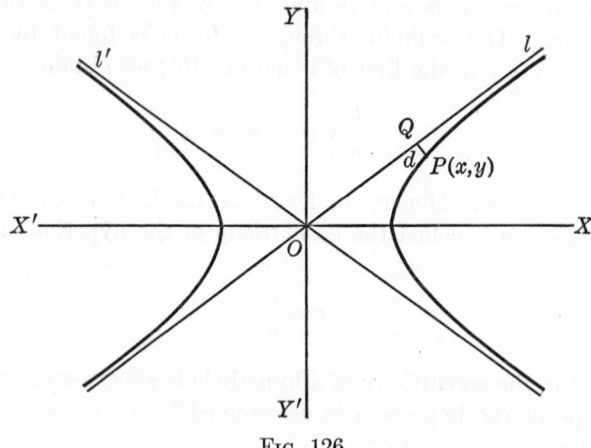

FIG. 126

point moves along the curve further and further from the origin, its distance from the line continually decreases, and approaches 0 as a limit when the distance of the point from the origin becomes infinite, then the straight line is called an ***asymptote*** to the curve. The discussion above suggests that the lines $y = \pm bx/a$ are asymptotes to the hyperbola. We may prove that this is the case as follows.

Let $P(x, y)$ be any variable point on the upper half of the right-hand branch of the hyperbola, and let d be the perpendicular distance between P and the line l whose equation is $y = bx/a$ or $bx - ay = 0$ (Fig. 126). By use of the formula for the distance from a line to a point (§ 38), since $y = \dfrac{b}{a}\sqrt{x^2 - a^2}$, we find

$$(b) \qquad d = \frac{bx - ay}{\sqrt{b^2 + a^2}} = \frac{bx - b\sqrt{x^2 - a^2}}{c}.$$

Now let us multiply numerator and denominator of (b) by $x + \sqrt{x^2 - a^2}$; we obtain

$$(c) \qquad d = \frac{b(x - \sqrt{x^2 - a^2})(x + \sqrt{x^2 - a^2})}{c(x + \sqrt{x^2 - a^2})} = \frac{b[x^2 - (x^2 - a^2)]}{c(x + \sqrt{x^2 - a^2})}$$

$$= \frac{ba^2}{c(x + \sqrt{x^2 - a^2})}.$$

It can be readily seen from this result that $d \to 0$ as $x \to \infty$. This proves that the upper right-hand portion of the hyperbola approaches the line $y = bx/a$ as an asymptote. In a similar way, it may be shown that the lower left-hand portion of the curve approaches the line $y = bx/a$ as an asymptote, and also that the lower right-hand portion and the upper left-hand portion approach the line $y = -bx/a$ asymptotically. Hence:

The branches of the hyperbola $b^2x^2 - a^2y^2 = a^2b^2$ approach the lines $y = \pm bx/a$ as asymptotes.

Since the equations of the asymptotes may be written $bx - ay = 0$ and $bx + ay = 0$, they may be represented by the single equation $b^2x^2 - a^2y^2 = 0$ (by § 48).

In order to sketch a given hyperbola, a convenient way is to draw the asymptotes first, then to locate the vertices and a few other points of the curve, and then to draw the curve approaching the asymptotes.

The relation between the constants a, b and c of the hyperbola is shown graphically in the right triangle OAC of Fig. 127. AC is drawn through the vertex A perpendicular to the transverse axis A′A up to the asymptote at C, then CB is drawn perpendicular to the conjugate axis. This gives a representation of the semi-conjugate axis b as a length OB. Note that a circle circumscribed about the ⁻ectangle passes through the foci.

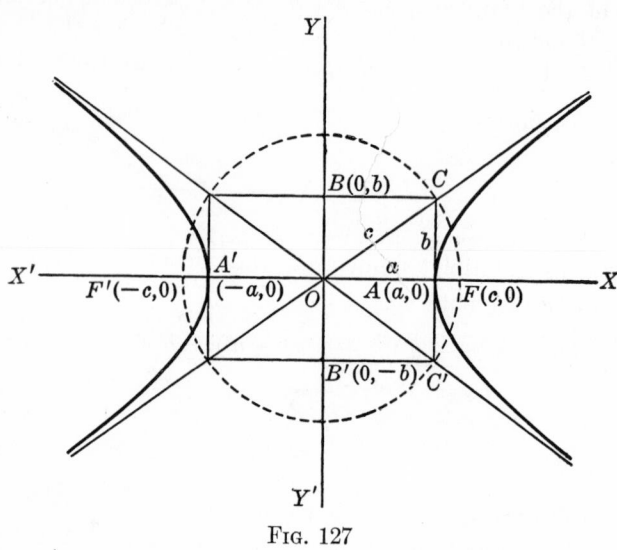

Fig. 127

EXAMPLE. For the hyperbola $9\,x^2 - 16\,y^2 = 144$, the equations of the asymptotes are $9\,x^2 - 16\,y^2 = 0$, or $3\,x - 4\,y = 0$ and $3\,x + 4\,y = 0$.

The eccentricity of a hyperbola has been defined as $e = c/a$; it is always greater than 1. The effect of changing the eccentricity upon the shape of the hyperbola may be analyzed as follows. If e is only slightly larger than 1, then c is slightly larger than a, and b is small compared to a, since $b = \sqrt{c^2 - a^2}$; it follows that the asymptotes make a small angle with the transverse axis. As e increases, the asymptotes make a larger angle with the transverse axis, approaching a right angle.

If two hyperbolas are so related that the transverse and conjugate axes of the one curve are respectively the conjugate and transverse axes of the other, each hyperbola is called the **conjugate** of the other, and together they are said to form a pair of *conjugate hyperbolas*.

If the equation of one hyperbola is $\dfrac{x^2}{a^2} - \dfrac{y^2}{b^2} = 1$, its conjugate has the equation $\dfrac{y^2}{b^2} - \dfrac{x^2}{a^2} = 1$. (Fig. 128.) The foci of one are on the X-axis and those of the other are on the Y-axis.

The foci of two conjugate hyperbolas are equally distant from the center, since $c^2 = a^2 + b^2$ for both curves. Two conjugate hyperbolas have the same asymptotes.

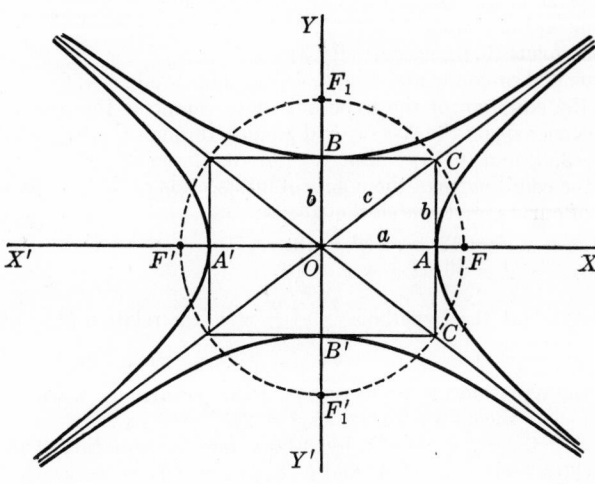

Fig. 128

237. Exercises

1. Find the lengths of the semi-axes, the coördinates of the vertices and the foci and the eccentricity of each of the following hyperbolas, and sketch each curve:
   (a) $4x^2 - 9y^2 = 36$;   (b) $9x^2 - 16y^2 = 144$;
   (c) $4x^2 - y^2 = 16$;   (d) $9y^2 - x^2 = 9$.

2. Proceed as in Exercise 1 with:
   (a) $x^2 - 4y^2 = 4$;   (b) $16y^2 - 25x^2 = 400$;
   (c) $16x^2 - 9y^2 = 144$;   (d) $x^2 - y^2 = 4$.

3. Find the equation of each hyperbola satisfying the following data, and sketch each curve:
   (a) foci $(\pm 5, 0)$, vertices $(\pm 3, 0)$;
   (b) vertices $(\pm 6, 0)$, eccentricity $\sqrt{2}$;
   (c) vertices $(\pm 12, 0)$, semi-conjugate axis 5;
   (d) foci $(0, \pm 8)$, ends of conjugate axis $(\pm 4, 0)$.

4. Proceed as in Exercise 3 with the following data:
   (a) vertices $(\pm 4, 0)$, foci $(\pm 6, 0)$;
   (b) foci $(\pm 6, 0)$, eccentricity $3/2$;
   (c) ends of conjugate axis $(\pm 6, 0)$, vertices $(0, \pm 4)$;
   (d) ends of transverse axis $(0, \pm 2)$, foci $(0, \pm 5)$.

5. Find the equation of each hyperbola with center at the origin and satisfying the following conditions:
   (a) transverse axis 8, foci on the X-axis, eccentricity $3/2$;
   (b) one vertex $(3, 0)$, passing through $(5, 3)$;
   (c) one focus $(0, 10)$, eccentricity $5/4$.

6. Proceed as in Exercise 5 with the following data:
   (a) one end of conjugate axis $(3, 0)$, eccentricity 2;
   (b) one focus $(0, 6)$, eccentricity 3;
   (c) one end of conjugate axis $(0, 4)$, passing through $(4, 6)$.

7. Find the equation of the hyperbola with center at the origin, with its transverse axis on the X-axis, and passing through the two points:
   (a) $(-3, 3)$ and $(6, 7)$;   (b) $(3, 1)$ and $(9, 5)$.

8. Find the coördinates of the points of intersection of each of the following pairs of curves, and sketch the curves:
   (a) $2 x^2 - 3 y^2 = 12$, $x^2 + y^2 = 16$;
   (b) $16 x^2 - y^2 = 16$, $x^2 + 4 y^2 = 16$.

9. Show that for the hyperbola $\dfrac{x^2}{a^2} - \dfrac{y^2}{b^2} = 1$, the relation $b^2 = a^2(e^2 - 1)$ always holds.

10. Find the equation of the hyperbola with eccentricity 2 which has the same foci as the ellipse $9 x^2 + 25 y^2 = 225$.

11. By use of the *definition* of a hyperbola, find the equation of the hyperbola whose foci are at $(4, 4)$ and $(-6, 4)$, and whose transverse axis is 8.

12. Show that all of the hyperbolas $\dfrac{x^2}{\cos^2 \alpha} - \dfrac{y^2}{\sin^2 \alpha} = 1$ have their foci at $(\pm 1, 0)$ for all values of α.

13. Find the equation of the hyperbola which has the foci of the ellipse $4 x^2 + 9 y^2 = 36$ for vertices and the vertices of the ellipse as foci.

14. Find the equations of the asymptotes of the hyperbolas:
   (a) $4 x^2 - 9 y^2 = 36$;   (b) $5 x^2 - 4 y^2 = 40$.

15. Find the equations of the asymptotes of the hyperbolas:
   (a) $16 x^2 - 25 y^2 = 400$;   (b) $9 y^2 - x^2 = 18$.

16. Find the equation of the hyperbola whose asymptotes are $y = \pm \frac{2}{3} x$, if the ends of the conjugate axis are $(0, \pm 4)$.

17. The vertices of a hyperbola are $(\pm 8, 0)$ and the equations of its asymptotes are $3 x \pm 4 y = 0$. Find the coördinates of the foci and the eccentricity.

18. Write the equations of the hyperbolas conjugate to the following, write the equations of the asymptotes, and sketch:
   (a) $4 x^2 - 9 y^2 = 36$;   (b) $4 y^2 - x^2 = 8$.

19. Proceed as in Exercise 18 with:
   (a) $16\,x^2 - 9\,y^2 = 144$; (b) $y^2 - 9\,x^2 = 9$.

20. Prove that the distance from a focus of a hyperbola to an asymptote is equal to the semi-conjugate axis.

21. Prove that the product of the perpendicular distances of any point on a hyperbola from its asymptotes is constant.

22. Find the equations of the tangent and the normal to each of the following hyperbolas at the point indicated:
   (a) $4\,x^2 - 16\,y^2 = 48$, $(4,\,-1)$; (b) $x^2 - y^2 = 5$, $(3,\,-2)$.

23. Find the equations of the tangents to the hyperbola $4\,x^2 - y^2 = 7$ which are perpendicular to the line $3\,x - 8\,y + 16 = 0$.

24. Prove that the equations of the tangents with given slope m to the hyperbola $b^2x^2 - a^2y^2 = a^2b^2$ are $y = mx \pm \sqrt{a^2m^2 - b^2}$.

25. Prove that the product of the perpendicular distances from the foci of a hyperbola to any tangent is constant.

26. Find the *vertical* distance between a point on the upper right hand portion of the hyperbola $b^2x^2 - a^2y^2 = a^2b^2$ and the corresponding asymptote. Then show that as x becomes infinite, this vertical distance approaches zero.

27. Prove that the eccentricity of a hyperbola is equal to the secant of half the angle between the asymptotes.

28. Prove that an ellipse and a hyperbola which have the same foci intersect at right angles.

238. Equilateral or Rectangular Hyperbola

A hyperbola in which the transverse and conjugate axes are equal is called an **equilateral hyperbola;** it is also frequently called a *rectangular hyperbola.*

If we put $a = b$ in the standard equation (9) of a hyperbola, we find that:

The equation of an equilateral hyperbola whose center is at the origin and whose foci are on the X-axis is

(13) $$x^2 - y^2 = a^2,$$

where a is the common value of the semi-transverse and semi-conjugate axis. If the foci are on the Y-axis, the equation of the hyperbola is evidently

$$y^2 - x^2 = a^2.$$

This is the conjugate of (13).

The asymptotes of the equilateral hyperbola (13) have the equations $x - y = 0$ and $x + y = 0$ (the bisectors of the quadrants). These asymptotes are perpendicular to each other; this is the reason for the name "rectangular" hyperbola.

The equilateral hyperbola bears the same relation to hyperbolas in general that the circle does to ellipses in general.

It will be shown later that when the asymptotes of the equilateral hyperbola are used as coördinate axes, the equation of the curve takes the form

$$xy = k.$$

239. Exercises

1. Sketch the following curves:

    (a) $x^2 - y^2 + 4 = 0$;   (b) $xy + 4 = 0$.

2. What is the eccentricity of an equilateral hyperbola?
3. Prove that each hyperbola $x^2 - y^2 = c$ is orthogonal to each hyperbola $xy = k$.
4. Prove that the area of a triangle formed by a tangent to the hyperbola $xy = a^2$ and the coördinate axes is a constant.

240. Construction of a Hyperbola

If the foci and the transverse axis of a hyperbola are given, the curve may be drawn by the following construction: Place two pins

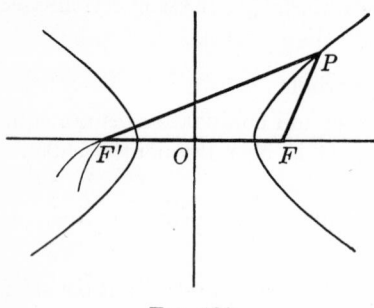

at the foci F and F' (Fig. 129), and fasten a pencil point to a string at P. Let one end of the string pass below F and both ends over F', as shown in the figure. Adjust the string so that $F'P$ exceeds FP by $2\,a$, the transverse axis. Hold the strings together below F' and pull them in or let them out, keeping the point P of the pencil firmly against the string;

Fig. 129

cil firmly against the string; then the point P will trace out one branch of the hyperbola. By reversing the arrangement, the other branch of the hyperbola may be drawn.

241. Applications of the Hyperbola

Some of the applications of the hyperbola are the following:

Range-finding in artillery work may be based on the intersection of two hyperbolas. If the time of the report of a gun is noted at each of two listening posts, the difference in time multiplied by the velocity of sound gives the difference of distances of the gun from these two fixed points. By the definition of the hyperbola, the gun is located on a hyperbola whose foci are the listening posts and whose transverse axis is the difference of distances. If the time of the report at a third listening post is obtained, another hyperbola is determined in a similar way, and the position of the gun is located at one of the intersections of the two hyperbolas.

By using the same general ideas as those described above in range-finding, a new method of navigation for locating the position of a ship at sea, called "Loran," has recently been developed, employing radio signals from selected stations and maps with systems of hyperbolas drawn in advance, having the stations as foci.

The orbits of some comets are hyperbolas.

The graphic representation of Boyle's law for gases is an equilateral hyperbola.

Indicator diagrams for the horsepower of an engine contain arcs of hyperbolas.

242. The Directrix Property of the Ellipse and Hyperbola

The distance FP or $F'P$ from a focus of an ellipse or hyperbola to any point P on the curve is called a *focal radius* of the point P.

Let $P(x, y)$ be any point on the ellipse $b^2x^2 + a^2y^2 = a^2b^2$, and let F be the focus $(c, 0)$. Since $c = ae$ and $e^2 = 1 - \dfrac{b^2}{a^2}$, and $y^2 = \dfrac{b^2}{a^2}(a^2 - x^2)$, and $c^2 + b^2 = a^2$, we have

$$(FP)^2 = (x - c)^2 + y^2 = x^2 - 2\,cx + c^2 + \frac{b^2}{a^2}(a^2 - x^2)$$

$$= \left(1 - \frac{b^2}{a^2}\right)x^2 - 2\,aex + c^2 + b^2$$

$$= e^2x^2 - 2\,aex + a^2 = (a - ex)^2.$$

Then $FP = a - ex$, since $a > ex$. Similarly, we find $F'P = a + ex$, where F' is the other focus $(-c, 0)$. Hence:

I. *The focal radii of any point $P(x, y)$ of the ellipse $b^2x^2 + a^2y^2 = a^2b^2$ are*

(14) $$FP = a - ex, \qquad F'P = a + ex,$$

where F is the focus $(c, 0)$ and F' is the focus $(-c, 0)$.

We may write $FP = e\left(\dfrac{a}{e} - x\right)$. Denote by d the line whose equation is $x = a/e$ (Fig. 130).   Then $\dfrac{a}{e} - x$ is the distance PR of P

from the line d, and we have $FP = e \cdot PR$.   Similarly, $F'P = e\left(\dfrac{a}{e} + x\right)$,

and if d' is the line whose equation is $x = -a/e$, then $\dfrac{a}{e} + x$ is the

distance PR' of P from the line d', and we have $F'P = e \cdot PR'$.

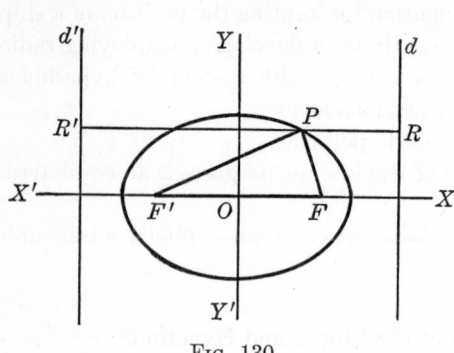

The lines d and d', whose equations are $x = a/e$ and $x = -a/e$, respectively, are called the **directrices** of the ellipse, each directrix being associated with a *corresponding* focus, d with F and d' with F'.   The preceding results may now be stated thus:

Fig. 130

II. *The ratio of the distance of any point of an ellipse from either focus to the distance of this point from the corresponding directrix is always equal to the eccentricity e:*

$$\frac{FP}{PR} = e, \qquad \frac{F'P}{PR'} = e.$$

In a similar way, it can be shown that if P is any point on the hyperbola $b^2x^2 - a^2y^2 = a^2b^2$, then

$$(FP)^2 = (ex - a)^2 \quad \text{and} \quad FP = |ex - a|; \quad \text{also} \quad F'P = |ex + a|.$$

Hence:

III. *The focal radii of any point $P(x, y)$ on the hyperbola*

$$b^2x^2 - a^2y^2 = a^2b^2$$

are

(15) $FP = |ex - a|, \qquad F'P = |ex + a|,$

where F is the focus $(c, 0)$ and F' is the focus $(-c, 0)$.

In a manner similar to that used for the ellipse, by use of the results (15), it may readily be shown that $FP = e \cdot PR$, $F'P = e \cdot PR'$, where PR is the distance of P from the line $x = a/e$ and PR' is the distance of P from the line $x = -a/e$.

The lines d and d', whose equations are $x = a/e$ and $x = -a/e$, respectively, are called the **directrices** of the hyperbola, each directrix being associated with a *corresponding* focus, d with F and d' with F'. We may now state the preceding results as follows:

IV. *The ratio of the distance of any point of a hyperbola from either focus to the distance of this point from the corresponding directrix is always equal to the eccentricity e:*

$$\frac{FP}{PR} = e, \qquad \frac{F'P}{PR'} = e.$$

If we recall the definition of the parabola (§ 218), we may formulate the following theorem:

V. *The ratio of the distance of any point of a parabola, ellipse or hyperbola from a focus to the distance of this point from the corresponding directrix is always equal to the eccentricity e. For a parabola $e = 1$, for an ellipse $e < 1$, and for a hyperbola $e > 1$.*

This property is frequently used as the basic definition of each of these curves.

243. Exercises

1. Locate the foci and directrices of the ellipses:
   (a) $4x^2 + 9y^2 = 36$;   (b) $4x^2 + y^2 = 4$.
2. Locate the foci and directrices of the ellipses:
   (a) $25x^2 + 169y^2 = 400$;   (b) $9x^2 + 4y^2 = 4$.
3. Find the equation of the ellipse with center at the origin, with directrices $x = 4$ and $x = -4$ and eccentricity $1/2$.
4. Find the equation of the ellipse with foci $(0, \pm2)$ and directrices $y = \pm8$.
5. Locate the foci and directrices of the hyperbolas:
   (a) $16x^2 - 25y^2 = 400$;   (b) $4x^2 - y^2 = 16$.
6. Locate the foci and directrices of the hyperbolas:
   (a) $9x^2 - 16y^2 = 144$;   (b) $x^2 - 4y^2 = 4$.
7. Find the equation of the hyperbola with center at the origin, with directrices $x = 5$ and $x = -5$ and eccentricity 2.
8. Find the equation of the hyperbola with foci $(\pm5, 0)$ and directrices $x = \pm\frac{16}{5}$.
9. Prove directly that the locus of a point which moves so that the ratio of its distance from the point $(ae, 0)$ to its distance from the line $x = \dfrac{a}{e}$ is

always equal to e is the ellipse $b^2x^2 + a^2y^2 = a^2b^2$, if $e < 1$ and $b^2 = a^2(1 - e^2)$.

10. Prove that the line joining a point P of an ellipse with the center and the line through a focus perpendicular to the tangent at P meet on a directrix.

244. Translation of Coördinate Axes

It is frequently useful to change from one set of coördinate axes to another set of axes; this process gives rise to a *transformation of coördinates.*

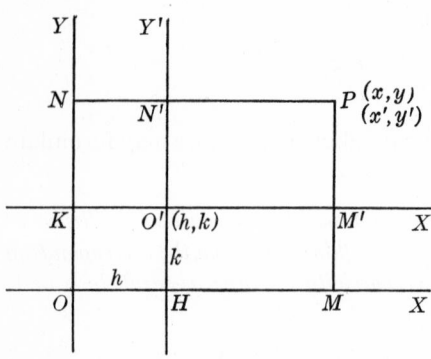

Fig. 131

Let OX and OY be the original rectangular axes (Fig. 131), and let $O'X'$ and $O'Y'$ be a new set of coördinate axes, having a new origin O' and *parallel* respectively to the old axes OX and OY, and having the same positive senses. The transformation in this case is called a ***translation of axes.***

Let the coördinates of the new origin O' with respect to the old axes be (h, k). In Fig. 131, let P be any point whose coördinates are (x, y) referred to the old axes and (x', y') referred to the new axes. Then

$$x = \overline{OM} = \overline{OH} + \overline{HM} = \overline{OH} + \overline{O'M'} = h + x',$$
$$y = \overline{MP} = \overline{MM'} + \overline{M'P} = \overline{HO'} + \overline{M'P} = k + y'.$$

Hence:

If a translation of axes is made to a new origin O' whose coördinates with respect to the old axes are (h, k), the relation between the old and new coördinates of any point is given by

(16) $$x = x' + h, \qquad y = y' + k,$$

where the primed letters represent coördinates referred to the new axes.

EXAMPLE 1. Transform the equation of the curve $y = 4x^2 + 16x + 13$ to a new set of axes parallel to the old axes, when the new origin is at the point $(3, 1)$.

Solution: The equations for the translation are

$$x = x' + 3, \qquad y = y' + 1.$$

The equation of the curve referred to the new axes is then

$$y' + 1 = 4(x' + 3)^2 + 16(x' + 3) + 13 = 4\,x'^2 + 40\,x' + 97,$$

or
$$y' = 4\,x'^2 + 40\,x' + 96.$$

EXAMPLE 2. Transform by a translation of axes the equation of the curve $4\,x^2 + 9\,y^2 - 24\,x + 36\,y + 36 = 0$ to a form in which the terms of the first degree in x and y are lacking.

Solution: We may complete the squares in the terms in x and y and obtain the form

$$4(x - 3)^2 + 9(y + 2)^2 = 36.$$

If we put $x - 3 = x'$ and $y + 2 = y'$, this equation becomes

$$4\,x'^2 + 9\,y'^2 = 36,$$

in which the first degree terms in x' and y' are lacking. The substitution $x - 3 = x'$, $y + 2 = y'$ or $x = x' + 3$, $y = y' - 2$ gives the desired translation; the new origin is $(3, -2)$.

245. Exercises

1. Transform the following equations by translation to the origin indicated in each case:
   (a) $x^2 + 9\,y^2 + 4\,x - 18\,y + 4 = 0$, $(-2, 1)$;
   (b) $y^2 - 6\,y + 5 = 4\,x$, $(-1, 3)$;
   (c) $4\,x^2 - y^2 - 12\,x - 6\,y + 24 = 0$, $(\frac{3}{2}, -3)$;
   (d) $x^2 - y^2 - 6\,x + 10\,y - 20 = 0$, $(3, 5)$.

2. Proceed as in Exercise 1 with:
   (a) $y^2 - 8\,y + 6\,x - 2 = 0$, $(3, 4)$;
   (b) $x^2 - 6\,x + 4\,y^2 + 8\,y = 5$, $(3, -1)$;
   (c) $x^2 - 6\,x + y^2 + 6\,y = 7$, $(3, -3)$;
   (d) $4\,x^2 - y^2 + 24\,x + 8\,y + 16 = 0$, $(-3, 4)$.

3. By translation, remove the first degree terms in x and y in the following equations and give the new origin:
   (a) $x^2 - 4\,x - 4\,y - 8 = 0$;
   (b) $9\,x^2 + 16\,y^2 + 18\,x - 128\,y + 121 = 0$.

4. Proceed as in Exercise 3 with:
   (a) $y^2 - 8\,x - 2\,y - 23 = 0$;
   (b) $25\,x^2 - 9\,y^2 - 50\,x - 36\,y - 236 = 0$.

246. More General Forms of the Equations of the Parabola, Ellipse and Hyperbola

If a parabola has its vertex at any point (h, k) or if an ellipse or hyperbola has its center at (h, k), and if the principal axis of either curve is parallel to one of the coördinate axes, the equations of the curves may be obtained from the previous standard equations by use

of a translation of coördinates.   If the coördinate axes are translated
to a new origin $O'(h, k)$, the equations for the transformation are

(a) $$x' = x - h, \qquad y' = y - k.$$

By writing the equation of the given curve in terms of the new co-
ordinates x', y' by use of the previous standard equations and making
the substitution (a), we obtain the required more general equations.
The results may be stated thus:

I. *Parabola with vertex at (h, k)*:

(17) $\qquad (y - k)^2 = 2\,p(x - h),$ *axis parallel to OX,*

(18) $\qquad (x - h)^2 = 2\,p(y - k),$ *axis parallel to OY.*

II. *Ellipse with center at (h, k)*:

(19) $\qquad \dfrac{(x - h)^2}{a^2} + \dfrac{(y - k)^2}{b^2} = 1,$ *major axis parallel to OX,*

(20) $\qquad \dfrac{(y - k)^2}{a^2} + \dfrac{(x - h)^2}{b^2} = 1,$ *major axis parallel to OY.*

III. *Hyperbola with center at (h, k)*:

(21) $\qquad \dfrac{(x - h)^2}{a^2} - \dfrac{(y - k)^2}{b^2} = 1,$ *transverse axis parallel to OX,*

(22) $\qquad \dfrac{(y - k)^2}{a^2} - \dfrac{(x - h)^2}{b^2} = 1,$ *transverse axis parallel to OY.*

EXAMPLE 1.   Find the equation of the parabola whose vertex is at $(-4, 2)$
and whose focus is at $(-2, 2)$.

Solution: Since the vertex and focus have the same ordinate 2, the axis of
the parabola is parallel to the X-axis, and the equation of the curve is of the
form (17), with $h = -4, k = 2$.   Since the focus is to the right of the vertex,
the curve opens to the right and p is positive; the distance between the
vertex and focus is $\frac{1}{2}\,p = 2$, so that $2\,p = 8$.   The required equation is
therefore

$$(y - 2)^2 = 8(x + 4) \qquad \text{or} \qquad y^2 - 8\,x - 4\,y - 28 = 0.$$

When multiplied out, the equations (17) and (18) of the parabola
take the forms

(b) $$y^2 + Dx + Ey + F = 0 \qquad (D \neq 0),$$

(c) $$x^2 + D'x + E'y + F' = 0 \qquad (E' \neq 0),$$

respectively.   Conversely, any equation of the form (b) or (c) can be put in the form (17) or (18) by completing the square in y or x respectively. Such an equation therefore represents a parabola with axis parallel to one of the coördinate axes.

An equation of the form (c) can also be written in the form $y = ax^2 + bx + c$. Hence, any quadratic function of x such as $y = ax^2 + bx + c$ is represented graphically by a parabola with axis parallel to the Y-axis.

Equations (19) and (20) of an ellipse, when multiplied out, take the form

(d) $$Ax^2 + Cy^2 + Dx + Ey + F = 0,$$

where A and C are unequal, different from zero and of the same sign. Similarly, the equations (21) and (22) of a hyperbola take the form (d) in which coefficients A and C are of opposite sign. Conversely, any equation of the form (d) can in general be put in one of the forms (19)–(22) by completing the squares in x and y. The graph of such an equation as (d) is therefore an ellipse or hyperbola, depending on the signs of A and C, with axes parallel to the coördinate axes (provided that the resulting numbers a^2 and b^2 are positive).

EXAMPLE 2. Show that the graph of the equation
$$9 x^2 + 16 y^2 + 36 x - 96 y + 36 = 0$$
is an ellipse, and find its semi-axes, and locate its center, vertices and foci.

Solution: We complete the squares in x and y thus:
$$9(x^2 + 4 x + 4) + 16(y^2 - 6 y + 9) = -36 + 36 + 144 = 144.$$
This may be written
$$\frac{[x - (-2)]^2}{16} + \frac{(y - 3)^2}{9} = 1.$$

This equation is of the form (19) and therefore represents an ellipse, with $h = -2$, $k = 3$, $a = 4$, $b = 3$. The center is at $(-2, 3)$, the semi-axes are 4 and 3, and the vertices are at $(2, 3)$ and $(-6, 3)$. Since $c^2 = a^2 + b^2$, we have $c = \sqrt{7}$; the foci are at $(-2 + \sqrt{7}, 3)$ and $(-2 - \sqrt{7}, 3)$.

247. Exercises

1. Find the equations of the parabolas satisfying the following conditions:
    (a) vertex at $(1, 3)$, focus at $(5, 3)$;
    (b) focus at $(-2, 6)$, directrix $y = -4$;
    (c) vertex at $(-1, 2)$, directrix $x - 3 = 0$.
2. Proceed as in Exercise 1 with:
    (a) focus at $(-2, 3)$, vertex at $(-2, -1)$;

(b) vertex at $(4, 3)$, directrix $y = -5$;

(c) focus at $(3, -2)$, directrix $x + 1 = 0$.

3. For each of the following parabolas, find the coördinates of the vertex and focus, and find the equation of the directrix and the equation of the axis; also sketch each curve:

(a) $y^2 - 4y - 6x + 10 = 0$;   (b) $x^2 + 6x - 8y + 41 = 0$;

(c) $3x^2 + 6x + 5y - 7 = 0$;   (d) $3y^2 + 12y + 16 = 4x$.

4. Proceed as in Exercise 3 with:

(a) $y^2 + 8y - 4x + 12 = 0$;   (b) $x^2 - 10x - 3y + 19 = 0$;

(c) $2x^2 + 7y - 5x - 2 = 0$;   (d) $y^2 - 5y = x - 7$.

5. Find the equation of the parabola with axis parallel to the Y-axis and passing through the points $(1, -2)$, $(2, 1)$ and $(-1, 4)$. [*Hint.* Assume the equation of the parabola to be $y = ax^2 + bx + c$, and use the fact that if a point lies on a curve, its coördinates satisfy the equation of the curve.]

6. Find the equation of the parabola with axis parallel to the X-axis and passing through the points $(2, 1)$, $(5, -2)$ and $(10, 3)$. [See the hint in Exercise 5.]

7. Find the equations of the ellipses satisfying the following conditions:

(a) center at $(2, 1)$, semi-axes $a = 5$, $b = 3$, major axis parallel to the X-axis;

(b) vertices at $(-4, 3)$ and $(6, 3)$, length of minor axis 8;

(c) foci at $(-1, -2)$ and $(3, -2)$, length of major axis 10;

(d) center at $(4, 2)$, major axis parallel to the Y-axis and of length 12, eccentricity $2/3$;

(e) vertices at $(-2, 1)$ and $(6, 1)$, one focus at $(4, 1)$;

(f) foci at $(-2, -3)$ and $(6, -3)$, eccentricity $1/2$.

8. Proceed as in Exercise 7 with the conditions:

(a) center at $(-1, 4)$, one vertex at $(4, 4)$, corresponding focus at $(3, 4)$;

(b) vertices at $(-2, 2)$ and $(-2, -6)$, length of minor axis 4;

(c) foci at $(2, 1)$ and $(14, 1)$ eccentricity $3/4$;

(d) vertices at $(-2, 5)$ and $(-2, -7)$, one focus at $(-2, -5)$;

(e) one vertex at $(0, -3)$, corresponding focus at $(2, -3)$, length of minor axis 8;

(f) one focus at $(-3, 3)$, length of major axis 10, minor axis on the line $x = 1$.

9. For each of the following ellipses find the coördinates of the center, vertices, foci, and sketch each curve:

(a) $16x^2 + 25y^2 - 32x + 100y - 284 = 0$;

(b) $25x^2 + 9y^2 + 225x - 36y + 36 = 0$;

(c) $x^2 + 4y^2 + 8x + 8y + 4 = 0$;

(d) $4x^2 + 8y^2 + 4x - 24y + 1 = 0$.

10. Proceed as in Exercise 9 with the equations:

(a) $9x^2 + 16y^2 + 36x - 16y - 104 = 0$;

(b) $4x^2 + y^2 - 24x + 8y + 48 = 0$;

(c) $5x^2 + 2y^2 - 20x + 16y + 42 = 0$;

(d) $8x^2 + 9y^2 + 32x - 18y + 23 = 0$.

11. Find the equations of the hyperbolas satisfying the following conditions:

(a) center at $(-1, 3)$, semi-axes $a = 3$, $b = 2$, transverse axis parallel to the X-axis;

(b) vertices at $(4, 4)$, $(-2, 4)$, length of conjugate axis 8;

(c) foci at $(-7, -3)$, $(3, -3)$, one vertex at $(2, -3)$;

(d) vertices at $(2, 4)$, $(2, -2)$, eccentricity 2;

(e) foci at $(-3, 5)$, $(7, 5)$, slope of an asymptote $3/4$;

(f) vertices at $(-3, 2)$, $(9, 2)$, asymptotes $x - 2y + 1 = 0$, $x + 2y - 7 = 0$.

12. Proceed as in Exercise 11 with the conditions:

(a) vertices at $(1, 3)$, $(9, 3)$, length of conjugate axis 6;

(b) center at $(-1, -2)$, one focus at $(3, -2)$, length of transverse axis 6;

(c) foci at $(-7, 2)$, $(-13, 2)$, one vertex at $(-11, 2)$;

(d) vertices at $(2, 4)$, $(2, -2)$, eccentricity $4/3$;

(e) vertices at $(-5, -3)$, $(7, -3)$, slope of an asymptote $1/2$;

(f) center at $(2, 4)$, one focus at $(7, 4)$, asymptotes $3x - 4y + 10 = 0$, $3x + 4y - 22 = 0$.

13. For each of the following hyperbolas, find the coördinates of the center, vertices, foci, the equations of the asymptotes, and sketch each curve:

(a) $9x^2 - 16y^2 - 18x + 96y - 279 = 0$;

(b) $x^2 - 4y^2 + 4x + 32y - 64 = 0$;

(c) $25x^2 - 9y^2 - 75x + 9y - 396 = 0$;

(d) $5y^2 - 4x^2 + 8x + 40y + 56 = 0$.

14. Proceed as in Exercise 13 with the equations:

(a) $4x^2 - 9y^2 - 16x + 18y - 9 = 0$;

(b) $25x^2 - 16y^2 + 50x + 96y - 219 = 0$;

(c) $9y^2 - x^2 - 6x - 72y + 126 = 0$;

(d) $x^2 - y^2 - 4x = 0$.

248. Conic Sections

The intersection of a circular conical surface by a plane is called a **conic section** or simply a *conic*.

It is evident that the shape of a section of a conical surface depends upon the position of the cutting plane. The following facts can be proved. Suppose first that this plane does not pass through the vertex of the cone. If the cutting plane is perpendicular to the axis of the cone, the section is a **circle** (Fig. 132 (a)). If the plane is not perpendicular to the axis but cuts all the elements of the conical surface on one side of the vertex, the section is an **ellipse** (Fig. 132 (b)). If the plane is parallel to an element and cuts all other elements on one side of the vertex, the section is a **parabola** (Fig. 132 (c)). If the plane cuts both nappes of the cone, the section is a *hyperbola* (Fig. 132 (*d*)). Suppose next that the cutting plane passes through the vertex. Then the intersection with the conical surface may be either a single point (the vertex), or a single straight line (an element of the cone), or two intersecting straight lines (passing through the vertex).

These conic sections were discussed by the ancient Greeks by methods of elementary geometry, and many of their properties were discovered by them.

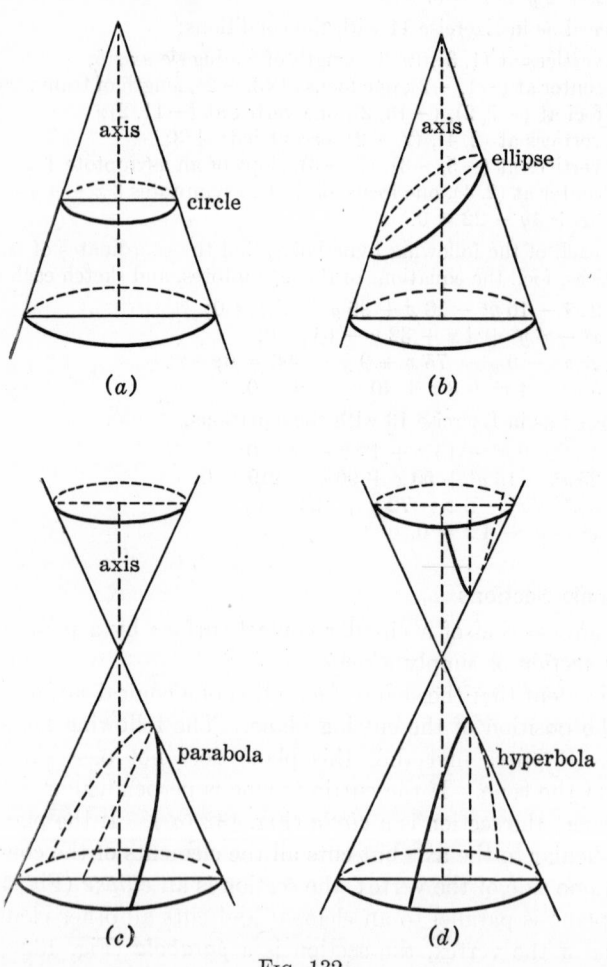

Fig. 132

The equations of the circle, the parabola, the ellipse and the hyperbola, as discussed previously, are all special forms of the general quadratic equation

$$Ax^2 + Bxy + Cy^2 + Dx + Ey + F = 0.$$

It can be proved that the graph of any equation of this form is either a *conic section* or *two parallel lines*, except that in certain cases the equation may have no real graph.

★ 249. Transformation of Coördinates by Rotation of Axes

The equation of a curve, referred to a given set of rectangular axes, can often be simplified by use of a new set of coördinate axes. If the original axes are moved parallel to themselves, we have a translation of axes, which has been already discussed in § 244. If the original axes are rotated about the origin through a certain angle, keeping the origin fixed, the new axes are said to be obtained by a *rotation of axes*.

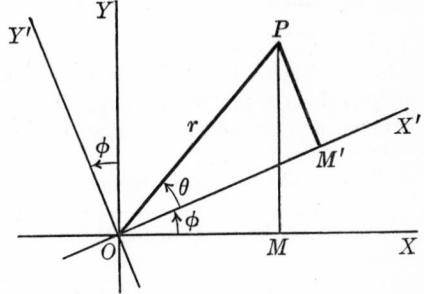

FIG. 133

Let the original axes be OX and OY (Fig. 133), and let OX' and OY' be new axes obtained by rotating OX and OY through an angle ϕ. Let P be any given point in the plane of these axes. Denote the coördinates of P, referred to the old axes, by (x, y), and referred to the new axes, by (x', y'). Then we need to express x and y in terms of x' and y', and vice versa.

Let $OP = r$ and angle $X'OP = \theta$; then angle $XOP = \phi + \theta$. From the definition of the sine and cosine, we have

$$\cos(\phi + \theta) = \frac{x}{r}, \qquad \sin(\phi + \theta) = \frac{y}{r}, \qquad \cos\theta = \frac{x'}{r}, \qquad \sin\theta = \frac{y'}{r}.$$

Therefore,

$$\begin{aligned} x &= r\cos(\phi + \theta) = r(\cos\phi\cos\theta - \sin\phi\sin\theta) \\ &= (r\cos\theta)\cos\phi - (r\sin\theta)\sin\phi = x'\cos\phi - y'\sin\phi, \\ y &= r\sin(\phi + \theta) = r(\sin\phi\cos\theta + \cos\phi\sin\theta) \\ &= (r\cos\theta)\sin\phi + (r\sin\theta)\cos\phi = x'\sin\phi + y'\cos\phi. \end{aligned}$$

Hence:

If a given set of rectangular axes is rotated about the origin through an angle ϕ, the old coördinates of any point are given in terms of the new coördinates by the transformation formulas:

$$\textbf{(23)} \qquad \begin{aligned} x &= x' \cos \phi - y' \sin \phi, \\ y &= x' \sin \phi + y' \cos \phi. \end{aligned}$$

If we solve these equations for x' and y' and simplify, we obtain

$$\textbf{(24)} \qquad \begin{aligned} x' &= x \cos \phi + y \sin \phi, \\ y' &= -x \sin \phi + y \cos \phi. \end{aligned}$$

When simplifying equations of curves by a transformation by rotation of axes, we find that a rotation through a positive acute angle is sufficient.

EXAMPLE. The equation of a rectangular hyperbola with center at the origin and foci on the X-axis is $x^2 - y^2 = a^2$. The asymptotes $y = \pm x$ of this hyperbola make angles of $\pm 45°$ with the X-axis. If the asymptotes are taken as new coördinate axes, the equation of the hyperbola takes an important new form.

Let us rotate the axes through an angle of $-45°$, then the asymptote $y = -x$ becomes the new X'-axis and the asymptote $y = x$ becomes the new Y'-axis. The equations (23) for the transformation become

$$x = x' \cos (-45°) - y' \sin (-45°) = x'(\tfrac{1}{2}\sqrt{2}) - y'(-\tfrac{1}{2}\sqrt{2}) = \frac{x' + y'}{\sqrt{2}},$$

$$y = x' \sin (-45°) + y' \cos (-45°) = x'(-\tfrac{1}{2}\sqrt{2}) + y'(\tfrac{1}{2}\sqrt{2}) = \frac{-x' + y'}{\sqrt{2}}.$$

If we substitute these values in the equation $x^2 - y^2 = a^2$, we get

$$\frac{(x' + y')^2}{2} - \frac{(-x' + y')^2}{2} = a^2;$$

when simplified, this becomes

$$(e) \qquad\qquad\qquad 2\,x'y' = a^2.$$

This is the equation of a rectangular hyperbola referred to its asymptotes as coördinate axes.

By a rotation of axes through a suitable angle, we may remove the xy term from any equation in x and y of the second degree. This greatly simplifies the analysis of the graph. This transformation is explained in the next article.

When these expressions are substit
plified, we find

$$9\,x''^2 + 4\,y''$$

(*j*) $$\frac{x''^2}{4} + \frac{y''^2}{9}$$

This is the equation of an ellipse i
axis and semi-axes of length 3 and
shown in Fig. 134.

If both translation and rotatic
the translation first in the case c
rotation first in the case of the

★ **251. Exercises**

1. For each of the following equati
   the given angle and find the tran
   (*a*) $8\,x^2 - 4\,xy + 5\,y^2 = 36,\ \phi =$
   (*b*) $x^2 + 4\,xy + y^2 = 16,\ \phi = 45$

2. Proceed as in Exercise 1 with:
   (*a*) $4\,x^2 + 15\,xy - 4\,y^2 = 20,\ \phi$
   (*b*) $x^2 + 4\,xy + 4\,y^2 - 36\,y = 0,$

3. By a suitable rotation of axes, tr
   into a form lacking the xy-term;
   graph:
   (*a*) $11\,x^2 + 24\,xy + 4\,y^2 = 20;$

4. Proceed as in Exercise 3 with:
   (*a*) $11\,x^2 + 6\,xy + 3\,y^2 = 20;$

5. By a suitable translation and rota
   lowing equations to a form lackin;
   and lacking the xy-term; draw bot
   (*a*) $5\,x^2 + 6\,xy + 5\,y^2 - 32\,x - 3$
   (*b*) $9\,x^2 - 24\,xy + 16\,y^2 - 56\,x -$

6. Proceed as in Exercise 5 with:
   (*a*) $13\,x^2 + 48\,xy + 27\,y^2 + 44\,x -$
   (*b*) $3\,x^2 - 4\,xy - 16\,x + 8\,y + 24$

★ **250. Graph of the General Equation of the Second Degree**

Each of the equations of curves derived in this chapter is a special case of the general equation of the second degree:

(*a*) $$ax^2 + bxy + cy^2 + dx + ey + f = 0,$$

where a, b and c are not all zero. It can be proved without difficulty that *the equation of any conic section in any position is always an equation of the second degree (in rectangular coördinates).*

Conversely, it can be proved that *the graph, if it exists, of every equation of the second degree in rectangular coördinates is a conic section or a pair of parallel lines.* This is shown by making a transformation of the equation by a translation or a rotation of axes or both. By a translation of axes, one can remove one or both of the first degree terms in x and y; by a rotation of axes, one can generally remove the xy-term.

We shall now derive a formula for the angle ϕ through which the axes are to be rotated in order to remove the xy-term. We shall assume that $b \neq 0$, and in equation (*a*) make the substitution (§ 249):

(*b*) $$x = x' \cos \phi - y' \sin \phi, \qquad y = x' \sin \phi + y' \cos \phi.$$

After collecting terms, we obtain

(*c*) $(a \cos^2 \phi + b \sin \phi \cos \phi + c \sin^2 \phi)x'^2$
$\qquad + (-2\,a \sin \phi \cos \phi - b \sin^2 \phi + b \cos^2 \phi + 2\,c \sin \phi \cos \phi)x'y'$
$\qquad + (a \sin^2 \phi - b \sin \phi \cos \phi + c \cos^2 \phi)y'^2$
$\qquad + (d \cos \phi + e \sin \phi)x' + (-d \sin \phi + e \cos \phi)y' + f = 0.$

We may remove the $x'y'$-term by putting its coefficient equal to zero, which gives

(*d*) $$b\,(\cos^2 \phi - \sin^2 \phi) - 2(a - c) \sin \phi \cos \phi = 0.$$

By trigonometry, $\cos^2 \phi - \sin^2 \phi = \cos 2\,\phi$, $2 \sin \phi \cos \phi = \sin 2\,\phi$. Then (*d*) may be written

$$b \cos 2\,\phi - (a - c) \sin 2\,\phi = 0, \qquad \text{or}$$

(25) $$\cot 2\,\phi = \frac{a - c}{b}.$$

If ϕ is chosen so as to satisfy (25), the coefficient of $x'y'$ in the transformed equation is zero. If $\cot 2\,\phi$ is positive, we make $2\,\phi$ acute;

and if cot 2ϕ is negativ

acute angle.   If $a = c$,

From (25) we find th

of $\cos\phi$ and $\sin\phi$ by use

(e) $\cos\phi = \sqrt{\dfrac{1+}{}}$

EXAMPLE. Discuss the g

(f) $5x^2 + 4xy$

Solution: We first transl

$x = x' + h,\ y = y' + k$ (§

collecting coefficients of the

(g) $5x'^2 + 4x'y' + 8y'^2 +$

$+ (5h^2 +$

We may remove the first deg

the coefficients of x' and y'

(h) $10h + 4k -$

If we solve these equations

$h = 2$ and $k = -1$. By su

obtain

(i) $5x'^2 +$

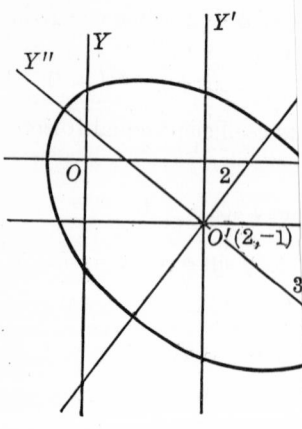

FIG. 134

$y' =$

CHAPTER XIII

Differentiation of Transcendental Functions

252. Transcendental Functions

A *transcendental function* was defined in § 85 as any function which is not algebraic. The elementary transcendental functions are: the trigonometric, inverse trigonometric, exponential, logarithmic and hyperbolic functions.

253. Radian Measure of Angles

For the purposes of calculus, it will be found that radian measure of angles is essential. Therefore we briefly review this concept, which is usually treated in works on trigonometry.

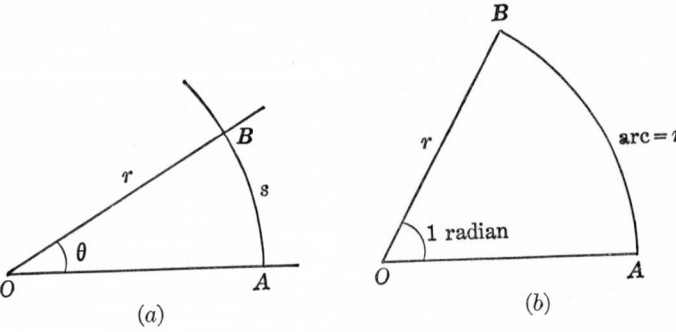

(a) $\qquad\qquad\qquad\qquad$ (b)

FIG. 135

The **radian measure** or **circular measure** of an angle whose vertex is at the center of a circle is defined as the ratio of the intercepted arc to the radius (Fig. 135 (a)):

(a) $\qquad\qquad\qquad\qquad$ $\theta = \dfrac{s}{r}.$

278

★ 250. Graph of the General Equation of the Second Degree

Each of the equations of curves derived in this chapter is a special case of the general equation of the second degree:

$$(a) \qquad ax^2 + bxy + cy^2 + dx + ey + f = 0,$$

where a, b and c are not all zero. It can be proved without difficulty that *the equation of any conic section in any position is always an equation of the second degree (in rectangular coördinates)*.

Conversely, it can be proved that *the graph, if it exists, of every equation of the second degree in rectangular coördinates is a conic section or a pair of parallel lines*. This is shown by making a transformation of the equation by a translation or a rotation of axes or both. By a translation of axes, one can remove one or both of the first degree terms in x and y; by a rotation of axes, one can generally remove the xy-term.

We shall now derive a formula for the angle ϕ through which the axes are to be rotated in order to remove the xy-term. We shall assume that $b \neq 0$, and in equation (a) make the substitution (§ 249):

$$(b) \qquad x = x' \cos \phi - y' \sin \phi, \qquad y = x' \sin \phi + y' \cos \phi.$$

After collecting terms, we obtain

$$(c) \quad (a \cos^2 \phi + b \sin \phi \cos \phi + c \sin^2 \phi)x'^2$$
$$+ (-2 a \sin \phi \cos \phi - b \sin^2 \phi + b \cos^2 \phi + 2 c \sin \phi \cos \phi)x'y'$$
$$+ (a \sin^2 \phi - b \sin \phi \cos \phi + c \cos^2 \phi)y'^2$$
$$+ (d \cos \phi + e \sin \phi)x' + (-d \sin \phi + e \cos \phi)y' + f = 0.$$

We may remove the $x'y'$-term by putting its coefficient equal to zero, which gives

$$(d) \qquad b (\cos^2 \phi - \sin^2 \phi) - 2(a - c) \sin \phi \cos \phi = 0.$$

By trigonometry, $\cos^2 \phi - \sin^2 \phi = \cos 2\phi$, $2 \sin \phi \cos \phi = \sin 2\phi$. Then (d) may be written

$$b \cos 2\phi - (a - c) \sin 2\phi = 0, \qquad \text{or}$$

$$(25) \qquad \cot 2\phi = \frac{a - c}{b}.$$

If ϕ is chosen so as to satisfy (25), the coefficient of $x'y'$ in the transformed equation is zero. If $\cot 2\phi$ is positive, we make 2ϕ acute;

and if $\cot 2\phi$ is negative, we make 2ϕ obtuse; in each case, ϕ is an acute angle. If $a = c$, we take $2\phi = 90°$, and $\phi = 45°$.

From (25) we find the value of $\cos 2\phi$; then we obtain the values of $\cos \phi$ and $\sin \phi$ by use of the half-angle formulas:

$$(e) \qquad \cos \phi = \sqrt{\frac{1 + \cos 2\phi}{2}}, \qquad \sin \phi = \sqrt{\frac{1 - \cos 2\phi}{2}}.$$

EXAMPLE. Discuss the graph of the equation

$$(f) \qquad 5x^2 + 4xy + 8y^2 - 16x + 8y - 16 = 0.$$

Solution: We first translate the origin to the point (h, k) by putting $x = x' + h$, $y = y' + k$ (§ 244). By substituting these values in (f) and collecting coefficients of the various types of terms in x' and y', we get

$$(g) \quad 5x'^2 + 4x'y' + 8y'^2 + (10h + 4k - 16)x' + (4h + 16k + 8)y'$$
$$+ (5h^2 + 4hk + 8k^2 - 16h + 8k - 16) = 0.$$

We may remove the first degree terms in x' and y' in this equation by putting the coefficients of x' and y' equal to zero:

$$(h) \qquad 10h + 4k - 16 = 0, \qquad 4h + 16k + 8 = 0.$$

If we solve these equations as a simultaneous system for h and k, we find $h = 2$ and $k = -1$. By substitution of these values of h and k in (g), we obtain

$$(i) \qquad 5x'^2 + 4x'y' + 8y'^2 - 16 = 0.$$

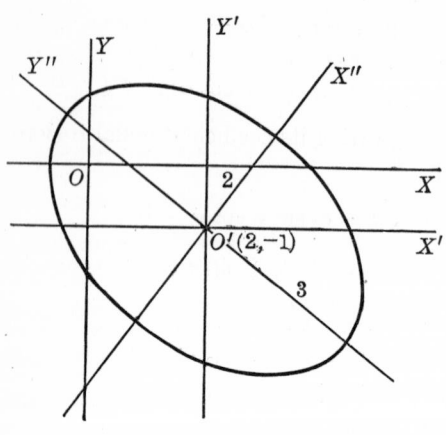

FIG. 134

We now apply formula (25) to this equation, with $a = 5$, $b = 4$ and $c = 8$, and we get $\cot 2\phi = -\frac{3}{4}$; from this we find $\cos 2\phi = -\frac{3}{5}$. By (e), we have

$$\cos \phi = \sqrt{\tfrac{1}{2}(1 - \tfrac{3}{5})} = \frac{1}{\sqrt{5}},$$

$$\sin \phi = \sqrt{\tfrac{1}{2}(1 + \tfrac{3}{5})} = \frac{2}{\sqrt{5}}.$$

If we substitute these values of $\cos \phi$ and $\sin \phi$ in the formulas for rotation of axes, we obtain

$$x' = \frac{1}{\sqrt{5}}x'' - \frac{2}{\sqrt{5}}y'',$$

$$y' = \frac{2}{\sqrt{5}}x'' + \frac{1}{\sqrt{5}}y''.$$

When these expressions are substituted in equation (i), and the result simplified, we find

$$9\,x''^2 + 4\,y''^2 - 36 = 0, \qquad \text{or}$$

(j)
$$\frac{x''^2}{4} + \frac{y''^2}{9} = 1.$$

This is the equation of an ellipse in the $X''Y''$-plane, with foci on the Y''-axis and semi-axes of length 3 and 2. The graph of the given equation is shown in Fig. 134.

If both translation and rotation are to be made, it is best to make the translation first in the case of the ellipse and hyperbola, and the rotation first in the case of the parabola.

★ 251. Exercises

1. For each of the following equations rotate the coördinate axes through the given angle and find the transformed equation in simplified form:

   (a) $8\,x^2 - 4\,xy + 5\,y^2 = 36$, $\phi = \text{Arc tan } 2$;

   (b) $x^2 + 4\,xy + y^2 = 16$, $\phi = 45°$.

2. Proceed as in Exercise 1 with:

   (a) $4\,x^2 + 15\,xy - 4\,y^2 = 20$, $\phi = \text{Arc tan } \frac{3}{5}$;

   (b) $x^2 + 4\,xy + 4\,y^2 - 36\,y = 0$, $\phi = \text{Arc tan } \frac{4}{3}$.

3. By a suitable rotation of axes, transform each of the following equations into a form lacking the xy-term; draw both sets of axes and draw each graph:

   (a) $11\,x^2 + 24\,xy + 4\,y^2 = 20$;   (b) $25\,x^2 + 14\,xy + 25\,y^2 = 288$.

4. Proceed as in Exercise 3 with:

   (a) $11\,x^2 + 6\,xy + 3\,y^2 = 20$;   (b) $3\,x^2 + 4\,xy = 4$.

5. By a suitable translation and rotation of axes, transform each of the following equations to a form lacking one or both of the first degree terms and lacking the xy-term; draw both sets of axes and draw each graph:

   (a) $5\,x^2 + 6\,xy + 5\,y^2 - 32\,x - 32\,y + 32 = 0$;

   (b) $9\,x^2 - 24\,xy + 16\,y^2 - 56\,x - 92\,y + 688 = 0$.

6. Proceed as in Exercise 5 with:

   (a) $13\,x^2 + 48\,xy + 27\,y^2 + 44\,x + 12\,y - 77 = 0$;

   (b) $3\,x^2 - 4\,xy - 16\,x + 8\,y + 24 = 0$.

Differentiation of Transcendental Functions

252. Transcendental Functions

A **transcendental function** was defined in § 85 as any function which is not algebraic. The elementary transcendental functions are: the trigonometric, inverse trigonometric, exponential, logarithmic and hyperbolic functions.

253. Radian Measure of Angles

For the purposes of calculus, it will be found that radian measure of angles is essential. Therefore we briefly review this concept, which is usually treated in works on trigonometry.

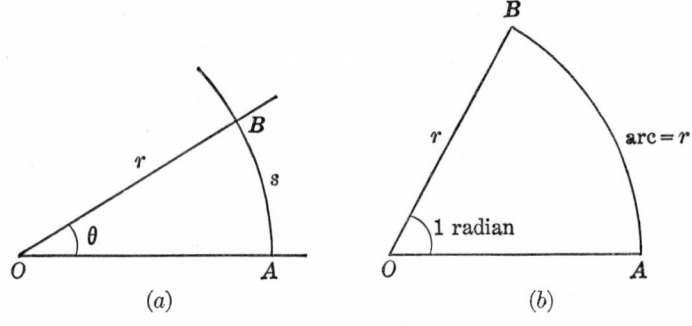

(a)   (b)

Fig. 135

*The **radian measure** or **circular measure** of an angle whose vertex is at the center of a circle is defined as the ratio of the intercepted arc to the radius* (Fig. 135 (a)):

(a)
$$\theta = \frac{s}{r}.$$

The reason for this particular choice of angular measure will be seen in §§ 261, 263.

It follows at once that: *the unit angle, a* **radian,** *is an angle which, when placed with its vertex at the center of a circle, intercepts an arc equal in length to the radius* (Fig. 135 (*b*)).

If an angle of radian measure θ intercepts an arc of length s in a circle of radius r, it follows at once from the definition of circular measure that:

$$(b) \qquad\qquad s = r \cdot \theta.$$

That is, *the length of the circular arc intercepted by an angle at the center is equal to the radius times the radian measure of the angle.*

Since the radian measure of an angle of 2 right angles is $(\pi r)/r = \pi$, the fundamental relation between radian measure and degree measure may be expressed by:

$$(c) \qquad\qquad \pi \text{ radians} = 180°.$$

From this formula, we obtain:

$$1 \text{ radian} = \left(\frac{180}{\pi}\right)° = 57.296° \text{ (approximately)},$$

$$1° = \left(\frac{\pi}{180}\right) \text{ radian} = 0.01745 \text{ radian (approximately)}.$$

By elementary geometry, any two sectors of the same circle are to each other as their corresponding angles, hence (Fig. 135 (*a*)):

$$\text{Area of sector } AOB : \text{area of circle} = \theta : 2\pi.$$

From this, since the area of the circle is πr^2, it follows that:

$$(d) \qquad\qquad \textbf{\textit{Area of sector AOB}} = \tfrac{1}{2}\, r^2\theta.$$

254. Trigonometric Functions

The **trigonometric functions** consist of the six functions: $\sin x$, $\cos x$, $\tan x$, $\csc x$, $\sec x$ and $\cot x$, defined and discussed in trigonometry. A summary of important properties and formulas for the trigonometric functions is given in the Appendix.

In calculus, angles are practically always expressed in radian measure, since all calculus formulas involving trigonometric functions are then much simpler.

It is shown in trigonometry that all six trigonometric functions are single-valued functions, that the sine, cosine, secant and cosecant are periodic functions with the period 2π radians ($360°$) and that the tangent and cotangent are periodic functions with the period π radians ($180°$). These properties and many others are well illustrated by the graphs of these functions, which are discussed in §§ 256, 257 and shown in Figs. 136, 137.

It can be shown* that the trigonometric functions $\sin x$ and $\cos x$ are continuous for all values of x, but that $\tan x$ is discontinuous (becomes infinite) for all odd multiples of $\frac{1}{2}\pi$ and is continuous elsewhere (see the graphs in Fig. 137). This is equivalent to the statements:

$$(a) \quad \begin{cases} \lim_{x \to a} (\sin x) = \sin a, & \lim_{x \to a} (\cos x) = \cos a, \\ \lim_{x \to a} (\tan x) = \tan a & \text{provided} \quad a \neq \tfrac{1}{2}(2n+1)\pi. \end{cases}$$

A small table of values of the trigonometric functions of angles expressed in radian measure is given in the Appendix, Table C.

255. Exercises

1. Evaluate each of the following limits:

   (a) $\lim_{x \to 0} (\sin x)$;   (b) $\lim_{x \to 0} (\cos x)$;

   (c) $\lim_{x \to \frac{1}{2}\pi} (\sin x)$;   (d) $\lim_{x \to \pi} (\cos x)$.

2. Evaluate each of the following limits:

   (a) $\lim_{x \to 0} (\tan x)$;   (b) $\lim_{x \to \frac{1}{2}\pi} (\cos x)$;

   (c) $\lim_{x \to \frac{1}{2}\pi} (\cot x)$;   (d) $\lim_{x \to \pi} (\sin x)$.

Find each of the limits in Exercises 3–8:

   3. $\lim_{x \to \pi} (\sin x + \cos x)$.   4. $\lim_{x \to \frac{1}{4}\pi} (\tan x + \cot x)$.

   5. $\lim_{x \to \frac{1}{2}\pi} (x^2 \sin x)$.   6. $\lim_{x \to \frac{1}{2}\pi} \left(\dfrac{\sin x}{x} \right)$.

   7. $\lim_{x \to \pi} \left(\dfrac{1 - \cos x}{x} \right)$.   8. $\lim_{x \to \frac{1}{2}\pi} \left(\dfrac{1 - \sin x}{x^2} \right)$.

Evaluate each of the indeterminate forms in Exercises 9–12 by first transforming to a more convenient form by use of a trigonometric identity:

   9. $\lim_{x \to 0} \left(\dfrac{\sin x}{\tan x} \right)$.   10. $\lim_{x \to 0} \left(\dfrac{\sin 2x}{\tan x} \right)$.

---

* See Fine, *Calculus*, § 61.

11. $\lim\limits_{x \to \frac{1}{2}\pi} (\sec x - \tan x)$.

12. $\lim\limits_{x \to 0} \left(\dfrac{\sec x - \cos x}{\tan x} \right)$.

Discuss the limiting behavior of:

13. $y = \cot x$ as $x \to 0$.

14. $y = \dfrac{\cos x}{\sin^2 x}$ as $x \to \pi$.

Find all the discontinuities of the following functions:

15. $\cot x$.

16. $\sec (x - 1)$.

17. $\dfrac{1}{1 - \cos x}$.

18. $\dfrac{\sin x}{\sin 2 x}$.

256. Graphs of the Sine and Cosine

The graph of the equation $y = \sin x$ may be constructed in the usual way by plotting, on a pair of rectangular axes, pairs of corresponding values of x and $\sin x$ by points and drawing a smooth curve through these points. The standard form of the graph is obtained by taking x in radian measure.

Let us draw two perpendicular axes $X'X$ and $Y'Y$, and use the same unit of length on both axes. We now form the following table of corresponding values of x and $y = \sin x$:

x	0	$\frac{1}{6}\pi$	$\frac{1}{3}\pi$	$\frac{1}{2}\pi$	$\frac{2}{3}\pi$	$\frac{5}{6}\pi$	π	$\frac{7}{6}\pi$	$\frac{4}{3}\pi$	$\frac{3}{2}\pi$	$\frac{5}{3}\pi$	$\frac{11}{6}\pi$	2π
$y = \sin x$	0	0.5	0.87	1	0.87	0.5	0	-0.5	-0.87	-1	-0.87	-0.5	0

If we plot these pairs of values of x and y on the axes of Fig. 136, and draw a smooth curve through these points, we obtain the wave-shaped curve of Fig. 136, which is the *graph of the sine function,* also called the *sine curve.*

Since $\sin n\pi = 0$, where n is any integer, the sine curve has the X-intercepts $x = 0$, $\pm\pi$, $\pm 2\,\pi$, $\pm 3\,\pi$, etc.; it has the one Y-intercept $y = 0$. The curve is symmetric with respect to the origin, because $\sin (-x) = -\sin x$; it is not symmetric with respect to the coördinate axes.

Since $\sin (\pi - x) = \sin x$, the sine curve has an arch between 0 and π which is symmetric about a line parallel to the Y-axis through the point $\frac{1}{2}\,\pi$. Because $\sin x$ is periodic with a period $2\,\pi$, the sine curve repeats itself during each interval of length $2\,\pi$, endlessly, for positive and negative values of x.

The highest points on the graph of $y = \sin x$ (the crests of the waves) have an ordinate equal to 1 and the lowest points (at the troughs of the waves) an ordinate equal to -1. The greatest height of the sine curve $y = \sin x$ is called the **amplitude** of the curve; it is equal to 1. The distance between two consecutive points at which the curve crosses the X-axis in the same direction is called the **wave-length** of the curve; it is equal to 2π for the graph of $y = \sin x$.

The sine curve is a wave form of the simplest type, and because of this it has many important applications in the study of wave motions

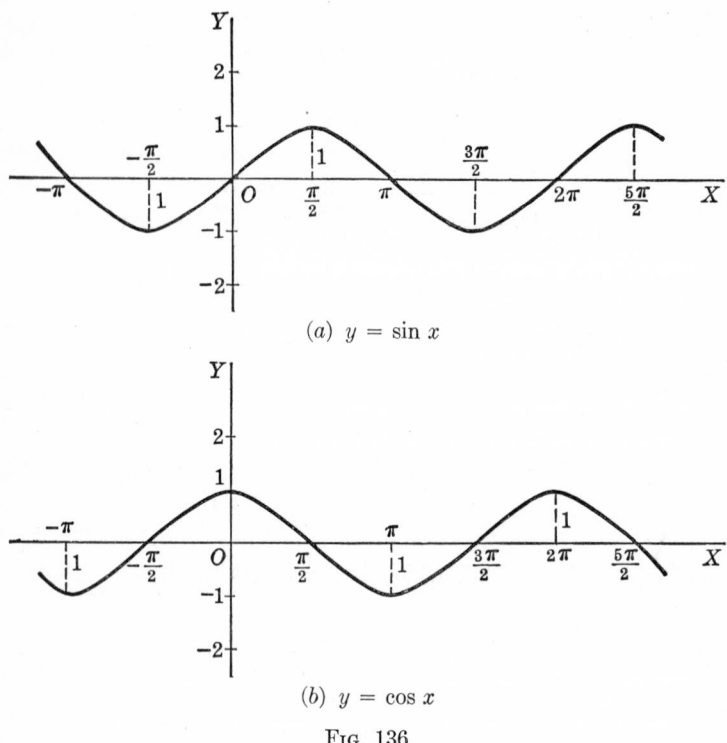

(a) $y = \sin x$

(b) $y = \cos x$

Fig. 136

and of periodic phenomena in general, in science and engineering. It is essential in the study of water waves, sound waves, alternating electric currents, electromagnetic waves, vibrating strings, pendulums, etc.

The graph of $y = \cos x$ may be plotted by similar methods, but this is not necessary, because the formula $\sin\left(\frac{1}{2}\pi + x\right) = \cos x$ shows that the graph of $y = \cos x$ is obtained by shifting the graph of $y = \sin x$ to the left a distance of $\frac{1}{2}\pi$. The resulting graph is

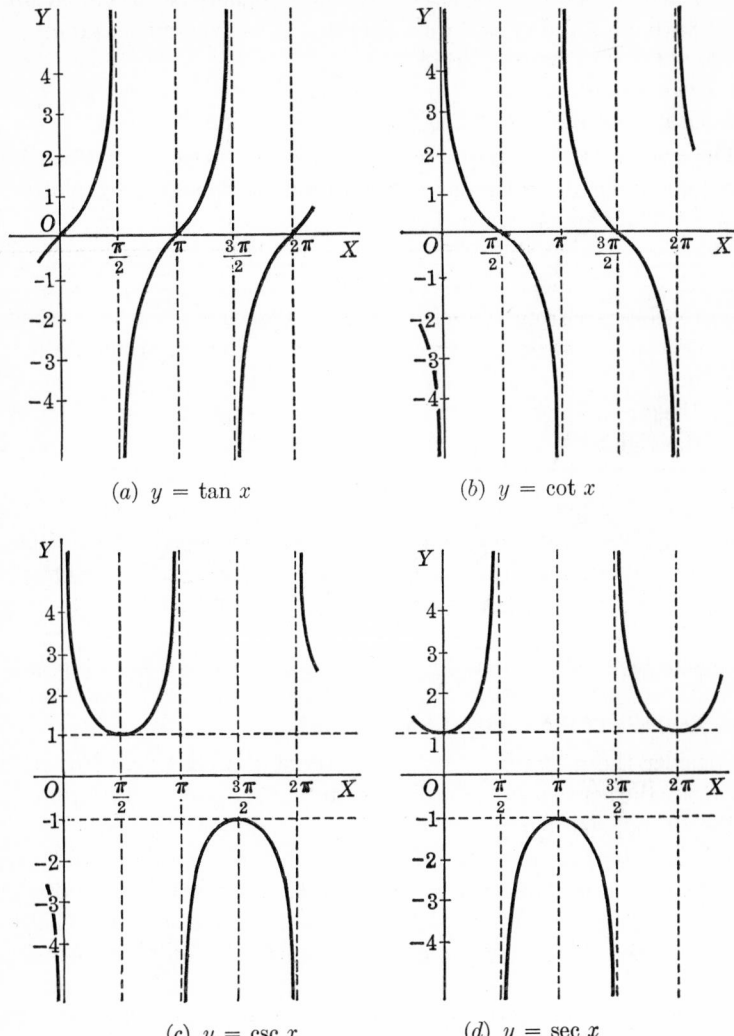

(a) $y = \tan x$

(b) $y = \cot x$

(c) $y = \csc x$

(d) $y = \sec x$

Fig. 137

shown in Fig. 136 (b). The cosine graph is therefore a simple sine curve with amplitude 1 and wave-length 2π, but we say that it *differs in phase* by $\frac{1}{2}\pi$ from the graph of $y = \sin x$.

257. Graphs of the Other Trigonometric Functions

The graphs of the other four trigonometric functions may be constructed in a manner similar to that used for the sine, by plotting points. They are shown in Fig. 137.

The discussion of the graph of $y = \tan x$ is typical of that of the other three functions. Since $\tan x$ becomes positively infinite when x approaches $\frac{1}{2}\pi$ from the left, it follows that the graph approaches the vertical line through $\frac{1}{2}\pi$ asymptotically upward from the left; since $\tan x$ becomes negatively infinite as x approaches $\frac{1}{2}\pi$ from the right, the graph approaches the line $x = \frac{1}{2}\pi$ asymptotically downward from the right. The graph has a similar behavior at $x = \frac{3}{2}\pi$, $\frac{5}{2}\pi$, etc., as also at $x = -\frac{1}{2}\pi$, $-\frac{3}{2}\pi$, etc. The curve is discontinuous at these odd multiples of $\frac{1}{2}\pi$, and has vertical asymptotes there. The graph consists of an endless number of disconnected pieces, called branches, in intervals of length π, having the same form as the branch from $\frac{1}{2}\pi$ to $\frac{3}{2}\pi$, since $\tan x$ is periodic with a period π.

The graphs of $y = \cot x$, $y = \sec x$ and $y = \csc x$ show somewhat analogous behavior to that of $y = \tan x$, as may be seen from Fig. 137.

258. Analysis of the General Sine Curve

Consider the graph of $y = a \sin x$, where a is positive. For each value of x the corresponding ordinate is a times as great as the ordinate of the simple sine curve $y = \sin x$ corresponding to this value of x. Since the amplitude of the graph of $y = \sin x$ is 1, it follows that the amplitude of the graph of $y = a \sin x$ is a. The wave-length of the graph of $y = a \sin x$ remains 2π, since $a \sin x$ has the period 2π. Therefore, the graph of $y = a \sin x$ is a simple wave-form curve with amplitude a and wave-length 2π, and passing through the origin. The graphs of $y = \sin x$, $y = 2 \sin x$ and $y = \frac{1}{2} \sin x$ are shown on the same axes in Fig. 138.

Now consider the graph of $y = \sin bx$, where b is positive. As bx varies from 0 to 2π, x varies from 0 to $2\pi/b$; therefore, in the interval $x = 0$ to $x = 2\pi/b$, the function $\sin bx$ goes through the same set of values that $\sin x$ takes in the interval from $x = 0$ to $x = 2\pi$. Hence, the graph of $y = \sin bx$ has the wave-length $2\pi/b$. The function $\sin bx$ takes the greatest value 1 and the least value -1

as x varies from 0 to $2\pi/b$, so that the amplitude of the graph of $y = \sin bx$ is 1. Therefore, the graph of $y = \sin bx$ is a simple wave-form curve with amplitude 1 and wave-length $2\pi/b$, and passing through the origin. The graphs of $y = \sin x$, $y = \sin 2x$ and $y = \sin \tfrac{1}{2}x$ are shown on the same axes in Fig. 139.

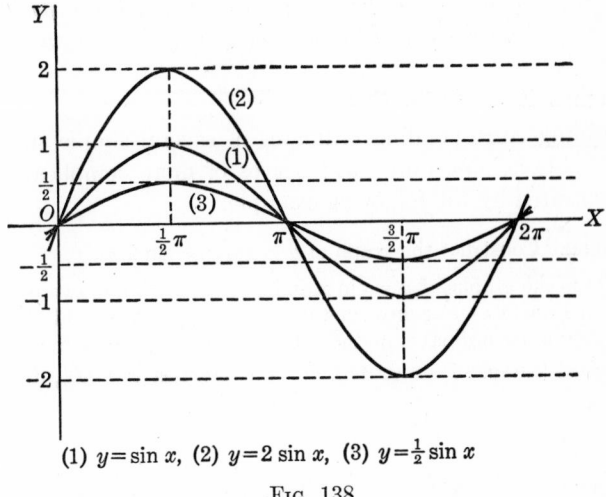

(1) $y = \sin x$, (2) $y = 2 \sin x$, (3) $y = \tfrac{1}{2}\sin x$

Fig. 138

The graph of $y = \sin(x + \alpha)$ may be obtained from that of $y = \sin x$ by shifting the origin a distance α to the left, if α is positive, and to the right if α is negative, according to the formulas for translation of axes in § 244. We say that the graph of $y = \sin(x + \alpha)$ *differs in phase* by α from the graph of $y = \sin x$. It has the same amplitude and the same wave-length. Therefore, the graph of

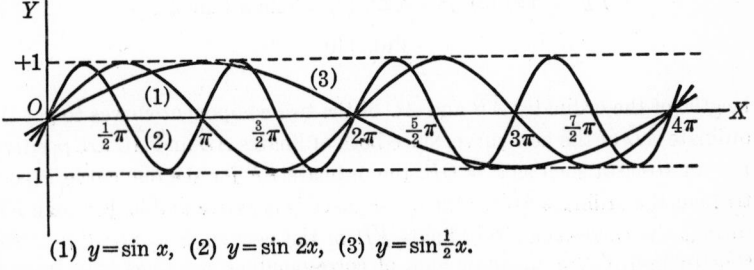

(1) $y = \sin x$, (2) $y = \sin 2x$, (3) $y = \sin \tfrac{1}{2}x$.

Fig. 139

$y = \sin (x + \alpha)$ is a simple wave-form curve with amplitude 1 and wave-length 2π, but passing through the point $x = -\alpha$ instead of the origin.

Combining the three preceding results, we have the following general theorem:

The graph of $y = a \sin (bx + c)$, where a and b are positive, is a simple wave-form curve with amplitude a and wave-length $2\pi/b$.

259. Composition of Sine Curves

By adding corresponding ordinates of several simple sine curves, we may obtain important wave curves of more complicated forms, as is illustrated by the following example.

EXAMPLE. Construct the graph of $y = \sin x + \sin 2x$.

Solution: The graphs of $y = \sin x$ and $y = \sin 2x$ are drawn on the same axes, as in Fig. 140. For any chosen value of x, we then add algebraically the corresponding ordinates of these two curves, to obtain the ordinate of the required curve. In Fig. 140, for the abscissa $x = \overline{OA}$, we add the

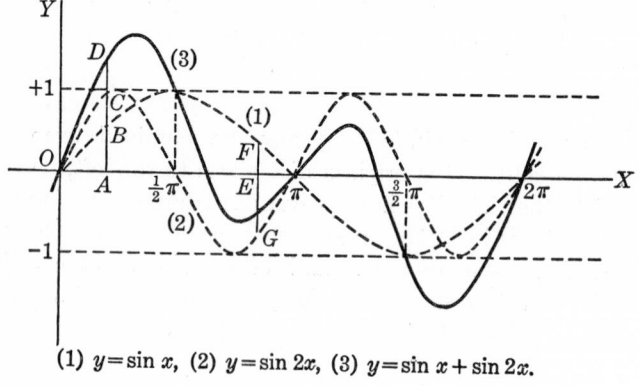

(1) $y = \sin x$, (2) $y = \sin 2x$, (3) $y = \sin x + \sin 2x$.

FIG. 140

lengths of the ordinates $\overline{AB}$ and $\overline{AC}$ of the two component curves to get the ordinate $\overline{AD}$ of the new curve, since both ordinates $\overline{AB}$ and $\overline{AC}$ are positive. For an abscissa such as $x = \overline{OE}$, the ordinate $\overline{EF}$ for the one curve is positive but the ordinate $\overline{EG}$ for the other curve is negative and longer than $\overline{EF}$, so that the corresponding ordinate $\overline{EH}$ of the new curve is negative. The construction of the algebraic sum of corresponding ordinates may be conveniently carried out by use of a pair of dividers, after drawing a set of vertical lines cutting the X-axis and the component curves at suitable intervals. The compound curve $y = \sin x + \sin 2x$ is shown by the full line in Fig. 140.

260. Exercises

1. Draw the graphs of: (a) $y = 3 \sin x$; (b) $y = \frac{1}{3} \sin x$, for one complete wave-length.
2. Draw the graphs of: (a) $y = \sin 3x$; (b) $y = \cos \frac{1}{3} x$, for one complete wave-length.
3. Draw the graphs of: (a) $y = 2 \sin 4x$; (b) $y = 3 \sin 3x$, for one complete wave-length.
4. Draw the graphs of: (a) $y = 2 \sin (x + \frac{1}{4} \pi)$; (b) $y = \sin (2x - \frac{1}{2} \pi)$, for one complete wave-length.
5. Draw the graphs of: (a) $y = 2 \tan 2x$; (b) $y = 3 \sec \frac{1}{2} x$, for one period.
6. Draw, by addition of ordinates, the graphs of:
   (a) $y = \sin x + \cos x$; (b) $y = \sin x + \frac{1}{2} \sin 2x$;
   (c) $y = \sin x - 2 \cos x$, for one complete cycle.

261. Limit of $\dfrac{\sin \theta}{\theta}$ as θ Approaches Zero

When we attempt to obtain a formula for the derivative of the sine function, we shall need to know the limit of the ratio $\dfrac{\sin \theta}{\theta}$ as θ approaches 0; we therefore investigate this limit now.

Let θ be the radian measure of any small positive angle (Fig. 141). Draw an arc CA of a circle of radius r about its vertex as center, and also draw AB perpendicular to OC and CD perpendicular to OC. Then it is geometrically evident that

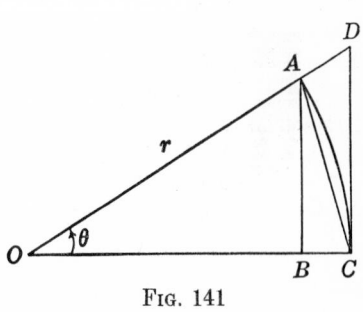

FIG. 141

(a) area $\triangle OCA$ < area sector OCA < area $\triangle OCD$.

But $BA = r \sin \theta$, $CD = r \tan \theta$, so that

$$\text{area } \triangle OCA = \tfrac{1}{2} OC \cdot BA = \tfrac{1}{2} r^2 \sin \theta,$$
$$\text{area } \triangle OCD = \tfrac{1}{2} OC \cdot CD = \tfrac{1}{2} r^2 \tan \theta;$$

also, by § 253, area sector $OCA = \tfrac{1}{2} r^2 \theta$. Hence, (a) becomes:

(b) $\tfrac{1}{2} r^2 \sin \theta < \tfrac{1}{2} r^2 \theta < \tfrac{1}{2} r^2 \tan \theta.$

Dividing by $\frac{1}{2} r^2 \sin \theta$, we get

$$1 < \frac{\theta}{\sin \theta} < \frac{1}{\cos \theta},$$

or, taking reciprocals,

(c) $$1 > \frac{\sin \theta}{\theta} > \cos \theta.$$

Now, since $\cos \theta \to 1$ as $\theta \to 0$, from (c) we obtain:

(d) $$\lim_{\theta \to 0} \frac{\sin \theta}{\theta} = 1.$$

This limit remains the same when θ is negative, since the value of the ratio $\frac{\sin \theta}{\theta}$ is unaltered when θ is replaced by $-\theta$. Hence:

When θ is expressed in radian measure,

(1) $$\lim_{\theta \to 0} \left(\frac{\sin \theta}{\theta} \right) = 1.$$

From formula (1), it follows that for sufficiently small values of θ, when θ is expressed in radian measure, $\sin \theta$ is very nearly equal to θ, or

(2) $$\sin \theta \approx \theta \qquad \textbf{if } \theta \textbf{ is small and in radians.}$$

This approximation is frequently used in applied problems.

We shall assume, throughout this book, unless stated otherwise, that all angles are expressed in radian measure.

EXAMPLE 1. Prove that $\lim_{x \to 0} \left(\dfrac{1 - \cos x}{x} \right) = 0$.

Solution: By trigonometry, $1 - \cos x = 2 \sin^2 \frac{1}{2} x$, hence

$$\lim_{x \to 0} \left(\frac{1 - \cos x}{x} \right) = \lim_{x \to 0} \left(\frac{2 \sin^2 \frac{1}{2} x}{x} \right) = \lim_{x \to 0} \left[\left(\frac{\sin \frac{1}{2} x}{\frac{1}{2} x} \right) \cdot \sin \frac{1}{2} x \right] = 1 \cdot 0 = 0.$$

EXAMPLE 2. Prove that $\lim_{x \to 0} \left(\dfrac{\tan x}{x} \right) = 1$.

Solution: Since $\tan x = \dfrac{\sin x}{\cos x}$, and since $\cos x \to 1$ as $x \to 0$, we have

$$\lim_{x \to 0} \left(\frac{\tan x}{x} \right) = \lim_{x \to 0} \left(\frac{\sin x}{x} \cdot \frac{1}{\cos x} \right) = \lim_{x \to 0} \left(\frac{\sin x}{x} \right) = 1.$$

262. Exercises

Evaluate each of the following limits:

1. $\lim_{x \to 0} \left(\dfrac{\sin 2x}{x} \right)$.

2. $\lim_{x \to 0} \left(\dfrac{x - \sin x}{x} \right)$.

3. $\displaystyle\lim_{x\to 0}\left(\frac{\tan x}{\sin x}\right).$

4. $\displaystyle\lim_{x\to 0}\left(\frac{\tan x}{\sin 2x}\right).$

5. $\displaystyle\lim_{x\to 0}\left(\frac{1-\cos x}{\sin x}\right).$

6. $\displaystyle\lim_{x\to 0}\left(\frac{\sin x}{\sqrt{x}}\right).$

7. $\displaystyle\lim_{x\to 0}\left(\frac{1-\cos x}{\sin^2 x}\right).$

8. $\displaystyle\lim_{x\to 0}\left(\frac{1-\cos x}{x\cos x}\right).$

9. $\displaystyle\lim_{x\to 0}\left(\frac{\sec x-1}{x^2}\right).$

10. $\displaystyle\lim_{x\to 0}\left(\frac{1}{x}\cdot\sin\tfrac12 x\right).$

11. $\displaystyle\lim_{x\to 0}\left(\frac{\tan x-\sin x}{x^3}\right).$

12. $\displaystyle\lim_{x\to \pi}\left(\frac{\sin x}{\pi-x}\right).$

263. Derivative of the Sine Function

The fundamental formula for the differentiation of the trigonometric functions is the formula for the derivative of the sine.

Let $y = \sin u$, where u is expressed in radian measure. If u is given an increment Δu, then y receives a corresponding increment Δy. From

$$y = \sin u \qquad \text{and} \qquad y + \Delta y = \sin (u + \Delta u),$$

we have

$$\Delta y = \sin (u + \Delta u) - \sin u,$$

(a)
$$\frac{\Delta y}{\Delta u} = \frac{\sin (u + \Delta u) - \sin u}{\Delta u}.$$

We now change the form of this ratio by applying the identity:

(b)
$$\sin A - \sin B = 2 \cos \tfrac12(A + B) \sin \tfrac12(A - B).$$

The ratio (a) then becomes

$$\frac{\Delta y}{\Delta u} = \frac{2 \cos (u + \tfrac12 \Delta u) \sin (\tfrac12 \Delta u)}{\Delta u},$$

which can be rearranged into the more convenient form:

(c)
$$\frac{\Delta y}{\Delta u} = \cos (u + \tfrac12 \Delta u)\cdot\frac{\sin (\tfrac12 \Delta u)}{\tfrac12 \Delta u}.$$

From this, since

$$\lim_{\Delta u\to 0} \cos (u + \tfrac12 \Delta u) = \cos u, \qquad \lim_{\Delta u\to 0}\frac{\sin (\tfrac12 \Delta u)}{\tfrac12 \Delta u} = 1 \text{ (by § 261)},$$

we obtain

(d)
$$D_u y = \cos u.$$

Now suppose that u is a function of x. By the composite function rule (§ 97), we have $D_x y = D_u y \cdot D_x u = \cos u \cdot D_x u$. Hence:

If u is a function of x, and if u is expressed in radian measure, then:

(3) $$D_x \sin u = \cos u \cdot D_x u.$$

EXAMPLE 1. $D_x \sin (2x + 1) = \cos (2x + 1) \cdot D_x(2x + 1)$
$$= \cos (2x + 1) \cdot 2 = 2 \cos (2x + 1).$$

EXAMPLE 2. Find $D_x(\sin^2 x)$.

Solution: Starting with the general power rule (§ 99), we find
$$D_x(\sin^2 x) = 2 \sin x \cdot D_x(\sin x) = 2 \sin x \cos x = \sin 2x.$$

264. Derivative of the Cosine Function

We may express $\cos u$ in terms of the sine function by use of the trigonometric formula: $\cos u = \sin (\frac{1}{2}\pi - u)$. By use of the fundamental formula (3) of § 263, we have

$$D_x \cos u = D_x \sin (\tfrac{1}{2}\pi - u)$$
$$= \cos (\tfrac{1}{2}\pi - u) \cdot D_x(\tfrac{1}{2}\pi - u) = \sin u \cdot (-D_x u).$$

Therefore:

(4) $$D_x \cos u = - \sin u \cdot D_x u.$$

EXAMPLE 1. $D_x \cos \sqrt{x} = - \sin \sqrt{x} \cdot D_x(\sqrt{x}) = - \dfrac{1}{2\sqrt{x}} \sin \sqrt{x}.$

EXAMPLE 2. Find $D_x(x^2 \cos 2x)$.

Solution: Starting with the product rule (§ 93), we get
$$D_x(x^2 \cos 2x) = x^2 \cdot D_x \cos 2x + \cos 2x \cdot D_x(x^2)$$
$$= -x^2 \sin 2x(2) + \cos 2x \cdot (2x)$$
$$= -2x^2 \sin 2x + 2x \cos 2x.$$

265. Exercises

In Exercises 1–20, differentiate each of the given functions:

1. $y = \sin 2x.$ 2. $y = \sin (3x + 2).$

3. $y = \sin^3 x.$ 4. $y = \sin^4 2x.$

5. $y = x \sin x.$ 6. $y = x^2 \sin x.$

7. $y = \sqrt{1 - \sin x}.$ 8. $y = \sqrt{\sin x}.$

9. $y = \dfrac{\sin x}{x}.$ 10. $s = a(t - \sin t).$

11. $y = \dfrac{x^2}{\sin x}.$ 12. $u = \dfrac{z}{\sin 4z}.$

13. $y = \cos(2x - 3)$.

14. $y = \cos^2 3x$.

15. $y = 2\cos^2 \frac{1}{2} x$.

16. $y = \dfrac{\cos x}{x}$.

17. $u = 2\sin x + 3\cos x$.

18. $w = \sin 2z \cos 3z$.

19. $s = t\sin t + \cos 2t$.

20. $s = t^2 \cos 2t$.

21. Find $f'(\frac{1}{2}\pi)$ and $f'(\frac{1}{6}\pi)$ if $f(x) = \sin^2 2x$.

22. Find $F'(\frac{1}{2})$ and $F'(\frac{1}{4})$ if $F(x) = x\cos(\pi x)$.

23. Find the first five successive derivatives of $y = \sin x$.

24. Find the first five successive derivatives of $y = \cos x$.

25. Show that:

(a) $D_x \sin ax = a\sin(ax + \frac{1}{2}\pi)$.

(b) $D_x \cos ax = a\cos(ax + \frac{1}{2}\pi)$.

26. Show that:

(a) $D_x{}^n \sin ax = a^n \sin(ax + \frac{1}{2} n\pi)$.

(b) $D_x{}^n \cos ax = a^n \cos(ax + \frac{1}{2} n\pi)$.

27. Show that $y = a\sin(kx + c)$ satisfies the equation $y'' + k^2 y = 0$ for all values of the constants a, k and c.

28. Show that $y = A\sin kx + B\cos kx$ satisfies the equation $y'' + k^2 y = 0$ for all values of the constants A, B and k.

266. Derivatives of the Other Trigonometric Functions

In order to obtain rules for differentiating the other trigonometric functions, we first express them in terms of the sine and cosine, and then apply the formulas already found for the derivatives of these two functions. Thus, applying the quotient rule (§ 94), we have

$$D_x \tan u = D_x \left(\frac{\sin u}{\cos u}\right)$$

$$= \frac{\cos u \cdot D_x \sin u - \sin u \cdot D_x \cos u}{\cos^2 u}$$

$$= \frac{\cos u \cdot \cos u - \sin u \cdot (-\sin u)}{\cos^2 u} \cdot D_x u$$

$$= \frac{\cos^2 u + \sin^2 u}{\cos^2 u} \cdot D_x u = \frac{1}{\cos^2 u} \cdot D_x u$$

$$= \sec^2 u \cdot D_x u.$$

Hence:

(5) $D_x \tan u = \sec^2 u \cdot D_x u.$

Similarly we obtain:

(6) $D_x \cot u = -\csc^2 u \cdot D_x u,$

(7)
$$D_x \sec u = \sec u \tan u \cdot D_x u,$$

(8)
$$D_x \csc u = - \csc u \cot u \cdot D_x u.$$

EXAMPLE 1. $D_x \tan (1 - 2x) = \sec^2 (1 - 2x) \cdot D_x(1 - 2x)$
$$= \sec^2 (1 - 2x)(-2) = -2 \sec^2 (1 - 2x).$$

EXAMPLE 2. $D_t \sec^2 3t = 2 \sec 3t \cdot D_t \sec 3t$
$$= 2 \sec 3t \cdot \sec 3t \tan 3t (3) = 6 \sec^2 3t \tan 3t.$$

267. Exercises

In Exercises 1–24, differentiate each of the given functions:

1. $y = \tan 2x.$
2. $y = 2 \tan \frac{1}{2} x.$
3. $y = 3 \cot (x - 1).$
4. $y = \sec (x + 2).$
5. $f(x) = \frac{1}{2} \sec 2x.$
6. $w = \cot (1 - 2z).$
7. $v = \csc (4x - 3).$
8. $u = \frac{1}{2} \csc (2x - 3).$
9. $u = \frac{1}{4} \tan (t^2).$
10. $s = 2 \sec (t^3).$
11. $F(z) = \sec \sqrt{z}.$
12. $f(x) = \tan \sqrt{x + 1}.$
13. $y = x \tan x.$
14. $y = \tan x - x.$
15. $y = \sec^2 x.$
16. $y = x \tan^2 x.$
17. $f(t) = \sec 2t - \tan 2t.$
18. $u = \sin x \tan x.$
19. $v = \tan^3 2t.$
20. $s = \tan \left(\dfrac{\pi}{4} - \dfrac{t}{2} \right).$
21. $w = z + \cot z.$
22. $w = \dfrac{z^2}{\cos z}.$
23. $g(x) = \dfrac{\tan x}{x^2}.$
24. $F(y) = \sec 2y \tan 2y.$

25. Write out in detail the proofs of the formulas of § 266 for the derivatives of cot u, sec u and csc u.
26. Write in differential notation all the differentiation rules of §§ 263, 264, 266.

Find the differential dy for each of the following functions in terms of x and dx:

27. $y = \sin 4x.$
28. $y = 2 \tan \frac{1}{2} x.$
29. $y = x \cos x.$
30. $y = a \sec^3 x.$

268. Applications of the Derivatives of the Trigonometric Functions

EXAMPLE 1. Locate the maximum and minimum points and the points of inflection of the curve $y = 3 \sin x - 4 \cos x$ in the interval $(0, 2\pi)$.

Solution: $y' = 3 \cos x + 4 \sin x,$ $y'' = -3 \sin x + 4 \cos x.$ For maximum and minimum points, we put $y' = 0$, which gives $3 \cos x = -4 \sin x$ or $\tan x = -\frac{3}{4}$; from this we find the critical values: $x = 2.50$ and $x = 5.64$ (from Table C, Appendix). Substituting $x = 2.50$ in y'', we get $y'' = -5$, and substituting $x = 5.64$ in y'', we get $y'' = +5$, which shows that y has a maximum at $x = 2.50$ and a minimum at $x = 5.64$. To find the points of inflection, we put $y'' = 0$, which gives $3 \sin x = 4 \cos x$ or $\tan x = \frac{4}{3}$, from which we find $x = 0.92$ and $x = 4.06$.   These values of x can be readily shown to make $y''' \neq 0$; this gives the location of the points of inflection.

EXAMPLE 2.   Find the dimensions of the right circular cylinder of maximum volume which can be inscribed in a given sphere of radius a.

Solution: In Fig. 142 (a), let θ be the angle AOB at the center of the sphere between the half-altitude OB and the radius OA of the sphere.   Then from

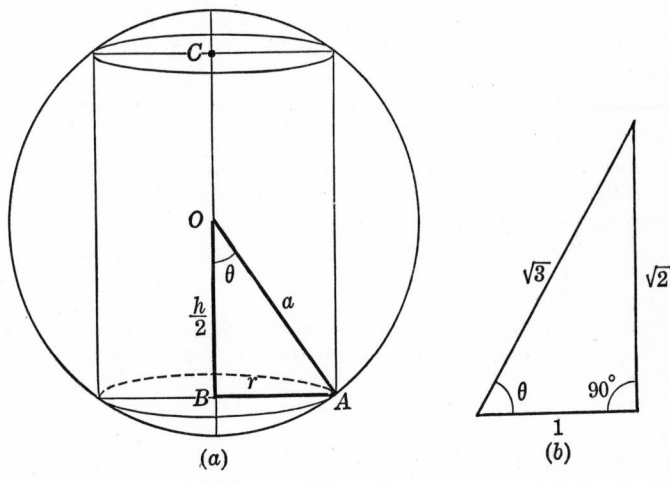

FIG. 142

the right triangle OBA, we have for the radius of base and altitude of the cylinder:

$$r = a \sin \theta, \qquad h = 2 a \cos \theta.$$

The volume of the cylinder is

$$V = \pi r^2 h = 2 \pi a^3 \sin^2 \theta \cos \theta = 2 \pi a^3 (\cos \theta - \cos^3 \theta).$$

Then

$$D_\theta V = -2 \pi a^3 \sin \theta (1 - 3 \cos^2 \theta).$$

If $D_\theta V = 0$, we have $\sin \theta = 0$ or $1 - 3 \cos^2 \theta = 0$.   If $\sin \theta = 0$, then $\theta = 0$ or π, which obviously does not give a maximum cylinder.   But if $1 - 3 \cos^2 \theta = 0$, then $\cos \theta = \frac{1}{3}\sqrt{3}$, which gives a maximum value for V. From $\cos \theta = \frac{1}{3}\sqrt{3}$, we find

$$r = a \sin \theta = \tfrac{1}{3} a\sqrt{6}, \qquad h = 2 a \cos \theta = \tfrac{2}{3} a\sqrt{3}.$$

269. Exercises

1. At what angle do the curves $y = \sin x$ and $y = \cos x$ intersect?
2. Find the angle of intersection of the curves $y = \tan x$ and $y = \cot x$.

3. Show analytically that the slope of the curve $y = \tan x$ is always positive and never less than 1.

4. Show analytically that the graph of $y = \cot x$ is everywhere falling, as x increases.

In Exercises 5–8, find the maximum and minimum points, the points of inflection and the direction of concavity of each of the given curves for all values of x near the origin:

5. $y = \sin x + \cos x$.

6. $y = 4 \sin x + 3 \cos x$.

7. $y = 2 \sin x + \cos x$.

8. $y = \tan x + \cot x$.

Find the velocity and acceleration of a particle moving along a straight line for which the equation of motion is:

9. $s = 2 \sin 2t$,   at $t = 0$.

10. $s = \cos t + \cos 2t$,   at $t = t_1$.

11. An isosceles triangle has equal sides 8 inches long and the included angle θ. If θ increases at the rate of $1°$ per minute, how fast is the area of the triangle changing when $\theta = 30°$?

12. An airplane 2000 feet above the earth is flying horizontally at the speed of 300 feet per second. How fast is the angle of elevation of the plane changing when this angle is $35°$?

13. A man on a wharf 32 feet above the water pulls in the rope of a rowboat so that the boat approaches the wharf at the rate of 4 feet per second. When it is 24 feet distant, at what rate is the rope being drawn in? [*Hint.* Use the angle between the rope and the water.]

14. In a certain engine, the distance x (feet) between the center of the driving-shaft and the head of the piston is given by,

$$x = \cos \theta + \sqrt{16.5 - \sin^2 \theta},$$

where θ is the angle between the crank and the path of the piston-head. If θ increases at the constant rate of 60 radians per second, find the speed of the piston-head when $\theta = \frac{1}{4}\pi$.

15. At a point 30 feet from its base on horizontal ground, a tree subtends an angle of $30°$. What is the error in the computed height of the tree due to an error of $30'$ in measuring this angle?

16. Two sides and the included angle of a triangle are measured as 30 feet, 40 feet and $60°$ respectively. Find the error in the third side caused by an error of $10'$ in measuring the included angle.

17. Find the relative dimensions of the maximum rectangle inscribed in a given circle.

18. Find the altitude of a right circular cone of maximum convex surface area inscribed in a given sphere.

19. Find the altitude of the right circular cone of maximum volume inscribed in a given sphere.

20. The sides of a V-shaped trough are 12 inches wide; what should be the angle between the sides for a trough of maximum capacity?

21. Find the length of the shortest beam that can be used to brace a wall, if the beam is to pass over a second wall 8 feet high and 10 feet from the first.

22. Two corridors, one of which is 5 feet wide, intersect at right angles (Fig. 143), and a beam 40 feet long is to be carried horizontally around the corner. We wish to find the minimum width of the second corridor which will just allow the beam to pass, no allowance being made for the width of the beam. [*Hint.* $5 \sec \theta + y \csc \theta = 40$; make y a maximum.]

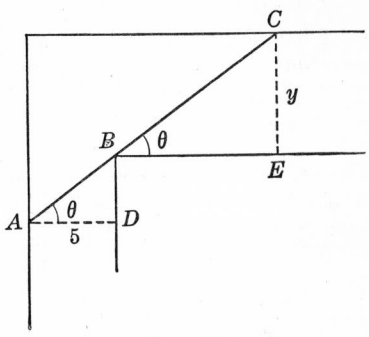

Fig. 143

23. Two corridors respectively 8 feet and 3 feet wide intersect at right angles. Find the length of the longest thin rod that will go horizontally around the corner.

24. When a plane surface, of inclination θ, is driven horizontally through the air at a fixed speed, the lifting power of the air resistance is proportional to $Q = \sin^2 \theta \cos \theta$. Find the value of θ which makes Q a maximum.

270. Inverse Trigonometric Functions

The **inverse trigonometric functions** are the six functions: arc sin x, arc cos x, arc tan x, arc cot x, arc sec x and arc csc x. These are defined in trigonometry as follows: If $x = \sin y$, then y regarded as a function of x is called the **inverse sine of x** and is denoted by $y = $ arc sin x; the others are defined similarly. These functions are also frequently denoted by: $\sin^{-1} x$, $\cos^{-1} x$, $\tan^{-1} x$, etc.

The graphs of the inverse trigonometric functions $y = $ arc sin x, $y = $ arc cos x, etc., are shown in Fig. 144; they are the same as the graphs of $y = \sin x$, $y = \cos x$, etc., with the X- and Y-axes interchanged.

The inverse trigonometric functions are *multiple-valued*; that is, for a given permissible value of x, there are many values of y. This is illustrated by the graphs, in which a vertical line that cuts one of them at any point also cuts it again in innumerable other points. For example, if $x = \frac{1}{2}$, then $y = $ arc sin $x = $ arc sin $\frac{1}{2} = \frac{1}{6} \pi$, $\frac{5}{6} \pi$, $\frac{13}{6} \pi$, $-\frac{7}{6} \pi$, etc.

It is highly desirable in problems involving inverse trigonometric functions to be able to deal with single-valued functions. For this purpose we define what are known as the *principal values* of the inverse trigonometric functions, which are indicated by writing the initial letter of the symbol of the function with a capital letter, thus, Arc sin x or Sin^{-1} x, etc. We define these **principal values** as follows:

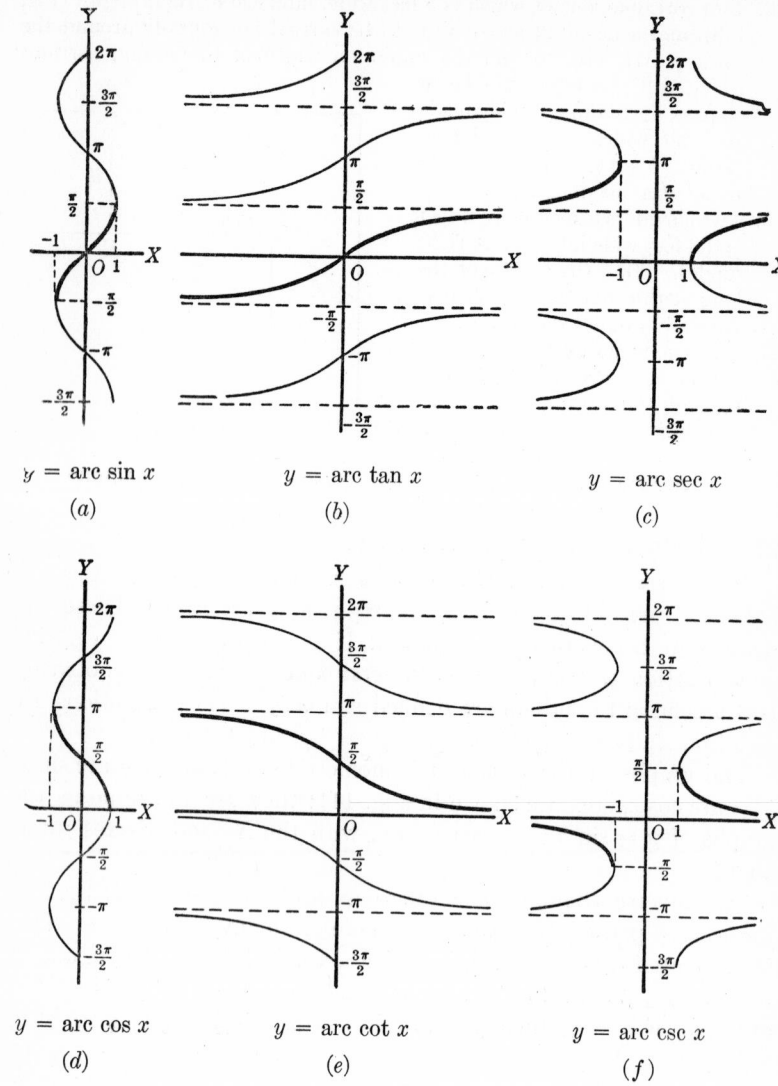

$y = \text{arc sin } x$

(a)

$y = \text{arc tan } x$

(b)

$y = \text{arc sec } x$

(c)

$y = \text{arc cos } x$

(d)

$y = \text{arc cot } x$

(e)

$y = \text{arc csc } x$

(f)

Fig. 144

*For a given value of x, the **principal value** of **arc sin x** or of **arc tan x** is the numerically smallest value of the function, and the **principal value** of **arc sec x** is the smallest positive (or zero) value of the function.* These principal values are contained in the following intervals:

$$-\frac{\pi}{2} \leqq \text{Arc sin } x \leqq \frac{\pi}{2}, \quad -\frac{\pi}{2} < \text{Arc tan } x < \frac{\pi}{2}, \quad 0 \leqq \text{Arc sec } x \leqq \pi.$$

*The **principal values** of the "**inverse co-functions**" are determined by subtracting the principal values of the other functions from $\frac{\pi}{2}$:*

(a) $\quad$ **Arc cos $x = \dfrac{\pi}{2} -$ Arc sin x,** $\qquad$ **Arc cot $x = \dfrac{\pi}{2} -$ Arc tan x,**

$$\textbf{Arc csc } x = \frac{\pi}{2} - \textbf{Arc sec } x.$$

These principal values are contained in the following intervals:

$$0 \leqq \text{Arc cos } x \leqq \pi, \quad 0 < \text{Arc cot } x < \pi, \quad -\frac{\pi}{2} \leqq \text{Arc csc } x \leqq \frac{\pi}{2}.$$

It should be noted that when $x > 0$, each principal value lies in the first quadrant, i.e., in the interval from 0 to $\frac{1}{2}\pi$.

The principal value of each inverse trigonometric function is shown in Fig. 144 by the heavy portion of the graph.

EXAMPLE. Arc sin $(\frac{1}{2}) = \frac{1}{6}\pi$, Arc sin $(-\frac{1}{2}\sqrt{2}) = -\frac{1}{4}\pi$, Arc sin $1 = \frac{1}{2}\pi$; Arc tan $1 = \frac{1}{4}\pi$, Arc tan $(-\sqrt{3}) = -\frac{1}{3}\pi$, Arc tan $0 = 0$; Arc sec $2 = \frac{1}{3}\pi$, Arc sec $(-\sqrt{2}) = \frac{3}{4}\pi$; $\quad$ Arc cos $(\frac{1}{2}) = \frac{1}{3}\pi$, $\quad$ Arc cos $(-\frac{1}{2}\sqrt{3}) = \frac{5}{6}\pi$, Arc cos $(-1) = \pi$; Arc cot $(-1) = \frac{3}{4}\pi$, Arc csc $(-\sqrt{2}) = -\frac{1}{4}\pi$.

It is to be understood hereafter that, unless stated otherwise, the principal values of the inverse trigonometric functions are to be used.

271. Exercises

1. Find: (a) Arc sin $(\frac{1}{2}\sqrt{3})$; (b) Arc sin $(-\frac{1}{2})$; (c) Arc sin (-1); (d) Arc cos $(\frac{1}{2}\sqrt{2})$; (e) Arc cos $(-\frac{1}{2})$; (f) Arc tan $(\sqrt{3})$; (g) Arc tan (-1); (h) Arc sec (-2); (i) Arc cot 1; (j) Arc csc $(-\sqrt{2})$.

2. Find: (a) Arc sin $(\frac{1}{2}\sqrt{2})$; (b) Arc sin $(-\frac{1}{2}\sqrt{3})$; (c) Arc cos $(\frac{1}{2}\sqrt{3})$; (d) Arc cos $(-\frac{1}{2}\sqrt{2})$; (e) Arc cos 1; (f) Arc tan $(\frac{1}{3}\sqrt{3})$; (g) Arc tan $(-\sqrt{3})$; (h) Arc sec $(-\sqrt{2})$; (i) Arc cot $(-\frac{1}{3}\sqrt{3})$; (j) Arc csc (2).

Find the inverse of each of the following functions:

3. $y = \sin 3\,x$.
4. $y = 2 \cos (\tfrac{1}{2}\,\pi + x)$.
5. $y = 2 \arcsin 2\,x$.
6. $y = \tfrac{1}{3} \arctan x$.
7. $y = \sin x \cos x$.
8. $y = \tan x - \cot x$.

272. Derivatives of the Inverse Trigonometric Functions

Let $y = \text{Arc} \sin u$, where u is a function of x. Then

(a)
$$u = \sin y.$$

By formula (3) of § 263, we have

(b)
$$D_y u = \cos y.$$

Now applying the inverse function formula of § 105, we get

(c)
$$D_u y = \frac{1}{D_y u} = \frac{1}{\cos y} = \frac{1}{\sqrt{1 - \sin^2 y}} = \frac{1}{\sqrt{1 - u^2}},$$

where the positive sign is used with the radical because $\cos y$ is positive for the values $-\tfrac{1}{2}\,\pi \leq y \leq \tfrac{1}{2}\,\pi$ of the principal value $\text{Arc} \sin u$. By use of the composite function formula of § 97, we obtain:

(9)
$$D_x(\text{Arc} \sin u) = \frac{1}{\sqrt{1 - u^2}} \cdot D_x u.$$

Since $\text{Arc} \cos u = \tfrac{1}{2}\,\pi - \text{Arc} \sin u$ by definition, we have:

(10)
$$D_x(\text{Arc} \cos u) = - \frac{1}{\sqrt{1 - u^2}} \cdot D_x u.$$

Now let $y = \text{Arc} \tan u$, where u is a function of x. Then

$$u = \tan y, \qquad D_y u = \sec^2 y,$$

and

$$D_u y = \frac{1}{D_y u} = \frac{1}{\sec^2 y} = \frac{1}{1 + \tan^2 y} = \frac{1}{1 + u^2}.$$

Hence:

(11)
$$D_x(\text{Arc} \tan u) = \frac{1}{1 + u^2} \cdot D_x u.$$

From $\text{Arc} \cot u = \tfrac{1}{2}\,\pi - \text{Arc} \tan u$ by definition, we have

(12)
$$D_x(\text{Arc} \cot u) = - \frac{1}{1 + u^2} \cdot D_x u.$$

In a manner similar to the preceding, we find:

(13) $$D_x(\text{Arc sec } u) = \frac{1}{\sqrt{u^2(u^2 - 1)}} \cdot D_x u,$$

(14) $$D_x(\text{Arc csc } u) = -\frac{1}{\sqrt{u^2(u^2 - 1)}} \cdot D_x u.$$

From the graph of $y = \text{Arc sec } x$ (Fig. 144), it can be seen that the derivative of Arc sec u must always be positive (except for $u = \pm 1$). This is the reason for writing the radical in (13) in the form $\sqrt{u^2(u^2 - 1)}$ rather than $u\sqrt{u^2 - 1}$.

EXAMPLE 1.   (a) $D_x \text{ Arc sin } (2x - 1) = \dfrac{1}{\sqrt{1 - (2x - 1)^2}} \cdot 2 = \dfrac{1}{\sqrt{x - x^2}};$

(b) $D_x \text{ Arc tan } \dfrac{1}{x} = \dfrac{1}{1 + \left(\dfrac{1}{x}\right)^2} \cdot \left(-\dfrac{1}{x^2}\right) = -\dfrac{1}{x^2 + 1}.$

EXAMPLE 2.   Differentiate $y = 2 \text{ Arc sin } \frac{1}{2} x - \frac{1}{2} x\sqrt{4 - x^2}$, and simplify.

Solution:

$$D_x y = 2 \cdot \frac{1}{\sqrt{1 - \frac{1}{4} x^2}} \cdot \frac{1}{2} - \frac{1}{2} x \cdot \frac{1}{2}(4 - x^2)^{-\frac{1}{2}}(-2x) - \frac{1}{2}(4 - x^2)^{\frac{1}{2}}$$

$$= \frac{2}{\sqrt{4 - x^2}} + \frac{x^2}{2\sqrt{4 - x^2}} - \frac{4 - x^2}{2\sqrt{4 - x^2}} = \frac{x^2}{\sqrt{4 - x^2}}.$$

273. Exercises

In Exercises 1–20, differentiate each of the given functions:

1. $y = \text{Arc sin } 2x.$

2. $y = \text{Arc sin } (1 - x).$

3. $y = \text{Arc tan } (x - 1).$

4. $y = \text{Arc tan } \left(\dfrac{1}{x}\right).$

5. $w = z \text{ Arc tan } z.$

6. $f(x) = x^2 \text{ Arc tan } (x^2).$

7. $u = \text{Arc sin } \sqrt{x}.$

8. $v = \text{Arc sin } \dfrac{z + 1}{\sqrt{2}}.$

9. $y = \text{Arc sec } (2 - x).$

10. $y = \text{Arc sec } (x^2).$

11. $F(x) = x \text{ Arc cot } \frac{1}{2} x.$

12. $y = x^2 \text{ Arc cos } x.$

13. $w = \dfrac{1}{z} \text{ Arc tan } z.$

14. $f(x) = \dfrac{1}{x} \text{ Arc cot } 2x.$

15. $s = t^2 \text{ Arc csc } \sqrt{t}.$

16. $u = \text{Arc csc } (z^2).$

17. $y = a^2 \text{ Arc sin } \dfrac{x}{a} - x\sqrt{a^2 - x^2}.$

18. $y = x \text{ Arc sin } x + \sqrt{1 - x^2}.$

19. $y = (x^2 + 1) \text{ Arc tan } x - x$.   20. $y = \dfrac{x}{\sqrt{a^2 - x^2}} - \text{Arc sin } \dfrac{x}{a}$.

Find the second derivative of each of the following functions:

21. $y = \text{Arc sin } \frac{1}{2} x$.   22. $y = x \text{ Arc tan } x$.

274. Applications of the Derivatives of the Inverse Trigonometric Functions

EXAMPLE 1. A revolving light 5 miles from a straight shore has a constant angular velocity. With what velocity does the light revolve if the spot of light moves along the shore at the rate of 15 miles per minute when the beam makes an angle of 60° with the shore line?

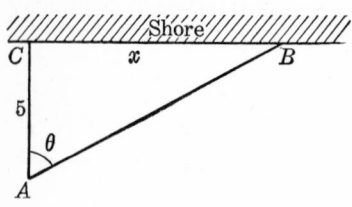

FIG. 145

Solution: From Fig. 145, we have

(a) $$x = 5 \tan \theta$$

or $$\theta = \text{Arc tan} \left(\frac{x}{5} \right).$$

(b) $$D_t\theta = \frac{1}{1 + \dfrac{x^2}{25}} \cdot \frac{1}{5} \cdot D_t x = \frac{5}{25 + x^2} \cdot D_t x.$$

But $D_t x = 15$ miles per minute; and when angle $ABC = 60°$, $\theta = 30°$, and from (a), $x = 5 \tan 30° = \frac{5}{3}\sqrt{3}$. Substituting these values in (b), we get

$$D_t\theta = \frac{5}{25 + \frac{25}{3}} \cdot 15 = \frac{9}{4} \text{ radians per minute,}$$

which is the required rate of revolution of the light.

EXAMPLE 2. A picture 7 feet in height is hung on a wall with the lower edge 9 feet above the level of the observer's eye. How far from the wall should the observer stand in order to obtain the most favorable view?

Solution: In Fig. 146, we must find the value of x which will make angle θ a maximum. From the figure, we see that

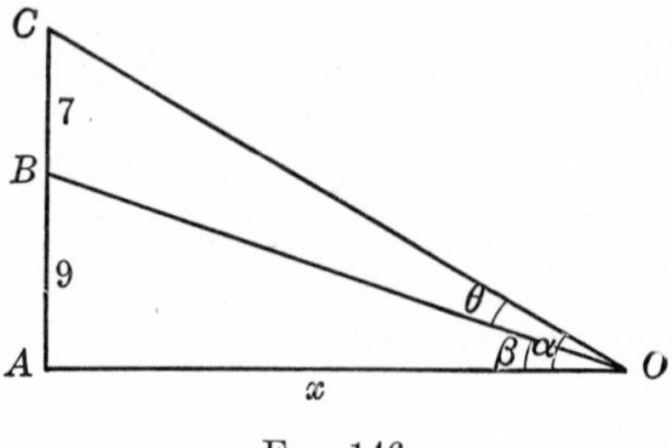

(c) $$\tan \alpha = \frac{16}{x}, \qquad \tan \beta = \frac{9}{x},$$

so that

FIG. 146

(d) $$\theta = \alpha - \beta = \text{Arc tan } \frac{16}{x} - \text{Arc tan } \frac{9}{x}.$$

Then

$$D_x\theta = \frac{1}{1 + \dfrac{256}{x^2}}\cdot\left(-\frac{16}{x^2}\right) - \frac{1}{1 + \dfrac{81}{x^2}}\left(-\frac{9}{x^2}\right)$$

$$= -\frac{16}{x^2 + 256} + \frac{9}{x^2 + 81}.$$

Putting $D_x\theta = 0$ for a maximum and solving for x, we have

$$16(x^2 + 81) = 9(x^2 + 256), \qquad \text{or} \qquad 7\,x^2 = 7\cdot 144,$$

from which $x = 12$. The observer should therefore stand 12 feet back from the wall.

275. Exercises

1. A man is walking at the rate of 4 miles per hour toward the foot of a tower 60 feet high standing on level ground. At what rate is the angle of elevation of the top changing when he is 80 feet from the foot of the tower?
2. A searchlight, located 100 feet from a straight road, is trained upon a car running along the road at 30 miles per hour; at what rate per minute is the light rotating when the car is 200 feet from the nearest point of the road to the light?
3. A sign board 10 feet high is erected with its lower edge 13 feet above the ground. At what distance would a man whose eyes are 5 feet above the ground obtain the clearest view of the sign?
4. An airplane 1 mile high is flying horizontally with a velocity of 100 miles per hour, directly away from an observer. At what rate is the angle of elevation of the airplane changing when the point directly under the airplane is $\frac{1}{5}$ mile from the observer?
5. A kite is 60 feet high, with 100 feet of cord out. If the kite is moving horizontally 4 miles per hour directly away from the boy who is flying it, find the rate of change of the angle of elevation of the cord, assuming the cord to be in a straight line.
6. A balloon rises vertically, starting from a point A on level ground. If observed from a point B on the ground 1000 feet from A, how fast is the angle of elevation increasing per foot rise, when the height is 600 feet?
7. Locate the point on the X-axis at which the chord of the curve $y^2 = 8\,x$ drawn from the point of the curve where $y = 4$ to the point where $y = 8$ subtends the maximum angle.
8. A revolving light 5 miles from a straight shore revolves at the rate of 5 radians per minute. Find the speed along the shore of the spot of light when it makes an angle of 60° with the shore.

276. The Exponential Function

Let b be any number greater than 1. The symbol b^x is defined in elementary algebra for all *rational* values of x. This symbol b^x may also be defined for *irrational* values of x as follows: If c is any irrational number, it can be proved that if $v \to c$ through rational values, then b^v will approach a limit, which is denoted by b^c. The expression b^x is then defined for all *real* values of x.

It can also be shown that the familiar laws of exponents hold for all real exponents, whether rational or irrational; thus, $b^x \cdot b^c = b^{x+c}$ for all real values of x and c.

An **exponential function** *is a function of the form* $y = b^x$, *where* b *is constant and* x *is the independent variable.* It has a *constant base* b and a *variable exponent* x. We shall take $b > 1$.

The exponential function b^x is a single-valued function, which is always positive and always increasing (if $b > 1$) as x increases.

It can be proved that

$$(a) \qquad \lim_{x \to a} (b^x) = b^a \qquad (b > 1)$$

whether a is rational or irrational; that is, b^x is *continuous* for all values of x. It can also be shown that, if $b > 1$:

$$(b) \quad b^x \to +\infty \quad \text{as} \quad x \to +\infty, \quad \text{and} \quad b^x \to 0 \quad \text{as} \quad x \to -\infty.$$

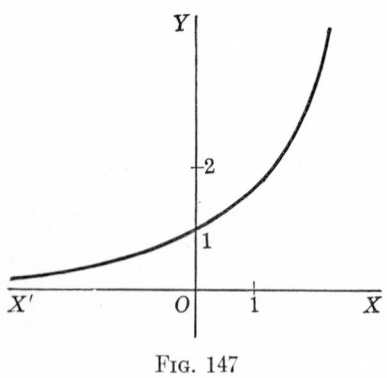

FIG. 147

The graph of the exponential function may be readily plotted in rectangular coördinates by making a table of values of the function and plotting points. It is shown in Fig. 147. It has no symmetry with respect to the coördinate axes or the origin. It has no X-intercept but has the Y-intercept 1. The curve is always above the X-axis, never crosses the X-axis, but is asymptotic to the negative X-axis. It rises from left to right.

277. The Logarithmic Function

The **logarithmic function** $y = \log_b x$ *is defined as the inverse of the exponential function, and is therefore defined by the relation* $x = b^y$. The base b must be positive and different from 1; we shall take $b > 1$.

The definition of a logarithm may also be stated: *The logarithm of a given number x to a given base is the exponent of the power to which the base must be raised to give the number x.*

This function $\log_b x$ is defined only for positive values of x, if we restrict ourselves to real values of the function. It is single-valued (for $x > 0$). It is always increasing as x increases. It is positive if $x > 1$ and negative if $0 < x < 1$, and for $x = 1$ we have $\log_b 1 = 0$. It is important to note that $\log_b b = 1$.

For change of base, we have from algebra,

(a) $$\log_a x = \log_b x \cdot \log_a b = \frac{\log_b x}{\log_b a}.$$

It can be proved that:

(b) $$\lim_{x \to a} (\log_b x) = \log_b a \qquad (a > 0);$$

hence, $\log_b x$ is continuous for all positive values of x. It can also be shown that, if $b > 1$:

(c) $\log_b x \to -\infty$ as $x \to 0^+$, and $\log_b x \to +\infty$ as $x \to +\infty$.

From the definition of a logarithm we have the following important formulas:

(d) $$b^{\log_b x} = x \qquad and \qquad \log_b (b^x) = x.$$

A summary of important properties and formulas for the exponential and logarithmic functions is given in the Appendix.

The graph of the logarithmic function $y = \log_b x$ is obtained from that of the exponential function $y = b^x$ by interchanging axes. The graph is shown in Fig. 148. It has no symmetry with respect to the coördinate axes or the origin, it has the X-intercept $x = 1$ and no Y-intercept, but is asymptotic to the negative Y-axis; there is no portion of the graph to the left of the Y-axis.

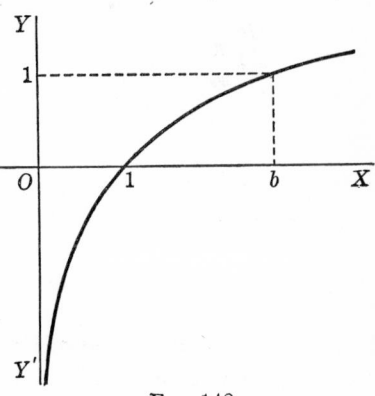

Fig. 148

278. Exercises

1. For what values of x are the following functions defined:
   (a) 2^x; (b) $\log_{10}(x - 1)$?

2. Show that:
$$\log_b (x^2\sqrt{x^2 - 1}) = 2 \log_b x + \tfrac{1}{2} \log_b (x + 1) + \tfrac{1}{2} \log_b (x - 1).$$

3. Change the implicit function form
$$2 \log_b x - \tfrac{1}{2} \log_b y = 2$$
to an explicit function form for y as a function of x.

4. Show that:
$$\frac{\log_b (x + h) - \log_b x}{h} = \log_b \left(1 + \frac{h}{x}\right)^{\frac{1}{h}}.$$

Find the inverse of each of the functions in Exercises 5–8:

5. $y = 10^{2x}$.
6. $y = 2^{x-1}$.

7. $y = \log_{10} (3\,x)$.
8. $y = 2 \log_2 (x + 1)$.

Evaluate each of the limits in Exercises 9–12:

9. $\lim\limits_{x \to 1} (x^2 \log_{10} x)$.
10. $\lim\limits_{x \to 0} (2^x + 2^{-x})$.

11. $\lim\limits_{x \to 10} \left(\dfrac{1 + x}{\log_{10} x}\right)$.
12. $\lim\limits_{x \to -\infty} \left(2 - \dfrac{1}{x}\right) \cdot 10^x$.

279. The Number *e*. Natural Logarithms

We now refer to another fundamental limit which is very important in later derivations.

It is proved in more advanced works* that:

When $h \to 0$, then $(1 + h)^{\frac{1}{h}}$ approaches a limit, which is denoted by e:

(15) $$\lim\limits_{h \to 0} (1 + h)^{\frac{1}{h}} = e.$$

This number e is a very important number in mathematics. It is an irrational number and cannot be expressed exactly in decimal form. Its approximate value correct to 5 decimal places is

$$e = 2.71828.$$

A method of calculation of the approximate numerical value of e will be given later (§ 457).

Logarithms to the base e are called **natural logarithms** (or sometimes Napierian logarithms, after John Napier, the inventor or discoverer of logarithms). They are used almost exclusively in calculus, because their use greatly simplifies many formulas. They are often denoted by $\log_e x$ (or in many calculus books by $\log x$, without the subscript e), but we shall use the convenient notation **ln x,** which is now widely used.

* See, for example, Fine, *Calculus*, page 71, or Smail, *Elements of the Theory of Infinite Processes*, pages 38–41.

Logarithms to the base 10 are called *common logarithms*, and are used chiefly for numerical calculation.

Table D (Appendix) gives the values of the natural logarithmic function $\ln x$.

Table E (Appendix) gives the values of the exponential functions e^x and e^{-x}.

For change of base between natural logarithms and common logarithms, we use the formulas:

(a) $$\log_{10} x = 0.43429 \ln x,$$

(b) $$\ln x = 2.30259 \log_{10} x,$$

where $0.43429 = \log_{10} e$ and $2.30259 = \ln 10$ (these values are only approximate).

280. Exercises

1. Simplify: (a) $e^{2 \ln x}$; (b) $e^{-\ln x}$; (c) $e^{-3 \ln x}$; (d) $e^{x+\ln x}$.
2. Simplify: (a) $e^{3 \ln x}$; (b) $e^{-2 \ln x}$; (c) $e^{x-\ln x}$.
3. Express as powers of e: (a) 10^x; (b) 10^{-2x}. [*Hint.* For (a), since $e^{\ln 10} = 10$, we have $10^x = (e^{\ln 10})^x = e^{x \ln 10}$.]
4. Express as powers of e: (a) 10^{3x}; (b) 10^{-4x}.
5. Solve the equation $e^x + e^{-x} = 3$ for x. [*Hint.* Replace e^{-x} by $1/e^x$, and solve the resulting equation for e^x.]
6. Solve the equation $e^x - e^{-x} = 2$ for x.
7. Using Table D, find: (a) $\ln 6.82$; (b) $\ln 34.6$; (c) $\ln 506$; (d) $\ln 0.163$; (e) $\ln 0.0419$.
8. Using Table D, find: (a) $\ln 2.08$; (b) $\ln 81.7$; (c) $\ln 345$; (d) $\ln 0.456$; (e) $\ln 0.0609$.
9. Use Table D to find x from: (a) $\ln x = 1.5390$; (b) $\ln x = 4.2047$; (c) $\ln x = 5.7462$; (d) $\ln x = 9.4166 - 10$.
10. Use Table D to find x from: (a) $\ln x = 1.2355$; (b) $\ln x = 4.1620$; (c) $\ln x = 5.5094$; (d) $\ln x = 9.2125 - 10$.
11. From Table E, find: (a) $e^{0.24}$; (b) $e^{1.45}$; (c) $e^{-0.45}$; (d) $e^{-1.10}$.
12. From Table E, find: (a) $e^{0.38}$; (b) $e^{1.20}$; (c) $e^{-0.65}$; (d) $e^{-1.3}$.

281. Derivative of the Logarithmic Function

Let $y = \log_a u$, where a is any base which is greater than 1. If u is given any increment Δu, then

$$y + \Delta y = \log_a (u + \Delta u),$$

$$\Delta y = \log_a (u + \Delta u) - \log_a u$$

$$= \log_a \left(\frac{u + \Delta u}{u}\right) = \log_a \left(1 + \frac{\Delta u}{u}\right),$$

(a)
$$\frac{\Delta y}{\Delta u} = \frac{1}{\Delta u} \log_a \left(1 + \frac{\Delta u}{u} \right)$$

$$= \frac{1}{u} \cdot \frac{u}{\Delta u} \log_a \left(1 + \frac{\Delta u}{u} \right)$$

(b)
$$= \frac{1}{u} \log_a \left(1 + \frac{\Delta u}{u} \right)^{\frac{u}{\Delta u}}.$$

Put $\dfrac{\Delta u}{u} = h$, then $\dfrac{u}{\Delta u} = \dfrac{1}{h}$; we have $h \to 0$ as $\Delta u \to 0$.   Then

(c)
$$\frac{\Delta y}{\Delta u} = \frac{1}{u} \log_a (1 + h)^{\frac{1}{h}}.$$

Since $(1 + h)^{\frac{1}{h}} \to e$ when $h \to 0$ (by § 279), we get

$$\lim_{\Delta u \to 0} \left(\frac{\Delta y}{\Delta u} \right) = \frac{1}{u} \log_a [\lim_{h \to 0} (1 + h)^{\frac{1}{h}}],^*$$

or

(d)
$$D_u y = \frac{1}{u} \cdot \log_a e.$$

Now suppose that u is a function of x.   By the composite function formula of § 97, we obtain

(e)
$$D_x y = D_u y \cdot D_x u = \frac{1}{u} \cdot \log_a e \cdot D_x u.$$

Therefore:

If u is a function of x, and a is any base which is greater than 1, then:

(16)
$$D_x (\log_a u) = \log_a e \cdot \frac{1}{u} \cdot D_x u.$$

In the preceding formula, put $a = e$; then $\log_a e = \ln e = 1$; hence:

(17)
$$D_x (\ln u) = \frac{1}{u} \cdot D_x u.$$

When $u = x$, formula (17) becomes:

(18)
$$D_x (\ln x) = \frac{1}{x}.$$

---

* We use here the limit theorem: lim (log v) = log (lim v), based on the continuity of the logarithmic function (§ 277).

A comparison of formulas (16) and (17) shows how the use of the base e for natural logarithms simplifies the formula for the differentiation of the logarithmic function.

EXAMPLE 1.   (a) $D_x(\ln x^3) = D_x(3 \ln x) = 3\left(\dfrac{1}{x}\right) = \dfrac{3}{x}$;

$$(b)\ D_x \ln\left(\dfrac{2}{x}\right) = D_x(\ln 2 - \ln x) = -\dfrac{1}{x};$$

$$(c)\ D_x \ln (ax^n) = D_x(\ln a + n \ln x) = n\left(\dfrac{1}{x}\right) = \dfrac{n}{x}.$$

EXAMPLE 2.   (a) $D_x(\ln \sin x) = \dfrac{1}{\sin x} \cdot D_x(\sin x) = \dfrac{1}{\sin x} \cdot \cos x = \cot x$;

$$(b)\ D_x(x \cdot \ln x) = x \cdot D_x(\ln x) + \ln x \cdot D_x(x) = x \cdot \dfrac{1}{x} + \ln x = 1 + \ln x.$$

EXAMPLE 3. $D_x \ln (x + \sqrt{1 + x^2}) = \dfrac{1}{x + \sqrt{1 + x^2}} \cdot D_x(x + \sqrt{1 + x^2})$

$$= \dfrac{1}{x + \sqrt{1 + x^2}}\left(1 + \dfrac{x}{\sqrt{1 + x^2}}\right) = \dfrac{1}{\sqrt{1 + x^2}}.$$

282. Exercises

In Exercises 1–24, differentiate each of the given functions:

1. $y = \ln (5 x^2)$.
2. $y = \ln \sqrt[3]{x^5}$.
3. $y = \ln (1/x)$.
4. $y = \ln (x^2 + 1)^2$.
5. $y = \ln \sqrt{x^2 - 1}$.
6. $y = \ln \tan x$.
7. $y = \ln \cos x$.
8. $y = x^2 \ln x$.
9. $w = \ln (\ln z)$.
10. $w = \sqrt{\ln z}$.
11. $v = \dfrac{\ln x}{x}$.
12. $u = \ln \sin^2 t$.
13. $y = \ln (x + \sqrt{x^2 + 4})$.
14. $y = \ln (x + \sqrt{x^2 - a^2})$.
15. $y = \ln (\sec x + \tan x)$.
16. $s = \ln (\sqrt{t + a} + \sqrt{t})$.
17. $z = \ln\left(\dfrac{y}{y^2 - 1}\right)$.
18. $w = \ln \sec^2 z$.
19. $u = \ln \sqrt{\dfrac{1 - z^2}{1 + z^2}}$.
20. $y = x \ln \sqrt{1 - x}$.
21. $y = x \operatorname{Arc} \tan \dfrac{x}{a} - \tfrac{1}{2} a \ln (x^2 + a^2)$.
22. $y = \tfrac{1}{4} \ln\left(\dfrac{x^2}{x^2 - 4}\right) - \dfrac{1}{x^2 - 4}$.
23. $y = \sqrt{a^2 + x^2} - a \ln \dfrac{a + \sqrt{a^2 + x^2}}{x}$.

24. $y = b \ln (a \cos x + b \sin x) + ax$.

25. Evaluate each of the following, using Table D:

$$(a)\ \ D_x(x^3 \ln x), \text{ for } x = 2; \quad (b)\ \ D_x\left(\frac{\ln x}{x^2}\right), \text{ for } x = 3.$$

26. Show that: $D_x \ln \tan \left(\dfrac{x}{2} + \dfrac{\pi}{4}\right) = \sec x$.

283. Logarithmic Differentiation

In order to differentiate complicated expressions involving products or quotients or powers, it is sometimes convenient to take logarithms of both sides of the functional equation and then differentiate; from this we may then obtain the required derivative.   This process is called *logarithmic differentiation.*

EXAMPLE 1.   Differentiate $y = \dfrac{(1 - x)^2 \sqrt{4 + x^2}}{x}$.

Solution: $\ln y = 2 \ln (1 - x) + \frac{1}{2} \ln (4 + x^2) - \ln x$,

$$\therefore \frac{1}{y} D_x y = \frac{2}{1 - x} \cdot (-1) + \frac{1}{2} \cdot \frac{1}{4 + x^2} \cdot 2\,x - \frac{1}{x}$$

$$= -\frac{2(x^3 + 2\,x + 2)}{x(1 - x)(4 + x^2)}.$$

Multiplying by y, we get

$$D_x y = -\frac{2(x^3 + 2\,x + 2)}{x(1 - x)(4 + x^2)} \cdot \frac{(1 - x)^2 \sqrt{4 + x^2}}{x}$$

$$= -\frac{2(1 - x)(x^3 + 2\,x + 2)}{x^2 \sqrt{4 + x^2}}.$$

If $y = f(x)$, the ratio $\dfrac{1}{y} \cdot D_x y = \dfrac{f'(x)}{f(x)}$, the ratio of the derivative of a function to the function itself, is called the **logarithmic derivative** of $f(x)$, because $f'(x)/f(x) = D_x \ln f(x)$.

The *relative error* (§ 145) may be found by *logarithmic differentiation,* since $d \ln y = \dfrac{dy}{y}$, which is, approximately, the relative error.

It is now possible to give a proof of the *general power rule* for any *real* exponent, irrational as well as rational.   Let $y = u^n$, where u is a function of x and n is any real number.   Then

(a) $\ln y = n \ln u$.

Differentiating with respect to x, we have:

$$\frac{1}{y} \cdot D_x y = n \cdot \frac{1}{u} \cdot D_x u;$$

hence

$$D_x y = n \cdot y \cdot \frac{1}{u} \cdot D_x u = n \cdot u^n \cdot \frac{1}{u} \cdot D_x u = n \, u^{n-1} D_x u.$$

We have therefore proved that the power rule: $D_x(u^n) = n \, u^{n-1} D_x u$ holds for any *real* exponent n.

284. Exercises

In Exercises 1–8, differentiate by logarithmic differentiation and simplify:

1. $y = \dfrac{(2\,x + 1)^2}{(x^2 + 2)^3}.$

2. $y = x(1 - x)\sqrt{1 + x^2}.$

3. $y = \sqrt{\dfrac{x + 1}{x - 1}}.$

4. $y = \sqrt{\dfrac{x^2 + 1}{x^2 - 1}}.$

5. $y = \dfrac{\sqrt{1 - x^2}}{(x + 1)^{\frac{2}{3}}}.$

6. $y = \dfrac{\sqrt[3]{1 - x^3}}{\sqrt{1 + x^2}}.$

7. $y = \dfrac{3\,x^2 - 1}{x\sqrt{1 - x^2}}.$

8. $y = \dfrac{x^2\sqrt{1 - x^2}}{\sqrt{1 - 2\,x^2}}.$

9. Find the derivative of $y = x^x$. [*Hint.* Take logarithms of both sides and then differentiate.]

285. Applications of the Derivative of the Logarithmic Function

EXAMPLE 1. Find the maxima and minima of $y = \dfrac{\ln x}{x}.$

Solution: $y' = \dfrac{x\left(\dfrac{1}{x}\right) - \ln x}{x^2} = \dfrac{1 - \ln x}{x^2}.$

If $y' = 0$, then $1 - \ln x = 0$ or $\ln x = 1$, so that $x = e$. If $x < e$, then $\ln x < 1$ and y' is positive, and if $x > e$, then $\ln x > 1$ and y' is negative; hence, y has a maximum at $x = e$. There are no other maxima, and no minima, since the equation $y' = 0$ has no other root than $x = e$.

EXAMPLE 2. In a certain type of chemical reaction, the weight x of substance formed varied thus with the elapsed time:

(a)
$$\frac{x}{a - x} = e^{ka(t - c)} \qquad (k > 0),$$

where a, k and c are constants. Find the rate of reaction; also find the value of t for which this rate is a maximum.

Solution: Taking the logarithm of each side of (*a*), we have

$$\ln x - \ln (a - x) = ka(t - c).$$

Then

$$\frac{1}{x} \cdot D_t x + \frac{1}{a - x} \cdot D_t x = ka.$$

If we denote the required rate of reaction by r, we then have

(*b*) $$r = D_t x = kx(a - x).$$

To find when this rate r is a maximum, we differentiate (*b*) with respect to x and get

$$D_x r = kx(-1) + k(a - x) = -2 kx + ka.$$

If $D_x r = 0$, we have $x = \frac{1}{2} a$. Since $D_x{}^2 r = -2 k < 0$, r has a maximum when $x = \frac{1}{2} a$. Putting $x = \frac{1}{2} a$ in equation (*a*), we find that the maximum rate occurs when $t = c$.

286. Exercises

In Exercises 1–6, find the maximum and minimum points and points of inflection of each of the given curves:

1. $y = x \ln x$.   2. $y = \dfrac{\ln x}{x}$.

3. $y = \ln \cos x$.   4. $y = \ln \sin x$.

5. $y = \ln (1 + x^2)$.   6. $y = x^2 \ln x$.

7. Show that the angle between the tangent at any point P and the line joining P to the origin is the same at all points of the curve

$$\ln \sqrt{x^2 + y^2} = k \text{ Arc tan } (y/x).$$

8. The speed of signalling in a submarine telegraphic cable varies as $x^2 \ln (1/x)$, where x is the ratio of the radius of the core to the thickness of the covering of the cable. Show that the greatest speed is attained when $x = 1/\sqrt{e}$.

9. The relation between the vapor pressure p of a substance and the absolute temperature T has been represented by the equation

$$\ln p = \frac{a}{T} + b \ln T + c,$$

where a, b and c are constants. Find $D_T p$.

10. The time required for a certain biological change is

$$T = \frac{a}{k} \ln \frac{x}{k - x} - k,$$

where a and k are constants, and x is the number of bacteria present. Find $D_x T$.

287. Derivative of the Exponential Function

Let $y = a^u$, where a is any base greater than 1 and u is a function of x. By the method of logarithmic differentiation, we have

$$\ln y = u \ln a \qquad \text{and} \qquad \frac{1}{y} D_x y = \ln a \cdot D_x u.$$

Hence, $\qquad D_x y = \ln a \cdot y \cdot D_x u = \ln a \cdot a^u \cdot D_x u,$ $\qquad$ or:

If u is a function of x, and if $a > 1$, then

(19) $\qquad\qquad\qquad D_x(a^u) = \ln a \cdot a^u \cdot D_x u.$

If we take $a = e$ in this formula, we have $\ln a = \ln e = 1$, hence:

(20) $\qquad\qquad\qquad D_x(e^u) = e^u \cdot D_x u.$

If we take $u = x$, formula (20) becomes:

(21) $\qquad\qquad\qquad D_x(e^x) = e^x.$

This result, which shows that the derivative of the exponential function e^x is equal to itself, is of very great importance in scientific applications of calculus.

EXAMPLE. $\quad(a)\ D_x(e^{x^2}) = e^{x^2} \cdot 2\,x = 2\,x\,e^{x^2};$

$\qquad\qquad(b)\ D_x(e^{\sin x}) = e^{\sin x} \cdot \cos x;$

$\qquad\qquad(c)\ D_x(2^{2x-1}) = \ln 2 \cdot (2^{2x-1}) \cdot 2 = 2^{2x} \ln 2.$

A comparison of formulas (19) and (20) shows again the great advantage of using the base e, since it simplifies the differentiation of the exponential function.

288. Exercises

In Exercises 1–24, differentiate each of the given functions:

1. $y = e^{\frac{1}{2}x}.$ $\qquad\qquad\qquad$ 2. $y = e^{\sqrt{x}}.$
3. $y = 2^{-x}.$ $\qquad\qquad\qquad$ 4. $y = a^x \cdot e^x.$
5. $y = e^x + e^{-x}.$ $\qquad\qquad\quad$ 6. $y = 10^{x^2 - x}.$
7. $y = e^{-\frac{1}{x}}.$ $\qquad\qquad\qquad$ 8. $y = x^2 \cdot e^x.$
9. $y = xe^x.$ $\qquad\qquad\qquad$ 10. $y = e^{-x}(1 - x).$
11. $y = e^{-x^2}.$ $\qquad\qquad\qquad$ 12. $y = e^{-x} \cdot \ln x.$
13. $y = e^{\tan x}.$ $\qquad\qquad\qquad$ 14. $y = \dfrac{\sin x + \cos x}{e^x}.$
15. $y = e^x \cdot \cos x.$ $\qquad\qquad\ $ 16. $f(x) = x^2 \cdot e^{-x}.$
17. $y = \dfrac{e^x}{x}.$ $\qquad\qquad\qquad$ 18. $u = e^x \cdot \ln \sin x.$
19. $y = e^x \cdot \ln x.$ $\qquad\qquad\ $ 20. $y = a^x \cdot x^a.$
21. $f(x) = \text{Arc} \tan e^x.$ $\qquad$ 22. $F(x) = e^{x^2 \ln x}.$
23. $\phi(x) = e^{\ln x}.$ $\qquad\qquad\ $ 24. $v = z \cdot e^{-z^2}.$

Find $D_x y$ from each of the following implicit functions:

25. $xy = x + e^{-y}.$ $\qquad\qquad$ 26. $xy = c\,e^{\frac{y}{x}}.$

27. If $\ln Q = kt$ (k constant), show that $D_t Q = k \cdot Q$.
28. Find the n-th derivative of e^x.
29. If $f(x) = Ae^{kx} + Be^{-kx}$, find $f'(x)$.
30. If $s = e^{-kt}(a \sin mt + b \cos mt)$, find $D_t s$.

289. Applications of the Derivative of the Exponential Function

EXAMPLE 1. Discuss fully the curve $y = e^{-x^2}$.

Solution: The curve is evidently symmetrical with respect to the Y-axis. The Y-intercept is $y = 1$ when $x = 0$. Since $e^{-x^2} > 0$ for all values of x, the curve has no X-intercept, and it lies entirely above the X-axis. We have

$$y' = -2x \cdot e^{-x^2}, \qquad y'' = (4x^2 - 2)e^{-x^2}.$$

If $y' = 0$, we have $x = 0$; y'' is negative when $x = 0$, hence the curve has a maximum point when $x = 0$. If $y'' = 0$, we have $4x^2 - 2 = 0$ or $x = \pm\frac{1}{2}\sqrt{2}$; y'' changes sign when x passes through $x = \frac{1}{2}\sqrt{2}$ and $x = -\frac{1}{2}\sqrt{2}$, therefore the curve has points of inflection at $x = \pm\frac{1}{2}\sqrt{2}$. Since y'' is negative if $x^2 < \frac{1}{2}$, the curve is concave downward between $x = -\frac{1}{2}\sqrt{2}$ and $x = \frac{1}{2}\sqrt{2}$; since y'' is positive if $x^2 > \frac{1}{2}$, the curve is concave upward to the right of $x = \frac{1}{2}\sqrt{2}$ and to the left of $x = -\frac{1}{2}\sqrt{2}$. Since $y \to 0$ when $x \to +\infty$ or $x \to -\infty$, the curve is asymptotic to the X-axis to the right and to the left. Using the information obtained above, we get the curve shown in Fig. 149.

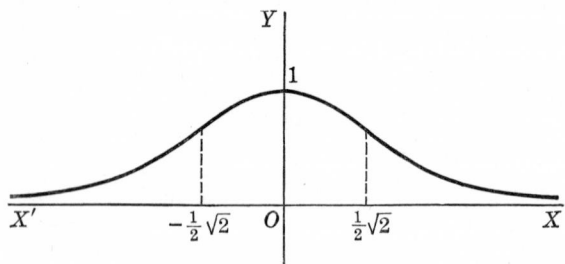

FIG. 149

This curve is a special form of the *probability curve*, which plays an important part in the theory of probability and in its applications, as for example in statistics.

EXAMPLE 2. The *damped vibration curve* $y = e^{-ax} \sin bx$ is of importance in many applications, such as the motion of musical strings, vibration of a pendulum and the current in a radio circuit. Let us examine it.

If $x = 0$, then $y = 0$. If $y = 0$, then $\sin bx = 0$ since e^{-ax} can never be zero. From $\sin bx = 0$, we find $bx = n\pi$ or $x = \dfrac{n\pi}{b}$, where n is any positive or negative integer or 0; this gives the X-intercepts, which are at a distance $\dfrac{\pi}{b}$ apart. As x increases, $\sin bx$ oscillates regularly between 1 and

−1, but e^{-ax} decreases and approaches 0 as $x \to +\infty$. Hence, the curve oscillates regularly but with a constantly decreasing amplitude.

When $\sin bx = 1$ or $x = \dfrac{\pi}{2\,b}, \dfrac{5\,\pi}{2\,b}, \dfrac{9\,\pi}{2\,b}$, etc., we have $y = e^{-ax}$, so that the damped vibration curve is in contact with the exponential curve $y = e^{-ax}$ at these values of x. Similarly, at the values $x = \dfrac{3\,\pi}{2\,b}, \dfrac{7\,\pi}{2\,b}, \dfrac{11\,\pi}{2\,b}$, etc., the damped vibration curve is in contact with the exponential curve $y = -e^{-ax}$. The damped vibration curve therefore oscillates between the two exponential guiding curves.

We find $y' = e^{-ax} (b \cos bx - a \sin bx)$. If $y' = 0$, since e^{-ax} cannot be 0, we must have $b \cos bx - a \sin bx = 0$, or $\tan bx = \dfrac{b}{a}$; hence, the values $x = \dfrac{1}{b} \arctan \dfrac{b}{a}$ give alternate maximum and minimum points of the damped vibration curve. These maximum and minimum points are to the left of the points of contact with the boundary curves.

Making use of the above facts, we obtain a graph as shown in Fig. 150.

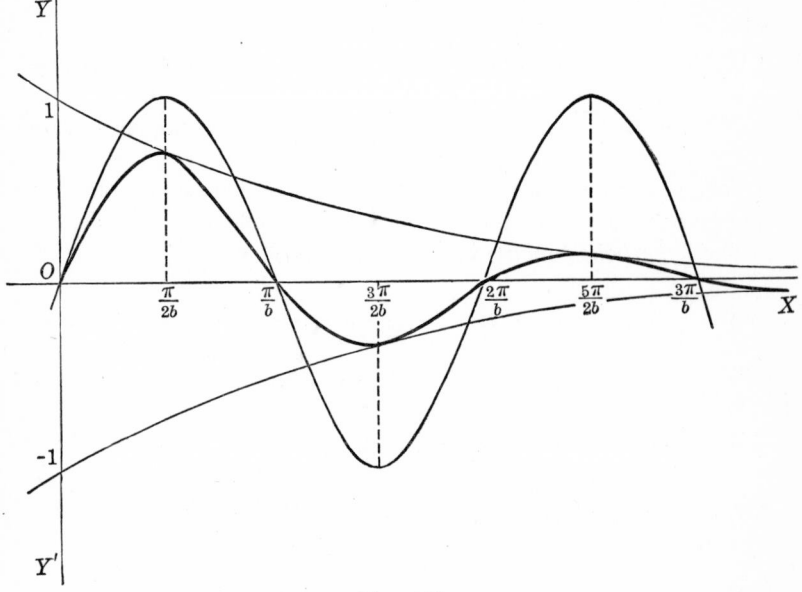

$$\text{F{\small IG}. 150}$$

290. Exercises

In Exercises 1–12, discuss fully the graph of each of the given functions, examining each for maximum and minimum points, points of inflection, direction of concavity, intercepts and asymptotes, and sketch each curve:

1. $y = e^x$.
2. $y = e^{-x}$.
3. $y = e^{\frac{1}{x}}$.
4. $y = e^x - e^{-x}$.
5. $y = e^x + e^{-x}$.
6. $y = xe^x$.
7. $y = xe^{-x}$.
8. $y = x^2 e^{-x}$.
9. $y = e^{-x} \cos x$.
10. $y = e^{-x} \sin 2x$.
11. $y = xe^{-x^2}$.
12. $y = x - e^x$.

13. Show that the maximum rectangle which can be inscribed under the curve $y = e^{-x^2}$ has two of its vertices at the points of inflection of the curve.

14. The number of bacteria in a certain culture was given by the formula $N = 1000\, e^{0.06t}$, where t is the time expressed in hours.   Find the number of bacteria at the end of 2 hours.   Also find the rate of change of N at that time.

15. An equation used in studying cells is $x = k(1 - e^{-at})$, where k and a are constants.   Find the rate of change of x with respect to t in terms of x.

16. The strength of electric current needed to excite a nerve x units long was found to be $S = \dfrac{ke^x}{e^x - 1}$, where k is constant.   Find the rate of change of S with respect to x.

291. Hyperbolic Functions

Certain combinations of exponential functions called *hyperbolic functions* occur so frequently in many problems of applied mathematics that they are given names and their properties are investigated. These hyperbolic functions are so called because they are related to a rectangular hyperbola in much the same way that the trigonometric functions (also called circular functions) are related to a circle.

The **hyperbolic functions** are defined as follows:

(22)   *hyperbolic sine:* $\sinh x = \frac{1}{2}(e^x - e^{-x})$,

(23)   *hyperbolic cosine:* $\cosh x = \frac{1}{2}(e^x + e^{-x})$,

(24)   *hyperbolic tangent:* $\tanh x = \dfrac{\sinh x}{\cosh x}$,

(25)   *hyperbolic cotangent:* $\coth x = \dfrac{1}{\tanh x} = \dfrac{\cosh x}{\sinh x}$,

(26)   *hyperbolic secant:* $\operatorname{sech} x = \dfrac{1}{\cosh x}$,

(27)   *hyperbolic cosecant:* $\operatorname{csch} x = \dfrac{1}{\sinh x}$.

By addition and subtraction of the defining equations (22) and (23), we get the useful formulas:

(28) $$\cosh x + \sinh x = e^x,$$

(29) $$\cosh x - \sinh x = e^{-x}.$$

Tables of values of the hyperbolic functions $\sinh x$, $\cosh x$ and $\tanh x$ are published in various collections of mathematical tables. A brief table, in *Table E,* will be found in the Appendix.

292. Identities Between the Hyperbolic Functions

There will be noticed a close resemblance between identities for the hyperbolic functions and those for the trigonometric functions.

One fundamental set of such identities is the following:

(30) $$\cosh^2 x - \sinh^2 x = 1,$$

(31) $$\tanh^2 x + \operatorname{sech}^2 x = 1,$$

(32) $$\coth^2 x - \operatorname{csch}^2 x = 1.$$

The first one of these may be proved directly from the definitions as follows:

$$\cosh^2 x - \sinh^2 x = \tfrac{1}{4}(e^x + e^{-x})^2 - \tfrac{1}{4}(e^x - e^{-x})^2$$
$$= \tfrac{1}{4}[(e^{2x} + 2 + e^{-2x}) - (e^{2x} - 2 + e^{-2x})] = 1.$$

The second identity may be obtained from the first by dividing each term by $\cosh^2 x$. The third identity may be derived similarly.

Numerous other identities may be derived, which are given as exercises in § 294. To illustrate the method of proof, consider the following example:

(a) $$\sinh (x + y) = \sinh x \cosh y + \cosh x \sinh y.$$

To prove this, we write

$$\sinh x \cosh y + \cosh x \sinh y$$
$$= \tfrac{1}{4}(e^x - e^{-x})(e^y + e^{-y}) + \tfrac{1}{4}(e^x + e^{-x})(e^y - e^{-y})$$
$$= \tfrac{1}{4}[(e^{x+y} - e^{-x+y} + e^{x-y} - e^{-x-y}) + (e^{x+y} + e^{-x+y} - e^{x-y} - e^{-x-y})]$$
$$= \tfrac{1}{2}[e^{(x+y)} - e^{-(x+y)}] = \sinh (x + y).$$

Another important set of identities, which follow at once from the definitions, is:

(33) $$\sinh (-x) = -\sinh x, \qquad \cosh (-x) = \cosh x.$$

293. Graphs of the Hyperbolic Functions

The graphs of $y = \cosh x$ and of $y = \sinh x$ may be readily sketched by drawing the curves $y = e^x$ and $y = e^{-x}$, adding and subtracting ordinates and taking half of each. They are shown in Fig. 151. By finding the first and second derivatives, and testing for maxima and minima, points of inflection and concavity, we may sketch the curves more accurately.

A *catenary*, which is the graph of the hyperbolic cosine, is a curve in which a homogeneous cord or chain hangs under its own weight.

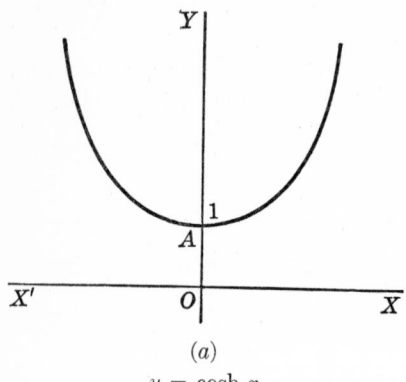

(a)
$y = \cosh x$

(b)
$y = \sinh x$

Fig. 151

294. Exercises

1. Show that:
   (a) $\sinh 0 = 0$;
   (b) $\cosh 0 = 1$;
   (c) $\tanh 0 = 0$.
2. Prove the identity:
   $\coth^2 x - \operatorname{csch}^2 x = 1$.
3. By use of Table E, find the values of: (a) $\sinh 0.5$; (b) $\cosh 1.2$; (c) $\tanh 0.8$; (d) $\cosh 0.45$.
4. By use of Table E, find the values of: (a) $\sinh 1.5$; (b) $\cosh 0.6$; (c) $\tanh 1.2$; (d) $\sinh 0.54$.

Prove the identities in Exercises 5–12:

5. $\cosh (x + y) = \cosh x \cosh y + \sinh x \sinh y$.
6. $\sinh (x - y) = \sinh x \cosh y - \cosh x \sinh y$.
7. $\cosh (x - y) = \cosh x \cosh y - \sinh x \sinh y$.
8. $\tanh (x + y) = \dfrac{\tanh x + \tanh y}{1 + \tanh x \tanh y}$.
9. $\sinh 2 x = 2 \sinh x \cosh x$.
10. $\cosh 2 x = \cosh^2 x + \sinh^2 x = 2 \cosh^2 x - 1 = 2 \sinh^2 x + 1$.
11. $\sinh \frac{1}{2} x = \pm \sqrt{\dfrac{\cosh x - 1}{2}}$.

12. $\cosh \frac{1}{2} x = \sqrt{\dfrac{\cosh x + 1}{2}}.$

295. Derivatives of the Hyperbolic Functions

Let $y = \sinh u$, where u is a function of x.   Then by the formula (20) of § 287, we have

$$D_x y = D_x \left[\tfrac{1}{2}\left(e^u - e^{-u}\right)\right] = \tfrac{1}{2}\left[e^u \cdot D_x u - e^{-u}(-1)\cdot D_x u\right]$$
$$= \tfrac{1}{2}\left(e^u + e^{-u}\right)\cdot D_x u = \cosh u \cdot D_x u.$$

Similarly we may find $D_x \cosh u$.   Hence:

If u is a function of x, then:

(34) $\qquad\qquad D_x\,(\sinh u) = \cosh u \cdot D_x u,$

(35) $\qquad\qquad D_x\,(\cosh u) = \sinh u \cdot D_x u.$

Let $y = \tanh u = \dfrac{\sinh u}{\cosh u}.$ By the quotient rule for derivatives (§ 94) and by use of the identity (30) of § 292, we get

$$D_x y = \frac{\cosh u \cosh u - \sinh u \sinh u}{\cosh^2 u}\cdot D_x u$$

$$= \frac{1}{\cosh^2 u}\cdot D_x u = \operatorname{sech}^2 u \cdot D_x u.$$

Similarly we may find $D_x \coth u$, etc.   Hence:

If u is a function of x, then:

(36) $\qquad\qquad D_x\,(\tanh u) = \operatorname{sech}^2 u \cdot D_x u,$

(37) $\qquad\qquad D_x\,(\coth u) = -\operatorname{csch}^2 u \cdot D_x u,$

(38) $\qquad\qquad D_x\,(\operatorname{sech} u) = -\operatorname{sech} u \tanh u \cdot D_x u,$

(39) $\qquad\qquad D_x\,(\operatorname{csch} u) = -\operatorname{csch} u \coth u \cdot D_x u.$

296. Exercises

In Exercises 1–16, differentiate each of the given functions:

1. $y = \cosh 2x.$
2. $y = \sinh \frac{1}{2} x.$
3. $y = \tanh (1 - x).$
4. $y = \coth (1 - x^2).$
5. $y = \sinh^2 x.$
6. $y = \cosh^2 x.$
7. $y = x \sinh 3x.$
8. $y = x^2 \cosh x.$
9. $u = \tanh z - \operatorname{sech} z.$
10. $w = z \sinh z - \cosh z.$
11. $v = \ln \sinh 2u.$
12. $u = \ln \tanh \frac{1}{2} t.$
13. $s = e^{-t} \cosh 2t.$
14. $v = e^{-2x} \sinh x.$
15. $y = \operatorname{Arc\,tan} (\sinh x).$
16. $z = \frac{1}{4} \sinh 2u + \frac{1}{2} u.$

17. Prove the formulas of § 295 for $D_x \cosh u$, $D_x \coth u$, $D_x \operatorname{sech} u$.

18. Show that if $y = \cosh x$, then $y'' = y$.

297. Inverse Hyperbolic Functions

*The **inverse hyperbolic sine** is denoted by* $\sinh^{-1} x$, *and is defined by*

$$y = \sinh^{-1} x \quad if \quad x = \sinh y.$$

Similarly the other inverse hyperbolic functions are defined; they are denoted by similar symbols.

It can be seen from the graphs of the direct hyperbolic functions in Fig. 151 that $\sinh^{-1} x$ is a single-valued function, but that $\cosh^{-1} x$ is a double-valued function, since the graph of $y = \cosh x$ is symmetric with respect to the Y-axis. We define the *principal value* of $\cosh^{-1} x$ as the positive value of the function and denote it by $\operatorname{Cosh}^{-1} x$, the other value being $-\operatorname{Cosh}^{-1} x$.

The inverse hyperbolic functions may be expressed in terms of natural logarithms as follows: Let $y = \cosh^{-1} x$, where $x \geqq 1$. Then $x = \cosh y = \frac{1}{2}(e^y + e^{-y})$. Multiplying by $2\,e^y$, we get

(a) $\qquad 2\,x\,e^y = e^{2y} + 1 \quad$ or $\quad (e^y)^2 - 2\,x(e^y) + 1 = 0.$

Solving this quadratic equation for the unknown e^y, we find

(b) $\qquad e^y = x \pm \sqrt{x^2 - 1} \quad$ or $\quad y = \ln(x \pm \sqrt{x^2 - 1}).$

Since $\operatorname{Cosh}^{-1} x$ is the larger of these two values of y, we get $\operatorname{Cosh}^{-1} x = \ln(x + \sqrt{x^2 - 1})$. Similarly we may treat the other inverse hyperbolic functions. Hence:

$(40) \qquad \sinh^{-1} x = \ln(x + \sqrt{x^2 + 1}) \qquad$ (any x),

$(41) \qquad \operatorname{Cosh}^{-1} x = \ln(x + \sqrt{x^2 - 1}) \qquad (x \geqq 1),$

$(42) \qquad \tanh^{-1} x = \frac{1}{2} \ln \dfrac{1 + x}{1 - x} \qquad\qquad (-1 < x < 1).$

298. Exercises

1. Evaluate: (a) $\sinh^{-1} 0$; (b) $\operatorname{Cosh}^{-1} 1$; (c) $\tanh^{-1} 0$; (d) $\cosh^{-1} 1$.

2. Draw the graphs of: (a) $y = \sinh^{-1} x$; (b) $y = \cosh^{-1} x$;
   (c) $y = \tanh^{-1} x$.

3. Prove formula (40) of § 297.

4. Prove formula (42) of § 297.

5. From Table E, find: (a) $\sinh^{-1} 0.8223$; (b) $\operatorname{Cosh}^{-1} 1.8107$;
   (c) $\tanh^{-1} 0.5005$.

6. From Table E, find: (a) $\sinh^{-1} 2.5075$; (b) $\operatorname{Cosh}^{-1} 1.6038$;
   (c) $\tanh^{-1} 0.9801$.

299. Derivatives of the Inverse Hyperbolic Functions

Let $y = \sinh^{-1} u$, where u is a function of x.   Then

$$u = \sinh y, \qquad D_y u = \cosh y;$$

$$D_u y = \frac{1}{D_y u} = \frac{1}{\cosh y} = \frac{1}{\sqrt{1 + \sinh^2 y}} = \frac{1}{\sqrt{u^2 + 1}},$$

$$D_x y = D_u y \cdot D_x u = \frac{1}{\sqrt{u^2 + 1}} \cdot D_x u.$$

Similarly we may treat the other inverse functions.   These derivatives may also be obtained by differentiating formulas (40), (41), (42) of § 297.   Hence:

If u is a function of x, then:

(43) $D_x (\sinh^{-1} u) = \dfrac{1}{\sqrt{u^2 + 1}} \cdot D_x u$ (all values of u),

(44) $D_x (\operatorname{Cosh}^{-1} u) = \dfrac{1}{\sqrt{u^2 - 1}} \cdot D_x u$ $(u > 1)$,

(45) $D_x (\tanh^{-1} u) = \dfrac{1}{1 - u^2} \cdot D_x u$ $(-1 < u < 1)$,

(46) $D_x (\coth^{-1} u) = \dfrac{-1}{u^2 - 1} \cdot D_x u$ $(u^2 > 1)$.

300. Exercises

In Exercises 1–10, differentiate each of the given functions:

1. $y = \sinh^{-1} 2 x$.
2. $y = \sinh^{-1} x^2$.
3. $y = x \sinh^{-1} x$.
4. $y = \operatorname{Cosh}^{-1} \frac{3}{4} x$.
5. $y = \operatorname{Cosh}^{-1} e^x$.
6. $y = \tanh^{-1} \left(\dfrac{1}{x}\right) + \tan^{-1} \left(\dfrac{1}{x}\right)$.
7. $y = \tanh^{-1} (1 - x)$.
8. $y = \operatorname{Cosh}^{-1} (\sec x)$.
9. $y = \tanh^{-1} (\tan \frac{1}{2} x)$.
10. $y = 2 \tanh^{-1} \frac{1}{2} x + \ln \dfrac{2 - x}{2 + x}$.

11. Prove the formulas in § 299 for $D_x \operatorname{Cosh}^{-1} u$ and $D_x \tanh^{-1} u$.
12. Prove the formulas in § 299 for $D_x \sinh^{-1} u$, $D_x \operatorname{Cosh}^{-1} u$ and $D_x \tanh^{-1} u$ by use of the logarithmic forms (40), (41), (42) of § 297.

301. Newton's Method for Solving Transcendental Equations

In § 151, we presented *Newton's method* for solving equations, and applied it to polynomial equations.   The method applies equally well

to transcendental equations.   We recall that the basic formula for
the solution of the equation $f(x) = 0$ is:

(a) $$a_2 = a_1 - \frac{f(a_1)}{f'(a_1)}.$$

EXAMPLE.   Find the real root of the equation $e^x + x - 2 = 0$ by use of
Newton's method, correct to four decimal places.

Solution: Put $f(x) = e^x + x - 2$, then $f'(x) = e^x + 1$.   A rough graph of
$f(x)$ indicates a root between 0 and 1, perhaps near 0.5.   From the table of
exponentials (Appendix) we find that $f(0.5) = +0.1487$ and $f(0.4) = -0.1082$,
so that the equation $f(x) = 0$ has a root between 0.5 and 0.4.   Let us take
$a_1 = 0.5$ in formula (a), then $f'(0.5) = 2.6487$, and we have

(b) $$a_2 = 0.5 - \frac{0.1487}{2.6487} = 0.5 - 0.056 = 0.444.$$

Now let us take $a_2 = 0.444$ in place of a_1 in formula (a), and we find

(c) $$a_3 = 0.444 - \frac{0.00293}{2.55893} = 0.44286.$$

The required root is therefore approximately 0.4429 to four decimal places.

302. Exercises

In Exercises 1–16, solve each of the given equations by Newton's method, to
find the smallest positive root, correct to three decimal places:

1. $e^x = 3\,x$.
2. $4\,x = e^x$.
3. $e^x - 4 \sin x = 0$.
4. $\sin x + x - 1 = 0$.
5. $\cos x = x^2$.
6. $\cos x = x$.
7. $x - \ln x - 2 = 0$.
8. $e^x - 4 \sin x = 0$.
9. $2 - 3\,x - \sin x = 0$.
10. $\tan x + x - 1 = 0$.
11. $e^{-x} - \cos x = 0$.
12. $1 + \sin x = x^2$.
13. $2\,x + \ln x = 0$.
14. $e^x + x - 3 = 0$.
15. $\cosh x = 2\,x$.
16. $\sinh x = 2\,x$.

17. The equation $x - e \sin x = M$, called Kepler's equation, occurs in
astronomy.   Solve it for x when $e = 0.2$, $M = 0.85$, correct to three
decimal places.
18. The equation $5\,e^{-x} + x - 5 = 0$ arises in the quantum theory of radia-
tion in physics.   Solve it, correct to three decimal places.
19. Find, correct to three decimal places, the value of x between 0 and $\frac{1}{2}\,\pi$
for which the function $x \cos x$ is a maximum.

303. Miscellaneous Exercises on Differentiation of Transcendental Functions

Differentiate and simplify:

1. $y = x \sin 2\,x$.
2. $u = \cos^3 x$.
3. $w = z \,\text{Arc} \sin z$.
4. $y = \text{Arc} \tan \frac{1}{2}\,x + \dfrac{2\,x}{4 + x^2}$.

5. $v = \ln (y^2 + 1)$.

6. $z = \ln (u - \sqrt{u^2 + a^2})$.

7. $y = \dfrac{x}{e^x}$.

8. $y = x^n + n^x$.

9. $y = \tanh \left(\dfrac{1}{x}\right)$.

10. $u = x^2 \tanh^{-1} x$.

11. $y = \ln \sin 2\, x$.

12. $v = \tan u + \sec u$.

13. $f(y) = e^{-y} \sin y$.

14. $w = \sqrt{1 - z^2}\ \mathrm{Arc}\ \sin z$.

15. $y = \sqrt{\sinh x}$.

16. $z = e^{-\frac{1}{w^2}}$.

17. $y = \mathrm{Arc}\ \sin (x - 1) + (x - 1)\ \sqrt{2\,x - x^2}$.

18. $y = \cosh e^x$.

19. $\phi(z) = \sqrt{1 + \sin z}$.

20. $y = 2\sqrt{x} - 2\ \mathrm{Arc}\ \tan \sqrt{x}$.

21. $y = e^{ax} (\sin ax - \cos ax)$.

22. $u = \sin v - \tfrac{1}{3} \sin^3 v$.

23. $z = \ln \sinh^2 x$.

24. $y = \dfrac{1 - \sin x}{1 + \sin x}$.

25. $y = \dfrac{8\,x}{x^2 + 4} - 4\ \mathrm{Arc}\ \tan \tfrac{1}{2}\, x + x$.

26. $u = \mathrm{Arc}\ \sin (2\,x - 1)$.

27. $x = \cosh^3 3\, y$.

28. $g(x) = \ln (x^2 - 2\,x)$.

29. $w = z^2\ \mathrm{Arc}\ \sin z$.

30. $v = x \ln e^x$.

31. $s = \sqrt{1 - \cos t}$.

32. $y = e^{-2x} \cos 3\, x$.

33. $u = \ln \sec z$.

34. $y = \mathrm{Arc}\ \tan \sqrt{v}$.

35. $y = \sin 2\, x \cdot \sin^2 x$.

36. $y = \ln \dfrac{x^2 + 1}{x^2 - 1}$.

37. $y = \mathrm{Arc}\ \sin \dfrac{x}{a} + \dfrac{\sqrt{a^2 - x^2}}{x}$.

38. $y = \sinh^{-1} e^x$.

39. $z = \dfrac{\sin^2 y}{y}$.

40. $y = e^{-x} \ln x$.

41. $y = 2 \sin 3\, x + 3 \cos 2\, x$.

42. $z = \dfrac{x}{e^{-x}}$.

43. $y = \mathrm{Arc}\ \cos \left(1 - \dfrac{x}{a}\right)$.

44. $u = \ln \sin^3 x$.

45. $w = \ln (\sqrt{z + a} + \sqrt{z})$.

46. $y = x^2\ \mathrm{Arc}\ \tan \left(\dfrac{1}{x}\right)$.

47. $F(x) = \tan x - x$.

48. $y = x\ \mathrm{Arc}\ \tan x + \ln \sqrt{1 + x^2}$.

49. $y = (\sin x)^x$.

50. $z = e^{\sin u}$.

51. $y = x^2\ \mathrm{Arc}\ \sin \left(\dfrac{2}{x}\right)$.

52. $y = \dfrac{1}{a} \ln \dfrac{x}{x + \sqrt{a^2 - x^2}}$.

53. $v = \sec^2 x + 2 \tan x$.

54. $u = \ln \tan^2 v$.

55. $y = -\dfrac{\sqrt{a^2 - x^2}}{x} + \mathrm{Arc}\ \cos \dfrac{x}{a}$.

56. $y = x \tanh^{-1} x$.

57. $y = \mathrm{Arc}\ \sin e^x$.

58. $v = \ln \sinh x$.

59. $s = a \sin (kt + \alpha)$.

60. $u = \mathrm{Arc}\ \sin (x^2)$.

CHAPTER XIV

Polar Coördinates

304. Polar Coördinates of a Point

The position of a point in a plane may be specified, not only by its directed distances from two perpendicular axes as in the case of rectangular coördinates, but also by means of its *direction* and *distance* from a fixed reference line and point.

Let O be a fixed reference point, called the **pole** (or origin), and let OX be a fixed reference half-line through O, called the **polar axis** (or initial line) (Fig. 152). The polar axis is usually drawn horizontally and to the right from the pole.

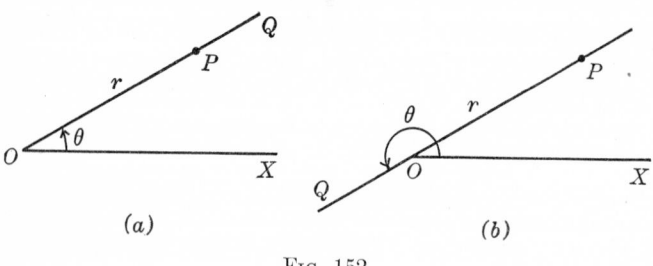

(a)   (b)

Fig. 152

The position of any point P (other than the pole O) is determined by the directed angle XOQ (Fig. 152), whose initial side is OX and whose terminal side OQ, or whose terminal side extended backward through O, contains the given point P, and by the directed distance $\overline{OP}$.

We shall consider the directed angle XOQ as positive when it is generated by counter-clockwise rotation of OQ about O from the initial position OX, and negative when the rotation is clockwise. We shall consider the directed distance $\overline{OP}$ as positive when $\overline{OP}$ and $\overline{OQ}$ agree in direction (Fig. 152 (a)), and negative when $\overline{OP}$ and $\overline{OQ}$ are opposite in direction (Fig. 152 (b)).

*The directed distance $\overline{OP}$ is called the **radius vector** of the point P, and the directed angle XOQ is called a **vectorial angle** of P.**

The radius vector and vectorial angle of a point P are together called the **polar coördinates** of P.

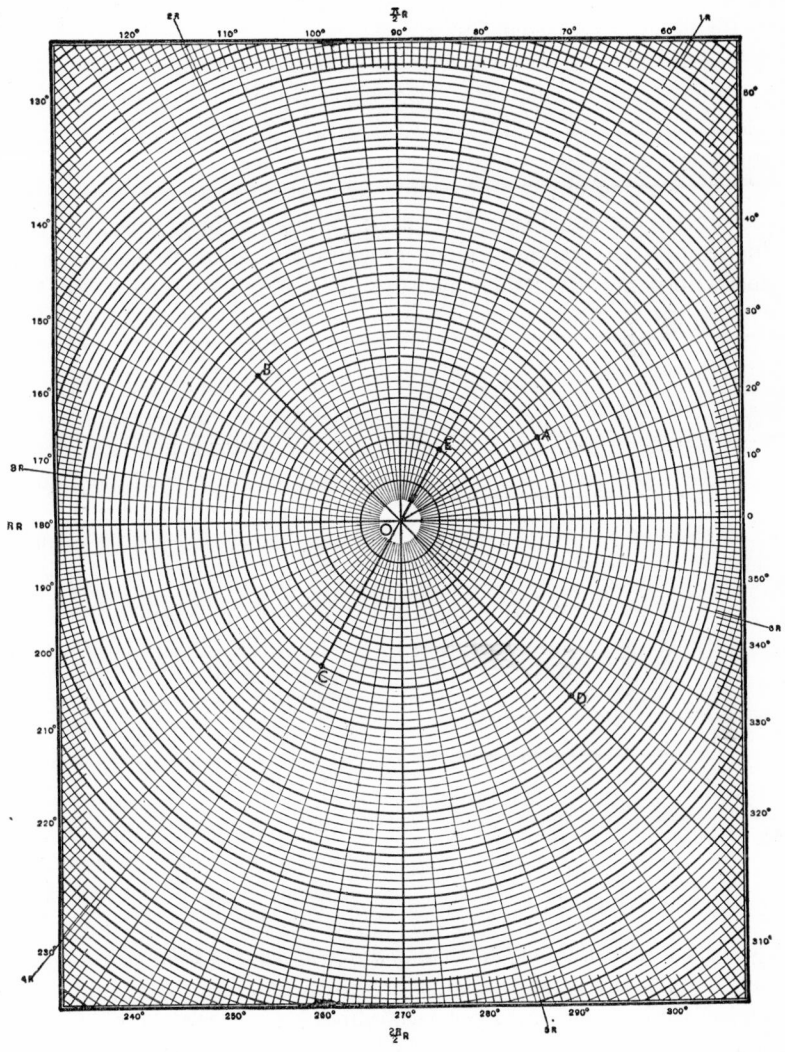

Fig. 153

* The term *radius vector* is also sometimes used to refer to the directed *line segment OP*.

The polar coördinates of the pole O are defined by taking the radius vector equal to 0 and the vectorial angle to be any angle we please.

The radius vector of a point is usually denoted in general by r (or sometimes by ρ), and the vectorial angle by θ. A point whose polar coördinates are r and θ is denoted by (r, θ), in which the radius vector is always written first.

According to the above agreement as to algebraic signs of the polar coördinates, the radius vector r is positive when P lies on the terminal side of the vectorial angle θ and is negative when P lies on the terminal side of θ extended backward through O.

The following obvious procedure for plotting a point whose polar coördinates are given may be stated: Taking the polar axis as initial side, lay off the vectorial angle θ, counterclockwise if positive and clockwise if negative; then measure off the radius vector r, on the terminal side of θ if r is positive and on the terminal side of θ extended backward through the pole if r is negative.

For plotting points in polar coördinates, it will be found convenient to use polar coördinate paper (Fig. 153), ruled into subdivisions by concentric circles and radial lines.

EXAMPLE. The points whose polar coördinates are: $A(4, 30°)$, $B(5, 135°), C(4, 240°), D(-6, 135°)$ and $E(2, 780°)$ are shown plotted on polar coördinate paper in Fig. 153.

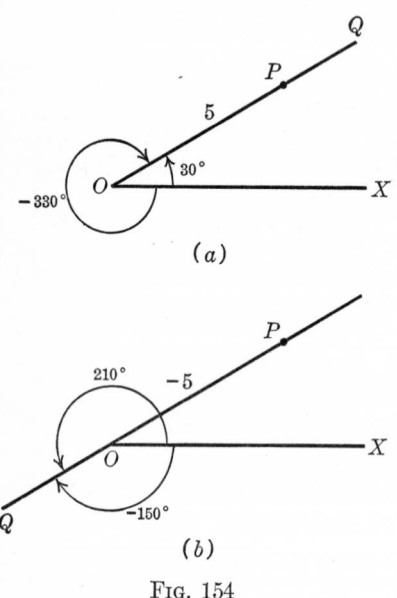

(a)

(b)

FIG. 154

A given pair of polar coördinates evidently determines a single point. The converse of this statement is not true. That is, *a given point may have many different pairs of polar coördinates.* For example, the point whose polar coördinates are $(5, 30°)$ is also represented by the pairs of polar coördinates $(5, -330°)$, $(-5, 210°)$, $(-5, -150°)$, and by other pairs with angles greater than $360°$ in numerical value (Fig. 154).

305. Exercises

1. Plot on polar coördinate paper the points whose polar coördinates are:
$A(5, -30°)$, $C(-5, 30°)$, $D(-5, -30°)$, $E(4, 240°)$, $F(-3, 180°)$, $G(6, 0°)$, $H(4, 90°)$, $J(4, \frac{1}{3}\pi)$, $K(-3, \frac{5}{3}\pi)$, $L(5, \frac{7}{4}\pi)$, $M(2, -\pi)$.

2. Proceed as in Exercise 1 with: $A(4, 45°)$, $B(-4, 45°)$, $C(5, 135°)$, $D(6, 180°)$, $E(3, 210°)$, $F(-5, 270°)$, $G(4, 315°)$, $H(-5, 0°)$, $J(6, \frac{2}{3}\pi)$, $K(4, -\frac{1}{6}\pi)$, $L(3, \pi)$, $M(2, -\frac{7}{4}\pi)$.

3. For each of the following points for which one pair of polar coördinates is given, find three other pairs of polar coördinates, including two for which r is negative: (a) $(4, 45°)$; (b) $(3, -60°)$; (c) $(5, 270°)$; (d) $(-4, \frac{7}{6}\pi)$.

4. Proceed as in Exercise 3 with: (a) $(5, 120°)$; (b) $(4, -45°)$; (c) $(3, 90°)$; (d) $(-6, 135°)$.

5. Show that the points whose polar coördinates are $A(0, 0)$, $B(5, \frac{1}{3}\pi)$ and $C(5, \frac{2}{3}\pi)$ are the vertices of an equilateral triangle.

6. Show that the points whose polar coördinates are $A(0, 0)$, $B(4, \frac{1}{6}\pi)$ and $C(4, \frac{1}{2}\pi)$ are the vertices of an equilateral triangle.

7. Where do all the points lie for which the radius vector is 4; for which the vectorial angle is $\frac{1}{4}\pi$?

8. Show that in general the same point is located by each of the following four pairs of polar coördinates: (a) (r, θ); (b) $(-r, \theta + \pi)$; (c) $[r, -(2\pi - \theta)]$; (d) $[-r, -(\pi - \theta)]$.

9. Show that: (a) the points (r, θ) and $(-r, \theta)$ are symmetric with respect to the pole; (b) the points (r, θ) and $(r, \theta + \pi)$ are symmetric with respect to the pole; (c) the points (r, θ) and $(r, \pi - \theta)$ are symmetric with respect to the 90°-line.

10. (a) Find the rectangular coördinates of the point whose polar coördinates are $(6, \frac{1}{3}\pi)$.

(b) Find the polar coördinates of the point whose rectangular coördinates are $(-4\sqrt{3}, 4)$.

11. Find the distance between the points whose polar coördinates are $(3, \frac{1}{6}\pi)$ and $(4, \frac{1}{2}\pi)$, by using the law of cosines of trigonometry.

12. Prove that the distance d between the points $P_1(r_1, \theta_1)$ and $P_2(r_2, \theta_2)$ is given by
$$d^2 = r_1{}^2 + r_2{}^2 - 2\,r_1 r_2 \cos(\theta_1 - \theta_2).$$
[*Hint.* Use the law of cosines of trigonometry.]

306. Graph of an Equation in Polar Coördinates

The *graph* (or locus) *of an equation in polar coördinates* is the set of all points whose polar coördinates satisfy the given equation.

The basic method for constructing a graph of an equation in polar coördinates r and θ is to calculate a table of corresponding values of r and θ from the given equation, plot the point representing each such pair of coördinates and then draw a curve through these points. Usually the equation is solved for r in terms of θ, convenient values are assigned to θ and the corresponding values of r are calculated.

EXAMPLE 1. Plot the graph of the equation $r = 1 - \cos \theta$.

Solution: We first calculate the following table of corresponding values of r and θ:

θ	0	$\frac{1}{6}\pi$	$\frac{1}{4}\pi$	$\frac{1}{3}\pi$	$\frac{1}{2}\pi$	$\frac{2}{3}\pi$	$\frac{3}{4}\pi$	$\frac{5}{6}\pi$	π
r	0	0.13	0.29	0.50	1.00	1.50	1.71	1.87	2.00

For the values of θ: $\frac{7}{6}\pi$, $\frac{5}{4}\pi$, $\frac{4}{3}\pi$, $\frac{3}{2}\pi$, $\frac{5}{3}\pi$, $\frac{7}{4}\pi$, $\frac{11}{6}\pi$, 2π, by trigonometry, the corresponding values of r will be the same as those in the table in reverse order. If we plot the points corresponding to the values of θ from 0 to 2π on polar coördinate paper, we obtain the points shown in Fig. 155, and by drawing a smooth curve through these points we have the graph of the given equation. Note that the curve is symmetric about the polar axis. This curve is called a *cardioid* because of its heart-like shape.

EXAMPLE 2. (*a*) The graph of the equation $r = 4$ is evidently a circle with center at the pole O and radius 4.

(*b*) The graph of the equation $\theta = \frac{1}{3}\pi$ is evidently a line through the pole, making an angle of $\frac{1}{3}\pi$ with the polar axis.

In order that a point may lie on the graph of a given equation in polar coördinates, it is necessary that at least one pair of coördinates of this point shall satisfy the equation. But since a given point has more than one pair of polar coördinates, it sometimes happens that only one pair of coördinates of a point on a graph, and sometimes more than one pair, will satisfy the equation of the graph. For the same reason, it sometimes happens that two different equations in polar coördinates may have the same graph; for example, the equations $r = 4$ and $r = -4$ are represented by the same circle.

307. Exercises

1. Plot the graphs of the following equations:

    (*a*) $r = 5$;
    (*b*) $\theta = \frac{1}{6}\pi$;

    (*c*) $r = 2\cos\theta$;
    (*d*) $r\cos\theta = 2$;

    (*e*) $r = 1 - \sin\theta$;
    (*f*) $r = \dfrac{2}{1 + \cos\theta}$.

2. Plot the graphs of the following equations:

    (*a*) $r = -5$;
    (*b*) $\theta = \frac{3}{4}\pi$;

    (*c*) $r = 4\sin\theta$;
    (*d*) $r\sin\theta = 4$;

    (*e*) $r = 2(1 + \sin\theta)$;
    (*f*) $r = \dfrac{8}{2 - \cos\theta}$.

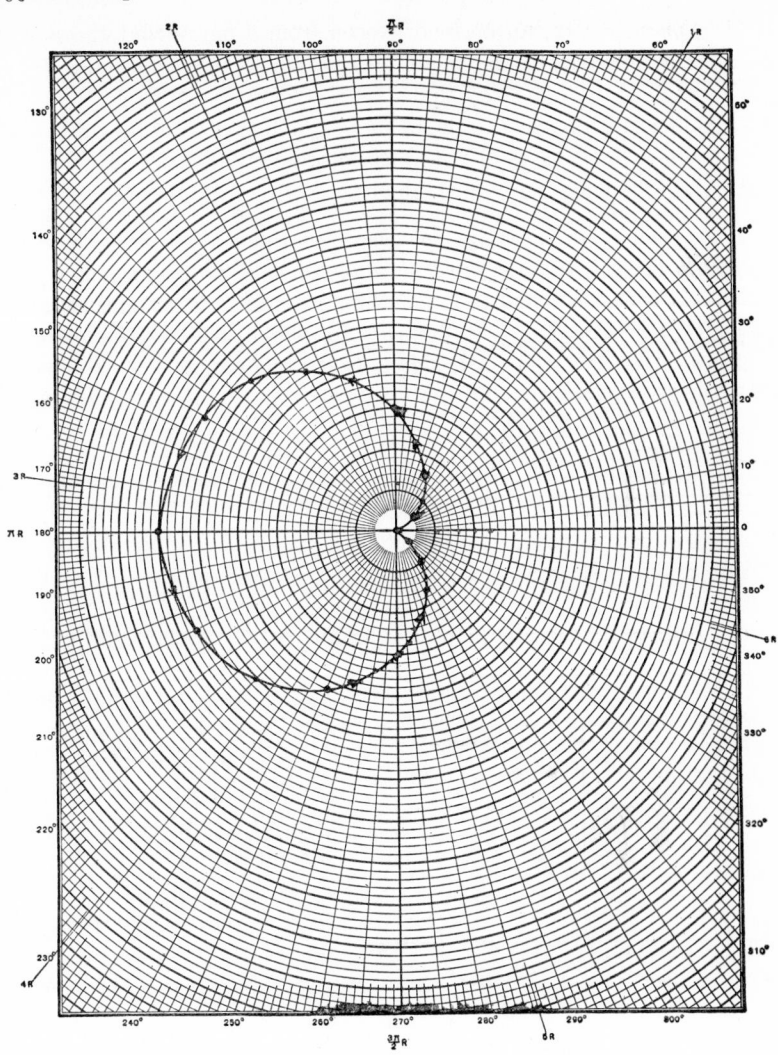

Fig. 155

308. Discussion of an Equation in Polar Coördinates

A preliminary analysis or discussion of an equation in polar co-ordinates in addition to plotting of particular points will generally simplify the construction of the graph. In this analysis we consider such properties as symmetry, extent, excluded values, intercepts, etc.

(1) *Symmetry:* It can be readily seen from a figure that the point (r, θ) is symmetric to the point $(-r, \theta)$ or to the point $(r, \pi + \theta)$ with respect to the pole; that (r, θ) is symmetric to $(r, -\theta)$ or $(-r, \pi - \theta)$ with respect to the polar axis; and that (r, θ) is symmetric to $(-r, -\theta)$ or $(r, \pi - \theta)$ with respect to the 90°-axis. Hence we have the following tests for symmetry:

The graph of an equation in polar coördinates is symmetric with respect to the pole if an equivalent equation is obtained when r is replaced by $-r$ or when θ is replaced by $\pi + \theta$; it is symmetric with respect to the polar axis if an equivalent equation is obtained when θ is replaced by $-\theta$ or when r is replaced by $-r$ and θ by $\pi - \theta$; it is symmetric with respect to the 90°-axis if an equivalent equation is obtained when θ is replaced by $\pi - \theta$ or when r is replaced by $-r$ and θ by $-\theta$.

(2) *Extent and excluded values:* Values of θ for which r is imaginary will give excluded regions. The extent of the graph is indicated by finding values, if any, which make r a maximum or minimum, or which make r become infinite, and by consideration of excluded regions, if any.

(3) *Intercepts:* Intercepts of the graph on the polar axis or its extension backward through the pole are evidently found by putting $\theta = 0$, $\pm\pi$, $\pm 2\pi$, etc., and solving for r. Similarly, intercepts on the 90°-axis or its extension backward are obtained by putting $\theta = \pm\frac{1}{2}\pi$, $\pm\frac{3}{2}\pi$, etc., and solving for r.

(4) *Tangents at the pole:* If a curve passes through the pole, the directions of any tangents to the curve at the pole are found by putting $r = 0$ in the equation of the curve and solving for θ.

When the given equation expresses r as a trigonometric function of θ, as occurs in many polar equations of

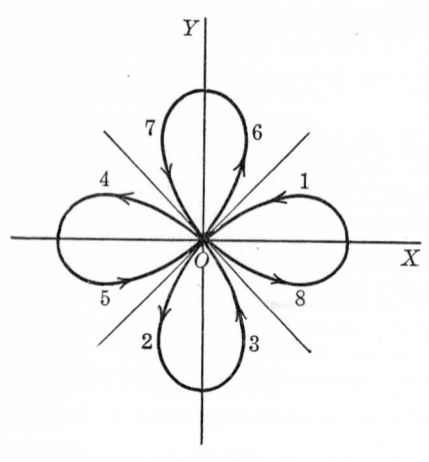

FIG. 156

curves, a knowledge of the variation of the trigonometric functions in the various quadrants and of the periodicity of these functions can be used to trace the variation of r as θ varies.

EXAMPLE 1. Discuss and draw the graph of the equation $r = \cos 2\,\theta$.

Solution: By use of the properties of the cosine, we see from the tests for symmetry that this graph is symmetric with respect to the polar axis and its extension, with respect to the 90°-axis and its extension and with respect to the pole.   If we put $r = 0$ in the equation of the curve, we have $\cos 2\,\theta = 0$, or $2\,\theta = \frac{1}{2}\,\pi,\ \frac{3}{2}\,\pi$, etc., so that $\theta = \frac{1}{4}\,\pi,\ \frac{3}{4}\,\pi$, etc.   These angles give the direction of the tangents to the curve at the pole.   As θ varies from 0 to $\frac{1}{4}\,\pi$, r varies from 1 to 0, and we obtain the half-loop labelled 1 in Fig. 156; as θ varies from $\frac{1}{4}\,\pi$ to $\frac{1}{2}\,\pi$, r varies from 0 to -1, giving the half-loop labelled 2 in the figure.   The remainder of the curve may now be drawn by use of the symmetries.   As θ varies from 0 to $2\,\pi$, the curve is traced out once as indicated by the numbers and arrows in Fig. 156.   This curve is called the *four-leafed rose*.

EXAMPLE 2. Discuss and draw the graph of $r^2 = a^2 \cos 2\,\theta$.

Solution: By the symmetry tests, this graph is symmetric with respect to the polar axis and the 90°-axis and their extensions and with respect to the pole.   When $r = 0$, we find $\theta = \frac{1}{4}\,\pi,\ \frac{3}{4}\,\pi$, etc.; this gives the direction of the tangents at the origin.   As θ varies from 0 to $\frac{1}{4}\,\pi$, $2\,\theta$ varies from 0 to $\frac{1}{2}\,\pi$, and $\cos 2\,\theta$ is positive and varies from 1 to 0, hence r is real and decreases from a to 0; this gives the half-loop numbered 1 in Fig. 157.   When θ is between $\frac{1}{4}\,\pi$ and $\frac{1}{2}\,\pi$, $2\,\theta$ is in the second quadrant, $\cos 2\,\theta$ is negative and r is imaginary, hence there are no points of the graph when θ varies from $\frac{1}{4}\,\pi$ to $\frac{1}{2}\,\pi$.   By symmetry the remainder of the graph may be drawn; it consists of two loops as shown in Fig. 157.   This curve is called a *lemniscate*.

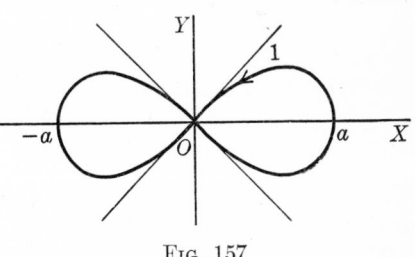

FIG. 157

309. Exercises

Discuss and draw the graphs of the following equations:

1. $r = 4 \sin \theta$.
2. $r = 5 \cos \theta$.
3. $r \cos \theta = 4$.
4. $r \sin \theta = -3$.
5. $r = 2 \sin 2\,\theta$ (rose).
6. $r = -3 \cos 2\,\theta$ (rose).
7. $r = 2 \cos 3\,\theta$ (rose).
8. $r = 4 \sin 3\,\theta$ (rose).
9. $r = 2(1 + \sin \theta)$ (cardioid).
10. $r = 2(1 + \cos \theta)$ (cardioid).
11. $r^2 = 4 \sin 2\,\theta$ (lemniscate).
12. $r^2 = 9 \sin \theta$.
13. $r = 2 \cos 4\,\theta$ (rose).
14. $r = 4 \sin 5\,\theta$ (rose).
15. $r = 2 - \cos \theta$ (limaçon).
16. $r = 2 + \sin \theta$ (limaçon).
17. $r = 2 + 3 \cos \theta$ (limaçon).
18. $r = 1 - 2 \sin \theta$ (limaçon).
19. $r = \cos^2 \theta$.
20. $r = 1 + \sin^2 \theta$.
21. $r(1 - \sin \theta) = 2$.
22. $r(1 - 2 \cos \theta) = 4$.
23. $r = 2 \tan \theta \sin \theta$ (cissoid).
24. $r = \sin \theta + \cos \theta$.
25. $r = 2\,\theta$ (spiral of Archimedes).

26. $r = e^{2\theta}$ (logarithmic spiral).
27. $r\theta = 4$ (reciprocal or hyperbolic spiral).
28. $r^2\theta = 2$ (lituus, a spiral).

310. Relation Between Polar and Rectangular Coördinates of a Point

Let $X'X$ and $Y'Y$ be a set of rectangular coördinate axes, and let a polar coördinate system be placed with its pole at the origin O and its polar axis along the positive X-axis OX (Fig. 158). Let P be any point with rectangular coördinates (x, y) and polar coördinates (r, θ).

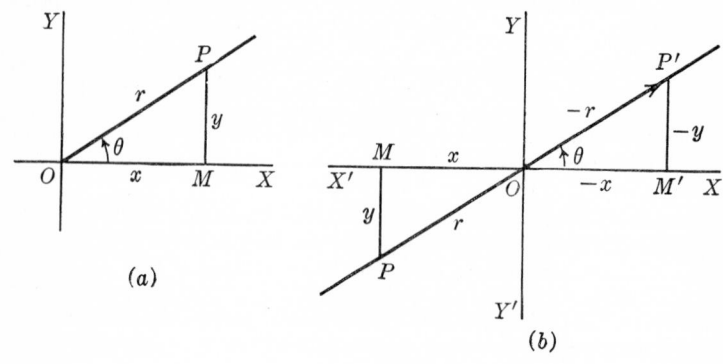

(a)
(b)

Fig. 158

(1) Suppose that r is *positive* (Fig. 158 (a)). From the definitions of the sine and cosine, we have

(a) $\qquad x = r \cos \theta, \qquad y = r \sin \theta.$

(2) If r is *negative* (Fig. 158 (b)), we locate the point P' whose rectangular coördinates and polar coördinates are $(-x, -y)$ and $(-r, \theta)$ respectively. Since $-r$ is now positive, we may apply the results of (1), and we have

$$-x = (-r) \cos \theta, \qquad -y = (-r) \sin \theta,$$

from which we get equations (a) again.

By squaring and adding, and by division, in equations (a) for both cases, we obtain

(b) $\qquad r^2 = x^2 + y^2, \qquad \tan \theta = \dfrac{y}{x}.$

Hence:

If the pole and polar axis of a polar coördinate system coincide with the origin and positive X-axis of a rectangular coördinate system, then the rectangular coördinates (x, y) and the polar coördinates (r, θ) of any point P are related by the following formulas:

(1) $\qquad\qquad x = r \cos \theta, \qquad y = r \sin \theta,$

(2) $\qquad\qquad r^2 = x^2 + y^2, \qquad \tan \theta = y/x.$

When r is to be found from the equation $r^2 = x^2 + y^2$, the positive square root may be taken for r if, in finding θ from the equation $\tan \theta = y/x$, the value of θ is used which corresponds to the quadrant in which P lies.

The equation $\tan \theta = y/x$ fails if $x = 0$; in this case we may use $\cot \theta = x/y$ unless $y = 0$. If both $x = 0$, $y = 0$, then $r = 0$ and θ may be taken to have any value.

From the formulas (1) and (2), we may obtain two other formulas which are sometimes useful, thus:

$$(c) \qquad \cos \theta = \frac{x}{r} = \frac{x}{\pm\sqrt{x^2 + y^2}}, \qquad \sin \theta = \frac{y}{r} = \frac{y}{\pm\sqrt{x^2 + y^2}}.$$

EXAMPLE 1. Find the rectangular coördinates of the point whose polar coördinates are $(5, \frac{1}{6}\pi)$.

Solution: By formulas (1), we have

$$x = 5 \cos \tfrac{1}{6}\pi = 5(\tfrac{1}{2}\sqrt{3}) = \tfrac{5}{2}\sqrt{3}, \qquad y = 5 \sin \tfrac{1}{6}\pi = 5(\tfrac{1}{2}) = \tfrac{5}{2}.$$

EXAMPLE 2. Find a pair of polar coördinates of the point whose rectangular coördinates are $(-8, 6)$; also write down three other pairs of corresponding polar coördinates for this point.

Solution: Since the point $(-8, 6)$ is in the second quadrant, θ must be an angle of the second quadrant or the fourth quadrant. From formulas (2) we find

$$r^2 = (-8)^2 + 6^2 = 100, \qquad r = \pm 10, \qquad \tan \theta = -\tfrac{6}{8} = -\tfrac{3}{4}.$$

Values of θ for which $\tan \theta = -\frac{3}{4}$ are $143°08'$, $-36°52'$, $323°08'$, $-216°52'$, etc. Hence, one pair of polar coördinates of the given point are $(10, 143°08')$. Other pairs of polar coördinates are: $(10, -216°52')$, $(-10, -36°52')$, $(-10, 323°08')$, etc.

It is frequently desirable to transform the equation of a given curve from polar coördinates to rectangular coördinates or vice versa. This may be done by use of equations (1) and (2).

EXAMPLE 3. Transform the equation $r = 2a \cos \theta$ from polar coördinates to rectangular coördinates.

Solution: We first multiply both sides of the equation by r to obtain $r^2 = 2\,a\,(r\cos\theta)$; then we replace r^2 by $x^2 + y^2$ and $r\cos\theta$ by x, and we get

$$x^2 + y^2 = 2\,ax.$$

EXAMPLE 4. Transform the equation $2\,xy = a^2$ from rectangular coördinates to polar coördinates.

Solution: Substituting $x = r\cos\theta$, $y = r\sin\theta$ in the given equation, we get $2\,r^2\sin\theta\cos\theta = a^2$. But by trigonometry, $2\sin\theta\cos\theta = \sin 2\,\theta$; therefore, the equation becomes

$$r^2\sin 2\,\theta = a^2.$$

311. Exercises

1. Find the rectangular coördinates of the points whose polar coördinates are: $A(10, \frac{1}{4}\,\pi)$, $B(3, \frac{5}{6}\,\pi)$, $C(5, -\frac{1}{4}\,\pi)$, $D(5, \frac{3}{2}\,\pi)$, $E(-4, \frac{2}{3}\,\pi)$.
2. Find the rectangular coördinates of the points whose polar coördinates are: $A(4, \frac{1}{3}\,\pi)$, $B(8, \frac{4}{3}\,\pi)$, $C(5, -\frac{5}{4}\,\pi)$, $D(6, \pi)$, $E(-10, -\frac{1}{6}\,\pi)$.
3. Find a pair of polar coördinates of the points whose rectangular coördinates are: $A(3, \sqrt{3})$, $B(-2, 2)$, $C(4, -5)$, $D(-3, 0)$, $E(0, 4)$.
4. Find a pair of polar coördinates of the points whose rectangular coördinates are: $A(4, 4)$, $B(-\sqrt{3}, -3)$, $C(-2, 4)$, $D(5, 0)$, $E(0, -3)$.
5. Transform the following equations of graphs from polar coördinates to rectangular coördinates, and draw the graphs:

   (a) $r = a$;   (b) $r\cos\theta = 4$;
   (c) $r = 2\,a\sin\theta$;   (d) $r = a\sin 2\,\theta$;
   (e) $r^2 = a^2\cos 2\,\theta$;   (f) $r = 2\cos\theta + 3\sin\theta$.

6. Proceed as in Exercise 5 with the following equations:

   (a) $\theta = \frac{1}{4}\,\pi$;   (b) $r\sin\theta = -3$;
   (c) $r = 2\,a\tan\theta$;   (d) $r = a\cos 2\,\theta$;
   (e) $r(1 - \cos\theta) = a$;   (f) $r^2\cos 2\,\theta = 4$.

7. Transform the following equations of graphs from rectangular coördinates to polar coördinates, and draw the graphs:

   (a) $x = 2$;   (b) $x^2 + y^2 = a^2$;
   (c) $x^2 + y^2 = 2\,ax$;   (d) $2\,x + y = 4$;
   (e) $y^2 = x^3$;   (f) $(x^2 + y^2)^2 = a^2(x^2 - y^2)$.

8. Proceed as in Exercise 7 with the following equations:

   (a) $y + 2 = 0$;   (b) $x^2 + y^2 - 4\,y = 0$;
   (c) $x + 3\,y = 5$;   (d) $x^2 - y^2 = 2\,ay$;
   (e) $y^2 = 4\,ax$;   (f) $x^2 + 4\,y^2 = 4$.

312. The Straight Line and Circle in Polar Coördinates

The polar equation of a straight line or circle in general position is usually not as convenient as the rectangular equation and is seldom used. When the line or circle is in one of certain special positions, however, the polar equation is simple and very useful.

Consider first a line perpendicular to the polar axis and with polar intercept a. Its equation in rectangular coördinates is $x = a$, which transforms by § 310 into $r \cos \theta = a$. Similarly, a line $y = b$ transforms into $r \sin \theta = b$. Clearly, also, a line through the pole making an angle α with the polar axis has $\theta = \alpha$ for all points on the line. Hence:

I. *The polar equation of a line perpendicular to the polar axis is*

$$(3) \qquad\qquad r \cos \theta = a,$$

if it passes through the point $(a, 0)$; *the equation of a line parallel to the polar axis is*

$$(4) \qquad\qquad r \sin \theta = b,$$

if it passes through the point $(b, \tfrac{1}{2} \pi)$. *The equation of a line passing through the pole is*

$$(5) \qquad\qquad \theta = \alpha,$$

where α *is the angle which the line makes with the polar axis.*

Now consider a circle of radius a with center on the polar axis and passing through the pole (Fig. 159), and let $P(r, \theta)$ be any point on this circle. Then angle OPA is a right angle (being inscribed in a semi-circle). From the right triangle OPA we have $r = 2\,a \cos \theta$. This is the polar equation of the circle. In a similar way, if the circle has its center on the 90°-axis and passes through the pole, its

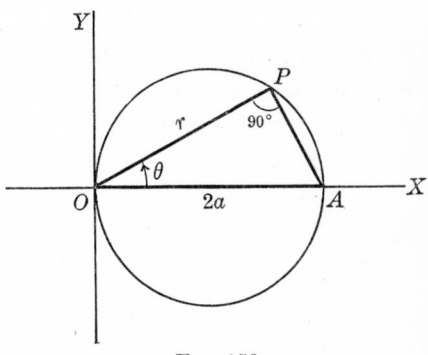

Fig. 159

equation is found to be $r = 2\,a \sin \theta$. If the circle has its center at the pole, its equation is evidently $r = a$. Hence:

II. *The polar equation of a circle passing through the pole is*

$$(6) \qquad\qquad r = 2\,a \cos \theta,$$

if its center is at $(a, 0)$, *and is*

$$(7) \qquad\qquad r = 2\,a \sin \theta,$$

if its center is at $(a, \frac{1}{2}\pi)$. *The equation of a circle of radius a and center at the pole is*

(8) $$r = a.$$

313. Conic Sections in Polar Coördinates

We first recall, from § 242, that the parabola, ellipse and hyperbola each have the property that the ratio of the distance of any point of

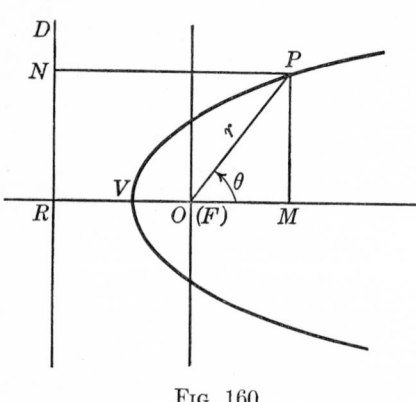

Fig. 160

the curve from a focus to its distance from the corresponding directrix is always equal to the eccentricity. By use of this property, we may find the polar equation of one of these curves in simplest form by taking a focus as pole and the line through the focus perpendicular to the directrix as polar axis. We shall first suppose that the directrix D is to the left of the focus O (Fig. 160). Let p be the distance RO from the directrix to the focus, and let e be the eccentricity of the conic. If $P(r, \theta)$ is any point on the conic, we have

(a) $$OP = e \cdot NP,$$

by the property mentioned above. But $\overline{NP} = \overline{RM} = \overline{RO} + \overline{OM} = p + r \cos \theta$. Therefore,

$$r = e(p + r \cos \theta) = ep + er \cos \theta.$$

Solving this equation for r, we get

(b) $$r = \frac{ep}{1 - e \cos \theta}.$$

Conversely, if the coördinates of a point P satisfy this equation, we find, by reversing the above steps, that $OP = e \cdot NP$, which shows that P lies on the conic. Hence:

The equation

(9) $$r = \frac{ep}{1 - e \cos \theta} \qquad (p > 0)$$

represents a parabola, ellipse or hyperbola, according as $e = 1$, $e < 1$ or $e > 1$. A focus is at the pole and the corresponding directrix is perpendicular to the polar axis and at the distance p to the left of the focus.

It can be shown readily in a similar way that if the directrix is perpendicular to the polar axis and to the right of the focus, the equation of the curve is

(c)
$$r = \frac{ep}{1 + e \cos \theta},$$

and that if the directrix is parallel to the polar axis, the equation is

(d)
$$r = \frac{ep}{1 \pm e \sin \theta},$$

according as the directrix is above or below the focus.

EXAMPLE 1. Discuss the graph of the equation $r = \dfrac{5}{2 - 2 \cos \theta}$.

Solution: The equation may be written

$$r = \frac{\frac{5}{2}}{1 - \cos \theta}.$$

This shows that the curve is a parabola, since $e = 1$, which is open to the right. Since $ep = \frac{5}{2}$ and $e = 1$, we have $p = \frac{5}{2}$; hence, the distance from the vertex to the focus is $\frac{5}{4}$.

EXAMPLE 2. Discuss the graph of the equation

$$r = \frac{16}{5 + 3 \cos \theta}.$$

Solution: The equation may be written

$$r = \frac{\frac{16}{5}}{1 + \frac{3}{5} \cos \theta}.$$

This is of the form (c) with $e = \frac{3}{5}$, hence the graph is an ellipse with one focus at the pole, the major axis along the

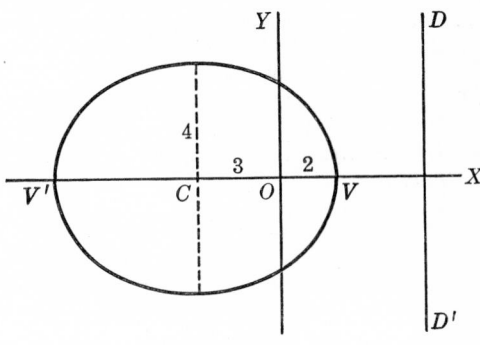

FIG. 161

polar axis and the corresponding directrix to the right of the focus. To locate the vertices, we put $\theta = 0$ and $\theta = \pi$; we get $r = 2$ and $r = 8$ respectively. Therefore, the vertices are 2 units to the right of the given focus (at the pole) and 8 units to the left. It follows that the major axis is $8 + 2 = 10$ units long, so that the semi-major axis is $a = 5$. Then $b^2 = a^2 (1 - e^2) = 25(1 - \frac{9}{25}) = 16$ and the semi-minor axis is $b = 4$;

the distance from the given focus to the center is $c = \sqrt{a^2 - b^2} = 3$. The graph is shown in Fig. 161.

314. Exercises

1. Draw the graphs of the following polar equations:
   (a) $r \cos \theta = 4$;   (b) $r \sin \theta = -3$;   (c) $\theta = \frac{1}{4} \pi$.

2. Draw the graphs of the following polar equations:
   (a) $r \sin \theta = 2$;   (b) $r = -5 \sec \theta$;   (c) $\theta = \frac{2}{3} \pi$.

3. Write the polar equations of the following lines: (a) perpendicular to the polar axis, through the point $(3, 0)$; (b) parallel to the polar axis, through the point $(5, \frac{1}{2} \pi)$; (c) through the pole and through the point $(3, \frac{1}{3} \pi)$.

4. Write the polar equations of the following lines: (a) perpendicular to the polar axis, through the point $(-4, 0)$; (b) parallel to the polar axis, through the point $(3, \frac{1}{4} \pi)$; (c) through the pole and through the point $(-2, \frac{5}{3} \pi)$.

5. Draw each of the following circles and give the center and radius:
   (a) $r = 8 \cos \theta$;   (b) $r = -5 \sin \theta$;   (c) $r = 3$.

6. Draw each of the following circles and give the center and radius:
   (a) $r = 10 \sin \theta$;   (b) $r = -4 \cos \theta$;   (c) $r = -2$.

7. Find the polar equations of the circles having the given center and radius:
   (a) $C(5, 0)$, $r = 5$;   (b) $C(6, \frac{1}{2} \pi)$, $r = 6$;   (c) $C(0, 0)$, $r = 5$.

8. Find the polar equations of the circles having the given center and radius:
   (a) $C(5, \frac{1}{2} \pi)$, $r = 5$;   (b) $C(0, 0)$, $r = 4$;   (c) $C(3, \pi)$, $r = 3$.

9. Draw a line such that the perpendicular from the pole to this line makes an angle ω with the polar axis and has the length p. Show that the equation of this line is $r \cos (\theta - \omega) = p$.

10. Show that the polar equation of a circle passing through the pole and having the polar intercept a and $90°$-intercept b is $r = a \cos \theta + b \sin \theta$. [*Hint.* Write the rectangular equation and transform to polar coördinates.]

11. Show that the polar equation of a circle of radius a and center (c, α) is $r^2 - 2 cr \cos (\theta - \alpha) + c^2 = a^2$.

12. Show that $r = 2 a \cos (\theta - \alpha)$ is the equation of a circle; locate its center and give its radius.

13. For each of the following equations name the type of graph and draw it:
    (a) $r = \dfrac{4}{1 - \cos \theta}$;   (b) $r = \dfrac{6}{2 + \cos \theta}$;
    (c) $r(1 - 2 \cos \theta) = 6$;   (d) $r(3 + 3 \sin \theta) = 20$.

14. Proceed as in Exercise 13 with:
    (a) $r = \dfrac{10}{1 + \sin \theta}$;   (b) $r = \dfrac{12}{3 - 4 \cos \theta}$;
    (c) $r(4 + \cos \theta) = 12$;   (d) $r(1 + 2 \sin \theta) = 8$.

15. Write the polar equation of each of the following curves, taking the pole at a focus:

(a) a parabola with axis on the polar axis, with the vertex at $(4, \pi)$, and open to the right;

(b) an ellipse, with eccentricity $\frac{3}{4}$ and a directrix parallel to the 90°-axis and 6 units to the left of it;

(c) a hyperbola, with eccentricity 2 and a directrix parallel to the polar axis and 4 units below it.

16. Show that the graph of $r = a \sec^2 \frac{1}{2} \theta$ is a parabola. In what position is it?

315. Derivation of Polar Equations of Curves

The *equation in polar coördinates of a given curve* is an equation such that at least one pair of polar coördinates of each point on the curve satisfies the equation, and conversely.

The polar equation of a given locus may be derived by methods similar to those used for rectangular coördinates. Polar coördinates are especially useful in finding the equation of a locus when the locus is described in terms of the variable distance of a moving point from a fixed point. The pole is usually chosen at a convenient position especially related to the curve, and the moving point which traces out the locus should be taken in a general position and its polar coördinates labelled (r, θ). The required equation is then obtained by expressing the condition which defines the locus in terms of r and θ.

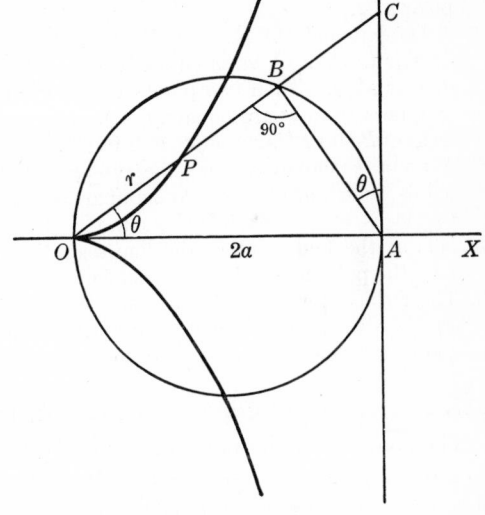

Fig. 162

EXAMPLE. A tangent is drawn to a circle at one end A of a fixed diameter (Fig. 162). Through the other end O of the diameter a variable line is drawn cutting the circle at B and the tangent at C. Find the equation of the locus of a point P on the line which is situated such that OP is always equal to BC.

Solution: We take O as the pole and OA as polar axis. Let $OA = 2a$. Let (r, θ) denote the polar coördinates of P. Draw AB; then angle OBA is a right angle and angle $BAC = \theta$. From right triangle OAC we have $AC = OA \tan \theta = 2\,a \tan \theta$; from the right triangle ABC we have $BC = AC \sin BAC = (2\,a \tan \theta) \sin \theta$. Then by definition,

$$r = OP = BC = 2\,a \tan \theta \sin \theta.$$

This is the required polar equation of the locus, which is a type of curve called a *cissoid*.

316. Exercises

1. A chord through one end of a diameter of a circle of radius a is extended the length of the diameter. Show that if the pole is taken at one end of the diameter and the polar axis along the diameter, the polar equation of the locus of the end of the line-segment is $r = 2\,a(1 + \cos \theta)$. Sketch the curve. (Cardioid.)

2. Find the polar equation of the locus of the mid-points of the chords of the circle $r = 2\,a \cos \theta$ drawn from the pole.

3. A fixed point O is at a distance a from a fixed line AB; a variable line through O cuts the fixed line AB at Q. Then two points P and P' are located on OQ at a constant distance b from Q on either side of Q. Find the polar equation of the locus of P and P'. Sketch the curve. (Conchoid.) [*Hint.* Take O as pole and the perpendicular from O to AB as polar axis.]

4. A line-segment OA is of length a; at A a straight line is drawn perpendicular to OA. A variable line is drawn through O cutting this perpendicular at Q. Then two points P and P' are taken on OQ so that their distances from Q are equal to AQ. Show that a polar equation of the locus of P and P' is $r = a(\sec \theta \pm \tan \theta)$. Sketch the curve. (Strophoid.)

5. A point P moves so that the product of its distances from two fixed points, which are a distance $2\,a$ apart, is a^2. Find the polar equation of the locus of P. Sketch the curve. (Lemniscate.) [*Hint.* Take the pole at the mid-point of the line segment joining the fixed points, and take the polar axis along this segment. Use the law of cosines.]

6. The radius of a circle whose center is at the pole is extended a distance equal to the ordinate of its extremity. Find the polar equation of the end of this line segment. (Cardioid.)

317. Intersection of Curves in Polar Coördinates

The solution of the polar equations of two curves as simultaneous equations gives the polar coördinates of points of intersection of the curves, for the pairs of coördinates found in this way satisfy both equations and therefore represent points on both curves. In many cases, the determination of the points of intersection leads to the problem of the solution of a trigonometric equation.

Not all of the intersections of curves are obtainable by this procedure in every case. This may be due to the fact that a given point has more than one pair of polar coördinates, or it may be due to the fact that at the pole, $r = 0$ but θ may have any value whatever. It may be that, at a given intersection, the pair of coördinates of this point which satisfy the first equation may not be the pair that satisfies the second equation. The pole is often a point of inter-

section but it is not always found by solving together the equations of the curves; for, the pole may lie on both curves and yet the values of θ that make $r = 0$ may be quite different for the two equations. In most cases, by drawing graphs of both equations on the same diagram, any intersections not

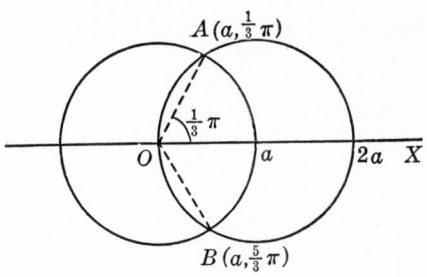

FIG. 163

found by solving the equations simultaneously may be detected. The graphs will also serve as a check on the analytical solution of the equations.

EXAMPLE 1. Find the points of intersection of the circles $r = 2\,a\cos\theta$ and $r = a$.

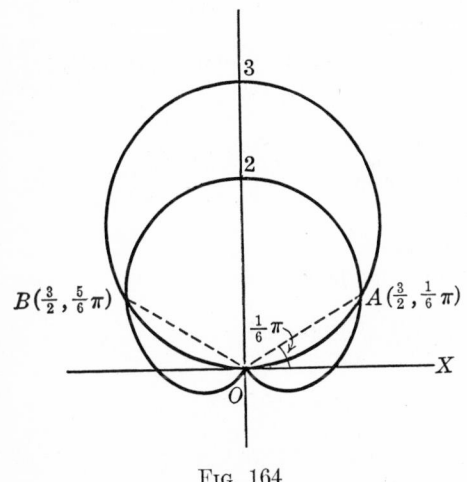

FIG. 164

Solution: To solve the equations simultaneously, we equate the two values of r and get

$$2\,a\cos\theta = a,$$
$$\cos\theta = \tfrac{1}{2},$$
$$\theta = \tfrac{1}{3}\,\pi \text{ or } \tfrac{5}{3}\,\pi.$$

For either value of θ, we get $r = a$. Therefore, two points of intersection are $A(a, \tfrac{1}{3}\,\pi)$ and $B(a, \tfrac{5}{3}\,\pi)$. From the graphs of the two equations (Fig. 163), we see that there are no other intersections.

EXAMPLE 2. Find the points of intersection of the cardioid $r = 1 + \sin\theta$ and the circle $r = 3\sin\theta$.

Solution: Equating the values of r, we obtain

$$3\sin\theta = 1 + \sin\theta, \qquad \sin\theta = \tfrac{1}{2}, \qquad \theta = \tfrac{1}{6}\,\pi \text{ or } \tfrac{5}{6}\,\pi;$$

$r = \tfrac{3}{2}$ for each of these values of θ. Two points of intersection are therefore $A(\tfrac{3}{2}, \tfrac{1}{6}\,\pi)$ and $B(\tfrac{3}{2}, \tfrac{5}{6}\,\pi)$. But the graphs (Fig. 164) show that the cardioid and the circle intersect not only at the points A and B, but also at the pole; $r = 0$ for the cardioid for $\theta = \frac{3}{2}\pi$ but $r = 0$ for the circle for $\theta = 0$ or π.

318. Exercises

Draw the graphs of each of the following pairs of equations on one set of axes, and find the polar coördinates of their points of intersection:

1. $r = 4 \sin \theta$, $r = 2$.
2. $r = 2a \cos \theta$, $r \cos \theta = a$.
3. $r \cos \theta = 6$, $r = 10$.
4. $r = 1 + \cos \theta$, $r = \frac{1}{2}$.
5. $r = a \cos \theta$, $r = a \sin \theta$.
6. $r = a(1 - \cos \theta)$, $r = a \cos \theta$.
7. $r = \sin \theta$, $r = \cos 2\theta$.
8. $r = \sin \theta$, $r = \sin 2\theta$.
9. $r^2 = 4a^2 \cos 2\theta$, $r = \sqrt{2}\,a$.
10. $r = \cos 2\theta$, $r = \frac{1}{2}$.
11. $r = 2\theta$, $r = 2$.
12. $r\theta = 4$, $r = 2$.
13. $r = 1 + \cos \theta$, $r(1 + \cos \theta) = 1$.

14. $r = 1 + \cos \theta$, $r = 1 - \cos \theta$.
15. $r = 1 + \cos \theta$, $r = \sin \theta$.
16. $r = 4(1 + \cos \theta)$, $r \cos \theta = 3$.

319. Slope of the Tangent to a Curve in Polar Coördinates

Let $P(r, \theta)$ be any point on a curve $r = f(\theta)$. Let r' denote the derivative $dr/d\theta$. We have $x = r \cos \theta$, $y = r \sin \theta$. The slope of the tangent to the given curve is given by $m = \dfrac{dy}{dx}$. If we differentiate the given values of x and y with respect to θ, remembering that r is a function of θ, we get

$$dx = (r' \cos \theta - r \sin \theta)\, d\theta, \qquad dy = (r' \sin \theta + r \cos \theta)\, d\theta.$$

Then

$$m = \frac{dy}{dx} = \frac{r' \sin \theta + r \cos \theta}{r' \cos \theta - r \sin \theta} = \frac{r' \tan \theta + r}{r' - r \tan \theta}.$$

Hence:

The slope of the curve $r = f(\theta)$ at the point (r, θ) is equal to

$$(10) \qquad\qquad m = \frac{r' \tan \theta + r}{r' - r \tan \theta}.$$

320. Exercises

In Exercises 1–6, find the slope of the tangent to each of the given curves at the point indicated:

1. $r = a \cos \theta$, at $\theta = \frac{1}{6}\pi$.
2. $r = a \cos 2\theta$, at $\theta = \frac{1}{6}\pi$.
3. $r = a(1 - \cos \theta)$, at $\theta = \frac{1}{2}\pi$.
4. $r = a(1 + \sin \theta)$, at $\theta = \frac{1}{6}\pi$.
5. $r^2 = a \sin 2\theta$, at $\theta = \theta_1$.
6. $r(2 - \cos \theta) = a$, at $\theta = \frac{1}{3}\pi$.

7. Find the angle of intersection of the curves $r = a \sin 2\theta$ and $r = a \cos 2\theta$.
   [*Hint.* Use the formula of § 22.]

8. Find the angle of intersection of the curves $r = a(1 - \cos \theta)$ and $r = a \cos \theta$. [See the hint to Exercise 7.]

9. Show that the curves $r = a \sin \theta$ and $r = a \cos \theta$ intersect at right angles.

10. Show that the cardioids $r = a(1 + \cos \theta)$ and $r = a(1 - \cos \theta)$ intersect at right angles.

CHAPTER XV

Parametric Equations;
Curvilinear Motion

321. Parametric Equations of a Curve

It is frequently convenient to represent a curve by a pair of equations expressing the coördinates of any point of the curve in terms of an auxiliary variable called a ***parameter***. By means of these equations, corresponding to each value of the parameter in a given range, there is determined a value of each coördinate, and therefore a point is determined for each value of the parameter. The locus of all such points is the graph of the given pair of equations. The equations are called ***parametric equations*** of the graph.

When a curve is given by a pair of parametric equations, its single equation in terms of x and y, which we shall call the *rectangular equation*, may usually be obtained by eliminating the parameter from the given equations. Ordinarily it is not desirable to make this change.

EXAMPLE 1. Consider the equations $x = a \cos \phi$, $y = b \sin \phi$, where ϕ is a parameter. We can write the equations in the form

$$(a) \qquad \frac{x}{a} = \cos \phi, \qquad \frac{y}{b} = \sin \phi.$$

The parameter ϕ may be eliminated by squaring and adding the members of (a). We obtain

$$\frac{x^2}{a^2} + \frac{y^2}{b^2} = \cos^2 \phi + \sin^2 \phi = 1.$$

The given equations are therefore parametric equations of the ellipse $b^2x^2 + a^2y^2 = a^2b^2$. In case $b = a$, the equations represent the circle $x^2 + y^2 = a^2$. The student should draw the figure for the circle, and see that in this case ϕ is the angle that the radius to $P(x, y)$ makes with the X-axis.

For a given curve, in a given position, an unlimited number of pairs of parametric equations is possible, depending on the choice of a parameter.

EXAMPLE 2. Consider the parabola whose rectangular equation is $y^2 = 2\,px$, and let us use the parameter m defined by $y = mx$. Combining the two equations, we find $m^2x^2 - 2\,px = 0$, or $x = \dfrac{2\,p}{m^2}$; from $y = mx$ we get $y = \dfrac{2\,p}{m}$. The two equations

$$x = \frac{2\,p}{m^2}, \qquad y = \frac{2\,p}{m}$$

form a pair of parametric equations of the parabola with m as the parameter.

322. Exercises

1. Show that $x = x_1 + a \cos \theta$, $y = y_1 + a \sin \theta$ are parametric equations of any circle. Where is the center and what is the radius?
2. Show that $x = x_1 + t(x_2 - x_1)$, $y = y_1 + t(y_2 - y_1)$ are parametric equations of the line through the points (x_1, y_1) and (x_2, y_2).
3. Show that $x = a \sec \theta$, $y = b \tan \theta$ are parametric equations of a hyperbola with semi-axes a and b.
4. Show that $x = at^2$, $y = 2\,at$ are parametric equations of a parabola.
5. Find the rectangular equations of the curves which are represented by the following pairs of parametric equations:

   (a) $x = t^2, y = t^3$; (b) $x = \dfrac{1 - t^2}{1 + t^2}, y = \dfrac{2\,t}{1 + t^2}$;

   (c) $x = \tfrac{1}{2}\,p \cot^2 \theta, y = p \cot \theta$; (d) $x = a \cos^3 \theta, y = a \sin^3 \theta$.

6. Proceed as in Exercise 5 with:

   (a) $x = at, y = \dfrac{a}{t}$; (b) $x = 1 + 2\,t, y = 2 - 3\,t$;

   (c) $x = \cos 2\,\phi, y = \cos \phi$; (d) $x = a \cosh t, y = b \sinh t$.

7. Find the parametric equations of the circle $x^2 + y^2 - 2\,x = 0$ by using the parameter m defined by $y = mx$.
8. Find the parametric equations of the curve $x^2 - y^2 = a^2$ by using the parameter t defined by $x = a \sec t$.
9. Find parametric equations of the following curves, by making the indicated substitution:

   (a) $b^2x^2 + a^2y^2 = a^2b^2$, $y = m(x + a)$ (ellipse);
   (b) $x^2 - y^2 - 2\,x - 2\,y = 0$, $y = tx$ (hyperbola);
   (c) $x^3 + y^3 = 3\,axy$, $y = tx$ (Folium of Descartes).

10. Proceed as in Exercise 9 with:

    (a) $x^2 + y^2 - 2\,y = 0$, $y = mx$ (circle);
    (b) $y^2 = 4\,ax$, $y = 2\,a \cot \theta$ (parabola);
    (c) $x^3 + xy^2 - 2\,ay^2 = 0$, $y = mx$ (cissoid).

323. Plotting a Curve from Its Parametric Equations

In order to plot the graph of a pair of parametric equations, we may assign various values to the parameter and from the equations find the corresponding values of the coördinates, then plot the points corresponding to these coördinates and draw a smooth curve through these points.

EXAMPLE. Plot the graph of the parametric equations

$$x = t - 4, \qquad y = 2 \pm 2\sqrt{t}.$$

Solution: We first make out a table of corresponding values of t, x and y, calculated from the given equations:

t	0	1	2	3	4	5	6	7	8	9
x	-4	-3	-2	-1	0	1	2	3	4	5
y	2	4 or 0	4.83 or -0.83	5.46 or -1.46	6 or -2	6.47 or -2.47	6.90 or -2.90	7.29 or -3.29	7.66 or -3.66	8 or -4

When we plot these corresponding pairs of values of x and y, we obtain the points shown in Fig. 165; the curve drawn through these points represents

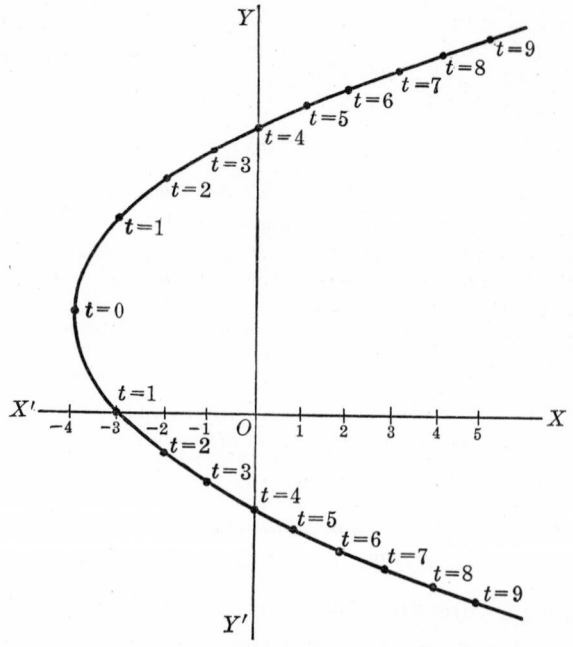

FIG. 165

the graph of the given parametric equations. The curve looks like a parabola; that it is actually a parabola is verified by eliminating the parameter t.

324. Exercises

Plot the curves representing the following pairs of parametric equations:

1. $x = t + 2, \quad y = t^2$.
2. $x = 2t, \quad y = t + 1$.
3. $x = \frac{1}{2} t, \quad y = \frac{8}{t}$.
4. $x = 5t, \quad y = \pm 3\sqrt{1 - t^2}$.
5. $x = 2 t^2, \quad y = 2 t^3$.
6. $x = t + \frac{1}{t}, \quad y = t - \frac{1}{t}$.
7. $x = \cos \theta, \quad y = \cos 2\theta$.
8. $x = 1 + 5 \cos \phi,$
   $y = -2 + 3 \sin \phi$.
9. $x = \phi - \sin \phi, y = 1 - \cos \phi$.
10. $x = \phi + \sin \phi, y = \phi - \sin \phi$.
11. $x = \tan \theta + \sin \theta, y = 1 + \cos \theta$.
12. $x = \sin^2 \theta, y = \tan \theta \sin^2 \theta$.
13. $x = a \cos^3 \phi, y = a \sin^3 \phi$ (hypocycloid of four cusps).

325. The Cycloid

Sometimes the geometric definition of a curve is such that the coördinates of any point on the curve may be easily and naturally expressed in terms of a parameter having a simple geometric meaning, but the direct derivation of the rectangular equation of the curve may be difficult. This is well illustrated in the case of the *cycloid*.

A **cycloid** *is defined as the curve traced out by a point fixed on the circumference of a circle which rolls without slipping on a fixed straight line.*

To find parametric equations of the cycloid in simplest form, we choose rectangular axes as follows: Take the fixed line on which the circle rolls as X-axis; and take as origin any one of the positions at

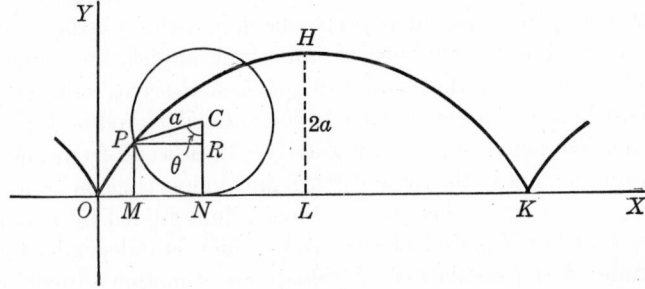

Fig. 166

which the tracing point comes in contact with the fixed line (Fig. 166). Let a be the radius of the rolling circle. Let $P(x, y)$ be any position of the tracing point; take for the parameter the angle θ (expressed in radian measure) through which the radius CP of the circle has turned from the position when P was at the origin.

Since the circle has rolled from O to N, we have

$$ON = \text{arc } NP = a\theta,$$

by definition of radian measure. We have $\overline{PR} = a \sin \theta$, $\overline{RC} = a \cos \theta$. The rectangular coördinates of P are then

$$x = \overline{OM} = \overline{ON} - \overline{MN} = \overline{ON} - \overline{PR} = a\theta - a \sin \theta = a(\theta - \sin \theta),$$
$$y = \overline{MP} = \overline{NR} = \overline{NC} - \overline{RC} = a - a \cos \theta = a(1 - \cos \theta).$$

Hence:

The cycloid has parametric equations

(1)
$$\begin{cases} x = a(\theta - \sin \theta), \\ y = a(1 - \cos \theta), \end{cases}$$

when the rectangular coördinate axes are placed as described above.

The rectangular equation of the cycloid may be obtained by eliminating the parameter θ from the equations (1) above, but this form is long and complicated and is almost never used.

When the circle rolls once around, θ varies from 0 to 2π, and the tracing point describes one *arch* of the cycloid (shown in Fig. 166). Since the circle can roll without limit, the cycloid consists of an endless number of similar arches. The base OK of one arch is evidently of length $2\pi a$. The point H for which $\theta = \pi$ or $x = \pi a$ is a maximum point of the curve. The points, such as O and K, at which the curve touches the X-axis are called *cusps*, and it can be shown that at a cusp the tangent is perpendicular to the X-axis.

The cycloid has a number of important applications, especially in mechanics. It is the "curve of quickest descent," the so-called brachistochrone; that is, a particle constrained to follow some path but otherwise acted on only by gravity will descend from one point to a lower one, not in the same vertical line, in less time on an inverted cycloid than on any other path. A pendulum guided by two arches of a cycloid has a period of oscillation which is independent of the amplitude of the oscillation. Cycloids are sometimes used in gear construction.

★ 326. Exercises

Derive parametric equations of the following curves which are defined geometrically.

1. *Cissoid:* A tangent is drawn to a fixed circle of radius a at one end A of a fixed diameter. Through the other end O of the diameter a line is drawn meeting the circle at Q and the tangent at T. A point P is taken on this line so that $OP = QT$. As the line OT rotates about O, the point P traces out a curve known as the *cissoid.* If O is the origin and the fixed diameter is the X-axis, and if angle $XOP = \theta$, show that the parametric equations of the cissoid are

$$x = 2\,a\sin^2\theta, \qquad y = 2\,a\tan\theta\sin^2\theta.$$

2. *Witch:* A circle of radius a is drawn tangent to the X-axis at the origin O and cutting the Y-axis at A. The tangent to the circle at A is drawn. Through O a line is drawn cutting the circle at R and the tangent at Q; a horizontal line through R and a vertical line through Q meet at P. As the line OQ rotates about O, the point P describes a curve called the *witch of Agnesi.* If angle $XOQ = \theta$, show that parametric equations of the witch are

$$x = 2\,a\cot\theta, \qquad y = 2\,a\sin^2\theta.$$

3. *Strophoid:* Let AQ be a variable line through the fixed point $A(-a, 0)$ and cutting the Y-axis at Q. On AQ take points P and P' so that $PQ = P'Q = OQ$. As the line AQ rotates about A, the points P and P' describe a curve known as the *strophoid.* If angle $OAP = \theta$, show that parametric equations of the strophoid are

$$x = a\sin\theta, \qquad y = a\tan\theta\,(1 + \sin\theta).$$

4. *Conchoid:* A line is drawn through the origin and cutting the line $y = a$ at Q. On OQ two points P and P' are taken so that QP and QP' are equal to a constant b. As the line OQ rotates about O, the points P and P' describe a curve called the *conchoid of Nicomedes.* Show that parametric equations of the conchoid are

$$x = a\cot\theta \pm b\cos\theta, \qquad y = a \pm b\sin\theta,$$

where $\theta =$ angle XOP.

327. Functions Defined by Parametric Equations

We have seen that it is frequently convenient to represent a curve by a pair of parametric equations which express the coördinates of a point in terms of an auxiliary variable. It is also often convenient to represent a functional relation in parametric form, even when no geometric interpretation is being considered.

Let two variables x and y be given as functions of an auxiliary variable t, as $x = f(t)$, $y = g(t)$. Then y is determined as a function of x by these parametric equations.

328. Derivative of a Function Defined by Parametric Equations

Let y be a function of x defined by the parametric equations $x = f(t)$, $y = g(t)$, where t is the parameter. Suppose that $f(t)$ and $g(t)$ are single-valued functions which are differentiable in a given interval, and also suppose that $f'(t) \neq 0$ for all values of t in that interval. It follows from these assumptions that the function $x = f(t)$ has an inverse $t = h(x)$ (by § 105); then the equations $y = g(t)$, $t = h(x)$ together define y as a function of x by the composite function method (§ 96). By § 97, $D_x y = D_t y \cdot D_x t$, and by § 105, $D_x t = \dfrac{1}{D_t x}$, hence $D_x y = \dfrac{D_t y}{D_t x}$. Therefore:

If y is a function of x defined by the parametric equations $x = f(t)$, $y = g(t)$, where $f(t)$ and $g(t)$ are single-valued and differentiable, then

$$(2) \qquad D_x y = \frac{D_t y}{D_t x} = \frac{g'(t)}{f'(t)},$$

provided $f'(t) \neq 0$.

Example. If $x = t^2$, $y = t^3$, find $D_x y$.

Solution: $D_t x = 2t$, $D_t y = 3t^2$, then $D_x y = \dfrac{3t^2}{2t} = \tfrac{3}{2}t$.

329. Exercises

1. Find $D_x y$ from each of the following pairs of parametric equations, without eliminating the parameter:

    (a) $x = 4t$, $y = 8t^2$;
    (b) $x = \tfrac{1}{3}t^3$, $y = \tfrac{1}{2}t^2$;

    (c) $x = t^2$, $y = \dfrac{1}{2t}$;
    (d) $x = \dfrac{t^2 - 1}{t^2 + 1}$, $y = \dfrac{2t}{t^2 + 1}$.

2. Proceed as in Exercise 1 with:

    (a) $x = 1 + t^2$, $y = 1 - t^2$;
    (b) $x = 2t$, $y = \tfrac{1}{3}t^3$;

    (c) $x = \dfrac{1}{1 + t}$, $y = \dfrac{t}{1 + t}$;
    (d) $x = \dfrac{3t}{1 + t^3}$, $y = \dfrac{3t^2}{1 + t^3}$.

3. Find the slope of the tangent to the curve: $x = t^2 + 1$, $y = t^2 - t$, at the point where $t = 3$.

4. Find the slope of the tangent to the curve: $x = \sqrt{t}$, $y = t + \dfrac{1}{t}$, at the point where $t = 4$.

5. Find the equations of the tangent and normal to the curve $x = t^2$, $y = t^3$ at the point where $t = -2$.

6. Find the equations of the tangent and normal to the curve $x = 25 - t^2$, $y = t^3$ at the point where $t = 4$.

7. Find $D_x{}^2 y$ from the parametric equations $x = 2t - 1$, $y = t^3 + 1$, without eliminating t.
   [*Hint.* $D_x{}^2 y = D_x(D_x y) = D_t(D_x y) \cdot D_x t = D_t(D_x y)/D_t x$.]

8. Find $D_x{}^2 y$ from the parametric equations $x = \dfrac{1}{t}$, $y = t + 1$ without eliminating t.   [See hint in Exercise 7.]

9. Find $D_x y$ from $x = a \cos \theta$, $y = a \sin \theta$.

10. Find $D_x y$ from $x = a(\theta - \sin \theta)$, $y = a(1 - \cos \theta)$.

11. Find the equations of the tangent and normal to the cycloid
$$x = a(\theta - \sin \theta), \qquad y = a(1 - \cos \theta)$$
   at the point where $\theta = \frac{1}{2}\pi$.

12. Find the maximum and minimum points and points of inflection of the curve $x = \theta + \sin \theta$, $y = 1 - \cos \theta$.

13. Find $D_x y$ from $x = a \ln t$, $y = \dfrac{a}{2}\left(t + \dfrac{1}{t}\right)$.

14. Find $D_x y$ from $x = t^2 e^t$, $y = t \ln t$.

330. Use of Differentials in Parametric Equations

When dealing with parametric equations, it is convenient to use differentials in finding derivatives, particularly for the derivatives of higher order. Thus, y' is obtained by dividing dy by dx, and y'' is obtained by dividing dy' by dx.

EXAMPLE. Find the first two derivatives of the function defined by $x = 1/t$, $y = t^2$.

Solution: $dx = -\dfrac{1}{t^2}\, dt, \quad dy = 2t\, dt, \quad \dfrac{dy}{dx} = -2t^3 = y'; \quad dy' = -6t^2\, dt,$

$dx = -\dfrac{1}{t^2}\, dt, \dfrac{d^2 y}{dx^2} = \dfrac{dy'}{dx} = 6t^4.$

331. Exercises

1. Find $\dfrac{dy}{dx}$ and $\dfrac{d^2 y}{dx^2}$ in terms of t for the following parametric equations:

    (a) $x = t^2$, $y = t^3$;
    (b) $x = 2t$, $y = 2\sqrt{1 - t^2}$;

    (c) $x = t^4$, $y = \dfrac{1}{t}$;
    (d) $x = \dfrac{3t}{1 + t^3}$, $y = \dfrac{3t^2}{1 + t^3}$.

2. Proceed as in Exercise 1 with:

    (a) $x = t^2 - 1$, $y = \dfrac{2}{t}$;
    (b) $x = 2t + 1$, $y = 4t - t^2$;

    (c) $x = \sqrt{1 + t}$, $y = \sqrt{1 - t}$;
    (d) $x = \dfrac{2t}{1 + t^2}$, $y = \dfrac{1 - t^2}{1 + t^2}$.

332. Integration Problems Involving Parametric Equations

If y is a function of x defined by a pair of parametric equations with a parameter t, a definite integral in the form $\int_a^b y\,dx$ may be evaluated by expressing both y and dx in terms of t and dt, and by replacing a and b by the corresponding values of t.

EXAMPLE 1. Evaluate $\int_{x=0}^{x=4} y\,dx$ when $x = 2\,t,\ y = t^2$.

Solution: From $x = 2\,t$, we get $dx = 2\,dt$; when $x = 4$, $t = 2$, and when $x = 0$, $t = 0$. Then

$$\int_{x=0}^{x=4} y\,dx = \int_{t=0}^{t=2} t^2 \cdot 2\,dt = \frac{2}{3}\,t^3\,\Big|_0^2 = \frac{16}{3}.$$

EXAMPLE 2. Find the area of the region bounded by the curve $x = 1 + t^2$, $y = 2\,t$, the X-axis and the line $x = 5$, and lying above the X-axis.

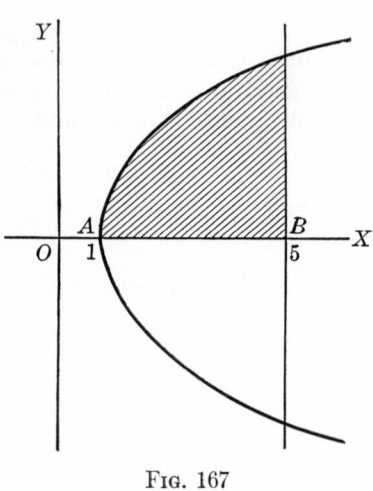

FIG. 167

Solution: The curve is the parabola of Fig. 167; the point A corresponds to $t = 0$ and point B corresponds to $t = 2$. The required area is that of the shaded region in the figure. Since $y = 2\,t$ and $dx = 2\,t\,dt$, we have

$$A = \int_1^5 y\,dx = \int_0^2 (2\,t)(2\,t\,dt)$$
$$= 4\int_0^2 t^2\,dt = \frac{32}{3}.$$

EXAMPLE 3. Find the length of the arc of the curve $x = t^2$, $y = t^3$ between the points for which $t = 0$ and $t = 2$.

Solution: $dx = 2\,t\,dt,\quad dy = 3t^2\,dt,$
$$y' = \frac{dy}{dx} = \frac{3\,t^2\,dt}{2\,t\,dt} = \frac{3}{2}\,t,$$

$1 + y'^2 = 1 + \dfrac{9}{4}\,t^2 = \tfrac{1}{4}(4 + 9\,t^2).$ Then

$$s = \int_a^b \sqrt{1 + y'^2}\,dx = \int_0^2 \tfrac{1}{2}\sqrt{4 + 9\,t^2}\,(2\,t\,dt) = \tfrac{8}{27}(10\sqrt{10} - 1).$$

333. Exercises

1. Evaluate $\int_{x=1}^{x=3} y\,dx$ when $x = 2\,t - 1,\ y = t^2 + 2$.

2. Evaluate $\displaystyle\int_{x=0}^{x=4} y\,dx$ when $x = \sqrt{t}$, $y = 1 - t$.

3. Find the area of the region bounded by the curve $x = t^2$, $y = 2 - t$ and the coördinate axes.

4. Find the area of the region bounded by the curve $3\,x = t^3$, $2\,y = t^2$, the Y-axis and the line $y = 2$.

5. Find the length of the curve $x = t^3$, $y = t^2$ between the points for which $t = 0$ and $t = 2$.

6. Find the length of the curve $x = 1 + t^2$, $y = 1 - t^2$ between the points for which $t = 1$ and $t = 4$.

334. Vectors

In order to be able to discuss many applications of mathematics to physical problems, it is found convenient to use the concept of a *vector*.

*A **vector** is a directed line-segment.   It has length and direction.*

A *vector quantity* is a quantity which has direction as well as magnitude and which may be represented by a vector having the same direction and whose length is equal to the magnitude of the quantity.   Examples of vector quantities are: displacement, velocity, acceleration and force.

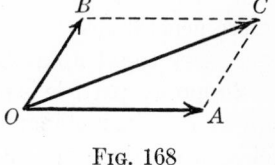

Fig. 168

For brevity, instead of "vector quantity," we shall use the single word *vector* to describe the vector quantity which the vector represents.

We use an arrow to indicate a vector, thus $\overrightarrow{AB}$.

*The **resultant** of two vectors $\overrightarrow{OA}$ and $\overrightarrow{OB}$ (Fig. 168) is defined to be the vector diagonal $\overrightarrow{OC}$ of the parallelogram having $\overrightarrow{OA}$ and $\overrightarrow{OB}$ as adjacent sides.*

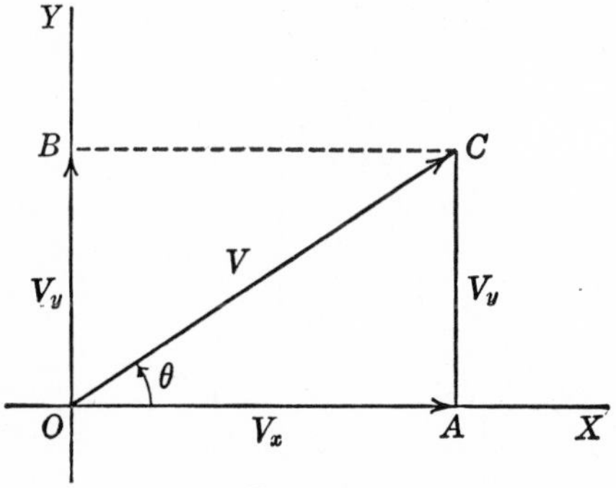

Fig. 169

In Fig. 169, let $\overrightarrow{OC}$ be a given vector, and let $\overrightarrow{OA}$ and $\overrightarrow{OB}$ be the projections of $\overrightarrow{OC}$ on a set of rectangular axes.   Then *the vectors $\overrightarrow{OA}$ and $\overrightarrow{OB}$ are called the rec-*

tangular components *of the vector* $\overrightarrow{OC}$ *referred to the given coördinate axes.* The given vector $\overrightarrow{OC}$ is the resultant of the vectors $\overrightarrow{OA}$ and $\overrightarrow{OB}$.

Let V denote the (undirected) length of the vector $\overrightarrow{OC}$, and let V_x and V_y denote the directed lengths $\overline{OA}$ and $\overline{OB}$, and let θ denote the angle AOC. Then

$$(3) \qquad V_x = V \cos \theta, \qquad V_y = V \sin \theta,$$

$$(4) \qquad V^2 = V_x{}^2 + V_y{}^2, \quad \tan \theta = \frac{V_y}{V_x}.$$

The quadrant in which θ lies is determined by equations (3).

335. Velocity in Curvilinear Motion

In our previous treatment of motion (§ 80), we defined and considered velocity in the case of motion in a straight line only. For the more general case of motion in a path of any kind, it is therefore necessary to set up a new definition of velocity.

Suppose a particle is moving along a plane curvilinear path in such a way that its rectangular coördinates x and y referred to a given set of axes are given in terms of the time t by the equations

$$(a) \qquad x = f(t), \qquad y = g(t).$$

These are called the *equations of motion*.

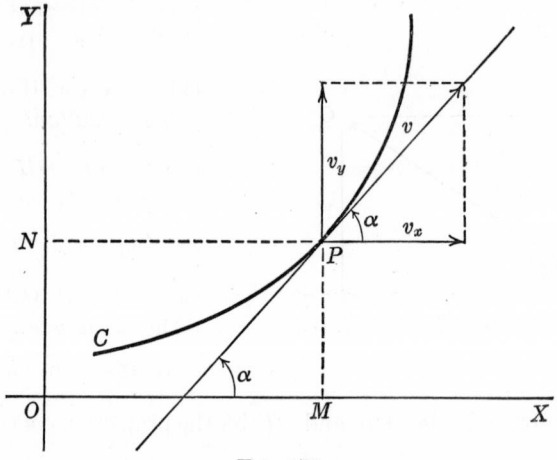

Fig. 170

We may regard the equations (a) as parametric equations of the path of the particle. If we eliminate t from these equations, we obtain the rectangular equation of the path in terms of x and y.

Let $P(x, y)$ be the position of the particle at any time t (Fig. 170), and let M and N be the projections of P on the X- and Y-axes respectively. Then, by § 80, the velocities of M and N along their respective axes are given by $D_t x$ and $D_t y$; these determine the motion of P. This leads to the following definition:

*For motion in a plane path given by equations (a), the **velocity** of the particle at any time t is the **vector** v whose rectangular components have the directed lengths:*

$$(5) \qquad v_x = D_t x = \frac{dx}{dt}, \qquad v_y = D_t y = \frac{dy}{dt}.$$

*The length (or magnitude) of the velocity vector is called the **speed** of the particle.*

This definition of velocity in plane motion evidently includes as a special case the previous definition of velocity in a rectilinear path.

From the definition of the velocity vector, it follows from § 334, formulas (3) and (4), that:

I. *The magnitude and direction of the velocity vector are given by:*

$$(6) \qquad v = \sqrt{v_x{}^2 + v_y{}^2}, \qquad \tan \alpha = \frac{v_y}{v_x},$$

where α is the angle between the X-axis and the velocity vector. Also,

$$(7) \qquad v_x = v \cos \alpha, \qquad v_y = v \sin \alpha.$$

The quadrant in which α lies is determined by equations (7).

An important property of the velocity vector may be obtained as follows: We have

$$\tan \alpha = \frac{v_y}{v_x} = \frac{D_t y}{D_t x} = D_x y,$$

by § 328. But $D_x y$ is the tangent of the angle which the geometrical tangent to the path makes with the X-axis. Hence, α is equal to the inclination of the tangent; therefore the velocity is in the direction of the tangent. Also,

$$v^2 = v_x{}^2 + v_y{}^2 = (D_t x)^2 + (D_t y)^2 = (D_t s)^2,$$

by § 195, so that $v = |D_t s|$. Hence:

II. *The velocity vector of a particle in plane curvilinear motion has the direction of the tangent to the path; and the speed of the particle is given by* $v = |D_t s| = |ds/dt|$, *where s is the distance along the curve of the particle from some fixed point on it.*

Problems involving the velocity of a particle moving in a plane path may be solved by use of one or more of the formulas (5), (6), (7).

EXAMPLE 1.   The equations of motion of a particle moving in a plane are $x = t^2$, $y = 3t - 1$, where t is the time and x, y are rectangular coördinates. Find the path of the particle, and find the speed and direction of motion at the instant when $t = 2$.

Solution: From $x = t^2$, $y = 3t - 1$, we find $v_x = 2t$, $v_y = 3$; when $t = 2$, we have $v_x = 4$, $v_y = 3$.   Then

$$v^2 = 4^2 + 3^2 = 25, \quad v = 5; \quad \tan \alpha = \tfrac{3}{4}, \quad \alpha = 36° \; 52',$$

since $\cos \alpha = \tfrac{4}{5}$ and $\sin \alpha = \tfrac{3}{5}$ are both positive.   Eliminating t from the equations of motion, we find that the path is the parabola

$$9x = (y + 1)^2.$$

EXAMPLE 2.   A particle describes the right-hand part of the curve $4y^3 = x^2$, with $v_y = 2$ at all times.   Find the speed and direction of motion at the point where $y = 4$.

Solution: Differentiating the equation of the path with respect to t, we have

$$12 y^2 \frac{dy}{dt} = 2x \frac{dx}{dt},$$

or

(a)
$$6 y^2 \cdot v_y = x \cdot v_x.$$

When $y = 4$, from the equation of the path we find $x = 16$.   Substituting these values of x and y and the value $v_y = 2$ in equation (a), and solving for v_x, we obtain $v_x = 12$.   Then

$$v^2 = v_x{}^2 + v_y{}^2 = 144 + 4 = 148, \quad v = 2\sqrt{37},$$

$$\tan \alpha = \frac{v_y}{v_x} = \frac{1}{6}, \quad \alpha = 9° \; 28',$$

since $\cos \alpha = \dfrac{6}{2\sqrt{37}}$ and $\sin \alpha = \dfrac{2}{2\sqrt{37}}$ are both positive.

EXAMPLE 3.   A particle moves to the right and upward along the portion of the parabola $y^2 = 8x$ which lies in the first quadrant.   If it passes through the point (2, 4) with a speed of 2, how fast is it rising vertically at that point?

Solution: From the equation of the curve we get $2y \, v_y = 8 v_x$, and at the point (2, 4) this becomes $8 v_y = 8 v_x$, or

(b)
$$v_y = v_x.$$

Since the speed is $v = 2$, we have also

(c)
$$v_x^2 + v_y^2 = v^2 = 4.$$

Solving equations (b) and (c) for v_y, we find $v_y = \sqrt{2}$.

336. Exercises

1. If the equations of motion of a particle are $x = t^2$, $y = 2\,t$, find the speed and direction of motion at the time $t = 2$, and also at any time t. Find the rectangular equation of the path.

2. If a particle moves according to the equations of motion $x = t^2$, $y = t^3$, find the speed and direction of motion at any time t, and also find the rectangular equation of the path.

3. If the equations of motion of a particle are $x = 4\cos t$, $y = 3\sin t$, find the speed and direction of motion at $t = \frac{1}{4}\,\pi$, and find the rectangular equation of the path.

4. A particle moves along the parabola $y = x^2$, with $v_x = 3$ at all times; find its speed and direction of motion when $x = 2$.

5. A particle moves along the right-hand branch of the hyperbola $xy = 8$ with a horizontal component of velocity of 6 at all times. Find the speed and direction of motion of the particle when it reaches the position $(4, 2)$.

6. Show that if a particle moves along the parabola $x^2 = 8\,y$ so that the horizontal component of velocity is inversely proportional to the abscissa of the particle, then the vertical component of velocity is constant.

7. If a moving particle describes the lower part of the curve $y^2 = 8\,x$ from left to right with a constant speed of 8, find the rectangular components of the velocity and the direction of motion at the point $(2, -4)$.

8. A point moves counter-clockwise along the ellipse $x^2 + 9\,y^2 = 81$ with a constant speed of 5; find the rectangular components of the velocity at the position $(3, 2\sqrt{2})$.

337. Acceleration in Curvilinear Motion

Consider again a particle moving in a plane path whose equations of motion are $x = f(t)$, $y = g(t)$, and whose velocity at any time t is given by the vector whose rectangular components have the directed lengths $v_x = dx/dt$ and $v_y = dy/dt$.

The previous definition of acceleration for rectilinear motion (§ 116) will not apply directly here. We therefore formulate the following new definition of acceleration, which will evidently include the previous definition as a special case.

*For plane curvilinear motion, the **acceleration** of a particle at any time t is the **vector** whose rectangular components have the directed lengths:*

(8)
$$a_x = \frac{dv_x}{dt} = \frac{d^2x}{dt^2}, \qquad a_y = \frac{dv_y}{dt} = \frac{d^2y}{dt^2}.$$

It follows at once from this definition and from § 334 that:

The magnitude and direction of the acceleration vector are given by:

(9)
$$a = \sqrt{a_x^2 + a_y^2}, \qquad \tan \phi = \frac{a_y}{a_x},$$

where ϕ is the angle between the X-axis and the acceleration vector.   Also,

(10)
$$a_x = a \cos \phi, \qquad a_y = a \sin \phi.$$

The quadrant in which ϕ lies is determined by equations (10).

It is important to note that in curvilinear motion, the acceleration vector does *not* in general lie along the tangent to the path (as does the velocity vector) but it can be shown that it is toward the concave side of the path, and also that the magnitude of the acceleration a is *not* given by dv/dt as in rectilinear motion.

EXAMPLE 1.   If a particle moves in a plane according to the equations of motion $x = -t^2$, $y = t^3$, find the magnitude and direction of the acceleration when $t = \frac{2}{3}$.

Solution: $v_x = \dfrac{dx}{dt} = -2\,t$, $v_y = \dfrac{dy}{dt} = 3\,t^2$; then

$$a_x = \frac{dv_x}{dt} = -2, \; a_y = \frac{dv_y}{dt} = 6\,t.$$

At $t = \frac{2}{3}$, we obtain $a_x = -2$, $a_y = 4$.   Then

$$a = \sqrt{a_x^2 + a_y^2} = 2\sqrt{5}, \; \tan \phi = \frac{4}{-2} = -2, \; \phi = 116° 34',$$

since $\cos \phi = -\dfrac{2}{2\sqrt{5}}$ is negative and $\sin \phi = \dfrac{4}{2\sqrt{5}}$ is positive.

EXAMPLE 2.   A particle moves along the curve $y = \frac{1}{3} x^3$ with $v_y = 8$ at all times; find the magnitude and direction of the acceleration when $x = 2$.

Solution: Differentiating both sides of the equation of the path with respect to t twice, we get

(a)
$$v_y = x^2 \cdot v_x,$$

(b)
$$a_y = x^2 \cdot a_x + 2\,x \cdot v_x^2.$$

But $v_y = 8$ for all values of t, so that $a_y = \dfrac{dv_y}{dt} = 0$ at all times.   Substitution of $x = 2$ and $v_y = 8$ in (a) gives $8 = 4\,v_x$ or $v_x = 2$.   Substitution of $x = 2$, $v_x = 2$ and $a_y = 0$ in (b) gives $0 = 4\,a_x + 16$, or $a_x = -4$.   Then from $a^2 = a_x^2 + a_y^2$ we find $a = 4$.   Also, since $a_y = 0$, it follows that the acceleration vector is parallel to the X-axis.

EXAMPLE 3.   A particle describes the path $x^2 = 4y$ from left to right with a constant speed of 8.   Find the acceleration (in magnitude and direction) at the position $(2, 1)$.

Solution: From the equation of the path, we get

$$(c) \qquad\qquad 2\,x\cdot v_x = 4\,v_y,$$

and for $x = 2$, we have $4\,v_x = 4\,v_y$, or

$$(d) \qquad\qquad v_x = v_y.$$

Since $v = 8$ at all times,

$$(e) \qquad\qquad v_x{}^2 + v_y{}^2 = v^2 = 64.$$

Solving equations (d) and (e) for v_x and v_y, we find $v_x = 4\sqrt{2} = v_y$.   Differentiating equations (c) and (e) with respect to t, we obtain

$$(f) \qquad\qquad 2\,x\cdot a_x + 2\,v_x{}^2 = 4\,a_y,$$

$$(g) \qquad\qquad 2\,v_x\cdot a_x + 2\,v_y\cdot a_y = 0.$$

Substituting $x = 2$, $v_x = 4\sqrt{2}$, $v_y = 4\sqrt{2}$ in (f) and (g), and solving the resulting equations for a_x and a_y, we find $a_x = -8$, $a_y = 8$.   Then

$$a = \sqrt{a_x{}^2 + a_y{}^2} = 8\sqrt{2}, \quad \tan\phi = \frac{8}{-8} = -1, \quad \phi = 135°,$$

since a_x is negative and a_y is positive.

338. Exercises

For each of the motions in Exercises 1–4, find v_x, v_y, v, a_x, a_y, and a, the direction of motion and the direction of the acceleration vector, and also the rectangular equation of the path:

1. $x = 2\,t$, $y = t^2$, at $t = 2$.
2. $x = 1 - t^2$, $y = t + t^2$, at $t = 1$.
3. $x = \sin 2\,t$, $y = \cos 2\,t$, at $t = \frac{1}{2}\,\pi$.
4. $x = \ln \cos t$, $y = t$, at $t = \frac{1}{4}\,\pi$.

5. If a particle moves according to the law of motion $x = 3 \cos 2\,\pi t$, $y = \sin 2\,\pi t$, find the magnitude and direction of the acceleration vector at $t = \frac{1}{6}$.

6. If a particle moves according to the law $x = e^{-2t} \cos 2\,t$, $y = e^{-2t} \sin 2\,t$, find the magnitude of the acceleration at any time t.

7. If the equations of motion of a particle are: $x = at$, $y = b \sin t$, show that: (a) the X-component of the velocity is constant; (b) the acceleration at any instant is proportional to the ordinate of the particle.

8. A particle moves along the parabola $y = 2\,x^2$ with a constant X-component of velocity of 2.   Find the Y-components of the velocity and acceleration at the point $(1, 2)$.

9. A particle moves counter-clockwise along the curve $16\,x^2 + 9\,y^2 = 144$ with $v_x = 12$.   Find v_y, v, a_x, a_y and a when $x = 2$.

10. A particle moves counter-clockwise with a constant speed of 25 around the circle $x^2 + y^2 = 25$.   Find v_x, v_y, a_x and a_y at the point $(3, 4)$.

CHAPTER XVI

Curvature of Plane Curves

339. Curvature

Let $P(x, y)$ be any point on the curve $y = f(x)$, and let α be the inclination of the tangent to this curve at P (Fig. 171). Let

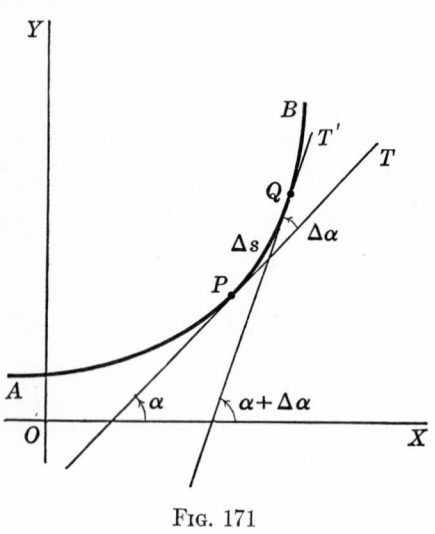

$Q(x + \Delta x, y + \Delta y)$ be a neighboring point on the curve, let $\alpha + \Delta\alpha$ be the inclination of the tangent at Q, and let Δs be the arc length PQ. Then $\Delta\alpha$ is the angle through which the tangent turns when a point moves a distance Δs along the curve from P to Q. The angle $\Delta\alpha$ is to be measured in radians. The ratio $\Delta\alpha/\Delta s$ represents the average change in direction of the curve per unit of arc length. This ratio $\Delta\alpha/\Delta s$ will in general approach a limit as $\Delta s \to 0$, which is the derivative $D_s\alpha$.

FIG. 171

The absolute value of the limit $\lim\limits_{\Delta s \to 0} (\Delta\alpha/\Delta s)$ *is called the* **curvature** *of the curve* $y = f(x)$ *at the point* P, *and is usually denoted by* K. *Then, by definition,*

(1) $$K = |D_s\alpha|.$$

Now let us apply our definition of curvature to a circle. In Fig. 172, angle SRQ = angle $POQ = |\Delta\alpha|$, $|\Delta s|$ = arc $PQ = r|\Delta\alpha|$. Then

$\left|\dfrac{\Delta\alpha}{\Delta s}\right| = \dfrac{1}{r}$, and therefore $K = \dfrac{1}{r}$ at all points of the circle.   Hence:

I. *The curvature of a circle is the same at every point on it, and it is equal to the reciprocal of the radius.*

In the case of a straight line, $\Delta\alpha = 0$ everywhere on the line, since the tangent coincides with the line. Then $\dfrac{\Delta\alpha}{\Delta s} = 0$, and therefore $K = 0$ at all points of the line.   Hence:

II. *The curvature of a straight line is everywhere zero.*

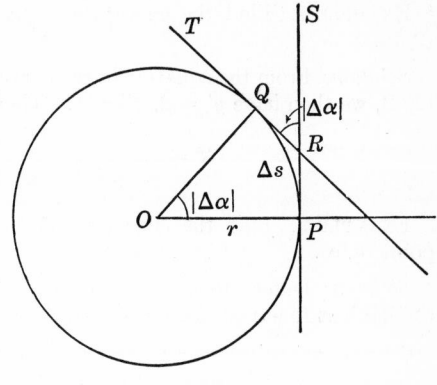

Fig. 172

340. Formula for Curvature, in Rectangular Coördinates

Let us now derive a formula for the curvature of the curve $y = f(x)$ at a given point $P(x, y)$ on it.   The slope of the tangent is $\tan\alpha = y'$, so that

(a) $$\alpha = \text{Arc tan } y'.$$

By definition of curvature, and by §§ 97, 105, we have

(b) $$K = |D_s\alpha| = |D_x\alpha \cdot D_s x| = \left|\frac{D_x\alpha}{D_x s}\right|.$$

From (a),

(c) $$D_x\alpha = \frac{1}{1 + y'^2} \cdot D_x y' = \frac{y''}{1 + y'^2}.$$

By § 195,

(d) $$D_x s = (1 + y'^2)^{\frac{1}{2}}.$$

Combining these last two results as indicated in (b), we obtain

$$K = \frac{|y''|}{1 + y'^2} \cdot \frac{1}{(1 + y'^2)^{\frac{1}{2}}} = \frac{|y''|}{(1 + y'^2)^{\frac{3}{2}}}.$$

Hence:

The curvature K of a curve $y = f(x)$ at a point $P(x, y)$ is given by:

(2)
$$K = \frac{|y''|}{(1 + y'^2)^{\frac{3}{2}}},$$

where y' and y'' are to be evaluated at P.

EXAMPLE 1. Find the curvature of the parabola $2\,y = x^2$ at the point $(2, 2)$.

Solution: From the equation of the curve, $y' = x$ and $y'' = 1$; at the point $(2, 2)$, we then have $y' = 2$, $y'' = 1$. Therefore,

$$K = \frac{1}{(1 + 4)^{\frac{3}{2}}} = \frac{1}{5\sqrt{5}} = \frac{1}{25}\sqrt{5}.$$

EXAMPLE 2. Find the curvature of the cissoid $y^2(2\,a - x) = x^3$ at the point (a, a).

Solution: Differentiating the equation of the curve with respect to x by the implicit function method, we get

(e) $$y^2(-1) + (2\,a - x)\cdot 2\,yy' = 3\,x^2,$$

and differentiating again, we obtain

(f) $$-2\,yy' + (2\,a - x)\cdot 2\,yy'' + (2\,a - x)\cdot 2\,y'y' + 2\,yy'(-1) = 6\,x.$$

Substituting $x = a$, $y = a$ in (e) and solving for y', we find $y' = 2$; substituting $x = a$, $y = a$ and $y' = 2$ in (f) and solving for y'', we find $y'' = \dfrac{3}{a}$.
Then

$$K = \frac{\dfrac{3}{a}}{(1 + 4)^{\frac{3}{2}}} = \frac{3}{5\sqrt{5}\,a}.$$

341. Exercises

In Exercises 1–22, find the curvature of each of the given curves:

1. $y = x^2$, at $(1, 1)$.
2. $y = 2\,x - x^2$, at $(1, 1)$.
3. $y = x^2 - x^3$, at $x = 1$.
4. $y = x^3$, at $x = 2$.
5. $y = \sqrt{x}$, at $x = 2$.
6. $y = 1/x$, at (x_1, y_1).
7. $y = x^{-\frac{3}{2}}$, at $x = 1$.
8. $y = 1/\sqrt{x}$, at (x_1, y_1).
9. $y^2 = x^3$, at $(1, 1)$.
10. $y^2 = 4\,ax$, at $(a, 2\,a)$.
11. $x^2 - y^2 = a^2$, at $x = 2\,a$.
12. $4\,x^2 + 9\,y^2 = 36$, at $(0, 2)$.
13. $xy = a^2$, at (x_1, y_1).
14. $x^{\frac{1}{2}} + y^{\frac{1}{2}} = a^{\frac{1}{2}}$, at (x_1, y_1).
15. $y = \cos x$, at $x = 0$.
16. $y = \sec x - 1$, at $x = \frac{1}{4}\,\pi$.
17. $y = e^x$, at $(0, 1)$.
18. $y = \ln(x + 1)$, at $x = 2$.
19. $y = \tan x$, at $x = \frac{1}{4}\,\pi$.
20. $y = \cosh x$, at (x_1, y_1).
21. $y = \ln \sec x$, at (x_1, y_1).
22. $y = e^{-x^2}$, at $(0, 1)$.

23. Find the curvature of the curve $x = t^2$, $y = 2/t$ at the point where $t = t_1$.
24. Find the curvature of the curve $x = 2\,t$, $y = t^3$ at the point where $t = t_1$.

25. Find the curvature of the cycloid $x = a(\theta - \sin \theta)$, $y = a(1 - \cos \theta)$ at the highest point of an arch.

26. A locomotive is running on a track which has the shape of the parabola $y = x^2$, a mile being the unit of length. At what rate per mile is its direction changing when $x = 1$?

27. Find the maximum curvature of the curve $y = \ln x$.

28. Find the point on the curve $y = e^x$ where the curvature is a maximum.

29. Find the curvature of the curve $y = x \ln x$ at the point whose ordinate is a minimum.

30. Show that the maximum point of the curve $y = 3x - x^3$ is not a point of maximum curvature.

31. At what points on a curve is the curvature 0?

32. What is the value of the curvature at a point where the tangent is parallel to the X-axis?

342. Circle of Curvature and Radius of Curvature

*The circle which is tangent to a given curve at a point P on its concave side and which has the same curvature as the given curve at P is called the **circle of curvature** of the given curve at P (Fig. 173).*

*The center of this circle is called the **center of curvature**, and its radius is called the **radius of curvature**, for the given curve at P.*

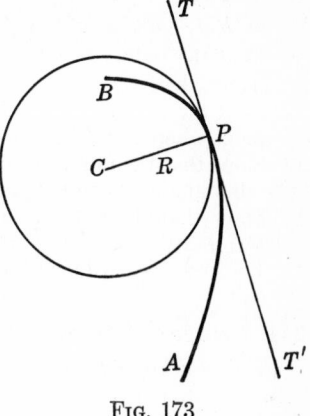

Fig. 173

Since the circle of curvature is tangent to the given curve at P, its center must lie on the normal to the given curve at P, on the concave side. Since, by § 339, the curvature of a circle is the reciprocal of its radius, it follows that the radius of curvature of the given curve is equal to the reciprocal of its curvature. Hence:

$$(3) \qquad R = \frac{1}{K}.$$

Using the formula (2) of § 340 for K, we have:

The radius of curvature of the curve $y = f(x)$ at any point (x, y) is given by:

$$(4) \qquad R = \frac{(1 + y'^2)^{\frac{3}{2}}}{|y''|}.$$

The circle of curvature at a point P is also sometimes called the *osculating circle*. It can be shown that it "fits" the curve near P more closely than does any other circle.

EXAMPLE. Find the radius of curvature of the semi-cubical parabola $3 y^2 = x^3$ at the point $(3, 3)$.

Solution: From the equation of the curve, $6 yy' = 3 x^2$ and $yy'' + y'^2 = x$. Substituting $x = 3$, $y = 3$ and solving for y' and y'', we find $y' = \frac{3}{2}$ and $y'' = \frac{1}{4}$. Formula (4) for R then gives

$$R = \frac{(1 + \frac{9}{4})^{\frac{3}{2}}}{\frac{1}{4}} = 4 \left(\frac{13}{4}\right)^{\frac{3}{2}} = \frac{13}{2} \sqrt{13}.$$

343. Exercises

In Exercises 1–10, find the radius of curvature of each of the given curves:

1. $y = x^3 - 6 x$, at $(1, -5)$.
2. $y = 1/x^2$, at $(-1, 1)$.
3. $y = \sin x$, at $x = \frac{1}{2} \pi$.
4. $y = e^{-x}$, at $(0, 1)$.
5. $x^2 + xy + y^2 = 3$, at $(1, 1)$.
6. $y^2 - y + x = 0$, at $(0, 0)$.
7. $2 xy = a^2$, at $(a, \frac{1}{2} a)$.
8. $x^3 + y^3 = 3 xy$, at $(\frac{3}{2}, \frac{3}{2})$.
9. $b^2x^2 + a^2y^2 = a^2b^2$, at (x_1, y_1).
10. $x^{\frac{2}{3}} + y^{\frac{2}{3}} = a^{\frac{2}{3}}$, at (x_1, y_1).

11. Find the radius of curvature of the curve $x = 3 t^2$, $y = 3 t - t^3$, at the point where $t = 1$.
12. Find the radius of curvature of the curve $x = \sin t$, $y = \cos 2 t$, at the point where $t = \frac{1}{4} \pi$.
13. Show that the radius of curvature of the parabola $y = ax^2 + bx + c$ is a minimum at its vertex.
14. Show that the radii of curvature at the ends of the axes of the ellipse $b^2x^2 + a^2y^2 = a^2b^2$ are b^2/a and a^2/b.
15. Find the least value of the radius of curvature of the curve $y = \ln x$.

344. Center of Curvature

Formulas for the coördinates of the center of curvature are sometimes needed; they may be derived as follows: In Fig. 174, let R be the radius of curvature at P_1 on the curve, and let ϕ be the acute angle that the tangent P_1T makes with the X-axis, so that angle $P_1CQ = \phi$ also. Let $C(\alpha, \beta)$ be the center of curvature for P_1. For the figure as drawn,

(a) $\qquad x_1 - \alpha = R \sin \phi, \qquad y_1 - \beta = -R \cos \phi.$

Since $\tan \phi = y'$, by trigonometry we have,

$$\sin \phi = \frac{y_1'}{\sqrt{1 + y_1'^2}}, \qquad \cos \phi = \frac{1}{\sqrt{1 + y_1'^2}}.$$

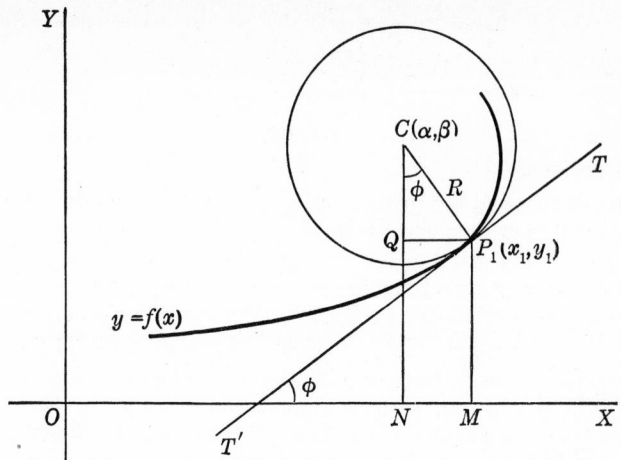

Fig. 174

For the figure as drawn, we may replace $|y_1''|$ by y_1'' in the formula (4) for R in § 342, since the curve is concave upward and y_1'' is therefore positive. If we substitute in (a) the preceding values of $\sin \phi$ and $\cos \phi$ and the value of R modified as just described, we obtain the result:

The coördinates (α, β) of the center of curvature of the curve $y = f(x)$ for the point $P_1(x_1, y_1)$ are given by:

$$(5) \qquad \alpha = x_1 - \frac{y_1'(1 + y_1'^2)}{y_1''}, \qquad \beta = y_1 + \frac{1 + y_1'^2}{y_1''}.$$

The foregoing proof of (5) is valid for the case represented by Fig. 174, where $y_1' > 0$ and C lies to the left of P_1 and above P_1. By examining suitable figures, and using the fact that $|y_1''| = -y_1''$ when the curve is concave downward at P_1, it can be shown readily that the formulas (5) are correct in all cases.

EXAMPLE. Find the coördinates of the center of curvature of the parabola $y^2 = 2px$ at any point (x_1, y_1).

Solution: From the equation of the curve, we find $y' = \dfrac{p}{y}$, $y'' = -\dfrac{p^2}{y^3}$. Then

$$\alpha = x_1 - \frac{\dfrac{p}{y_1}\left(1 + \dfrac{p^2}{y_1{}^2}\right)}{-\dfrac{p^2}{y_1{}^3}} = x_1 + \frac{y_1{}^2}{p}\left(1 + \frac{p^2}{y_1{}^2}\right) = \frac{3\,y_1{}^2 + 2\,p^2}{2\,p} = 3\,x_1 + p,$$

$$\beta = y_1 + \frac{1 + \dfrac{p^2}{y_1{}^2}}{-\dfrac{p^2}{y_1{}^3}} = y_1 - \frac{y_1{}^3}{p^2}\left(1 + \frac{p^2}{y_1{}^2}\right) = -\frac{y_1{}^3}{p^2}.$$

345. Exercises

In Exercises 1–8, find the coördinates of the center of curvature for each of the given curves at the point indicated:

1. $y = x^2$, at $x = 1$.
2. $y = x^3$, at $x = 2$.
3. $y = \sin x$, at $x = \frac{1}{2}\pi$.
4. $y = e^{2x}$, at $x = 0$.
5. $xy = 4$, at $x = 2$.
6. $x^3 + xy^2 - 6y^2 = 0$, at $x = 3$.
7. $x^{\frac{2}{3}} + y^{\frac{2}{3}} = a^{\frac{2}{3}}$, at (x_1, y_1).
8. $b^2x^2 + a^2y^2 = a^2b^2$, at (x_1, y_1).

9. Show that the coördinates (α, β) of the center of curvature for the parabola $x^{\frac{1}{2}} + y^{\frac{1}{2}} = a^{\frac{1}{2}}$ satisfy the relation $\alpha + \beta = 3(x + y)$.

10. Show that if the center of curvature of the ellipse $b^2x^2 + a^2y^2 = a^2b^2$ at one end of the minor axis lies at the other end, then the eccentricity of the ellipse is $\frac{1}{2}\sqrt{2}$.

11. Show that the circle of curvature is the circle through P such that y' and y'' have the same values for the circle as for the curve at P.

CHAPTER XVII

Integration by Standard Forms

346. Standard Integrals

Rules for integration may be obtained by reversing the rules of differentiation. By reversing most of the fundamental formulas of differentiation derived in Chapters VI and XIII, we obtain a certain set of formulas of integration which are called *standard forms for integration.* We now proceed to discuss these.

347. The Power Formula

In Chapter IX we have already seen that by reversing the power rule for differentiation, $d(u^n) = nu^{n-1} du$, we obtain the *power formula* for *integration:*

$$(1) \qquad \int u^n \, du = \frac{u^{n+1}}{n+1} + C \qquad (n \neq -1).$$

We have already used this rule extensively in previous chapters. By recognizing the standard differential forms for transcendental functions and using the substitution method, we may integrate many additional forms; thus, we may use: $\cos x \, dx = d \sin x$, $\sec^2 x \, dx = d \tan x$, $dx/x = d \ln x$, $e^x \, dx = d(e^x)$, etc.

EXAMPLE. (a) $\displaystyle \int \sin x \cos x \, dx = \int \sin x \, (\cos x \, dx)$

$$= \int \sin x \cdot d \, (\sin x) = \tfrac{1}{2} \sin^2 x + C;$$

(b) $\displaystyle \int \sqrt{\tan x} \, \sec^2 x \, dx = \int (\tan x)^{\frac{1}{2}} \cdot (\sec^2 x \, dx)$

$$= \int (\tan x)^{\frac{1}{2}} \, d(\tan x) = \tfrac{2}{3}(\tan x)^{\frac{3}{2}} + C;$$

(c) $\displaystyle \int e^x (e^x + 2)^3 \, dx = \int (e^x + 2)^3 \, (e^x \, dx)$

$$= \int (e^x + 2)^3 \cdot d(e^x + 2) = \tfrac{1}{4}(e^x + 2)^4 + C.$$

348. Exercises

Evaluate each of the following integrals:

1. $\int \sin^2 x \cos x \, dx.$

2. $\int \cos^2 x \sin x \, dx.$

3. $\int \tan^3 x \sec^2 x \, dx.$

4. $\int \sqrt{\sin x} \cos x \, dx.$

5. $\int \frac{\cos y \, dy}{\sin^2 y}.$

6. $\int \frac{\sec^2 z \, dz}{(1 + \tan z)^2}.$

7. $\int \sec^2 t \, (\sec t \tan t) \, dt.$

8. $\int (1 + \sin^2 x) \sin x \cos x \, dx.$

9. $\int (\ln x)^2 \cdot \frac{dx}{x}.$

10. $\int \frac{dv}{\tan^3 v \cos^2 v}.$

11. $\int \sqrt{1 + e^x} \cdot e^x \, dx.$

12. $\int (1 + e^x)^2 \, e^x \, dx.$

13. $\int \frac{\sec^2 y \, dy}{\sqrt{1 + \tan y}}.$

14. $\int \frac{2 + \ln x}{x} \, dx.$

15. $\int \sinh^2 x \cosh x \, dx.$

16. $\int \frac{\text{Arc tan } x}{1 + x^2} \, dx.$

349. The Logarithmic Form

Since $d \ln u = \dfrac{du}{u}$, we have $\int \dfrac{du}{u} = \ln u + C$ when $u > 0$; also,

when $u < 0, \int \dfrac{du}{u} = \int \dfrac{-du}{-u} = \int \dfrac{d(-u)}{-u} = \ln (-u) + C$.   These

two results can be combined into the single standard form:

(2) $$\int \frac{du}{u} = \ln |u| + C \qquad \textit{if } u \neq 0.$$

This formula fills the gap in the formula for $\int u^n \, du$ when $n = -1$.

EXAMPLE 1. $(a) \int \dfrac{dx}{x} = \ln |x| + C;$

$(b) \int \dfrac{dx}{x + 1} = \int \dfrac{d(x + 1)}{x + 1} = \ln |x + 1| + C;$

$(c) \int \dfrac{x \, dx}{x^2 + 1} = \frac{1}{2} \int \dfrac{d(x^2 + 1)}{x^2 + 1} = \frac{1}{2} \ln (x^2 + 1) + C.$

EXAMPLE 2. $(a) \int \dfrac{x^2 + 1}{x} \, dx = \int \left(x + \dfrac{1}{x} \right) dx = \frac{1}{2} x^2 + \ln |x| + C;$

$(b) \int \dfrac{x + 1}{x + 2} \, dx = \int \left(1 - \dfrac{1}{x + 2} \right) dx = x - \ln |x + 2| + C.$

350. Exercises

Evaluate each of the following integrals:

1. $\displaystyle\int \frac{dx}{2\,x+3}.$

2. $\displaystyle\int \frac{dx}{1-x}.$

3. $\displaystyle\int \frac{1+2\,x}{x^2+x}\,dx.$

4. $\displaystyle\int \frac{(x-1)\,dx}{x^2-2\,x+3}.$

5. $\displaystyle\int \frac{x\,dx}{a^2-x^2}.$

6. $\displaystyle\int \frac{x^2\,dx}{x^3+1}.$

7. $\displaystyle\int \frac{1+x}{x^2}\,dx.$

8. $\displaystyle\int \frac{x+2}{x+5}\,dx.$

9. $\displaystyle\int_0^2 \frac{x^2-x}{x+1}\,dx.$

10. $\displaystyle\int_0^4 \frac{y^3\,dy}{y+1}.$

11. $\displaystyle\int_1^3 \frac{(z-1)(z+2)}{z+1}\,dz.$

12. $\displaystyle\int_1^5 \frac{6\,x-9}{x^2-3\,x+5}\,dx.$

13. $\displaystyle\int \frac{4\,e^x\,dx}{2\,e^x-1}.$

14. $\displaystyle\int \frac{e^{-u}\,du}{4+e^{-u}}.$

15. $\displaystyle\int \frac{\cos\theta\,d\theta}{2\sin\theta-1}.$

16. $\displaystyle\int \frac{1-\cos 3\,t}{3\,t-\sin 3\,t}\,dt.$

17. $\displaystyle\int \frac{\sec^2\phi\,d\phi}{\tan\phi+1}.$

18. $\displaystyle\int \frac{dx}{\tan x\,\cos^2 x}.$

19. $\displaystyle\int \frac{\sqrt{x}\,dx}{1+x\sqrt{x}}.$

20. $\displaystyle\int \frac{\sin 2\,x}{1+\sin^2 x}\,dx.$

21. $\displaystyle\int \frac{\sin t\,\cos t\,dt}{4+\sin^2 t}.$

22. $\displaystyle\int \frac{1+\cos x}{x+\sin x}\,dx.$

23. $\displaystyle\int \frac{dv}{v\,\ln v}.$

24. $\displaystyle\int \frac{dx}{(x-2)^{\frac{1}{2}}+(x-2)^{\frac{2}{3}}}.$

351. Exponential Forms

Since $d(e^u)=e^u\,du$ and $d(a^u)=a^u\ln a\,du$, it follows at once that:

$$(3) \qquad\qquad \int e^u\,du = e^u + C,$$

$$(4) \qquad\qquad \int a^u\,du = \frac{a^u}{\ln a} + C.$$

EXAMPLE. (a) $\displaystyle\int (e^x - e^{-x})\,dx = \int e^x\,dx + \int e^{-x}\,d(-x) = e^x + e^{-x} + C;$

(b) $\displaystyle\int x\,e^{-x^2}\,dx = -\tfrac{1}{2}\int e^{-x^2}(-2\,x\,dx) = -\tfrac{1}{2}\int e^{-x^2}\,d(-x^2) = -\tfrac{1}{2}\,e^{-x^2} + C;$

(c) $\int \sec^2 \theta \cdot e^{\tan \theta} \, d\theta = \int e^{\tan \theta} \cdot d(\tan \theta) = e^{\tan \theta} + C;$

(d) $\int a^{2x-1} \, dx = \frac{1}{2} \int a^{2x-1} \, d(2x - 1) = \frac{1}{2} \frac{a^{2x-1}}{\ln a} + C.$

352. Exercises

Evaluate each of the following integrals:

1. $\int e^{2x+3} \, dx.$

2. $\int a e^{-mt} \, dt.$

3. $\int (e^x + e^{-x}) \, dx.$

4. $\int (e^x - e^{-x})^2 \, dx.$

5. $\int \frac{2 \, dx}{e^x}.$

6. $\int a^x e^x \, dx.$

7. $\int 2^x \, dx.$

8. $\int \frac{a^{\tan t} \, dt}{\cos^2 t}.$

9. $\int x \cdot 10^{-x^2} \, dx.$

10. $\int x^2 \, e^{x^3} \, dx.$

11. $\int_0^5 \frac{dt}{\sqrt{e^t}}.$

12. $\int_1^2 \frac{(e^x + 1)^2}{e^{2x}} \, dx.$

13. $\int_0^{\frac{\pi}{2}} e^{\sin x} \cos x \, dx.$

14. $\int_1^4 \frac{e^{\sqrt{x}} \, dx}{\sqrt{x}}.$

15. $\int \frac{e^{\frac{1}{x}} \, dx}{x^2}.$

16. $\int \frac{x \, dx}{e^{1-x^2}}.$

17. $\int e^{\ln x} \, dx.$

18. $\int \frac{x \, dx}{e^{x^2}}.$

19. $\int \frac{e^x \, dx}{e^x - 1}.$

20. $\int e^{z^2 + \ln z} \, dz.$

353. Trigonometric Forms

By reversal of the differentiation formulas for the six trigonometric functions, we obtain at once the standard integration forms:

(5) $\int \sin u \, du = - \cos u + C,$

(6) $\int \cos u \, du = \sin u + C,$

(7) $\int \sec^2 u \, du = \tan u + C,$

(8)
$$\int \csc^2 u \, du = -\cot u + C,$$

(9)
$$\int \sec u \tan u \, du = \sec u + C,$$

(10)
$$\int \csc u \cot u \, du = -\csc u + C.$$

EXAMPLE 1. (a) $\displaystyle\int \sin 2\,ax \, dx = -\frac{1}{2a} \cos 2\,ax + C$;

(b) $\displaystyle\int \cos \tfrac{1}{2}\,\theta \, d\theta = 2 \int \cos \tfrac{1}{2}\,\theta \, d(\tfrac{1}{2}\,\theta) = 2 \sin \tfrac{1}{2}\,\theta + C$;

(c) $\displaystyle\int \frac{dv}{\cos^2 v} = \int \sec^2 v \, dv = \tan v + C$;

(d) $\displaystyle\int \frac{\sin \phi \, d\phi}{\cos^2 \phi} = \int \tan \phi \sec \phi \, d\phi = \sec \phi + C.$

EXAMPLE 2. $\displaystyle\int (\tan \theta + \sec \theta)^2 \, d\theta$

$$= \int (\tan^2 \theta + 2 \tan \theta \sec \theta + \sec^2 \theta) \, d\theta$$

$$= \int (\sec^2 \theta - 1 + 2 \tan \theta \sec \theta + \sec^2 \theta) \, d\theta$$

$$= \int 2 \sec^2 \theta \, d\theta + \int 2 \tan \theta \sec \theta \, d\theta - \int d\theta$$

$$= 2 \tan \theta + 2 \sec \theta - \theta + C.$$

Formulas for $\int \tan u \, du, \int \sec u \, du$, etc., are not obtainable by direct reversal of standard differentiation formulas. Such integration formulas are, however, readily derived as follows:

$$\int \tan u \, du = \int \frac{\sin u}{\cos u} \, du = \int \frac{-d \cos u}{\cos u}$$
$$= -\ln |\cos u| + C = \ln |\sec u| + C;$$

similarly we may treat $\int \cot u \, du$.

$$\int \sec u \, du = \int \frac{\sec u \, (\sec u + \tan u)}{\sec u + \tan u} \, du$$
$$= \int \frac{(\sec^2 u + \sec u \tan u) \, du}{\tan u + \sec u} = \int \frac{d(\tan u + \sec u)}{\tan u + \sec u}$$
$$= \ln |\tan u + \sec u| + C;$$

similarly we may treat $\int \csc u \, du$. Our results are then:

(11) $\qquad \int \tan u \, du = -\ln |\cos u| + C = \ln |\sec u| + C,$

(12) $\qquad \int \cot u \, du = \ln |\sin u| + C = -\ln |\csc u| + C,$

(13) $\qquad \int \sec u \, du = \ln |\sec u + \tan u| + C.$

(14) $\qquad \int \csc u \, du = \ln |\csc u - \cot u| + C.$

EXAMPLE 3. $\quad \int \dfrac{1 + \sin x}{\cos x} \, dx = \int (\sec x + \tan x) \, dx$

$= \ln |\sec x + \tan x| + \ln |\sec x| + \ln c = \ln |\sec^2 x + \sec x \tan x| + \ln c.$

354. Exercises

Evaluate each of the following integrals:

1. $\int \cos(2x + 1) \, dx.$

2. $\int \sin (2 \pi n t) \, dt.$

3. $\int \sec^2 2 \, mx \, dx.$

4. $\int \csc^2 \tfrac{1}{4} \, \theta \, d\theta.$

5. $\int x \sin (x^2) \, dx.$

6. $\int 4 \sin (100 \, \pi t + 0.6) \, dt.$

7. $\int \tan 2 \, y \, dy.$

8. $\int \cot (v - 1) \, dv.$

9. $\int \dfrac{\sin y \, dy}{\cos^2 y}.$

10. $\int \dfrac{\sin x - \cos x}{\cos x} \, dx.$

11. $\int \tan^2 3 \, z \, dz.$

12. $\int (1 + \sec 2 \, w)^2 \, dw.$

13. $\int_{\frac{\pi}{4}}^{\frac{\pi}{2}} \dfrac{1 + \cos x}{\sin^2 x} \, dx.$

14. $\int_{0}^{1} \dfrac{\cos^2 z}{1 + \sin z} \, dz.$

15. $\int_{0}^{\frac{\pi}{3}} (\sec \theta - \tan \theta)^2 \, d\theta.$

16. $\int_{\frac{\pi}{4}}^{\frac{\pi}{2}} \dfrac{dr}{\sin r \tan r}.$

17. $\int (1 + \tan v)^2 \, dv.$

18. $\int \dfrac{dt}{\cos^2 t}.$

19. $\int \csc^2 \theta \cot^2 \theta \, d\theta.$

20. $\int \dfrac{1 - \cos x}{1 + \cos x} \, dx.$

355. Inverse Trigonometric Forms

By the formulas of § 272, we have

$$d\left(\text{Arc tan } \frac{u}{a}\right) = \frac{1}{1 + \dfrac{u^2}{a^2}} \cdot \frac{1}{a}\, du = \frac{a\, du}{a^2 + u^2},$$

$$d\left(\text{Arc sin } \frac{u}{a}\right) = \frac{1}{\sqrt{1 - \dfrac{u^2}{a^2}}} \cdot \frac{1}{a}\, du = \frac{du}{\sqrt{a^2 - u^2}}, \qquad \text{if } a > |u| \geqq 0.$$

Hence:

(15) $\displaystyle \int \frac{du}{a^2 + u^2} = \frac{1}{a} \text{ Arc tan } \frac{u}{a} + C,$

(16) $\displaystyle \int \frac{du}{\sqrt{a^2 - u^2}} = \text{Arc sin } \frac{u}{a} + C,$ \qquad if $u^2 < a^2$, if $a > 0$.

EXAMPLE. (a) $\displaystyle \int \frac{dx}{4 + x^2} = \frac{1}{2} \text{ Arc tan } \frac{x}{2} + C;$

(b) $\displaystyle \int \frac{dx}{4\,x^2 + 9} = \frac{1}{2} \int \frac{d(2\,x)}{3^2 + (2\,x)^2} = \frac{1}{6} \text{ Arc tan } \frac{2\,x}{3} + C;$

(c) $\displaystyle \int \frac{dx}{\sqrt{4 - x^2}} = \text{Arc sin } \frac{x}{2} + C;$

(d) $\displaystyle \int \frac{dx}{\sqrt{4 - 9\,x^2}} = \frac{1}{3} \int \frac{d(3\,x)}{\sqrt{2^2 - (3\,x)^2}} = \frac{1}{3} \text{ Arc sin } \frac{3\,x}{2} + C.$

356. Exercises

Evaluate each of the following integrals:

1. $\displaystyle \int \frac{dx}{x^2 + 9}.$
2. $\displaystyle \int \frac{dy}{y^2 + 1}.$

3. $\displaystyle \int \frac{dx}{9\,x^2 + 16}.$
4. $\displaystyle \int \frac{dx}{4\,x^2 + 25}.$

5. $\displaystyle \int \frac{dx}{\sqrt{16 - x^2}}.$
6. $\displaystyle \int \frac{dz}{\sqrt{1 - z^2}}.$

7. $\displaystyle \int \frac{dy}{\sqrt{25 - 9\,y^2}}.$
8. $\displaystyle \int_0^{\frac{1}{4}} \frac{dv}{\sqrt{1 - 4\,v^2}}.$

9. $\displaystyle \int \frac{dt}{5 + 6\,t^2}.$
10. $\displaystyle \int \frac{dx}{3\,x^2 + 2}.$

11. $\displaystyle \int \frac{dz}{\sqrt{3 - 4\,z^2}}.$
12. $\displaystyle \int \frac{dx}{\sqrt{5 - 2\,x^2}}.$

13. $\displaystyle\int_0^{\frac{1}{2}a\sqrt{2}} \frac{x\,dx}{\sqrt{a^4 - x^4}}.$

14. $\displaystyle\int_0^a \frac{x\,dx}{a^4 + x^4}.$

15. $\displaystyle\int \frac{dy}{\sqrt{y}(1+y)}.$

16. $\displaystyle\int \frac{\cos x}{a^2 + \sin^2 x}\,dx.$

17. $\displaystyle\int_0^{\frac{\pi}{2}} \frac{\sin\theta\,d\theta}{\cos^2\theta + 4}.$

18. $\displaystyle\int \frac{e^{\frac{1}{2}x}\,dx}{1 + e^x}.$

19. $\displaystyle\int \frac{\sec^2 t\,dt}{\tan^2 t + 1}.$

20. $\displaystyle\int \frac{dv}{v[1 + (\ln v)^2]}.$

357. Hyperbolic Forms

Reversal of the differentiation formulas for the six hyperbolic functions gives directly:

$$\textbf{(17)} \qquad \int \sinh u\,du = \cosh u + C,$$

$$\textbf{(18)} \qquad \int \cosh u\,du = \sinh u + C,$$

$$\textbf{(19)} \qquad \int \text{sech}^2 u\,du = \tanh u + C,$$

$$\textbf{(20)} \qquad \int \text{csch}^2 u\,du = -\coth u + C,$$

$$\textbf{(21)} \qquad \int \text{sech } u \tanh u\,du = -\text{sech } u + C,$$

$$\textbf{(22)} \qquad \int \text{csch } u \coth u\,du = -\text{csch } u + C.$$

To find $\int \tanh u\,du$, we proceed thus:

$$\int \tanh u\,du = \int \frac{\sinh u\,du}{\cosh u} = \int \frac{d\cosh u}{\cosh u} = \ln \cosh u + C.$$

Similarly we treat $\int \coth u\,du$. Therefore:

$$\textbf{(23)} \qquad \int \tanh u\,du = \ln \cosh u + C,$$

$$\textbf{(24)} \qquad \int \coth u\,du = \ln |\sinh u| + C.$$

358. Exercises

Evaluate each of the following integrals:

1. $\int \sinh \frac{1}{2} x \, dx$.

2. $\int \cosh (1 - x) \, dx$.

3. $\int \operatorname{sech}^2 2 v \, dv$.

4. $\int \operatorname{csch}^2 \frac{1}{2} y \, dy$.

5. $\int \operatorname{sech} 2 w \tanh 2 w \, dw$.

6. $\int \coth 3 v \, dv$.

7. $\int \tanh (2 x - 1) \, dx$.

8. $\int \tanh^2 z \, dz$.

359. Certain Logarithmic Forms

To integrate $\int \dfrac{du}{u^2 - a^2}$, we use the identity

$$\frac{1}{u^2 - a^2} = \frac{1}{2 \, a(u - a)} - \frac{1}{2 \, a(u + a)}.$$

Hence,

$$\int \frac{du}{u^2 - a^2} = \frac{1}{2 \, a} \int \frac{du}{u - a} - \frac{1}{2 \, a} \int \frac{du}{u + a} = \frac{1}{2 \, a} \ln \left| \frac{u - a}{u + a} \right| + C,$$

or

(25) $$\int \frac{du}{u^2 - a^2} = \frac{1}{2 \, a} \ln \left| \frac{u - a}{u + a} \right| + C \qquad \text{if } u \neq a.$$

To integrate $\int \dfrac{du}{\sqrt{u^2 + a^2}}$, we substitute $u = a \tan \theta, du = a \sec^2 \theta \, d\theta$, getting

$$\int \frac{du}{\sqrt{u^2 + a^2}} = \int \frac{a \sec^2 \theta \, d\theta}{a \sqrt{\tan^2 \theta + 1}} = \int \frac{\sec^2 \theta \, d\theta}{\sec \theta} = \int \sec \theta \, d\theta$$

$$= \ln |\tan \theta + \sec \theta| + C' = \ln |u + \sqrt{u^2 + a^2}| + C.$$

To integrate $\int \dfrac{du}{\sqrt{u^2 - a^2}}$, we substitute $u = a \sec \theta$. We thus obtain:

(26) $$\int \frac{du}{\sqrt{u^2 + a^2}} = \ln |u + \sqrt{u^2 + a^2}| + C,$$

(27) $$\int \frac{du}{\sqrt{u^2 - a^2}} = \ln |u + \sqrt{u^2 - a^2}| + C \qquad \text{if } u^2 > a^2.$$

EXAMPLE 1.   (a) $\int \dfrac{dx}{x^2 - 9} = \frac{1}{6} \ln \dfrac{x - 3}{x + 3} + C$ if $x > 3$;

(b) $\int \dfrac{dy}{\sqrt{4\,y^2 + 25}} = \frac{1}{2} \ln |2\,y + \sqrt{4\,y^2 + 25}| + C$;

(c) $\int \dfrac{dz}{\sqrt{9\,z^2 - 49}} = \frac{1}{3} \ln (3\,z + \sqrt{9\,z^2 - 49}) + C$ if $3\,z > 7$.

EXAMPLE 2. $\int_6^8 \dfrac{dx}{\sqrt{x^2 - 16}} = \ln (x + \sqrt{x^2 - 16}) \Big|_6^8$

$$= \ln (8 + \sqrt{48}) - \ln (6 + \sqrt{20}) \approx \ln 14.93 - \ln 10.47 \approx 0.35.$$

Expressions for these integral types in terms of inverse hyperbolic functions will be given in the next section.

360. Inverse Hyperbolic Forms

By use of the formulas of § 299 for the derivatives of the inverse hyperbolic functions, we obtain readily the following integral forms:

(28) $\int \dfrac{du}{a^2 - u^2} = \dfrac{1}{a} \tanh^{-1} \dfrac{u}{a} + C$ if $u^2 < a^2$,

(29) $\int \dfrac{du}{u^2 - a^2} = -\dfrac{1}{a} \coth^{-1} \dfrac{u}{a} + C$ if $u^2 > a^2$,

(30) $\int \dfrac{du}{\sqrt{u^2 + a^2}} = \sinh^{-1} \dfrac{u}{a} + C,$

(31) $\int \dfrac{du}{\sqrt{u^2 - a^2}} = \operatorname{Cosh}^{-1} \dfrac{u}{a} + C$ if $u > a > 0$.

EXAMPLE 1.   (a) $\int \dfrac{dx}{1 - x^2} = \tanh^{-1} x + C$;

(b) $\int \dfrac{dx}{\sqrt{4\,x^2 + 1}} = \frac{1}{2} \sinh^{-1} 2\,x + C$;

(c) $\int \dfrac{dx}{\sqrt{4\,x^2 - 9}} = \frac{1}{2} \operatorname{Cosh}^{-1} \dfrac{2\,x}{3} + C$ if $2\,x > 3$.

EXAMPLE 2. $\int_6^8 \dfrac{dx}{\sqrt{x^2 - 16}} = \operatorname{Cosh}^{-1} \dfrac{x}{4} \Big|_6^8 = \operatorname{Cosh}^{-1} 2 - \operatorname{Cosh}^{-1} 1.5$

$$\approx 1.32 - 0.97 \approx 0.35.$$

361. Exercises

Evaluate each of the following integrals:

1. $\int \dfrac{dx}{x^2 - 4}$.

2. $\int \dfrac{dy}{4 - y^2}$.

3. $\int \dfrac{dx}{\sqrt{x^2 - 4}}$.

4. $\int \dfrac{dv}{\sqrt{v^2 - 16}}$.

5. $\int \dfrac{dz}{\sqrt{z^2 + 9}}$.

6. $\int_0^1 \dfrac{dx}{3\,x^2 - 4}$.

7. $\int \dfrac{dv}{9\,v^2 - 16}$.

8. $\int_4^8 \dfrac{dz}{\sqrt{3\,z^2 - 4}}$.

9. $\int_{\frac{4}{3}}^2 \dfrac{dt}{\sqrt{9\,t^2 - 16}}$.

10. $\int \dfrac{dr}{\sqrt{3\,r^2 + 2}}$.

11. $\int_1^3 \dfrac{dx}{\sqrt{16 + 9\,x^2}}$.

12. $\int \dfrac{dt}{a^2 - b^2 t^2}$.

13. $\int_0^{0.8} \dfrac{x\,dx}{1 - x^4}$.

14. $\int \dfrac{w^2\,dw}{1 - w^6}$.

15. $\int \dfrac{y\,dy}{\sqrt{y^4 - 1}}$.

16. $\int_0^1 \dfrac{u\,du}{\sqrt{u^4 + 1}}$.

17. $\int \dfrac{\sec^2 \theta\,d\theta}{9 - 4\tan^2 \theta}$.

18. $\int \dfrac{\cos x\,dx}{\sqrt{4\sin^2 x - 1}}$.

19. $\int \dfrac{e^w\,dw}{\sqrt{e^{2w} + 1}}$.

20. $\int \dfrac{\cos v\,dv}{1 - \sin^2 v}$.

362. Miscellaneous Exercises on Integration by Standard Forms

Evaluate the following integrals:

1. $\int (x^2 + ax + a^2)\,dx$.

2. $\int \sin m\theta \cos m\theta\,d\theta$.

3. $\int \dfrac{x\,dx}{\sqrt{4 - x^2}}$.

4. $\int \left(v + \dfrac{1}{v}\right)^2 dv$.

5. $\int \dfrac{x\,dx}{a^2 + x^2}$.

6. $\int e^{-2t}\,dt$.

7. $\int \sin (1 - x)\,dx$.

8. $\int \dfrac{dz}{\sin^2 z}$.

9. $\int \cos^2 3\,x \sin 3\,x\,dx$.

10. $\int \dfrac{ds}{1 + 2\,s^2}$.

11. $\int y\sqrt{1 + y}\,dy$.

12. $\int e^{-k^2 x}\,dx$.

13. $\int_3^7 \dfrac{dz}{(z-1)^2}.$

14. $\int \dfrac{y\,dy}{9-4\,y^2}.$

15. $\int_{\frac{\pi}{6}}^{\frac{\pi}{3}} (\tan\theta + \cot\theta)^2\,d\theta.$

16. $\int \dfrac{x^3\,dx}{x^2+5}.$

17. $\int x^2\sqrt{x-2}\,dx.$

18. $\int \sqrt{2\,px}\,dx.$

19. $\int \dfrac{e^t\,dt}{\sqrt{1-e^t}}.$

20. $\int_0^{\frac{\pi}{6}} \sec^2 2\,v\,dv.$

21. $\int \sin^n\theta \cos\theta\,d\theta.$

22. $\int \dfrac{e^{2x}\,dx}{e^x+1}.$

23. $\int \dfrac{\sqrt{x+2}-1}{x+3}\,dx.$

24. $\int_2^4 \dfrac{z\,dz}{z+1}.$

25. $\int_0^a x^3(a^2-x^2)\,dx.$

26. $\int_0^1 \dfrac{y\,dy}{y^4+1}.$

27. $\int e^{3x+4}\,dx.$

28. $\int (\tan 2\,\theta + \cot 3\,\theta)\,d\theta.$

29. $\int (x+1)\sqrt{x^2+2\,x}\,dx.$

30. $\int \dfrac{(1-t)^2}{t^2}\,dt.$

31. $\int \dfrac{(z+3)\,dz}{z\sqrt{z+2}}.$

32. $\int \tan^n x \sec^2 x\,dx.$

33. $\int \dfrac{(2\,ax+b)\,dx}{ax^2+bx+c}.$

34. $\int \dfrac{e^{\ln 2x}}{x}\,dx.$

35. $\int \dfrac{t\,dt}{(4-t^2)^2}.$

36. $\int \dfrac{v^2-1}{v+2}\,dv.$

37. $\int \dfrac{dy}{3^y}.$

38. $\int \cos^2 3\,\theta \sin 3\,\theta\,d\theta.$

39. $\int \dfrac{2\csc^2\phi\,d\phi}{\cot\phi+4}.$

40. $\int (x^{\frac{1}{2}} + a^{\frac{1}{2}})^2\,dx.$

41. $\int \dfrac{(x+3)\,dx}{x^2+6\,x-5}.$

42. $\int \tan(2\,x+1)\,dx.$

43. $\int_0^1 \dfrac{dw}{4\,w^2+1}.$

44. $\int \dfrac{e^{2x}\,dx}{e^{2x}+9}.$

45. $\int \dfrac{dy}{(y-1)\sqrt{y+2}}.$

46. $\int \dfrac{(y+1)\,dy}{\sqrt{y^2+2\,y-1}}.$

47. $\int \cos\dfrac{2\,\pi t}{n}\,dt.$

48. $\int_1^3 \dfrac{dx}{4\,x^2-1}.$

49. $\int x^2\sqrt{ax+b}\,dx.$

50. $\int \dfrac{t\,dt}{\sqrt{1-t^4}}.$

363. Compound Interest Law or Law of Organic Growth

We have seen in § 287 that the derivative of an exponential function is proportional to itself: $D_x(e^{kx}) = k\,e^{kx}$; that is, *an exponential function increases at a rate proportional to itself.* This is perhaps the most characteristic property of the exponential function.

Conversely, we can easily show that: *If a function increases at a rate proportional to itself, then it is an exponential function.* For, if

$$\frac{dy}{dx} = ky, \qquad \text{then} \qquad \frac{dy}{y} = kdx.$$

Integrating, we get

$$\ln y = kx + c \qquad \text{or} \qquad y = e^{kx+c} = e^c \cdot e^{kx} = Ce^{kx}.$$

*When a function varies according to this law: $dy/dx = ky$ or its equivalent: $y = Ce^{kx}$, it is said to follow the "**exponential law**" or the "**compound interest law**" or the "**law of growth or decay.**"*

This exponential mode of variation was called the "compound interest law" by Lord Kelvin because it expresses the way in which a sum of money increases in value when placed at compound interest if interest is compounded "continuously." The name "law of organic growth" is often applied to it because cases are frequently met in biological investigations where forms of growth or increase follow this law. For example, the growth of bacteria in a culture, the growth of a tree or animal, or the increase of population of a country, follow this law very closely under certain conditions. Other examples of the law are: Newton's law of cooling, radioactive change, absorption of light in passing through a medium, change of air pressure with altitude, fluid resistance, healing of wounds, and many problems in chemistry.

It is very important, for applications, to remember that:

$$(32) \qquad \boxed{\quad \textit{if } \ \frac{dy}{dx} = ky, \qquad \textit{then} \qquad y = Ce^{kx}. \quad}$$

It should be noted that C is the value of y when $x = 0$, i.e., it is the initial value of y. Writing y_0 for this initial value of y, we may write:

$$(a) \qquad \text{if} \qquad \frac{dy}{dx} = ky, \qquad \text{then} \qquad y = y_0 e^{kx}.$$

EXAMPLE 1. *Atmospheric pressure:* It can be shown that if the temperature is constant, the rate of change of the atmospheric pressure p at any height h is proportional to the pressure at that height:

$$(b) \qquad \frac{dp}{dh} = -kp$$

(the minus sign being used since the pressure decreases as the height increases). It follows that $p = p_0 e^{-kh}$, where p_0 is the pressure at zero elevation $h = 0$.

EXAMPLE 2. *Newton's law of cooling:* According to this law, the rate at which a body cools is proportional to the difference in temperature between the body and the surrounding medium:

$$(c) \qquad \frac{dT}{dt} = -k(T - T_0),$$

where T is the temperature of the body, T_0 is the temperature of the surrounding medium and t is the time. Then $T - T_0 = (T_1 - T_0)e^{-kt}$, where T_1 is the value of T when $t = 0$.

EXAMPLE 3. *Chemical reaction:* For example, cane sugar in solution is decomposed into other substances through the presence of acids, and the rate at which the reaction takes place is proportional to the mass of sugar still unchanged; we then have

$$(d) \qquad \frac{dx}{dt} = k(a - x),$$

where x is the amount of sugar converted in time t and a is the original amount of sugar. Then we find $x = a(1 - e^{-kt})$.

EXAMPLE 4. *Electric currents:* The general equation expressing the relation between electromotive force and current in a circuit is:

$$(e) \qquad E = Ri + L\frac{di}{dt},$$

where E is the electromotive force, R is the resistance, L is the inductance, i is the current and t is the time. Let the electromotive force be removed, and at the instant of removal when $t = 0$, let the current be i_0. Then the general equation (e) becomes $0 = Ri + L(di/dt)$, from which we get

$$(f) \qquad \frac{di}{dt} = -\frac{Ri}{L};$$

the solution of this equation is $i = i_0 e^{-Rt/L}$.

364. Exercises

1. When bacteria grow in the presence of unlimited food, they increase at a rate proportional to the number present. Express that number as a function of the time.

2. If, in a certain culture of bacteria, the number present at a certain instant was 1000, and if the number present ten hours later was 8000, find an expression for the number of bacteria at the end of fifteen hours. (See Exercise 1.)

3. The natural law of increase of population, under normal conditions, is that at any time the time-rate of increase is considered to be proportional to the population at that time. If P_0 is the population at time $t = 0$, express the population P at any later time t.

4. A town had a population of 18,000 in 1935; in 1945 this had increased to 25,000. Assuming that the population growth follows the exponential law (see Exercise 3), find the expected population in 1955.

5. The population of England and Wales in 1881 was 25.974 millions, and in 1891 it was 29.003 millions. What should it have been in 1901 if the increase had followed the law indicated in Exercise 3? (The actual census population then was 32.528 millions.)

6. Radium decomposes at a time-rate which is proportional to the amount present. If half the original quantity disappears in 1800 years, what percentage disappears in 100 years?

7. A body is cooling according to Newton's law of cooling (§ 363, Example 2). Let T be the difference in temperature of the body and the surrounding medium. If T falls from $65°$ C. to $50°$ C. in 180 seconds, find T at the end of 400 seconds. How long will it take for T to fall to $35°$ C.?

8. When an iron rod was heated, its length increased so that $dL/dT = 10^{-5}L$, where T is the temperature. If the value of L was 75 when $T = 0$, express L in terms of T.

9. Under certain conditions, the atmospheric pressure p varies with the height h above sea-level at the rate $dp/dh = -kp$ (see § 363, Example 1). If $p = 30$ when $h = 0$, and $p = 29.6$ when $h = 1200$, find h when $p = 28.8$.

10. Passing through dark glass, the intensity of light I varied with the distance x thus: $dI/dx = -0.25\,I$. If I was originally 100, derive a formula for I at any distance x.

11. According to the law of mass action, the velocity of a chemical reaction is proportional to the concentration of the substance, so that we have $dx/dt = k(s - x)$, where s is the original amount of substance per unit volume, x is the amount transformed in time t, and $s - x$ is the amount remaining unchanged at the end of time t. Express x in terms of t.

12. Sugar in solution decomposes into other substances at a time-rate proportional to the amount x still unchanged. (a) Show that $x = Ce^{-kt}$. What does C represent? (b) If 30 pounds of sugar reduces to 10 pounds in 4 hours, when will 95 percent of the sugar be decomposed?

13. An electric current died out according to the law: $di/dt = -60\,i$; find i in terms of t, if $i = 15$ when $t = 0$.

14. An electric current left to die out in a certain circuit drops to $1/e$ of its value in 0.1 second. How long will it take to drop to one-millionth of its value, assuming that it decreases at a time-rate proportional to itself?

15. In economics, in such problems as the valuation of property and ma-

y, the compound interest law is sometimes applied. Suppose that
.chine costing $2000 new is worth only the scrap value $20 at the end
10 years. Assuming that the rate of depreciation is proportional to
.e value at the time under consideration, find the value of the machine
at the end of 5 years.

★ 365. Projectiles

Suppose that a projectile is fired at an inclination α with the
horizontal plane and with an initial velocity v_0 (Fig. 175). If we
select the starting point as the origin and the Y-axis as positive
upward, so that the X-axis is horizontal, then the horizontal and
vertical components of the initial velocity are:

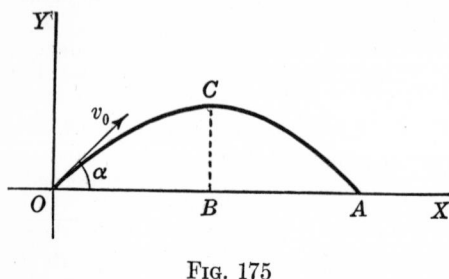

(a) $\qquad v_x = v_0 \cos \alpha,$
$\qquad\qquad v_y = v_0 \sin \alpha$
when $\quad t = 0,$

and the initial position
gives

(b) $\qquad x = 0,$
$\qquad\qquad y = 0$
when $\qquad t = 0.$

FIG. 175

The only force acting on the projectile is that of gravity, acting
vertically downward (if we neglect air-resistance); there is no horizontal force. Using the horizontal and vertical components of the
acceleration of the projectile at any time t, the differential equations
of motion are:

(c) $\qquad a_x = \dfrac{d^2x}{dt^2} = \dfrac{dv_x}{dt} = 0, \qquad a_y = \dfrac{d^2y}{dt^2} = \dfrac{dv_y}{dt} = -g;$

the initial conditions are (a) and (b).

Integrating equations (c), we get

(d) $\qquad\qquad\qquad v_x = c_1, \qquad v_y = -gt + c_2;$

using the initial conditions (a), we have $c_1 = v_0 \cos \alpha$, $c_2 = v_0 \sin \alpha$.
Therefore,

(e) $\qquad v_x = \dfrac{dx}{dt} = v_0 \cos \alpha, \qquad v_y = \dfrac{dy}{dt} = -gt + v_0 \sin \alpha.$

Integrating again in these equations, we obtain

(f) $\qquad x = (v_0 \cos \alpha)t + c_3, \qquad y = -\tfrac{1}{2} gt^2 + (v_0 \sin \alpha)t + c_4;$

using the initial conditions (b), we find $c_3 = 0$, $c_4 = 0$.   The position of the projectile at any time t is therefore given by the equations:

(g) $\qquad\qquad x = (v_0 \cos \alpha)t, \qquad y = -\tfrac{1}{2} gt^2 + (v_0 \sin \alpha)t.$

These equations may be regarded as the parametric equations of the path of the projectile, with t as the parameter.   Eliminating t from these equations (g), we find

(h) $\qquad\qquad y = - \dfrac{g}{2\,v_0^2 \cos^2 \alpha} \cdot x^2 + x \tan \alpha,$

which is the equation of a parabola with vertical axis of symmetry (Fig. 175).

★ 366. Exercises

In the following problems, assume $g = 32$, and neglect air-resistance.

1. A projectile was fired at an angle of 30° with the horizontal at an initial velocity of 1024 feet per second.   What was its range, the time of flight and the greatest height reached?   (The *range* is the distance along the horizontal to the point where the projectile falls on the horizontal plane.)

2. A projectile was fired with an initial velocity of 1600 feet per second, and at an angle of inclination of Arc tan $(\tfrac{3}{4})$.   Find the equation of the path, and find the range.

3. Show that the projectile of § 365 attains its greatest height H when $t = (v_0 \sin \alpha)/g$, and that $H = (v_0^2 \sin^2 \alpha)/2\,g$.

4. Show that the range of the projectile of § 365 is $R = (v_0^2 \sin 2\,\alpha)/g$.

5. Show that the maximum range of the projectile of § 365 occurs when $\alpha = \tfrac{1}{4}\,\pi$, and has the value $R = v_0^2/g$.

6. Show that the speed of the projectile of § 365 is least when the projectile is at its highest point.

7. If a body, projected from the top of a tower at an angle of 45° above the horizontal plane, in 5 seconds strikes the ground at a distance from the bottom of the tower equal to its height, find the height of the tower.

8. A bullet is fired with a velocity of 3000 feet per second at an inclination of 45° from a point 100 feet above level ground.   Find where the bullet will strike the ground.

CHAPTER XVIII

Integration by Other Methods

367. Integration by Parts

An important method of integration is a process called *integration by parts*, based on the inversion of the formula for differentiation of a product.

Let u and v be given functions of x. Since $d(uv) = u\,dv + v\,du$, we have $u\,dv = d(uv) - v\,du$. Integrating both sides of this, we get:

$$(1) \qquad \int u\,dv = uv - \int v\,du.$$

This is the formula for *integration by parts*.

EXAMPLE 1. Find $\int xe^x\,dx$.

Solution: Put $u = x$, $dv = e^x\,dx$, then $du = dx$, $v = e^x$. Hence,

$$\int xe^x\,dx = xe^x - \int e^x\,dx = xe^x - e^x + C.$$

EXAMPLE 2. Find $\int \text{Arc tan } x\,dx$.

Solution: Put $u = \text{Arc tan } x$, $dv = dx$, then $du = \dfrac{dx}{1 + x^2}$, $v = x$, and

$$\int \text{Arc tan } x\,dx = x\,\text{Arc tan } x - \int \frac{x\,dx}{1 + x^2}$$
$$= x\,\text{Arc tan } x - \tfrac{1}{2}\ln(1 + x^2) + C.$$

In order to be able to use the method of integration by parts to advantage, we must obviously be able to choose u and dv so that we may integrate dv readily and so that the integral $\int v\,du$ is easier to evaluate than the original integral.

Sometimes it is necessary to apply the integration by parts two or more times.

EXAMPLE 3.   Evaluate $\int x^2 \sin x \, dx$.

Solution: Take $u = x^2$, $dv = \sin x \, dx$; then $du = 2 \, x \, dx$, $v = -\cos x$, and we get

(a) $$\int x^2 \sin x \, dx = -x^2 \cos x + \int 2 \, x \cos x \, dx.$$

Now apply integration by parts to the last integral in (a).   Put $u = 2 \, x$, $dv = \cos x \, dx$, then $du = 2 \, dx$, $v = \sin x$, and

(b) $$\int 2 \, x \cos x \, dx = 2 \, x \sin x - 2 \int \sin x \, dx = 2 \, x \sin x + 2 \cos x + C.$$

Combining (a) and (b), we have

(c) $$\int x^2 \sin x \, dx = -x^2 \cos x + 2 \, x \sin x + 2 \cos x + C$$

$$= (2 - x^2) \cos x + 2 \, x \sin x + C.$$

368. Exercises

Evaluate each of the following integrals:

1. $\int x e^{-x} \, dx.$

2. $\int x \sin nx \, dx.$

3. $\int x \cos x \, dx.$

4. $\int x e^{2x} \, dx.$

5. $\int y \sec^2 y \, dy.$

6. $\int t \ln t \, dt.$

7. $\int \text{Arc} \sin x \, dx.$

8. $\int x^2 \, \text{Arc} \sin x \, dx.$

9. $\int \ln x \, dx.$

10. $\int_0^{\frac{\pi}{4}} y \tan^2 y \, dy.$

11. $\int x \, \text{Arc} \tan x \, dx.$

12. $\int_0^1 x^2 e^{-3x} \, dx.$

13. $\int_0^2 x^2 e^x \, dx.$

14. $\int x^2 \cos x \, dx.$

15. $\int_0^{\frac{\pi}{2}} z^2 \sin z \, dz.$

16. $\int \dfrac{x^2}{e^x} \, dx.$

17. $\int t^n \ln t \, dt.$

18. $\int \sinh^{-1} x \, dx.$

19. $\int y \sinh y \, dy.$

20. $\int x \, \text{Cosh}^{-1} x \, dx.$

369. Evaluation of $\int e^{ax} \cos bx\, dx$ and $\int e^{ax} \sin bx\, dx$

The integrals $\int e^{ax} \cos bx\, dx$ and $\int e^{ax} \sin bx\, dx$ occur in many applications. They can be evaluated by integration by parts as follows:

To evaluate $\int e^{ax} \sin bx\, dx$, take $u = e^{ax}$, $dv = \sin bx\, dx$, then $du = ae^{ax}\, dx$, $v = -\dfrac{1}{b} \cos bx$, and we have

$$(a) \qquad \int e^{ax} \sin bx\, dx = -\frac{1}{b} e^{ax} \cos bx + \frac{a}{b} \int e^{ax} \cos bx\, dx.$$

We now integrate $\int e^{ax} \cos bx\, dx$, which occurs here, by parts, putting $u = e^{ax}$, $dv = \cos bx\, dx$; then $du = ae^{ax}\, dx$, $v = \dfrac{1}{b} \sin bx$, and we get

$$(b) \qquad \int e^{ax} \cos bx\, dx = \frac{1}{b} e^{ax} \sin bx - \frac{a}{b} \int e^{ax} \sin bx\, dx.$$

Substituting (b) in (a), we have

$$(c) \quad \int e^{ax} \sin bx\, dx = -\frac{1}{b} e^{ax} \cos bx + \frac{a}{b^2} e^{ax} \sin bx - \frac{a^2}{b^2} \int e^{ax} \sin bx\, dx.$$

Transposing the last term of (c) to the left side and combining terms, we obtain

$$(d) \quad \left(1 + \frac{a^2}{b^2}\right) \int e^{ax} \sin bx\, dx = \frac{e^{ax}}{b^2} (a \sin bx - b \cos bx) + C';$$

hence:

$$(2) \qquad \int e^{ax} \sin bx\, dx = \frac{e^{ax}}{a^2 + b^2} (a \sin bx - b \cos bx) + C.$$

In a similar way, or by substituting this result in (b) above, we find:

$$(3) \qquad \int e^{ax} \cos bx\, dx = \frac{e^{ax}}{a^2 + b^2} (a \cos bx + b \sin bx) + C.$$

370. Evaluation of $\int \sec^3 x\, dx$

The integral form $\int \sec^3 x\, dx$ occurs so often that it is worth while to give the derivation of a formula for it here; it is based on integration by parts.

Putting $u = \sec x$, $dv = \sec^2 x \, dx$, we get $du = \sec x \tan x \, dx$, $v = \tan x$, so that

(a) $$\int \sec^3 x \, dx = \sec x \tan x - \int \sec x \tan^2 x \, dx.$$

In the last integral of (a), put $\tan^2 x = \sec^2 x - 1$; then (a) becomes

$$\int \sec^3 x \, dx = \sec x \tan x - \int \sec^3 x \, dx + \int \sec x \, dx.$$

Transposing the second term of the right-hand side, we get

$$2 \int \sec^3 x \, dx = \sec x \tan x + \ln |\sec x + \tan x| + C'.$$

Hence:

(4) $$\int \sec^3 x \, dx = \frac{1}{2} \sec x \tan x + \frac{1}{2} \ln |\sec x + \tan x| + C.$$

371. Exercises

Evaluate each of the following integrals by using the *process* of § 369 but not substituting in the formulas (2) and (3):

1. $\int e^x \sin x \, dx.$
2. $\int e^x \cos 2 x \, dx.$

3. $\int e^{-x} \cos 3 x \, dx.$
4. $\int e^{-2x} \sin 4 x \, dx.$

5. $\int \dfrac{\cos 2 x}{e^{3x}} \, dx.$
6. $\int e^{ax} \cos ax \, dx.$

372. Integrands with Quadratic Expressions in Denominator

Integrals of the types

$$\int \frac{dx}{ax^2 + bx + c} \quad \text{and} \quad \int \frac{dx}{\sqrt{ax^2 + bx + c}},$$

with quadratic expressions in the denominators, can be reduced to standard forms by completing the square in the quadratic expressions.

Example 1. Evaluate $\int \dfrac{dx}{3 x^2 - 6 x + 15}$.

Solution: Since

$$3 x^2 - 6 x + 15 = 3(x^2 - 2 x + 1 + 4) = 3[(x - 1)^2 + 2^2],$$

$$\int \frac{dx}{3 x^2 - 6 x + 15} = \tfrac{1}{3} \int \frac{d(x - 1)}{(x - 1)^2 + 2^2} = \tfrac{1}{6} \text{ Arc tan } \frac{x - 1}{2} + C.$$

EXAMPLE 2. Evaluate $\displaystyle\int \frac{dx}{\sqrt{5 - 4\,x - x^2}}$.

Solution: Since

$$5 - 4\,x - x^2 = 5 - (x^2 + 4\,x) = 9 - (x^2 + 4\,x + 4) = 3^2 - (x + 2)^2,$$

$$\int \frac{dx}{\sqrt{5 - 4\,x - x^2}} = \int \frac{d(x + 2)}{\sqrt{3^2 - (x + 2)^2}} = \text{Arc sin}\ \frac{x + 2}{3} + C.$$

Integrals of the types

$$\int \frac{Ax + B}{ax^2 + bx + c}\,dx \qquad \text{and} \qquad \int \frac{Ax + B}{\sqrt{ax^2 + bx + c}}\,dx,$$

with linear numerators and quadratic expressions in the denominators may be evaluated by splitting them up into several integrals.

EXAMPLE 3. $\displaystyle\int \frac{x + 2}{x^2 + 16}\,dx = \int \frac{x\,dx}{x^2 + 16} + \int \frac{2\,dx}{x^2 + 16}$

$$= \tfrac{1}{2}\int \frac{2\,x\,dx}{x^2 + 16} + 2 \int \frac{dx}{x^2 + 16} = \tfrac{1}{2}\ln\,(x^2 + 16) + \tfrac{1}{2}\,\text{Arc tan}\,\frac{x}{4} + C.$$

EXAMPLE 4. Evaluate $\displaystyle\int \frac{(4\,x - 3)\,dx}{x^2 - 6\,x + 5}$.

Solution: Since $x^2 - 6\,x + 5 = x^2 - 6\,x + 9 - 4 = (x - 3)^2 - 2^2$,

$$\int \frac{(4\,x - 3)\,dx}{x^2 - 6\,x + 5} = \int \frac{4\,x - 12 + 9}{x^2 - 6\,x + 5}\,dx = \int \frac{2(2\,x - 6)\,dx}{x^2 - 6\,x + 5} + \int \frac{9\,dx}{x^2 - 6\,x + 5}$$

$$= 2 \int \frac{d(x^2 - 6\,x + 5)}{x^2 - 6\,x + 5} + 9 \int \frac{d(x - 3)}{(x - 3)^2 - 2^2}$$

$$= 2 \ln\,|x^2 - 6\,x + 5| + 9\cdot\tfrac{1}{4} \ln \left|\frac{x - 3 - 2}{x - 3 + 2}\right| + C$$

$$= 2 \ln\,|x^2 - 6\,x + 5| + \tfrac{9}{4} \ln \left|\frac{x - 5}{x - 1}\right| + C,$$

$$= 2 \ln\,|x^2 - 6\,x + 5| - \tfrac{9}{2} \coth^{-1} \frac{x - 3}{2} + C.$$

EXAMPLE 5. $\displaystyle\int \frac{5\,x - 2}{\sqrt{x^2 + 2\,x}}\,dx = \tfrac{5}{2} \int \frac{2\,x - \frac{4}{5}}{\sqrt{x^2 + 2\,x}}\,dx$

$$= \tfrac{5}{2} \int \frac{(2\,x + 2)\,dx}{\sqrt{x^2 + 2\,x}} - \tfrac{5}{2}\cdot\tfrac{14}{5} \int \frac{dx}{\sqrt{x^2 + 2\,x}}$$

$$= \tfrac{5}{2} \int \frac{d(x^2 + 2\,x)}{(x^2 + 2\,x)^{\frac{1}{2}}} - 7 \int \frac{d(x + 1)}{\sqrt{(x + 1)^2 - 1^2}}$$

$$= 5\sqrt{x^2 + 2\,x} - 7 \ln |x + 1 + \sqrt{x^2 + 2\,x}| + C,$$

or

$$= 5\sqrt{x^2 + 2\,x} - 7 \operatorname{Cosh}^{-1}(x + 1) + C.$$

373. Exercises

Evaluate each of the following integrals:

1. $\displaystyle\int \frac{dx}{x^2 + 2\,x + 5}.$

2. $\displaystyle\int \frac{dy}{y^2 - 6\,y + 18}.$

3. $\displaystyle\int \frac{dx}{\sqrt{3 + 2\,x - x^2}}.$

4. $\displaystyle\int \frac{dx}{\sqrt{2 + x - x^2}}.$

5. $\displaystyle\int \frac{dx}{\sqrt{2\,ax - x^2}}.$

6. $\displaystyle\int \frac{dt}{\sqrt{t(1 - t)}}.$

7. $\displaystyle\int \frac{dt}{t^2 - t + 1}.$

8. $\displaystyle\int \frac{dz}{4\,z^2 + 4\,z + 3}.$

9. $\displaystyle\int \frac{ds}{1 + 3\,s + s^2}.$

10. $\displaystyle\int \frac{dx}{5 + 4\,x - x^2}.$

11. $\displaystyle\int \frac{dx}{\sqrt{x^2 + 4\,x + 5}}.$

12. $\displaystyle\int \frac{dz}{\sqrt{z(z - 4)}}.$

13. $\displaystyle\int \frac{x + 1}{x^2 + 1}\, dx.$

14. $\displaystyle\int \frac{2\,x + 3}{x^2 + 9}\, dx.$

15. $\displaystyle\int \frac{1 + 2\,y}{\sqrt{4 - y^2}}\, dy.$

16. $\displaystyle\int \frac{5\,x + 6}{\sqrt{x^2 + 4\,x}}\, dx.$

17. $\displaystyle\int \frac{(x - 4)\, dx}{\sqrt{8 + 6\,x - x^2}}.$

18. $\displaystyle\int \frac{3\,z - 2}{\sqrt{3 - 2\,z^2}}\, dz.$

19. $\displaystyle\int_0^1 \frac{2\,x - 5}{x^2 + 6\,x + 25}\, dx.$

20. $\displaystyle\int \frac{3\,y - 2}{4\,y^2 + 1}\, dy.$

21. $\displaystyle\int \frac{px + q}{a^2 + b^2 x^2}\, dx.$

22. $\displaystyle\int_0^1 \frac{t^2 - 1}{t^2 + 1}\, dt.$

23. $\displaystyle\int_2^3 \frac{3\,t - 2}{\sqrt{4\,t - t^2}}\, dt.$

24. $\displaystyle\int_{\frac{1}{2}}^{\frac{3}{4}} \sqrt{\frac{1 - x}{1 + x}}\, dx = \int_{\frac{1}{2}}^{\frac{3}{4}} \frac{1 - x}{\sqrt{1 - x^2}}\, dx.$

374. Trigonometric Integrals

Type I: $\displaystyle\int \sin^m x \cos^n x\, dx,$ *where either* m *or* n *is an odd positive integer.*

Suppose that n is an odd positive integer.   We write the integral in the form

$$\int \sin^m x \cos^{n-1} x \cdot \cos x\, dx = \int \sin^m x \cos^{n-1} x\, d(\sin x).$$

Since n is odd, $\cos^{n-1} x$ is an even power of $\cos x$, which can therefore be expressed rationally in terms of $\sin x$ by use of the identity $\cos^2 x = 1 - \sin^2 x$, and we then obtain a set of powers of $\sin x$ each multiplied by $d(\sin x)$, which can be integrated by means of the power rule. Similarly we may proceed if m is an odd positive integer, by using $d(\cos x)$.

EXAMPLE 1. $\displaystyle\int \sin^2 x \cos^3 x \, dx = \int \sin^2 x \cos^2 x \, (\cos x \, dx)$

$\displaystyle = \int \sin^2 x \, (1 - \sin^2 x) \, d(\sin x) = \int \sin^2 x \, d(\sin x) - \int \sin^4 x \, d(\sin x)$

$\displaystyle = \tfrac{1}{3} \sin^3 x - \tfrac{1}{5} \sin^5 x + C.$

Type II: $\displaystyle\int \sin^m x \cos^n x \, dx$, *where both m and n are even positive integers.*

The integrand can be transformed into an integrable expression in terms of sines and cosines of multiple angles by use of the trigonometric double-angle formulas:

$$(a) \qquad \begin{cases} \sin^2 u = \tfrac{1}{2} (1 - \cos 2 u), \\ \cos^2 u = \tfrac{1}{2} (1 + \cos 2 u), \\ \sin u \cos u = \tfrac{1}{2} \sin 2 u. \end{cases}$$

EXAMPLE 2. $\displaystyle\int \sin^4 x \, dx = \int (\sin^2 x)^2 \, dx = \int \left(\frac{1 - \cos 2 x}{2} \right)^2 dx$

$\displaystyle = \tfrac{1}{4} \int (1 - 2 \cos 2 x + \cos^2 2 x) \, dx = \tfrac{1}{4} \int \left(1 - 2 \cos 2 x + \frac{1 + \cos 4 x}{2} \right) dx$

$\displaystyle = \tfrac{1}{4}(\tfrac{3}{2} x - \sin 2 x + \tfrac{1}{8} \sin 4 x) + C = \tfrac{3}{8} x - \tfrac{1}{4} \sin 2 x + \tfrac{1}{32} \sin 4 x + C.$

Type III: $\displaystyle\int \sin mx \cos nx \, dx$, $\displaystyle\int \sin mx \sin nx \, dx$ or $\displaystyle\int \cos mx \cos nx \, dx$.

For this case, we use the trigonometric identities:

$$(b) \qquad \begin{cases} 2 \sin A \cos B = \sin (A + B) + \sin (A - B), \\ 2 \sin A \sin B = \cos (A - B) - \cos (A + B), \\ 2 \cos A \cos B = \cos (A + B) + \cos (A - B). \end{cases}$$

EXAMPLE 3.

(a) $\displaystyle\int \sin 5 x \cos 3 x \, dx = \tfrac{1}{2} \int [\sin(5 x + 3 x) + \sin(5 x - 3 x)] \, dx$

$\displaystyle = \tfrac{1}{2} \int \sin 8 x \, dx + \tfrac{1}{2} \int \sin 2 x \, dx = -\tfrac{1}{16} \cos 8 x - \tfrac{1}{4} \cos 2 x + C$

(b) $\int \cos 3x \cos 2x \, dx = \frac{1}{2} \int [\cos (3x + 2x) + \cos (3x - 2x)] \, dx$

$$= \frac{1}{2} \int \cos 5x \, dx + \frac{1}{2} \int \cos x \, dx = \frac{1}{10} \sin 5x + \frac{1}{2} \sin x + C.$$

Type IV: $\int \tan^n x \, dx$ *or* $\int \cot^n x \, dx$.

Here we use the trigonometric identities:

(c) $\qquad \tan^2 u = \sec^2 u - 1, \qquad \cot^2 u = \csc^2 u - 1.$

EXAMPLE 4. $\int \tan^3 x \, dx = \int \tan x \, (\sec^2 x - 1) \, dx$

$$= \int \tan x \, (\sec^2 x \, dx) - \int \tan x \, dx = \frac{1}{2} \tan^2 x + \ln|\cos x| + C.$$

Type V: $\int \tan^m x \sec^n x \, dx$ *or* $\int \cot^m x \csc^n x \, dx$.

EXAMPLE 5. $\int \tan^3 x \sec^4 x \, dx = \int \tan^3 x \sec^2 x \, (\sec^2 x \, dx)$

$= \int \tan^3 x \, (1 + \tan^2 x)(\sec^2 x \, dx) = \int \tan^3 x \cdot d \, (\tan x) + \int \tan^5 x \cdot d \, (\tan x)$

$$= \frac{1}{4} \tan^4 x + \frac{1}{6} \tan^6 x + C.$$

EXAMPLE 6. $\int \tan^3 x \sec x \, dx = \int \tan^2 x \, (\sec x \tan x \, dx)$

$$= \int (\sec^2 x - 1) \, d \, (\sec x) = \frac{1}{3} \sec^3 x - \sec x + C.$$

EXAMPLE 7. $\int \sec^4 x \, dx = \int \sec^2 x \, (\sec^2 x \, dx)$

$$= \int (1 + \tan^2 x) \, d \, (\tan x) = \tan x + \frac{1}{3} \tan^3 x + C.$$

375. Exercises

Evaluate each of the following integrals:

1. $\int \sin^3 x \, dx.$ $\qquad$ 2. $\int \cos^5 x \, dx.$

3. $\int \sin x \cos x \, dx.$ $\qquad$ 4. $\int \sin^3 y \cos^2 y \, dy.$

5. $\int \sin^3 v \cos^3 v \, dv.$ $\qquad$ 6. $\int \sin^6 v \cos^3 v \, dv.$

7. $\int \sin^4 y \cos^3 y \, dy.$

8. $\int \sin^5 z \cos^5 z \, dz.$

9. $\int \sqrt{\cos x} \sin^3 x \, dx.$

10. $\int \dfrac{\sin^5 y}{\sqrt{\cos y}} \, dy.$

11. $\int_0^{\frac{\pi}{3}} \dfrac{\sin x}{\cos^2 x} \, dx.$

12. $\int_0^{\frac{\pi}{3}} \dfrac{\sin^3 z}{\cos^2 z} \, dz.$

13. $\int \sin^2 x \, dx.$

14. $\int \cos^2 x \, dx.$

15. $\int \cos^4 y \, dy.$

16. $\int_0^{\frac{\pi}{2}} \sin^4 2 \, v \, dv.$

17. $\int_{\frac{\pi}{6}}^{\frac{\pi}{4}} \sin^2 \theta \cos^2 \theta \, d\theta.$

18. $\int \sin^2 t \cos^4 t \, dt.$

19. $\int \sin^4 x \cos^2 x \, dx.$

20. $\int \cos^6 \frac{1}{2} z \sin^2 \frac{1}{2} z \, dz.$

21. $\int \sin 3 \, x \cos x \, dx.$

22. $\int \sin 2 \, x \cos 2 \, x \, dx.$

23. $\int \cos 4 \, x \cos 2 \, x \, dx.$

24. $\int \cos \theta \sin 2 \, \theta \, d\theta.$

25. $\int \sin 3 \, y \sin 2 \, y \, dy.$

26. $\int \cos 5 \, z \sin 3 \, z \, dz.$

27. $\int \cos 4 \, y \cos y \, dy.$

28. $\int \sin 2 \, t \sin 4 \, t \, dt.$

29. $\int \tan^4 x \, dx.$

30. $\int \cot^6 \theta \, d\theta.$

31. $\int \cot^3 2 \, y \, dy.$

32. $\int \tan^5 v \, dv.$

33. $\int_0^{\frac{\pi}{2}} \tan^2 \frac{1}{2} t \, dt.$

34. $\int \dfrac{dz}{\tan^4 2 \, z}.$

35. $\int \cot^7 3 \, x \, dx.$

36. $\int_0^{\frac{\pi}{2}} \tan^7 \frac{1}{2} x \, dx.$

37. $\int \tan^2 x \sec^4 x \, dx.$

38. $\int \tan^2 x \sec x \, dx.$

39. $\int \cot^3 z \csc^5 z \, dz.$

40. $\int \tan^2 \theta \sec^2 \theta \, d\theta.$

41. $\displaystyle\int_{\frac{\pi}{6}}^{\frac{\pi}{4}} \tan y \sec^5 y \, dy.$

42. $\displaystyle\int \tan \tfrac{1}{2} w \sec^4 \tfrac{1}{2} w \, dw.$

43. $\displaystyle\int \tan^5 2\,\theta \sec^3 2\,\theta \, d\theta.$

44. $\displaystyle\int_{0}^{\frac{\pi}{3}} \tan^3 y \sec^3 y \, dy.$

45. $\displaystyle\int \sec^6 x \, dx.$

46. $\displaystyle\int \csc^6 y \, dy.$

47. $\displaystyle\int \csc^4 \tfrac{1}{2} v \, dv.$

48. $\displaystyle\int \sec^8 \theta \, d\theta.$

49. $\displaystyle\int \frac{\cos^3 x \, dx}{\sin^4 x}.$

50. $\displaystyle\int \sin^{\frac{2}{3}} x \cos^3 x \, dx.$

51. $\displaystyle\int \frac{\sec^4 x}{\tan^2 x} \, dx.$

52. $\displaystyle\int \frac{\tan^2 x}{\cos x} \, dx.$

53. $\displaystyle\int \sqrt{\tan y} \sec^4 y \, dy.$

54. $\displaystyle\int \frac{\sec^3 z}{\tan^5 z} \, dz.$

55. $\displaystyle\int (\tan \theta + \cot \theta)^2 \, d\theta.$

56. $\displaystyle\int \frac{\sec^2 y \, dy}{\tan^2 y}.$

57. Evaluate $\displaystyle\int \frac{dx}{1 - \sin x}$ by using:

$$\int \frac{dx}{1 - \sin x} = \int \frac{1 + \sin x}{\cos^2 x} \, dx = \int (\sec^2 x + \sec x \tan x) \, dx.$$

58. Evaluate $\displaystyle\int \frac{dx}{1 + \cos x}.$

376. Exercises

Evaluate each of the following integrals:

1. $\displaystyle\int \sinh^3 x \, dx.$

2. $\displaystyle\int \cosh^5 x \, dx.$

3. $\displaystyle\int \cosh^2 x \, dx.$

4. $\displaystyle\int \sinh^2 y \, dy.$

5. $\displaystyle\int \tanh^2 z \, dz.$

6. $\displaystyle\int \tanh^4 v \, dv.$

7. $\displaystyle\int \tanh^3 2\,t \, dt.$

8. $\displaystyle\int \coth^5 2\,z \, dz.$

9. $\displaystyle\int \operatorname{sech}^4 x \, dx.$

10. $\displaystyle\int \operatorname{csch}^3 x \, dx.$

377. Integration by Trigonometric Substitutions

By use of the trigonometric identities:

(a) $$1 - \sin^2 \theta = \cos^2 \theta,$$

(b) $$1 + \tan^2 \theta = \sec^2 \theta,$$

(c) $$\sec^2 \theta - 1 = \tan^2 \theta,$$

we obtain substitutions which enable us to integrate expressions involving $\sqrt{a^2 - u^2}$, $\sqrt{a^2 + u^2}$ and $\sqrt{u^2 - a^2}$.

> *If $\sqrt{a^2 - u^2}$ occurs, substitute $u = a \sin \theta$;*
> *if $\sqrt{a^2 + u^2}$ occurs, substitute $u = a \tan \theta$;*
> *if $\sqrt{u^2 - a^2}$ occurs, substitute $u = a \sec \theta$.*

For, if $u = a \sin \theta$, then

$$\sqrt{a^2 - u^2} = a\sqrt{1 - \sin^2 \theta} = a \cos \theta, \text{ and } du = a \cos \theta \, d\theta;$$

if $u = a \tan \theta$, then

$$\sqrt{a^2 + u^2} = a\sqrt{1 + \tan^2 \theta} = a \sec \theta, \text{ and } du = a \sec^2 \theta \, d\theta;$$

if $u = a \sec \theta$, then

$$\sqrt{u^2 - a^2} = a\sqrt{\sec^2 \theta - 1} = a \tan \theta, \text{ and } du = a \sec \theta \tan \theta \, d\theta.$$

EXAMPLE 1. Find $\int \sqrt{a^2 - x^2} \, dx$.

Solution: Put $x = a \sin \theta$, then $\sqrt{a^2 - x^2} = a \cos \theta$ and $dx = a \cos \theta \, d\theta$, so that

$$\int \sqrt{a^2 - x^2} \, dx = \int a \cos \theta \cdot a \cos \theta \, d\theta = a^2 \int \cos^2 \theta \, d\theta$$

$$= \tfrac{1}{2} a^2 \int (1 + \cos 2\theta) \, d\theta = \tfrac{1}{2} a^2 (\theta + \tfrac{1}{2} \sin 2\theta) + C$$

$$= \tfrac{1}{2} a^2 (\theta + \sin \theta \cos \theta) + C = \tfrac{1}{2} a^2 \left[\text{Arc sin} \frac{x}{a} + \frac{x}{a} \cdot \frac{\sqrt{a^2 - x^2}}{a} \right] + C$$

$$= \tfrac{1}{2} a^2 \text{ Arc sin} \frac{x}{a} + \tfrac{1}{2} x\sqrt{a^2 - x^2} + C.$$

EXAMPLE 2. Evaluate $\int \frac{dx}{x^2\sqrt{x^2 + 4}}$.

Solution: Put $x = 2 \tan \theta$, then $\sqrt{x^2 + 4} = 2 \sec \theta$ and $dx = 2 \sec^2 \theta \, d\theta$,

$$\therefore \int \frac{dx}{x^2\sqrt{x^2 + 4}} = \int \frac{2 \sec^2 \theta \, d\theta}{4 \tan^2 \theta \cdot 2 \sec \theta} = \tfrac{1}{4} \int \frac{\sec \theta \, d\theta}{\tan^2 \theta}$$

$$= \tfrac{1}{4} \int \frac{\cos \theta \, d\theta}{\sin^2 \theta} = \tfrac{1}{4} \int \cot \theta \csc \theta \, d\theta = -\tfrac{1}{4} \csc \theta + C = -\frac{\sqrt{x^2 + 4}}{4x} + C.$$

EXAMPLE 3.   Evaluate $\int \dfrac{\sqrt{x^2 - 1}}{x} \, dx.$

Solution: Put $x = \sec \theta$, then $\sqrt{x^2 - 1} = \tan \theta$ and $dx = \sec \theta \tan \theta \, d\theta.$

$$\therefore \int \frac{\sqrt{x^2 - 1}}{x} \, dx = \int \frac{\tan \theta \cdot \sec \theta \tan \theta \, d\theta}{\sec \theta} = \int \tan^2 \theta \, d\theta$$

$$= \int (\sec^2 \theta - 1) \, d\theta = \tan \theta - \theta + C = \sqrt{x^2 - 1} - \text{Arc sec } x + C.$$

EXAMPLE 4.   Evaluate $\int \dfrac{x \, dx}{\sqrt{4\,x - x^2}}.$

Solution: $4\,x - x^2 = 2^2 - (x - 2)^2$, hence put $x - 2 = 2 \sin \theta$, then $x = 2 + 2 \sin \theta$, $dx = 2 \cos \theta \, d\theta$, and $\sqrt{4\,x - x^2} = 2 \cos \theta.$

$$\int \frac{x \, dx}{\sqrt{4\,x - x^2}} = \int \frac{(2 + 2 \sin \theta) \cdot 2 \cos \theta \, d\theta}{2 \cos \theta} = \int (2 + 2 \sin \theta) \, d\theta$$

$$= 2\,\theta - 2 \cos \theta + C = 2 \text{ Arc sin } \frac{x - 2}{2} - \sqrt{4\,x - x^2} + C.$$

Sometimes expressions involving integral powers of $a^2 - u^2$ or $a^2 + u^2$ or $u^2 - a^2$ may be most conveniently integrated by a trigonometric substitution.

EXAMPLE 5.   Evaluate $\int \dfrac{dx}{(x^2 + 4)^2}.$

Solution: Put $x = 2 \tan \theta$, then $x^2 + 4 = 4(1 + \tan^2 \theta) = 4 \sec^2 \theta$, $(x^2 + 4)^2 = 16 \sec^4 \theta$, $dx = 2 \sec^2 \theta \, d\theta.$ Therefore,

$$\int \frac{dx}{(x^2 + 4)^2} = \int \frac{2 \sec^2 \theta \, d\theta}{16 \sec^4 \theta} = \tfrac{1}{8} \int \cos^2 \theta \, d\theta = \tfrac{1}{16} \int (1 + \cos 2 \, \theta) \, d\theta$$

$$= \tfrac{1}{16} (\theta + \tfrac{1}{2} \sin 2 \, \theta) + C = \tfrac{1}{16} (\theta + \sin \theta \cos \theta) + C$$

$$= \tfrac{1}{16} \text{ Arc tan } \tfrac{1}{2} \, x + \frac{x}{16 \sqrt{x^2 + 4}} \cdot \frac{2}{\sqrt{x^2 + 4}} + C$$

$$= \tfrac{1}{16} \text{ Arc tan } \tfrac{1}{2} \, x + \frac{x}{8 \, (x^2 + 4)} + C.$$

378. Exercises

Evaluate each of the following integrals:

1. $\int \dfrac{\sqrt{a^2 - x^2}}{x^2} \, dx.$ 2. $\int x^2 \sqrt{1 - x^2} \, dx.$

3. $\displaystyle\int \sqrt{a^2 + x^2}\, dx.$

4. $\displaystyle\int \frac{dx}{x\sqrt{x^2 + 4}}.$

5. $\displaystyle\int \frac{dy}{y\sqrt{y^2 - 4}}.$

6. $\displaystyle\int \sqrt{x^2 - a^2}\, dx.$

7. $\displaystyle\int \frac{dx}{(a^2 - x^2)^{\frac{3}{2}}}.$

8. $\displaystyle\int \frac{x^2\, dx}{\sqrt{9 - x^2}}.$

9. $\displaystyle\int (a^2 + x^2)^{\frac{3}{2}}\, dx.$

10. $\displaystyle\int \frac{dz}{(a^2 + z^2)^{\frac{3}{2}}}.$

11. $\displaystyle\int \frac{t^2\, dt}{\sqrt{t^2 - 9}}.$

12. $\displaystyle\int \frac{dt}{t^2\sqrt{9\, t^2 + 4}}.$

13. $\displaystyle\int \frac{\sqrt{x^2 + a^2}}{x^2}\, dx.$

14. $\displaystyle\int \frac{dy}{y\sqrt{3 - y^2}}.$

15. $\displaystyle\int (a^2 - y^2)^{\frac{3}{2}}\, dy.$

16. $\displaystyle\int \frac{dx}{(x^2 - a^2)^{\frac{3}{2}}}.$

17. $\displaystyle\int_{\frac{5}{2}\sqrt{2}}^{\frac{7}{2}} \frac{dv}{v^2\sqrt{4\, v^2 - 25}}.$

18. $\displaystyle\int_{0}^{2} \frac{dy}{(y^2 + 4)^{\frac{5}{2}}}.$

19. $\displaystyle\int_{0}^{\frac{1}{2}\sqrt{2}} \frac{dx}{(1 - x)\sqrt{1 - x^2}}.$

20. $\displaystyle\int_{1}^{\sqrt{2}} \frac{ds}{(s + 1)\sqrt{s^2 - 1}}.$

21. $\displaystyle\int \frac{dx}{(2\, ax - x^2)^{\frac{3}{2}}}.$

22. $\displaystyle\int \frac{dx}{x\sqrt{2\, ax + x^2}}.$

23. $\displaystyle\int \frac{y\, dy}{\sqrt{2\, y - y^2}}.$

24. $\displaystyle\int \frac{dt}{t\sqrt{t^2 - 2\, t}}.$

25. $\displaystyle\int \frac{y\, dy}{\sqrt{3 + 2\, y - y^2}}.$

26. $\displaystyle\int \frac{dx}{(x^2 + 2\, x + 2)^{\frac{3}{2}}}.$

27. $\displaystyle\int \frac{dx}{(x^2 - 9)^2}.$

28. $\displaystyle\int \frac{dx}{(a^2 - x^2)^3}.$

29. $\displaystyle\int \frac{dx}{(1 + x^2)^3}.$

30. $\displaystyle\int \frac{dx}{(4 - x^2)^2}.$

379. Integration by Partial Fractions

The integration of *rational fractions* can be performed by use of certain standard integral forms together with the use, in many cases, of the algebraic method of **partial fractions**.*

* For a discussion of the general theory of partial fractions, see, for example, Barnard and Child, *Higher Algebra*, Chapter VII, or Osgood, *Advanced Calculus*, Chapter I. or Chrystal, *Algebra*, Chapter VIII.

It should be recalled that by definition a rational algebraic function is expressible as a quotient of two polynomials. A rational fraction in which the polynomial in the numerator is of lower degree than the polynomial in the denominator is called a *proper fraction*, otherwise an improper fraction. Any improper fraction can be reduced by division to a mixed form, consisting of the sum of a polynomial and a proper fraction.

EXAMPLE 1. $\dfrac{x^4 + 3\,x^2 + 2}{x^2 - 3\,x} = x^2 + 3\,x + 12 + \dfrac{36\,x + 2}{x^2 - 3\,x}.$

In the method of partial fractions, we assume always that the fraction to be resolved is a *proper fraction*.

According to the fundamental theorem of algebra, any polynomial in x with real coefficients can be expressed as a product of factors of one or both of the following types: (a) **linear factors** of the form $ax + b$ (where a and b are real numbers), and (b) **irreducible quadratic factors** of the form $ax^2 + bx + c$ (where a, b and c are real numbers), which cannot be factored into real linear factors.

EXAMPLE 2. $x^4 + x^3 - x^2 + x - 2 = (x - 1)(x + 2)(x^2 + 1).$

The *method of integration by partial fractions* consists in separating the given rational fractional integrand into a sum of simpler fractions and integrating these by standard integration forms. It will be seen that *the integral of every rational function can be expressed in terms of algebraic, logarithmic and inverse trigonometric expressions.*

When a rational fraction is separated into partial fractions, the result is an *identity*; that is, it is true for all values of the variable for which the expressions involved have a meaning. A general method for the evaluation of the coefficients of the partial fractions is based on the following theorem from the theory of equations of algebra:

If two polynomials of the same degree are identical, i.e., are equal for all values of the variable, then the coefficients of like powers of the variable in both polynomials must be equal.

Several cases arise, according to the nature of the factors of the denominator of the integrand.

380. Case I: Distinct Linear Factors

To each linear factor, as $ax + b$, occurring once in the denominator of the integrand, there corresponds a single partial fraction of the form

$\dfrac{A}{ax + b}$, *where A is a constant to be determined.*

EXAMPLE. Evaluate $\displaystyle\int \frac{7x - 4}{x(x-1)(x+2)}\, dx$.

Solution: We assume for the integrand the partial fractional form:

$$(a) \qquad \frac{7x - 4}{x(x-1)(x+2)} = \frac{A}{x} + \frac{B}{x-1} + \frac{C}{x+2},$$

where A, B and C are constants as yet undetermined. Clearing of fractions we get

$$(b) \qquad 7x - 4 = A(x-1)(x+2) + Bx(x+2) + Cx(x-1)$$

$$(c) \qquad\quad = (A+B+C)x^2 + (A+2B-C)x - 2A,$$

which is an identity, valid for all values of x. To determine the constants A, B, C, there are two methods available in this case.

According to the general method for all cases, we equate coefficients of like powers of x on both sides of (c). Equating coefficients of x^2, x and constant terms (terms in x^0), we obtain:

$$(d) \qquad 0 = A + B + C, \quad 7 = A + 2B - C, \quad -4 = -2A.$$

Solving this system of linear equations, we find $A = 2$, $B = 1$, $C = -3$.

A shorter method for this case is the following: Since (b) is an identity, we may substitute any convenient particular values of x. If we substitute first $x = 0$, then $x = 1$ and then $x = -2$ in (b), in each case we make two of the coefficients of A, B, C equal to 0. If $x = 0$, we get $-4 = -2A$, so that $A = 2$; if $x = 1$, we get $3 = 3B$, so that $B = 1$; and if $x = -2$, we get $-18 = 6C$, so that $C = -3$. This gives the same results for A, B and C as before, but with less labor.

Hence, by either method,

$$(e) \qquad \frac{7x - 4}{x(x-1)(x+2)} = \frac{2}{x} + \frac{1}{x-1} - \frac{3}{x+2}.$$

Integrating (e) term by term, we get

$$(f) \quad \int \frac{7x-4}{x(x-1)(x+2)}\, dx = 2\int \frac{dx}{x} + \int \frac{dx}{x-1} - 3\int \frac{dx}{x+2}$$

$$= 2\ln|x| + \ln|x-1| - 3\ln|x+2| + C = \ln\left|\frac{cx^2(x-1)}{(x+2)^3}\right|,$$

where the arbitrary constant C in (f) has been replaced by $\ln c$.

381. Exercises

Evaluate each of the integrals in Exercises 1–12:

1. $\displaystyle\int \frac{(x+3)\, dx}{x^2 + 3x + 2}$.

2. $\displaystyle\int \frac{5x + 6}{2 - x - x^2}\, dx$.

3. $\displaystyle\int \frac{dx}{x^3 + 5x^2 + 4x}$.

4. $\displaystyle\int \frac{(x+2)\, dx}{x(x+1)}$.

5. $\displaystyle\int \frac{x^2\, dx}{x^2 - 9}$.

6. $\displaystyle\int \frac{x^3\, dx}{x^2 + 3x + 2}$.

7. $\displaystyle\int \frac{dy}{y(a^2 - y^2)}.$

8. $\displaystyle\int \frac{2\,x^3 + x - 1}{x^3 + x^2 - 4\,x - 4}\,dx.$

9. $\displaystyle\int \frac{dx}{(x^2 - 4)(x^2 - 9)}.$

10. $\displaystyle\int \frac{(x^2 + 2)\,dx}{x^3 - 2\,x^2 - 9\,x + 18}.$

11. $\displaystyle\int_1^4 \frac{x^2 + 3\,x + 3}{2\,x^3 + 5\,x^2 - 3\,x}\,dx.$

12. $\displaystyle\int_2^5 \frac{t^4 + t^3 - 3}{t^3 - 2\,t}\,dt.$

13. The rate of growth of certain young animals and of certain plants is given by $dx/dt = kx(a - x)$, where a and k are constants.   Express x as a function of t.

14. In a bimolecular reaction, the rate of reaction is given by

$$dx/dt = k(a - x)(b - x),$$

where x is the amount of substance reacting, a is the initial concentration of one reacting substance and b is the initial concentration of the second substance.   Express x as a function of t.

382. Case II: Repeated Linear Factors

To each linear factor, as $ax + b$, occurring r times in the denominator of the integrand, there corresponds a set of r partial fractions of the form

$$\frac{A_1}{ax + b} + \frac{A_2}{(ax + b)^2} + \cdots + \frac{A_r}{(ax + b)^r},$$

where A_1, A_2, $\cdots$, A_r are constants to be determined.

EXAMPLE 1.   Evaluate $\displaystyle\int \frac{x^2 - 9\,x + 17}{x^3 - 3\,x^2 + 4}\,dx.$

Solution: The denominator of the integrand factors into

$$x^3 - 3\,x^2 + 4 = (x + 1)(x - 2)^2;$$

we therefore write

(a) $$\frac{x^2 - 9\,x + 17}{x^3 - 3\,x^2 + 4} = \frac{A}{x + 1} + \frac{B}{x - 2} + \frac{C}{(x - 2)^2},$$

where A, B and C are undetermined coefficients.   Clearing of fractions gives

(b) $$x^2 - 9\,x + 17 = A(x - 2)^2 + B(x - 2)(x + 1) + C(x + 1).$$

Picking out the coefficients of x^2, x and constant terms on the right hand side, and equating coefficients of these powers of x on both sides, we obtain

(c) $$1 = A + B, \quad -9 = -4\,A - B + C, \quad 17 = 4\,A - 2\,B + C.$$

Solving this system of equations, we find $A = 3$, $B = -2$, $C = 1$.   Hence,

(d) $$\frac{x^2 - 9\,x + 17}{x^3 - 3\,x^2 + 4} = \frac{3}{x + 1} - \frac{2}{x - 2} + \frac{1}{(x - 2)^2}.$$

We might have found A and C more easily by substituting $x = -1$ and then $x = 2$ in (b), so that $27 = 9\,A$ or $A = 3$, and $3 = 3\,C$ or $C = 1$; then B

could be found by equating coefficients of some power of x, or by substituting any value of x other than -1 or 2.

Integrating (d) term by term, we find

$$\int \frac{x^2 - 9\,x + 17}{x^3 - 3\,x^2 + 4}\,dx = 3\int \frac{dx}{x + 1} - 2\int \frac{dx}{x - 2} + \int (x - 2)^{-2}\,dx$$

$$(e) \qquad = 3\ln|x + 1| - 2\ln|x - 2| - \frac{1}{x - 2} + C.$$

Another form of this result is

$$(f) \qquad \int \frac{x^2 - 9\,x + 17}{x^3 - 3\,x^2 + 4}\,dx = \ln\left|\frac{c(x + 1)^3}{(x - 2)^2}\right| - \frac{1}{x - 2},$$

where the arbitrary constant C in (e) has been replaced by $\ln c$.

EXAMPLE 2. Evaluate $\displaystyle\int \frac{x^2 - 9\,x + 20}{(x - 3)^3}\,dx.$

Solution: The most convenient method here is to make the change of variable: $x - 3 = u$, so that $x = u + 3$, $dx = du$, and

$$x^2 - 9\,x + 20 = (u + 3)^2 - 9(u + 3) + 20 = u^2 - 3\,u + 2.$$

Then

$$\int \frac{x^2 - 9\,x + 20}{(x - 3)^3}\,dx = \int \frac{u^2 - 3\,u + 2}{u^3}\,du = \int \frac{du}{u} - 3\int u^{-2}\,du + 2\int u^{-3}\,du$$

$$= \ln|u| + \frac{3}{u} - \frac{1}{u^2} + C = \ln|x - 3| + \frac{3}{x - 3} - \frac{1}{(x - 3)^2} + C.$$

383. Exercises

Evaluate each of the following integrals:

1. $\displaystyle\int \frac{dx}{x^3 + x^2}.$

2. $\displaystyle\int \frac{dx}{x^3 - x^2}.$

3. $\displaystyle\int \frac{dx}{x^3 + 6\,x^2 + 9\,x}.$

4. $\displaystyle\int \frac{dy}{y^2(y^2 - 1)}.$

5. $\displaystyle\int \frac{x^2 - 3\,x - 8}{x^2 - 2\,x + 1}\,dx.$

6. $\displaystyle\int \frac{(x - 8)\,dx}{x^3 - 4\,x^2 + 4\,x}.$

7. $\displaystyle\int \frac{x\,dx}{(1 - x^2)^2}.$

8. $\displaystyle\int \frac{dy}{(y^2 - 1)^2}.$

9. $\displaystyle\int \frac{(x^2 + 1)\,dx}{(x + 2)^2}.$

10. $\displaystyle\int \frac{x\,dx}{(x + 2)^4}.$

11. $\displaystyle\int_3^6 \frac{x^3 - 6}{x^4 - 2\,x^3}\,dx.$

12. $\displaystyle\int_3^4 \frac{z^3 - 1}{z(z + 1)^3}\,dz.$

384. Case III: Distinct Quadratic Factors

To each irreducible quadratic factor, as $ax^2 + bx + c$, occurring once in the denominator of the integrand, there corresponds a single partial *fraction of the form* $\dfrac{Ax + B}{ax^2 + bx + c}$, *where A and B are constants to be determined.*

EXAMPLE 1.   Evaluate $\displaystyle\int \dfrac{3x^2 + 5x + 8}{(x + 2)(x^2 + 1)}\,dx$.

Solution: Put

(a)
$$\frac{3x^2 + 5x + 8}{(x + 2)(x^2 + 1)} = \frac{A}{x + 2} + \frac{Bx + C}{x^2 + 1},$$

where A, B and C are undetermined constants.   Clearing of fractions, we have

(b)
$$3x^2 + 5x + 8 = A(x^2 + 1) + (Bx + C)(x + 2).$$

Equating coefficients of x^2, x and the constant term on both sides gives the equations

(c)
$$3 = A + B, \qquad 5 = 2B + C, \qquad 8 = A + 2C.$$

Solving these equations for A, B, C, we find: $A = 2$, $B = 1$, $C = 3$.   Hence,

(d)
$$\frac{3x^2 + 5x + 8}{(x + 2)(x^2 + 1)} = \frac{2}{x + 2} + \frac{x + 3}{x^2 + 1}.$$

As an alternative method for finding A, B and C, we might have first put $x = -2$ in (b), producing $5A = 10$ or $A = 2$.   We might then have equated coefficients of like powers of x in (b) to find B and C, or we might have substituted in (b) any two values of x other than $x = -2$, thus obtaining $B = 1$, $C = 3$.

Integrating (d), we find

$$\int \frac{3x^2 + 5x + 8}{(x + 2)(x^2 + 1)}\,dx = 2\int \frac{dx}{x + 2} + \int \frac{x\,dx}{x^2 + 1} + 3\int \frac{dx}{x^2 + 1}$$
$$= 2\ln |x + 2| + \tfrac{1}{2}\ln (x^2 + 1) + 3\,\text{Arc}\tan x + C.$$

EXAMPLE 2.   Evaluate $\displaystyle\int \dfrac{27x^3 - 166x^2 + 320x - 169}{(x - 3)^2(x^2 + x + 1)}\,dx$.

Solution: It will be more convenient for the integration to assume the partial fractions in the form

(e)
$$\frac{27x^3 - 166x^2 + 320x - 169}{(x - 3)^2(x^2 + x + 1)} = \frac{A}{x - 3} + \frac{B}{(x - 3)^2} + \frac{C(2x + 1) + E}{x^2 + x + 1},$$

since the differential of $(x^2 + x + 1)$ is $(2x + 1)\,dx$.   Clearing of fractions, we have

(f) $27x^3 - 166x^2 + 320x - 169 = A(x - 3)(x^2 + x + 1) + B(x^2 + x + 1)$
$$+ C(2x + 1)(x - 3)^2 + E(x - 3)^2.$$

Putting $x = 3$, we obtain $26 = 13B$ or $B = 2$.   Equating coefficients of x^3, x and the constant term, we get the equations

(g) $27 = A + 2C$, $320 = -2A + B + 12C - 6E$,
$$-169 = -3A + B + 9C + 9E.$$

Solving these equations together with $B = 2$, we find $A = 3$, $C = 12$, $E = -30$. Then

$$\int \frac{27\,x^3 - 166\,x^2 + 320\,x - 169}{(x - 3)^2(x^2 + x + 1)}\,dx$$

$$= 3\int \frac{dx}{x - 3} + 2\int (x - 3)^{-2}\,dx + 12\int \frac{(2\,x + 1)\,dx}{x^2 + x + 1} - 30\int \frac{dx}{x^2 + x + 1}$$

$$= 3\ln|x - 3| - \frac{2}{x - 3} + 12\ln(x^2 + x + 1) - 30\cdot\frac{2}{\sqrt{3}}\,\text{Arc tan}\,\frac{2\,x + 1}{\sqrt{3}} + C.$$

385. Exercises

Evaluate each of the following integrals:

1. $\displaystyle\int \frac{x + 1}{x^3 + 4\,x}\,dx.$ 2. $\displaystyle\int \frac{10\,dx}{x(4\,x^2 - 4\,x + 5)}.$

3. $\displaystyle\int \frac{t\,dt}{t^4 + 6\,t^2 + 5}.$ 4. $\displaystyle\int \frac{x^3 - 1}{x^3 + 3\,x}\,dx.$

5. $\displaystyle\int \frac{3\,x^2 + 1}{x^3 + x^2 + x}\,dx.$ 6. $\displaystyle\int \frac{2\,dr}{r^3 + r^2 + r + 1}.$

7. $\displaystyle\int \frac{dy}{y^3 + 1}.$ 8. $\displaystyle\int \frac{dx}{x^3(1 + x^2)}.$

9. $\displaystyle\int \frac{dx}{(x^2 + 1)(x^2 + x)}.$ 10. $\displaystyle\int \frac{4\,z^2 - 3\,z + 1}{2\,z^5 + z^3}\,dz.$

11. $\displaystyle\int \frac{(x^3 - 2\,x)\,dx}{x^4 - 81}.$ 12. $\displaystyle\int \frac{dy}{y^4 - 16}.$

386. Case IV: Repeated Quadratic Factors

To each irreducible quadratic factor, as $ax^2 + bx + c$, occurring r times in the denominator of the integrand, there corresponds a set of r partial fractions of the form

$$\frac{A_1 x + B_1}{ax^2 + bx + c} + \frac{A_2 x + B_2}{(ax^2 + bx + c)^2} + \cdots + \frac{A_r x + B_r}{(ax^2 + bx + c)^r},$$

where A_1, B_1, A_2, B_2, $\cdots$, A_r, B_r are constants to be determined.

EXAMPLE. Evaluate $\displaystyle\int \frac{10\,x^2 + x + 36}{(x - 4)(x^2 + 4)^2}\,dx.$

Solution: Put

(a) $$\frac{10\,x^2 + x + 36}{(x - 4)(x^2 + 4)^2} = \frac{A}{x - 4} + \frac{Bx + C}{x^2 + 4} + \frac{Ex + F}{(x^2 + 4)^2}.$$

Clearing of fractions, we have

(b) $10\,x^2 + x + 36$
$$= A(x^2 + 4)^2 + (Bx + C)(x - 4)(x^2 + 4) + (Ex + F)(x - 4).$$

For $x = 4$, we have $200 = 400\,A$, or $A = \tfrac{1}{2}$. Equating coefficients of x^4, x^3, x^2 and the constant term, we get

(c) $A + B = 0,\; C - 4\,B = 0,\; 8\,A + 4\,B - 4\,C + E = 10,$
$$16\,A - 16\,C - 4\,F = 36.$$

Solving these equations together with $A = \tfrac{1}{2}$, we find: $B = -\tfrac{1}{2},\; C = -2,$ $E = 0,\; F = 1$. Hence,

$$\int \frac{10\,x^2 + x + 36}{(x - 4)(x^2 + 4)^2}\, dx = \tfrac{1}{2}\int \frac{dx}{x - 4} - \tfrac{1}{2}\int \frac{x + 4}{x^2 + 4}\, dx + \int \frac{dx}{(x^2 + 4)^2}$$

$$= \tfrac{1}{2}\ln |x - 4| - \tfrac{1}{4}\int \frac{2\,x\,dx}{x^2 + 4} - 2\int \frac{dx}{x^2 + 4} + \int \frac{dx}{(x^2 + 4)^2}$$

$$= \tfrac{1}{2}\ln |x - 4| - \tfrac{1}{4}\ln (x^2 + 4) - 2\cdot\tfrac{1}{2}\,\text{Arc tan }\tfrac{1}{2}\,x + \int \frac{dx}{(x^2 + 4)^2}.$$

To evaluate the last term $\displaystyle\int \frac{dx}{(x^2 + 4)^2}$, we may use the trigonometric substitution $x = 2 \tan \theta$, then

$$\int \frac{dx}{(x^2 + 4)^2} = \tfrac{1}{8}\int \cos^2 \theta\, d\theta = \tfrac{1}{8}(\tfrac{1}{2}\,\theta + \tfrac{1}{4}\sin 2\,\theta) + C$$

$$= \tfrac{1}{16}\,\text{Arc tan }\tfrac{1}{2}\,x + \tfrac{1}{16}\cdot\frac{2\,x}{x^2 + 4} + C.$$

The final result is then

(e) $$\tfrac{1}{4}\ln \frac{(x - 4)^2}{x^2 + 4} - \tfrac{15}{16}\,\text{Arc tan }\tfrac{1}{2}\,x + \tfrac{1}{8}\cdot\frac{x}{x^2 + 4} + C.$$

387. Exercises

Evaluate each of the following integrals:

1. $\displaystyle\int \frac{6\,x^3\,dx}{(x^2 + 1)^2}.$
2. $\displaystyle\int \frac{x - 1}{(x^2 + 4)^2}\, dx.$

3. $\displaystyle\int \frac{dy}{(1 - y^2)^2}.$
4. $\displaystyle\int \frac{dy}{(y^2 - 9)^3}.$

5. $\displaystyle\int \frac{dx}{x(x^2 + 1)^2}.$
6. $\displaystyle\int \frac{dt}{(t^2 + 2\,t + 5)^2}.$

7. $\displaystyle\int \frac{dz}{z^2(z^2 + 1)^2}.$
8. $\displaystyle\int \frac{x^3\,dx}{(x^3 + 1)^2}.$

388. Integration of Rational Functions of the Trigonometric Functions

Any integral whose integrand is a rational function of $\sin \theta$ and $\cos \theta$ may be reduced to the form of an integral of a rational function of t

by means of the substitution

(a)
$$\tan \tfrac{1}{2}\theta = t.$$

For, if we take $\tan \tfrac{1}{2}\theta = t$, then

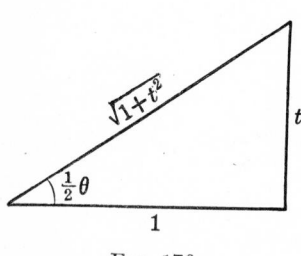

$(b)\quad \theta = 2 \text{ Arc tan } t, \quad d\theta = \dfrac{2\,dt}{1+t^2},$

$(c)\qquad \sin \theta = 2 \sin \tfrac{1}{2}\theta \cos \tfrac{1}{2}\theta$

$\qquad\qquad = 2 \cdot \dfrac{t}{\sqrt{1+t^2}} \cdot \dfrac{1}{\sqrt{1+t^2}}$

$\qquad\qquad = \dfrac{2t}{1+t^2} \quad \text{(Fig. 176)},$

Fig. 176

$(d)\qquad \cos \theta = \cos^2 \tfrac{1}{2}\theta - \sin^2 \tfrac{1}{2}\theta$

$\qquad\qquad = \dfrac{1}{1+t^2} - \dfrac{t^2}{1+t^2} = \dfrac{1-t^2}{1+t^2}.$

Hence:

(5)
$$\begin{cases} \theta = 2 \text{ Arc tan } t, \qquad d\theta = \dfrac{2\,dt}{1+t^2}, \\[2mm] \sin \theta = \dfrac{2t}{1+t^2}, \qquad \cos \theta = \dfrac{1-t^2}{1+t^2}, \\[2mm] t = \tan \tfrac{1}{2}\theta. \end{cases}$$

EXAMPLE. Evaluate $\displaystyle\int \frac{d\theta}{\sin \theta + \cos \theta}$.

Solution: Substituting from (5), we find

$$\int \frac{d\theta}{\sin \theta + \cos \theta} = \int \frac{2\,dt}{2t + 1 - t^2} = 2 \int \frac{dt}{2 - (t-1)^2}$$

$$= -2 \cdot \frac{1}{2\sqrt{2}} \ln \left| \frac{t - 1 - \sqrt{2}}{t - 1 + \sqrt{2}} \right| + C = -\tfrac{1}{2}\sqrt{2} \ln \left| \frac{\tan \tfrac{1}{2}\theta - 1 - \sqrt{2}}{\tan \tfrac{1}{2}\theta - 1 + \sqrt{2}} \right| + C,$$

or

$$= 2 \cdot \frac{1}{\sqrt{2}} \tanh^{-1}\left(\frac{t-1}{\sqrt{2}} \right) + C = \sqrt{2} \tanh^{-1}\left(\frac{\tan \tfrac{1}{2}\theta - 1}{\sqrt{2}} \right) + C.$$

389. Exercises

Evaluate each of the following integrals:

1. $\displaystyle\int \frac{dx}{2 + \cos x}$.

2. $\displaystyle\int \frac{dx}{1 + \sin x}$.

3. $\displaystyle\int \frac{dx}{1 + 2 \sin 2x}$.

4. $\displaystyle\int \frac{dy}{5 - 3 \cos y}$.

5. $\displaystyle\int \frac{dx}{3 \sin x + 4 \cos x}.$

6. $\displaystyle\int \frac{dz}{5 \sin z + 12 \cos z}.$

7. $\displaystyle\int \frac{dy}{\sin y + \tan y}.$

8. $\displaystyle\int \frac{dx}{1 + \cot x} = \int \frac{\sin x\, dx}{\sin x + \cos x}.$

9. By use of the substitution $\tan \frac{1}{2}\, x = t$, show that:

(a) $\displaystyle\int \csc x\, dx = \ln |\tan \tfrac{1}{2}\, x| + C;$

(b) $\displaystyle\int \sec x\, dx = \ln |\tan (\tfrac{1}{2}\, x + \tfrac{1}{4}\, \pi)| + C.$

390. Reduction Formulas for Integration

Certain types of integrals may be evaluated most readily by use of so-called *reduction-formulas*. By means of a reduction formula, a given integral is reduced by successive steps to simpler forms until a type is reached which can be evaluated by the preceding methods.

The derivation of many reduction formulas is based on integration by parts.

One such reduction formula, which is sometimes useful in the integration of rational fractions, is the following:

(6)

$$\int \frac{dx}{(x^2 + a^2)^n} = \frac{1}{2(n-1)a^2}\left[\frac{x}{(x^2 + a^2)^{n-1}} + (2\,n - 3)\int \frac{dx}{(x^2 + a^2)^{n-1}}\right],$$

where n is a positive integer.   By use of this formula the exponent n is reduced successively by 1 until the form $\displaystyle\int \frac{dx}{x^2 + a^2}$ is reached.   This formula is obtained by integration by parts.

Among the most useful reduction formulas are those for integrals of the following forms:

(1) *binomial algebraic differentials:* $\displaystyle\int x^m(a + bx^n)^p\, dx;$

(2) *trigonometric differentials:* $\displaystyle\int \sin^n x\, dx,$ $\displaystyle\int \cos^n x\, dx,$

$\displaystyle\int \sin^m x \cos^n x\, dx,$ $\displaystyle\int \tan^m x \sec^n x\, dx,$ $\displaystyle\int \cot^m x \csc^n x\, dx.$

EXAMPLE.   Derive a reduction formula for $\displaystyle\int \sin^m x \cos^n x\, dx.$

Solution: Suppose that m and n are positive integers. Integrate by parts, putting $u = \cos^{n-1} x$, $dv = \sin^m x \cos x \, dx$; then

$$du = -(n-1) \cos^{n-2} x \sin x \, dx \text{ and } v = \frac{\sin^{m+1} x}{m+1}.$$

(a) $\therefore \int \sin^m x \cos^n x \, dx = \frac{\sin^{m+1} x \cos^{n-1} x}{m+1} + \frac{n-1}{m+1} \int \sin^{m+2} x \cos^{n-2} x \, dx.$

Now

(b) $\int \sin^{m+2} x \cos^{n-2} x \, dx = \int \sin^m x (1 - \cos^2 x) \cos^{n-2} x \, dx$

$$= \int \sin^m x \cos^{n-2} x \, dx - \int \sin^m x \cos^n x \, dx.$$

Substituting this in (a) and combining like terms, we get

(c) $\left(1 + \frac{n-1}{m+1}\right) \int \sin^m x \cos^n x \, dx$

$$= \frac{1}{m+1} \sin^{m+1} x \cos^{n-1} x + \frac{n-1}{m+1} \int \sin^m x \cos^{n-2} x \, dx,$$

and therefore

(7)

$$\int \sin^m x \cos^n x \, dx = \frac{\sin^{m+1} x \cos^{n-1} x}{m+n} + \frac{n-1}{m+n} \int \sin^m x \cos^{n-2} x \, dx.$$

The effect of this reduction formula is to reduce the exponent of $\cos x$ by 2.

Many useful reduction formulas are given in the Table of Integrals in the Appendix.

391. Tables of Integrals

The methods of integration discussed up to this point are very far from exhausting all the known methods of integration. In order to save time in evaluating integrals occurring in applications, the more frequently occurring integral forms have been tabulated in various more or less extensive *Tables of Integrals*. The formulas in such a table are usually arranged systematically, according to the type of function in the integrand.

However, a table of integrals cannot be relied on for finding all the integrals occurring in ordinary practical problems; a knowledge of the principal *methods of integration* must be used to supplement the use of an integral table.

A brief Table of Integrals, sufficiently extensive for many practical purposes, will be found in the Appendix.

The two best-known larger collections of integrals are the following books:

B. O. Peirce, *A Short Table of Integrals* (Ginn and Co.).

H. B. Dwight, *Tables of Integrals and Other Mathematical Data* (The Macmillan Co.).

392. Exercises

Evaluate the following integrals by use of the Table of Integrals in the Appendix:

1. $\displaystyle\int \frac{x^2\,dx}{2\,x + 3}$.

2. $\displaystyle\int \frac{dx}{x(x + 4)^2}$.

3. $\displaystyle\int 3\,x\sqrt{2\,x - 1}\,dx$.

4. $\displaystyle\int \frac{dx}{x^2 + x + 1}$.

5. $\displaystyle\int \frac{dx}{(x^2 - 9)^{\frac{3}{2}}}$.

6. $\displaystyle\int 3\,x \sin 2\,x\,dx$.

7. $\displaystyle\int \frac{dx}{x\sqrt{x^2 + 4}}$.

8. $\displaystyle\int \text{Arc}\cos x\,dx$.

9. $\displaystyle\int \cos^5 x\,dx$.

10. $\displaystyle\int e^{-x} \sin 3\,x\,dx$.

11. $\displaystyle\int x^3 e^{2x}\,dx$.

12. $\displaystyle\int \sqrt{x^2 - x + 1}\,dx$.

13. $\displaystyle\int_0^{\frac{\pi}{2}} x \cos x\,dx$.

14. $\displaystyle\int_1^2 x^2(x^2 + 4)^{\frac{1}{2}}\,dx$.

15. $\displaystyle\int_0^{0.2} e^{3x} \cos 4\,x\,dx$.

16. $\displaystyle\int_0^{\pi} \sin^4 x\,dx$.

17. $\displaystyle\int x^2\sqrt{x + 2}\,dx$.

18. $\displaystyle\int x^2\sqrt{4 - x^2}\,dx$.

19. $\displaystyle\int (x^2 + 4)^{\frac{3}{2}}\,dx$.

20. $\displaystyle\int \frac{x\,dx}{\sqrt{4\,x + 1}}$.

21. $\displaystyle\int \sqrt{8\,x - x^2}\,dx$.

22. $\displaystyle\int (x^2 - 16)^{\frac{3}{2}}\,dx$.

23. $\displaystyle\int \frac{\sqrt{16 - x^2}}{x^2}\,dx$.

24. $\displaystyle\int \cos^3 x\,dx$.

25. $\displaystyle\int_{\frac{3}{2}}^2 \frac{dx}{x^2\sqrt{x^2 - 1}}$.

26. $\displaystyle\int x^2 e^{4x}\,dx$.

27. $\displaystyle\int \sin^3 x \cos^2 x\,dx$.

28. $\displaystyle\int \frac{dx}{x^2(2\,x + 1)}$.

29. $\displaystyle\int_0^{\frac{\pi}{2}} x^2 \sin x \, dx.$

30. $\displaystyle\int_0^{\frac{\pi}{6}} \sec^3 2 \, x \, dx.$

31. $\displaystyle\int x^2 \cos 3 \, x \, dx.$

32. $\displaystyle\int_1^2 x \sinh x \, dx.$

393. Integrals Not Expressible in Terms of Elementary Functions

We have seen that the derivatives of all elementary functions are elementary functions; but integrals of elementary functions are *not* all expressible (in finite form) in terms of elementary functions.

Simple examples of integrals of elementary functions which are not expressible in terms of elementary functions are:

$$\int \frac{\sin x}{x} \, dx, \qquad \int \frac{\cos x}{x} \, dx, \qquad \int \frac{e^x \, dx}{x}, \qquad \int \frac{dx}{\sqrt{1 - x^3}}.$$

An important class of integral forms not expressible in general in terms of elementary functions is that of the so-called *elliptic integrals*. An **elliptic integral** is defined as any integral of the form $\int R(x, \sqrt{P(x)}) \, dx$, where $P(x)$ is a polynomial function of degree 3 or 4, and R denotes any rational function.

The problems of finding the length of arc of an ellipse and of finding the time of oscillation of a pendulum (for arbitrary angle of oscillation) lead to elliptic integrals. Numerous other problems of geometry, mechanics and other subjects lead to elliptic integrals.

394. Miscellaneous Exercises on Integration

Evaluate the following integrals:

1. $\displaystyle\int x^2(x^2 - 2) \, dx.$

2. $\displaystyle\int \sqrt{ax + b} \, dx.$

3. $\displaystyle\int \frac{dx}{x^2 + 4 \, x + 20}.$

4. $\displaystyle\int x\sqrt{x + 2} \, dx.$

5. $\displaystyle\int \sec^2 2 \, \theta \, d\theta.$

6. $\displaystyle\int \frac{y^3 + y}{y + 1} \, dy.$

7. $\displaystyle\int \frac{\sqrt{x} \, dx}{1 + x}.$

8. $\displaystyle\int \sec^3 \phi \tan \phi \, d\phi.$

9. $\displaystyle\int \frac{t \, dt}{9 + t^2}.$

10. $\displaystyle\int \frac{dt}{9 + t^2}.$

11. $\displaystyle\int \cot^2 \theta \, d\theta.$

12. $\displaystyle\int \frac{x \, dx}{(1 + x)^4}.$

13. $\int e^{\cos x} \sin x \, dx.$

14. $\int \sin^3 \phi \, d\phi.$

15. $\int x \sin 2\, x \, dx.$

16. $\int \dfrac{(y-2)\, dy}{y^2 - 4\, y + 2}.$

17. $\int (z^2 + 4)^2 \, dz.$

18. $\int v \csc^2 v \, dv.$

19. $\int t^3 \sqrt{2 - t} \, dt.$

20. $\int x(1 - x^2)\, dx.$

21. $\int \sin^2 x \cos^3 x \, dx.$

22. $\int (4 - x^2)^{\frac{3}{2}} \, dx.$

23. $\int \dfrac{dy}{\sqrt{2\, y + 1}}.$

24. $\int \dfrac{3\, x^2 + 1}{x^3 + 2\, x^2 - 3\, x} \, dx.$

25. $\int \dfrac{e^{2t} \, dt}{e^t - 2}.$

26. $\int \dfrac{2\, z + 3}{\sqrt{1 + 2\, z}} \, dz.$

27. $\int \tanh 2\, v \, dv.$

28. $\int \dfrac{dy}{5 + 4\, y + 4\, y^2}.$

29. $\int \dfrac{\sin x + \cos x}{\tan x} \, dx.$

30. $\int \dfrac{e^{2x} \, dx}{e^{2x} + 1}.$

31. $\int \dfrac{x \, dx}{x^4 - 4}.$

32. $\int x^3 \, e^{x^2} \, dx.$

33. $\int \dfrac{dx}{x \ln x}.$

34. $\int \dfrac{y^2 \, dy}{(y + 1)^3}.$

35. $\int \tan \left(\tfrac{1}{4}\, \pi - \theta \right) d\theta.$

36. $\int \dfrac{x + 1}{x\sqrt{x - 2}} \, dx.$

37. $\int a^x b^x \, dx.$

38. $\int \sin^2 \theta \csc^2 2\, \theta \, d\theta.$

39. $\int \sqrt{\dfrac{a + x}{a - x}} \, dx.$

40. $\int \dfrac{dx}{\sqrt{16 + 4\, x - 2\, x^2}}.$

41. $\int \dfrac{x^3 - 2\, x}{x - 1} \, dx.$

42. $\int \ln (1 - y) \, dy.$

43. $\int (3\, y^2 - 6\, y)^3 \, (y - 1) \, dy.$

44. $\int \cos^n \theta \sin \theta \, d\theta.$

45. $\int \dfrac{3\, x^2 \, dx}{1 - x}.$

46. $\int x^2 \, e^x \, dx.$

47. $\int \cos^3 3\, x \, dx.$

48. $\int \dfrac{dy}{\sqrt{2 + 3\, y^2}}.$

49. $\int \dfrac{x^2 \, dx}{4 - x^2}.$

50. $\int \csc^4 x \, dx.$

51. $\displaystyle\int x^2 \operatorname{Arc\,sin} x \, dx.$

52. $\displaystyle\int \frac{\sec^2 z \, dz}{a + b \tan z}.$

53. $\displaystyle\int \frac{(3\,t + 2)\ dt}{t\sqrt{t + 1}}.$

54. $\displaystyle\int e^{\frac{1}{2}y} \, dy.$

55. $\displaystyle\int x \cos^2 x \, dx.$

56. $\displaystyle\int \frac{dv}{\sqrt{3\,v - v^2}}.$

57. $\displaystyle\int \frac{dx}{x^2 + ax}.$

58. $\displaystyle\int \sin^4 y \cos^4 y \, dy.$

59. $\displaystyle\int \frac{w^3 \, dw}{1 - w^2}.$

60. $\displaystyle\int \frac{\cos^2 mx \, dx}{\sin^3 mx}.$

CHAPTER XIX

Further Applications of Definite Integrals

395. Plane Areas: Rectangular Coördinates

Methods for finding plane areas were discussed in § 181; we can now solve area problems which involve integrals that could not have been evaluated at that point.

EXAMPLE 1. Find the area under one arch of the curve $y = \sin x$.

Solution: The first arch of this curve to the right of the Y-axis extends from $x = 0$ to $x = \pi$, and lies above the X-axis, hence the required area is

$$A = \int_0^\pi y \, dx = \int_0^\pi \sin x \, dx = -\cos x \Big|_0^\pi = -(-1 - 1) = 2.$$

EXAMPLE 2. Find the area in the first quadrant bounded by the circle $x^2 + y^2 = 16$, the coördinate axes and the line $x = 2\sqrt{2}$.

Solution: We have $A = \int_0^{2\sqrt{2}} y \, dx = \int_0^{2\sqrt{2}} \sqrt{16 - x^2} \, dx$. To evaluate this integral, let us take $x = 4 \cos \theta$; then as x varies from 0 to $2\sqrt{2}$, θ varies from $\frac{1}{2}\pi$ to $\frac{1}{4}\pi$. Since $\sqrt{16 - x^2} = 4 \sin \theta$ and $dx = -4 \sin \theta \, d\theta$, we get

$$A = \int_{\frac{\pi}{2}}^{\frac{\pi}{4}} 4 \sin \theta \, (-4 \sin \theta \, d\theta) = -16 \int_{\frac{\pi}{2}}^{\frac{\pi}{4}} \sin^2 \theta \, d\theta$$

$$= 8 \int_{\frac{\pi}{4}}^{\frac{\pi}{2}} (1 - \cos 2\theta) \, d\theta = 8 \left[\theta - \tfrac{1}{2} \sin 2\theta \right]_{\frac{\pi}{4}}^{\frac{\pi}{2}} = 2\pi + 4.$$

EXAMPLE 3. Find the entire area of the ellipse $x = a \cos \theta$, $y = b \sin \theta$.

Solution: As θ varies from $\frac{1}{2}\pi$ to 0, the part of the curve in the first quadrant is traced out, and by symmetry the entire area of the ellipse is 4 times the area in the first quadrant. Hence,

$$A = 4 \int_0^a y \, dx = 4 \int_{\frac{\pi}{2}}^0 (b \sin \theta)(-a \sin \theta \, d\theta) = 4 \, ab \int_0^{\frac{\pi}{2}} \sin^2 \theta \, d\theta = \pi \, ab.$$

396. Exercises

In each of the following problems, draw a figure carefully and shade the area to be found.

1. Find the area of one arch of the curve $y = 2 \sin \frac{1}{2} x$.
2. Find the area of one arch of the curve $y = \cos 2 x$.
3. Find the area bounded by the hyperbola $xy = a^2$, the X-axis and the lines $x = a$ and $x = 2 a$.
4. Find the area bounded by the curve $xy = 1$, the X-axis and the lines $y = x$ and $x = 3$.
5. Find the area bounded by the curve $y(1 + x^2) = 1$, the coördinate axes and the line $x = 2$.
6. Find the area between the curve $y = e^x$, the coördinate axes and the line $x = 1$.
7. Find the area bounded by the curve $y = \dfrac{x}{1 + x^2}$, the X-axis and the line $x = 8$.
8. Find the area bounded by the curve $y = x\,e^x$, the X-axis and the line $x = 4$.
9. Find the area between the hyperbola $x^2 - y^2 = a^2$ and the line $x = 2 a$.
10. Find the area bounded by the hyperbola $y^2 - 4 x^2 = 16$ and the line $y = 8$.
11. Find the area bounded by the curve $xy = 36$ and the line $x + y = 15$.
12. Find the area included between the parabola $x^2 = 4 ay$ and the witch $y(x^2 + 4 a^2) = 8 a^3$.
13. Find the area bounded by the curves $x^2 + y^2 = 5$ and $x^2 = 4 y$.
14. Find one of the smaller areas bounded by $y^2 = 2 x$ and $y^2 = 6 x - x^2$.
15. Find the area bounded by the catenary $y = \cosh x$, the coördinate axes and the line $x = 1$.
16. Find the area bounded by the catenary $y = \cosh x$ and the line $y = 2$.
17. Find the area of one arch of the cycloid $x = a(\theta - \sin \theta)$, $y = a(1 - \cos \theta)$.
18. Find the total area enclosed by the hypocycloid $x = a \cos^3 \theta$, $y = a \sin^3 \theta$.

397. Plane Areas: Polar Coördinates

Let us now consider the problem of finding the area of a plane region whose boundary is expressed in polar coördinates. Let the region AOB in Fig. 177 be bounded by the curve $r = f(\theta)$ and the radii vectors OA and OB which correspond to $\theta = \alpha$ and $\theta = \beta$ respectively, and for definiteness suppose that $\alpha < \beta$.

Divide the region AOB into n parts by lines through O, and let $\Delta\theta_k$ be the angle of a typical part. Let r_k be any radius vector in this typical part, and through its extremity P_k draw an arc of a circle forming a circular sector of angle $\Delta\theta_k$ and radius r_k. Let the same be done for each of the n parts of the region AOB. The area of the typical circular sector is $\frac{1}{2} r_k^2 \Delta\theta_k$. Let us form the sum of the areas of all the circular sectors:

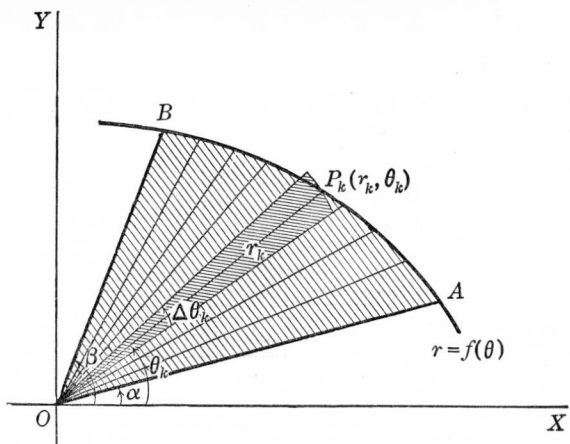

Fig. 177

$$(a) \qquad S_n = \sum_{k=1}^{n} \tfrac{1}{2}\, r_k^2 \Delta\theta_k.$$

If $r = f(\theta)$ is continuous, as $\delta \to 0$ (where δ is defined as usual), the sum S_n approaches the limit $\int_{\alpha}^{\beta} \tfrac{1}{2} r^2\, d\theta$. It can be proved that this limit is equal to the area of the region AOB as defined in § 169. Hence:

The area bounded by the curve $r = f(\theta)$ and two radii vectors $\theta = \alpha$ and $\theta = \beta$ is given by:

$$(1) \qquad A = \tfrac{1}{2} \int_{\alpha}^{\beta} r^2\, d\theta.$$

EXAMPLE 1. Find the area bounded by the cardioid

$$r = a(1 - \cos\theta).$$

Solution: The curve is shown in Fig. 178. The entire region bounded by the cardioid is swept out as the radius vector rotates from $\theta = 0$ to $\theta = 2\pi$; by symmetry, the required area is twice the area from $\theta = 0$ to $\theta = \pi$. Therefore,

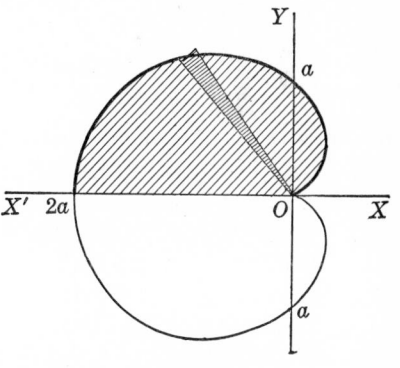

Fig. 178

$$A = 2 \cdot \tfrac{1}{2} \int_{0}^{\pi} a^2 (1 - \cos\theta)^2\, d\theta = \tfrac{3}{2}\, \pi a^2.$$

To find an area, in polar coördinates, bounded by two curves and perhaps one or two radii vectors, we may subtract areas as in the case of rectangular coördinates. In this case, we may also set up the integral for the area by taking as an element of the integral a "truncated circular sector" formed by taking away a smaller sector from a larger sector (as illustrated in Fig. 179).

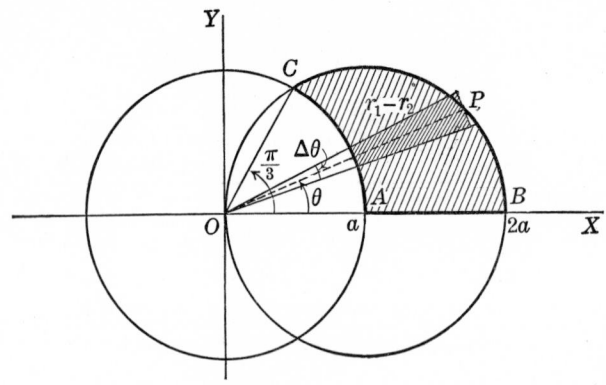

Fig. 179

EXAMPLE 2. Find the area inside the circle $r = 2a\cos\theta$ and outside the circle $r = a$ (Fig. 179).

Solution: By solving the given equations of the curves simultaneously, we find the coördinates of the intersection point C to be $(a, \frac{1}{3}\pi)$. By symmetry, the required area is twice the area ABC, shaded in Fig. 179; for this area, θ varies from 0 to $\frac{1}{3}\pi$. Putting $r_2 = 2a\cos\theta$ and $r_1 = a$, and using the "truncated sector" element shown in the figure, we find the element of area to be

$$\tfrac{1}{2} r_2{}^2 \Delta\theta - \tfrac{1}{2} r_1{}^2 \Delta\theta = \tfrac{1}{2}(r_2{}^2 - r_1{}^2)\Delta\theta.$$

The required area is given by

$$A = 2 \cdot \tfrac{1}{2} \int_0^{\frac{\pi}{3}} (r_2{}^2 - r_1{}^2)\,d\theta = \int_0^{\frac{\pi}{3}} (4a^2\cos^2\theta - a^2)\,d\theta = (\tfrac{1}{3}\pi + \tfrac{1}{2}\sqrt{3})a^2.$$

398. Exercises

In each of the following problems, draw a figure carefully and shade the area to be found.

In Exercises 1–4, find the area bounded by each of the given curves and the given radii vectors:

1. $r = a\cos\theta$, $\theta = 0$ to $\theta = \frac{1}{4}\pi$.   2. $r = a\theta$, $\theta = 0$ to $\theta = 2\pi$.
3. $r = e^{2\theta}$, $\theta = 0$ to $\theta = \frac{1}{2}\pi$.   4. $r = a\sec^2\frac{1}{2}\theta$, $\theta = 0$ to $\theta = \frac{1}{2}\pi$.

In Exercises 5–8, find the entire area of each of the given curves:

     5. $r = 1 + \cos \theta$ (cardioid).   6. $r = 2 \sin^2 \frac{1}{2} \theta$ (cardioid).

     7. $r = 2 + \cos \theta$ (limaçon).   8. $r = a \cos^3 \frac{1}{3} \theta$.

In Exercises 9–14, find the area of one loop of each of the given curves:

     9. $r = a \cos 2 \theta$ (four-leaved rose).   10. $r = a \sin 3 \theta$ (three-leaved rose).

     11. $r = 2 - \sec \theta$.   12. $r = a \cot \frac{1}{2} \theta$.

     13. $r^2 = a^2 \cos 2 \theta$ (lemniscate).   14. $r = a \cos^2 \theta$.

In Exercises 15–20, find the area bounded by each of the given pairs of curves:

     15. Inside $r = 2 a \sin \theta$,   outside $r = a$.

     16. Inside $r = 4 \cos \theta$,   outside $r = 2$.

     17. Inside $r = \sin \theta$,   outside $r = 1 - \cos \theta$.

     18. Inside $r^2 = 4 a^2 \cos 2 \theta$,   outside $r = \sqrt{2} \, a$.

     19. Inside $r = 2 \cos \theta + 4$,   outside $r = 5$.

     20. Between the line $r \cos \theta = 6$ and the circle $r = 10$.

21. Find the area inside the circle $r = 8 \cos \theta$ and to the right of the line $r = 2 \sec \theta$.

22. Find the area inside the circle $r = 10 \sin \theta$ and above the line $r = 2 \csc \theta$.

23. Find the area bounded by the circle $r = 3 \cos \theta$ and the cardioid $r = 1 + \cos \theta$, outside the cardioid and inside the circle.

24. Find the area inside the circle $r = \sin \theta$ and outside the cardioid $r = 1 + \cos \theta$.

25. Show that the area bounded by any two radii vectors of the hyperbolic spiral $r \, \theta = a$ is proportional to the difference between the lengths of these radii.

26. Find the area of the small loop of the curve $r = 1 + 2 \cos \theta$.

399. Volumes of Solids

In Chapter XI, methods were given for finding volumes of solids, by use of cylindrical disks, by washers, by cylindrical shells and by parallel slicing. By use of the additional methods of integration given in Chapters XVII and XVIII, we may now consider further problems in finding volumes.

EXAMPLE 1. Find the volume generated by revolving about the X-axis the area under the first arch of the curve $y = \sin x$; also find the volume when this area is revolved about the Y-axis.

Solution: (a) To find the volume generated when the given area is revolved about the X-axis, the simplest method is the cylindrical disk method (§ 186). This gives

$$V = \pi \int_0^{\pi} y^2 \, dx = \pi \int_0^{\pi} \sin^2 x \, dx = \tfrac{1}{2} \pi^2.$$

(b) To find the volume when the given area is revolved about the Y-axis, the simplest method is the cylindrical shell method (§ 190). In this case, we have

$$V = 2\pi \int_0^\pi xy\, dx = 2\pi \int_0^\pi x\sin x\, dx = 2\pi^2.$$

EXAMPLE 2. Find the volume of the solid generated by revolving about their common chord the area common to the circles $x^2 + y^2 = 16$ and $x^2 + y^2 = 8x$ (Fig. 180).

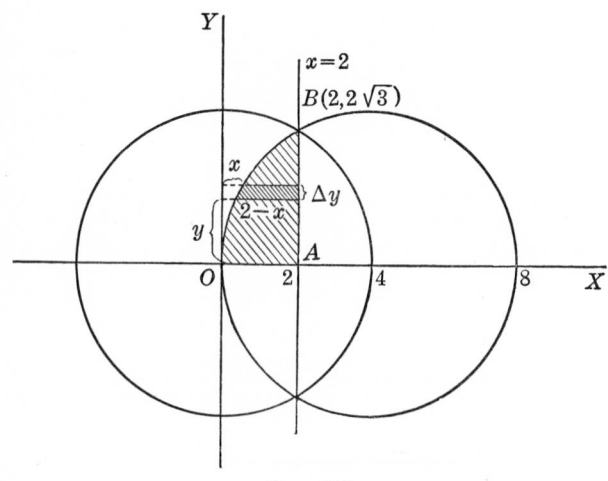

FIG. 180

Solution: By use of the cylindrical disk method, we have

$$V = 2\pi \int_0^{2\sqrt{3}} (2 - x)^2\, dy = 2\pi \int_0^{2\sqrt{3}} (-2 + \sqrt{16 - y^2})^2\, dy$$

$$= 2\pi \int_0^{2\sqrt{3}} (20 - y^2 - 4\sqrt{16 - y^2})\, dy$$

$$= 2\pi \left[20y - \tfrac{1}{3}y^3 - 2y\sqrt{16 - y^2} - 32\,\mathrm{Arc}\sin\frac{y}{4} \right]_0^{2\sqrt{3}}$$

$$= 48\pi\sqrt{3} - \tfrac{64}{3}\pi^2.$$

EXAMPLE 3. Find the volume of the solid generated by revolving about the X-axis the region in the first quadrant bounded by the hypocycloid $x = a\cos^3\theta$, $y = a\sin^3\theta$ and the coördinate axes.

Solution: Using the method of cylindrical disks, we have $V = \pi \int_0^a y^2\, dx$; but $y^2 = a^2\sin^6\theta$ and $dx = -3a\cos^2\theta\sin\theta\, d\theta$. Therefore,

$$V = \pi \int_{\frac{\pi}{2}}^0 (a^2\sin^6\theta)(-3a\cos^2\theta\sin\theta\, d\theta)$$

$$= 3\,\pi\,a^3 \int_{\frac{\pi}{2}}^{0} \sin^6 \theta \cos^2 \theta\, (d \cos \theta)$$

$$= 3\,\pi\,a^2 \int_{\frac{\pi}{2}}^{0} \cos^2 \theta\, (1 - \cos^2 \theta)^3\, (d \cos \theta) = \tfrac{16}{105}\,\pi a^3.$$

400. Exercises

1. The region bounded by the curve $y = e^x$, the X-axis and the lines $x = 1$ and $x = 3$ is revolved about the X-axis; find the volume of the solid generated.

2. Find the volume of the solid formed by revolving about the X-axis the region in the first quadrant bounded by the curve $xy^2 = 1$, the X-axis and the lines $x = 1$ and $x = 2$.

3. Find the volume generated by revolving the region bounded by one arch of the curve $y = 2 \sin x$ and the line $y = 1$ about the line $y = 1$.

4. Find the volume generated by revolving about the Y-axis the segment of the circle $x^2 + y^2 + 2\,x = 3$ to the right of the Y-axis.

5. Find the volume generated by revolving about the Y-axis the region bounded by the curve $y = e^{-x^2}$, the coördinate axes and the line $x = 1$.

6. Find the volume generated by revolving about the Y-axis the region between the curve $xy = 4$ and the line $x + y = 5$.

7. Find the volume generated by revolving the region inside the ellipse $x = a \cos \theta$, $y = b \sin \theta$ about: (a) the X-axis; (b) the Y-axis.

8. Find the volume generated by revolving about the X-axis the region in the first quadrant under the hyperbola $x = a \sec \theta$, $y = a \tan \theta$ between $x = a$ and $x = 2\,a$.

9. Find the volume generated by revolving the region under the first arch of the cycloid $x = a(\theta - \sin \theta)$, $y = a(1 - \cos \theta)$ about the X-axis.

10. Find the volume generated by revolving the region under the first arch of the cycloid $x = a(\theta - \sin \theta)$, $y = a(1 - \cos \theta)$ about the Y-axis.

11. Find the volume generated by revolving the region inside the circle $r = 2\,a \cos \theta$ about the Y-axis.

$$[\text{Hint.}\quad V = 4\,\pi \int_{0}^{2a} xy\, dx,\ x = r \cos \theta = 2\,a \cos^2 \theta,$$

$$y = r \sin \theta = 2\,a \cos \theta \sin \theta.]$$

12. Find the volume generated by revolving about the polar axis the region inside the cardioid $r = a(1 - \cos \theta)$ and lying to the left of the Y-axis.

401. Lengths of Curves: Rectangular Coördinates

Formulas for finding lengths of arcs of curves in rectangular co-ordinates were derived and used in Chapter XI (§ 194). Additional applications of these formulas are now possible with the further methods of integration given in Chapters XVII and XVIII.

EXAMPLE 1. Find the length of arc of the curve $y = \ln \cos x$ from $x = 0$ to $x = \frac{1}{4}\pi$.

Solution: We use the formula $s = \int_a^b \sqrt{1 + y'^2}\, dx$.

$$y = \ln \cos x,\ y' = -\tan x,\ \sqrt{1 + y'^2} = \sqrt{1 + \tan^2 x} = \sec x,$$

$$\therefore\ s = \int_0^{\frac{\pi}{4}} \sec x\, dx = \ln |\sec x + \tan x|\ \Big|_0^{\frac{\pi}{4}} = \ln (\sqrt{2} + 1).$$

EXAMPLE 2. Find the length of arc of one arch of the cycloid

$$x = a(\theta - \sin \theta),\quad y = a(1 - \cos \theta).$$

Solution: $dx = a(1 - \cos \theta)\, d\theta,\quad dy = a \sin \theta\, d\theta,$

$$(ds)^2 = (dx)^2 + (dy)^2 = [a^2(1 - \cos \theta)^2 + a^2 \sin^2 \theta](d\theta)^2$$

$$= 2\, a^2(1 - \cos \theta)(d\theta)^2 = 4\, a^2 \sin^2 \tfrac{1}{2}\, \theta\, (d\theta)^2,$$

$$\therefore\ s = \int_0^{2\pi} 2\, a \sin \tfrac{1}{2}\, \theta\, d\theta = 8\, a.$$

402. Exercises

In Exercises 1–10, find the length of each of the given curves:

1. $y = \ln \sec x$, from $x = 0$ to $x = \frac{1}{6}\pi$.
2. $y = x^2$, from $x = 0$ to $x = 1$.
3. $y^2 = 4\, x$, from $x = 0$ to $x = 1$.
4. $y = 2\, e^{\frac{1}{2}x}$, from $x = 0$ to $x = 2$.
5. $y = 12 \ln x$, from $x = 5$ to $x = 9$.
6. $y = \ln \csc x$, from $x = \frac{1}{6}\pi$ to $x = \frac{1}{2}\pi$.
7. $y = e^x$, from $x = 0$ to $x = 1$.
8. $3\, y^2 = x(x - 1)^2$, one loop.
9. $y = \cosh x$, from $x = 0$ to $x = 1$.
10. $8\, y = x^2 - 8 \ln x$, from $x = 1$ to $x = 2$.

11. Find the length of the arc in the first quadrant of the curve $y^2 = 6\, x - x^2$ cut off by the line $y = x$.
12. Find, by integration, the entire length of the curve $x^2 + y^2 - 4\, ax = 0$; check by another method.
13. Find the length of the arc of the parabola $y^2 = 4\, ax$ from the vertex to one end of the latus rectum.
14. Find the length of the arc of the parabola $x^2 = 4\, y$ from $(0, 0)$ to $(4, 4)$.

Find the length of each of the curves in Exercises 15, 16:

15. Parabola $x = 4\, at^2$, $y = 4\, at$, from $t = 0$ to $t = \frac{1}{2}$.
16. Hypocycloid $x = a \cos^3 t$, $y = a \sin^3 t$, total length.

403. Length of Arc in Polar Coördinates

Let $r = f(\theta)$ be the equation of a curve in polar coördinates. We start with the formula

(a) $$(ds)^2 = (dx)^2 + (dy)^2$$

of § 195. Since $x = r \cos \theta$, $y = r \sin \theta$, we get

$$dx = -r \sin \theta \, d\theta + \cos \theta \, dr, \qquad dy = r \cos \theta \, d\theta + \sin \theta \, dr.$$

Substituting these in (a) and simplifying, we find

(2) $$(ds)^2 = r^2 (d\theta)^2 + (dr)^2.$$

Dividing by $(d\theta)^2$ and putting $dr/d\theta = r'$, we have

(b) $$ds = \sqrt{r^2 + r'^2} \, d\theta.$$

Hence:

The length of the arc of the curve $r = f(\theta)$ from $\theta = \alpha$ to $\theta = \beta$ is given by:

(3) $$s = \int_\alpha^\beta \sqrt{r^2 + r'^2} \, d\theta,$$

where $r' = dr/d\theta$.

EXAMPLE. Find the entire length of the cardioid $r = a(1 - \cos \theta)$. (See Fig. 178.)

Solution: The entire cardioid is traced out when θ varies from 0 to 2π. Since $r' = a \sin \theta$,

$$r^2 + r'^2 = a^2 (1 - \cos \theta)^2 + a^2 \sin^2 \theta = 2 a^2 (1 - \cos \theta) = 4 a^2 \sin^2 \tfrac{1}{2} \theta.$$

The entire length of the cardioid is then given by

$$s = \int_0^{2\pi} \sqrt{r^2 + r'^2} \, d\theta = 2 a \int_0^{2\pi} \sin \tfrac{1}{2} \theta \, d\theta$$

$$= -4 a \cos \tfrac{1}{2} \theta \Big|_0^{2\pi} = -4 a(-1 - 1) = 8 a.$$

404. Exercises

1. Find the perimeter of the cardioid $r = a(1 + \cos \theta)$.
2. Find the length of arc of the equiangular spiral $r = e^{a\theta}$ from $\theta = 0$ to $\theta = \alpha$.
3. Find the length of arc of the spiral of Archimedes $r = a\theta$ from $\theta = 0$ to $\theta = \alpha$.
4. Find the arc length of the parabola $r = a \sec^2 \tfrac{1}{2} \theta$ from $\theta = 0$ to $\theta = \tfrac{1}{2}\pi$.
5. Find the arc length of the cissoid $r = 2 a \tan \theta \sin \theta$ from $\theta = 0$ to $\theta = \tfrac{1}{3}\pi$.

405. Area of a Surface of Revolution

Let the arc CD of the smooth curve $y = f(x)$ (Fig. 181 (a)) be revolved about the X-axis, generating a surface of revolution, whose area we wish to find. By analogy with the basic procedure used in defining length of curve and area under a curve, we *define* the **area of this surface of revolution** as the limit of the area generated by the n parts of a broken line inscribed in the arc CD when $n \to \infty$.

Let a and b be the abscissas of points C and D; then, as usual, divide the interval (a, b) into n parts Δx_k as in Fig. 181 (a), erect ordinates at the division points and join their extremities by chords, forming the inscribed broken line. Fig. 181 (b) shows the typical

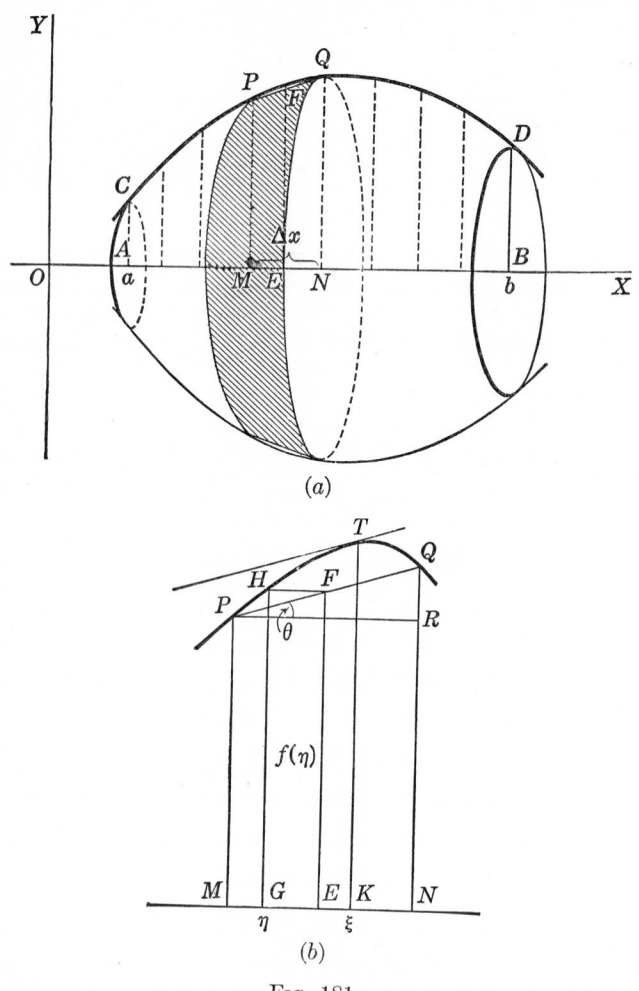

(a)

(b)

Fig. 181

(k-th) sub-interval Δx_k and its corresponding ordinates and chord PQ, enlarged. The chord PQ generates the lateral surface of a frustum of a right circular cone of which PQ is the slant height (Fig. 181 (a)). Since the area of a frustum of a cone of revolution is equal to the circumference of the middle section multiplied by the slant height, the area of the surface of the frustum generated by chord PQ is $2\pi \cdot EF \cdot PQ$, where F is the mid-point of PQ. Since $f(x)$ is continuous, there is evidently some point η in Δx_k such that $EF = f(\eta)$. By the mean-value theorem for derivatives, there is some point ξ in Δx_k such that the tangent to CD at T (whose abscissa is ξ) is parallel to the chord PQ, so that $\tan \theta = f'(\xi)$, where θ is the inclination of PQ. Then

$$PQ = \Delta x_k \cdot \sec \theta = \Delta x_k \cdot \sqrt{1 + \tan^2 \theta} = \Delta x_k \cdot \sqrt{1 + [f'(\xi)]^2}.$$

The sum of the areas generated by the broken line is therefore

(a)
$$S_n = \sum_{k=1}^{n} 2\pi \cdot f(\eta) \cdot \sqrt{1 + [f'(\xi)]^2} \cdot \Delta x_k.$$

By Bliss' theorem (§ 177), the limit of this sum when $n \to \infty$ and $\delta \to 0$, where δ is the length of the longest Δx_k, is the definite integral

(b)
$$S = 2\pi \int_a^b f(x)\sqrt{1 + [f'(x)]^2}\, dx.$$

This, by definition, is the required area of the surface of revolution.

The formula (b) can be put in another form which is often more convenient, by using the formula for arc-length:

$$\sqrt{1 + [f'(x)]^2}\, dx = \sqrt{1 + y'^2}\, dx = ds.$$

Formula (b) then becomes

(c)
$$S = 2\pi \int_{x=a}^{x=b} y\, ds,$$

where the notation $\int_{x=a}^{x=b} y\, ds$ is used to mean "the integral of y with respect to s from the value of s for which $x = a$ to the value of s for which $x = b$." Hence:

If the arc of the curve $y = f(x)$ between $x = a$ and $x = b$ is revolved about the X-axis, the area of the surface generated is given by:

(4)
$$S = 2\pi \int_{x=a}^{x=b} y\, ds.$$

In using this formula, we may substitute the values of y and ds in terms of x and dx, as in (b), or in terms of any other convenient variable.

EXAMPLE. Find the area of the surface generated by revolving about the X-axis the arc of the parabola $y^2 = 4\,x$ between $x = 0$ and $x = 8$.

Solution: $y^2 = 4\,x$, $2\,yy' = 4$, $y' = \dfrac{2}{y}$, $1 + y'^2 = 1 + \dfrac{4}{y^2} = \dfrac{y^2 + 4}{y^2}$,

$$y\,ds = y\sqrt{1 + y'^2}\,dx = y \cdot \frac{1}{y} \cdot \sqrt{y^2 + 4}\,dx = \sqrt{4\,x + 4}\,dx = 2\sqrt{x + 1}\,dx,$$

$$S = 2\,\pi \cdot 2 \int_0^8 \sqrt{x + 1}\,dx = 4\,\pi \cdot \tfrac{2}{3}\,(x + 1)^{\frac{3}{2}}\Big|_0^8 = \tfrac{208}{3}\,\pi.$$

If an arc of a curve $y = f(x)$ or $x = g(y)$ between $y = c$ and $y = d$ is revolved about the Y-axis, the area of the surface generated is evidently given by

(d)
$$S = 2\,\pi \int_{y=c}^{y=d} x\,ds,$$

where x and ds may be expressed in terms of y and dy or x and dx, or some other convenient variable.

406. Exercises

1. Find the area of the surface of a sphere of radius a, by revolving the circle $x^2 + y^2 = a^2$ about the X-axis.
2. Show that the area of a zone of altitude h on a sphere of radius a is $2\,\pi a h$.

In Exercises 3–6, find the area of the surface generated by revolving about the X-axis each of the given arcs:

3. $y^2 = 9\,x$, from $x = 0$ to $x = 4$.
4. $y^2 = 4 - x$, in the first quadrant.
5. $y = x^3$, from $x = 0$ to $x = 1$.
6. $y^3 = ax^2$, from $y = 0$ to $y = 5\,a$.

In Exercises 7–10, find the area of the surface generated by revolving about the Y-axis each of the given arcs:

7. $y = x^2$, from $y = 0$ to $y = 2$.
8. $y = x^3$, from $x = 0$ to $x = \tfrac{1}{3}\sqrt{3}$.
9. $x = y^3$, from $y = 0$ to $y = 3$.
10. $x^2 - y^2 = a^2$, from $y = 0$ to $y = 2\,a$.

In Exercises 11–14, find the area of the surface generated by revolving about the X-axis each of the given arcs:

11. $y = \sin x$, one arch.
12. $y = 2 \sec x$, from $x = 0$ to $x = \tfrac{1}{4}\,\pi$.
13. $y = e^x$, from $x = 0$ to $x = 1$.
14. $y = \cosh x$, from $x = 0$ to $x = 1$.

15. The loop of the curve $9\,y^2 = x(x - 3)^2$ is revolved about the X-axis; find the area of surface generated.

16. The arc of the catenary $y = \cosh x$ between $x = 0$ and $x = 1$ is revolved about the Y-axis; find the area of the surface generated.

17. A torus is generated by revolving a circle of radius a about a line in the plane of the circle at a distance $b > a$ from the center of the circle. Find the area of the surface of the torus.

18. The arc of the parabola $y^2 = 4\,x$ from $(0, 0)$ to $(3, 2\sqrt{3})$ is revolved about the Y-axis; find the surface area generated.

19. Find the area of the surface generated by revolving about the X-axis the arc of the parabola $y^2 = 4\,ax$ between $x = 0$ and $x = a$.

20. One arch of the cycloid $x = a(t - \sin t)$, $y = a(1 - \cos t)$ is revolved about its base (X-axis); find the area of the surface generated.

21. Find the area of the surface generated by revolving about the X-axis the portion of the hypocycloid $x = a\cos^3\theta$, $y = a\sin^3\theta$ in the first quadrant.

22. Find the area of the surface generated by revolving about the polar axis the upper half of the circle $r = 2\,a\cos\theta$.

23. The upper half of the cardioid $r = a(1 + \cos\theta)$ is revolved about the polar axis; find the area of the surface generated.

24. The lemniscate $r^2 = a^2\cos 2\,\theta$ is revolved about the polar axis; find the area of the surface generated.

407. Centroids of Plane Arcs and of Surfaces of Revolution

In Chapter XI we discussed centroids of plane areas and solids of revolution. We shall now consider centroids of two other types of geometric figures.

Let CD be an arc of the curve $y = f(x)$ between $x = a$ and $x = b$ (Fig. 182). Divide this arc into n parts, and on a typical sub-arc Δs_k choose an arbitrary point (ξ_k, η_k), and form the sum $\sum\limits_{k=1}^{n} \xi_k\,\Delta s_k$ for all the parts of CD. Let δ be the length of the longest sub-arc Δs_k. By analogy with the previous definitions

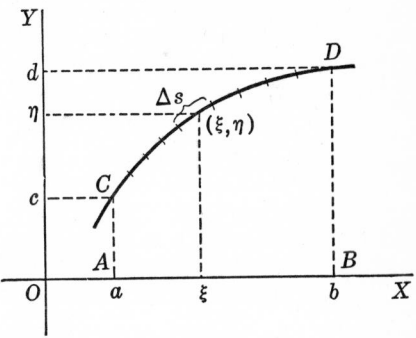

FIG. 182

of first moments and centroids, we take the limit of this sum as $\delta \to 0$. Then:

*The **first moment** of arc CD with respect to the Y-axis is defined by:*

$$(5) \qquad M_y = \lim_{\delta \to 0} \sum_{k=1}^{n} \xi_k \Delta s_k = \int_{x=a}^{x=b} x\,ds.$$

Similarly, *the **first moment** of arc CD with respect to the X-axis is defined by:*

(6) $$M_x = \lim_{\delta \to 0} \sum_{k=1}^{n} \eta_k \Delta s_k = \int_{x=a}^{x=b} y \, ds.$$

*The **centroid** of arc CD is defined as the point $(\bar{x}, \bar{y})$ whose coördinates satisfy the relations:*

(7) $$s\,\bar{x} = M_y, \qquad s\,\bar{y} = M_x,$$

where s is the length of arc CD.

The arc length s may be found from

(a) $$s = \int_a^b \sqrt{1 + y'^2} \, dx.$$

EXAMPLE. Find the coördinates of the centroid of the first quadrant arc of the circle $x^2 + y^2 = a^2$.

Solution: $x^2 + y^2 = a^2$, $2x + 2yy' = 0$, $y' = -\dfrac{x}{y}$,

$$1 + y'^2 = 1 + \frac{x^2}{y^2} = \frac{x^2 + y^2}{y^2} = \frac{a^2}{y^2}, \quad ds = \sqrt{1 + y'^2}\, dx = \frac{a}{y}\, dx,$$

$$M_y = \int_{x=0}^{x=a} x\, ds = a \int_0^a \frac{x}{y}\, dx = a \int_0^a \frac{x\, dx}{\sqrt{a^2 - x^2}} = a^2 \ (\text{see } \S\,417).$$

$$\therefore\ \bar{x} = \frac{M_y}{s} = \frac{a^2}{\tfrac{1}{2}\,\pi a} = \frac{2\,a}{\pi}.$$

By symmetry, $\bar{y} = \bar{x} = \dfrac{2\,a}{\pi}.$ Otherwise:

$$M_x = \int_{x=0}^{x=a} y\, ds = \int_0^a y \cdot \frac{a}{y}\, dx = a \int_0^a dx = a^2,$$

$$\therefore\ \bar{y} = \frac{M_x}{s} = \frac{a^2}{\tfrac{1}{2}\,\pi a} = \frac{2\,a}{\pi}.$$

Let the arc CD of Fig. 182 be revolved about the X-axis, generating a surface of revolution. By analogy with the previous definition of centroid of arc, and with reference to the formula for the area of a surface of revolution in § 405, we define the centroid of surface as follows:

*The **first moment** with respect to a plane through the origin perpendicular to the X-axis of the surface generated by revolution of arc CD about the X-axis is defined by:*

$$(8) \qquad M = \lim_{\delta \to 0} \sum_{k=1}^{n} \xi_k \cdot 2\,\pi\eta_k \Delta s_k = 2\,\pi \int_{x=a}^{x=b} xy\, ds\,;$$

the **centroid** *of this surface is defined as the point on the X-axis whose abscissa $\bar{x}$ satisfies the relation*

$$(9) \qquad\qquad S\,\bar{x} = M,$$

where S is the surface area, given by

$$(b) \qquad\qquad S = 2\,\pi \int_{x=a}^{x=b} y\, ds.$$

408. Pappus' Theorems

Let a plane region A in the XY-plane be revolved about the X-axis, generating a solid of revolution. By the cylindrical shell method, the volume generated is

$$(a) \qquad\qquad V = 2\,\pi \int_{c}^{d} y\, h(y)\, dy,$$

where $h(y)$ is the width of the region A corresponding to the ordinate y, and c and d are the extreme values of y for the region A. But by § 201, the integral $\int_{c}^{d} y\, h(y)\, dy$ is the first moment of the area A with respect to the X-axis, so that

$$(b) \qquad\qquad \int_{c}^{d} y\, h(y)\, dy = A\,\bar{y},$$

where $\bar{y}$ is the ordinate of the centroid of area A. From (a) and (b), we have

$$(c) \qquad\qquad V = 2\,\pi\,\bar{y} \cdot A.$$

This result may be stated:

I. *If a plane area is revolved about a line in the plane not cutting the area, the volume generated is equal to the product of the area and the length of the circular path described by the centroid of the area.*

This theorem holds if the revolution is through only a part of a complete turn.

Now let CD be an arc of the curve $y = f(x)$, and let CD be revolved about the X-axis to generate a surface of revolution. As in § 405, the area of the surface generated is given by

$$(d) \qquad\qquad S = 2\,\pi \int_{x=a}^{x=b} y\, ds.$$

But by § 407, the integral $\int_{x=a}^{x=b} y \, ds$ is the first moment of the arc CD with respect to the X-axis, so that

$$\int_{x=a}^{x=b} y \, ds = s \, \bar{y},$$

where $\bar{y}$ is the ordinate of the centroid of the arc CD and s is the length of the arc CD. Hence:

(e) $S = 2 \pi \, \bar{y} \cdot s.$

This gives the theorem:

II. *If an arc of a plane curve is revolved about a line in the plane not cutting the arc, the area of the surface generated is equal to the product of the length of the given arc and the length of the circular path described by the centroid of the arc.*

In this case, also, the rotation may be through only a part of a complete turn.

The two theorems I and II are known as **Pappus' theorems,** after the ancient Greek geometer Pappus.

Pappus' theorems may be used to find volumes or areas of surfaces of revolution when the centroids of the generating figures are known, or to find the centroids of certain figures when the corresponding volumes or surface areas are known.

409. Exercises

In Exercises 1-10, use the methods of §§ 201, 203:

1. Find the coördinates of the centroid of the area bounded by the curve $y = \cos x$ and the coördinate axes, from $x = 0$ to $x = \frac{1}{2}\pi$.
2. Locate the centroid of the area bounded by the curve $y = e^x$, the coordinate axes and the line $x = 1$.
3. Find the centroid of the area bounded by the parabola $x^{\frac{1}{2}} + y^{\frac{1}{2}} = a^{\frac{1}{2}}$ and the coördinate axes.
4. Find the centroid of the area bounded by $y = xe^{-x}$, the X-axis and the line $x = 2$.
5. Locate the centroid of the area under one arch of the cycloid $x = a(\theta - \sin \theta)$, $y = a(1 - \cos \theta)$.
6. Find the centroid of the area in the first quadrant bounded by the ellipse $x = a \cos \theta$, $y = b \sin \theta$ and the coördinate axes.
7. Find the centroid of area of the upper half of the circle $r = 2 a \cos \theta$.
8. Locate the centroid of area of one loop of the lemniscate $r^2 = a^2 \cos 2 \theta$.

9. Find the coördinates of the centroid of the solid of revolution generated by revolving about the X-axis the area under one arch of the curve $y = \sin x$.

10. Find the centroid of the solid of revolution generated by revolving about the X-axis the area under one arch of the cycloid $x = a(\theta - \sin \theta)$, $y = a(1 - \cos \theta)$.

In Exercises 11-20, use the methods of § 407:

11. Find the coördinates of the centroid of the upper semi-circular arc of the circle $x^2 + y^2 = a^2$.

12. Locate the centroid of the upper arc of the parabola $y^2 = 4x$ from $x = 0$ to $x = 2$.

13. Find the centroid of the first quadrant arc of the hypocycloid $x^{\frac{2}{3}} + y^{\frac{2}{3}} = a^{\frac{2}{3}}$.

14. Find the centroid of arc of one arch of the cycloid $x = a(\theta - \sin \theta)$, $y = a(1 - \cos \theta)$.

15. Locate the centroid of the arc of the circle $r = a$ between $\theta = -\alpha$ and $\theta = \alpha$.

16. Locate the centroid of the upper arc of the cardioid $r = a(1 + \cos \theta)$.

17. Find the centroid of the surface of a hemisphere.

18. Find the position of the centroid of the lateral surface of a right circular cone of altitude h.

19. Locate the centroid of surface of a spherical segment in a sphere of radius a, cut off by a plane b units from the center.

20. Find the centroid of the surface of a paraboloid of revolution 2 feet high, with radius of base 4 feet.

In Exercises 21-24, use the methods of § 205:

21. Find the second moment of the area bounded by the curve $y = e^x$, the coördinate axes and the line $x = 1$, with respect to: (a) the Y-axis; (b) the X-axis.

22. Find the second moment of the area bounded by the catenary $y = \cosh x$, the coördinate axes and the line $x = 1$, with respect to: (a) the Y-axis; (b) the X-axis.

23. Find the second moment with respect to the Y-axis of the area bounded by the curve $y = \ln x$, the X-axis and the line $x = 2$.

24. Find the second moment of the area under one arch of the cycloid $x = a(\theta - \sin \theta)$, $y = a(1 - \cos \theta)$, with respect to: (a) the Y-axis; (b) the X-axis.

25. Use one of the theorems of Pappus to find the volume of a torus.

26. Use one of the theorems of Pappus to find the surface area of a torus.

27. Apply one of Pappus' theorems to find the location of the centroid of a semi-circular arc.

28. Use one of Pappus' theorems to locate the centroid of a semi-circular area.

CHAPTER XX

Approximate Integration

410. Approximate Integration

Methods of *approximate integration* are useful when the integral cannot be expressed in terms of elementary functions, and also when the integrand is defined by an empirical table of values or by an empirical graph.

Most of the methods of approximate integration are based on the fact that we may represent a definite integral by an area under a curve (§ 169), so that any method of approximating this area will give an approximate value of the integral.

Two of the most widely used methods of approximate integration by numerical calculation are the *trapezoidal rule* and *Simpson's rule*, which will be discussed in detail in §§ 411, 414. Another useful method is based on the use of *series* (§ 459). Various instruments such as planimeters, integraphs and integrators, are also available, by means of which the area of any plane figure can be found easily.

411. Trapezoidal Rule

The trapezoidal rule is based on the idea of representing a definite integral by an area under a curve and on approximating this area by a set of inscribed trapezoids, which amounts to replacing the arc of the curve by a set of chords.

Suppose that we are to evaluate $\int_a^b f(x)\, dx$ approximately. Let the arc CD in Fig. 183 be part of the graph of the integrand function $y = f(x)$; the integral is then represented by the area of the region $ABDC$ bounded by the arc CD, the X-axis and the ordinates AC and BD. Divide the interval (a, b) into n equal parts each of length h, so that $h = (b - a)/n$; let the end-points and the division-points be $x_0 = a, x_1, x_2, \cdots, x_{n-1}, x_n = b$, and let the corresponding ordinates be $y_0, y_1, y_2, \cdots, y_{n-1}, y_n$, as indicated in the figure. Join the ex-

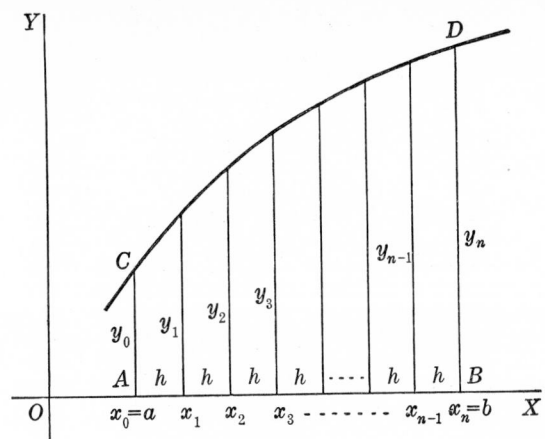

Fig. 183

tremities of consecutive ordinates by straight line segments (chords), forming trapezoids.   We then replace each strip under the curve by a corresponding trapezoid, and the sum of the areas of the trapezoids is taken as an approximation to the area under the curve.   Since the area of a trapezoid is equal to half the sum of the parallel sides times the altitude, we have for the sum of the areas of the trapezoids:

(a) $A = \frac{1}{2}(y_0 + y_1)h + \frac{1}{2}(y_1 + y_2)h + \frac{1}{2}(y_2 + y_3)h + \cdots$

$$+ \frac{1}{2}(y_{n-2} + y_{n-1})h + \frac{1}{2}(y_{n-1} + y_n)h$$

$$= \frac{1}{2} h(y_0 + 2 y_1 + 2 y_2 + \cdots + 2 y_{n-1} + y_n).$$

Hence, we have the **trapezoidal rule:**

If $y = f(x)$, and $\int_a^b f(x)\, dx = \int_a^b y\, dx$ is to be evaluated approximately, then

(1) $\int_a^b y\, dx \approx \dfrac{h}{2} (y_0 + 2\, y_1 + 2\, y_2 + 2\, y_3 + \cdots + 2\, y_{n-1} + y_n),$

where the interval (a, b) is divided into n equal sub-intervals each of length h, and where $y_0, y_1, y_2, \cdots, y_n$ are the values of y for $x = a$, $a + h, a + 2\, h, \cdots, b$.

Evidently, the greater the value of n, or the smaller the value of h, the closer the approximation will be, in general.

EXAMPLE 1. Evaluate $\int_0^1 \dfrac{dx}{1+x^2}$ by the trapezoidal rule, taking $n = 4$.

Solution: With $n = 4$, we have $h = \frac{1}{4}(b - a) = \frac{1}{4}$. Let $y = \dfrac{1}{1 + x^2}$; then $x_0 = 0$, $x_1 = \frac{1}{4}$, $x_2 = \frac{1}{2}$, $x_3 = \frac{3}{4}$, $x_4 = 1$, and

$$y_0 = \frac{1}{1 + 0} = 1, \; y_1 = \frac{1}{1 + (\frac{1}{4})^2} = \frac{16}{17} \approx 0.941,$$

$$y_2 = \frac{1}{1 + (\frac{1}{2})^2} = \frac{4}{5} = 0.8, \; y_3 = \frac{1}{1 + (\frac{3}{4})^2} = \frac{16}{25} = 0.64,$$

$$y_4 = \frac{1}{1 + 1} = \frac{1}{2} = 0.5.$$

By the trapezoidal rule, we get

$$\int_0^1 \frac{dx}{1 + x^2} \approx \frac{1}{2} \cdot \frac{1}{4} \left[1 + 2(0.941) + 2(0.8) + 2(0.64) + 0.5 \right] \approx 0.783.$$

The exact value of the integral is $\frac{1}{4}\pi$, which is 0.7854 to four decimal places.

EXAMPLE 2. A tree trunk is 140 inches long. At a distance x inches from one end its cross-sectional area, A, is given in square inches by the following table at intervals of 20 inches:

x	0	20	40	60	80	100	120	140
A	120	124	128	130	132	136	144	158

Find the volume of the tree trunk.

Solution: By § 192, the volume is $V = \int_0^{140} A \, dx$. Let us take $n = 7$ and $h = 20$. By the trapezoidal rule,

$$V \approx \tfrac{20}{2} [120 + 2(124) + 2(128) + 2(130) + 2(132) + 2(136) + 2(144) + 158]$$
$$= 18{,}660 \text{ cubic inches.}$$

412. Exercises

In Exercises 1–8, evaluate each of the given integrals by the trapezoidal rule, to three decimal places, using the value of n indicated in each case; then compare with the exact value of the integral:

1. $\int_0^2 x^2 \, dx$, $\quad n = 4$.

2. $\int_0^3 \dfrac{x \, dx}{\sqrt{4 + x^2}}$, $\quad n = 6$.

3. $\int_1^4 \dfrac{dx}{x^2}$, $\quad n = 6$.

4. $\int_0^3 (1 + x^2)^{\frac{3}{2}} \, dx$, $\quad n = 6$.

5. $\int_2^{10} \dfrac{dx}{1 + x}$, $\quad n = 8$.

6. $\int_0^4 x\sqrt{16 - x^2} \, dx$, $\quad n = 8$.

7. $\int_0^3 x\sqrt{9 - x^2}\, dx, \quad n = 6.$ 8. $\int_1^3 \frac{dx}{x}, \quad n = 8.$

In Exercises 9–12, evaluate each of the given integrals by the trapezoidal rule, to three decimal places, using the value of n indicated in each case; the exact value cannot be found by integration in terms of elementary functions:

9. $\int_0^2 \sqrt{4 + x^3}\, dx, \quad n = 4.$ 10. $\int_0^4 \frac{dx}{\sqrt{1 + x^3}}, \quad n = 4.$

11. $\int_0^\pi \frac{\sin x}{x}\, dx.$ **Take $n = 6$, $y_0 = 1.$**   12. $\int_0^2 e^{-x^2}\, dx, \quad n = 10.$

13. Find the length of the arc of the ellipse $x = 2 \cos \theta$, $y = \sin \theta$ in the first quadrant, by use of the trapezoidal rule, to three decimal places, by dividing the interval $0 \le \theta \le \frac{1}{2}\pi$ into five equal parts.

14. Find the length of the arc of the ellipse $9 x^2 + 100 y^2 = 900$ in the first quadrant from $x = 0$ to $x = 8$, by use of the trapezoidal rule, to three decimal places, by dividing the interval $0 \le x \le 8$ into four equal parts.

15. In the following table, S is the area in square yards of the cross-section of a railroad cutting, and x yards the corresponding distance along the line:

x	0	25	50	75	100	125	150
S	105	118	142	120	110	90	78

Calculate the number of cubic yards of earth removed to make the cutting from $x = 0$ to $x = 150$, using the trapezoidal rule.

16. A series of soundings taken across a river channel is given in the following table, x being the distance from one shore and y the corresponding depth:

x (ft.)	0	10	20	30	40	50	60	70	80
y (ft.)	5	10	13.2	15	15.6	12	6	4	0

Draw the section, and find its area, by the trapezoidal rule.

17. In the following table, F is the force in pounds acting on a body in its direction of motion and s is the displacement in feet:

s	0	5	10	15	20	25	30	35	40	45	50
F	100	80	66	56	50	45	40	36	33	30	28

Calculate the total work done by the force from: (a) $s = 0$ to $s = 20$, and (b) $s = 0$ to $s = 50$, using the trapezoidal rule.

18. Find the second moments about the X-axis and about the Y-axis of the area bounded by the curve represented by the following table of values and the ordinate $x = 3$:

x	0	0.5	1.0	1.5	2.0	2.5	3.0
y	0	2.83	4.0	4.9	5.66	6.32	6.93

413. Area Under a Parabolic Arc

As a preliminary to the derivation of Simpson's rule, we need to find a formula for the area under a parabolic arc.

Let the curve in Fig. 184 represent the parabola $y = ax^2 + bx + c$. Draw the ordinates to this curve at $x = -h$ and at $x = h$; and denote the ordinates at $x = -h$, $x = 0$ and $x = h$ by y_0, y_1 and y_2 respectively. The area under the parabola, above the X-axis and bounded by the ordinates y_0 and y_2 is given by

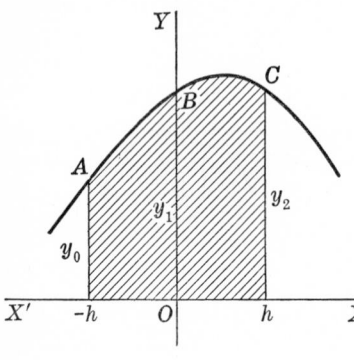

$$(a) \quad \text{Area} = \int_{-h}^{h} y \, dx$$

$$= \int_{-h}^{h} (ax^2 + bx + c) \, dx$$

$$= a\frac{x^3}{3} + b\frac{x^2}{2} + cx \Big|_{-h}^{h}$$

$$= \frac{2}{3} ah^3 + 2\,ch = \frac{h}{3} (2\,ah^2 + 6\,c).$$

Fig. 184

Since the three points $A(-h, y_0)$, $B(0, y_1)$ and $C(h, y_2)$ lie on the curve, their coördinates satisfy the equation $y = ax^2 + bx + c$, and we have

$$(b) \quad \begin{cases} y_0 = ah^2 - bh + c, \\ y_1 = \qquad\quad c, \\ y_2 = ah^2 + bh + c. \end{cases}$$

Then
$$y_0 + y_2 = 2\,ah^2 + 2\,c,$$

and therefore
$$y_0 + y_2 + 4\,y_1 = 2\,ah^2 + 6\,c.$$

Substituting this in the area formula (a), we get

$$(c) \qquad \text{Area} = \frac{h}{3} (y_0 + 4\,y_1 + y_2).$$

This formula (c) depends only upon the three ordinates and the distance h, and so is independent of the position of the y-axis. We may state the result as follows:

If a parabola with vertical axis is passed through the extremities of three equidistant ordinates y_0, y_1, y_2, with the distance h between consecutive ordinates, the area bounded by the parabola, the X-axis and the extreme ordinates y_0 and y_2 is given by:

$$(2) \qquad A = \frac{h}{3}\,(y_0 + 4\,y_1 + y_2).$$

414. Simpson's Rule

Simpson's rule is obtained by interpreting the definite integral by an area under a curve, and by approximating the curve by a set of parabolic arcs. By using such parabolic arcs instead of chords, as in the derivation of the trapezoidal rule, we would expect to get a closer

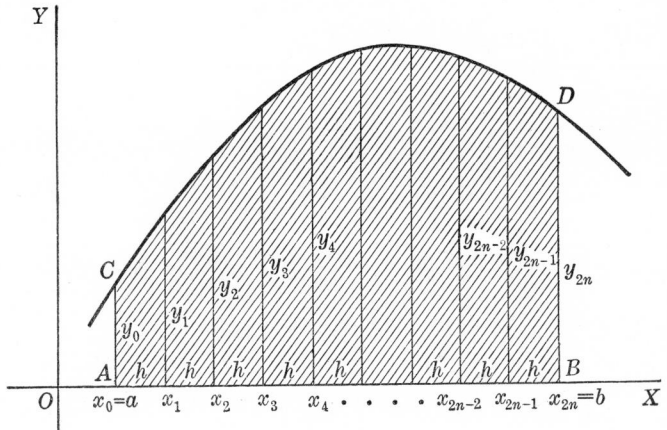

FIG. 185

approximation to the area. We recall that a parabola with vertical axis can be passed through three points not in the same straight line.

Let $\int_a^b f(x)\,dx$ be the integral to be approximated; and let the area $ABDC$ of Fig. 185 be the graphical representation of the integral. Divide the interval (a, b) into an *even number* $2\,n$ of equal sub-intervals, each of length $h = (b - a)/2\,n$. Let the corresponding points on the X-axis be $x_0 = a, x_1, x_2, \cdots, x_{2n-1}, x_{2n} = b$, and the corresponding ordinates $y_0, y_1, y_2, \cdots, y_{2n-1}, y_{2n}$; arrange these ordinates in groups of three, the last ordinate of each group being the same as the first ordinate of the next group. Through the extremities of the first three ordinates, pass an arc of a parabola with vertical axis; by § 413, formula (2), the area under this parabola between the ordinates y_0 and y_2 is

$$(a) \qquad A_1 = \frac{h}{3} (y_0 + 4 y_1 + y_2).$$

Through the extremities of the next three ordinates y_2, y_3, y_4, pass a parabolic arc; the corresponding area is

$$(b) \qquad A_2 = \frac{h}{3} (y_2 + 4 y_3 + y_4).$$

Similarly, the area under the next parabolic arc is

$$(c) \qquad A_3 = \frac{h}{3} (y_4 + 4 y_5 + y_6),$$

etc. Finally, the area under the last parabolic arc, between the ordinates y_{2n-2} and y_{2n} is

$$(d) \qquad A_n = \frac{h}{3} (y_{2n-2} + 4 y_{2n-1} + y_{2n}).$$

Adding these partial areas, we obtain for the total area under all the parabolic arcs:

$$
\begin{aligned}
(e) \quad A &= \frac{h}{3} [(y_0 + 4 y_1 + y_2) + (y_2 + 4 y_3 + y_4) + (y_4 + 4 y_5 + y_6) \\
&\quad + \cdots + (y_{2n-4} + 4 y_{2n-3} + y_{2n-2}) \\
&\quad + (y_{2n-2} + 4 y_{2n-1} + y_{2n})] \\
&= \frac{h}{3} (y_0 + 4 y_1 + 2 y_2 + 4 y_3 + 2 y_4 + \cdots \\
&\quad + 2 y_{2n-2} + 4 y_{2n-1} + y_{2n}).
\end{aligned}
$$

Hence, we have **Simpson's rule:**

If $y = f(x)$, where $f(x) \geqq 0$ when $a \leqq x \leqq b$, and $\int_a^b y \, dx$ is to be evaluated approximately, then

$$
(3) \qquad \int_a^b y \, dx \approx \frac{h}{3} (y_0 + 4 y_1 + 2 y_2 + 4 y_3 + 2 y_4 + \cdots \\
+ 2 y_{2n-2} + 4 y_{2n-1} + y_{2n}),
$$

where the interval (a, b) is divided into an even number $2n$ of equal subintervals each of length h, and where y_0, y_1, y_2, $\cdots$, y_{2n} are the values of y for $x = a$, $a + h$, $a + 2h$, $\cdots$, b.

As in the case of the trapezoidal rule, the larger the value of n (i.e. the smaller the value of h), the closer will be the approximation by Simpson's rule, in general.

EXAMPLE.   Evaluate $\int_0^1 \dfrac{dx}{1 + x^2}$ by Simpson's rule, with $2\,n = 4$.   (See § 411, Example 1.)

Solution: Using the values of y from Example 1 of § 411, we have

$$\int_0^1 \frac{dx}{1 + x^2} \approx \frac{1}{3}\cdot\frac{1}{4}\,[1 + 4(0.941) + 2(0.8) + 4(0.64) + 0.5] \approx 0.785.$$

The correct value, by integration, to four decimal places, is 0.7854.

It can be proved* that the error between the exact value of the integral and the approximate value given by Simpson's rule is less than $\dfrac{M(b - a)}{180}\cdot h^4$, where M is the greatest value of $|f^{(4)}(x)|$ in the interval (a, b).

415. Exercises

In Exercises 1–8, evaluate each of the given integrals by Simpson's rule, to three decimal places, taking the value of n indicated in each case; compare with the value found by exact integration:

1. $\displaystyle\int_0^{10} x^2\, dx, \quad 2\,n = 10.$ 2. $\displaystyle\int_1^4 \frac{dx}{x^2}, \quad 2\,n = 6.$

3. $\displaystyle\int_1^9 \frac{dx}{x}, \quad 2\,n = 8.$ 4. $\displaystyle\int_0^4 x\sqrt{25 - x^2}\, dx, \quad 2\,n = 4.$

5. $\displaystyle\int_2^8 \sqrt{64 - x^2}\, dx, \quad 2\,n = 6.$ 6. $\displaystyle\int_0^1 \frac{dx}{1 + x}, \quad 2\,n = 8.$

7. $\displaystyle\int_0^{\pi} \sin x\, dx, \quad 2\,n = 6.$ 8. $\displaystyle\int_0^1 \frac{dx}{1 + x^3}, \quad 2\,n = 4.$

In Exercises 9–12, evaluate each of the given integrals by Simpson's rule, to three decimal places, taking the value of n indicated in each case:

9. $\displaystyle\int_0^1 \sqrt{1 + x^3}\, dx, \quad 2\,n = 6.$ 10. $\displaystyle\int_0^2 e^{-x^2}\, dx, \quad 2\,n = 10.$

11. $\displaystyle\int_0^3 \sqrt{16 - x^2}\, dx, \quad 2\,n = 6.$ 12. $\displaystyle\int_0^4 \frac{dx}{\sqrt{4 + x^3}}, \quad 2\,n = 8.$

Calculate each of the following integrals by both the trapezoidal rule and Simpson's rule, and compare results:

13. $\displaystyle\int_3^6 \frac{x\, dx}{4 + x^2}, \quad$ using six sub-intervals.

* See Fine, *Calculus*, page 219.

14. $\displaystyle\int_0^1 \frac{dx}{1 + x^2}$, using ten sub-intervals.

15. $\displaystyle\int_4^7 \sqrt{9 + x^2}\, dx$, using six sub-intervals.

16. $\displaystyle\int_0^{\frac{\pi}{2}} \sqrt{\sin x}\, dx$, using four sub-intervals.

17. Find the length of the arc of the ellipse $x = 3 \sin \phi$, $y = 4 \cos \phi$ in the first quadrant, by use of Simpson's rule, to three decimal places, by dividing the interval $0 \leq \phi \leq \frac{1}{2}\pi$ into six equal parts.

18. Calculate the maximum possible error in the approximation of $\displaystyle\int_1^2 \frac{dx}{x^2}$ by Simpson's rule, with $2\,n = 8$.

19. Find the area between the curve given by the following pairs of rectangular coördinates:

x	2.0	2.4	2.8	3.2	3.6	4.0	4.4
y	3.03	4.61	5.80	6.59	7.76	8.46	9.19

the X-axis and the ordinates $x = 2$ and $x = 4.4$, by Simpson's rule.

20. The area of the horizontal section of a reservoir is A square feet at a height x feet from the bottom; corresponding values of x and A are given in the following table:

x	0	2.5	5	7.5	10	12.5	15	17.5	20	22.5	25
A	0	2510	3860	4870	5160	5590	5810	6210	6890	7680	8270

Find the volume of the water when the depth is 25 feet, by use of the trapezoidal rule and also by Simpson's rule.

21. A gas expands from a volume of 1 cubic foot to 2.5 cubic feet; values of the volume and pressure during the expansion are given in the following table:

v	1	1.25	1.5	1.75	2	2.25	2.5
p	68.7	55.0	45.8	39.3	34.4	30.5	27.5

(p is in pounds per square inch). Calculate the total work done in the expansion, using Simpson's rule.

22. For the area between the curve given by the following pairs of rectangular coördinates:

x	2	3	4	5	6	7	8
y	0.77	1.20	1.26	1.18	0.80	0.33	0.10

the X-axis and the ordinates $x = 2$ and $x = 8$, find: (a) the volume of the solid of revolution generated by revolving this area about the X-axis; (b) the second moment of this area with respect to the Y-axis, by Simpson's rule.

CHAPTER XXI

Improper Integrals

416. Improper Integrals

In the definition of the definite integral $\int_a^b f(x)\,dx$ given in Chapter X, it was assumed that the integrand $f(x)$ is *finite* in the interval (a, b), and that both limits of integration a and b are *finite*. If either of these conditions is not fulfilled, the previous definition does not apply, and a new definition is necessary. In such a case, the integral is called an *improper integral*.

There are therefore two types of improper integrals: (1) integrals with infinite discontinuous integrands, and (2) integrals with infinite limits. These will be considered separately.

417. Improper Integrals with Discontinuous Integrand

An improper integral with discontinuous integrand is defined as follows:

I. *If the integrand $f(x)$ becomes infinite at the lower limit of integration, a, and if the integral $\int_{a+h}^b f(x)\,dx$ has a limit l when $h \to 0$ through positive values, then we say that the improper integral $\int_a^b f(x)\,dx$ is* **convergent** *with the* **value** *l:*

(a) $$\int_a^b f(x)\,dx = \lim_{h \to 0} \int_{a+h}^b f(x)\,dx \qquad (h > 0);$$

but if $\int_{a+h}^b f(x)\,dx$ does not have a limit when $h \to 0$, we say that the improper integral $\int_a^b f(x)\,dx$ is **divergent** *and has no value.*

II. *If $f(x)$ becomes infinite at the upper limit of integration, b, the* *convergence* and *value*, or *divergence*, *of the improper integral* $\int_a^b f(x)\ dx$

depend in a similar way on the existence and value of $\lim\limits_{h \to 0} \int_a^{b-h} f(x)\ dx$

$(h > 0)$.

III. *If* $f(x)$ *becomes infinite at a point* $x = c$, *where* $a < c < b$, *the improper integral* $\int_a^b f(x)\ dx$ *is said to* **converge** *to the* **value**

$$(b) \qquad \int_a^b f(x)\ dx = \int_a^c f(x)\ dx + \int_c^b f(x)\ dx,$$

if each improper integral on the right-hand side converges; if either of them diverges, so does $\int_a^b f(x)\ dx$, *which then has no value.*

EXAMPLE 1. Examine the improper integral $\int_2^3 \dfrac{dx}{\sqrt{x-2}}$.

Solution: The integrand $1/\sqrt{x-2}$ becomes infinite as x approaches the lower limit of the integral; we must therefore apply definition I. We have

$$\int_{2+h}^3 \frac{dx}{\sqrt{x-2}} = 2(x-2)^{\frac{1}{2}}\Big|_{2+h}^3 = 2(1 - h^{\frac{1}{2}}).$$

Since $2(1 - h^{\frac{1}{2}}) \to 2$ as $h \to 0$, it follows that the given integral is convergent and has the value 2, and we write

$$\int_2^3 \frac{dx}{\sqrt{x-2}} = 2.$$

EXAMPLE 2. Examine the integral $\int_0^1 \dfrac{dx}{x^2}$.

Solution: The integrand $(1/x^2)$ becomes infinite as $x \to 0$. We form the integral

$$\int_h^1 \frac{dx}{x^2} = -\frac{1}{x}\Big|_h^1 = -1 + \frac{1}{h};$$

but $-1 + \dfrac{1}{h} \to +\infty$ when $h \to 0$ (through positive values), so that the integral $\int_0^1 \dfrac{dx}{x^2}$ is divergent and has no value.

EXAMPLE 3. Examine the integral $\int_0^1 \dfrac{dx}{\sqrt{1-x^2}}$.

Solution: In this case, the integrand $1/\sqrt{1-x^2}$ becomes infinite as x approaches the upper limit of the integral. Since

$$\int_0^{1-h} \frac{dx}{\sqrt{1-x^2}} = \text{Arc sin } x \,\Big|_0^{1-h} = \text{Arc sin } (1-h),$$

and Arc sin $(1-h) \to \frac{1}{2}\pi$ as $h \to 0$, by definition II the given integral converges to the value $\frac{1}{2}\pi$.

EXAMPLE 4. Examine the integral $\int_{-1}^{1} \frac{dx}{x^2}$.

Solution: The integrand becomes infinite at $c = 0$ between the upper and lower limits of the integral; we therefore examine the improper integrals

$$\int_{-1}^{0} \frac{dx}{x^2} \text{ and } \int_0^1 \frac{dx}{x^2}. \text{ Since}$$

$$\int_{-1}^{-h} \frac{dx}{x^2} = \frac{1}{h} - 1 \quad \text{and} \quad \int_h^1 \frac{dx}{x^2} = -1 + \frac{1}{h},$$

we see that both improper integrals mentioned above are divergent. Therefore, the given integral diverges.

It is of interest to note that if we substitute the limits -1 and 1 in the indefinite integral $\int \frac{dx}{x^2}$ directly, we get

$$-\frac{1}{x}\,\Big|_{-1}^{1} = -1 - 1 = -2,$$

which is *incorrect*.

In the first type of improper integral, where $f(x)$ becomes infinite at the lower limit a, by interpreting the integral $\int_{a+h}^{b} f(x)\,dx$ as the area under a curve, we may obtain a geometric interpretation of the improper integral $\int_a^b f(x)\,dx$ as the *limit of an area* when the integral is convergent. Similarly for the other types.

418. Exercises

In the improper integrals in Exercises 1–22, determine which of them are convergent and which of them are divergent, and evaluate each of those that are convergent:

1. $\int_0^1 \frac{dx}{\sqrt{x}}$.

2. $\int_0^1 \frac{dx}{x^3}$.

3. $\int_0^1 \frac{dx}{x}$.

4. $\int_4^6 \frac{dx}{\sqrt{x-4}}$.

5. $\int_0^a \frac{dx}{\sqrt{a-x}}$.

6. $\int_1^5 \frac{x\,dx}{\sqrt{5-x}}$.

7. $\displaystyle\int_0^{\frac{\pi}{4}} \tan 2\,x\,dx.$

8. $\displaystyle\int_0^{\frac{\pi}{2}} \csc x\,dx.$

9. $\displaystyle\int_{-1}^1 \frac{dx}{\sqrt[3]{x}}.$

10. $\displaystyle\int_0^3 \frac{dx}{(x-2)^2}.$

11. $\displaystyle\int_0^{2a} \frac{dx}{(x-a)^2}.$

12. $\displaystyle\int_a^{3a} \frac{2\,x\,dx}{(x^2-a^2)^{\frac{3}{2}}}.$

13. $\displaystyle\int_0^1 \frac{dx}{1-x^2}.$

14. $\displaystyle\int_1^2 \frac{dx}{\sqrt{x^2-1}}.$

15. $\displaystyle\int_0^a \frac{x^2\,dx}{\sqrt{a^2-x^2}}.$

16. $\displaystyle\int_0^3 \frac{x\,dx}{(9-x^2)^{\frac{3}{2}}}.$

17. $\displaystyle\int_{-a}^a \frac{dx}{\sqrt{a^2-x^2}}.$

18. $\displaystyle\int_0^1 \frac{\ln x\,dx}{x}.$

19. $\displaystyle\int_0^a \frac{dx}{\sqrt{a^2-x^2}}.$

20. $\displaystyle\int_a^{2a} \frac{x\,dx}{\sqrt{x^2-a^2}}.$

21. $\displaystyle\int_1^2 \frac{dx}{(2-x)^{\frac{3}{4}}}.$

22. $\displaystyle\int_0^4 \frac{dx}{\sqrt{8\,x-x^2}}.$

23. Find the "limiting area" between the cissoid $(2\,a-x)\,y^2 = x^3$ and its asymptote.

419. Improper Integrals with Infinite Limits

When the interval of integration of a definite integral is infinite, the resulting improper integral is often called an *infinite integral* (by analogy with infinite series). This type of improper integral is defined as follows:

I. *If the integrand* $f(x)$ *is continuous for* $x \geqq a$, *and if the integral* $\displaystyle\int_a^t f(x)\,dx$ *has a limit* l *when* $t \to +\infty$, *we say that the improper integral* $\displaystyle\int_a^\infty f(x)\,dx$ *is* **convergent** *with the* **value** l:

(a) $$\int_a^\infty f(x)\,dx = \lim_{t\to+\infty} \int_a^t f(x)\,dx;$$

but if $\displaystyle\int_a^t f(x)\,dx$ *does not have a limit when* $t \to +\infty$, *we say that the improper integral* $\displaystyle\int_a^\infty f(x)\,dx$ *is* **divergent** *and has no value.*

II. *Similarly, if* $f(x)$ *is continuous for* $x \leqq b$, *the improper integral*

$\int_{-\infty}^{b} f(x)\, dx$ is said to **converge** to the **value** $\lim\limits_{t\to-\infty} \int_{t}^{b} f(x)\, dx$ if that limit exists, but otherwise it **diverges** and has no value.

III. If $f(x)$ is continuous for all values of x, the improper integral $\int_{-\infty}^{\infty} f(x)\, dx$ is said to **converge** to the **value**

(b) $$\int_{-\infty}^{\infty} f(x)\, dx = \int_{-\infty}^{c} f(x)\, dx + \int_{c}^{\infty} f(x)\, dx,$$

if each improper integral on the right-hand side converges for a suitable value of c; if either of them diverges, so does $\int_{-\infty}^{\infty} f(x)\, dx$, which then has no value.

EXAMPLE 1. Examine the improper integral $\int_{0}^{\infty} \dfrac{dx}{1 + x^2}$.

Solution: Since

$$\int_{0}^{t} \frac{dx}{1 + x^2} = \text{Arc tan } t,$$

and since Arc tan $t \to \frac{1}{2}\pi$ as $t \to +\infty$, it follows from the definition I that the given integral converges to the value $\frac{1}{2}\pi$.

EXAMPLE 2. Consider the integral $\int_{1}^{\infty} \dfrac{dx}{x}$.

Solution: Since $\int_{1}^{t} \dfrac{dx}{x} = \ln|t|$, and since $\ln t \to +\infty$ as $t \to +\infty$, the given integral is divergent.

EXAMPLE 3. Examine the infinite integral $\int_{-\infty}^{\infty} \dfrac{dx}{x^2 + 2x + 2}$.

Solution: We have

$$\int_{0}^{t} \frac{dx}{x^2 + 2x + 2} = \text{Arc tan }(x + 1)\,\Big|_{0}^{t} = \text{Arc tan }(t + 1) - \tfrac{1}{4}\pi,$$

$$\int_{t'}^{0} \frac{dx}{x^2 + 2x + 2} = \text{Arc tan }(x + 1)\,\Big|_{t'}^{0} = \tfrac{1}{4}\pi - \text{Arc tan }(t' + 1).$$

Since Arc tan $(t + 1) \to \frac{1}{2}\pi$ when $t \to +\infty$, and Arc tan $(t' + 1) \to -\frac{1}{2}\pi$ when $t' \to -\infty$, the given integral is convergent with the value π.

If the interval of integration is infinite and if the integrand becomes infinite at a finite number of points, we divide the range of integration into a finite number of intervals within each of which the resulting improper integral is of one of the types previously discussed. If *each* of these integrals converges, the value of the given integral is defined as the sum of their values.

By interpreting the integral $\int_a^t f(x)\, dx$ as an area under a curve, we may obtain a geometric interpretation of the infinite integral $\int_a^\infty f(x)\, dx$ as a *limit of an area* when the integral is convergent. Similar statements hold for the other cases of integrals with infinite limits of integration.

420. Exercises

In the improper integrals in Exercises 1–24, determine which of them are convergent and which of them are divergent, and evaluate each of those that are convergent:

1. $\int_1^\infty \dfrac{dx}{x^2}.$

2. $\int_0^\infty e^{-x}\, dx.$

3. $\int_0^\infty e^{2x}\, dx.$

4. $\int_1^\infty \dfrac{dx}{\sqrt{x}}.$

5. $\int_0^\infty \dfrac{x\, dx}{\sqrt{x+1}}.$

6. $\int_3^\infty \dfrac{dx}{(x-1)^4}.$

7. $\int_0^\infty x\, e^{-x^2}\, dx.$

8. $\int_0^\infty \cos x\, dx.$

9. $\int_1^\infty \dfrac{x\, dx}{(1+x^2)^2}.$

10. $\int_0^\infty \dfrac{x\, dx}{1+x^2}.$

11. $\int_0^\infty e^{-x} \cos x\, dx.$

12. $\int_1^\infty \dfrac{dx}{x(1+x^2)}.$

13. $\int_{-\infty}^0 \dfrac{dx}{x^2+4}.$

14. $\int_{-\infty}^2 \dfrac{dx}{\sqrt{4-x}}.$

15. $\int_{-\infty}^1 \dfrac{x\, dx}{\sqrt{2-x}}.$

16. $\int_{-\infty}^0 e^x\, dx.$

17. $\int_{-\infty}^\infty \dfrac{dx}{x^2+a^2}.$

18. $\int_{-\infty}^\infty \dfrac{dx}{(x+1)^2}.$

19. $\int_{-\infty}^\infty \dfrac{dx}{x^{\frac{2}{3}}}.$

20. $\int_{-\infty}^\infty \dfrac{dx}{x^2+4x+5}.$

21. $\int_{2a}^\infty \dfrac{dx}{x^2-a^2}.$

22. $\int_2^\infty \dfrac{dx}{x\sqrt{x^2-1}}.$

23. $\int_1^\infty \dfrac{dx}{x^4+x^2}.$

24. $\int_{-\infty}^\infty \dfrac{dx}{e^x+e^{-x}}.$

25. Find the "limiting area" between the witch $y = \dfrac{8\,a^3}{x^2 + 4\,a^2}$ and its asymptote.

26. In a problem in electrical theory, the following integral occurs:

$$W = \int_0^\infty Ri^2\, dt,$$

where $i = I\,e^{-\frac{Rt}{L}}$, $(R,\ I$ and L constant); evaluate it.

27. The magnetic potential at a point on the axis of a circular coil is given by

$$u = \frac{2\,\pi N I r}{10} \int_x^\infty \frac{dy}{(r^2 + y^2)^{\frac{3}{2}}},$$

where $N,\ I,\ r$ and x are constants; evaluate it.

28. The field intensity around a long ("infinite") straight wire carrying electric current is given by the integral

$$F = \frac{rIm}{10} \int_{-\infty}^\infty \frac{dy}{(r^2 + y^2)^{\frac{3}{2}}},$$

where $r,\ I$ and m are constants; evaluate it.

CHAPTER XXII

Indeterminate Forms

---

421. Indeterminate Forms

We have met *indeterminate forms* before in § 72. In some special cases we found methods of evaluating them. We now consider more general methods for evaluating indeterminate forms.

If $u(x) \to 0$ and $v(x) \to 0$ as $x \to a$, we say that $F(x) = \dfrac{u(x)}{v(x)}$ has the indeterminate form $\dfrac{0}{0}$ at $x = a$. If $u(x) \to \infty$ and $v(x) \to 0$ as $x \to a$, we say that $F(x) = u^v$ has the *indeterminate form* ∞^0 at $x = a$. In a similar way we may obtain the following indeterminate forms for a function $F(x)$:

$$\frac{0}{0}, \quad \frac{\infty}{\infty}, \quad 0 \cdot \infty, \quad \infty - \infty, \quad 0^0, \quad \infty^0, \quad 1^\infty.$$

In these cases, the function $F(x)$ is not defined for $x = a$ and it is discontinuous there. But if $\lim\limits_{x \to a} F(x)$ exists, it is convenient to assign this value to $F(a)$, for this re-definition makes $F(x)$ continuous at $x = a$. Hence:

If $F(x)$ becomes indeterminate for $x = a$, then we define $F(a)$ as $\lim\limits_{x \to a} F(x)$, *if this limit exists.*

Indeterminate forms may also arise when $x \to \infty$, as well as when x approaches some number a.

422. More General Mean-Value Theorem for Derivatives

In § 150, we derived a mean-value theorem for derivatives which involved one function. For use in this chapter, we need a somewhat more general mean-value theorem involving two functions. It may be stated as follows:

443

If $f(x)$ and $g(x)$ are continuous in the interval $a \leq x \leq b$, and if the derivatives $f'(x)$ and $g'(x)$ exist at every point of the interval $a < x < b$, and if $g'(x)$ is not zero at any point within the interval (a, b), except possibly at a or b, then there is at least one value ξ of x between a and b such that

(1) $$\frac{f(b) - f(a)}{g(b) - g(a)} = \frac{f'(\xi)}{g'(\xi)}, \qquad (a < \xi < b).$$

This theorem may be proved in a manner similar to that used in § 150 for the previous mean-value theorem. We construct the auxiliary function:

(a) $$F(x) = f(x) - f(a) - \frac{f(b) - f(a)}{g(b) - g(a)} [g(x) - g(a)].$$

Since $g'(x) \neq 0$ at all points within the interval (a, b), it follows from Rolle's theorem (§ 149) that $g(a) \neq g(b)$. From the form of $F(x)$ and the hypotheses on $f(x)$ and $g(x)$, it follows that $F(x)$ is continuous in the interval $a \leq x \leq b$, and that it has a derivative at all points where $a < x < b$. Evidently $F(a) = F(b) = 0$. We have

(b) $$F'(x) = f'(x) - \frac{f(b) - f(a)}{g(b) - g(a)} g'(x).$$

By Rolle's theorem, $F'(x)$ must vanish for some value $x = \xi$ between a and b. Hence,

(c) $$F'(\xi) = f'(\xi) - \frac{f(b) - f(a)}{g(b) - g(a)} g'(\xi) = 0,$$

from which formula (1) follows at once since $g'(\xi) \neq 0$.

It should be noted that the mean-value theorem of § 150 is a special case of this theorem, for the case when $g(x) = x$.

423. Evaluation of the Indeterminate Form 0/0

Consider the fractional form $F(x) = \frac{f(x)}{g(x)}$, where $f(a) = 0$ and $g(a) = 0$. Then the function $F(x)$ is indeterminate for $x = a$, and is of the form $\frac{0}{0}$. According to the general definition of § 421, it is then necessary to investigate $\lim\limits_{x \to a} \frac{f(x)}{g(x)}$. In this case, we cannot evaluate this limit by taking the quotient of the limits of $f(x)$ and $g(x)$, by the rule of § 70, III.

Let us suppose that $f(x)$ and $g(x)$ are continuous in an interval containing the point $x = a$, and also suppose that their derivatives exist in this interval and that $g'(x) \neq 0$ within this interval except possibly at $x = a$. Let us now apply the general mean-value theorem of § 422 to $F(x)$, taking x in place of b. Since $f(a) = 0$ and $g(a) = 0$, the formula (1) of § 422 becomes

$$(a) \qquad \frac{f(x)}{g(x)} = \frac{f'(\xi)}{g'(\xi)}, \quad (\xi \text{ between } a \text{ and } x).$$

Evidently, $\xi \to a$ when $x \to a$ since ξ is between a and x. If $\lim\limits_{x \to a} \dfrac{f'(x)}{g'(x)}$ exists, from (a) we get

$$(b) \qquad \lim_{x \to a} \frac{f(x)}{g(x)} = \lim_{x \to a} \frac{f'(x)}{g'(x)}.$$

Hence:

If $f(x)$ and $g(x)$ are continuous in an interval including $x = a$, and if their derivatives $f'(x)$ and $g'(x)$ exist and $g'(x) \neq 0$ in this interval (except possibly at $x = a$), and if $f(a) = 0$ and $g(a) = 0$, then:

$$(2) \qquad \lim_{x \to a} \frac{f(x)}{g(x)} = \lim_{x \to a} \frac{f'(x)}{g'(x)},$$

provided the latter limit exists.

This is known as *l'Hospital's rule.*

EXAMPLE 1. Evaluate the indeterminate form $\lim\limits_{x \to 1} \dfrac{\ln x}{x - 1}$.

Solution: If we put $f(x) = \ln x$, $g(x) = x - 1$, then

$$\frac{f'(x)}{g'(x)} = \frac{\dfrac{1}{x}}{1} = \frac{1}{x}.$$

By l'Hospital's rule, the required limit is $\lim\limits_{x \to 1} \left(\dfrac{1}{x}\right) = 1$.

It may happen that, when we apply the rule (2) to $\dfrac{f(x)}{g(x)}$, the derivatives $f'(x)$ and $g'(x)$ both approach 0. In this case, we may again apply formula (2) to find the limit of $\dfrac{f'(x)}{g'(x)}$.

EXAMPLE 2. Evaluate the limit $\lim\limits_{x \to 0} \dfrac{x - \sin x}{x^2}$.

Solution: If we take $f(x) = x - \sin x$, $g(x) = x^2$, then

$$\frac{f'(x)}{g'(x)} = \frac{1 - \cos x}{2\,x},$$

which is indeterminate when $x = 0$. Applying l'Hospital's rule again, since $\dfrac{f''(x)}{g''(x)} = \dfrac{\sin x}{2}$, we have

$$\lim_{x \to 0} \frac{x - \sin x}{x^2} = \lim_{x \to 0} \frac{1 - \cos x}{2\,x} = \lim_{x \to 0} \frac{\sin x}{2} = 0.$$

The required limit is therefore 0.

It will simplify the work if, before each step in applying l'Hospital's rule, the fraction involved is reduced to its simplest form. Sometimes a never-ending set of indeterminate forms will be obtained unless some transformation (algebraic or trigonometric) is made at the appropriate stage.

EXAMPLE 3. Find $\displaystyle\lim_{x \to 0} \frac{\tan x - x}{x - \sin x}$.

Solution: By the rule (2):

$$\lim_{x \to 0} \frac{\tan x - x}{x - \sin x} = \lim_{x \to 0} \frac{\sec^2 x - 1}{1 - \cos x},$$

which is indeterminate of the form $0/0$. If we apply the rule to this form as it stands, we get another indeterminate form. But if we transform the last fraction thus:

$$\frac{\sec^2 x - 1}{1 - \cos x} = \frac{\dfrac{1}{\cos^2 x} - 1}{1 - \cos x} = \frac{1 - \cos^2 x}{\cos^2 x(1 - \cos x)} = \frac{1 + \cos x}{\cos^2 x},$$

we see that the limit of the last expression as $x \to 0$ is 2. The required limit is therefore 2.

It can be shown that: if $\dfrac{f(x)}{g(x)}$ takes the form $\dfrac{0}{0}$ when $x \to \infty$, then

(c)
$$\lim_{x \to \infty} \frac{f(x)}{g(x)} = \lim_{x \to \infty} \frac{f'(x)}{g'(x)},$$

if the latter limit exists.

It can also be shown that: if $\dfrac{f(x)}{g(x)}$ takes the form $\dfrac{0}{0}$ when $x \to a$ or $x \to \infty$, and if $\dfrac{f'(x)}{g'(x)} \to \infty$, then $\dfrac{f(x)}{g(x)} \to \infty$.

A common mistake is to *differentiate the quotient* $\dfrac{f(x)}{g(x)}$ instead of finding the *quotient of the derivatives* of $f(x)$ and $g(x)$ separately.

424. Exercises

Evaluate each of the limits in Exercises 1–40:

1. $\lim\limits_{x\to 2} \dfrac{x^2 + x - 6}{x^2 - 3x + 2}$.

2. $\lim\limits_{x\to -1} \dfrac{x^2 + 5x + 4}{x^2 - 4x - 5}$.

3. $\lim\limits_{x\to 1} \dfrac{2x^3 + 5x^2 - 4x - 3}{x^3 + x^2 - 10x + 8}$.

4. $\lim\limits_{x\to 0} \dfrac{x^3 - 3x^2 + 5x}{x^3 - x}$.

5. $\lim\limits_{x\to 1} \dfrac{\ln x}{x^2 - 1}$.

6. $\lim\limits_{x\to 1} \dfrac{\sin \pi x}{x - 1}$.

7. $\lim\limits_{x\to 0} \dfrac{e^x - e^{-x}}{\sin x}$.

8. $\lim\limits_{x\to 0} \dfrac{\tan 2x}{\ln (1 + x)}$.

9. $\lim\limits_{x\to \pi} \dfrac{1 + \cos x}{\sin 2x}$.

10. $\lim\limits_{x\to 0} \dfrac{\ln (1 - x)}{e^x - 1}$.

11. $\lim\limits_{x\to 0} \dfrac{\sin^2 x}{x}$.

12. $\lim\limits_{x\to 0} \dfrac{\tan x - x}{\sin x}$.

13. $\lim\limits_{x\to 0} \dfrac{e^x + e^{-x} - 2}{x^2}$.

14. $\lim\limits_{x\to 0} \dfrac{e^x + e^{-x} - 2}{\sin^2 x}$.

15. $\lim\limits_{x\to 0} \dfrac{\cos x - 1}{\cos 2x - 1}$.

16. $\lim\limits_{x\to 0} \dfrac{e^x - 1 - \sin x}{1 - \cos x}$.

17. $\lim\limits_{x\to 0} \dfrac{\sin x - x}{x^3}$.

18. $\lim\limits_{x\to 0} \dfrac{\tan x - x}{\cos x - 1}$.

19. $\lim\limits_{x\to 0} \dfrac{e^x - e^{-x} - 2\sin x}{3x^3}$.

20. $\lim\limits_{x\to 0} \dfrac{\tan x - \sin x}{x^3}$.

21. $\lim\limits_{x\to 0} \dfrac{x e^{4x} - x}{1 - \cos 2x}$.

22. $\lim\limits_{x\to 0} \dfrac{x \tan x}{1 - \cos x}$.

23. $\lim\limits_{x\to \frac{\pi}{4}} \dfrac{1 + \cos 4x}{\sec^2 x - 2\tan x}$.

24. $\lim\limits_{x\to 0} \dfrac{\tan x - \sin x}{x^2 \tan x}$.

25. $\lim\limits_{x\to 0} \dfrac{2^x - 1}{3^x - 1}$.

26. $\lim\limits_{x\to 0} \dfrac{a^x - b^x}{x}$.

27. $\lim\limits_{x\to \frac{\pi}{4}} \dfrac{\cos^2 2x}{1 - \tan x}$.

28. $\lim\limits_{x\to 0} \dfrac{\text{Arc} \tan x}{x}$.

29. $\lim\limits_{x\to 0} \dfrac{e^x - \ln (1 + x) - 1}{x^2}$.

30. $\lim\limits_{x\to 0} \dfrac{2x - \text{Arc} \sin x}{2\,\text{Arc} \tan x - x}$.

31. $\lim\limits_{x\to 0} \dfrac{x - \text{Arc} \tan x}{x^3}$.

32. $\lim\limits_{x\to 0} \dfrac{\tan 3x}{x \cos x}$.

33. $\lim\limits_{x \to 0} \dfrac{e^{2x} - 1}{x^2 - \sin x}$.

34. $\lim\limits_{x \to 0} \dfrac{\sin 2x - \sin x}{\tan 3x}$.

35. $\lim\limits_{x \to 0} \dfrac{\text{Arc tan } x}{\text{Arc sin } x}$.

36. $\lim\limits_{x \to 0} \dfrac{\ln \sec 2x}{\ln \sec x}$.

37. $\lim\limits_{x \to 0} \dfrac{\sinh x}{x}$.

38. $\lim\limits_{x \to 0} \dfrac{\cosh x - 1}{x^2}$.

39. $\lim\limits_{x \to 0} \dfrac{\ln \cosh x}{x}$.

40. $\lim\limits_{x \to 0} \dfrac{\tanh^{-1} x}{x}$.

41. Discuss the behavior of $\dfrac{\sin x + \tan x}{e^x + e^{-x} - 2}$ as $x \to 0$.

42. Discuss the behavior of $\dfrac{1 - \cos x - x \sin x}{2 - 2 \cos x - \sin^2 x}$ as $x \to 0$.

425. Evaluation of the Indeterminate Form ∞ /∞

It can be proved* that indeterminate forms of the type ∞ / ∞ may be evaluated by a process like that for the type $0/0$, as indicated by the following theorem:

If $f(x) \to \infty$ and $g(x) \to \infty$ as $x \to a$, then

$$(3) \qquad \lim_{x \to a} \frac{f(x)}{g(x)} = \lim_{x \to a} \frac{f'(x)}{g'(x)},$$

provided the latter limit exists. The corresponding result holds for the limits as $x \to +\infty$ or as $x \to -\infty$ instead of the limits as $x \to a$.

EXAMPLE. Evaluate the limit $\lim\limits_{x \to +\infty} \dfrac{x^2}{e^x}$.

Solution: $\lim\limits_{x \to +\infty} \dfrac{x^2}{e^x} = \lim\limits_{x \to +\infty} \dfrac{2x}{e^x} = \lim\limits_{x \to +\infty} \dfrac{2}{e^x} = 0$.

426. Exercises

Evaluate each of the following limits:

1. $\lim\limits_{x \to 0} \dfrac{\ln x}{\cot x}$.

2. $\lim\limits_{x \to 0} \dfrac{\ln x}{\dfrac{1}{x}}$.

3. $\lim\limits_{x \to \frac{\pi}{2}} \dfrac{\sec x + 1}{\tan x}$.

4. $\lim\limits_{x \to 0} \dfrac{\ln \sin 2x}{\ln \sin x}$.

5. $\lim\limits_{x \to +\infty} \dfrac{\ln x}{x}$.

6. $\lim\limits_{x \to 0} \dfrac{\ln \sin x}{\ln \tan x}$.

* See, for example, Fine, *Calculus*, page 109.

7. $\lim\limits_{x \to +\infty} \dfrac{x}{e^x}$.

8. $\lim\limits_{x \to +\infty} \dfrac{x^4 + x^3}{e^x + 1}$.

9. $\lim\limits_{x \to 0} \dfrac{\cot x}{\cot 2x}$.

10. $\lim\limits_{x \to +\infty} \dfrac{\ln x}{a^x}$.

11. $\lim\limits_{x \to +\infty} \dfrac{x^2 + x - 1}{e^x + e^{-x}}$.

12. $\lim\limits_{x \to +\infty} \dfrac{x + \ln x}{x \ln x}$.

13. $\lim\limits_{x \to +\infty} \dfrac{\ln (\ln x)}{\ln x}$.

14. $\lim\limits_{x \to \frac{1}{2}} \dfrac{\ln (1 - 2x)}{\tan \pi x}$.

15. $\lim\limits_{x \to 1} \dfrac{\ln (1 - x)}{\cot \pi x}$.

16. $\lim\limits_{x \to 0} \dfrac{\csc x}{\cot^2 x}$.

17. $\lim\limits_{x \to +\infty} \dfrac{\ln x}{x^k} \ (k > 0)$.

18. $\lim\limits_{x \to +\infty} \dfrac{\ln x}{e^x}$.

19. $\lim\limits_{x \to +\infty} \dfrac{x^k}{e^x} \ (k > 0)$.

20. $\lim\limits_{x \to +\infty} \dfrac{\cosh x}{x}$.

427. Evaluation of the Indeterminate Forms $0 \cdot \infty$ and $\infty - \infty$

I. *Type* $0 \cdot \infty$.

If a function $F(x) = f(x) \cdot g(x)$ takes the indeterminate form $0 \cdot \infty$, we may write the product in the quotient form

$$(a) \qquad f(x) \cdot g(x) = f(x) \Big/ \dfrac{1}{g(x)} \qquad \text{or} \qquad g(x) \Big/ \dfrac{1}{f(x)},$$

which will produce one of the indeterminate forms $0/0$ or ∞/∞, which may then be treated by the method of § 423 or § 425.

EXAMPLE 1. Find the value of $\lim\limits_{x \to 0} (x \ln x)$.

Solution: Since $\ln x. \to -\infty$ when $x \to 0$, the product $x \ln x$ takes the indeterminate form $0 \cdot \infty$ when $x \to 0$. If we write $x \ln x = \dfrac{\ln x}{\dfrac{1}{x}}$, this fraction takes the indeterminate form ∞/∞ when $x \to 0$. Applying the rule of § 425, we get

$$\lim_{x \to 0} (x \ln x) = \lim_{x \to 0} \left(\dfrac{\ln x}{\dfrac{1}{x}} \right) = \lim_{x \to 0} \left(-\dfrac{1}{x} \Big/ \dfrac{1}{x^2} \right) = \lim_{x \to 0} (-x) = 0.$$

II. *Type* $\infty - \infty$.

If a function $F(x)$ takes the indeterminate form $\infty - \infty$, it is generally possible to make a transformation (frequently algebraic or trigonometric) which will change $F(x)$ to the form of a fraction which will assume one of the indeterminate forms $0/0$ or ∞/∞.

EXAMPLE 2.   Evaluate the indeterminate form $\lim\limits_{x\to 0}\left(\dfrac{1}{\sin x}-\dfrac{1}{x}\right)$.

Solution: Since $\dfrac{1}{\sin x}\to\infty$ and $\dfrac{1}{x}\to\infty$ when $x\to 0$, the given function takes the indeterminate form $\infty-\infty$. We may write

$$\frac{1}{\sin x}-\frac{1}{x}=\frac{x-\sin x}{x\sin x},$$

which becomes $0/0$ when $x\to 0$. Applying l'Hospital's rule twice, we obtain

$$\lim_{x\to 0}\left(\frac{1}{\sin x}-\frac{1}{x}\right)=\lim_{x\to 0}\frac{x-\sin x}{x\sin x}=\lim_{x\to 0}\frac{1-\cos x}{x\cos x+\sin x}$$

$$=\lim_{x\to 0}\frac{\sin x}{-x\sin x+\cos x+\cos x}=0.$$

428. Evaluation of the Exponential Indeterminate Forms 1^{∞}, 0^0 and ∞^0

A function of the form $[f(x)]^{g(x)}$ may take one of the indeterminate forms 1^{∞}, 0^0 or ∞^0. To treat this form, we put

(a) $$y=[f(x)]^{g(x)},$$

and take logarithms, obtaining:

(b) $$\ln y=g(x)\cdot\ln f(x),$$

which takes the form $0\cdot\infty$. This may be evaluated by the method of § 427, and then $\lim (\ln y)$ is known; from this we find $\lim (y)$.

EXAMPLE 1.   Evaluate $\lim\limits_{x\to 0}(x+1)^{\cot x}$.

Solution: This takes the form 1^{∞}. Put $y=(x+1)^{\cot x}$; then

$$\ln y=\cot x\cdot\ln (x+1)=\frac{\ln (x+1)}{\tan x}.$$

By l'Hospital's rule,

$$\lim_{x\to 0}(\ln y)=\lim_{x\to 0}\frac{\left(\dfrac{1}{x+1}\right)}{\sec^2 x}=\lim_{x\to 0}\frac{\cos^2 x}{x+1}=1.$$

Since $\ln y\to 1$ as $x\to 0$, we have $y\to e$. The required limit is therefore e.

EXAMPLE 2.   Find $\lim\limits_{x\to\frac{\pi}{2}}(\tan x)^{\cos x}$.

Solution: This takes the form ∞^0. Put $y = (\tan x)^{\cos x}$, then

$$\ln y = \cos x \cdot \ln \tan x = \frac{\ln \tan x}{\sec x}.$$

$$\lim_{x \to \frac{\pi}{2}} (\ln y) = \lim_{x \to \frac{\pi}{2}} \frac{\dfrac{1}{\tan x} \cdot \sec^2 x}{\sec x \tan x} = \lim_{x \to \frac{\pi}{2}} \frac{\sec x}{\tan^2 x} = \lim_{x \to \frac{\pi}{2}} \frac{\cos x}{\sin^2 x} = 0,$$

$$\therefore \lim_{x \to \frac{\pi}{2}} (y) = e^0 = 1.$$

429. Exercises

Evaluate each of the limits in Exercises 1–36:

1. $\lim\limits_{x \to 0} (x \cot x)$.

2. $\lim\limits_{x \to \frac{\pi}{2}} (1 - \sin x) \tan x$.

3. $\lim\limits_{x \to +\infty} x(e^{\frac{1}{x}} - 1)$.

4. $\lim\limits_{x \to 0} (x^2 \ln x)$.

5. $\lim\limits_{x \to 0} (x \ln \sin x)$.

6. $\lim\limits_{x \to +\infty} (x\, e^{-x})$.

7. $\lim\limits_{x \to \frac{\pi}{2}} (\tan x \cdot \ln \sin x)$.

8. $\lim\limits_{x \to 0} [\csc x \cdot \ln (x + 1)]$.

9. $\lim\limits_{x \to 0} (x^2 \csc x \cot x)$.

10. $\lim\limits_{x \to \frac{\pi}{4}} (1 - \tan x) \sec 2\, x$.

11. $\lim\limits_{x \to -\infty} (x^2 e^x)$.

12. $\lim\limits_{x \to +\infty} (x - 1)\, e^{-x^2}$.

13. $\lim\limits_{x \to 0} (x^n \ln x) \quad (n > 0)$.

14. $\lim\limits_{x \to a} (a^2 - x^2) \tan \dfrac{\pi x}{2\, a}$.

15. $\lim\limits_{x \to 1} (1 - x) \tan \tfrac{1}{2}\, \pi x$.

16. $\lim\limits_{x \to 0} (\sin x \cdot \ln \sin x)$.

17. $\lim\limits_{x \to \frac{\pi}{2}} (\sec x - \tan x)$.

18. $\lim\limits_{x \to 0} (\csc \tfrac{1}{2}\, x - \cot \tfrac{1}{2}\, x)$.

19. $\lim\limits_{x \to 0} \left(\cot x - \dfrac{1}{x} \right)$.

20. $\lim\limits_{x \to 1} \left(\dfrac{1}{\ln x} - \dfrac{x}{\ln x} \right)$.

21. $\lim\limits_{x \to 0} \left(\dfrac{1}{x} - \dfrac{1}{e^x - 1} \right)$.

22. $\lim\limits_{x \to 1} \left(\dfrac{x}{x - 1} - \dfrac{1}{\ln x} \right)$.

23. $\lim\limits_{x \to 1} \left(\dfrac{1}{\ln x} - \dfrac{1}{x - 1} \right)$.

24. $\lim\limits_{x \to \frac{\pi}{2}} \left(x \tan x - \dfrac{\pi}{2} \sec x \right)$.

25. $\lim\limits_{x \to 0} (x^x)$.

26. $\lim\limits_{x \to 0} (1 + x^2)^{\frac{1}{x^2}}$.

27. $\lim\limits_{x \to \frac{\pi}{2}} (\sin x)^{\tan x}$.

28. $\lim\limits_{x \to 0} (\csc x)^{\sin x}$.

29. $\lim\limits_{x \to 0} (1 + \sin x)^{\cot x}$.

30. $\lim\limits_{x \to 0} \left(\dfrac{1}{x}\right)^{\sin x}$.

31. $\lim\limits_{x \to +\infty} (1 + x^2)^{\frac{1}{x}}$.

32. $\lim\limits_{x \to 0} (\cos x)^{\frac{1}{x}}$.

33. $\lim\limits_{x \to 1} (1 - x)^{\tan \pi x}$.

34. $\lim\limits_{x \to 0} (e^x + x)^{\frac{1}{x}}$.

35. $\lim\limits_{x \to 0} \left(\dfrac{\sin x}{x}\right)^{\frac{1}{x}}$.

36. $\lim\limits_{x \to \frac{\pi}{2}} (\csc x)^{\tan^2 x}$.

37. Find $\lim\limits_{x \to +\infty} P(x) \cdot e^{-x}$, where $P(x)$ is a polynomial function of x.

38. Find $\lim\limits_{x \to +\infty} [\ln (x + 1) - \ln (x - 1)]$.

39. Evaluate by integrating by parts:

$\quad (a)\ \displaystyle\int_0^\infty x\, e^{-x}\, dx;$ $\qquad (b)\ \displaystyle\int_0^1 x \ln x\, dx.$

40. Show that:

$$\int_0^\infty x^n e^{-x}\, dx = n \int_0^\infty x^{n-1} e^{-x}\, dx \quad (n > 0)$$

by integration by parts.

CHAPTER XXIII

Infinite Series

430. Infinite Sequences

A set of numbers arranged in a one-to-one correspondence with the positive integers 1, 2, 3, $\cdots$, *and determined according to some rule, is* called *an **infinite sequence**.*

The numbers of the set constituting an infinite sequence are called the *terms* of the sequence. In an infinite sequence there is a first term, each term is followed by another term and there is no last term.

EXAMPLE 1. Examples of infinite sequences are: (a) $1, \frac{1}{2}, \frac{1}{3}, \frac{1}{4}, \frac{1}{5}, \cdots$; (b) $\frac{1}{2}, \frac{3}{4}, \frac{7}{8}, \frac{15}{16}, \frac{31}{32}, \cdots$; (c) $\frac{1}{2}, -\frac{2}{3}, \frac{3}{4}, -\frac{4}{5}, \frac{5}{6}, -\frac{6}{7}, \cdots$; (d) $1, 3, 5, 7, \cdots$; (e) $1, -1, 1, -1, 1, \cdots$.

If the first few terms of a given infinite sequence are denoted in general by $a_1, a_2, a_3, \cdots$, the n-th term (where n is any positive integer) is denoted by a_n, and the sequence itself may be conveniently denoted by

$$a_1, a_2, a_3, \cdots, a_n, \cdots,$$

or more briefly by $\{a_n\}$. The n-th term is sometimes called the *general term*. The n-th term may be regarded as a function of n.

The rule defining a sequence is often expressed by an explicit formula for its n-th term in terms of the index n. Sometimes a sequence is indicated by a sufficient number of the first few terms so that a natural choice for the n-th term is suggested.

EXAMPLE 2. (a) If $a_n = \frac{n^2 + 1}{n}$, and if we put $n = 1, 2, 3, 4, \cdots$, we obtain for the first few terms of the sequence: $2, \frac{5}{2}, \frac{10}{3}, \frac{17}{4}, \cdots$; (b) if $a_n = (-1)^n \cdot \frac{1}{n^2}$, the first few terms of the sequence are: $-1, \frac{1}{4}, -\frac{1}{9}, \frac{1}{16}, -\frac{1}{25} \cdots$.

EXAMPLE 3. For the indicated infinite sequence: $\frac{1}{2}, -\frac{2}{3}, \frac{3}{4}, -\frac{4}{5}, \cdots$, the simplest general term suggested is: $a_n = (-1)^{n+1} \frac{n}{n+1}$.

431. Limits of Infinite Sequences; Convergence and Divergence

Since the n-th term of an infinite sequence is a function of the index n, we may apply to it the definition of limit of a function in § 68.

For this case, the definition may be restated thus: *An infinite sequence $\{a_n\}$ has a **limit** A if the difference between a_n and A is less in absolute value than an arbitrarily small positive number for all integral values of n that are sufficiently large.* We then write:

$$A = \lim_{n \to \infty} a_n, \quad \text{or} \quad a_n \to A \quad \text{as } n \to \infty.$$

*An infinite sequence which has a limit is called **convergent**; one which has no limit is called non-convergent or **divergent**.*

EXAMPLE. (*a*) The infinite sequence $\frac{1}{2}$, $\frac{2}{3}$, $\frac{3}{4}$, $\frac{4}{5}$, $\cdots$ has the n-th term $\frac{n}{n+1}$. Since $\frac{n}{n+1} \to 1$ as $n \to \infty$, this sequence has the limit 1 and is convergent.

(*b*) In the infinite sequence $\frac{1}{2}$, $-\frac{2}{3}$, $\frac{3}{4}$, $-\frac{4}{5}$, $\cdots$, the n-th term is $(-1)^{n+1}\frac{n}{n+1}$. This n-th term does not approach a limit as $n \to \infty$, but oscillates between values getting nearer, alternately, to 1 and -1; this sequence has no limit and is divergent.

(*c*) In the infinite sequence 1, 4, 9, 16, 25, $\cdots$, the n-th term is n^2, which becomes infinite as $n \to \infty$; hence the sequence is divergent.

The limit theorems of § 70 for functions in general apply also to infinite sequences. We may therefore write:

(1) $$\lim_{n \to \infty} (a_n + b_n) = \lim_{n \to \infty} a_n + \lim_{n \to \infty} b_n,$$

(2) $$\lim_{n \to \infty} (a_n \cdot b_n) = \lim_{n \to \infty} a_n \cdot \lim_{n \to \infty} b_n,$$

(3) $$\lim_{n \to \infty} (a_n/b_n) = \lim_{n \to \infty} a_n / \lim_{n \to \infty} b_n, \quad (\text{if } \lim_{n \to \infty} b_n \neq 0),$$

provided the right-hand limits exist.

Two additional limit theorems, which will be of importance in this chapter, will now be stated without proof:[*]

I. *If the terms of an infinite sequence steadily increase but remain less than some constant c, then the sequence has a limit and is convergent; this limit is either c or some number less than c.*

[*] See, for example, Smail, *Infinite Processes*, §§ 28, 29, or Fine, *Calculus*, § 328.

II. *If the terms of an infinite sequence steadily decrease but remain greater than some constant c', then the sequence has a limit and is convergent; this limit is either c' or some number greater than c'.*

432. Exercises

In Exercises 1–4, write out the first five terms of each of the infinite sequences for which the n-th term is:

1. $\dfrac{n}{n^2 + 1}.$

2. $\dfrac{\sqrt{n}}{n + 2}.$

3. $(-1)^{n+1} \dfrac{n}{(n + 1)(n + 2)}.$

4. $(-1)^n \dfrac{x^n}{n!}.$

In Exercises 5–8, find the n-th term of each of the given infinite sequences:

5. $1, \frac{1}{3}, \frac{1}{5}, \frac{1}{7}, \cdots.$

6. $2, \frac{4}{3}, \frac{6}{5}, \frac{8}{7}, \cdots.$

7. $\frac{1}{2}, -\frac{1}{5}, \frac{1}{10}, -\frac{1}{17}, \frac{1}{26}, \cdots.$

8. $\dfrac{2}{1 \cdot 3}, \dfrac{3}{2 \cdot 4}, \dfrac{4}{3 \cdot 5}, \dfrac{5}{4 \cdot 6}, \cdots.$

In Exercises 9–16, determine which of the given infinite sequences are convergent and which are divergent, and in case of convergence, find the limit:

9. $\frac{3}{2}, \frac{4}{3}, \frac{5}{4}, \frac{6}{5}, \cdots.$

10. $\frac{1}{2}, \frac{4}{3}, \frac{3}{4}, \frac{6}{5}, \frac{5}{6}, \cdots.$

11. $\frac{1}{2}, -\frac{3}{4}, \frac{5}{6}, -\frac{7}{8}, \cdots.$

12. $\frac{1}{2}, -\frac{4}{3}, \frac{3}{4}, -\frac{6}{5}, \frac{5}{6}, \cdots.$

13. $1, -\frac{1}{2}, \frac{1}{3}, -\frac{1}{4}, \frac{1}{5}, \cdots.$

14. $1, -1, 1, -1, 1, \cdots.$

15. $1, -3, 5, -7, 9, \cdots.$

16. $1, -\frac{1}{2}, \frac{1}{4}, -\frac{1}{8}, \frac{1}{16}, \cdots.$

In Exercises 17–24, discuss the limiting behavior, when $n \to \infty$, of each of the given expressions:

17. $1 + \dfrac{1}{n^2}.$

18. $2 - \dfrac{1000}{n}.$

19. $n + (-1)^n.$

20. $n^2 - 2\,n.$

21. $\frac{1}{2}[1 + (-1)^n].$

22. $(-\frac{1}{2})^n.$

23. $\dfrac{2^n}{2^n + 1}.$

24. $(-1)^n.$

Evaluate each of the limits in Exercises 25–32:

25. $\displaystyle\lim_{n \to \infty} \dfrac{2\,n^2 + 3\,n - 5}{3\,n^2 - 4\,n - 1}.$

26. $\displaystyle\lim_{n \to \infty} \dfrac{2\,n^2 + 5\,n - 5}{2\,n^2 - n + 2}.$

27. $\displaystyle\lim_{n \to \infty} \dfrac{n(2\,n + 1)}{(n + 1)^2}.$

28. $\displaystyle\lim_{n \to \infty} \dfrac{n(n + 3)}{(n + 1)(n + 4)}.$

29. $\displaystyle\lim_{n \to \infty} \dfrac{2\,n - 1}{n^2 + n - 2}.$

30. $\displaystyle\lim_{n \to \infty} \dfrac{3\,n^2}{(n - 1)^2(n + 1)}.$

31. $\displaystyle\lim_{n \to \infty} \left(2 - \dfrac{1}{2^{n-1}}\right).$

32. $\displaystyle\lim_{n \to \infty} \left[\dfrac{1}{(n + 1)!} \Big/ \dfrac{1}{n!}\right].$

433. Infinite Series

Let

$$(a) \qquad a_1, a_2, a_3, \cdots, a_n, \cdots$$

be a given infinite sequence. The indicated sum

$$(b) \qquad a_1 + a_2 + a_3 + \cdots + a_n + \cdots$$

has no meaning in the ordinary sense of a sum, for it is impossible to carry out the operation of adding infinitely many numbers. However, as will be seen in § 435, a meaning can sometimes be assigned to such an expression.

An indicated sum of the terms of an infinite sequence $\{a_n\}$ of the form (b) is called an **infinite series**, and $a_1, a_2, a_3, \cdots, a_n, \cdots$ are called the *terms* of the series. We sometimes denote the series (b) by $\sum_{n=1}^{\infty} a_n$ for brevity.

Associated with the sequence $\{a_n\}$ is another infinite sequence $\{s_n\}$, where

$$(c) \qquad s_1 = a_1, \; s_2 = a_1 + a_2, \; s_3 = a_1 + a_2 + a_3, \cdots,$$
$$s_n = a_1 + a_2 + \cdots + a_n, \cdots$$

That is, s_n is the sum of the first n terms of the infinite series. The sum s_n is called the n-th *partial sum* of the series $\sum_{n=1}^{\infty} a_n$.

EXAMPLE 1. In the infinite series $\frac{1}{2} + \frac{1}{4} + \frac{1}{8} + \cdots + \frac{1}{2^n} + \cdots$, the general term is $\frac{1}{2^n}$. The first four partial sums are

$$s_1 = \tfrac{1}{2}, \; s_2 = \tfrac{1}{2} + \tfrac{1}{4} = \tfrac{3}{4}, \; s_3 = \tfrac{1}{2} + \tfrac{1}{4} + \tfrac{1}{8} = \tfrac{7}{8}, \; s_4 = \tfrac{1}{2} + \tfrac{1}{4} + \tfrac{1}{8} + \tfrac{1}{16} = \tfrac{15}{16}.$$

EXAMPLE 2. For the infinite series $\sum_{n=1}^{\infty} \frac{n}{n^2 + 1}$, the first few terms are:

$$\tfrac{1}{2} + \tfrac{2}{5} + \tfrac{3}{10} + \tfrac{4}{17} + \tfrac{5}{26} + \cdots.$$

EXAMPLE 3. For the infinite series

$$\frac{3}{2} - \frac{4}{3} \cdot \frac{1}{3} + \frac{5}{4} \cdot \frac{1}{3^2} - \frac{6}{5} \cdot \frac{1}{3^3} + \frac{7}{6} \cdot \frac{1}{3^4} - \cdots,$$

the n-th term is $(-1)^{n+1} \dfrac{n+2}{n+1} \cdot \dfrac{1}{3^{n-1}}$.

When no ambiguity can arise from its use, the notation $\sum a_n$ is often used instead of $\sum_{n=1}^{\infty} a_n$ for indicating an infinite series in general.

434. Exercises

In Exercises 1–8, write out the first five terms of each of the given infinite series:

1. $\displaystyle\sum_{n=1}^{\infty} \frac{2n}{n^2 + 1}$.

2. $\displaystyle\sum_{n=1}^{\infty} \frac{1}{n(n + 1)}$.

3. $\displaystyle\sum_{n=1}^{\infty} \frac{2^{n-1}}{n!}$.

4. $\displaystyle\sum_{n=1}^{\infty} (-1)^{n+1} \frac{1}{(2n - 1)^2}$.

5. $\displaystyle\sum_{n=1}^{\infty} (-1)^{n+1} \frac{n}{2^n}$.

6. $\displaystyle\sum_{n=1}^{\infty} \frac{1}{n^n}$.

7. $\displaystyle\sum_{n=1}^{\infty} \frac{x^n}{\sqrt{n}}$.

8. $\displaystyle\sum_{n=1}^{\infty} \frac{(x - a)^{n-1}}{n(n + 2)}$.

In Exercises 9–16, find the n-th term of each of the given infinite series:

9. $1 + \dfrac{1}{2^2} + \dfrac{1}{3^2} + \dfrac{1}{4^2} + \dfrac{1}{5^2} + \cdots$.

10. $1 + \dfrac{2}{2} + \dfrac{3}{2^2} + \dfrac{4}{2^3} + \dfrac{5}{2^4} + \cdots$.

11. $1 - \dfrac{1}{2!} + \dfrac{1}{3!} - \dfrac{1}{4!} + \dfrac{1}{5!} - \cdots$.

12. $1 - \dfrac{1}{4} + \dfrac{1}{7} - \dfrac{1}{10} + \dfrac{1}{13} - \cdots$.

13. $\dfrac{1}{1\cdot 3} + \dfrac{1}{2\cdot 4} + \dfrac{1}{3\cdot 5} + \dfrac{1}{4\cdot 6} + \cdots$.

14. $\dfrac{1}{2} + \dfrac{1\cdot 3}{2\cdot 4} + \dfrac{1\cdot 3\cdot 5}{2\cdot 4\cdot 6} + \dfrac{1\cdot 3\cdot 5\cdot 7}{2\cdot 4\cdot 6\cdot 8} + \cdots$.

15. $x - \dfrac{x^2}{2} + \dfrac{x^3}{3} - \dfrac{x^4}{4} + \cdots$.

16. $\dfrac{x^2}{\sqrt{2}} + \dfrac{x^4}{\sqrt{4}} + \dfrac{x^6}{\sqrt{6}} + \dfrac{x^8}{\sqrt{8}} + \cdots$.

In Exercises 17–20, calculate the first four partial sums of each of the given infinite series:

17. $1 + \frac{1}{2} + \frac{1}{3} + \frac{1}{4} + \cdots$.

18. $\dfrac{1}{1\cdot 2} + \dfrac{1}{2\cdot 3} + \dfrac{1}{3\cdot 4} + \dfrac{1}{4\cdot 5} + \cdots$.

19. $1 - \frac{1}{2} + \frac{1}{4} - \frac{1}{8} + \cdots$.

20. $1 - \frac{2}{3} + \frac{3}{9} - \frac{4}{27} + \cdots$.

435. Convergence and Divergence of an Infinite Series

An infinite series

$$(a) \qquad \sum_{n=1}^{\infty} a_n = a_1 + a_2 + a_3 + \cdots + a_n + \cdots$$

is said to **converge** or **diverge** according as the associated sequence of partial sums $\{s_n\}$ converges or diverges. If the infinite series $\sum_{n=1}^{\infty} a_n$ is convergent, the limit of the sequence $\{s_n\}$ is called the **sum** or **value** of the series. A divergent series has no sum or value according to this definition.

In other words: *An infinite series $\sum a_n$ is **convergent** if the sum s_n of the first n terms approaches a limit s when $n \to \infty$ and s is then called the **sum** or **value** of the series; the series is **divergent** if s_n does not approach a limit.*

Recalling the definition of a limit and of convergence of an infinite sequence in § 431, we may say:

An infinite series $\sum a_n$, in which s_n is the sum of the first n terms, is convergent, with sum s, if $|s - s_n|$ is less than an arbitrarily small positive number for all values of n that are sufficiently large.

EXAMPLE 1. (a) The infinite series $\frac{1}{2} + \frac{1}{4} + \frac{1}{8} + \frac{1}{16} + \cdots$ is convergent with the sum 1, since the associated sequence of partial sums is $\frac{1}{2}, \frac{3}{4}, \frac{7}{8}, \frac{15}{16}, \cdots$, which has the limit 1.

(b) The infinite series $1 + 1 + 1 + \cdots$ is divergent, since the sequence of partial sums is $1, 2, 3, \cdots, n, \cdots$, which has no limit but becomes infinite as $n \to \infty$.

EXAMPLE 2. Consider the infinite series

$$\frac{1}{1 \cdot 2} + \frac{1}{2 \cdot 3} + \frac{1}{3 \cdot 4} + \frac{1}{4 \cdot 5} + \cdots.$$

We may write the sum of the first n terms:

$$\begin{aligned}
s_n &= \frac{1}{1 \cdot 2} + \frac{1}{2 \cdot 3} + \frac{1}{3 \cdot 4} + \frac{1}{4 \cdot 5} + \cdots + \frac{1}{(n-1)n} + \frac{1}{n(n+1)} \\
&= (1 - \tfrac{1}{2}) + (\tfrac{1}{2} - \tfrac{1}{3}) + (\tfrac{1}{3} - \tfrac{1}{4}) + (\tfrac{1}{4} - \tfrac{1}{5}) + \cdots \\
&\qquad\qquad\qquad + \left(\frac{1}{n-1} - \frac{1}{n}\right) + \left(\frac{1}{n} - \frac{1}{n+1}\right) \\
&= 1 - \frac{1}{n+1},
\end{aligned}$$

since the terms cancel in pairs except for the first and last. Then $s_n \to 1$ as

$n \to \infty$, since $\dfrac{1}{n+1} \to 0$, and therefore the series is convergent with sum 1. (This is an example of a so-called telescopic series.)

It is important to remember that the sum of a convergent infinite series, as defined above, is a *limit* and not a sum in the sense of a sum of terms of a polynomial, for example. We must therefore not assume without proof that the properties of a finite sum in algebra will necessarily hold for the sum of an infinite series.

Since *convergent* series are the only ones which have a value attached to them by the definition above, they are the only series which are used in elementary calculus. An important problem in the treatment of infinite series is therefore to find methods for testing a given series for convergence or divergence.

It is seldom possible to find a single compact expression representing the partial sum s_n as a function of n; and so the determination of convergence cannot usually be based directly on the definition of convergence. We must therefore find tests of convergence which depend only on the knowledge of the form of the general term.

Since $\lim\limits_{n\to\infty} (k \cdot s_n) = k \cdot \lim\limits_{n\to\infty} s_n$ (by § 431), it follows that: *If a series* $a_1 + a_2 + a_3 + \cdots$ *is convergent, with sum* s, *then the series* $ka_1 + ka_2 + ka_3 + \cdots$ *is also convergent, with sum* ks.

It follows from the definition of convergence and divergence that: *the convergence or divergence of an infinite series is not affected by discarding a finite number of terms from the beginning of the series, or by adding a finite number of terms at the beginning of the series.*

436. A Necessary Condition for Convergence

Let $a_1 + a_2 + a_3 + \cdots + a_n + \cdots$ be a given *convergent* series, and let s_n be the n-th partial sum and s the sum; then, by definition, $s_n \to s$ as $n \to \infty$. Since $a_n = s_n - s_{n-1}$, it follows that

$$\lim_{n\to\infty} a_n = \lim_{n\to\infty} s_n - \lim_{n\to\infty} s_{n-1} = s - s = 0.$$

Hence:

If the infinite series $\sum a_n$ *is convergent, then*

$$(a) \qquad\qquad \lim_{n\to\infty} a_n = 0 \, ;$$

that is, the n-th term of a convergent series must approach zero as n becomes infinite.

This condition is called a *necessary condition* for convergence, since it necessarily holds for *any convergent* series. The condition is *not*, however, a *sufficient condition* for convergence, since we shall soon meet with many series whose general term approaches zero, but which nevertheless diverge.

The preceding theorem may also be stated as follows:

If the n-th term of an infinite series $\sum a_n$ does not approach 0 as $n \to \infty$, the series must be divergent.

437. The Geometric Series

One of the simplest illustrations of infinite series and their convergence and divergence is furnished by the *geometric series*.

The infinite series

$$(a) \qquad 1 + r + r^2 + r^3 + \cdots r^n + \cdots = \sum_{n=0}^{\infty} r^n,$$

*in which the ratio of any term to the preceding term is a constant r, is called a **geometric series**.*

EXAMPLE 1. The series

$$1 + \tfrac{1}{2} + \tfrac{1}{4} + \tfrac{1}{8} + \cdots, \quad 1 + \tfrac{3}{2} + \tfrac{9}{4} + \tfrac{27}{8} + \cdots,$$

and $1 - \tfrac{2}{3} + \tfrac{4}{9} - \tfrac{8}{27} + \cdots$ are geometric series. The first two have positive ratios $r = \tfrac{1}{2}$ and $r = \tfrac{3}{2}$ respectively, and the last has a negative ratio $r = -\tfrac{2}{3}$.

Let us investigate the convergence or divergence of the geometric series.

Let $r \neq 1$. Then, by the formula for the sum of a geometric progression in algebra, the sum of the first n terms of the series (a) is:

$$(b) \qquad s_n = \frac{1 - r^n}{1 - r} = \frac{1}{1 - r} - \frac{r^n}{1 - r}.$$

(1) If $|r| < 1$, i.e., if $-1 < r < 1$, we have $\lim_{n \to \infty} (r^n) = 0$ (by § 71, Exercise 23). Hence, by (b),

$$\lim_{n \to \infty} s_n = \frac{1}{1 - r}.$$

The series (a) is therefore convergent when $|r| < 1$, with the sum $\dfrac{1}{1 - r}$.

(2) Let $r > 1$. Then $r^n \to +\infty$ as $n \to \infty$ (by § 71, Exercise 24); hence by (b) $s_n \to +\infty$, and the series is divergent.

(3) Let $r < -1$. Then r^n oscillates between positive and negative values, which in absolute value become infinite, so that s_n does not approach a limit, and the series is divergent.

(4) If $r = 1$, the series becomes $1 + 1 + 1 + \cdots$, which is obviously divergent, since $s_n = n$ and $s_n \to +\infty$ as $n \to \infty$. If $r = -1$, the series becomes $1 - 1 + 1 - 1 + \cdots$, which is also evidently divergent, since the partial sums are alternately 1 and 0.

Hence:

The geometric series $1 + r + r^2 + r^3 + \cdots + r^n + \cdots$ *is convergent if* $|r| < 1$, *with sum* $\dfrac{1}{1-r}$, *and is divergent for all other values of* r.

EXAMPLE 2. (a) The series $1 + \frac{1}{2} + \frac{1}{4} + \frac{1}{8} + \cdots$ is convergent since $r = \frac{1}{2}$, and its sum is $s = \dfrac{1}{1 - \frac{1}{2}} = 2$.

(b) The series $\frac{1}{2} + \frac{3}{4} + \frac{9}{8} + \frac{27}{16} + \cdots$ is divergent since $r = \frac{3}{2}$.

(c) The series $1 - \frac{2}{3} + \frac{4}{9} - \frac{8}{27} + \cdots$ is convergent since $r = -\frac{2}{3}$, so that $|r| = \frac{2}{3}$, and its sum is $s = \dfrac{1}{1 - (-\frac{2}{3})} = \frac{3}{5}$.

438. General Test for Convergence of a Series of Positive Terms

Suppose that a given infinite series $a_1 + a_2 + a_3 + \cdots + a_n + \cdots$ has all its terms positive; if we add more and more terms, the sums increase, so that the partial sums s_n steadily increase as n increases. Now suppose also that all the partial sums are bounded, i.e., remain less than a constant c. It follows from theorem I of § 431 that s_n approaches a limit which is less than or equal to c, as $n \to \infty$. By definition, the series is therefore convergent, and its sum $s \leq c$. Hence:

A series of positive terms $\sum a_n$ *is convergent if, for all values of* n, *the partial sums* s_n *remain less than some constant* c, *and in this case, the sum of the series is less than or equal to* c.

Evidently, in a convergent series of positive terms the partial sums s_n are all less than the sum s of the series.

439. The Harmonic Series

The infinite series

$$(a) \qquad 1 + \frac{1}{2} + \frac{1}{3} + \frac{1}{4} + \cdots + \frac{1}{n} + \cdots = \sum_{n=1}^{\infty} \frac{1}{n}$$

is called the **harmonic series.**

Let us group the terms as follows:

$$(b) \quad 1 + \tfrac{1}{2} + (\tfrac{1}{3} + \tfrac{1}{4}) + (\tfrac{1}{5} + \tfrac{1}{6} + \tfrac{1}{7} + \tfrac{1}{8}) + (\tfrac{1}{9} + \cdots + \tfrac{1}{16})$$
$$+ (\tfrac{1}{17} + \cdots + \tfrac{1}{32}) + \cdots,$$

taking twice as many terms in each group as in the previous group. The sum of the terms in each parenthesis is greater than $\frac{1}{2}$. Therefore, by taking enough of these groups we can evidently make the sum of these terms as large as we please. Therefore, the sum of n terms becomes infinite as $n \to \infty$. Hence:

The harmonic series $\sum \dfrac{1}{n}$ *is divergent.*

440. The Hyperharmonic Series

The infinite series

$$(a) \qquad 1 + \frac{1}{2^k} + \frac{1}{3^k} + \frac{1}{4^k} + \cdots + \frac{1}{n^k} + \cdots = \sum_{n=1}^{\infty} \frac{1}{n^k}$$

is called the **hyperharmonic series;** it includes the harmonic series as a special case, for $k = 1$.

Let us investigate the convergence of this series.

(1) Let $k > 1$. Group the terms of the series as follows:

$$(b) \quad 1 + \left(\frac{1}{2^k} + \frac{1}{3^k} \right) + \left(\frac{1}{4^k} + \frac{1}{5^k} + \frac{1}{6^k} + \frac{1}{7^k} \right)$$
$$+ \left(\frac{1}{8^k} + \cdots + \frac{1}{15^k} \right) + \left(\frac{1}{16^k} + \cdots + \frac{1}{31^k} \right) + \cdots,$$

in which each group contains twice as many terms as the preceding group. Since $k > 1$, we have

$$\frac{1}{2^k} + \frac{1}{3^k} < \frac{1}{2^k} + \frac{1}{2^k} = \frac{2}{2^k} = \frac{1}{2^{k-1}},$$

$$\frac{1}{4^k} + \frac{1}{5^k} + \frac{1}{6^k} + \frac{1}{7^k} < \frac{1}{4^k} + \frac{1}{4^k} + \frac{1}{4^k} + \frac{1}{4^k} = \frac{4}{4^k} = \frac{1}{4^{k-1}} = \frac{1}{(2^{k-1})^2},$$

$$\frac{1}{8^k} + \frac{1}{9^k} + \cdots + \frac{1}{15^k} < \frac{1}{8^k} + \frac{1}{8^k} + \cdots + \frac{1}{8^k}$$

$$= \frac{8}{8^k} = \frac{1}{8^{k-1}} = \frac{1}{(2^{k-1})^3},$$

. . . .

Thus, each group of terms in (b) is less than the corresponding term of the series

(c) $$1 + \frac{1}{2^{k-1}} + \frac{1}{(2^{k-1})^2} + \frac{1}{(2^{k-1})^3} + \cdots$$

Then the sum of any number of groups of terms of the series (b) is less than the sum of the corresponding number of terms of (c). But series (c) is a geometric series whose ratio is $r = 1/2^{k-1}$ which is less than 1 since $k > 1$. It therefore converges, and its partial sums are all less than its value, which is

$$s = \frac{1}{1-r} = \frac{1}{1 - \dfrac{1}{2^{k-1}}} = \frac{2^{k-1}}{2^{k-1} - 1}.$$

Therefore, the partial sums of series (a) are less than this number s. By the general test for convergence of § 438, it follows that the series (a) is convergent.

(2) Let $k = 1$. In this case we have the harmonic series, which has already been shown (in § 439) to be divergent.

(3) Let $k < 1$. Each term $\frac{1}{n^k}$ of the series (a) is greater than the corresponding term $\frac{1}{n}$ of the harmonic series, for each value of $n > 1$. Then each partial sum of the series (a) is greater than the corresponding partial sum of the harmonic series, which becomes infinite as $n \to \infty$, so that the same is true for series (a). Hence, the series (a) is divergent for $k < 1$.

Therefore:

The hyperharmonic series $\sum \frac{1}{n^k}$ is convergent when $k > 1$, and is divergent when $k \leqq 1$.

Example. The series

$$1 + \frac{1}{2^2} + \frac{1}{3^2} + \frac{1}{4^2} + \cdots + \frac{1}{n^2} + \cdots$$

is convergent, while the series

$$1 + \frac{1}{\sqrt{2}} + \frac{1}{\sqrt{3}} + \frac{1}{\sqrt{4}} + \cdots + \frac{1}{\sqrt{n}} + \cdots$$

is divergent.

441. Exercises

Test the following series for convergence.

1. $1 + \dfrac{1}{\sqrt{2^5}} + \dfrac{1}{\sqrt{3^5}} + \dfrac{1}{\sqrt{4^5}} + \cdots.$

2. $1 + \dfrac{1}{8} + \dfrac{1}{27} + \dfrac{1}{64} + \dfrac{1}{125} + \cdots.$

3. $1 + \dfrac{1}{\sqrt[3]{2}} + \dfrac{1}{\sqrt[3]{3}} + \dfrac{1}{\sqrt[3]{4}} + \cdots.$

4. $1 + \dfrac{1}{\sqrt{8}} + \dfrac{1}{\sqrt{27}} + \dfrac{1}{\sqrt{64}} + \dfrac{1}{\sqrt{125}} + \cdots.$

5. $1 + \dfrac{1}{2\sqrt[3]{2}} + \dfrac{1}{3\sqrt[3]{3}} + \dfrac{1}{4\sqrt[3]{4}} + \cdots.$

442. Comparison Tests for Convergence and Divergence

The following tests apply only to *series of positive terms;* for convenience we shall call these *positive series.*

Let $c_1 + c_2 + c_3 + \cdots + c_n + \cdots$ be a known convergent series of positive terms, let C_n be the n-th partial sum and let C be the sum of this series; then (by § 438), $C_n < C$. Let $a_1 + a_2 + a_3 + \cdots + a_n + \cdots$ be a given positive series to be tested, and let s_n be its n-th partial sum. Suppose that $a_1 \leqq c_1,\ a_2 \leqq c_2,\ a_3 \leqq c_3,\ \cdots,$ $a_n \leqq c_n,\ \cdots$ for every value of n; then for every value of n, $s_n \leqq C_n$, and therefore $s_n < C$. By the general test for positive series (§ 438), it follows that the series $a_1 + a_2 + a_3 + \cdots$ is convergent, with sum $\leqq C$. Hence:

I. *A positive series $\sum a_n$ is convergent if each of its terms is less than or equal to the corresponding term of a known convergent positive series $\sum c_n$.*

EXAMPLE 1. The series $1 + \dfrac{1}{2!} + \dfrac{1}{3!} + \dfrac{1}{4!} + \cdots + \dfrac{1}{n!} + \cdots$ is convergent. For $\dfrac{1}{n!} < \dfrac{1}{2^{n-1}}$ for all values of $n > 2$, and the series

$$1 + \frac{1}{2} + \frac{1}{2^2} + \frac{1}{2^3} + \cdots + \frac{1}{2^{n-1}} + \cdots$$

is a geometric series which is convergent since its ratio is $\frac{1}{2}$ (§ 437).

Now let $d_1 + d_2 + d_3 + \cdots + d_n + \cdots$ be a known divergent series of positive terms, and let D_n be the n-th partial sum of this series; then by definition, $D_n \rightarrow +\infty$ as $n \rightarrow \infty$. Let $a_1 + a_2 + \cdots + a_n + \cdots$ be a given positive series to be tested, and let s_n be its n-th partial sum. Suppose that $a_1 \geqq d_1$, $a_2 \geqq d_2$, $\cdots$, $a_n \geqq d_n$, $\cdots$ for every value of n; then $s_n \geqq D_n$ for every n. Since $D_n \rightarrow +\infty$, it follows that $s_n \rightarrow +\infty$ as $n \rightarrow \infty$, which shows that the series $a_1 + a_2 + \cdots + a_n + \cdots$ is divergent. Hence:

II. *A positive series $\sum a_n$ is divergent if each of its terms is greater than or equal to the corresponding term of a known divergent positive series $\sum d_n$.*

EXAMPLE 2. The series $\dfrac{4}{1 \cdot 3} + \dfrac{5}{2 \cdot 4} + \dfrac{6}{3 \cdot 5} + \cdots + \dfrac{n+3}{n(n+2)} + \cdots$ is

divergent since $a_n = \dfrac{n+3}{n(n+2)} = \dfrac{n+3}{n+2} \cdot \dfrac{1}{n} > \dfrac{1}{n}$ for every n, and $\dfrac{1}{n}$ is the

n-th term of the known divergent harmonic series.

When it is found difficult to apply the comparison test in the form I, because of trouble in finding an inequality $a_n \leqq c_n$, the following modified form of the comparison test may be found useful:

III. *If $\sum a_n$ is a positive series to be tested and if $\sum c_n$ is a known convergent positive series, and if $\lim\limits_{n \to \infty} \dfrac{a_n}{c_n}$ exists, then the series $\sum a_n$ is convergent.*

For, if $\lim\limits_{n \to \infty} \dfrac{a_n}{c_n} = l$, we may write $\dfrac{a_n}{c_n} = l + \delta_n$, where $\delta_n \rightarrow 0$ as $n \rightarrow \infty$. Then a positive constant δ exists such that $|\delta_n| < \delta$ for every value of n; we then have $\dfrac{a_n}{c_n} < l + \delta$ for every n. From this we get $a_n < (l + \delta)c_n$. But $(l + \delta)c_n$ is the general term of a known convergent series; hence, by I, $\sum a_n$ is convergent.

EXAMPLE 3. The series $\sum\limits_{n=1}^{\infty} \dfrac{2n+1}{n^3+n}$ is convergent, since $\sum \dfrac{1}{n^2}$ is convergent (§ 440) and

$$\lim_{n \to \infty} \left(\frac{2n+1}{n^3+n} \div \frac{1}{n^2} \right) = \lim_{n \to \infty} \frac{n^2(2n+1)}{n(n^2+1)} = 2.$$

Similarly, when the comparison test in the form II is not convenient to apply, we may use the following modified form:

IV. *If $\sum a_n$ is a positive series to be tested, and if $\sum d_n$ is a known divergent positive series, and if $\lim\limits_{n\to\infty} \dfrac{a_n}{d_n}$ exists, different from 0, then the series $\sum a_n$ is divergent. Also, if $\dfrac{a_n}{d_n} \to +\infty$, then $\sum a_n$ diverges.*

Let $\lim\limits_{n\to\infty} \dfrac{a_n}{d_n} = l'$. Since $l' \neq 0$ by hypothesis, and since the series have positive terms, we have $l' > 0$. Then if δ' is any number such that $0 < \delta' < l'$, it follows from the definition of a limit of a sequence that for all sufficiently large values of n,

$$\frac{a_n}{d_n} > \delta' > 0, \qquad \text{or} \qquad a_n > \delta' \cdot d_n.$$

But $\delta' \cdot d_n$ is the general term of a known positive divergent series; then by theorem II it follows that $\sum a_n$ is divergent.

EXAMPLE 4. The series $\sum\limits_{n=1}^{\infty} \dfrac{2n-1}{(n+1)(n+2)}$ is divergent, since $\sum \dfrac{1}{n}$ is divergent and

$$\lim_{n\to\infty} \left(\frac{2n-1}{(n+1)(n+2)} \div \frac{1}{n} \right) = \lim_{n\to\infty} \frac{n(2n-1)}{(n+1)(n+2)} = 2.$$

For use in applying the preceding comparison tests, we need some known convergent and divergent series. The following *comparison series* are already available:

(1) the geometric series $\sum r^n$, which is convergent for $|r| < 1$ and divergent for all other values of r (§ 437);

(2) the harmonic series $\sum \dfrac{1}{n}$, which is divergent (§ 439);

(3) the hyperharmonic series $\sum \dfrac{1}{n^k}$, which is convergent for $k > 1$ and divergent for $k \leqq 1$ (§ 440);

(4) the special telescopic series $\sum \dfrac{1}{n(n+1)}$, which is convergent (§ 435, Example 2);

(5) the series $\sum \dfrac{1}{n!}$, which is convergent (§ 442, Example 1).

Other series which can be used for comparison purposes will be found presently.

443. Exercises

In Exercises 1–6, test each of the given series for convergence or divergence by use of a comparison test, as indicated:

1. $\dfrac{1}{1\cdot2} + \dfrac{1}{2\cdot3} + \dfrac{1}{3\cdot4} + \cdots + \dfrac{1}{n(n+1)} + \cdots$, compare with $\sum \dfrac{1}{n^2}$.

2. $1 + \dfrac{1}{2!} + \dfrac{1}{3!} + \dfrac{1}{4!} + \cdots + \dfrac{1}{n!} + \cdots$, compare with preceding series.

3. $\dfrac{1}{2} + \dfrac{\sqrt{2}}{3} + \dfrac{\sqrt{3}}{4} + \dfrac{\sqrt{4}}{5} + \cdots + \dfrac{\sqrt{n}}{n+1} + \cdots$, compare with $\sum \dfrac{1}{\sqrt{n}}$ or $\sum \dfrac{1}{n}$.

4. $\dfrac{1}{1\cdot2} + \dfrac{1}{3\cdot2^2} + \dfrac{1}{5\cdot2^3} + \cdots + \dfrac{1}{(2n-1)2^n} + \cdots$, compare with $\sum \dfrac{1}{2^n}$.

5. $\dfrac{1}{\sqrt{1\cdot2}} + \dfrac{1}{\sqrt{2\cdot3}} + \dfrac{1}{\sqrt{3\cdot4}} + \cdots + \dfrac{1}{\sqrt{n(n+1)}} + \cdots$, compare with $\sum \dfrac{1}{n}$.

6. $\dfrac{1}{1\cdot2\cdot3} + \dfrac{1}{2\cdot3\cdot4} + \dfrac{1}{3\cdot4\cdot5} + \cdots + \dfrac{1}{n(n+1)(n+2)} + \cdots$, compare with $\sum \dfrac{1}{n^3}$.

In Exercises 7–14, examine each of the given series for convergence or divergence by use of one of the comparison tests:

7. $\dfrac{1}{2} + \dfrac{1}{5} + \dfrac{1}{10} + \dfrac{1}{17} + \cdots + \dfrac{1}{n^2+1} + \cdots$.

8. $\dfrac{1}{3} + \dfrac{1}{5} + \dfrac{1}{9} + \dfrac{1}{17} + \cdots + \dfrac{1}{2^n+1} + \cdots$.

9. $1 + \dfrac{1}{2^2} + \dfrac{1}{3^3} + \dfrac{1}{4^4} + \cdots + \dfrac{1}{n^n} + \cdots$.

10. $1 + \dfrac{1}{\sqrt{3}} + \dfrac{1}{\sqrt{5}} + \dfrac{1}{\sqrt{7}} + \cdots + \dfrac{1}{\sqrt{2n-1}} + \cdots$.

11. $\dfrac{3}{2\cdot4} + \dfrac{4}{4\cdot6} + \dfrac{5}{6\cdot8} + \cdots + \dfrac{n+2}{2n(2n+2)} + \cdots$.

12. $\dfrac{1}{2\cdot4} + \dfrac{2}{3\cdot8} + \dfrac{3}{4\cdot16} + \cdots + \dfrac{n-1}{n\cdot2^n} + \cdots$.

13. $\dfrac{2+1}{2^3-1} + \dfrac{3+1}{3^3-1} + \dfrac{4+1}{4^3-1} + \cdots + \dfrac{(n+1)+1}{(n+1)^3-1} + \cdots$.

14. $\dfrac{1}{2} + \dfrac{1}{1 + \sqrt{2}} + \dfrac{1}{1 + \sqrt{3}} + \cdots + \dfrac{1}{1 + \sqrt{n}} + \cdots.$

In Exercises 15–20, test each of the given series for convergence or divergence by a comparison test:

15. $\displaystyle\sum_{1}^{\infty} \dfrac{1}{n\sqrt{n^2 + 1}}.$ 16. $\displaystyle\sum_{1}^{\infty} \dfrac{n}{(2\,n + 1)^2}.$

17. $\displaystyle\sum_{1}^{\infty} \dfrac{1}{n \cdot 3^n}.$ 18. $\displaystyle\sum_{2}^{\infty} \dfrac{\sqrt{n}}{n^2 - 1}.$

19. $\displaystyle\sum_{2}^{\infty} \dfrac{1}{n^2 - 1}.$ 20. $\displaystyle\sum_{1}^{\infty} \dfrac{1}{\sqrt{n^2 + 1}}.$

444. The Ratio Test

Let $a_1 + a_2 + a_3 + \cdots + a_n + \cdots$ be a given positive series. Let us form the ratio $\dfrac{a_{n+1}}{a_n}$ of a general term to the preceding term, and let us suppose that this ratio approaches a limit l as $n \to \infty$.

(1) Suppose that $l < 1$.

Let r be any number between l and 1. Since $\lim\limits_{n\to\infty} \dfrac{a_{n+1}}{a_n} = l$, by definition of limit we can find a number m such that for all values of $n \geqq m$ the ratio $\dfrac{a_{n+1}}{a_n}$ will differ from l by as little as we please, and will therefore be less than r. Then

$$\dfrac{a_{m+1}}{a_m} < r \qquad \text{or} \qquad a_{m+1} < ra_m,$$

$$\dfrac{a_{m+2}}{a_{m+1}} < r \qquad \text{or} \qquad a_{m+2} < ra_{m+1} < r^2 a_m,$$

$$\dfrac{a_{m+3}}{a_{m+2}} < r \qquad \text{or} \qquad a_{m+3} < ra_{m+2} < r^3 a_m,$$

$$\cdot \quad \cdot \quad \cdot \quad \cdot \quad \cdot \quad \cdot \quad \cdot \quad \cdot \quad \cdot \quad \cdot$$

From these inequalities it will be seen that each term of the series $a_{m+1} + a_{m+2} + a_{m+3} + \cdots$ is less than the corresponding term of the geometric series $a_m r + a_m r^2 + a_m r^3 + \cdots$, which is convergent since $|r| < 1$. The series $a_{m+1} + a_{m+2} + a_{m+3} + \cdots$ is therefore convergent, by the comparison test (§ 442, I), and hence the series $a_1 + a_2 + a_3 + \cdots + a_{m+1} + a_{m+2} + \cdots$ is convergent.

(2) Suppose that $l > 1$.

Since $\lim\limits_{n\to\infty} \dfrac{a_{n+1}}{a_n} > 1$, we can find a number m such that for all values

of $n \geqq m$ the ratio $\dfrac{a_{n+1}}{a_n} > 1$. The same is true if $\dfrac{a_{n+1}}{a_n} \to +\infty$ as

$n \to \infty$. Then

$$\frac{a_{m+1}}{a_m} > 1 \qquad \text{or} \qquad a_{m+1} > a_m,$$

$$\frac{a_{m+2}}{a_{m+1}} > 1 \qquad \text{or} \qquad a_{m+2} > a_{m+1},$$

$$\frac{a_{m+3}}{a_{m+2}} > 1 \qquad \text{or} \qquad a_{m+3} > a_{m+2},$$

. . . .

It follows from these inequalities that a_n cannot approach 0 as $n \to \infty$, since the terms steadily increase. By the necessary condition of § 436, the series $a_{m+1} + a_{m+2} + \cdots$ cannot converge, and hence the series $a_1 + a_2 + a_3 + \cdots + a_{m+1} + \cdots$ is divergent.

(3) If $l = 1$, the test fails, because it will be found that $l = 1$ for

both the series $\sum \dfrac{1}{n}$ and the series $\sum \dfrac{1}{n^2}$, the first of which is diver-

gent (§ 439) and the second is convergent (§ 440). For, the series $\sum \dfrac{1}{n}$

has the test ratio $\dfrac{1}{n+1} \div \dfrac{1}{n} = \dfrac{n}{n+1}$, and the series $\sum \dfrac{1}{n^2}$ has the

test ratio $\dfrac{1}{(n+1)^2} \div \dfrac{1}{n^2} = \left(\dfrac{n}{n+1}\right)^2$, both of which approach the

limit 1 as $n \to \infty$.

We may now summarize the preceding results as follows:

If, in a positive series $\sum a_n$, the ratio $\dfrac{a_{n+1}}{a_n}$ of a general term to the preceding term approaches a limit l as $n \to \infty$, then the series $\sum a_n$ is convergent if $l < 1$, and is divergent if $l > 1$; it is also divergent if $\dfrac{a_{n+1}}{a_n} \to +\infty$ as $n \to \infty$. If $l = 1$, no information concerning the convergence of the series is given by the ratio test.

EXAMPLE 1. Test the series $\dfrac{1}{2} + \dfrac{2}{2^2} + \dfrac{3}{2^3} + \cdots + \dfrac{n}{2^n} + \cdots$ for convergence by the ratio test.

Solution: For this series, $a_n = \dfrac{n}{2^n}$ and $a_{n+1} = \dfrac{n+1}{2^{n+1}}$, then

$$\frac{a_{n+1}}{a_n} = \frac{n+1}{2^{n+1}} \cdot \frac{2^n}{n} = \frac{1}{2} \cdot \frac{n+1}{n} = \frac{1}{2}\left(1 + \frac{1}{n}\right);$$

the limit of this ratio is $l = \frac{1}{2}$. Since $l < 1$ in this case, the given series is convergent.

EXAMPLE 2. Test the series $1 + \dfrac{2^2}{2!} + \dfrac{3^3}{3!} + \cdots + \dfrac{n^n}{n!} + \cdots$ for convergence by the ratio test.

Solution: For this series,

$$\frac{a_{n+1}}{a_n} = \frac{(n+1)^{n+1}}{(n+1)!} \div \frac{n^n}{n!} = \frac{(n+1)^{n+1}}{(n+1)!} \cdot \frac{n!}{n^n} = \frac{(n+1)^{n+1}}{n+1} \cdot \frac{1}{n^n}$$

$$= \frac{(n+1)^n}{n^n} = \left(1 + \frac{1}{n}\right)^n.$$

But by § 279, $\left(1 + \dfrac{1}{n}\right)^n \to e$ as $n \to \infty$. In this case, since $e \approx 2.7$, we have $l > 1$, and the given series is divergent.

445. Exercises

Test each of the following series for convergence or divergence by the ratio test:

1. $\dfrac{1 \cdot 3}{2} + \dfrac{3 \cdot 5}{2^2} + \dfrac{5 \cdot 7}{2^3} + \cdots + \dfrac{(2n-1)(2n+1)}{2^n} + \cdots.$

2. $\dfrac{1}{1 \cdot 2} + \dfrac{1}{3 \cdot 2^2} + \dfrac{1}{5 \cdot 2^3} + \dfrac{1}{7 \cdot 2^4} + \cdots.$

3. $\frac{2}{3} + 2(\frac{2}{3})^2 + 3(\frac{2}{3})^3 + \cdots + n(\frac{2}{3})^n + \cdots.$

4. $1 + \dfrac{2!}{3} + \dfrac{3!}{3^2} + \dfrac{4!}{3^3} + \dfrac{5!}{3^4} + \cdots.$

5. $1 + \dfrac{1}{2!} + \dfrac{1}{3!} + \dfrac{1}{4!} + \cdots + \dfrac{1}{n!} + \cdots.$

6. $\dfrac{10}{2!} + \dfrac{10^2}{4!} + \dfrac{10^3}{6!} + \dfrac{10^4}{8!} + \cdots.$

7. $\dfrac{5}{1^2} + \dfrac{5^2}{2^2} + \dfrac{5^3}{3^2} + \dfrac{5^4}{4^2} + \cdots + \dfrac{5^n}{n^2} + \cdots.$

8. $\dfrac{1}{3} + \dfrac{1 \cdot 3}{3 \cdot 6} + \dfrac{1 \cdot 3 \cdot 5}{3 \cdot 6 \cdot 9} + \dfrac{1 \cdot 3 \cdot 5 \cdot 7}{3 \cdot 6 \cdot 9 \cdot 12} + \cdots.$

9. $1 + \dfrac{2}{2!} + \dfrac{3}{4!} + \dfrac{4}{6!} + \cdots + \dfrac{n}{(2n-2)!} + \cdots.$

10. $\dfrac{2!}{5} + \dfrac{4!}{5^2 \cdot 3} + \dfrac{6!}{5^3 \cdot 3^2} + \dfrac{8!}{5^4 \cdot 3^3} + \cdots.$

11. $1 + \dfrac{1 \cdot 2}{1 \cdot 3} + \dfrac{1 \cdot 2 \cdot 3}{1 \cdot 3 \cdot 5} + \dfrac{1 \cdot 2 \cdot 3 \cdot 4}{1 \cdot 3 \cdot 5 \cdot 7} + \cdots.$

12. $1 + \dfrac{1 \cdot 4}{1 \cdot 3} \cdot \dfrac{1}{2^2} + \dfrac{1 \cdot 4 \cdot 7}{1 \cdot 3 \cdot 5} \cdot \dfrac{1}{3^2} + \dfrac{1 \cdot 4 \cdot 7 \cdot 10}{1 \cdot 3 \cdot 5 \cdot 7} \cdot \dfrac{1}{4^2} + \cdots.$

13. $\dfrac{2}{1 \cdot 2} + \dfrac{2^2}{2 \cdot 3} + \dfrac{2^3}{3 \cdot 4} + \cdots + \dfrac{2^n}{n(n+1)} + \cdots.$

14. $\dfrac{1!}{1^2 \cdot 2^2} + \dfrac{2!}{2^2 \cdot 3^2} + \dfrac{3!}{3^2 \cdot 4^2} + \dfrac{4!}{4^2 \cdot 5^2} + \cdots.$

15. $\displaystyle\sum_{1}^{\infty} \dfrac{n^3}{n!}.$

16. $\displaystyle\sum_{1}^{\infty} \dfrac{n!}{n^n}.$

17. $\displaystyle\sum_{1}^{\infty} \dfrac{3^{2n-1}}{n^2 + 1}.$

18. $\displaystyle\sum_{1}^{\infty} \dfrac{n!}{(2n-1)^2 (2n)^2}.$

19. $\displaystyle\sum_{1}^{\infty} \dfrac{n(n+2)}{3^n}.$

20. $\displaystyle\sum_{1}^{\infty} \dfrac{n}{(2n-1)!}.$

446. The Alternating Series Test

An infinite series whose terms are alternately positive and negative is called an *alternating series*. Such a series may be written in the form $a_1 - a_2 + a_3 - a_4 + \cdots$, where the a's are all positive.

A very useful test for convergence for such an alternating series may be obtained as follows: Consider the alternating series $a_1 - a_2 + a_3 - a_4 + \cdots$, where each a_n is positive. Suppose that each term is numerically less than the preceding term: $a_n < a_{n-1}$ for all values of n, and suppose also that the n-th term a_n approaches 0 as $n \to \infty$. If n is *even*, the sum of the first n terms may be written in either of the forms

(a) $\qquad s_n = (a_1 - a_2) + (a_3 - a_4) + \cdots + (a_{n-1} - a_n),$

or

(b) $\qquad s_n = a_1 - (a_2 - a_3) - \cdots - (a_{n-2} - a_{n-1}) - a_n.$

Since $a_n < a_{n-1}$ for each value of n, each parenthesis in (a) and in (b) is positive, and from (a) we see that s_n increases with n and from (b) we see that $s_n < a_1$. Since s_n is bounded and increasing, by § 431, I, s_n approaches a limit s as $n \to \infty$ through even values. If n is even, $n + 1$ is odd. But s_{n+1} also approaches the same limit s as $n \to \infty$, since $s_{n+1} = s_n + a_{n+1}$ and $a_{n+1} \to 0$ by hypothesis. Hence, s_n approaches a single limit s when $n \to \infty$ through even values and through odd values, and therefore the series is convergent. We have then obtained the following alternating series theorem:

I. *An alternating series $a_1 - a_2 + a_3 - a_4 + \cdots$ is convergent if each term a_n is numerically less than the preceding term a_{n-1}, and if the limit of the n-th term is 0.*

EXAMPLE 1. The series $1 - \frac{1}{2} + \frac{1}{3} - \frac{1}{4} + \cdots$ is convergent by the alternating series test, since $a_n = \frac{1}{n} \to 0$ as $n \to \infty$, and a_n decreases steadily as n increases.

An important characteristic of a *convergent* alternating series is that in this case it is possible to estimate readily the error made by taking a partial sum as an approximation to the sum of the series.

II. *In a convergent alternating series in which each term is numerically less than the preceding term, the error made in taking the sum of the first n terms as an approximation to the sum of the series is numerically less than the $(n + 1)$-st term:*

(c) $$|E_n| < a_{n+1}.$$

For, if n is *even*,

$$s - s_n = a_{n+1} - (a_{n+2} - a_{n+3}) - \cdots < a_{n+1},$$

and if n is *odd*,

$$s_n - s = a_{n+1} - (a_{n+2} - a_{n+3}) - \cdots < a_{n+1};$$

in either case,

$$|s - s_n| < a_{n+1},$$

which is the result stated.

EXAMPLE 2. The series

$$1 - \frac{1}{2!}\left(\frac{1}{2}\right)^2 + \frac{1}{4!}\left(\frac{1}{2}\right)^4 - \frac{1}{6!}\left(\frac{1}{2}\right)^6 + \cdots$$

is convergent by the alternating series test. If we take the sum of the first three terms as an approximation to the sum, the error is

$$|E_3| < \frac{1}{6!}\left(\frac{1}{2}\right)^6 < 0.00003.$$

EXAMPLE 3. Compute the value, correct to four decimal places, of the sum of the series

$$\frac{1}{3}\cdot\frac{1}{2!} - \frac{1}{5}\cdot\frac{1}{3!} + \frac{1}{7}\cdot\frac{1}{4!} - \frac{1}{9}\cdot\frac{1}{5!} + \cdots$$

Solution: This is a convergent alternating series. The computation may be arranged systematically as follows:

$$\frac{1}{2!} = 0.50000 \qquad \frac{1}{3}\cdot\frac{1}{2!} = 0.16667$$

$$\frac{1}{3!} = 0.16667 \qquad \frac{1}{5}\cdot\frac{1}{3!} = 0.03333$$

$$\frac{1}{4!} = 0.04167 \qquad \frac{1}{7}\cdot\frac{1}{4!} = 0.00595$$

$$\frac{1}{5!} = 0.00833 \qquad \frac{1}{9}\cdot\frac{1}{5!} = 0.00093$$

$$\frac{1}{6!} = 0.00139 \qquad \frac{1}{11}\cdot\frac{1}{6!} = 0.00013$$

$$\frac{1}{7!} = 0.00020 \qquad \frac{1}{13}\cdot\frac{1}{7!} = 0.00002$$

By theorem II, the error after five terms is less numerically than the sixth term, so that $|E_5| < 0.00002$. Hence, we obtain the sum of the series, correct to four decimal places, if we use the first five terms. Taking the values of these terms with their proper signs, we have:

$$
\begin{array}{lll}
+0.16667 & -0.03333 & +0.17275 \\
0.00595 & 0.00093 & -0.03426 \\
\underline{0.00013} & \underline{-0.03426} & \underline{+0.13849} \\
+0.17275 & -0.03426 & +0.13849
\end{array}
$$

Therefore, the required value of the sum of the given series is 0.1385, to four decimal places.

447. Exercises

In Exercises 1–8, test each of the given series for convergence or divergence

1. $1 - \dfrac{1}{3} + \dfrac{1}{5} - \dfrac{1}{7} + \cdots.$

2. $1 - \dfrac{1}{2!} + \dfrac{1}{3!} - \dfrac{1}{4!} + \cdots.$

3. $\dfrac{3}{2} - \dfrac{4}{3} + \dfrac{5}{4} - \dfrac{6}{5} + \cdots.$

4. $\dfrac{1}{1\cdot 2} - \dfrac{1}{3\cdot 2^2} + \dfrac{1}{5\cdot 2^3} - \dfrac{1}{7\cdot 2^4} + \cdots.$

5. $\dfrac{1}{1\cdot 2} - \dfrac{1}{2\cdot 3} + \dfrac{1}{3\cdot 4} - \dfrac{1}{4\cdot 5} + \cdots.$

6. $\dfrac{1}{2} - \dfrac{3}{4} + \dfrac{5}{8} - \dfrac{9}{16} + \dfrac{17}{32} - \cdots.$

7. $1 - \dfrac{1}{\sqrt{3}} + \dfrac{1}{\sqrt{5}} - \dfrac{1}{\sqrt{7}} + \cdots.$

8. $\dfrac{1}{\ln 3} - \dfrac{1}{\ln 5} + \dfrac{1}{\ln 7} - \dfrac{1}{\ln 9} + \cdots$.

In Exercises 9–14, estimate the error made by taking the sum of the first n terms of each of the given convergent series as an approximation to the sum, for the indicated value of n:

9. $1 - \dfrac{1}{2^2} + \dfrac{1}{3^2} - \dfrac{1}{4^2} + \cdots$, $n = 20$.

10. $1 - \dfrac{1}{2!} + \dfrac{1}{3!} - \dfrac{1}{4!} + \cdots$, $n = 8$.

11. $\dfrac{1}{2 \cdot 1^2} - \dfrac{1}{4 \cdot 2^2} + \dfrac{1}{6 \cdot 3^2} - \dfrac{1}{8 \cdot 4^2} + \cdots$, $n = 10$.

12. $1 - \dfrac{1}{\sqrt{2}} + \dfrac{1}{\sqrt{3}} - \dfrac{1}{\sqrt{4}} + \cdots$, $n = 100$.

13. $\dfrac{1}{5} - \dfrac{1}{3}\left(\dfrac{1}{5}\right)^3 + \dfrac{1}{5}\left(\dfrac{1}{5}\right)^5 - \dfrac{1}{7}\left(\dfrac{1}{5}\right)^7 + \cdots$, $n = 6$.

14. $1 - \dfrac{1}{2!} + \dfrac{2}{3!} - \dfrac{3}{4!} + \cdots$, $n = 8$.

Compute the sum of each of the following series correct to three decimal places:

15. $1 - \dfrac{1}{2!} + \dfrac{1}{3!} - \dfrac{1}{4!} + \cdots$.

16. $1 - \dfrac{1}{2^4} + \dfrac{1}{3^4} - \dfrac{1}{4^4} + \dfrac{1}{5^4} - \cdots$.

17. $\dfrac{1}{3} - \dfrac{1}{3}\left(\dfrac{1}{3}\right)^3 + \dfrac{1}{5}\left(\dfrac{1}{3}\right)^5 - \dfrac{1}{7}\left(\dfrac{1}{3}\right)^7 + \cdots$.

18. $1 - \dfrac{1}{2} + \dfrac{1}{2!}\left(\dfrac{1}{2}\right)^2 - \dfrac{1}{3!}\left(\dfrac{1}{2}\right)^3 + \cdots$.

448. Absolute Convergence

Let us now consider infinite series with infinitely many positive terms and infinitely many negative terms. Let $u_1 + u_2 + u_3 + \cdots + u_n + \cdots$ be a given series with positive and negative terms, and let $u_1' + u_2' + u_3' + \cdots + u_n' + \cdots$ denote the series obtained by changing the signs of the negative terms of the first series, so that $u_n' = |u_n|$ for every n. Also let s_n be the sum of the first n terms of the first series and s_n' that of the second series.

Suppose that there are p positive terms and q negative terms in s_n, and let P_p and $-N_q$ be the sums of these terms, where $p + q = n$. Then

(a) $$s_n = P_p - N_q, \qquad s_n' = P_p + N_q.$$

Let us suppose that the series $u_1' + u_2' + u_3' + \cdots + u_n' + \cdots$ (with all positive terms) is convergent; then s_n' approaches a limit s' when $n \to \infty$. Since P_p, N_q and s_n' are all positive, by (a) we have $P_p \leqq s_n'$, $N_q \leqq s_n'$; also P_p, N_q and s_n' all increase as n increases, and s_n' remains less than s'. It follows that P_p and N_q both remain less than s' but are increasing; then, by § 431, I, P_p and N_q approach limits P and N respectively. From (a), we see that $s_n = P_p - N_q$ approaches the limit $P - N$; since s_n approaches a limit as $n \to \infty$, it follows that the series $u_1 + u_2 + \cdots + u_n + \cdots$ converges. We have now obtained the following important theorem:

An infinite series $\sum u_n$ which has both positive and negative terms is convergent if the series of absolute values $\sum |u_n|$ is convergent.

It can be readily shown by examples that the converse of this theorem is not true; that is, if $\sum u_n$ is convergent, it does not follow that $\sum |u_n|$ is convergent. For example, the series $1 - \frac{1}{2} + \frac{1}{3} - \frac{1}{4} + \cdots$ is convergent (by the alternating series test); but $1 + \frac{1}{2} + \frac{1}{3} + \frac{1}{4} + \cdots$ is not.

Based on the preceding theorem, we have the following definition:

*An infinite series $\sum u_n$ is called **absolutely convergent** if the series of absolute values $\sum |u_n|$ is convergent. A convergent series which is not absolutely convergent is called **conditionally convergent**.*

EXAMPLE 1. (a) The series $1 - \dfrac{1}{2^2} + \dfrac{1}{3^2} - \dfrac{1}{4^2} + \cdots$ is absolutely convergent since the series of absolute values $1 + \dfrac{1}{2^2} + \dfrac{1}{3^2} + \dfrac{1}{4^2} + \cdots$ is convergent (hyperharmonic series). (b) The series $1 - \frac{1}{2} + \frac{1}{3} - \frac{1}{4} + \cdots$ is convergent, by the alternating series test, but it is not absolutely convergent since the series of absolute values $1 + \frac{1}{2} + \frac{1}{3} + \frac{1}{4} + \cdots$ is the divergent harmonic series. It is therefore conditionally convergent.

It can be proved* that we can operate with absolutely convergent series as if they were finite sums, but this is not necessarily true for conditionally convergent series. Thus, a change in the order of the terms of a conditionally convergent series may affect its convergence or the value of the series.

The absolute convergence of a given series may frequently be tested by applying the ratio test to the absolute value series.

* See Smail, *Infinite Processes*, Chapter X.

EXAMPLE 2. Test for absolute convergence the series

$$\frac{x}{1\cdot3} + \frac{x^2}{2\cdot4} + \frac{x^3}{3\cdot5} + \cdots + \frac{x^n}{n(n+2)} + \cdots$$

Solution: Consider the absolute value series

$$\frac{|x|}{1\cdot3} + \frac{|x|^2}{2\cdot4} + \frac{|x|^3}{3\cdot5} + \cdots + \frac{|x|^n}{n(n+2)} + \cdots$$

Let $a_n = \dfrac{|x|^n}{n(n+2)}$, then

$$\frac{a_{n+1}}{a_n} = \frac{|x|^{n+1}}{(n+1)(n+3)}\cdot\frac{n(n+2)}{|x|^n} = \frac{n(n+2)}{(n+1)(n+3)}\cdot|x|,$$

which approaches $|x|$ as a limit when $n \to \infty$. The absolute value series therefore converges when $|x| < 1$ and diverges for $|x| > 1$. The given series is then absolutely convergent for $|x| < 1$. It is also absolutely convergent for $|x| = 1$, as we see by comparison with $\sum(1/n^2)$.

It can be readily seen that the ratio test for series of positive and negative terms may be stated:

If $\lim\limits_{n\to\infty} \left|\dfrac{u_{n+1}}{u_n}\right| = l$, *the series* $\sum u_n$ *is absolutely convergent if* $l < 1$, *and is divergent if* $l > 1$; *the test fails if* $l = 1$.

449. Exercises

Test each of the series in Exercises 1–8 for absolute convergence:

1. $1 - \dfrac{1}{3} + \dfrac{1}{9} - \dfrac{1}{27} + \dfrac{1}{81} - \cdots.$

2. $1 - \dfrac{1}{2^3} + \dfrac{1}{3^3} - \dfrac{1}{4^3} + \cdots.$

3. $1 - \dfrac{1}{\sqrt{2}} + \dfrac{1}{\sqrt{3}} - \dfrac{1}{\sqrt{4}} + \cdots.$

4. $1 - \dfrac{1}{3} + \dfrac{1}{5} - \dfrac{1}{7} + \dfrac{1}{9} - \cdots.$

5. $1 - \dfrac{2}{2!} + \dfrac{4}{3!} - \dfrac{8}{4!} + \dfrac{16}{5!} - \cdots.$

6. $2 - \dfrac{3}{2\sqrt{2}} + \dfrac{4}{3\sqrt{3}} - \dfrac{5}{4\sqrt{4}} + \cdots.$

7. $1 - \dfrac{1\cdot3}{2\cdot5} + \dfrac{1\cdot3\cdot5}{2\cdot5\cdot8} - \dfrac{1\cdot3\cdot5\cdot7}{2\cdot5\cdot8\cdot11} + \cdots.$

8. $1 - \dfrac{1\cdot2}{1\cdot3} + \dfrac{1\cdot2\cdot3}{1\cdot3\cdot5} - \dfrac{1\cdot2\cdot3\cdot4}{1\cdot3\cdot5\cdot7} + \cdots.$

9. Show that the series $e^{-x} \cos x + e^{-2x} \cos 2\,x + e^{-3x} \cos 3\,x + \cdots$ is absolutely convergent for all positive values of x. [*Hint.* Use $|\cos \theta| \leqq 1$.]

10. What can you say about the convergence of the series
$$1 + r \cos \theta + r^2 \cos 2\,\theta + r^3 \cos 3\,\theta + \cdots ?$$

450. Power Series

An infinite series of the form

(a) $\qquad a_0 + a_1 x + a_2 x^2 + \cdots + a_n x^n + \cdots = \sum_{n=0}^{\infty} a_n x^n,$

where the coefficients $a_0, a_1, a_2, \cdots$ are independent of x (constants) and x is a variable, is called a ***power series in x.*** A series of the form

(b) $\qquad a_0 + a_1 (x - a) + a_2 (x - a)^2 + \cdots$
$$+ a_n (x - a)^n + \cdots = \sum_{n=0}^{\infty} a_n (x - a)^n$$

is called a ***power series in $(x - a)$.***

A power series in x may converge for all values of x, or for no values of x except $x = 0$, or it may converge for some values and diverge for others.

EXAMPLE 1. (a) The series
$$1 + x + \frac{x^2}{2!} + \frac{x^3}{3!} + \cdots$$

converges for all values of x (as shown by the ratio test); (b) the series
$$1 + x + 2!\,x^2 + 3!\,x^3 + \cdots$$

converges for $x = 0$ but diverges for other values of x (as shown by the ratio test); (c) the series
$$1 + x + x^2 + x^3 + \cdots$$

converges for $|x| < 1$ and diverges for all other values of x (§ 437).

It can be proved* that a power series in x which does not converge for all values of x but does converge for some values of $x \neq 0$, is absolutely convergent within an interval $(-r, r)$ symmetric about $x = 0$, and is divergent outside this integral; at the values $x = r$ and $x = -r$, it may converge or diverge, according to circumstances. The interval $(-r, r)$ is called the ***interval of convergence;*** the number r is called the *radius of convergence.* Similarly, a power series in $x - a$ is absolutely convergent within an interval $(a - r, a + r)$ and divergent outside.

---

* See Smail, *Infinite Processes*, § 170.

It can be shown* that a power series in x defines a function which is a continuous function of x within the interval of convergence.

Frequently, the interval of convergence may be determined by use of the ratio test; the end-points of the interval must be tested by some other test.

EXAMPLE 2. Find the interval of convergence of the power series

$$x + \frac{x^2}{2^2} + \frac{x^3}{3^2} + \cdots + \frac{x^n}{n^2} + \cdots,$$

and test the end-points of the interval for convergence.

Solution: By the ratio test, if $u_n = \left| \dfrac{x^n}{n^2} \right|$,

$$\frac{u_{n+1}}{u_n} = \frac{|x|^{n+1}}{(n+1)^2} \cdot \frac{n^2}{|x|^n} = \frac{n^2}{(n+1)^2} \cdot |x|,$$

which approaches $|x|$ as $n \to \infty$. Then the series of positive terms $\sum \dfrac{|x|^n}{n^2}$ converges absolutely if $|x| < 1$ and diverges if $|x| > 1$. The interval of convergence is therefore $|x| < 1$ or $-1 < x < 1$. Testing the end-points of the interval: if $x = 1$, the given series becomes $1 + \dfrac{1}{2^2} + \dfrac{1}{3^2} + \dfrac{1}{4^2} + \cdots$, which is convergent (§ 440); if $x = -1$, the series becomes $-1 + \dfrac{1}{2^2} - \dfrac{1}{3^2} + \cdots$, which is convergent (§ 446). Hence, the given series is convergent for $-1 \leqq x \leqq 1$, and divergent for $x > 1$ and $x < -1$. (Fig. 186)

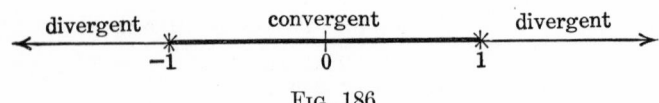

divergent   convergent   divergent

−1   0   1

FIG. 186

EXAMPLE 3. Determine the interval of convergence of the power series

$$(x - 1) - \tfrac{1}{2}(x - 1)^2 + \tfrac{1}{3}(x - 1)^3 - \tfrac{1}{4}(x - 1)^4 + \cdots,$$

and examine the end points of the interval.

Solution: If we put $u_n = (-1)^{n+1} \dfrac{(x - 1)^n}{n}$, we have

$$\left| \frac{u_{n+1}}{u_n} \right| = \frac{|x - 1|^{n+1}}{n + 1} \cdot \frac{n}{|x - 1|^n} = \frac{n}{n + 1} |x - 1|,$$

which approaches $|x - 1|$ as $n \to \infty$. The given series therefore converges absolutely for $|x - 1| < 1$ and diverges for $|x - 1| > 1$. The interval of

---

* See Smail, *Infinite Processes*, § 170.

convergence is $|x - 1| < 1$, or $-1 < x - 1 < 1$, or $0 < x < 2$. To test the end-points of the interval, we put $x = 0$, and the given series becomes $-1 - \frac{1}{2} - \frac{1}{3} - \frac{1}{4} - \cdots$, which is divergent since it is the negative of the harmonic series; putting $x = 2$, we get the series $1 - \frac{1}{2} + \frac{1}{3} - \frac{1}{4} + \cdots$, which is convergent by the alternating series test. The given series therefore converges for $0 < x \leqq 2$, and diverges for $x \leqq 0$ and $x > 2$. (Fig. 187)

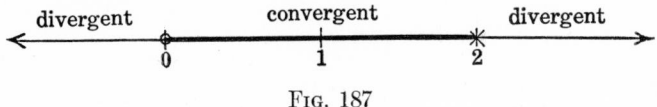

Fig. 187

Another important property of power series, which is proved in more advanced works,* is the following:

If a power series in powers of x or in powers of $(x - a)$ is differentiated term by term with respect to x, the resulting power series converges in the same interval of convergence as the original series (with the possible exception of the end-points of the interval), and the sum of the new series is equal to the derivative of the sum of the original series.

451. Exercises

Find the interval of convergence for each of the following power series, and determine whether the series converges or diverges at the end-points of the interval:

1. $\dfrac{x}{1 \cdot 2} + \dfrac{x^2}{2 \cdot 3} + \dfrac{x^3}{3 \cdot 4} + \dfrac{x^4}{4 \cdot 5} + \cdots$.

2. $1 + x + \dfrac{x^2}{2!} + \dfrac{x^3}{3!} + \cdots$.

3. $1 + \dfrac{2}{3} x + \dfrac{3}{9} x^2 + \dfrac{4}{27} x^3 + \cdots$.

4. $1 - 2 x + 3 x^2 - 4 x^3 + \cdots$.

5. $1 - x + \dfrac{x^2}{2!} - \dfrac{x^3}{3!} + \cdots$.

6. $1 - \dfrac{3}{2} x + \dfrac{5}{4} x^2 - \dfrac{7}{8} x^3 + \dfrac{9}{16} x^4 - \cdots$.

7. $1 + x + 2! \, x^2 + 3! \, x^3 + \cdots$.

8. $x + \dfrac{x^3}{3!} + \dfrac{x^5}{5!} + \dfrac{x^7}{7!} + \cdots$.

9. $x - \dfrac{x^3}{3!} + \dfrac{x^5}{5!} - \dfrac{x^7}{7!} + \cdots$.

* See, for example, Smail, *Infinite Processes*, § 173.

10. $1 - \dfrac{x^2}{2!} + \dfrac{x^4}{4!} - \dfrac{x^6}{6!} + \cdots.$

11. $x - \dfrac{x^2}{2} + \dfrac{x^3}{3} - \dfrac{x^4}{4} + \cdots.$

12. $1 + \dfrac{2^2}{5} x + \dfrac{3^2}{5^2} x^2 + \dfrac{4^2}{5^3} x^3 + \cdots.$

13. $x + 2^4 \cdot \dfrac{x^2}{2!} + 3^4 \cdot \dfrac{x^3}{3!} + 4^4 \cdot \dfrac{x^4}{4!} + \cdots.$

14. $\dfrac{3}{1^2 \cdot 4} x + \dfrac{3^2}{3^2 \cdot 4^2} x^2 + \dfrac{3^3}{5^2 \cdot 4^3} x^3 + \dfrac{3^4}{7^2 \cdot 4^4} x^4 + \cdots.$

15. $1 - 2(x - 1) + 3(x - 1)^2 - 4(x - 1)^3 + \cdots.$

16. $\dfrac{x + 3}{1 \cdot 3} - \dfrac{(x + 3)^2}{3 \cdot 5} + \dfrac{(x + 3)^3}{5 \cdot 7} - \dfrac{(x + 3)^4}{7 \cdot 9} + \cdots.$

17. $2(x - 2) + \dfrac{3(x - 2)^2}{2!} + \dfrac{4(x - 2)^3}{3!} + \dfrac{5(x - 2)^4}{4!} + \cdots.$

18. $(x + 1) - \dfrac{2}{4} (x + 1)^2 + \dfrac{2^2}{9} (x + 1)^3 - \dfrac{2^3}{16} (x + 1)^4 + \cdots.$

CHAPTER XXIV

Expansion of Functions in Series

---

452. Taylor's and Maclaurin's Series

In this chapter we shall consider the problem of representing a given function by means of a power series.

Let the function $f(x)$ and all of its derivatives be continuous at a given point $x = a$. Let us *assume* that within some interval including the point $x = a$ the function $f(x)$ can be represented by a power series in powers of $x - a$:

$$(a) \qquad f(x) = c_0 + c_1(x - a) + c_2(x - a)^2 + \cdots + c_n(x - a)^n + \cdots.$$

We shall investigate later the conditions under which this assumption is justified. Let $-r < x - a < r$ be the interval of convergence of the series (a). By the theorem on differentiation of a power series (at the end of § 450), for $|x - a| < r$ we have:

$$(b) \quad \left\{ \begin{aligned} f'(x) &= c_1 + 2\,c_2(x - a) + 3\,c_3(x - a)^2 + \cdots, \\ f''(x) &= 2\,c_2 + 3 \cdot 2\,c_3(x - a) + 4 \cdot 3\,c_4(x - a)^2 + \cdots, \\ f'''(x) &= 3 \cdot 2\,c_3 + 4 \cdot 3 \cdot 2\,c_4(x - a) + 5 \cdot 4 \cdot 3\,c_5(x - a)^2 + \cdots, \text{etc.} \end{aligned} \right.$$

If we put $x = a$ in these equations (a) and (b), we get $f(a) = c_0$, $f'(a) = c_1$, $f''(a) = 2\,c_2$, $f'''(a) = 3 \cdot 2\,c_3$, etc., or

$$c_0 = f(a), \ c_1 = f'(a), \ c_2 = \frac{1}{2} f''(a) = \frac{f''(a)}{2!}, \ c_3 = \frac{1}{3 \cdot 2} f'''(a) = \frac{f'''(a)}{3!},$$

and for the general coefficient, $c_n = \dfrac{f^{(n)}(a)}{n!}$. Substituting these values for the coefficients in (a), we have the following result:

If $f(x)$ and its derivatives are continuous at $x = a$, and if $f(x)$ has a representation by a power series in $x - a$, this representation is:

$$(1) \qquad f(x) = f(a) + f'(a)(x - a) + \frac{1}{2!} f''(a)(x - a)^2 + \cdots$$
$$+ \frac{1}{n!} f^{(n)}(a)(x - a)^n + \cdots.$$

This series is known as ***Taylor's series*** for the function $f(x)$. The function $f(x)$ is said to be *expanded in powers of* $(x - a)$ *by Taylor's theorem,* or to be *expanded about the point* $x = a$ or *in the neighborhood of* $x = a$.

For the special case in which $a = 0$, the series (1) becomes:

$$(2) \quad f(x) = f(0) + f'(0)x + \frac{1}{2!}f''(0)x^2 + \cdots + \frac{1}{n!}f^{(n)}(0)x^n + \cdots.$$

This series is called ***Maclaurin's series*** for the function $f(x)$. It is said to be the *expansion of* $f(x)$ *in powers of* x *by Maclaurin's theorem,* or the *expansion about the point* $x = 0$ or *in the neighborhood of* $x = 0$.

The constant a which occurs in Taylor's series (1) may be chosen arbitrarily except that $f(x)$ and all of its derivatives must be continuous for $x = a$, and the values $f(a)$, $f'(a)$, $f''(a)$, etc., must be known. It will be seen later how a is chosen for convenience in practical applications.

EXAMPLE 1. Assuming that e^x can be represented by a power series in powers of x, find the Maclaurin series for this function.

Solution: We may arrange the calculation of the coefficients of the series thus:

$$
\begin{array}{ll}
f(x) = e^x, & f(0) = 1, \\
f'(x) = e^x, & f'(0) = 1, \\
f''(x) = e^x, & f''(0) = 1, \\
\cdots\cdots & \cdots\cdots \\
f^{(n)}(x) = e^x, & f^{(n)}(0) = 1, \\
\cdots\cdots & \cdots\cdots
\end{array}
$$

Hence, the Maclaurin expansion of e^x is:

$$(c) \qquad e^x = 1 + x + \frac{x^2}{2!} + \frac{x^3}{3!} + \cdots + \frac{x^n}{n!} + \cdots.$$

By the ratio test we find that this series converges for all values of x.

EXAMPLE 2. For the function $\sin x$, find the Maclaurin expansion and also the Taylor expansion about the point $x = \frac{1}{3}\pi$, assuming that such expansions are possible.

Solution: (a) For the Maclaurin series, we find the coefficients as follows:

$$
\begin{array}{ll}
f(x) = \sin x, & f(0) = 0, \\
f'(x) = \cos x, & f'(0) = 1, \\
f''(x) = -\sin x, & f''(0) = 0, \\
f'''(x) = -\cos x, & f'''(0) = -1, \\
f^{(4)}(x) = \sin x, & f^{(4)}(0) = 0, \\
\cdots\cdots\cdots & \cdots\cdots\cdots \\
f^{(n)}(x) = \sin\left(x + \tfrac{1}{2}n\pi\right)^*, & f^{(n)}(0) = \sin\tfrac{1}{2}n\pi, \\
\cdots\cdots\cdots & \cdots\cdots\cdots
\end{array}
$$

The Maclaurin expansion is therefore

* See § 265, Exercise 26.

(d) $\sin x = x - \dfrac{x^3}{3!} + \dfrac{x^5}{5!} - \cdots + (-1)^{m+1} \dfrac{x^{2m-1}}{(2m-1)!} + \cdots.$

This series converges for all values of x, as may be seen by the ratio test.

(b) To obtain the Taylor series, we take the values of $f(x)$, $f'(x)$, $f''(x)$, etc., found above and substitute $a = \frac{1}{3}\pi$, and we get

$$f(\tfrac{1}{3}\pi) = \tfrac{1}{2}\sqrt{3}, \quad f'(\tfrac{1}{3}\pi) = \tfrac{1}{2}, \quad f''(\tfrac{1}{3}\pi) = -\tfrac{1}{2}\sqrt{3}, \quad f'''(\tfrac{1}{3}\pi) = -\tfrac{1}{2},$$

$$f^{(4)}(\tfrac{1}{3}\pi) = \tfrac{1}{2}\sqrt{3}, \cdots, \quad f^{(n)}(\tfrac{1}{3}\pi) = \sin\left(\tfrac{1}{3}\pi + \tfrac{1}{2}n\pi\right), \cdots.$$

The Taylor expansion is then

$$\sin x = \tfrac{1}{2}\sqrt{3} + \tfrac{1}{2}(x - \tfrac{1}{3}\pi) - \tfrac{1}{2}\sqrt{3}\cdot\frac{1}{2!}(x - \tfrac{1}{3}\pi)^2$$

$$- \frac{1}{2}\frac{1}{3!}(x - \tfrac{1}{3}\pi)^3 + \cdots + \frac{1}{n!}\sin\left(\tfrac{1}{3}\pi + \tfrac{1}{2}n\pi\right)(x - \tfrac{1}{3}\pi)^n + \cdots.$$

At this stage of our discussion of the expansion of functions in series, it should be remembered that we started with the *assumption* that the given function is representable by a power series of a given form. On this assumption we have found what form the coefficients have. Examples are known for which the Taylor series for a given function converges and yet the series does not represent the function, that is, for which the sum of the series is not equal to the value of the function. Such examples do not occur in elementary work. It will be shown in § 455 how to determine whether the Taylor series derived from a function actually represents the function.

Unless the function and all of its derivatives exist for $x = a$, the function cannot be represented by a Taylor series in powers of $(x - a)$. Examples of functions that are not representable by a Maclaurin series (where $a = 0$) are $\ln x$, $\cot x$, and $\sqrt{x}$.

453. Exercises

Find the Maclaurin expansion of each of the following functions, on the assumption that such an expansion exists:

1. e^{-x}.
2. 2^x.
3. $\ln(1 + x)$.
4. $1/(1 - x)$.
5. $\cos x$.
6. $\cosh x$.
7. $\sqrt{1 + x}$.
8. $\cos(x + \tfrac{1}{6}\pi)$.

Find the Taylor expansion of each of the following functions, for the given value of a, on the assumption that such an expansion exists:

9. e^x, $a = 1$.
10. e^{-x}, $a = 2$.
11. $\sin x$, $a = \tfrac{1}{4}\pi$.
12. $\cos x$, $a = \tfrac{1}{3}\pi$.
13. $\ln x$, $a = 1$.
14. $\sinh x$, $a = 1$.
15. $1/x$, $a = 2$.
16. $\sqrt{x}$, $a = 2$.

Find the first three non-zero terms of the Maclaurin expansion of each of the following functions, on the assumption that such an expansion exists:

17. $\tan x$.
18. $\sec x$.
19. $\operatorname{Arc} \tan x$.
20. $\operatorname{Arc} \sin x$.
21. $\ln \cos x$.
22. $\sin^2 x$.
23. $e^x \cos x$.
24. e^{-x^2}.

25. Show that $\ln x$ and $\cot x$ cannot have Maclaurin expansions.

454. Taylor's Formula with a Remainder

Let us consider the Taylor's series for a given function $f(x)$, and let R_n denote the *remainder* in the series after the n-th term, that is, let R_n be defined by

$$(a) \quad f(x) = f(a) + f'(a)(x - a) + \frac{1}{2!} f''(a)(x - a)^2 + \cdots$$

$$+ \frac{1}{(n-1)!} f^{(n-1)}(a)(x - a)^{n-1} + R_n.$$

We wish to derive a formula for the remainder R_n in terms of $f(x)$.

Let us suppose that $f(x)$ has derivatives of orders 1 to n in an interval containing the point a. Let K be determined by the equation

$$(b) \quad f(x) = f(a) + f'(a)(x - a) + \frac{1}{2!} f''(a)(x - a) + \cdots$$

$$+ \frac{1}{(n-1)!} f^{(n-1)}(a)(x - a)^{n-1} + K \cdot \frac{1}{n!} (x - a)^n,$$

and then define a function $F(u)$ by:

$$(c) \quad F(u) = f(x) - f(u) - f'(u)(x - u) - \frac{1}{2!} f''(u)(x - u)^2 - \cdots$$

$$- \frac{1}{(n-1)!} f^{(n-1)}(u)(x - u)^{n-1} - \frac{1}{n!} K(x - u)^n.$$

Then $F(x) = 0$ from (c), and $F(a) = 0$ from (b). Now we find from (c):

$$(d) \quad F'(u) = 0 - f'(u) + f'(u) - f''(u)(x - u) + f''(u)(x - u)$$

$$- \frac{1}{2!} f'''(u)(x - u)^2 + \frac{1}{2!} f'''(u)(x - u)^2 - \cdots$$

$$- \frac{1}{(n-1)!} f^{(n)}(u)(x - u)^{n-1} + K \cdot \frac{1}{(n-1)!} (x - u)^{n-1}.$$

All but the last two terms in (d) cancel in pairs, so that (d) reduces to:

$$(e) \qquad F'(u) = -\frac{(x-u)^{n-1}}{(n-1)!}\,[f^{(n)}(u) - K].$$

We may now apply Rolle's theorem (§ 149) to $F(u)$, since this function satisfies the conditions of that theorem. By Rolle's theorem, a number ξ between a and x exists such that $F'(\xi) = 0$. By (e) we get

$$F'(\xi) = -\frac{(x-\xi)^{n-1}}{(n-1)!}\,[f^{(n)}(\xi) - K] = 0,$$

from which it follows that $K = f^{(n)}(\xi)$. If we take this value of K in (b) and compare with (a), we have $R_n = \dfrac{1}{n!} f^{(n)}(\xi)(x-a)^n$. We have now obtained the following important result:

Taylor's formula with a remainder: *If the function $f(x)$ has derivatives of orders 1 to n in an interval about $x = a$, then:*

$$(3) \quad f(x) = f(a) + f'(a)(x-a) + \frac{1}{2!}f''(a)(x-a)^2 + \cdots$$

$$+ \frac{1}{(n-1)!} f^{(n-1)}(a)(x-a)^{n-1} + R_n,$$

in which

$$(4) \qquad R_n = \frac{1}{n!} f^{(n)}(\xi)(x-a)^n,$$

where ξ is a properly chosen number between a and x.

This formula for R_n is called **Lagrange's form** of the remainder. Other forms of the remainder are known, but they will not be needed in our work.

It should be noted that the mean-value formula of § 150 is a special case of Taylor's formula, for $n = 1$. For this reason, Taylor's formula with a remainder is sometimes called "the extended mean-value theorem."

We shall make two important applications of Taylor's formula. First, we shall use the formula to determine under what conditions the Taylor series for a given function will actually *represent* the function; and second, we shall use the remainder formula (4) to estimate the error when the sum of the first n terms of the Taylor series is used as an approximation to the value of the function.

455. Condition for Representation of a Function by Taylor's Series

We have seen in § 454 that a function $f(x)$ may be represented by Taylor's formula with a remainder, if $f(x)$ and its first $n - 1$ derivatives are continuous in an interval about $x = a$ and if it has an n-th derivative within this interval. Let s_n denote the sum of the first n terms of Taylor's formula and R_n the remainder. This sum s_n is also the sum of the first n terms of the Taylor's series for $f(x)$. Then

$$(a) \qquad f(x) = s_n + R_n.$$

If $R_n \to 0$ as $n \to \infty$, then it follows from (a) that $s_n \to f(x)$ as $n \to \infty$. Since s_n approaches a limit, the Taylor series for $f(x)$ is *convergent*; and since s_n has the limit $f(x)$, the Taylor series *represents* the function $f(x)$ because the sum of the series is equal to the value of the function. Conversely, if $s_n \to f(x)$ as $n \to \infty$, then it follows from (a) that $R_n \to 0$ as $n \to \infty$. Hence, we have the important theorem:

The Taylor's series for $f(x)$:

$$(5) \quad f(x) = f(a) + f'(a)(x - a) + \frac{1}{2!} f''(a)(x - a)^2 + \cdots$$

$$+ \frac{1}{(n - 1)!} f^{(n-1)}(a)(x - a)^{n-1} + \cdots$$

*converges and **represents the function** $f(x)$ for those values of x, and only those values, for which all the derivatives of $f(x)$ exist and for which the remainder $R_n \to 0$ as $n \to \infty$. The remainder R_n is expressed by:*

$$(6) \qquad R_n = \frac{1}{n!} f^{(n)}(\xi)(x - a)^n \qquad (\xi \text{ between } a \text{ and } x).$$

This theorem gives a necessary and sufficient condition for the *representation* of a function by the corresponding Taylor series.

When $a = 0$, we have the special result for Maclaurin's series.

456. Some Important Particular Series

We shall now apply the theorem of § 455 to several important special cases of Maclaurin's series.

Let us first consider the exponential function $f(x) = e^x$. The Maclaurin expansion for this function was obtained in Example 1 of § 452; to determine whether this series actually represents the function, we examine the remainder R_n.   Since $f^{(n)}(x) = e^x$ for each value of n, we have

$$(a) \qquad\qquad R_n = \frac{1}{n!} \cdot e^{\xi} x^n \qquad (\xi \text{ between } 0 \text{ and } x).$$

By the ratio test (§ 444), the series $\sum \dfrac{x^n}{n!}$ converges for all values of x, and by § 436 the n-th term of a convergent series has the limit 0 as $n \to \infty$; therefore,

$$(b) \qquad\qquad \lim_{n \to \infty} \left(\frac{x^n}{n!}\right) = 0 \qquad \text{for all values of } x.$$

For any fixed value of x, e^{ξ} remains bounded (since $0 < |\xi| < |x|$), and since $\dfrac{x^n}{n!} \to 0$ as $n \to \infty$, it follows that $R_n \to 0$ as $n \to \infty$, for all values of x.   Hence, by referring to Example 1 of § 452, we see that

$$(7) \qquad e^x = 1 + x + \frac{x^2}{2!} + \frac{x^3}{3!} + \cdots + \frac{x^n}{n!} + \cdots,$$

which *converges* and *represents* e^x for all values of x.   This is called the *exponential series*.

Next consider the function $f(x) = \sin x$, whose Maclaurin expansion was obtained in Example 2 of § 452.   Since $f^{(n)}(x) = \sin (x + \frac{1}{2} n\pi)$ (§ 265, Exercise 26), we have

$$(c) \qquad R_n = \sin (\xi + \tfrac{1}{2} n\pi) \frac{x^n}{n!} \qquad \text{for all values of } x.$$

By trigonometry, $|\sin (\xi + \tfrac{1}{2} n\pi)| \leqq 1$ for all values of n and of x, and by (b) above, $\dfrac{x^n}{n!} \to 0$ as $n \to \infty$; therefore, $R_n \to 0$ as $n \to \infty$, for all values of x.   When n is odd, $\sin [\tfrac{1}{2}(n - 1)\pi] = 0$, and when n is even, $\sin [\tfrac{1}{2}(n - 1)\pi] = (-1)^{\frac{n}{2}+1}$.   Hence,

$$(8) \qquad \sin x = x - \frac{x^3}{3!} + \frac{x^5}{5!} - \cdots + (-1)^{n+1} \frac{x^{2n-1}}{(2n-1)!} + \cdots,$$

which converges and represents $\sin x$ for all values of x.

In a similar way we may show that

$$(9) \qquad \cos x = 1 - \frac{x^2}{2!} + \frac{x^4}{4!} - \cdots + (-1)^{n+1} \frac{x^{2n-2}}{(2n-2)!} + \cdots,$$

which converges and represents $\cos x$ for all values of x.

By applying Maclaurin's theorem to $\ln(1+x)$, we obtain the *logarithmic series:*

$$(10)\quad \ln(1+x) = x - \frac{x^2}{2} + \frac{x^3}{3} - \frac{x^4}{4} + \cdots + (-1)^{n+1}\frac{x^n}{n} + \cdots.$$

It can be proved* that this series converges and represents $\ln(1+x)$ for all values of x in the interval $-1 < x \le 1$.

When Maclaurin's theorem is applied to $(1+x)^m$, we obtain the *binomial series:*

$$(11)\quad (1+x)^m \doteq 1 + mx + \frac{m(m-1)}{2!}x^2 + \frac{m(m-1)(m-2)}{3!}x^3 + \cdots$$

$$+ \frac{m(m-1)(m-2)\cdots(m-n+1)}{n!}x^n + \cdots.$$

It can be proved† that this series converges and represents $(1+x)^m$ for all values of x in the interval $-1 < x < 1$, for all values of m.

457. Computation of Functions by Maclaurin and Taylor Series

Maclaurin's and Taylor's series are very useful for the calculation of approximate values of functions for given numerical values of the variable, since the partial sums are polynomials, which are especially convenient for numerical computation. The accuracy of the result can be tested by the remainder. In certain cases, the series may be a convergent alternating series, in which circumstance the accuracy of the result may be easily tested by examining the next term beyond the point at which the series is broken off.

EXAMPLE 1. Compute the value of e correctly to five decimal places, by use of Maclaurin's formula.

Solution: In § 456 we saw that in Maclaurin's expansion for e^x the remainder is given by $R_n = \frac{1}{n!}e^{\xi}x^n$ (where ξ is between 0 and x). By substituting $x = 1$ in this expansion with the remainder, we get

$$(a)\quad e = 1 + 1 + \frac{1}{2!} + \frac{1}{3!} + \cdots + \frac{1}{(n-1)!} + \frac{1}{n!}e^{\xi},\quad 0 < \xi < 1.$$

Correctly to six decimal places, the first ten terms are:

---

* See, for example, Phillips, *Analysis*, pages 136–137.
† See, for example, Sokolnikoff, *Advanced Calculus*, pages 301–305.

$$1 = 1.000000$$
$$1 = 1.000000$$
$$1/2! = 0.500000 \quad \text{(divide by 3)}$$
$$1/3! = 0.166667 \quad \text{(divide by 4)}$$
$$1/4! = 0.041667 \quad \text{(divide by 5)}$$
$$1/5! = 0.008333 \quad \text{(divide by 6)}$$
$$1/6! = 0.001389 \quad \text{(divide by 7)}$$
$$1/7! = 0.000198 \quad \text{(divide by 8)}$$
$$1/8! = 0.000025 \quad \text{(divide by 9)}$$
$$1/9! = \underline{0.000003}$$
$$\text{Sum} = 2.718282$$

With more careful rounding off, from (a), to six decimal places,

(b)
$$2.718281 < e < 2.718282 + \frac{e^\xi}{10!}.$$

Since evidently $e > 1$, we know that e^x is everywhere an increasing function. Therefore, when $0 < \xi < 1$, we have $1 < e^\xi < e$. Consequently, from (b), neglecting numbers beyond the sixth decimal place, we have

(c)
$$2.718281 < e < 2.718282 + \frac{e}{10!}.$$

Therefore,

$$e\left(1 - \frac{1}{10!}\right) < 2.718282 \quad \text{or} \quad e(1 - 0.0000003) < 2.718282,$$

and

$$e < 2.718282 \div 0.9999997 = 2.718283.$$

Since e lies between 2.718281 and 2.718283, it follows that, correctly to five decimal places, $e = 2.71828$.

EXAMPLE 2. Calculate the value of $\sin 0.4$ by Maclaurin's series, correctly to five decimal places.

Solution: If we substitute $x = 0.4$ in the Maclaurin expansion of $\sin x$ in § 452 (d), we get

(d)
$$\sin 0.4 = 0.4 - \frac{(0.4)^3}{3!} + \frac{(0.4)^5}{5!} - \cdots.$$

The first three terms of (d) are

$$0.4, \quad -0.010667, \quad 0.000085,$$

correct to six decimal places. This suggests taking the sum of these terms as the required approximation. Since the series (d) is a convergent alternating series, we find (by § 446, II) that the error is less than the next term, $\frac{(0.4)^7}{7!} \approx 0.0000003$. This shows that the sum of the first three terms of (d) gives the necessary degree of accuracy. Then

$$\sin 0.4 \approx 0.4 - 0.010667 + 0.000085 = 0.389418,$$

which rounded off to five decimal places gives: $\sin 0.4 = 0.38942$.

The accuracy of this calculation could also have been tested by use of the remainder.

It frequently happens that for the values of x to be used, the calculation of $f(x)$ to a given degree of accuracy by Maclaurin's series is not feasible because the powers of x in that series do not decrease sufficiently fast, or because $f(x)$ or some of its derivatives are not defined at $x = 0$. In this case, Taylor's series with $a \neq 0$ may be used to advantage. By choosing a number a near the value of x in question, we can make $x - a$ small; then the successive powers of $x - a$ that appear in Taylor's series decrease so rapidly that relatively few terms are needed. The value of a which is chosen must be such that the values of $f(x)$ and of its derivatives for $x = a$ are known.

EXAMPLE 3. Compute the value of cos 32° by Taylor's formula, correctly to five decimal places.

Solution: In this case we choose for a a value near 32° for which the values of the sine and cosine are known. The difference between 32° and 30° is 2° or $\pi/90$ radian, which is small. Therefore, we take $a = \pi/6$ radian; then $x - a = \pi/90$ radian. The expansion by Taylor's formula of $\cos x$ in powers of $x - \frac{1}{6}\pi$ by § 454, is found to be:

$$\cos x = \tfrac{1}{2}\sqrt{3} - \tfrac{1}{2}(x - \tfrac{1}{6}\pi) - \frac{1}{2!}\cdot\frac{1}{2}\sqrt{3}(x - \tfrac{1}{6}\pi)^2 + \frac{1}{3!}\cdot\frac{1}{2}(x - \tfrac{1}{6}\pi)^3 - \cdots + R_n,$$

$$R_n = \frac{1}{n!}(x - \tfrac{1}{6}\pi)^n \cos(\xi + \tfrac{1}{2}n\pi) \qquad (\xi \text{ between } \tfrac{1}{6}\pi \text{ and } x).$$

If we substitute $x - \tfrac{1}{6}\pi = \dfrac{\pi}{90}$ in this formula, we have

$$(e) \quad \begin{cases} \cos 32° = \tfrac{1}{2}\sqrt{3} - \dfrac{1}{2}\left(\dfrac{\pi}{90}\right) - \dfrac{1}{2!}\cdot\dfrac{1}{2}\sqrt{3}\left(\dfrac{\pi}{90}\right)^2 + \dfrac{1}{3!}\cdot\dfrac{1}{2}\left(\dfrac{\pi}{90}\right)^3 - \cdots + R_n, \\[2mm] R_n = \dfrac{1}{n!}\left(\dfrac{\pi}{90}\right)^n \cos(\xi + \tfrac{1}{2}n\pi), \qquad \dfrac{\pi}{6} < \xi < \dfrac{\pi}{6} + \dfrac{\pi}{90}. \end{cases}$$

The first four terms of (e), correct to six decimal places, are:

$$0.866025, \qquad -0.017453, \qquad -0.000528, \qquad 0.000004.$$

Since the fourth term is so small, we calculate the remainder R_4 after four terms, to check the accuracy of the computation. We find

$$R_4 = \frac{1}{4!}\left(\frac{\pi}{90}\right)^4 \cos(\xi + \tfrac{4}{2}\pi)$$

$$< \frac{1}{4!}\left(\frac{\pi}{90}\right)^4 \qquad \text{since } \cos x \leqq 1$$

$$< 0.00000006.$$

Hence, the first four terms of (e) give the result correctly to five decimal places. Adding them, we find $\cos 32° = 0.84805$, which is correct to five places.

458. Exercises

In Exercises 1–10, compute the value, correct to five decimal places, of each of the given functions by use of Maclaurin's series:

1. $e^{-0.2}$.

2. $e^{-0.3}$.

3. $\sin 0.2$.

4. $\cos 0.1$.

5. $\ln 1.05$.

6. $\ln 0.97$.

7. $\sqrt{1.02}$.

8. $\sqrt{3.92} = \sqrt{4 - 0.08}$
$$= 2\sqrt{1 - 0.02}.$$

9. $\cosh 0.1$.

10. $\sinh 0.2$.

In Exercises 11–18, compute the value, correct to four decimal places, of each of the given functions by use of Taylor's series:

11. $e^{2.1}$ (using $e^2 \approx 7.3891$).

12. $e^{-3.1}$ (using $e^{-3} \approx 0.0498$).

13. $\sin 62°$.

14. $\sin 48°$.

15. $\cos 47°$.

16. $\cos 62°$.

17. $\cosh 1.2$ (using $\cosh 1 \approx 1.5431$).

18. $\sinh 1.2$ (using $\sinh 1 \approx 1.1752$).

459. Operations with Power Series

Let $f(x) = a_0 + a_1 x + a_2 x^2 + \cdots$, $g(x) = b_0 + b_1 x + b_2 x^2 + \cdots$.
The following theorems concerning operations with power series are proved in more advanced works:[*]

I. *Two power series in x may be added term by term for every value of x for which both series are convergent:*

(a) $\quad f(x) + g(x) = (a_0 + b_0) + (a_1 + b_1)x + (a_2 + b_2)x^2 + \cdots$.

EXAMPLE 1. From the exponential series (§ 456),

$$e^x = 1 + x + \frac{x^2}{2!} + \frac{x^3}{3!} + \cdots, \qquad e^{-x} = 1 - x + \frac{x^2}{2!} - \frac{x^3}{3!} + \cdots,$$

we obtain by adding term by term:

$$\cosh x = \tfrac{1}{2}(e^x + e^{-x}) = 1 + \frac{x^2}{2!} + \frac{x^4}{4!} + \cdots.$$

This series converges for all values of x, since the exponential series does.

II. *Two power series in x may be multiplied together by the following rule:*

---

[*] See, for example, Smail, *Infinite Processes*, §§ 87, 144, 146, 173, 175.

(b) $\quad f(x)\cdot g(x) = a_0b_0 + (a_0b_1 + a_1b_0)x + (a_0b_2 + a_1b_1 + a_2b_0)x^2$
$$+ (a_0b_3 + a_1b_2 + a_2b_1 + a_3b_0)x^3 + \cdots,$$

for every value of x for which both series are absolutely convergent.

EXAMPLE 2. If we multiply the series for e^x and $\sin x$ (§ 456):

$$e^x = 1 + x + \frac{1}{2!} x^2 + \frac{1}{3!} x^3 + \frac{1}{4!} x^4 + \cdots,$$

$$\sin x = 0 + x + 0\cdot x^2 - \frac{1}{3!} x^3 + 0\cdot x^4 - \frac{1}{5!} x^5 + \cdots,$$

we obtain:

$$e^x \sin x = (1\cdot 0) + (1\cdot 1 + 0\cdot 1)x + \left(1\cdot 0 + 1\cdot 1 + 0\cdot \frac{1}{2!}\right)x^2$$
$$+ \left(-1\cdot \frac{1}{3!} + 1\cdot 0 + \frac{1}{2!}\cdot 1 + \frac{1}{3!}\cdot 0\right)x^3 + \cdots$$
$$= x + x^2 + \frac{x^3}{3} + \cdots.$$

The two original series converge absolutely for all values of x, hence the new product series converges absolutely for all values of x.

III. *A power series in x may be differentiated term by term with respect to x for every value of x inside its interval of convergence:*

(c) $\qquad f'(x) = a_1 + 2\,a_2x + 3\,a_3x^2 + 4\,a_4x^3 + \cdots.$

(This was already stated at the end of § 450 and used in § 452).

IV. *A power series in x may be integrated term by term with respect to x if the limits of integration lie inside the interval of convergence of the original series.*

EXAMPLE 3. By Maclaurin's theorem,

$$\frac{1}{1+t} = 1 - t + t^2 - t^3 + \cdots,$$

which is convergent for $-1 < t < 1$. Integrating this series term by term, we get

$$\int_0^x \frac{dt}{1+t} = t - \frac{t^2}{2} + \frac{t^3}{3} - \frac{t^4}{4} + \cdots \,\Big|_0^x$$

or

$$\ln (1 + x) = x - \frac{x^2}{2} + \frac{x^3}{3} - \frac{x^4}{4} + \cdots,$$

which agrees with the result obtained directly by Maclaurin's theorem applied to $\ln (1 + x)$

We have noted in § 393 that certain integrals cannot be expressed in terms of elementary functions by a finite set of terms. Such integrals, in the form of definite integrals with given numerical limits, can frequently be evaluated approximately by use of power series.

EXAMPLE 4. Compute $\displaystyle\int_0^{\frac{1}{2}} \frac{e^x - 1}{x}\, dx$, correct to four decimal places.

Solution: $e^x = 1 + x + \dfrac{x^2}{2!} + \dfrac{x^3}{3!} + \dfrac{x^4}{4!} + \cdots,$

$$\frac{e^x - 1}{x} = 1 + \frac{x}{2!} + \frac{x^2}{3!} + \frac{x^3}{4!} + \cdots,$$

$$\int_0^{\frac{1}{2}} \frac{e^x - 1}{x}\, dx = \left(x + \frac{x^2}{2\cdot 2!} + \frac{x^3}{3\cdot 3!} + \frac{x^4}{4\cdot 4!} + \cdots \right)\Big|_0^{\frac{1}{2}}$$

$$= \frac{1}{2} + \frac{1}{2\cdot 2!}\left(\frac{1}{2}\right)^2 + \frac{1}{3\cdot 3!}\left(\frac{1}{2}\right)^3 + \frac{1}{4\cdot 4!}\left(\frac{1}{2}\right)^4 + \cdots \approx 0.5701.$$

460. Exercises

1. Find the first four non-zero terms of the expansion of $\cos^2 x$ in powers of x, by using the identity $\cos^2 x = \frac{1}{2}(1 + \cos 2x)$ and the power series for $\cos x$ in § 456.

2. Find the first four non-zero terms of the expansion of $\sinh x$ in powers of x, by using the exponential series.

3. Find the first four non-zero terms of the expansion of $e^x \cos x$ in powers of x, by multiplication of series.

4. Find the first four non-zero terms of the expansion of $e^x \ln(1 + x)$ in powers of x, by multiplication of series.

5. Derive the expansion

$$\text{Arc sin } x = x + \frac{1}{2}\cdot\frac{x^3}{3} + \frac{1\cdot 3}{2\cdot 4}\cdot\frac{x^5}{5} + \frac{1\cdot 3\cdot 5}{2\cdot 4\cdot 6}\cdot\frac{x^7}{7} + \cdots,$$

by using $\text{Arc sin } x = \displaystyle\int_0^x \frac{dt}{\sqrt{1 - t^2}}$, expanding $(1 - t^2)^{-\frac{1}{2}}$ by the binomial series in powers of t, and integrating term by term.

6. Expand $\text{Arc tan } x$ into a power series in powers of x by using

$$\text{Arc tan } x = \int_0^x \frac{dt}{1 + t^2}.$$

Compute the value correct to four decimal places of each of the following definite integrals, by use of series:

7. $\displaystyle\int_0^1 \frac{\sin x}{x}\, dx.$ \qquad 8. $\displaystyle\int_0^1 \frac{\sin x}{\sqrt{x}}\, dx.$

9. $\displaystyle\int_0^1 \frac{\cos x}{\sqrt{x}}\, dx.$

10. $\displaystyle\int_0^{0.1} \frac{-\ln(1-x)}{x}\, dx.$

11. $\displaystyle\int_0^{0.1} \frac{\ln(1+x)}{x}\, dx.$

12. $\displaystyle\int_0^1 \frac{e^x - 1 - x}{x^2}\, dx.$

13. $\displaystyle\int_0^{0.5} e^{-x^2}\, dx.$

14. $\displaystyle\int_0^{0.2} \frac{dx}{\sqrt{1 - x^3}}.$

15. $\displaystyle\int_0^{0.5} \sqrt{1 - x^3}\, dx.$

16. $\displaystyle\int_0^1 \sin(x^2)\, dx.$

★ 461. Calculation of Logarithms

It might be thought at first that the formula (10) of § 456:

$$(a) \qquad \ln(1 + x) = x - \frac{x^2}{2} + \frac{x^3}{3} - \frac{x^4}{4} + \cdots,$$

could be used directly for the computation of logarithms of numbers. But this series converges only for x in the interval $-1 < x \leq 1$, and unless x is small numerically, the series converges so slowly that too many terms would be required for practical use. A suitable formula for calculation of logarithms may be obtained as follows:

In formula (a) put $-x$ in place of x, then:

$$(b) \qquad \ln(1 - x) = -x - \frac{x^2}{2} - \frac{x^3}{3} - \frac{x^4}{4} - \cdots.$$

By subtracting (b) from (a), we obtain

$$(c) \qquad \ln \frac{1 + x}{1 - x} = 2\left(x + \frac{x^3}{3} + \frac{x^5}{5} + \cdots\right).$$

This series converges for $|x| < 1$. Now let N be a positive integer and put $x = \dfrac{1}{2N + 1}$; it is then found that $\dfrac{1 + x}{1 - x} = \dfrac{N + 1}{N}$. Then $|x| < 1$ for all values of N. Substituting in (c), we get the useful formula:

$$(12) \quad \ln(N + 1) = \ln N + 2\left[\frac{1}{2N + 1} + \frac{1}{3}\left(\frac{1}{2N + 1}\right)^3 \right.$$
$$\left. + \frac{1}{5}\left(\frac{1}{2N + 1}\right)^5 + \cdots\right].$$

This series converges for all positive values of N.

Let us now start by putting $N = 1$ in (12); we obtain

$$(d) \quad \ln 2 = 2[\tfrac{1}{3} + \tfrac{1}{3}(\tfrac{1}{3})^3 + \tfrac{1}{5}(\tfrac{1}{3})^5 + \cdots] = 0.69315.$$

Now put $N = 2$, then

(e) $\ln 3 = \ln 2 + 2[\frac{1}{5} + \frac{1}{3}(\frac{1}{5})^3 + \frac{1}{5}(\frac{1}{5})^5 + \cdots] = 1.09861.$

We may continue in this way, taking $N = 3, 4, 5$, etc.; but it is only necessary to calculate logarithms of prime numbers by the series because logarithms of composite numbers (non-primes) can be found by adding logarithms of prime numbers, thus: $\ln 4 = 2 \ln 2$, $\ln 6 = \ln 2 + \ln 3$, etc. In this way, a table of natural logarithms can be calculated. Common logarithms can be obtained from the natural logarithms by multiplying by $\log_{10} e = 0.43429$.

★ **462. Calculation of π**

An interesting use of series is in the computation of the approximate value of π. One method is to use the power series for Arc tan x in powers of x. The easiest way to obtain this power series is to start with Arc tan $x = \int_0^x \frac{dt}{1 + t^2}$, expand the integrand:

$$\frac{1}{1 + t^2} = 1 - t^2 + t^4 - t^6 + \cdots \qquad (-1 < t < 1),$$

integrate term by term, and get

(a) Arc tan $x = x - \dfrac{x^3}{3} + \dfrac{x^5}{5} - \cdots.$

This series (called *Gregory's series*) converges for $-1 \leq x \leq 1$.

We can obtain a series for $\frac{1}{4}\pi$ by putting $x = 1$ in (a), but this series converges very slowly and is useless for computation. We can obtain a more rapidly convergent series by using the identity:

(b) Arc tan $1 = $ Arc tan $\frac{1}{2} + $ Arc tan $\frac{1}{3}$,

which is easily proved by trigonometry. Substituting $x = \frac{1}{2}$ and also $x = \frac{1}{3}$ in the series (a), we have

(c) $\frac{1}{4}\pi = [\frac{1}{2} - \frac{1}{3}(\frac{1}{2})^3 + \frac{1}{5}(\frac{1}{2})^5 - \cdots] + [\frac{1}{3} - \frac{1}{3}(\frac{1}{3})^3 + \frac{1}{5}(\frac{1}{3})^5 - \cdots]$
            $= 0.78540,$

from which we get $\pi = 3.1416$ approximately.

A number of other trigonometric identities analogous to (b) have been used for this purpose, such as

Arc tan $1 = 2$ Arc tan $\frac{1}{3} + $ Arc tan $\frac{1}{7}$,

Arc tan $1 = 4$ Arc tan $\frac{1}{5} - $ Arc tan $\frac{1}{239}$.

CHAPTER XXV

Solid Analytic Geometry

463. Rectangular Coördinates in Space

In plane analytic geometry it was seen that the position of a point in the plane could be determined by means of its directed distances from two perpendicular coördinate axes. In solid analytic geometry, in order to fix the position of a point in space, we may use its directed distances from three perpendicular coördinate planes. These directed distances are called the *rectangular coördinates* of the point with respect to the three reference planes.

Let us choose three mutually perpendicular planes as a reference frame for locating points in space (Fig. 188). The point of intersection O is called the **origin;** the three lines of intersection OX,

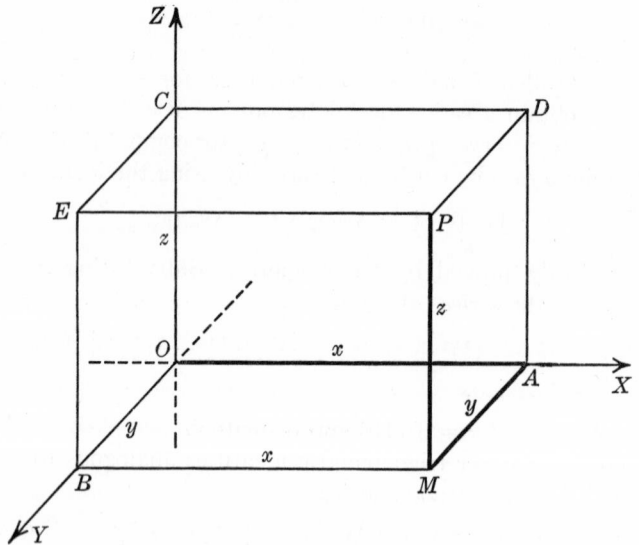

FIG. 188
496

OY and OZ are called the **coördinate axes,** and are referred to as the X-axis, Y-axis and Z-axis, respectively. The given planes XOY, YOZ and ZOX are called the **coördinate planes,** and are referred to as the XY-plane, the YZ-plane and the ZX-plane, respectively. It is customary to think of the XY-plane as horizontal and the Z-axis as vertical. The positive directions on the coördinate axes are indicated by arrowheads.

The X- and Y-axes may be arranged in two different orders, and both of the resulting systems are in common use. We shall adopt the arrangement shown in Fig. 188, which is known as a *left-hand system.* The other, a right-hand system, is found by interchanging the X- and Y-axes. According to our system, a directed distance measured on or parallel to the X-axis is positive to the right and negative to the left; one measured on or parallel to the Y-axis is positive to the front and negative to the back; and one measured on or parallel to the Z-axis is positive upward and negative downward.

Now let P be any given point in space. To determine the coördinates of P with reference to the above system of coördinate planes, we pass planes through P parallel to the three coördinate planes and denote the points of intersection of these planes with the X-, Y- and Z-axes by A, B and C respectively (Fig. 188).

*The **rectangular coördinates** of the point P are defined as the directed distances $x = \overline{OA}, y = \overline{OB}$ and $z = \overline{OC}$.* The point whose rectangular coördinates are x, y, z is denoted by the symbol (x, y, z).

It is usually found convenient in drawing figures to represent the coördinates x, y and z of a point P by the equivalent directed distances $\overline{OA}$, $\overline{AM}$ and $\overline{MP}$ of Fig. 188, respectively.

Every point in space has a unique set of rectangular coördinates, and conversely, every set of three real numbers determines one and only one point in rectangular coördinates.

The three coördinate planes divide space into eight parts, called **octants.** The octant in which all of the rectangular coördinates of a point are positive is called the **first octant.** The other octants are not numbered.

In order to represent a figure in space on a plane surface, it is necessary to make certain distortions. In the left-hand system, we represent the X- and Z-axes by lines that are actually perpendicular to each other, and the Y-axis is usually represented by a line that makes an angle of 135° with each of the other two. We use parallel projection, in which parallel lines are actually drawn parallel. Distances parallel to the ZX-plane are represented correctly to scale, but distances parallel to the Y-axis are shortened in the ratio of 1 to $\sqrt{2}$. In order to use the solid geometry diagrams properly, it is necessary for the student to visualize the actual relations in space by forming a mental picture of the figure as it actually exists in space.

464. Exercises

1. Plot the following points: $A(3, 2, 3)$, $B(-2, 1, 2)$, $C(2, -1, 3)$, $D(-3, -1, -2)$.
2. Plot the following points: $A(4, 3, 3)$, $B(4, -2, 1)$, $C(-3, 2, -3)$, $D(-2, 3, -1)$.
3. Find the coördinates of the projections of the point $(2, 4, -3)$ on each of the coördinate planes.
4. Find the coördinates of the feet of the perpendiculars from the point $(-3, 1, 2)$ to each of the coördinate planes.
5. Describe the location of all points in space for which: (a) $z = 0$; (b) $y = 2$; (c) $x = 2$ and $z = 3$; (d) $x = y$.
6. Describe the location of all points in space for which: (a) both $y = 0$ and $z = 0$; (b) both $x = 0$ and $y = 0$; (c) $x = 2$ and $y = 1$; (d) $x = y = z$.
7. What equation is satisfied by the coördinates of all points of the XY-plane? of the YZ-plane? of the ZX-plane?
8. What equation is satisfied by the coördinates of all points in space which are: (a) 5 units above the XY-plane? (b) 3 units to the left of the YZ-plane?
9. Find the perpendicular distance of the point $(3, 4, 2)$: (a) from the Z-axis; (b) from the Y-axis.
10. What are the coördinates of the points symmetric to the point (a, b, c) with respect to: (a) the XY-plane; (b) the YZ-plane; (c) the origin; (d) the X-axis?
11. Show that the directed lengths of the projections of the line-segment from $P_1(x_1, y_1, z_1)$ to $P_2(x_2, y_2, z_2)$ on the coördinate axes are $x_2 - x_1$, $y_2 - y_1$ and $z_2 - z_1$. (See Fig. 189.) [*Hint.* Use method similar to that used in § 7.]
12. Derive formulas for the coördinates of the mid-point of the segment P_1P_2, where P_1 is (x_1, y_1, z_1) and P_2 is (x_2, y_2, z_2). [*Hint.* Use method similar to that given in § 11.]

465. Distance Between Two Points

Let $P_1(x_1, y_1, z_1)$ and $P_2(x_2, y_2, z_2)$ be two given points. Draw planes through P_1 and through P_2 parallel to the coördinate planes, as in Fig. 189, forming a rectangular parallelopiped (box), of which P_1P_2 is a diagonal. Then P_1Q is perpendicular to QR and P_1R is perpendicular to RP_2. In the right triangle P_1RP_2, we have

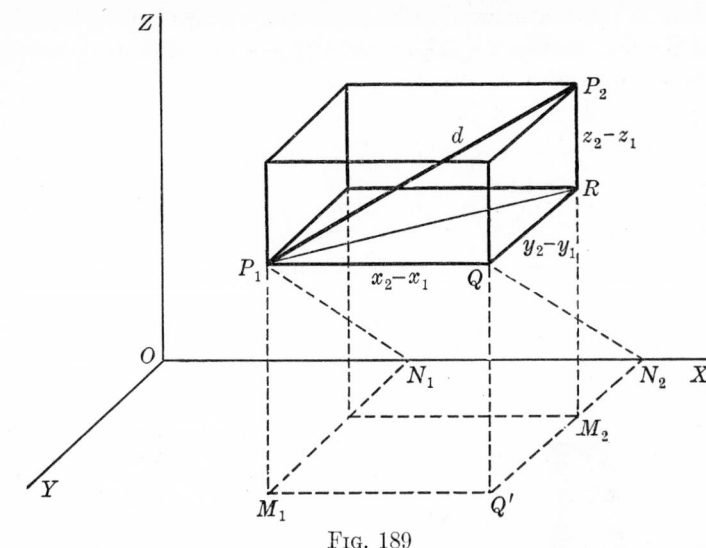

F<small>IG</small>. 189

$(\overline{P_1P_2})^2 = (\overline{P_1R})^2 + (\overline{RP_2})^2$, and in the right triangle P_1QR, we have $(\overline{P_1R})^2 = (\overline{P_1Q})^2 + (\overline{QR})^2$.   Therefore,

(a) $$(\overline{P_1P_2})^2 = (\overline{P_1Q})^2 + (\overline{QR})^2 + (\overline{RP_2})^2.$$

From the definitions of the rectangular coördinates, it follows readily that $\overline{P_1Q} = x_2 - x_1$, $\overline{QR} = y_2 - y_1$ and $\overline{RP_2} = z_2 - z_1$ (§ 464, Exercise 11).   Then by (a), we have

(b) $$(\overline{P_1P_2})^2 = (x_2 - x_1)^2 + (y_2 - y_1)^2 + (z_2 - z_1)^2.$$

Hence, we have the fundamental result:

The distance d between any two points $P_1(x_1, y_1, z_1)$ and $P_2(x_2, y_2, z_2)$ is given by

(1) $$d = \sqrt{(x_2 - x_1)^2 + (y_2 - y_1)^2 + (z_2 - z_1)^2}.$$

E<small>XAMPLE</small>.   The distance between the points $(3, 1, -2)$ and $(2, -3, 1)$ is

$$d = \sqrt{(2 - 3)^2 + (-3 - 1)^2 + (1 + 2)^2} = \sqrt{26}.$$

466. Exercises

1. Find the distance between each of the following pairs of points:
   (a) $(4, 1, 3)$ and $(1, -3, 3)$;   (b) $(2, 6, 9)$ and $(3, 2, 1)$;
   (c) $(3, 1, 2)$ and $(5, 3, -2)$;   (d) $(0, 0, 0)$ and $(1, -4, 5)$.

2. Find the distance between each of the following pairs of points:

    (a) $(6, -2, 7)$ and $(1, -2, -5)$;   (b) $(2, -1, 4)$ and $(1, 3, -1)$;
    (c) $(4, 1, -3)$ and $(2, -2, 0)$;   (d) $(2, -3, 4)$ and $(0, 0, 1)$.

3. Show that $(3, 4, -1)$, $(4, 6, 2)$ and $(6, 3, 1)$ are the vertices of an equilateral triangle.

4. Show that $(-2, 3, -6)$, $(3, 4, -2)$ and $(-3, 7, -1)$ are the vertices of an isosceles triangle.

5. Show that $(6, 7, 0)$, $(3, 1, -2)$ and $(8, 4, 6)$ are the vertices of a right triangle.

6. Show that $(0, 4, -2)$, $(-3, -2, -4)$ and $(2, 1, 4)$ are the vertices of a right triangle.

7. Find an equation which is satisfied by the coördinates of any point $P(x, y, z)$ which is such that its distance from the point $(3, 1, -2)$ is always equal to 4. What is the locus of P?

8. What is the locus of the equation $(x - 2)^2 + (y + 3)^2 + (z - 1)^2 = 16$?

9. Show that the distance of the point (x, y, z) from the Z-axis is $\sqrt{x^2 + y^2}$. What is the distance from the Y-axis, and from the X-axis?

10. Find the equation of the locus of a point (x, y, z) which is equidistant from the Y-axis and from the point $(2, -1, 3)$.

467. Direction of a Line

The angle between two intersecting directed lines in space is defined as the angle, between $0°$ and $180°$, between the positive directions of the lines. Two lines in space may not intersect; the angle between two directed lines which do not intersect is defined as the angle between the positive directions of two intersecting lines which are

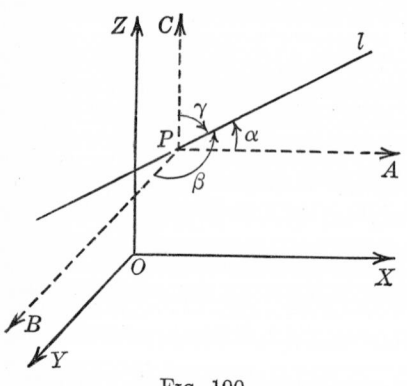

parallel respectively to the given lines and have the same positive directions. If the given lines are parallel to each other, the angle between them is said to be either $0°$ or $180°$, according as their positive directions agree or do not agree.

Let l be any given directed line in space. To specify its *direction* relative to a given system of rectangular coördinate axes, we choose an arbi-

Fig. 190

trary point P on the line and draw lines PA, PB and PC parallel, respectively, to the coördinate axes OX, OY and OZ, with the same positive senses as the axes (Fig. 190). Then the direction of l is determined by the angles α, β and γ which the positive direction of l makes with PA, PB and PC, respectively. These angles α, β and γ are called the **direction angles** of the line l.

In plane analytic geometry, the direction of a line is usually indicated by means of its slope. In solid analytic geometry, the direction of a line is most conveniently given by the cosines of its direction angles, $\cos \alpha$, $\cos \beta$ and $\cos \gamma$, which are called the **direction cosines** of the line.

Let $P_1(x_1, y_1, z_1)$ and $P_2(x_2, y_2, z_2)$ be two points on a line l. Draw planes through P_1 and P_2 parallel to the coördinate planes, as was done in § 465, forming the rectangular parallelepiped of Fig. 191.

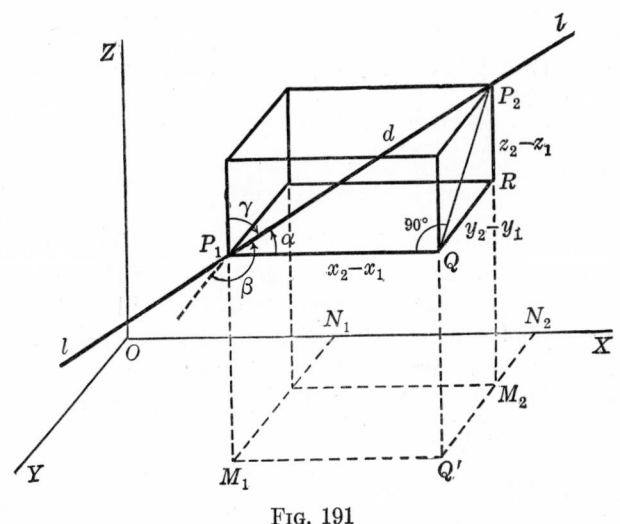

FIG. 191

By elementary solid geometry, QP_2 is perpendicular to P_1Q; in the right triangle P_1QP_2, the angle QP_1P_2 is the direction angle α and P_1P_2 is the hypotenuse. Then, by definition of the trigonometric functions, we have $\cos \alpha = P_1Q/P_1P_2$. But $P_1Q = x_2 - x_1$ and $P_1P_2 = d$ (the distance between P_1 and P_2); therefore, $\cos \alpha = (x_2 - x_1)/d$. Similarly we find corresponding expressions for $\cos \beta$ and $\cos \gamma$. Hence:

I. *The direction cosines of a line l passing from $P_1(x_1, y_1, z_1)$ through $P_2(x_2, y_2, z_2)$ are given by*

(2) $\cos \alpha = \dfrac{x_2 - x_1}{d}$, $\cos \beta = \dfrac{y_2 - y_1}{d}$, $\cos \gamma = \dfrac{z_2 - z_1}{d}$,

where d is the distance $P_1 P_2$.

EXAMPLE. Find the direction cosines of the line from $(2, 3, 1)$ through $(5, 3, 5)$.

Solution: $x_2 - x_1 = 3$, $y_2 - y_1 = 0$, $z_2 - z_1 = 4$, and $d^2 = 3^2 + 0^2 + 4^2 = 5^2$, therefore

$$\cos \alpha = \tfrac{3}{5}, \qquad \cos \beta = 0, \qquad \cos \gamma = \tfrac{4}{5}.$$

The direction angles of a line are not independent. For, if we square the terms in (2) and add, we get

$$\cos^2 \alpha + \cos^2 \beta + \cos^2 \gamma = \frac{(x_2 - x_1)^2 + (y_2 - y_1)^2 + (z_2 - z_1)^2}{d^2} = 1$$

by formula (1) of § 465. Hence:

II. *The sum of the squares of the direction cosines of any line is equal to* 1:

(3) $$\cos^2 \alpha + \cos^2 \beta + \cos^2 \gamma = 1.$$

It follows from (3) that the three direction cosines are *not independent;* when any two of them are given, the third is determined, except for sign. Because of symmetry, it is usually better to keep all three direction cosines rather than to eliminate one of them by formula (3); but it frequently becomes necessary to use the relation (3) in simplifying expressions involving direction cosines.

468. Direction Numbers of a Line

Any three real numbers a, b, c (not all 0*) which are proportional to the direction cosines of a line are called* **direction numbers** *of the line.* For many purposes, they serve to determine the direction of the line as well as the direction cosines and in many cases are more convenient.

It follows immediately from the formulas (2) of § 467 that:

I. *The numbers* $x_2 - x_1$, $y_2 - y_1$ *and* $z_2 - z_1$ *are direction numbers of the line* $P_1 P_2$.

If a, b, c are proportional to $\cos \alpha, \cos \beta, \cos \gamma$, there is a number k such that

(a) $$a = k \cos \alpha, \qquad b = k \cos \beta, \qquad c = k \cos \gamma.$$

Squaring and adding, we get

(b) $a^2 + b^2 + c^2 = k^2(\cos^2 \alpha + \cos^2 \beta + \cos^2 \gamma) = k^2$

by formula (3).   Therefore, $k = \pm\sqrt{a^2 + b^2 + c^2}$.   Substituting this expression for k in (a), we find expressions for the direction cosines in terms of a, b, c.   This result may be stated:

II. *The direction cosines of a line which has direction numbers a, b, c may be obtained by dividing each direction number by the square root of the sum of the squares of these numbers:*

$$(4)\quad \cos \alpha = \frac{a}{\pm\sqrt{a^2 + b^2 + c^2}}, \quad \cos \beta = \frac{b}{\pm\sqrt{a^2 + b^2 + c^2}},$$

$$\cos \gamma = \frac{c}{\pm\sqrt{a^2 + b^2 + c^2}}.$$

The algebraic sign in these formulas is to be taken as positive throughout or negative throughout.*

EXAMPLE.   If a line has direction numbers $1, -4, 8$, find its direction cosines.

Solution: Since $1^2 + (-4)^2 + 8^2 = 81 = 9^2$, we have

$$\cos \alpha = \tfrac{1}{9}, \qquad \cos \beta = -\tfrac{4}{9}, \qquad \cos \gamma = \tfrac{8}{9}.$$

We could equally well have taken each of these values with the opposite sign, in which case the direction of the line would have been reversed.

469. Exercises

1. Find the direction cosines of the line segments joining each of the following pairs of points:
   (a) $(4, 1, 3)$ and $(2, 3, 4)$;   (b) $(3, 1, -2)$ and $(5, 3, 1)$.
2. Proceed as in Exercise 1 with:
   (a) $(1, 3, -2)$ and $(3, 4, 0)$;   (b) $(0, 0, 0)$ and $(2, 1, 2)$.
3. What are the direction cosines of each of the coördinate axes?
4. Find the direction cosines of a line in the first octant passing through the origin and equally inclined to each of the coördinate axes.
5. If two of the direction angles of a line are $60°$ and $45°$, what is the third direction angle, if the line passes through the origin and the first octant?
6. If $\alpha = 45°$ and $\beta = 45°$, find γ.
7. Find the direction cosines of each of the lines whose direction numbers are: (a) $2, -3, 6$; (b) $1, -2, 3$.
8. Proceed as in Exercise 7 with: (a) $3, 0, -4$; (b) $3, 1, 2$.

---

* When the $+$ sign is used, the line is directed in one way, and when the $-$ sign is used, the line is directed in the opposite sense.

470. Angle Between Two Lines

We frequently need a formula for the angle between two lines in terms of the direction cosines of the lines. Let l_1 and l_2 be two lines in space, having direction cosines $\cos \alpha_1$, $\cos \beta_1$, $\cos \gamma_1$, and $\cos \alpha_2$, $\cos \beta_2$, $\cos \gamma_2$. Draw lines l_1' and l_2' through the origin parallel to the given lines l_1 and l_2 respectively (Fig. 192), if l_1 and l_2 do not themselves

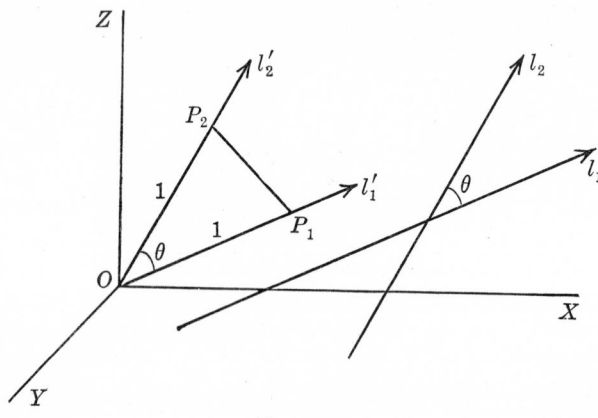

Fig. 192

pass through the origin. Take points P_1 and P_2 on lines l_1' and l_2' respectively, at unit distance from the origin O, so that $OP_1 = OP_2 = 1$. Let θ be the angle between l_1' and l_2', and therefore the angle between l_1 and l_2. By the law of cosines of trigonometry,

$$(a) \qquad (P_1P_2)^2 = 1 + 1 - 2 \cos \theta.$$

By theorem I of § 468, the coördinates of P_1 are $(\cos \alpha_1, \cos \beta_1, \cos \gamma_1)$ and those of P_2 are $(\cos \alpha_2, \cos \beta_2, \cos \gamma_2)$. Then by the distance formula of § 465, we have

$$
\begin{aligned}
(b) \quad (P_1P_2)^2 &= (\cos \alpha_1 - \cos \alpha_2)^2 + (\cos \beta_1 - \cos \beta_2)^2 \\
&\qquad\qquad + (\cos \gamma_1 - \cos \gamma_2)^2 \\
&= (\cos^2 \alpha_1 + \cos^2 \beta_1 + \cos^2 \gamma_1) + (\cos^2 \alpha_2 + \cos^2 \beta_2 + \cos^2 \gamma_2) \\
&\qquad - 2 (\cos \alpha_1 \cos \alpha_2 + \cos \beta_1 \cos \beta_2 + \cos \gamma_1 \cos \gamma_2) \\
&= 1 + 1 - 2 (\cos \alpha_1 \cos \alpha_2 + \cos \beta_1 \cos \beta_2 + \cos \gamma_1 \cos \gamma_2),
\end{aligned}
$$

by use of formula (3) of § 468. Comparing equations (a) and (b), we find

(c) $\cos \theta = \cos \alpha_1 \cos \alpha_2 + \cos \beta_1 \cos \beta_2 + \cos \gamma_1 \cos \gamma_2.$

Hence:

I. *If $\cos \alpha_1$, $\cos \beta_1$, $\cos \gamma_1$ and $\cos \alpha_2$, $\cos \beta_2$, $\cos \gamma_2$ are the direction cosines of two lines, the angle θ between them is given by:*

(5) $\cos \theta = \cos \alpha_1 \cos \alpha_2 + \cos \beta_1 \cos \beta_2 + \cos \gamma_1 \cos \gamma_2.$

This formula may be stated and remembered in words as follows: *The cosine of the angle between two lines is equal to the sum of the products of corresponding direction cosines of the lines.*

If two lines l_1 and l_2 are parallel, the corresponding direction angles are either equal or supplementary, so that their corresponding direction numbers are proportional. Conversely, if the corresponding direction numbers are proportional, then the direction angles are either equal or supplementary, and the lines are therefore parallel. Hence:

II. *Two lines l_1 and l_2 are parallel if and only if their corresponding direction numbers are proportional:*

(6) $$\frac{a_1}{a_2} = \frac{b_1}{b_2} = \frac{c_1}{c_2}.$$

Now suppose that the line l_1 is perpendicular to the line l_2, then the angle between them is $\theta = \frac{1}{2}\pi$, and $\cos \theta = 0$. Therefore, by formula (5),

(d) $\cos \alpha_1 \cos \alpha_2 + \cos \beta_1 \cos \beta_2 + \cos \gamma_1 \cos \gamma_2 = 0.$

Conversely, if condition (d) is satisfied, then $\cos \theta = 0$, and the lines l_1 and l_2 are perpendicular. Hence:

III. *Two lines l_1 and l_2 with direction cosines $\cos \alpha_1$, $\cos \beta_1$, $\cos \gamma_1$ and $\cos \alpha_2$, $\cos \beta_2$, $\cos \gamma_2$ are perpendicular if and only if the sum of the products of their corresponding direction cosines is zero:*

(7) $\cos \alpha_1 \cos \alpha_2 + \cos \beta_1 \cos \beta_2 + \cos \gamma_1 \cos \gamma_2 = 0.$

If we remember that the direction numbers of a line are proportional to its corresponding direction cosines, and if we multiply each term of formula (7) by the proportionality factor, we obtain the following useful form of the preceding theorem:

IV. *Two lines l_1 and l_2 with direction numbers a_1, b_1, c_1 and a_2, b_2, c_2 are perpendicular if and only if the sum of the products of their corresponding direction numbers is zero:*

(8) $$a_1a_2 + b_1b_2 + c_1c_2 = 0.$$

EXAMPLE. Show that the line through the points $P_1(3, 1, 2)$ and $P_2(2, -3, 4)$ is perpendicular to the line through $P_3(-1, 2, 1)$ and $P_4(1, 4, 6)$.

Solution: Since, by § 468, $x_2 - x_1$, $y_2 - y_1$ and $z_2 - z_1$ are direction numbers of a line P_1P_2, we find direction numbers of P_1P_2 are $a_1 = -1$, $b_1 = -4$, $c_1 = 2$, and direction numbers of P_3P_4 are $a_2 = 2$, $b_2 = 2$, $c_2 = 5$. Then

$$a_1a_2 + b_1b_2 + c_1c_2 = (-1)(2) + (-4)(2) + (2)(5) = 0;$$

therefore P_1P_2 is perpendicular to P_3P_4.

471. Exercises

1. Find the angle between the lines whose direction numbers are:
   (a) $4, 2, -3$ and $2, -4, 1$;   (b) $2, -1, 3$ and $4, 1, -1$.
2. Proceed as in Exercise 1 with:
   (a) $2, -1, 4$ and $3, 3, -3$;   (b) $3, 0, -4$ and $5, 1, 0$.
3. Show that the line through the points $(2, -1, 4)$ and $(4, 2, -1)$ is parallel to the line through $(1, 3, -2)$ and $(5, 9, -12)$.
4. Show that the points $(1, 4, -2)$, $(5, 8, 1)$ and $(-7, -4, -8)$ are in the same straight line.
5. Show that the lines having direction numbers $2, -1, 5$ and $1, 2, 0$ are perpendicular to each other.
6. Show that the lines whose direction numbers are $7, -2, 4$ and $2, 1, -3$ are perpendicular to each other.
7. Show that the line through $(3, 2, 4)$ and $(1, 5, 8)$ is perpendicular to the line through $(-1, 9, -2)$ and $(-7, 1, 1)$.
8. By use of direction numbers show that each of the following sets of points are vertices of a right triangle:
   (a) $(6, 7, 0)$, $(3, 1, -2)$, $(8, 4, 6)$;   (b) $(0, 4, -2)$, $(-3, -2, -4)$, $(2, 1, 4)$.
9. Show that the points $A(2, 6, -5)$, $B(-1, 0, -7)$ and $C(4, 3, 1)$ are the vertices of a right triangle.
10. Show that the angle between two lines whose direction numbers are a_1, b_1, c_1 and a_2, b_2, c_2 is given by
$$\cos \theta = \frac{a_1a_2 + b_1b_2 + c_1c_2}{\pm\sqrt{a_1{}^2 + b_1{}^2 + c_1{}^2}\cdot\sqrt{a_2{}^2 + b_2{}^2 + c_2{}^2}}.$$

472. Loci in Space

The *locus (or graph) of a given equation* in x, y, z is the set of all those points and only those points whose coördinates x, y, z satisfy this equation. Such a locus is in general a surface. An *equation of a surface* is an equation which is satisfied by the coördinates of all points of the surface and by the coördinates of no other point.   The *graph of an explicit function f(x, y) of two variables* is the locus of the equation $z = f(x, y)$; and the graph of an *implicit function defined by F(x, y, z) = 0* is the locus of the equation $F(x, y, z) = 0$.

EXAMPLE 1.   The locus of the equation $x^2 + y^2 + z^2 = a^2$ is the spherical surface with center at the origin and radius a, since the equation states that the square of the distance between the origin and the point (x, y, z) is equal to the constant a^2.

The *locus of two given equations* in x, y, z is the set of all those points and only those points which are common to the loci of both equations.   This locus is in general a *curve,* the curve of intersection of the two surfaces represented by the given equations.

EXAMPLE 2.   We shall see presently that each of the equations $x + 2y - 3z = 4$ and $2x - y + 4z = -3$ is represented by a plane, and therefore the two equations taken simultaneously are represented by the line of intersection of the two planes.

473. The Plane in Space

A plane is completely determined in position if the length and direction of the perpendicular to the plane from the origin are given. We shall obtain the equation of a plane in terms of these elements.

Let ABC in Fig. 193 be any given plane, and let N be the foot of the perpendicular from the origin to the plane.   A perpendicular

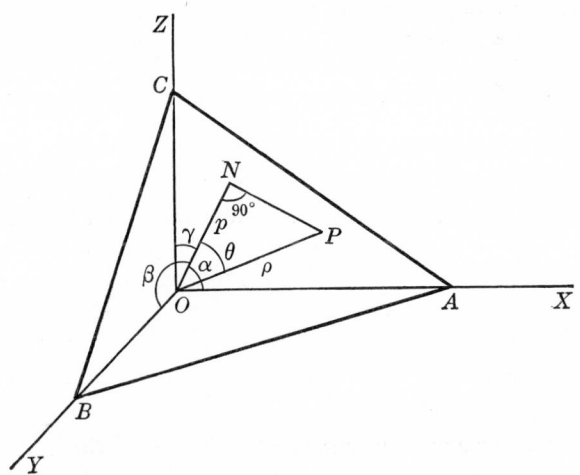

FIG. 193

to a plane is called a *normal* to the plane. Let p be the length of the normal ON, and let α, β, γ be the direction angles of ON. Let $P(x, y, z)$ be any point in the given plane; draw OP and denote its length by ρ and its direction angles by α', β', γ', and denote the angle NOP by θ. Since ON is perpendicular to NP (by elementary solid geometry), in the right triangle ONP we have

(a) $$p = \rho \cos \theta.$$

From formula (5) of § 470,

(b) $$\cos \theta = \cos \alpha' \cos \alpha + \cos \beta' \cos \beta + \cos \gamma' \cos \gamma.$$

Then from equation (a), we have

(c) $$p = \rho \cos \alpha' \cos \alpha + \rho \cos \beta' \cos \beta + \rho \cos \gamma' \cos \gamma.$$

But from formulas (2) of § 467,

$$\rho \cos \alpha' = x, \qquad \rho \cos \beta' = y, \qquad \rho \cos \gamma' = z.$$

Equation (c) then becomes

(d) $$p = x \cos \alpha + y \cos \beta + z \cos \gamma.$$

This equation is satisfied by the coördinates (x, y, z) of any point in the plane, but not by the coördinates of any point not in the plane, and is therefore the equation of the given plane. Hence:

I. *If p is the perpendicular distance of a given plane from the origin and if α, β, γ are the direction angles of a normal to the plane, the equation of the plane is*

(9) $$x \cos \alpha + y \cos \beta + z \cos \gamma = p.$$

This is called the **normal form** of the equation of a plane.

The normal form (9) of the equation of a plane is an equation of the first degree (a linear equation) in x, y, z. Since any plane can be represented by such an equation, it follows that:

II. *The equation of any plane is a linear equation, i.e., an equation of the first degree, in x, y, z. Conversely, every linear equation in x, y, z is represented by a plane.*

For, any linear equation in x, y, z can be put in the form

$$Ax + By + Cz + D = 0,$$

where A, B, C are not all zero. Let us divide both sides of this equation by $\pm\sqrt{A^2 + B^2 + C^2}$, obtaining

(e)
$$\frac{A}{\pm\sqrt{A^2 + B^2 + C^2}} x + \frac{B}{\pm\sqrt{A^2 + B^2 + C^2}} y$$
$$+ \frac{C}{\pm\sqrt{A^2 + B^2 + C^2}} z = \frac{-D}{\pm\sqrt{A^2 + B^2 + C^2}}. *$$

By formulas (4) of § 468, the coefficients of x, y, z in (e) are direction cosines of a line, which is normal to some plane. Therefore, equation (e) has the form of the normal equation (9), and its locus is consequently a plane.

The form $Ax + By + Cz + D = 0$ is called the *general form* of the equation of a plane. From the above discussion it follows that the general form of the equation of a plane may be reduced to the normal form by dividing each term by a square root of the sum of the squares of the coefficients of x, y, z.

EXAMPLE 1. Reduce the equation $2x - 3y + 4z - 12 = 0$ to the normal form, and find the direction cosines of the normal and the value of p.

Solution: Since $2^2 + (-3)^2 + 4^2 = 29$, the normal form is

$$\frac{2}{\sqrt{29}} x - \frac{3}{\sqrt{29}} y + \frac{4}{\sqrt{29}} z = \frac{12}{\sqrt{29}},$$

where we have chosen the positive sign for the radical so that the value of p is positive. Then

$$p = \frac{12}{\sqrt{29}}, \qquad \cos\alpha = \frac{2}{\sqrt{29}}, \qquad \cos\beta = -\frac{3}{\sqrt{29}}, \qquad \cos\gamma = \frac{4}{\sqrt{29}}.$$

From equation (e) there follows immediately the very important result:

III. *The coefficients A, B and C in the general equation*

$$Ax + By + Cz + D = 0$$

of a plane are direction numbers of any normal to the plane.

Some special forms of the equation of a plane are worth noting. An equation $z = 0$ represents the XY-plane, and an equation of the form $z = k$ represents a plane parallel to the XY-plane, at a distance

---

* The sign of the radical in (e) is usually taken opposite to that of D, when $D \neq 0$, so that the normal intercept p is positive. If $D = 0$, some other rule for the sign may be adopted.

k from it. Similar statements are true for the equations $x = 0$, $y = 0$, $x = k$, and $y = k$. An equation of the form $Ax + By + D = 0$, in which the z-term is missing, represents a plane perpendicular to the XY-plane (or parallel to the Z-axis), since $\cos \gamma = 0$. A similar statement holds for an equation lacking the term in x or the term in y.

The lines of intersection of a given plane with the coördinate planes are called its *traces* on those planes. The directed distances cut off on the coördinate axes by the given plane are called its *intercepts* on those axes. The XY-trace is evidently obtained by putting $z = 0$ in the equation of the plane; similar statements hold for the other traces. The X-intercept is evidently obtained by putting $y = 0$ and $z = 0$ in the equation of the plane; similar statements hold for the other two intercepts. A plane is usually represented in a figure by means of its traces.

EXAMPLE 2. The plane $3x + 4y + 6z - 12 = 0$ has the intercepts $x = \overline{OA} = 4$, $y = \overline{OB} = 3$, $z = \overline{OC} = 2$, and it has the traces AB, BC and AC (Fig. 194).

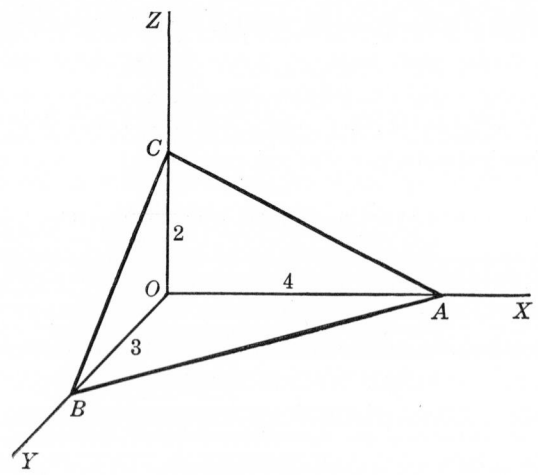

FIG. 194

The equation of a plane has three essential constants, for we may divide by one of the four coefficients A, B, C or D, and denote the three ratios of these coefficients by new letters, as for example, $rx + sy + tz + 1 = 0$, where $r = A/D$, $s = B/D$, $t = C/D$, if the plane does not go through the origin. Since the equation contains only three essential constants, it follows that: *a plane can be made to satisfy three conditions in general.* To find the equation of this plane, we express the conditions in terms of the three essential coefficients, and solve for these coefficients.

EXAMPLE 3. Find the equation of the plane passing through the three points $A(3, 2, -2)$, $B(2, 1, -1)$, $C(-2, 2, 4)$.

Solution: Let us assume the equation of the plane to be $rx + sy + tz + 1 = 0$. Since each given point lies in the plane, its coördinates must satisfy the equation of the plane. Substituting these coördinates in the equation $rx + sy + tz + 1 = 0$, we get the three equations

$$\begin{cases} 3\,r + 2\,s - 2\,t + 1 = 0, \\ 2\,r + \ s - \ t + 1 = 0, \\ -2\,r + 2\,s + 4\,t + 1 = 0. \end{cases}$$

Solving these equations for r, s, t, we find $r = -1$, $s = \frac{1}{6}$, $t = -\frac{5}{6}$. The equation of the required plane is then

$$-x + \tfrac{1}{6}\,y - \tfrac{5}{6}\,z + 1 = 0 \qquad \text{or} \qquad 6\,x - y + 5\,z - 6 = 0.$$

474. Relations Between Planes

The direction of a plane is determined by the direction of its normal; and the coefficients A, B, C in the equation of a plane $Ax + By + Cz + D = 0$ are direction numbers of the normal (by § 473, III). Many problems involving planes and lines are solved by use of this fundamental fact.

We often need to determine whether two given planes are parallel or perpendicular. Let the equations of the given planes be

$$A_1x + B_1y + C_1z + D_1 = 0 \qquad \text{and} \qquad A_2x + B_2y + C_2z + D_2 = 0.$$

The two given planes are parallel to each other if and only if their normals are parallel. By theorem III of § 473, direction numbers of the normals to these planes are A_1, B_1, C_1 and A_2, B_2, C_2. Now applying the condition (6) of § 470 for parallel lines, we obtain the result:

I. *Two planes whose equations are*

$$A_1x + B_1y + C_1z + D_1 = 0 \ \text{and} \ A_2x + B_2y + C_2z + D_2 = 0$$

are parallel if and only if

(10) $$\frac{A_1}{A_2} = \frac{B_1}{B_2} = \frac{C_1}{C_2}.$$

Similarly, by using formula (8) of § 470 for perpendicular lines, we obtain the theorem:

II. *Two planes whose equations are*

$$A_1x + B_1y + C_1z + D_1 = 0 \text{ and } A_2x + B_2y + C_2z + D_2 = 0$$

are perpendicular if and only if

(11) $$A_1A_2 + B_1B_2 + C_1C_2 = 0.$$

EXAMPLE. Find the equation of the plane through the point $P_1(3, -1, 5)$ and perpendicular to the planes

$$x - 6y - 2z - 2 = 0 \text{ and } 4x - 4y - 3z + 1 = 0.$$

Solution: Let the equation of the required plane be $Ax + By + Cz + D = 0$. Since P_1 lies in the plane, its coördinates satisfy the equation of the plane; this gives

(a) $$3A - B + 5C + D = 0.$$

Since the required plane is perpendicular to the first given plane, by theorem II we have

(b) $$A - 6B - 2C = 0;$$

and since the required plane is perpendicular to the second given plane, we have

(c) $$4A - 4B - 3C = 0.$$

Solving these three equations (a), (b) and (c) for A, B and C in terms of D, we find $\dfrac{A}{D} = -\dfrac{2}{27}, \dfrac{B}{D} = \dfrac{1}{27}, \dfrac{C}{D} = -\dfrac{4}{27}$, whence the equation of the required plane is

$$-\frac{2}{27}Dx + \frac{1}{27}Dy - \frac{4}{27}Dz + D = 0, \quad \text{or} \quad 2x - y + 4z - 27 = 0.$$

475. Exercises

1. Find the intercepts and traces of each of the following planes, and draw the plane:
    (a) $3x + 2y + 4z = 24$; (b) $2x + 3y = 6$.
2. Proceed as in Exercise 1 with:
    (a) $2x - 3y + z + 6 = 0$; (b) $2y - z = 4$.
3. Reduce the equation of each of the following planes to the normal form:
    (a) $2x - y - 2z = 6$; (b) $3x - 2y + z + 3 = 0$.
4. Proceed as in Exercise 3 with:
    (a) $4x + 7y - 4z - 5 = 0$; (b) $4x - 3y + 5z = 12$.
5. Find the equation of the plane perpendicular to the XY-plane, with X-intercept equal to 3 and Y-intercept equal to -4.

6. Find the equation of the plane parallel to the YZ-plane, with X-intercept equal to 5.

7. Find the equation of the plane through the point $(4, -5, 2)$ and perpendicular to the line whose direction numbers are $2, -1, 4$.

8. Find the equation of the plane through the point $(1, -3, 2)$ and perpendicular to the line joining the points $(0, 0, 3)$ and $(1, -3, -4)$.

9. Find the equation of the plane passing through the points $(2, 3, 1)$, $(1, -2, 2)$ and $(3, 1, -2)$.

10. Find the equation of the plane passing through the points $(1, 2, -1)$, $(2, -1, 3)$ and $(2, 1, 2)$.

11. Find the equation of the plane which is parallel to the plane $3x - y + 2z = 5$ and which passes through the point $(2, 1, -2)$.

12. Find the equation of the plane which is perpendicular to the XY-plane and which passes through the points $(2, -1, 0)$ and $(3, 0, 5)$.

13. Show that the plane $2x - y + 4z = 3$ is parallel to the plane $6x - 3y + 12z = 17$ and is perpendicular to the plane
$$x + 6y + z - 5 = 0.$$

14. Find the equation of the plane through the point $(2, -1, 3)$ and parallel to the plane $x + 2y - 4z + 6 = 0$.

15. Find the equation of the plane that passes through the point $(4, 3, -1)$ and is perpendicular to each of the planes $2x - y + 3z + 4 = 0$ and $x + 5y - 2z = 7$.

16. Find the equation of the plane through the point $(2, 1, 1)$ and perpendicular to the planes $2x + y - z = 0$ and $3x - 2y + z = 5$.

17. Find the equation of the plane that passes through the points $(1, -2, 1)$ and $(2, 3, -2)$ and is perpendicular to the plane $x + 2y - 3z = 4$.

18. Find the equation of the plane that is perpendicular to the plane $7x + 4y - 4z + 20 = 0$ and passes through the points $(2, 1, -1)$ and $(1, 1, 2)$.

19. Find the equation of the plane that passes through the point $(1, -1, 5)$, is perpendicular to the plane $4x + 2y - 3z = 8$ and has its Y-intercept equal to 2.

20. Find the equation of the plane through the point $(4, -3, 1)$ and perpendicular to the line joining the points $(3, 1, -6)$ and $(-2, 4, 7)$.

21. Find the equation of the plane such that the foot of the perpendicular to the plane from the origin is the point $(2, 3, 6)$.

22. Find the equation of the plane whose distance from the origin is 10 units and which has equal intercepts on the coördinate axes.

23. Prove that the equation of the plane with X-, Y- and Z-intercepts equal to a, b, c respectively may be written
$$\frac{x}{a} + \frac{y}{b} + \frac{z}{c} = 1.$$

This is called the *intercept form* of the equation of a plane. [*Hint.* Start with the general equation of a plane, using the fact that the points $(a, 0, 0)$, $(0, b, 0)$ and $(0, 0, c)$ lie in this plane.]

24. Find the equation of the plane whose intercepts on the coördinate axes are 3, 2 and -1.

25. A plane has equal intercepts on the coördinate axes and passes through the point $(2, -1, 4)$; find its equation.

26. Find the coördinates of the point of intersection of the planes $3x - 4y + 2z = 1$, $2x + 3y - 3z = -1$, $5x - 5y + 4z = 7$.

27. Find the cosine of the angle between the planes $2x + y + z = 3$ and $3x - y - z + 1 = 0$. [*Hint*. The angle between the planes is the same as the angle between their normals.]

28. Prove that the angle between the planes $A_1x + B_1y + C_1z + D_1 = 0$ and $A_2x + B_2y + C_2z + D_2 = 0$ is given by

$$\cos \theta = \pm \frac{A_1A_2 + B_1B_2 + C_1C_2}{\sqrt{A_1{}^2 + B_1{}^2 + C_1{}^2} \cdot \sqrt{A_2{}^2 + B_2{}^2 + C_2{}^2}}.$$

29. Prove that the distance from the plane $x \cos \alpha + y \cos \beta + z \cos \gamma = p$ to the point $P_1(z_1, y_1, z_1)$ is given by

$$d = x_1 \cos \alpha + y_1 \cos \beta + z_1 \cos \gamma - p.$$

[*Hint*. Find the distance from the given plane to a parallel plane through P_1.]

30. Find the perpendicular distance from the plane $x - 2y - 2z = 6$ to the point $(3, -2, 4)$.

476. The Straight Line in Space

A line in space is determined by the intersection of two planes. Since each plane can be represented by an equation of the first degree in x, y, z, the line may be represented by a pair of linear equations in x, y, z. Thus, one form of representation of a line is by means of two equations of the form

$$(a) \qquad \begin{cases} A_1x + B_1y + C_1z + D_1 = 0, \\ A_2x + B_2y + C_2z + D_2 = 0. \end{cases}$$

This will be referred to as the *general form* of the equations of a straight line.

A special form of the equations of a line, which is the most useful form for most purposes, is in terms of a given point on the line and its direction. They may be derived as follows. Let $P_1(x_1, y_1, z_1)$ be a given point on the line, and let $\cos \alpha$, $\cos \beta$, $\cos \gamma$ be the direction cosines of the line. Let $P(x, y, z)$ be any point on the line. By formulas (2) of § 467, we have

$$(b) \qquad \cos \alpha = \frac{x - x_1}{d}, \qquad \cos \beta = \frac{y - y_1}{d}, \qquad \cos \gamma = \frac{z - z_1}{d},$$

where d is the distance between P_1 and P. If we eliminate d by solving each equation for d and equating the values so obtained, we get the following result:

I. *The equations of a line with direction angles α, β, γ and passing through the fixed point $P_1(x_1, y_1, z_1)$ may be written in the form:*

(12)
$$\frac{x - x_1}{\cos \alpha} = \frac{y - y_1}{\cos \beta} = \frac{z - z_1}{\cos \gamma}.$$

This is called the **symmetric form** of the equations of a line.

The symmetric form fails if the given line is perpendicular to one of the coördinate planes. If, for example, the line is perpendicular to the X-axis, we have $\cos \alpha = 0$, and the equations (12) must be replaced by $x - x_1 = 0$ and $\dfrac{y - y_1}{\cos \beta} = \dfrac{z - z_1}{\cos \gamma}$. If the line is perpendicular to both X- and Y-axes, then $\cos \alpha = 0$ and $\cos \beta = 0$, and the equations (12) must be replaced by $x - x_1 = 0$ and $y - y_1 = 0$.

Since any direction numbers of a line are proportional to the corresponding direction cosines, we can evidently replace $\cos \alpha$, $\cos \beta$, $\cos \gamma$ in equations (12) by direction numbers a, b, c of the line. We then have the following *alternative form* of the *symmetric equations* of a line:

II. *The equations of a line with direction numbers a, b, c and passing through a fixed point $P_1(x_1, y_1, z_1)$ may be written:*

(13)
$$\frac{x - x_1}{a} = \frac{y - y_1}{b} = \frac{z - z_1}{c}.$$

EXAMPLE 1. Find the symmetric equations of the line through the point $P_1(2, -3, 1)$ and parallel to the line determined by the points $A(3, 1, 2)$ and $B(1, -3, 4)$.

Solution: Direction numbers of the line AB are obtained by subtracting the corresponding coördinates, so that we may take $a = 3 - 1 = 2$, $b = 1 - (-3) = 4$, $c = 2 - 4 = -2$. The required equations of the line are therefore

$$\frac{x - 2}{2} = \frac{y + 3}{4} = \frac{z - 1}{-2}.$$

If a line is determined by two planes whose equations are given in the general form $Ax + By + Cz + D = 0$, the symmetric equations of the line may be obtained by the method illustrated by the following example:

EXAMPLE 2. Reduce the equations of the line of intersection of the planes $x + 2y + 6z - 5 = 0$, $3x - 2y - 10z - 7 = 0$ to the symmetric form.

Solution: Eliminating y from the two given equations, by adding, we get $z = x - 3$; eliminating x, we get $z = -\frac{1}{7}(2y - 2)$. Equating these values of z, we have $x - 3 = -\frac{2}{7}(y - 1) = z$, which may be written

$$(c) \qquad \frac{x - 3}{1} = \frac{y - 1}{-\frac{7}{2}} = \frac{z - 0}{1}, \qquad \text{or} \qquad \frac{x - 3}{2} = \frac{y - 1}{-7} = \frac{z - 0}{2}.$$

This is one form of the symmetric equations of the line. It exhibits the point $(3, 1, 0)$ as a point P_1 on the line and direction numbers of the line as $2, -7, 2$.

We might equally well have found y in terms of x and z, or x in terms of y and z, and so have obtained other sets of equations, each of which would represent the given line. Other particular points on the line would have been obtained, but the same or proportional direction numbers would have been found.

477. Relative Positions of Lines and Planes

Solutions of problems concerning the relations between two lines or between a line and a plane are generally based on the important facts that the denominators in the symmetric equations of a line are direction numbers of the line, and that the coefficients of x, y, z in the equation of a plane are direction numbers of a normal to the plane. We may also need the conditions for parallelism or perpendicularity of two lines.

EXAMPLE 1. Show that the lines $\dfrac{x - 3}{2} = \dfrac{y + 1}{-3} = \dfrac{z - 2}{-4}$ and $\dfrac{x + 4}{5} = \dfrac{y}{2} = \dfrac{z - 5}{1}$ are perpendicular to each other.

Solution: Taking direction numbers of the lines as $2, -3, -4$ and $5, 2, 1$, and applying the condition (7) for two lines to be perpendicular we have $(2)(5) + (-3)(2) + (-4)(1) = 0$, which proves that the given lines are perpendicular.

EXAMPLE 2. Show that the line $\dfrac{x - 1}{2} = \dfrac{y - 2}{-3} = \dfrac{z + 2}{6}$ is parallel to the plane $3x + 6y + 2z = 8$.

Solution: If the given line is perpendicular to a normal to the given plane, it is parallel to the plane. Direction numbers of the line are $2, -3, 6$ and direction numbers of the normal are $3, 6, 2$. Applying the perpendicularity condition, we have $(2)(3) + (-3)(6) + (6)(2) = 0$, which shows that the line is perpendicular to the normal, and therefore is parallel to the given plane.

EXAMPLE 3. Find equations of the line passing through the point $P_1(-1, 2, 6)$ and perpendicular to each of the lines $(x = 2z - 4, y = -z + 2)$ and $(y = x + 5, z = 2x - 8)$.

Solution: The symmetric equations of the required line is of the form

$$(a) \qquad \frac{x + 1}{a} = \frac{y - 2}{b} = \frac{z - 6}{c},$$

where the direction numbers a, b, c are to be found. If we reduce the equations of the first given line to the symmetric form (as in Example 2 of § 476), we find

(b)
$$\frac{x+4}{2} = \frac{y-2}{-1} = \frac{z-0}{1},$$

and similarly for the second given line,

(c)
$$\frac{x-0}{1} = \frac{y-5}{1} = \frac{z+8}{2}.$$

Writing the perpendicularity condition for lines (a) and (b), and for lines (a) and (c), we get the equations

(d)
$$\begin{cases} 2\,a - b + c = 0, \\ a + b + 2\,c = 0. \end{cases}$$

Solving these equations for a and b in terms of c, we find $a = -c$, $b = -c$; substituting these values in (a), we have for the required line

$$\frac{x+1}{-c} = \frac{y-2}{-c} = \frac{z-6}{c}, \quad \text{or} \quad \frac{x+1}{1} = \frac{y-2}{1} = \frac{z-6}{-1}.$$

478. Exercises

1. Find equations of each of the following lines:
   (a) through the point $(2, 1, 3)$, with direction numbers $1, -2, 3$;
   (b) through the point $(1, -5, 6)$, parallel to the line through $(2, 4, 1)$ and $(-4, 7, 2)$.

2. Find equations of each of the following lines:
   (a) through the point $(1, -3, 2)$, with direction numbers $2, 3, 1$;
   (b) through the point $(2, -4, 3)$, parallel to the line through $(3, -1, 2)$ and $(1, 3, 2)$.

3. Find equations of the line through $(4, 1, -3)$ and parallel to the line
$$\frac{x-2}{2} = \frac{y+1}{-3} = \frac{z}{-1}.$$

4. Find equations of the line through the point $(3, 1, -2)$ and parallel to the Z-axis.

5. Find symmetric equations of the line passing through the points $(3, 1, -2)$ and $(4, -2, 3)$.

6. Find equations of the line through the points $(3, 4, 1)$ and $(-2, 1, 3)$.

7. Show that the lines $\dfrac{x-4}{3} = \dfrac{y-1}{2} = \dfrac{z+3}{-2}$ and $\dfrac{x+1}{6} = \dfrac{y+5}{4} = \dfrac{z-2}{-4}$ are parallel.

8. Show that the lines $\dfrac{x-2}{2} = \dfrac{y+1}{-3} = \dfrac{z}{4}$ and $\dfrac{x+1}{4} = \dfrac{y-3}{-6} = \dfrac{z+4}{8}$ are parallel.

9. Show that the lines $\dfrac{x-1}{2} = \dfrac{y+1}{3} = \dfrac{z-2}{-1}$ and $\dfrac{x-5}{4} = \dfrac{y-6}{-2} = \dfrac{z+1}{2}$ are perpendicular to each other.

10. Show that the line $\dfrac{x + 3}{3} = \dfrac{y - 1}{6} = \dfrac{z - 4}{2}$ is perpendicular to the line $\dfrac{x - 1}{2} = \dfrac{y - 2}{-3} = \dfrac{z + 2}{6}.$

11. Reduce the following equations of lines to the symmetric form:
    (a) $2x + 3y - z = 4$, $x - 2y + z = -1$;
    (b) $3x - 2y + 5z = 8$, $y + 3z = 6$.

12. Reduce the following equations of lines to the symmetric form:
    (a) $4x + 2y - 5z = 2$, $x - y + 3z + 3 = 0$;
    (b) $2x - y = 4$; $x + y + 3z = 5$.

13. Show that the lines $(x + 2y - z = 7,\ 2x - y - z + 6 = 0)$ and $(3x + 6y - 3z = 8,\ 2x - y - z = 0)$ are parallel.

14. Show that the lines $(2x - y = 1,\ y + 4z = 35)$ and $(x - y = 0,\ z - 6x = 3)$ are perpendicular to each other.

15. Find equations of the line through the point $(3, -1, -2)$ and parallel to the line $(4x - 3y - z = 1,\ 2x + 4y + z = 5)$.

16. Find the equation of the plane through the point $(3, 2, -1)$ which is perpendicular to the line $(x - y + 2z - 2 = 0,\ 2x + y - 3z - 6 = 0)$.

17. Show that the line $\dfrac{x + 3}{-2} = \dfrac{y + 4}{-7} = \dfrac{z}{3}$ is parallel to the plane $4x - 2y - 2z = 9.$

18. Show that the line $\dfrac{x - 5}{3} = \dfrac{y + 1}{-4} = \dfrac{z}{2}$ is perpendicular to the plane $3x - 4y + 2z = 7.$

19. Find equations of the line through the point $(3, -2, 1)$ and perpendicular to the plane $3x + y - 3z = 9.$

20. Find the cosine of the acute angle between the lines $\dfrac{x - 3}{4} = \dfrac{y + 2}{-8} = \dfrac{z - 6}{1}$ and $\dfrac{x - 2}{4} = \dfrac{y - 5}{4} = \dfrac{z}{7}.$

21. Find the coördinates of the points in which the line $\dfrac{x - 1}{2} = \dfrac{y - 1}{3} = \dfrac{z + 1}{-1}$ cuts the coördinate planes.

22. Find the coördinates of the point of intersection of the line $\dfrac{x - 3}{2} = \dfrac{y - 4}{3} = \dfrac{z - 7}{4}$ with the plane $4x - 5y + 3z = 3.$

23. Show that the line $\dfrac{x - 2}{3} = \dfrac{y - 10}{5} = \dfrac{z - 5}{20}$ lies in the plane $5x + y - z = 15.$

24. Show that the line $(x - 2y + 3z = 5,\ 2x + y - z = 3)$ lies in the plane $x + 3y - 4z + 2 = 0.$

25. Show that the line $(x + 2y - z + 3 = 0,\ 3x - y + 2z + 1 = 0)$ intersects the line $(2x - 2y + 3z - 2 = 0,\ x - y - z + 3 = 0)$, and find the coördinates of the point of intersection.

26. Find the equation of the plane through the line $(2\,x - y + 3\,z = 5,$ $x + 4\,y - z = -2)$ and the point $(1, -1, 2)$.

27. Find the equation of the plane determined by the intersecting lines
$$\frac{x - 3}{4} = \frac{y - 5}{3} = \frac{z + 1}{2} \quad \text{and} \quad \frac{x - 3}{1} = \frac{y - 5}{2} = \frac{z + 1}{3}.$$

28. Find the equation of the plane determined by the parallel lines
$$\frac{x - 1}{1} = \frac{y - 2}{2} = \frac{z - 3}{3} \quad \text{and} \quad \frac{x + 2}{1} = \frac{y - 3}{2} = \frac{z - 5}{3}.$$

479. The Sphere

Since a sphere is defined as the surface each point of which is at a given fixed distance (the radius) from a given fixed point (the center), by use of the distance formula we have:

The equation of a sphere of radius a and center at the point (h, k, l) is:

(14) $$(x - h)^2 + (y - k)^2 + (z - l)^2 = a^2.$$

This is often called the **standard equation** of the sphere.

By expanding and simplifying the equation (14), we can reduce this equation to the form

(a) $$x^2 + y^2 + z^2 + Ax + By + Cz + D = 0.$$

This is called the **general form** of the equation of a sphere.

Any equation of the form (a) can be reduced to the form (14) by completing the squares.

EXAMPLE. Find the center and radius of the sphere whose equation is
$$x^2 + y^2 + z^2 - 2\,x + 6\,y - 4\,z - 11 = 0.$$

Solution: Completing the squares, we get
$$(x^2 - 2\,x + 1) + (y^2 + 6\,y + 9) + (z^2 - 4\,z + 4) = 11 + 1 + 9 + 4 = 25,$$
or $$(x - 1)^2 + (y + 3)^2 + (z - 2)^2 = 5^2.$$
The center is therefore at $(1, -3, 2)$ and the radius is 5.

The equation of a sphere has *four essential constants;* a sphere may therefore be determined to satisfy four given conditions, as, for example, to pass through four given points not all in the same plane.

480. Cylindrical Surfaces

A surface generated by a straight line which moves so that it is always parallel to a given fixed line and always intersects a given fixed curve is called a **cylindrical surface.** Any position of the generating line is called an *element* of the cylindrical surface, and the fixed curve is called the *directing curve* or *directrix*.

According to this definition, we may have elliptical cylindrical surfaces or parabolic cylindrical surfaces, etc., as well as circular cylindrical surfaces.

Any equation in only two of the three variables x, y, z is represented by a cylindrical surface whose elements are parallel to the axis of the third variable. For example, in plane geometry, $x^2 + y^2 = a^2$ is represented by a circle in the XY-plane, but in solid geometry, it is represented by a circular cylindrical surface with its axis along the Z-axis and with radius a. *Conversely, every cylindrical surface whose elements are parallel to one of the coördinate axes has an equation involving only two variables.*

For, let the curve C in Fig. 195 be the graph of the equation $f(x, y) = 0$ in the XY-plane. If we take any point M on the curve C

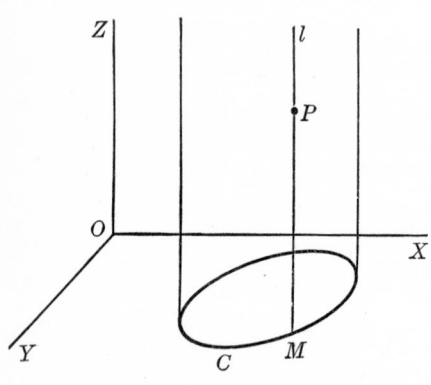

FIG. 195

and draw a line l through M parallel to the Z-axis, then the X- and Y-coördinates of any point P on the line l are the same as those of M. It follows that any point on the cylindrical surface directed by C and with elements parallel to the Z-axis has coördinates that satisfy the equation

$$f(x, y) = 0.$$

Moreover, the coördinates of any point not on the cylindrical surface fail to satisfy that equation, since the coördinates of its projection on the XY-plane fail to do so. The cylindrical surface is therefore the locus of the equation $f(x, y) = 0$. Similarly, it can be seen that equations of the form $g(y, z) = 0$ or $h(z, x) = 0$, containing only two variables, represent cylindrical surfaces whose elements are parallel to the X-axis or the Y-axis, respectively.

EXAMPLE. (*a*) The equation $4y^2 + 9z^2 = 36$ represents an elliptic cylindrical surface with elements parallel to the X-axis.

(*b*) The equation $y^2 = 4x$ represents a parabolic cylindrical surface with elements parallel to the Z-axis.

It should not be inferred that all cylindrical surfaces have equations in which one variable is lacking, since this would not be the case if the elements were not parallel to one of the coördinate axes.

481. Exercises

1. Find the equation of the sphere with center at $(4, 1, -2)$ and radius 3.
2. Find the equation of the sphere with center at $(-2, 1, 3)$ and passing through the point $(3, -2, 1)$.
3. Find the center and radius of each of the following spheres:
   (a) $x^2 + y^2 + z^2 - 4x + 2y - 6z - 2 = 0$;
   (b) $x^2 + y^2 + z^2 + 6x - 5y - z - 2 = 0$.
4. Find the center and radius of each of the following spheres:
   (a) $x^2 + y^2 + z^2 - 2x - 8y + 6z - 10 = 0$;
   (b) $x^2 + y^2 + z^2 - 3x + 4y + 7z = 0$.
5. Find the equation of the sphere having as a diameter the line-segment joining the points $(3, 1, -5)$ and $(1, -3, 1)$.
6. Find the equation of the sphere whose center is at $(3, 1, 4)$ and which is tangent to the XY-plane.
7. Describe and sketch the surface represented by each of the following equations:
   (a) $x^2 + y^2 = 16$;   (b) $4x^2 + y^2 = 36$;
   (c) $x^2 = z$;   (d) $y^2 + z^2 = 4y$.
8. Proceed as in Exercise 7 with:
   (a) $x^2 + z^2 - 2x = 0$;   (b) $4z^2 + 9y^2 = 36$;
   (c) $x^2 - 4y^2 = 36$;   (d) $xy = 4$.
9. Find the equation of the right circular cylinder with radius 5 and having the X-axis for its axis.
10. Find the equation of the right circular cylinder whose axis is the line $x = 4$, $y = 3$ and whose radius is 2.
11. Find the equation of the plane tangent to the sphere
$$x^2 + y^2 + z^2 - 4x + 6y - 4z - 32 = 0$$
at the point $(8, -1, 5)$.

482. Surfaces of Revolution

*The surface generated by revolving a plane curve about a line in its plane is called a **surface of revolution.*** Familiar examples are: the sphere, a right circular cylindrical surface and a right circular conical surface.

The equation of a surface of revolution whose axis of rotation is one of the coördinate axes may be written down readily from the equation of the generating curve by a method which may be derived as follows: Let the curve SR in Fig. 196 in the XZ-plane be represented

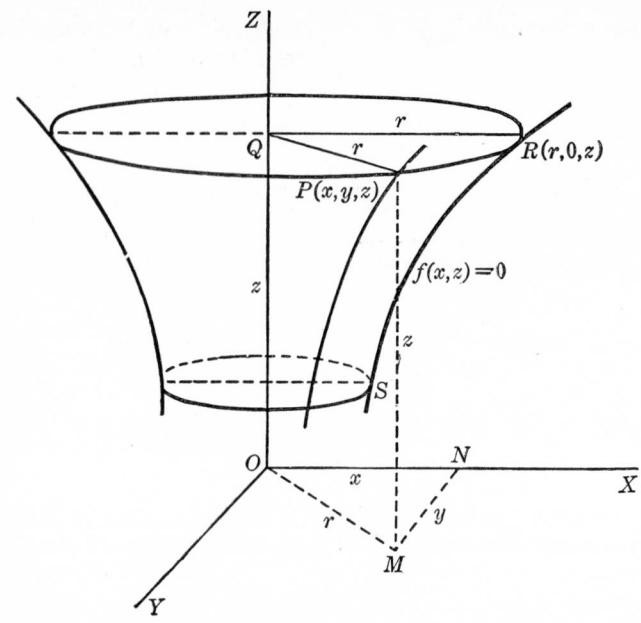

Fig. 196

by the equation $f(x, z) = 0$, and let this curve be revolved about the Z-axis to generate a surface of revolution. Let $P(x, y, z)$ be any point on this surface. Then P lies on a circle perpendicular to the Z-axis with center at Q and radius $QP = r$. Now

$$(a) \qquad x^2 + y^2 = r^2.$$

The point $R(r, 0, z)$ lies on the generating curve, so that $f(r, z) = 0$. Substituting the value of r from (a) in this equation $f(r, z) = 0$, we have

$$(b) \qquad f(\pm\sqrt{x^2 + y^2}, z) = 0.$$

This is satisfied by the coördinates of any point P on the surface, but not by the coördinates of a point not on the surface, therefore it is the required equation of the surface of revolution.

The preceding result leads to the following general procedure for writing the equation of a surface of revolution generated by revolving a given curve that lies in one of the coördinate planes about one of the coördinate axes of that plane:

Substitute in the equation of the given curve the square root of the sum of the squares of the two variables not measured along the axis of revolution in place of that one of these two variables which occurs in the equation of the curve.

EXAMPLE. Find the equation of the surface of revolution generated by revolving the parabola $y^2 = 4\,x$ about the X-axis.

Solution: In the equation of the curve, we replace y by $\sqrt{y^2 + z^2}$ and therefore y^2 by $y^2 + z^2$, which gives

$$y^2 + z^2 = 4\,x$$

as the required equation of the surface of revolution.

483. Exercises

1. Find the equation of the surface of revolution generated by revolving each of the following curves about the line indicated:
   (a) $x^2 + z^2 = 4$ in the XZ-plane, about the X-axis;
   (b) $y^2 = 4\,z$ in the YZ-plane, about the Z-axis;
   (c) $2\,x + 3\,y = 6$ in the XY-plane, about the Y-axis.

2. Proceed as in Exercise 1 with:
   (a) $4\,x^2 + 9\,y^2 = 36$ in the XY-plane, about the X-axis;
   (b) $4\,x^2 - 9\,z^2 = 36$ in the XZ-plane, about the Z-axis;
   (c) $y^2 = 4\,z$ in the YZ-plane, about the Y-axis.

3. Describe each of the following surfaces:
   (a) $x^2 + y^2 = 4\,az$;   (b) $x^2 + 4\,y^2 + 4\,z^2 = 16$.

4. Describe each of the following surfaces:
   (a) $x^2 + z^2 = 2\,ay$;   (b) $4\,x^2 + 4\,y^2 - z^2 = 4$.

5. Find the equation of the surface generated by revolving the circle $(x - a)^2 + y^2 = b^2$, $(a > b)$, about the Y-axis. (This surface is called a *torus* or *anchor ring*.)

6. Find the equation of the conical surface generated by revolving the line $2\,x - y + 1 = 0$ about the line $y = 1$.

484. Discussion of Surfaces

To learn something of the nature of a surface represented by a given equation, we may discuss it in a manner somewhat analogous to that used in studying curves in plane analytic geometry by discussing their equations. Important notions to be investigated in the case of surfaces are: symmetry, extent, intercepts and sections parallel to the coördinate planes.

If the given equation is left essentially unchanged by replacing x by $-x$, the surface is *symmetric* with respect to the YZ-plane; there is a similar statement for symmetry with respect to the other two coördinate planes. *Symmetry* with respect to a coördinate *axis* may be tested by changing the signs of two of the variables in the given equation. Thus, if the equation is left essentially unchanged by replacing y by $-y$ and z by $-z$, the surface is symmetric with respect to the X-axis. *Symmetry* with respect to the *origin* is tested by changing the signs of all of the variables in the equation.

The *intercepts* of a surface on the coördinate axes are the directed distances cut off on the axes from the origin by the surface. To find the intercepts, we must obviously put two of the variables equal to zero in the equation and solve the resulting equation for real values of the third variable.

The *traces* of the surface are the sections (curves) of the surface made by the coördinate planes. To find the equations of the traces, we put one of the variables equal to zero; then the resulting equation in two variables gives the required trace. *Sections* of the surface made by planes parallel to the coördinate planes, found by putting $x =$ constant, or $y =$ constant, or $z =$ constant, are also needed in forming an idea of the surface.

By putting all of these results together, we form a picture of the surface.

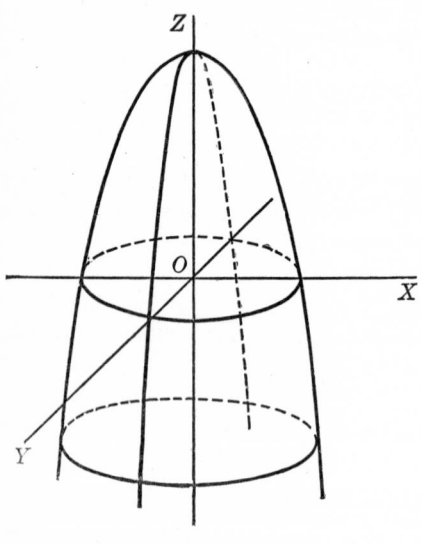

Fig. 197

EXAMPLE. Discuss the surface represented by the equation $x^2 + y^2 = 4 - z$.

Solution: (a) By inspection we see that the surface is symmetric with respect to the YZ-plane and the ZX-plane, but not with respect to the XY-plane. It is symmetric with respect to the Z-axis but not with respect to the other two axes. It is not symmetric with respect to the origin.

(b) Since $x^2 + y^2$ is negative for $z > 4$, the surface does not extend above the plane $z = 4$, but it extends without limit below that, and it extends without limit in the directions of the X- and Y-axes (see Fig. 197).

(c) By putting $y = z = 0$, we find $x = \pm 2$, the X-intercepts; by putting $x = z = 0$, we find $y = \pm 2$, the Y-intercepts; and by putting $x = y = 0$, we find $z = 4$, the Z-intercept (see Fig. 197).

(d) If we put $z = 0$, we get the XY-trace: $x^2 + y^2 = .4$, a *circle*; if we put $y = 0$, we get the ZX-trace: $x^2 = 4 - z$, a *parabola*; and if we put $x = 0$, we get the YZ-trace: $y^2 = 4 - z$, a *parabola* (see Fig. 197).

(e) The section made by a plane $z = k$ (a constant) is $x^2 + y^2 = 4 - k$, which is a *circle* if $k < 4$, a point if $k = 4$, and no locus if $k > 4$. If $k < 4$, as k decreases algebraically, the circular section increases in size, always having its center on the Z-axis. The section by a plane $y = k$ perpendicular to the Y-axis is $x^2 = 4 - k^2 - z$, which is a *parabola* for all values of k, with vertex varying in position as k varies. The sections by planes $x = k$ are *parabolas* like those for $y = k$.

The surface may be pictured by putting together these various results. It is called a *circular paraboloid* or a *paraboloid of revolution*, because one set of sections consists of circles and two sets of sections consist of parabolas.

485. Exercises

1. Discuss and sketch the surface represented by each of the following equations:

   (a) $4 x^2 + 4 y^2 + z^2 = 16$; (b) $y^2 + z^2 = 4 x$;
   (c) $x^2 + y^2 - z^2 = 1$; (d) $x^2 - y^2 - z^2 = 1$.

2. Proceed as in Exercise 1 with:

   (a) $4 x^2 + 9 y^2 + 16 z^2 = 144$; (b) $z^2 + x^2 - 9 y = 9$;
   (c) $x^2 + y^2 - z^2 = 0$; (d) $z = 4 - y - x^2$.

486. The Quadric Surfaces

The locus of an equation of the second degree in x, y, z is called a *quadric surface*. Just as the curves of the second degree in plane analytic geometry are classified into certain type forms: ellipse, parabola, etc., so the quadric surfaces may be classified into certain *typical forms*. We shall now discuss briefly the *standard equations* of the various types of quadric surfaces.

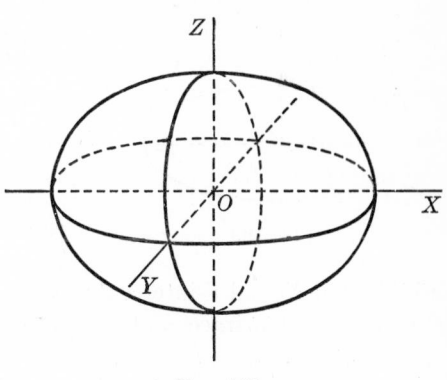

Fig. 198

I. *Ellipsoid:*

$$(15) \quad \frac{x^2}{a^2} + \frac{y^2}{b^2} + \frac{z^2}{c^2} = 1$$

(Fig. 198).

This surface is evidently symmetric with respect to each of the coördinate planes, each of the coördinate axes and the origin. The intercepts are $x = \pm a$, $y = \pm b$, $z = \pm c$. The traces and real sections are all ellipses. Thus, the XY-trace is the ellipse $\frac{x^2}{a^2} + \frac{y^2}{b^2} = 1$, which has its center at the origin and semi-axes a and b. The section by a plane $z = k$ is $\frac{x^2}{a^2} + \frac{y^2}{b^2} = 1 - \frac{k^2}{c^2}$; if $k^2 < c^2$, these sections are ellipses decreasing in size as k increases up to $k = c$, but if $k^2 > c^2$ there is no real section. Similarly we find the other traces and

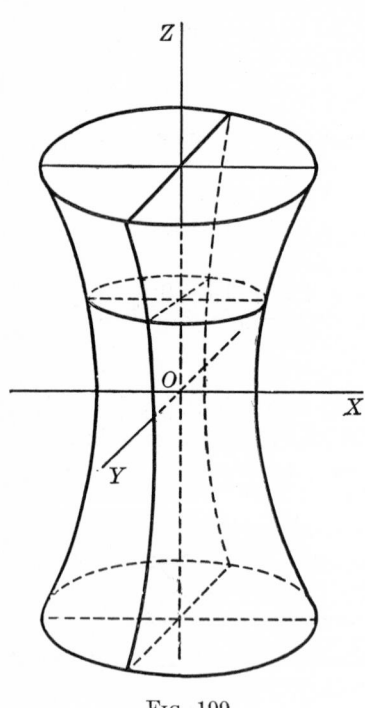

sections, which are ellipses. The origin is the *center* of the ellipsoid. The positive numbers a, b, c are called the semi-axes of the ellipsoid.

If $b = c$ but $a > b$, the ellipsoid is called a *prolate spheroid;* this is a surface of revolution obtained by revolving an ellipse about its longer axis. If $a = b$ but $c < a$, the ellipsoid is called an *oblate spheroid;* it is a surface of revolution obtained by revolving an ellipse about its shorter axis. The figure of the earth is approximately an oblate spheroid. If $a = b = c$, the surface is a *sphere.*

II. *Elliptic hyperboloid of one sheet:*

(16) $\dfrac{x^2}{a^2} + \dfrac{y^2}{b^2} - \dfrac{z^2}{c^2} = 1$ (Fig. 199).

This surface is symmetric with respect to each of the coördinate planes, the coördinate axes and the

Fig. 199

origin. The X- and Y-intercepts are $x = \pm a$, $y = \pm b$, but there is no Z-intercept. The traces and real sections are ellipses and hyperbolas. The XY-trace is the ellipse $\frac{x^2}{a^2} + \frac{y^2}{b^2} = 1$. The section by a plane $z = k$ is $\frac{x^2}{a^2} + \frac{y^2}{b^2} = 1 + \frac{k^2}{c^2}$, which is an ellipse for all values of k. This ellipse is smallest for $k = 0$ and increases without bound as k increases in absolute value, and the surface extends indefinitely far from the origin above and below. Similarly, we find that the XZ- and YZ-traces and sections are hyperbolas. The surface consists of *one* connected piece, therefore it is called an elliptic hyperboloid of one sheet, since it has one set of elliptical sections and two sets of hyperbolic sections.

If $a = b$, the elliptical sections become circles, and the surface is called a *circular hyperboloid of one sheet*, or a *hyperboloid of revolution of one sheet*. It may be generated by revolving a hyperbola about its conjugate axis.

III. *Elliptic hyperboloid of two sheets:*

(17) $$\frac{x^2}{a^2} - \frac{y^2}{b^2} - \frac{z^2}{c^2} = 1$$ (Fig. 200).

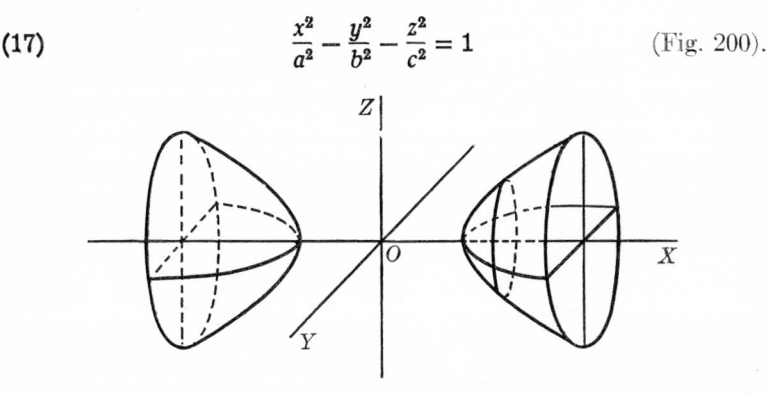

Fig. 200

The discussion of this surface is similar to that of the preceding one. The surface is symmetric with respect to each of the coördinate planes, the coördinate axes and the origin. It has the X-intercepts $x = \pm a$, but no Y- or Z-intercepts. The XY-trace and the XZ-trace are hyperbolas, but there is no YZ-trace. The section by a plane $x = k$ is $\frac{y^2}{b^2} + \frac{z^2}{c^2} = \frac{k^2}{a^2} - 1$. If $k^2 > a^2$, this is an ellipse which increases in size as k increases in absolute value; if $k^2 = a^2$, the equation represents a point; if $k^2 < a^2$, the equation has no locus. Thus, the surface has a gap between $x = a$ and $x = -a$, but for $x > a$ or $x < -a$, the surface extends without bound with increasing elliptical sections. The sections parallel to the XY- and XZ-planes are hyperbolas. The surface consists of *two* distinct pieces and is therefore called an elliptic hyperboloid of two sheets.

If $b = c$, the YZ-sections are circles for $x^2 > a^2$, and the surface is called a *circular hyperboloid of two sheets* or a *hyperboloid of revolution of two sheets*. It may be generated by revolving a hyperbola about its transverse axis.

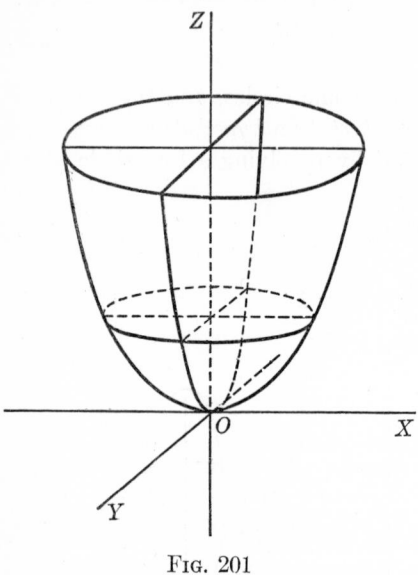

Fɪɢ. 201

IV. *Elliptic paraboloid:*

(18) $\dfrac{x^2}{a^2} + \dfrac{y^2}{b^2} = z$ (Fig. 201).

This surface is symmetric with respect to the YZ-plane and the XZ-plane, but not with respect to the XY-plane. It passes through the origin and has no intercepts other than $x = y = z = 0$. It has no center of symmetry. The XY-trace is a point, and the YZ- and XZ-traces are parabolas $x^2 = a^2z$ and $y^2 = b^2z$. The section made by

$$z = k \text{ is } \frac{x^2}{a^2} + \frac{y^2}{b^2} = k,$$

which is an ellipse if $k > 0$, a point if $k = 0$; there is no locus if $k < 0$. The surface therefore does not extend below the XY-plane but extends without bound upward, with increasing elliptical sections. The YZ- and XZ-sections are parabolas. The surface consists of one piece or sheet.

If $a = b$, the XY-sections are circles for $z > 0$, and the surface is then called a *circular paraboloid* or a *paraboloid of revolution*. It may be generated by revolving a parabola about its axis of symmetry.

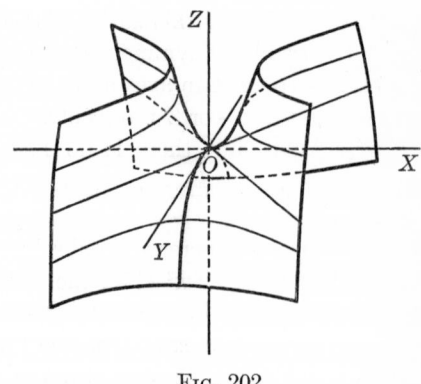

Fɪɢ. 202

V. *Hyperbolic paraboloid:*

(19) $\dfrac{x^2}{a^2} - \dfrac{y^2}{b^2} = z$ (Fig. 202).

This surface is symmetric with respect to the YZ- and XZ-planes, but not with respect to the XY-plane; it has no center of symmetry. It passes through the origin, but has no other intercepts than $x = y = z = 0$. The XY-trace is $\dfrac{x^2}{a^2} - \dfrac{y^2}{b^2} = 0$, which is a pair of intersecting straight lines. The sections parallel to the XY-plane above the XY-plane are hyperbolas with transverse axis parallel to the X-axis, but sections below the XY-plane are hyperbolas with transverse axis parallel to the Y-axis. The sections parallel to the other two coördinate planes are parabolas; those parallel to the XZ-plane open upward and those parallel to the YZ-plane open downward. The surface is best described as *saddle-shaped*, or in the form of a pass through a mountain range.

VI. *Elliptic cone:*

(20) $\qquad \dfrac{x^2}{a^2} + \dfrac{y^2}{b^2} = \dfrac{z^2}{c^2} \qquad$ (Fig. 203).

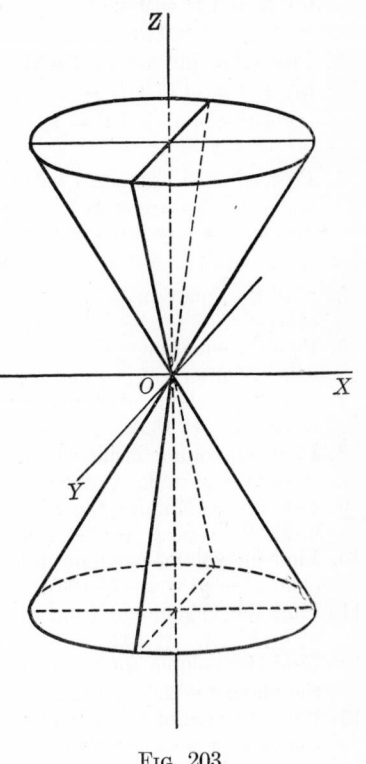

FIG. 203

This surface is symmetric with respect to each of the coördinate planes, and has a center at the origin. The sections by planes parallel to the XY-plane are ellipses, increasing in size as we go upward or downward. The traces in the XZ- and YZ-planes are pairs of intersecting straight lines; and the sections parallel to these planes are hyperbolas. The surface is a *conical surface* with vertex at the origin and axis along the Z-axis.

If $a = b$, the XY-sections are circles, and the surface is then a *right circular cone* or a *cone of revolution*.

Another type of quadric surface is the *cylindrical surface* whose equation is of the second degree, which has already been discussed.

487. Exercises

1. Discuss, name and sketch the surface represented by each of the following equations:

   (a) $4 x^2 + y^2 + 9 z^2 = 36$;   (b) $4 x^2 + 9 y^2 = 4 z$;
   (c) $x^2 + 4 y^2 - 9 z^2 = 36$;   (d) $x^2 - y^2 - z^2 = 9$;
   (e) $x^2 - y^2 = 6 z$;   (f) $x^2 + y^2 - 4 z^2 = 0$.

2. Proceed as in Exercise 1 with:

   (a) $4 x^2 + 9 y^2 + z^2 = 36$;   (b) $y^2 + 4 z^2 - 9 x^2 = 0$;
   (c) $z^2 + 4 x^2 = 9 y$;   (d) $4 y^2 - z^2 = x^2 + 1$;
   (e) $x^2 - z^2 = 4 y$;   (f) $4 y^2 + 4 z^2 = x^2$.

3. Proceed as in Exercise 1 with:

   (a) $4 x^2 + y^2 = 4 - z$;   (b) $4 x^2 + 9 y^2 - z^2 + 36 = 0$;
   (c) $4 x^2 + 4 y^2 + 4 z^2 = 1$;   (d) $x^2 + y^2 + z^2 - 4 x - 5 = 0$;
   (e) $y^2 + z^2 = 4$;   (f) $x + y = z^2$.

4. Proceed as in Exercise 1 with:

   (a) $x^2 + 4 y^2 - z = 4$;   (b) $2 x + z^2 = 4 y$;
   (c) $x^2 + y^2 + z^2 + 2 x - 4 y = 6$;   (d) $4 x^2 - 9 y^2 - z^2 = 0$;
   (e) $z^2 = 4 x$;   (f) $12 y^2 + 144 = 16 x^2 + 25 z^2$.

5. Find the equation of the paraboloid of revolution of height h and radius of base r.

6. Find the equation of the paraboloid of revolution whose axis is the Z-axis, whose Z-intercept is 4 and the radius of whose XY-trace is 2.

7. Find the volume of a paraboloid of revolution of altitude h and radius of base r.   (§ 186).

8. Find the volume inside the paraboloid $y^2 + z^2 = x$ and outside the cone $x^2 - y^2 - z^2 = 0$.   (§ 188).

9. Find the volume of the part of the sphere $x^2 + y^2 + z^2 = 8$ that lies inside the cone $x^2 + y^2 - z^2 = 0$.   (§ 190).

10. Find the volume common to the sphere $x^2 + y^2 + z^2 = 6$ and the paraboloid $x^2 + y^2 = z$.   (§ 190).

11. Find the volume cut from the elliptic paraboloid $x^2 + 4 y^2 = z$ by the plane $z = 1$.   (§ 192).

12. Find the volume cut from the elliptic paraboloid $x^2 + 4 y^2 = 4 - z$ by the plane $z = 2$.   (§ 192).

13. Find the area of the surface of the paraboloid $x^2 + y^2 = 4 az$ cut off by the plane $z = a$.   (§ 405).

14. Find the location of the centroid of the surface of a paraboloid of revolution 2 feet high, with radius of base 4 feet.   (§ 407).

15. Find the moment of inertia with respect to the Z-axis of the solid cut from the cylinder $x^2 + y^2 = a^2$ by the sphere $x^2 + y^2 + z^2 = 4 a^2$.   (§ 207).

16. Find the radius of gyration with respect to the Z-axis of the solid inside the paraboloid $x^2 + y^2 = az$ and outside the cone $x^2 + y^2 - z^2 = 0$.   (§ 207).

488. Curves in Space

A *curve in space* may be regarded as the intersection of two surfaces. If the equations of the surfaces are $F_1(x, y, z) = 0$ and $F_2(x, y, z) = 0$, these two equations taken together are *equations of the curve*.

If we eliminate z between these two equations $F_1 = 0$ and $F_2 = 0$, the resulting equation, of the form $g_1(x, y) = 0$, represents a cylinder, which is called the *projecting cylinder of the curve on the XY-plane*. This projecting cylinder contains the curve on it and has its elements perpendicular to the XY-plane. Similarly, by eliminating y or eliminating x between the equations $F_1 = 0$ and $F_2 = 0$, we obtain equations of the form $g_2(x, z) = 0$ or $g_3(y, z) = 0$, which are the projecting cylinders of the curve on the XZ-plane or the YZ-plane, respectively. Any two of the equations $g_1 = 0$, $g_2 = 0$, $g_3 = 0$ taken together represent the curve.

EXAMPLE 1.   (a) The curve whose equations are $x^2 + y^2 = 25$, $z = 4$ is a circle cut from the cylindrical surface $x^2 + y^2 = 25$ by the plane $z = 4$. It lies in a plane parallel to the XY-plane and 4 units above; its center is on the Z-axis and its radius is 5.

(b) The equations $x^2 + y^2 + z^2 = 25$, $x^2 + y^2 = 16$ represent the two circles cut from the sphere $x^2 + y^2 + z^2 = 25$ by the cylinder $x^2 + y^2 = 16$. To find the intersection, we subtract the two given equations and get $z^2 = 9$ or $z = \pm 3$. Therefore, the given equations represent two circles which lie in planes parallel to the XY-plane, one 3 units above and the other 3 units below; the center of each circle is on the Z-axis and the radius of each is 4.

It is often found convenient to represent a curve in space by *parametric equations* giving the three coördinates of a point on it in terms of a *parameter*, as for example by equations of the form $x = f(t)$, $y = g(t)$, $z = h(t)$.

EXAMPLE 2.   The equations

$$x = a \cos kt, \qquad y = a \sin kt, \qquad z = ct,$$

where t is the parameter, and a, b, c are constants, represent a space curve called a *cylindrical helix*, which winds around the cylinder $x^2 + y^2 = a^2$. It is the locus of a point which revolves about the Z-axis with uniform angular velocity k and at the same time moves parallel to the Z-axis with uniform linear velocity c. The thread of a bolt has the form of a cylindrical helix.

489. Exercises

1. Describe the curve in space represented by each of the following pairs of equations:

(a) $x^2 + y^2 + z^2 = 25$, $z = 3$;   (b) $x^2 + y^2 = 4z$, $z = 4$;
(c) $x^2 + y^2 = 25$, $y = 4$;   (d) $x^2 + y^2 - z = 0$, $x^2 + y^2 = 4$.

2. Proceed as in Exercise 1:

(a) $x^2 + z^2 = 16$, $y + 2 = 0$;   (b) $x^2 + y^2 + z^2 = 100$, $y^2 + z^2 = 64$;
(c) $x^2 + y^2 = 4 - z$, $z = 2$;   (d) $x^2 + y^2 - z^2 = 4$, $z + 2 = 0$.

3. Show that the equations $x = at \cos \omega t$, $y = at \sin \omega t$, $z = ct$ represent a curve (conical helix) which lies on the cone $\dfrac{x^2}{a^2} + \dfrac{y^2}{a^2} - \dfrac{z^2}{c^2} = 0$.

490. Cylindrical Coördinates

Instead of always using rectangular coördinates, it is often convenient to use another system of coördinates, which consists of a combination of polar coördinates in the XY-plane and the rectangular z-coördinate. These new coördinates are especially useful in problems involving axial symmetry.

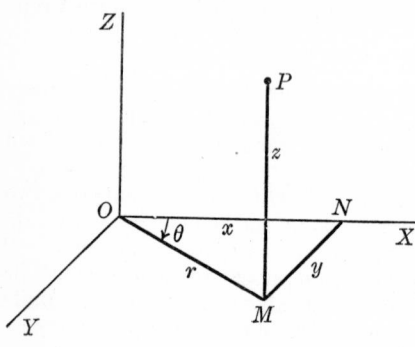

Fig. 204

Let OX, OY, OZ in Fig. 204 be any set of three mutually perpendicular axes. Let P be any point in space; draw PM perpendicular to the XY-plane, with M the foot of the perpendicular in the XY-plane. Let (r, θ) be the plane polar coördinates of M in the XY-plane, and let z be the rectangular Z-coördinate of P. Then *the three numbers r, θ, z are called the* **cylindrical coördinates** *of P*, and are written in order (r, θ, z).

If r is held constant and θ and z are allowed to vary, the point P will move on a circular cylindrical surface perpendicular to the XY-plane (whence the name: cylindrical coördinates). If θ is held constant and r and z are allowed to vary, P will move in a plane through the Z-axis. If z is held constant and r and θ are allowed to vary, P will move in a plane perpendicular to the Z-axis. These three surfaces are mutually perpendicular.

The relations between the rectangular coördinates and the cylindrical coördinates of a point are given by:

(a) $$x = r \cos \theta, \qquad y = r \sin \theta, \qquad z = z,$$

(b) $$r^2 = x^2 + y^2, \qquad \tan \theta = \frac{y}{x}, \qquad z = z.$$

These results follow at once from the relations between rectangular and polar coördinates in a plane.

Equations of certain surfaces are much simpler when expressed in cylindrical coördinates.

491. Exercises

1. Find the rectangular coördinates of the points whose cylindrical coördinates are:

   (a) $(3, \frac{1}{4}\pi, 5)$; (b) $(2, \frac{1}{2}\pi, 3)$.

2. Proceed as in Exercise 1 with:

   (a) $(4, \frac{1}{3}\pi, 2)$; (b) $(3, \frac{5}{6}\pi, 2)$.

3. Find cylindrical coördinates of the points whose rectangular coördinates are:

   (a) $(3, 4, 5)$; (b) $(3, 3, -4)$.

4. Proceed as in Exercise 3 with:

   (a) $(8, 15, -6)$; (b) $(\sqrt{3}, -2, 1)$.

5. Write each of the following equations in cylindrical coördinates, and sketch their loci:

   (a) $x^2 + y^2 = 16$; (b) $x^2 + y^2 = 4z$;
   (c) $4x^2 + 4y^2 - 9z^2 = 36$; (d) $x = 2$.

6. Proceed as in Exercise 5 with:

   (a) $4x^2 + 4y^2 = 25 - 4z^2$; (b) $9z = 4x^2 + 4y^2$;
   (c) $z^2 + 9 = x^2 + y^2$; (d) $x^2 + y^2 = 16$.

7. Find the equation in rectangular coördinates of each of the following surfaces whose equations are given in cylindrical coördinates, and sketch their loci:

   (a) $r^2 + 4z^2 = 16$; (b) $r = z$;
   (c) $r = 4\cos\theta$; (d) $r^2 - 4z = 0$.

8. Proceed as in Exercise 7 with:

   (a) $r^2 = -6z$; (b) $z^2 - r^2 = 1$;
   (c) $r = 5$; (d) $z = 9r^2$.

9. Discuss the surface represented by each of the following equations in cylindrical coördinates:

   (a) $r^2 = z$; (b) $4r^2 + z^2 = 36$.

10. Proceed as in Exercise 9 with:

    (a) $r^2 + z^2 = a^2$; (b) $r = z$.

11. Find the equation in cylindrical coördinates of each of the following surfaces:

    (a) the sphere with center at the origin and radius a;

(b) the right circular cylinder of radius a, with axis along the Z-axis;

(c) the plane passing through the Z-axis and bisecting the first octant.

12. Proceed as in Exercise 11 with:

(a) the right circular cylinder of radius a, with axis parallel to the Z-axis and passing through the points whose rectangular coördinates are $(0, 0, 0)$ and $(a, 0, 0)$;

(b) the plane parallel to the XY-plane and 5 units above it;

(c) the right circular cone with vertex at the origin, axis along the Z-axis and having the semi-vertical angle $30°$.

★ 492. Spherical Coördinates

Another set of space coördinates, which are especially useful in problems dealing with spheres and cones, is the system of spherical coördinates.

Let OX, OY, OZ in Fig. 205 be any set of three mutually perpendicular axes. Let P be any point in space, and let M be its projection on the XY-plane. Let θ be the angle XOM measured from OX to OM, let ϕ be the angle ZOP measured from OZ to OP, and let ρ be the positive distance OP. Then *the three numbers ρ, θ, ϕ are called the* **spherical coördinates** *of P*, and are written in order (ρ, θ, ϕ). The angles θ and ϕ correspond to longitude and co-latitude (complement of the latitude) of a point on the earth's surface in geography.

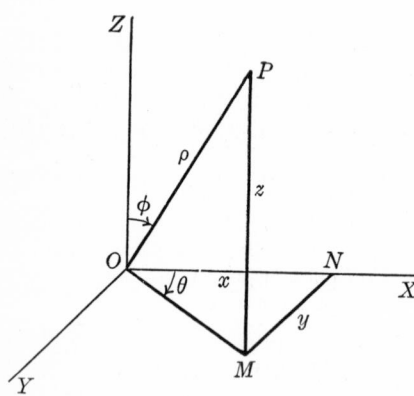

Fig. 205

If ρ is held constant and θ and ϕ are allowed to vary, the point P will move on a spherical surface (whence the name: spherical coördinates). If θ is held constant and ρ and ϕ are allowed to vary, P will move in a plane through the Z-axis. If ϕ is held constant and ρ and θ are allowed to vary, P will move on a conical surface with its axis along the Z-axis. These three surfaces are mutually perpendicular.

The relations between the rectangular coördinates and the spherical coördinates of a point are given by:

(a) $\qquad x = \rho \sin \phi \cos \theta, \qquad y = \rho \sin \phi \sin \theta, \qquad z = \rho \cos \phi,$

since $\quad x = OM \cos \theta, \quad y = OM \sin \theta, \quad z = \rho \sin (90° - \phi) \quad$ and $OM = \rho \sin \phi$.

The equations of certain surfaces are simpler when expressed in spherical coördinates.

★ 493. Exercises

1. Find the rectangular coördinates of the points whose spherical coördinates are:

   (a) $(2, \frac{1}{2} \pi, \frac{1}{6} \pi)$; $\qquad$ (b) $(3, \frac{1}{3} \pi, \frac{5}{6} \pi)$.

2. Proceed as in Exercise 1 with:

   (a) $(4, \frac{1}{4} \pi, \frac{1}{3} \pi)$; $\qquad$ (b) $(5, \frac{3}{2} \pi, \frac{1}{3} \pi)$.

3. Find spherical coördinates of the points whose rectangular coördinates are:

   (a) $(1, 1, 2)$; $\qquad$ (b) $(3, 4, 0)$.

4. Proceed as in Exercise 3 with:

   (a) $(4, 2, -4)$; $\qquad$ (b) $(2, 0, 3)$.

5. Show that the spherical coördinates of a point are expressed in terms of the rectangular coördinates of the point by:

$$\rho^2 = x^2 + y^2 + z^2, \qquad \tan \theta = \frac{y}{x}, \qquad \cos \phi = \frac{z}{\pm \sqrt{x^2 + y^2 + z^2}}.$$

6. Show that the cylindrical coördinates of a point are related to the spherical coördinates of the point by:

$$r = \rho \sin \phi, \qquad \theta = \theta, \qquad z = \rho \cos \phi.$$

7. Write each of the following equations in spherical coördinates:

   (a) $x^2 + y^2 + z^2 = 16$; $\qquad$ (b) $x^2 + y^2 - 4 z^2 = 0$;
   (c) $x^2 + y^2 = 4 z$; $\qquad$ (d) $x^2 + y^2 = 9$.

8. Proceed as in Exercise 7 with:

   (a) $x^2 + y^2 = 4 - z^2$; $\qquad$ (b) $4 y^2 = z - 4 x^2$;
   (c) $x^2 + y^2 = 12 z^2$; $\qquad$ (d) $x^2 + y^2 = 4 - 4 z^2$.

9. Write each of the following equations in rectangular coördinates:

   (a) $\rho = 6$; $\qquad$ (b) $\rho = 4 \cos \phi$; $\qquad$ (c) $\rho = a \sin \phi \sin \theta$.

10. Proceed as in Exercise 9 with:

    (a) $\rho \cos \phi = 2$; (b) $\rho = 2 \sin \phi$; $\qquad$ (c) $\rho^2 \cos 2 \phi = a^2$.

11. Find the equation in spherical coördinates of each of the following surfaces:

    (a) a sphere with center at the origin and radius a;
    (b) a right circular cylinder of radius a, with axis along the Z-axis;
    (c) a plane passing through the Z-axis and bisecting the first octant.

12. Proceed as in Exercise 11 with:

    (a) a right circular cylinder of radius a, with axis parallel to the Z-axis, and passing through the point whose rectangular coördinates are $(a, 0, 0)$;

   (b) a plane parallel to the XY-plane and 5 units above it;

   (c) a right circular cone with vertex at the origin, axis along the Z-axis and having the semi-vertical angle $30°$.

13. Discuss the surface represented by each of the following equations in spherical coördinates:

   (a) $\rho = a \cos \phi$;   (b) $\rho = 4 \cot \phi \csc \phi$.

14. Proceed as in Exercise 13 with:

   (a) $\rho \sin \phi = a$;   (b) $\cos 2\theta = 0$.

15. Find the direction cosines of the line from the origin to the point whose spherical coördinates are (ρ, θ, ϕ).

16. Discuss the surface represented by $\rho^2(\sin^2 \phi + \cos^2 \theta) = a^2$ in spherical coördinates.

CHAPTER XXVI

Partial Derivatives

494. Functions of Several Variables

In this chapter, we shall consider derivatives of functions of two or more independent variables.

The concept of a *function of several variables* should be recalled from § 60. A function of two variables x and y may be defined as an *explicit function* $f(x, y)$ or by an *implicit function* relation $F(x, y, z) = 0$.

It should be recalled from the previous chapter that an equation $z = f(x, y)$ or an equation $F(x, y, z) = 0$ can in general be represented graphically by a *surface* in space.

This surface is the graphic representation of the *function z* of two variables defined by either of the given equations.

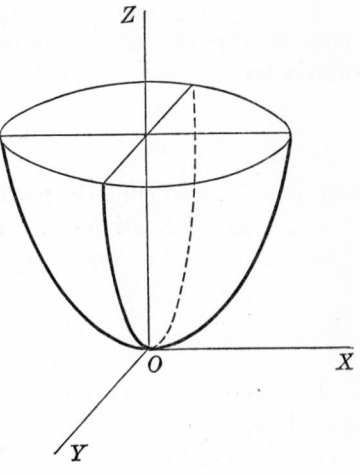

EXAMPLE. The function $z = x^2 + y^2$ is represented by the circular paraboloid shown in Fig. 206.

A *limit* of a function of several variables is defined in a manner quite analogous to that (in § 67) for a function of a single variable:

FIG. 206

*A function $f(x, y)$ is said to approach a **limit** l as x and y approach a and b respectively, if the difference $|f(x, y) - l|$ is less than an arbitrary positive number for all pairs of values of x and y for which both $|x - a|$ and $|y - b|$ are sufficiently small but for which at least one of the differences $x - a$, $y - b$ is different from zero.* Then we write:

$$l = \lim_{x \to a, \, y \to b} f(x, y).$$

A limit of a function of three or more variables is defined similarly.

*A function $f(x, y)$ is said to be **continuous for $x = a, y = b$**, or at the point (a, b), if $f(a, b)$ exists, if $\lim\limits_{x \to a,\ y \to b} f(x, y)$ exists, and if*

$$(a) \qquad \lim_{x \to a,\ y \to b} f(x, y) = f(a, b).$$

*A function is **continuous in a region** if it is continuous at all points of the region.*

Continuity of a function of three or more variables is defined similarly.

495. Partial Derivatives

Corresponding to the fundamental concept of *the derivative* of a function of one variable, we have the following concept of *partial derivatives* of a function of several variables:

*If $u = f(x, y)$, and if y is kept fixed, then u becomes a function of x only; the derivative of this function with respect to x is called the **partial derivative** of u with respect to x, and is denoted by one of the symbols:*

$$(a) \qquad \frac{\partial u}{\partial x} \quad or \quad \frac{\partial f}{\partial x} \quad or \quad u_x \quad or \quad f_x(x, y) \quad or \quad u_x(x, y).$$

Similarly, we define the **partial derivative** of u with respect to y, as the ordinary derivative of u with respect to y when x is held fixed, and it is denoted by one of the symbols:

$$(b) \qquad \frac{\partial u}{\partial y} \quad or \quad \frac{\partial f}{\partial y} \quad or \quad u_y \quad or \quad f_y(x, y) \quad or \quad u_y(x, y).$$

In order to find partial derivatives of given functions of several variables, the only processes needed are those already considered for derivatives of functions of one variable.

EXAMPLE 1.   The partial derivatives of $u = x^2 + xy + 3\,y^2$ are:

$$\frac{\partial u}{\partial x} = 2\,x + y, \quad \frac{\partial u}{\partial y} = x + 6\,y.$$

To denote the value at a particular point $P_1(x_1, y_1)$ of a partial derivative of a function $f(x, y)$, we may use the notation:

$$(c) \qquad \left.\frac{\partial f}{\partial x}\right|_{P_1} \quad and \quad \left.\frac{\partial f}{\partial y}\right|_{P_1}, \quad or \quad f_x(x_1, y_1) \quad and \quad f_y(x_1, y_1).$$

Using the definition of an ordinary derivative in § 77, we may write the defining equations for partial derivatives as follows:

$$(d) \qquad f_x(x_1, y_1) = \lim_{\Delta x \to 0} \frac{f(x_1 + \Delta x, y_1) - f(x_1, y_1)}{\Delta x},$$

$$(e) \qquad f_y(x_1, y_1) = \lim_{\Delta y \to 0} \frac{f(x_1, y_1 + \Delta y) - f(x_1, y_1)}{\Delta y}.$$

The preceding definition of a partial derivative of a function of two variables may be extended at once to functions of three or more variables, by holding constant all the independent variables except one and then taking the ordinary derivative of this resulting function of one variable. Thus, if $u = F(x, y, z)$, we may form three partial derivatives: $\dfrac{\partial F}{\partial x}, \dfrac{\partial F}{\partial y}, \dfrac{\partial F}{\partial z}$, or F_x, F_y, F_z.

496. Geometric Interpretation of Partial Derivatives

Let the function $z = f(x, y)$ be represented by the surface ABC of Fig. 207. Let $P_1(x_1, y_1, z_1)$ be any point on this surface; through P_1 let the plane $y = y_1$ be drawn parallel to the XZ-plane, cutting the

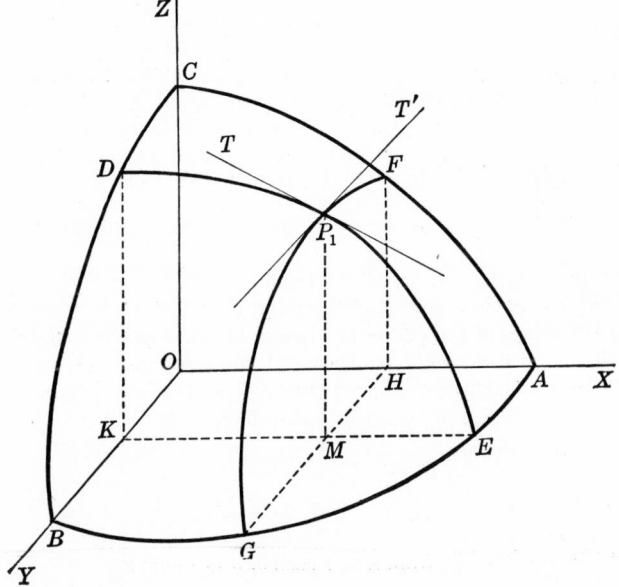

Fig. 207

surface in the curve DE. Since y is constant at each point of this curve DE, equations of this curve are $z = f(x, y)$, $y = y_1$. The slope of this curve at P_1 is given by the derivative of z with respect to x, with y constant ($= y_1$) which is the partial derivative $f_x(x_1, y_1)$. Similarly, if the surface is cut by the plane $x = x_1$ through P_1 parallel to the YZ-plane, the slope of the curve of intersection FG at P_1 is equal to $f_y(x_1, y_1)$. Hence:

The partial derivatives $\dfrac{\partial z}{\partial x}$ and $\dfrac{\partial z}{\partial y}$, where $z = f(x, y)$, are interpreted geometrically as the slopes of the curves of intersection of the surface $z = f(x, y)$ by the planes $y = $ constant and $x = $ constant, respectively.

497. Exercises

In Exercises 1–20, find the partial derivatives of each of the given functions with respect to each of the independent variables:

1. $u = x^2y + xy^2$.
2. $u = x^2y^2 + xy^3$.
3. $u = (x^2 + y^2)^2$.
4. $u = \sqrt{x^2 - y^2}$.
5. $\phi(x, y) = e^x \sin y$.
6. $u = \sin x \cos y$.
7. $u = \ln \sqrt{x^2 + y^2}$.
8. $u = e^{x^2y}$.
9. $f(x, y) = \dfrac{x}{y} + \dfrac{y}{x}$.
10. $f(x, y) = (x^2 - y^2)^{\frac{3}{2}}$.
11. $F(x, y) = \dfrac{1}{\sqrt{x^2 + y^2}}$.
12. $\phi(x, y) = $ Arc tan (xy).
13. $u = $ Arc tan (y/x).
14. $u = e^x \cosh y$.
15. $u = xy + yz + zx$.
16. $u = x^2 - y^2 + z^2 + yz$.
17. $u = xy \sin z - yz \sin x$.
18. $u = xe^y + ye^z - ze^x$.
19. $u = \dfrac{x + y}{z}$.
20. $f(x,y,z) = \dfrac{1}{\sqrt{x^2 + y^2 + z^2}}$.

21. If $f(x, y) = \sqrt{x^2 - y^2}$, find $f_x(2, 1)$ and $f_y(2, -1)$.
22. If $F(x, y) = e^x \sin y$, find $F_x(0, \frac{1}{6}\pi)$ and $F_y(0, \frac{1}{6}\pi)$.
23. Find the slopes of the curves at $(1, -2, 1)$ cut from the surface $z = 4x^2 - y^2 + 1$ by the planes $x = 1$ and $y = -2$.
24. Interpret geometrically $f_x(1, -\frac{1}{3})$ and $f_y(1, -\frac{1}{3})$ if
$$z = f(x, y) = 4x^2 + 9y^2 - 12.$$
25. Find $\dfrac{\partial x}{\partial r}$, $\dfrac{\partial x}{\partial \theta}$, $\dfrac{\partial y}{\partial r}$, $\dfrac{\partial y}{\partial \theta}$ from:

    (a) $x = r \cos \theta$, $y = r \sin \theta$;   (b) $x = r \sec \theta$, $y = r \tan \theta$

26. Find $\dfrac{\partial x}{\partial r}$, $\dfrac{\partial x}{\partial \theta}$, $\dfrac{\partial y}{\partial r}$, $\dfrac{\partial y}{\partial \theta}$ from $x = r \cosh \theta$, $y = r \sinh \theta$.

498. Partial Derivatives of Higher Order

If $u = f(x, y)$, then the partial derivatives

$$\frac{\partial u}{\partial x} \quad \text{or} \quad f_x(x, y) \qquad \text{and} \qquad \frac{\partial u}{\partial y} \quad \text{or} \quad f_y(x, y)$$

are themselves functions of x and y, and their partial derivatives can be found in turn. They are denoted by the following notation:

$$\frac{\partial}{\partial x}\left(\frac{\partial u}{\partial x}\right) = \frac{\partial^2 u}{\partial x^2} = f_{xx}(x, y),$$

$$\frac{\partial}{\partial y}\left(\frac{\partial u}{\partial x}\right) = \frac{\partial^2 u}{\partial y \partial x} = f_{yx}(x, y),$$

$$\frac{\partial}{\partial x}\left(\frac{\partial u}{\partial y}\right) = \frac{\partial^2 u}{\partial x \partial y} = f_{xy}(x, y),$$

$$\frac{\partial}{\partial y}\left(\frac{\partial u}{\partial y}\right) = \frac{\partial^2 u}{\partial y^2} = f_{yy}(x, y).$$

These are called the **second partial derivatives** of u.

Similarly we may obtain *third and higher partial derivatives*, thus:

$$\frac{\partial}{\partial x}\left(\frac{\partial^2 u}{\partial x^2}\right) = \frac{\partial^3 u}{\partial x^3}, \qquad \frac{\partial}{\partial x}\left(\frac{\partial^2 u}{\partial x \partial y}\right) = \frac{\partial^3 u}{\partial x^2 \partial y}, \text{ etc.}$$

Similar notation is used for higher partial derivatives of functions of three or more variables.

EXAMPLE. If $u = x^2 y^3$, then

$$\frac{\partial u}{\partial x} = 2\,xy^3, \qquad \frac{\partial u}{\partial y} = 3\,x^2 y^2, \frac{\partial^2 u}{\partial x^2} = 2\,y^3, \qquad \frac{\partial^2 u}{\partial y^2} = 6\,x^2 y,$$

$$\frac{\partial^2 u}{\partial y \partial x} = 6\,xy^2, \quad \frac{\partial^2 u}{\partial x \partial y} = 6\,xy^2, \frac{\partial^3 u}{\partial x^3} = 0, \qquad \frac{\partial^3 u}{\partial x^2 \partial y} = 6\,y^2, \text{ etc.}$$

It is proved in more advanced works* that:

If $u = f(x, y)$, and if $\dfrac{\partial u}{\partial x}$, $\dfrac{\partial u}{\partial y}$ and $\dfrac{\partial^2 u}{\partial x \partial y}$ are continuous, then

$$(1) \qquad\qquad \frac{\partial^2 u}{\partial x \partial y} = \frac{\partial^2 u}{\partial y \partial x};$$

i.e., the order of differentiation is immaterial.

* See, for example, Fine, *Calculus*, page 245, or Franklin, *Treatise on Advanced Calculus*, pages 334–335, or Sokolnikoff, *Advanced Calculus*, pages 87–89.

499. Exercises

In Exercises 1–12, find all the second partial derivatives of the given functions:

    1. $u = x^2y + xy^2$.   2. $u = x^3y^2 + x^5$.

    3. $u = x \sin y$.   4. $u = \sin (xy)$.

    5. $u = ce^{xy}$.   6. $f(x, y) = x^2 \cos y + y^2 \sin x$.

    7. $u = \text{Arc} \sin (y/x)$.   8. $u = (x^2 + y^2) \text{Arc} \tan (y/x)$.

    9. $u = xy + yz + zx$.   10. $F(x, y, z) = e^{xyz}$.

   11. $F(x, y, z) = e^x \sin y + e^y \sin z$.   12. $u = z \text{ Arc} \tan (y/x)$.

13. Verify $u_{xy} = u_{yx}$ for each of the following functions:

    (a) $u = x^2 - y^2$;   (b) $u = xy^2z$;

    (c) $u = e^x \sin y$;   (d) $u = x \sin y + y \sin x$.

In Exercises 14–16, show that:

14. If $u = \cos (x + y) + \cos (x - y)$, then $\dfrac{\partial^2 u}{\partial x^2} - \dfrac{\partial^2 u}{\partial y^2} = 0$.

15. If $u = z \text{ Arc} \tan (x/y)$, then $\dfrac{\partial^2 u}{\partial x^2} + \dfrac{\partial^2 u}{\partial y^2} + \dfrac{\partial^2 u}{\partial z^2} = 0$.

16. Show that $u = e^{-a^2 t} \sin \alpha x$ satisfies the equation $\dfrac{\partial u}{\partial t} = \dfrac{\partial^2 u}{\partial x^2}$ for all values of α.

500. Fundamental Increment Formula

We shall now derive a fundamental formula for the *total change* of a function of several variables when *all* of the variables on which it depends change. This formula forms the basis for the derivation of numerous important formulas in connection with partial derivatives.

Let $u = f(x, y)$ be a continuous function of two variables. Let us start with initial values $x = x_1$, $y = y_1$, and let x and y take increments Δx and Δy. Then the corresponding increment Δu of the function is

$$\Delta u = f(x_1 + \Delta x, y_1 + \Delta y) - f(x_1, y_1).$$

This may be written:

(a) $\Delta u = [f(x_1 + \Delta x, y_1 + \Delta y) - f(x_1, y_1 + \Delta y)]$
$$+ [f(x_1, y_1 + \Delta y) - f(x_1, y_1)],$$

where we have subtracted and then added the same term $f(x_1, y_1 + \Delta y)$. In the first bracketed expression in (a), y retains the same value, $y_1 + \Delta y$, and x has changed by the increment Δx; in the second bracketed expression, x retains the same value, x_1, and y has changed by the increment Δy. Let us now suppose that the partial derivatives of u are continuous, and let us denote them for convenience by

$f_x(x, y)$ and $f_y(x, y)$.   We may then apply the mean-value theorem for derivatives to the expressions in both brackets in (a).   We obtain:

(b) $f(x_1 + \Delta x, y_1 + \Delta y) - f(x_1, y_1 + \Delta y) = f_x(\xi, y_1 + \Delta y) \cdot \Delta x,$

(c) $f(x_1, y_1 + \Delta y) - f(x_1, y_1) = f_y(x_1, \eta) \cdot \Delta y,$

where ξ is a properly chosen number between x_1 and $x_1 + \Delta x$, and η is between y_1 and $y_1 + \Delta y$.   Substituting (b) and (c) in (a), we get

(d) $\Delta u = f_x(\xi, y_1 + \Delta y) \cdot \Delta x + f_y(x_1, \eta) \cdot \Delta y.$

Since $f_x(x, y)$ and $f_y(x, y)$ are continuous functions of x and y, $f_x(\xi, y_1 + \Delta y) \to f_x(x_1, y_1)$ and $f_y(x_1, \eta) \to f_y(x_1, y_1)$ as $\Delta x \to 0$ and $\Delta y \to 0$; hence

(e) $\begin{cases} f_x(\xi, y_1 + \Delta y) = f_x(x_1, y_1) + \epsilon_1, \\ \quad f_y(x_1, \eta) = f_y(x_1, y_1) + \epsilon_2, \end{cases}$

where $\epsilon_1 \to 0$ and $\epsilon_2 \to 0$ as $\Delta x \to 0$ and $\Delta y \to 0$.   Therefore, by (d):

If $u = f(x, y)$ and its partial derivatives $\dfrac{\partial u}{\partial x}$ and $\dfrac{\partial u}{\partial y}$ are continuous, and if x and y are given increments Δx and Δy starting at $x = x_1$, $y = y_1$, then the corresponding total increment Δu of the function is given by:

(2) $$\Delta u = \frac{\partial u}{\partial x} \Delta x + \frac{\partial u}{\partial y} \Delta y + \epsilon_1 \Delta x + \epsilon_2 \Delta y,$$

where the partial derivatives $\dfrac{\partial u}{\partial x}$ and $\dfrac{\partial u}{\partial y}$ are formed at the point (x_1, y_1), and where $\epsilon_1 \to 0$ and $\epsilon_2 \to 0$ when $\Delta x \to 0$ and $\Delta y \to 0$.

This formula is analogous to the corresponding formula

$$\Delta y = D_x y \cdot \Delta x + \epsilon \cdot \Delta x$$

for a function of one independent variable.

EXAMPLE.   If $u = x^2 + xy + y^2$, then

$\Delta u = [(x + \Delta x)^2 + (x + \Delta x)(y + \Delta y) + (y + \Delta y)^2] - (x^2 + xy + y^2)$

$\quad = (2x + y) \Delta x + (x + 2y) \Delta y + (\Delta x + \Delta y) \Delta x + (\Delta y) \Delta y.$

Since $\dfrac{\partial u}{\partial x} = 2x + y$ and $\dfrac{\partial u}{\partial y} = x + 2y$, by comparison with formula (2), we see that $\epsilon_1 = \Delta x + \Delta y$ and $\epsilon_2 = \Delta y$.

There is a formula similar to (2) for a function $u = F(x, y, z)$ of three variables:

$$(3) \qquad \Delta u = \frac{\partial u}{\partial x} \Delta x + \frac{\partial u}{\partial y} \Delta y + \frac{\partial u}{\partial z} \Delta z + \epsilon_1 \Delta x + \epsilon_2 \Delta y + \epsilon_3 \Delta z,$$

where ϵ_1, ϵ_2, $\epsilon_3 \to 0$ when Δx, Δy, $\Delta z \to 0$. A similar formula holds for a function of more variables.

It will be assumed in this chapter that all functions and derivatives used are continuous.

501. Total Differential

Consider the total increment formula:

$$(a) \qquad \Delta u = \frac{\partial u}{\partial x} \Delta x + \frac{\partial u}{\partial y} \Delta y + \epsilon_1 \Delta x + \epsilon_2 \Delta y,$$

where ϵ_1, $\epsilon_2 \to 0$ when Δx, $\Delta y \to 0$. If Δx and Δy are sufficiently small, ϵ_1 and ϵ_2 are small, and each of the last two terms consists of a product of small numbers which is considerably smaller than either of the factors. Each of the first two terms consists of a product of a constant by a small number. Hence, when Δx and Δy are sufficiently small, the first two terms predominate over the last two.

EXAMPLE 1. If $u = x^2 + xy$, and if $x = 2, y = 3$, and if we take $\Delta x = 0.01$, $\Delta y = 0.02$, then we find $u = 10$, $u + \Delta u = (2.01)^2 + (2.01)(3.02) = 10.1103$, so that $\Delta u = 0.1103$. We also find $\dfrac{\partial u}{\partial x} = 2x + y = 7$, $\dfrac{\partial u}{\partial y} = x = 2$, so that $\dfrac{\partial u}{\partial x} \Delta x + \dfrac{\partial u}{\partial y} \Delta y = 0.11$. Hence, $\epsilon_1 \Delta x + \epsilon_2 \Delta y = 0.0003$.

Because of the importance of the first two terms of formula (a), we give them a special name and notation, as follows:

*If $u = f(x, y)$, the sum of the first two terms of the total increment formula is called the **total differential** of the function u, and is denoted by **du**:*

$$(4) \qquad\qquad du = \frac{\partial u}{\partial x} \Delta x + \frac{\partial u}{\partial y} \Delta y.$$

For convenience, the differentials of the independent variables x and y are defined by:

$$(5) \qquad\qquad dx = \Delta x, \qquad dy = \Delta y.$$

Then

$$(6) \qquad\qquad du = \frac{\partial u}{\partial x} dx + \frac{\partial u}{\partial y} dy.$$

This definition of total differential should be compared with that in § 141 for the differential of a function of a single variable:

$$dy = D_x y \cdot \Delta x = D_x y \cdot dx.$$

EXAMPLE 2. If $u = \text{Arc tan}\left(\dfrac{y}{x}\right)$, show that $du = \dfrac{x\,dy - y\,dx}{x^2 + y^2}$.

Solution: $\dfrac{\partial u}{\partial x} = -\dfrac{y}{x^2 + y^2}$, $\dfrac{\partial u}{\partial y} = \dfrac{x}{x^2 + y^2}$,

$$\therefore\ du = -\frac{y}{x^2 + y^2}\,dx + \frac{x}{x^2 + y^2}\,dy = \frac{-y\,dx + x\,dy}{x^2 + y^2}.$$

For a function $u = F(x, y, z)$, the **total differential** is defined, in a similar way, by:

$$(7) \qquad\qquad du = \frac{\partial u}{\partial x}\,dx + \frac{\partial u}{\partial y}\,dy + \frac{\partial u}{\partial z}\,dz,$$

where $dx = \Delta x$, $dy = \Delta y$, $dz = \Delta z$ are arbitrary increments of the independent variables. For a function of more variables, a similar definition applies.

The following theorem will be needed later:

If P and Q are functions of x and y, and if a function $u = f(x, y)$ exists such that

$$(b) \qquad\qquad du = P\,dx + Q\,dy,$$

then $P = \dfrac{\partial u}{\partial x}$ and $Q = \dfrac{\partial u}{\partial y}$. A similar result holds for three or more variables.

Proof: By definition, $du = \dfrac{\partial u}{\partial x}\,dx + \dfrac{\partial u}{\partial y}\,dy$. Then

$$(c) \qquad\qquad P\,dx + Q\,dy = \frac{\partial u}{\partial x}\,dx + \frac{\partial u}{\partial y}\,dy.$$

Since dx and dy are arbitrary, their coefficients on both sides of the equation (c) are respectively equal, and $P = \dfrac{\partial u}{\partial x}$, $Q = \dfrac{\partial u}{\partial y}$.

502. Approximation of Total Increments; Small Errors

It follows at once from the discussion in § 501 and the definition of total differential that:

The total differential du of a function of several variables is an approximation to the total increment Δu of the function:

(8) $\Delta u \approx du,$

provided the increments of the independent variables are taken sufficiently small.

Since it is usually much easier to find the differential than to find the increment, the total differential is often used for finding *approximations* to a total increment.

EXAMPLE 1.   Find the approximate change in volume of a right circular cylinder caused by changing the radius of the base from 4 inches to 4.02 inches and the altitude from 8 inches to 7.99 inches.

Solution: $V = \pi r^2 h$, $dV = \dfrac{\partial V}{\partial r}\, dr + \dfrac{\partial V}{\partial h}\, dh = 2\,\pi r h\, dr + \pi r^2\, dh$; but

$$r = 4,\ h = 8,\ dr = 0.02,\ dh = -0.01. \quad \text{Then}$$
$$dV = 64\,\pi(0.02) + 16\,\pi(-0.01) = 1.12\,\pi.$$

Hence, $\Delta V \approx 1.12\,\pi = 3.52$ cubic inches.

If the values of the independent variables x, y, etc., are determined by measurement, they are subject to *errors*, which may be interpreted as increments dx, dy, etc., and any function u of these variables will have a corresponding error which will be Δu, but which may be approximated by taking the total differential du.

EXAMPLE 2.   If the dimensions of a right circular cone were measured as: radius of base 4 inches and altitude 6 inches, and if it is found later that there was a shortage of 0.01 inch per inch in the measure used, what is the corresponding error in the volume?

Solution: $V = \frac{1}{3}\pi r^2 h$, error in $V = \Delta V \approx dV = \frac{2}{3}\pi r h\, dr + \frac{1}{3}\pi r^2\, dh$. Since the error in r is -0.01 inch per inch, the error dr is -0.04 inch, and similarly, $dh = -0.06$ inch. $dV = \frac{2}{3}\pi(24)(-0.04) + \frac{1}{3}\pi(16)(-0.06) = -0.96\,\pi$. Hence, the error in V is: $\Delta V \approx -0.96\,\pi$, or a shortage of 3.02 cubic inches.

The **relative error** in a measurement is the error per unit. *The relative error in an independent variable x is then dx/x, and the relative error in a function u is approximately du/u.*

EXAMPLE 3.   If errors up to 2% and 1% may be made in measuring the radius of base and altitude, respectively, of a right circular cylinder, show that the maximum error in the calculated volume will be 5%, approximately.

Solution: $V = \pi r^2 h$, $dV = 2\,\pi r h\, dr + \pi r^2\, dh$,

(a) $\therefore \dfrac{dV}{V} = \dfrac{2\,\pi r h\, dr}{\pi r^2 h} + \dfrac{\pi r^2\, dh}{\pi r^2 h} = 2 \cdot \dfrac{dr}{r} + \dfrac{dh}{h}.$

The possible relative errors in r and h are: $\dfrac{dr}{r} = 0.02$ and $\dfrac{dh}{h} = 0.01$ in numerical value. We find from (a) that the *maximum possible* relative error in V is approximately:

$$\frac{dV}{V} = 2(0.02) + (0.01) = 0.05.$$

503. Exercises

In Exercises 1–12, find the total differential of each of the given functions:

1. $u = x^2 y + x y^2$.
2. $u = e^{-x} \cos y$.
3. $u = x^2 + 2\, y^2$.
4. $u = x \sin y + y \sin x$.
5. $u = x\sqrt{1 - y^2}$.
6. $u = \text{Arc} \sin (x/y)$.
7. $u = xy + yz + zx$.
8. $u = xyz$.
9. $u = x^2 - y^2 + z^2$.
10. $u = \dfrac{x + y}{z}$.
11. $u = ze^{xy}$.
12. $u = \ln (xyz)$.

13. Find a formula for the maximum error in the area of a circular sector due to errors in measuring the radius and the central angle.
14. Find approximately the amount of metal in an open can 4 inches in diameter and 5 inches high, if the metal is 0.01 inch thick.
15. The sides of a rectangle were found to be 8 feet and 10 feet, with a possible error of 1 inch in each measurement. Find approximately the maximum possible error in the calculated area. Also find the relative error in the area in terms of the relative errors in the two sides.
16. A tank consists of a hemisphere surmounted by a cylinder of equal radius. The altitude and radius of base of the cylinder are measured as 14 feet and 6 feet respectively, but it is found later that the measuring scale is in error by 0.2 inch per foot. What is the maximum possible error in the calculated volume of the tank?
17. Two sides of a triangular piece of land are measured as 100 feet and 125 feet and the included angle as 60°. If possible errors of 0.2 foot occur in measuring the sides and 1° in measuring the angle, what is the maximum possible error in the calculated area of the triangle?
18. Express the maximum relative error in the volume of a right circular cone in terms of relative errors in the radius of base and altitude.

504. Total Derivative

Let $u = f(x, y)$ be a given continuous function of two variables with continuous partial derivatives $\dfrac{\partial u}{\partial x}$ and $\dfrac{\partial u}{\partial y}$, and suppose that x and y are not independent variables but are differentiable functions of an independent variable t. If we give t an increment Δt, then x and y receive corresponding increments Δx and Δy, and thereby u receives an increment Δu (a total increment). We may then form the ratio $\Delta u/\Delta t$ and take its limit when $\Delta t \to 0$.

The limit $\lim\limits_{\Delta t \to 0} (\Delta u/\Delta t)$ *is called the* **total derivative** *of u, and is denoted by* $\dfrac{du}{dt}$.

We need a formula for finding the total derivative in terms of the partial derivatives; this may be derived as follows: Let t take an increment Δt and let Δx, Δy and Δu be the corresponding increments of x, y, and u. By the fundamental increment formula of § 500:

$$\Delta u = \frac{\partial u}{\partial x}\,\Delta x + \frac{\partial u}{\partial y}\,\Delta y + \epsilon_1\,\Delta x + \epsilon_2\,\Delta y.$$

Dividing both sides of this equation by Δt, we have

$$(a) \qquad \frac{\Delta u}{\Delta t} = \frac{\partial u}{\partial x}\frac{\Delta x}{\Delta t} + \frac{\partial u}{\partial y}\frac{\Delta y}{\Delta t} + \epsilon_1\frac{\Delta x}{\Delta t} + \epsilon_2\frac{\Delta y}{\Delta t}.$$

Since x and y are functions of one independent variable t, the limits of $\dfrac{\Delta x}{\Delta t}$ and of $\dfrac{\Delta y}{\Delta t}$ when $\Delta t \to 0$ are the ordinary derivatives $\dfrac{dx}{dt}$ and $\dfrac{dy}{dt}$, and the limit of $\dfrac{\Delta u}{\Delta t}$ is the total derivative $\dfrac{du}{dt}$. We have also $\Delta x \to 0$ and $\Delta y \to 0$ when $\Delta t \to 0$, so that $\epsilon_1 \to 0$ and $\epsilon_2 \to 0$. Taking limits in (a) as $\Delta t \to 0$, we obtain

$$\frac{du}{dt} = \frac{\partial u}{\partial x}\frac{dx}{dt} + \frac{\partial u}{\partial y}\frac{dy}{dt}.$$

Hence:

I. *If* $u = f(x, y)$ *and if* $x = g(t)$, $y = h(t)$, *the total derivative of u with respect to t is given by:*

$$(9) \qquad \frac{du}{dt} = \frac{\partial u}{\partial x}\frac{dx}{dt} + \frac{\partial u}{\partial y}\frac{dy}{dt}.$$

A similar formula holds for a function of more variables.

EXAMPLE 1. If $u = x^2 - xy + y^2$, and if $x = 1 + t^2$, $y = 1 - t^2$, the total derivative of u is

$$\frac{du}{dt} = (2\,x - y)(2\,t) + (2\,y - x)(-2\,t) = 6\,t(x - y).$$

If in the total derivative formula (9) we interpret the variable t as the time, we have a means of finding time-rates of change of related variables.

EXAMPLE 2. If the altitude of a cylinder is increasing at the rate of 0.1 inch per minute and the radius of the base is decreasing at the rate of 0.2 inch per minute, how fast is the volume of the cylinder changing when the altitude is 12 inches and the radius of the base is 8 inches?

Solution: $V = \pi r^2 h, \dfrac{dV}{dt} = 2\pi rh \dfrac{dr}{dt} + \pi r^2 \dfrac{dh}{dt};$

but $\qquad\qquad r = 8, h = 12, \dfrac{dr}{dt} = -0.2, \dfrac{dh}{dt} = 0.1.$

$$\therefore \frac{dV}{dt} = 2\pi(8)(12)(-0.2) + \pi(64)(0.1) = -32\pi.$$

Therefore, the volume is decreasing at the rate of 32π cubic inches per minute.

It sometimes happens that, when $u = f(x, y)$, the variables x and y are not independent but are related to each other by some functional relation $y = \phi(x)$. We may then find the total derivative $\dfrac{du}{dx}$ by taking $t = x$ in formula (9). Then we have:

II. *If $u = f(x, y)$ and $y = \phi(x)$, then*

(10) $$\frac{du}{dx} = \frac{\partial u}{\partial x} + \frac{\partial u}{\partial y}\frac{dy}{dx}.$$

The student should notice the difference between $\dfrac{du}{dx}$ and $\dfrac{\partial u}{\partial x}$ in this formula. The partial derivative $\dfrac{\partial u}{\partial x}$ is the derivative of $f(x, y)$ with respect to its first variable x when the second variable y is held constant; the total derivative $\dfrac{du}{dx}$ is the derivative of $f(x, \phi(x))$ with respect to its single variable x.

Similarly, if $u = F(x, y, z)$ and $y = g(x), z = h(x)$, then

(11) $$\frac{du}{dx} = \frac{\partial u}{\partial x} + \frac{\partial u}{\partial y}\frac{dy}{dx} + \frac{\partial u}{\partial z}\frac{dz}{dx}.$$

EXAMPLE 3. If $u = xy + yz + zx$, and $y = e^x$ and $z = \sin x$, then

$$\frac{\partial u}{\partial x} = y + z, \frac{\partial u}{\partial y} = x + z, \frac{\partial u}{\partial z} = y + x, \frac{dy}{dx} = e^x, \frac{dz}{dx} = \cos x,$$

$$\therefore \frac{du}{dx} = y + z + (x + z)e^x + (x + y)\cos x.$$

505. Exercises

In Exercises 1–10, find the total derivative $\dfrac{du}{dt}$ of each of the given functions.

    1. $u = 2\,x^2 + 3\,xy + 4\,y^2$, if $x = \tan t,\ y = \sin^2 t$.
    2. $u = (1 + x)(1 - y)$, if $x = t^2,\ y = t^3$.
    3. $u = \ln (x^2 - y^2)$, if $x = a \cos t,\ y = a \sin t$.
    4. $u = \operatorname{Arc\,tan} (x/y)$, if $x = 2\,t,\ y = 1 - t^2$.
    5. $u = \sin (xy) - x \sin y$, if $x = e^t,\ y = te^t$.
    6. $u = e^{xy}$, if $x = \sin t,\ y = \cos t$.

    7. $u = \dfrac{x}{y} + \dfrac{y}{z}$, if $x = 2\,t,\ y = \dfrac{1}{t},\ z = t^2$.

    8. $u = \ln (x^2 + y^2 + z^2)$, if $x = t,\ y = t^2,\ z = t^3$.
    9. $u = x^2y + y^2z + z^2x$, if $x = e^t,\ y = te^t,\ z = t^2 e^t$.

    10. $u = \dfrac{x}{y} + \dfrac{y}{z} + \dfrac{z}{x}$, if $x = \dfrac{1}{t},\ y = \dfrac{1}{t^2},\ z = \dfrac{1}{t^3}$.

In Exercises 11–18, find the total derivative $\dfrac{du}{dx}$ for each of the given functions:

    11. $u = x^2 + xy$, if $y = 2\,x$.   12. $u = x^2 + y^3$, if $y = \ln x$.

    13. $u = x^2 - y^2$, if $y = \tan x$.   14. $u = \operatorname{Arc\,tan} \dfrac{y}{x}$, if $y = e^x$.

    15. $u = \ln (x^2 + y^2)$, if $y = \dfrac{1}{x}$.   16. $u = \sin (xy)$, if $y = x^2 - 1$.

    17. $u = xy + yz + zx$, if $y = e^x,\ z = e^{-x}$.

    18. $u = \sqrt{x^2 + y^2 + z^2}$, if $y = \dfrac{1}{x},\ z = x^2$.

506. Change of Variables in Partial Derivatives

Let $u = f(x, y)$ be a continuous function of two variables x and y, with continuous partial derivatives, and let us make a change of variable from the first set x, y to a new set of independent variables r, s, when x and y are given as functions of r and s. Then u may be regarded as a function of the new variables r and s. It is frequently necessary to express the derivatives of u with respect to r and s in terms of the derivatives of u with respect to x and y.

Let us derive formulas for this transformation. Let s be held fixed and let r be given an increment Δr. This produces increments Δx and Δy and consequently an increment Δu. By the fundamental increment formula of § 500, we have

$$(a) \qquad \Delta u = \frac{\partial u}{\partial x}\,\Delta x + \frac{\partial u}{\partial y}\,\Delta y + \epsilon_1\,\Delta x + \epsilon_2\,\Delta y,$$

where ϵ_1, $\epsilon_2 \to 0$ when Δx, $\Delta y \to 0$. Dividing by Δr in (a), we get

(b)
$$\frac{\Delta u}{\Delta r} = \frac{\partial u}{\partial x}\frac{\Delta x}{\Delta r} + \frac{\partial u}{\partial y}\frac{\Delta y}{\Delta r} + \epsilon_1\frac{\Delta x}{\Delta r} + \epsilon_2\frac{\Delta y}{\Delta r}.$$

Now
$$\Delta x \to 0,\ \Delta y \to 0,\ \epsilon_1 \to 0,\ \epsilon_2 \to 0,$$

$$\frac{\Delta x}{\Delta r} \to \frac{\partial x}{\partial r},\ \frac{\Delta y}{\Delta r} \to \frac{\partial y}{\partial r},\ \frac{\Delta u}{\Delta r} \to \frac{\partial u}{\partial r}$$

when $\Delta r \to 0$. Therefore, by (b),

(c)
$$\frac{\partial u}{\partial r} = \frac{\partial u}{\partial x}\frac{\partial x}{\partial r} + \frac{\partial u}{\partial y}\frac{\partial y}{\partial r}.$$

We get a similar formula for $\dfrac{\partial u}{\partial s}$ by keeping r fixed and letting s take an increment Δs. Hence:

I. *If $u = f(x, y)$ is continuous and has continuous partial derivatives, and if x and y are continuous functions of r and s, with continuous partial derivatives, then*

(12)
$$\begin{cases} \dfrac{\partial u}{\partial r} = \dfrac{\partial u}{\partial x}\dfrac{\partial x}{\partial r} + \dfrac{\partial u}{\partial y}\dfrac{\partial y}{\partial r}, \\[2mm] \dfrac{\partial u}{\partial s} = \dfrac{\partial u}{\partial x}\dfrac{\partial x}{\partial s} + \dfrac{\partial u}{\partial y}\dfrac{\partial y}{\partial s}. \end{cases}$$

EXAMPLE 1. If $u = x^3 + y^3 - 3\,xy$, and $x = r^2 + s$, $y = r + s^2$, find $\dfrac{\partial u}{\partial r}$ and $\dfrac{\partial u}{\partial s}$.

Solution: $\dfrac{\partial u}{\partial x} = 3\,x^2 - 3\,y,\ \dfrac{\partial u}{\partial y} = 3\,y^2 - 3\,x,$

$$\frac{\partial x}{\partial r} = 2\,r,\ \frac{\partial x}{\partial s} = 1,\ \frac{\partial y}{\partial r} = 1,\ \frac{\partial y}{\partial s} = 2\,s,$$

$$\therefore \frac{\partial u}{\partial r} = (3\,x^2 - 3\,y)\,2\,r + (3\,y^2 - 3\,x) = 6\,x^2r - 6\,yr + 3\,y^2 - 3\,x,$$

$$\frac{\partial u}{\partial s} = (3\,x^2 - 3\,y) + (3\,y^2 - 3\,x)\,2\,s = 3\,x^2 - 3\,y + 6\,y^2s - 6\,xs.$$

We may obviously generalize the preceding theorem to the case of more variables as follows:

II. *If $u = f(x, y, z, \cdots)$ is a continuous function of n variables $x, y, z, \cdots$, with continuous partial derivatives, and if $x, y, z, \cdots$ are* *continuous functions of m independent variables r, s, t, $\cdots$, with continuous partial derivatives, then*

$$(13) \quad \begin{cases} \dfrac{\partial u}{\partial r} = \dfrac{\partial u}{\partial x}\dfrac{\partial x}{\partial r} + \dfrac{\partial u}{\partial y}\dfrac{\partial y}{\partial r} + \dfrac{\partial u}{\partial z}\dfrac{\partial z}{\partial r} + \cdots, \\[2ex] \dfrac{\partial u}{\partial s} = \dfrac{\partial u}{\partial x}\dfrac{\partial x}{\partial s} + \dfrac{\partial u}{\partial y}\dfrac{\partial y}{\partial s} + \dfrac{\partial u}{\partial z}\dfrac{\partial z}{\partial s} + \cdots, \\[2ex] \dfrac{\partial u}{\partial t} = \dfrac{\partial u}{\partial x}\dfrac{\partial x}{\partial t} + \dfrac{\partial u}{\partial y}\dfrac{\partial y}{\partial t} + \dfrac{\partial u}{\partial z}\dfrac{\partial z}{\partial t} + \cdots, \\[2ex] \cdot \quad \cdot \quad \cdot \quad \cdot \quad \cdot \quad \cdot \quad \cdot \quad \cdot \quad \cdot \quad \cdot \end{cases}$$

In this set of equations there are n terms on the right in each equation and there are m equations.

It is to be understood, in the use of the formulas (12) or (13), that if there is only one variable in either set of variables, in any derivative with respect to that variable the symbol for a partial derivative is to be replaced by the symbol for the ordinary derivative.

In either of the sets of formulas (12) or (13), the roles of $x, y, z, \cdots$ and $r, s, t, \cdots$ can of course be interchanged.

In § 501, we defined the *total differential du* for a function $u = f(x, y)$ by the formula

$$(e) \qquad du = \frac{\partial u}{\partial x}\,dx + \frac{\partial u}{\partial y}\,dy,$$

when x and y are independent variables. The question arises as to whether the formula (e) will still hold when x and y are not independent variables but are functions of new independent variables. Let us investigate this problem.

Suppose that x and y are functions of two independent variables r and s; then, by the definition of § 501,

$$(f) \qquad \begin{cases} dx = \dfrac{\partial x}{\partial r}\,dr + \dfrac{\partial x}{\partial s}\,ds, \\[2ex] dy = \dfrac{\partial y}{\partial r}\,dr + \dfrac{\partial y}{\partial s}\,ds. \end{cases}$$

Since u is now a function of the *independent variables r* and s, we have

$$(g) \qquad du = \frac{\partial u}{\partial r}\,dr + \frac{\partial u}{\partial s}\,ds.$$

But from formulas (12),

$$(h) \quad \begin{cases} \dfrac{\partial u}{\partial r} = \dfrac{\partial u}{\partial x}\dfrac{\partial x}{\partial r} + \dfrac{\partial u}{\partial y}\dfrac{\partial y}{\partial r}, \\[3mm] \dfrac{\partial u}{\partial s} = \dfrac{\partial u}{\partial x}\dfrac{\partial x}{\partial s} + \dfrac{\partial u}{\partial y}\dfrac{\partial y}{\partial s}. \end{cases}$$

Substituting (h) in (g), we have

$$(i) \qquad du = \left(\dfrac{\partial u}{\partial x}\dfrac{\partial x}{\partial r} + \dfrac{\partial u}{\partial y}\dfrac{\partial y}{\partial r}\right) dr + \left(\dfrac{\partial u}{\partial x}\dfrac{\partial x}{\partial s} + \dfrac{\partial u}{\partial y}\dfrac{\partial y}{\partial s}\right) ds.$$

By rearrangement of terms, this becomes

$$(j) \quad \begin{cases} du = \dfrac{\partial u}{\partial x}\left(\dfrac{\partial x}{\partial r}\, dr + \dfrac{\partial x}{\partial s}\, ds\right) + \dfrac{\partial u}{\partial y}\left(\dfrac{\partial y}{\partial r}\, dr + \dfrac{\partial y}{\partial s}\, ds\right) \\[3mm] \quad = \dfrac{\partial u}{\partial x}\, dx + \dfrac{\partial u}{\partial y}\, dy, \end{cases}$$

by use of equations (f).   Hence, we have the theorem:

III. *If $u = f(x, y)$, then*

$$du = \dfrac{\partial u}{\partial x}\, dx + \dfrac{\partial u}{\partial y}\, dy,$$

whether x and y are independent variables or are functions of other variables.   A similar statement applies to functions of any number of variables.

507. Exercises

In Exercises 1–6, find $\dfrac{\partial u}{\partial r}$ and $\dfrac{\partial u}{\partial s}$ in terms of x, y and r, s:

1. $u = x^2 - xy + y^2$, $x = rs$, $y = r^2 + s^2$.

2. $u = \dfrac{\cos y}{x^2}$, $x = r^2 - s^2$, $y = e^s$.

3. $u = e^{xy}$, $x = \sqrt{r^2 + s^2}$, $y = \text{Arc tan } (s/r)$.

4. $u = xe^y + ye^x$, $x = rs$, $y = \dfrac{r}{s}$.

5. Write out in full the equations (13) of § 506 when: (a) $n = 2$, $m = 3$; (b) $n = 1$, $m = 2$.

6. Write out in full the equations (13) of § 506 when: (a) $n = 3$, $m = 2$; (b) $n = 3$, $m = 1$.

In Exercises 7, 8, find $\dfrac{\partial u}{\partial r}$ and $\dfrac{\partial u}{\partial s}$ in terms of x, y, z and r, s:

7. $u = xy + yz - zx$, $x = r + s$, $y = rs$, $z = s$.

8. $u = \sqrt{x^2 + y^2 + z^2}$, $x = r \cos s$, $y = r \sin s$, $z = \sqrt{r^2 + s^2}$.

9. If $u = f(x, y)$, and if we change variables from rectangular coördinates (x, y) to polar coördinates (r, θ), where $x = r \cos \theta$, $y = r \sin \theta$, show that:

$(a)\ \dfrac{\partial u}{\partial r} = \cos \theta \dfrac{\partial u}{\partial x} + \sin \theta \dfrac{\partial u}{\partial y};$ $(b)\ \dfrac{1}{r} \dfrac{\partial u}{\partial \theta} = -\sin \theta \dfrac{\partial u}{\partial x} + \cos \theta \dfrac{\partial u}{\partial y}.$

10. If $u = f(x, y)$, and if $x = r \cos \theta$, $y = r \sin \theta$, show that:

$(a)\ \dfrac{\partial u}{\partial x} = \cos \theta \dfrac{\partial u}{\partial r} - \dfrac{\sin \theta}{r} \dfrac{\partial u}{\partial \theta};$ $(b)\ \dfrac{\partial u}{\partial y} = \sin \theta \dfrac{\partial u}{\partial r} + \dfrac{\cos \theta}{r} \dfrac{\partial u}{\partial \theta}.$

508. Differentiation of Implicit Functions

If y is given as an implicit function of x by a functional relation $f(x, y) = 0$, it is often either desirable or necessary to be able to find the derivative $\dfrac{dy}{dx}$ without having to solve the equation $f(x, y) = 0$ in order to express y as an explicit function of x. A formula for this purpose may be obtained as follows:

Put, temporarily, $u = f(x, y)$, and suppose that $f(x, y)$ and its first partial derivatives are continuous. Since y is defined as a function of x by the functional relation $f(x, y) = 0$, we may write the total derivative formula

(a) $$\frac{du}{dx} = \frac{\partial f}{\partial x} + \frac{\partial f}{\partial y} \frac{dy}{dx}$$

by (10) of § 504. But $u = 0$ for all corresponding pairs of values of x and y determined by the implicit function definition, and therefore $\dfrac{du}{dx} = 0$. Then

(b) $$\frac{\partial f}{\partial x} + \frac{\partial f}{\partial y} \frac{dy}{dx} = 0,$$

from which we get

(c) $$\frac{dy}{dx} = -\frac{\dfrac{\partial f}{\partial x}}{\dfrac{\partial f}{\partial y}},$$

provided $\dfrac{\partial f}{\partial y} \neq 0$. Hence:

I. *If y is defined as an implicit function of x by the equation $f(x, y) = 0$, where $f(x, y)$ and its first partial derivatives are continuous, then the derivative of y with respect to x is given by:*

(14) $$\frac{dy}{dx} = -\frac{f_x}{f_y}, \qquad if\ f_y \neq 0.$$

EXAMPLE 1. If $x^2y + xy^2 = 1$, find $\frac{dy}{dx}$.

Solution: If we put $f(x, y) = x^2y + xy^2 - 1$, then $\frac{\partial f}{\partial x} = 2\,xy + y^2$, $\frac{\partial f}{\partial y} = x^2 + 2\,xy$; hence by (15),

$$\frac{dy}{dx} = -\frac{2\,xy + y^2}{x^2 + 2\,xy}.$$

Similarly, we may treat implicit functions of more independent variables. Let z be defined as a function of x and y by the equation $F(x, y, z) = 0$. By reasoning similar to that used above, we may show that

(d) $$\frac{\partial F}{\partial x} + \frac{\partial F}{\partial z}\frac{\partial z}{\partial x} = 0, \qquad \frac{\partial F}{\partial y} + \frac{\partial F}{\partial z}\frac{\partial z}{\partial y} = 0.$$

Solving these equations for $\frac{\partial z}{\partial x}$ and $\frac{\partial z}{\partial y}$, we obtain:

II. *If z is defined as a function of x and y by the equation $F(x, y, z) = 0$, then*

(15) $$\frac{\partial z}{\partial x} = -\frac{F_x}{F_z}, \qquad \frac{\partial z}{\partial y} = -\frac{F_y}{F_z} \qquad if\ F_z \neq 0.$$

EXAMPLE 2. If $x^2 + 2\,y^2 + 3\,z^2 = 6$, find $\frac{\partial z}{\partial x}$ and $\frac{\partial z}{\partial y}$.

Solution: Put $F = x^2 + 2\,y^2 + 3\,z^2 - 6$, then

$$\frac{\partial F}{\partial x} = 2\,x, \quad \frac{\partial F}{\partial y} = 4\,y, \quad \frac{\partial F}{\partial z} = 6\,z;$$

hence

$$\frac{\partial z}{\partial x} = -\frac{2\,x}{6\,z} = -\frac{x}{3\,z}, \quad \frac{\partial z}{\partial y} = -\frac{4\,y}{6\,z} = -\frac{2\,y}{3\,z} \quad (\text{if } z \neq 0).$$

509. Exercises

In Exercises 1–10, find $\frac{dy}{dx}$ for each of the given implicit functions:

1. $x^3 + y^3 - 3\,axy = 0$.   2. $x^2 + y^2 = 4\,ax$.
3. $x^4 + x^2y^2 + y^4 = 4$.   4. $x^3y + xy^3 = 6$.
5. $x \sin y + y \sin x = 2$.   6. $(x^2 + y^2)^2 = a^2x^2$.

7. $e^x \sin y - e^y \sin x = 1$.   8. $\sin \dfrac{x}{y} + \sin \dfrac{y}{x} = 1$.

9. $e^x \sin y = 5$.   10. $\ln y + e^x = 6$.

In Exercises 11–18, find $\dfrac{\partial z}{\partial x}$ and $\dfrac{\partial z}{\partial y}$ for each of the given implicit functions:

11. $x^2 + y^2 + z^2 = a^2$.   12. $x^2 + y^2 - 2z^2 = a^2$.
13. $xy - yz + zx = 0$.   14. $x^3 + y^3 + z^3 - 3axyz = 0$.
15. $z^2 + xz - y^2 = 2$.   16. $\sin(x + y) + \sin(y + z) = 1$.
17. $x^2y^2 + y^2z^2 + z^2x^2 = 1$.   18. $xe^{yz} + ye^{zx} + ze^{xy} = 3$.

510. Tangents and Normals to Curves and Surfaces

Let us first consider a tangent line to a space curve; it is defined as follows. Let P_1 be a fixed point on a space curve C and let Q be any neighboring point on C. If we let Q approach P_1 along the curve, and if the secant line P_1Q approaches a limiting position P_1T, then this limiting line P_1T is called the *tangent line* to the curve C at the point P_1.

Suppose that the parametric equations of the curve C are: $x = g(t)$, $y = h(t)$, $z = k(t)$ (§ 488). Let the point $P_1(x_1, y_1, z_1)$ on the curve C be fixed, and let the variable neighboring point Q have coördinates $(x_1 + \Delta x, y_1 + \Delta y, z_1 + \Delta z)$, and let Δt be the corresponding increment of t. By § 467, the direction cosines $\cos \alpha'$, $\cos \beta'$, $\cos \gamma'$ of the secant line P_1Q are proportional to Δx, Δy, Δz, so that

$$(a) \qquad \frac{\cos \alpha'}{\dfrac{\Delta x}{\Delta t}} = \frac{\cos \beta'}{\dfrac{\Delta y}{\Delta t}} = \frac{\cos \gamma'}{\dfrac{\Delta z}{\Delta t}}.$$

Now let Q approach P_1 along the curve C. Then $\Delta x \to 0$, $\Delta y \to 0$, $\Delta z \to 0$ as $\Delta t \to 0$, and the secant line P_1Q approaches the tangent line to C as a limiting position, by definition. Let $\cos \alpha$, $\cos \beta$, $\cos \gamma$ be the direction cosines of the tangent. From (a), in the limit when $\Delta t \to 0$, we have

$$(b) \qquad \frac{\cos \alpha}{\dfrac{dx}{dt}} = \frac{\cos \beta}{\dfrac{dy}{dt}} = \frac{\cos \gamma}{\dfrac{dz}{dt}},$$

where the derivatives are to be formed at P_1. Hence:

I. *The tangent line to a space curve $x = g(t)$, $y = h(t)$, $z = k(t)$ at a point P_1 has the derivatives $\dfrac{dx}{dt}, \dfrac{dy}{dt}, \dfrac{dz}{dt}$ formed at P_1 as a set of direction numbers.*

Now let us consider a surface S whose equation is $F(x, y, z) = 0$, and let us assume that $\dfrac{\partial F}{\partial x}, \dfrac{\partial F}{\partial y}, \dfrac{\partial F}{\partial z}$ are continuous at a given point P_1 and that at least one of these partial derivatives is different from zero at P_1. We define a tangent line to a curve C lying on the surface S as a *tangent to the surface*. Let $P_1(x_1, y_1, z_1)$ be a fixed point on the surface S, let Q be a neighboring point on the surface, and let C be a curve on the surface passing through P_1 and Q. Let the equations of the curve C be: $x = g(t)$, $y = h(t)$, $z = k(t)$. Then for all values of t to be considered, these values of x, y, z satisfy the equation $F(x, y, z) = 0$, since C lies on S. If Q is made to approach P_1 along the curve C, the secant P_1Q approaches as a limiting position a tangent line to the surface S at P_1.

If $u = F(x, y, z)$, its total derivative at P is

$$\frac{du}{dt} = \frac{\partial F}{\partial x}\frac{dx}{dt} + \frac{\partial F}{\partial y}\frac{dy}{dt} + \frac{\partial F}{\partial z}\frac{dz}{dt},$$

where these derivatives are formed at P_1. But since $u = 0$ for all points on the surface, we have $du = 0$, and the preceding equation becomes

$$(c) \qquad \frac{\partial F}{\partial x}\cdot\frac{dx}{dt} + \frac{\partial F}{\partial y}\cdot\frac{dy}{dt} + \frac{\partial F}{\partial z}\cdot\frac{dz}{dt} = 0.$$

By theorem I, $\dfrac{dx}{dt}, \dfrac{dy}{dt}, \dfrac{dz}{dt}$ are direction numbers of a line tangent to C and therefore to S at P_1. By § 470, two lines whose direction numbers are a, b, c and a', b', c' are perpendicular if $aa' + bb' + cc' = 0$. It follows from (c) that the tangent line at P_1 is perpendicular to the line through P_1 whose direction numbers are $\dfrac{\partial F}{\partial x}, \dfrac{\partial F}{\partial y}, \dfrac{\partial F}{\partial z}$. But this line through P_1 has a fixed position independent of the tangent line to the particular curve C which was used. Call this line N. It follows that all the tangent lines to the surface at P_1 are perpendicular to this line N and therefore lie in a plane. Hence:

II. *All the tangent lines to a surface S (satisfying the conditions on the function F mentioned above) at a given point P_1 lie in a plane, which is called the **tangent plane** to the surface at P_1.*

*The line N, which is perpendicular to the tangent plane at P_1, is called the **normal line** to the surface at P_1.*

A very important result follows at once from the preceding discussion:

III. *The normal line to a surface $F(x, y, z) = 0$ at any point P_1 has the values of $\dfrac{\partial F}{\partial x}, \dfrac{\partial F}{\partial y}, \dfrac{\partial F}{\partial z}$ at that point as a set of direction numbers, if these partial derivatives satisfy the conditions specified above.*

It is evident from § 473, that the equation of a plane through P_1 with direction numbers a, b, c for its normal is

$$a(x - x_1) + b(y - y_1) + c(z - z_1) = 0,$$

and from §476 that equations of a line through P_1 with direction numbers a, b, c are

$$\frac{x - x_1}{a} = \frac{y - y_1}{b} = \frac{z - z_1}{c}.$$

Using the result of theorem III, together with these equations, we have:

IV. *The equation of the tangent plane to a surface $F(x, y, z) = 0$ at a point $P_1(x_1, y_1, z_1)$, if the function F satisfies the conditions specified above, is:*

$$(16) \qquad \frac{\partial F}{\partial x}(x - x_1) + \frac{\partial F}{\partial y}(y - y_1) + \frac{\partial F}{\partial z}(z - z_1) = 0;$$

and equations of the normal line to this surface are:

$$(17) \qquad \frac{x - x_1}{\dfrac{\partial F}{\partial x}} = \frac{y - y_1}{\dfrac{\partial F}{\partial y}} = \frac{z - z_1}{\dfrac{\partial F}{\partial z}},$$

where the derivatives are to be formed at P_1.

EXAMPLE. Find the equations of the tangent plane and normal line to the paraboloid $x^2 + y^2 = 4z$ at the point $(6, 8, 25)$.

Solution: Put $F(x, y, z) = x^2 + y^2 - 4z$; then

$$\frac{\partial F}{\partial x} = 2x, \qquad \frac{\partial F}{\partial y} = 2y, \qquad \frac{\partial F}{\partial z} = -4.$$

At the given point $(6, 8, 25)$, these derivatives have the values 12, 16, -4. Hence, the equation of the tangent plane is

$$12(x - 6) + 16(y - 8) - 4(z - 25) = 0, \quad \text{or} \quad 3x + 4y - z = 25;$$

and equations of the normal line are

$$\frac{x - 6}{12} = \frac{y - 8}{16} = \frac{z - 25}{-4}, \quad \text{or} \quad \frac{x - 6}{3} = \frac{y - 8}{4} = \frac{z - 25}{-1}.$$

511. Exercises

In Exercises 1–10, find the equations of the tangent plane and normal line to each of the given surfaces at the point indicated:

1. $x^2 + 2 y^2 + 3 z^2 = 12$, at $(1, -2, 1)$.
2. $3 x^2 + z^2 = 4 y$, at $(1, 3, -3)$.
3. $x^2 - y^2 - z^2 = 1$, at $(3, 2, 2)$.
4. $z = x^2 + xy - 2 y^2$, at $(1, 2, -5)$.
5. $z = x^2 - y^2$, at $(1, 1, 0)$.
6. $3 x^2 - 2 y^2 + z^2 - 5 x + z = 0$, at $(2, 1, -1)$.
7. $x + y - z^2 = 3$, at $(3, 4, 2)$.
8. $z = xy$, at $(2, 3, 6)$.
9. $x^2y + y^2 + z^2 = 7$, at $(1, 2, -1)$.
10. $x^2y + y^2z + z^2x = 1$, at $(-1, 1, 0)$.

Show that the equations of the tangent planes to the following quadric surfaces at the point $P_1(x_1, y_1, z_1)$ may be written as indicated:

11. $x^2 + y^2 + z^2 = a^2$, $x_1x + y_1y + z_1z = a^2$.

12. $\dfrac{x^2}{a^2} + \dfrac{y^2}{b^2} - \dfrac{z^2}{c^2} = 1$, $\dfrac{x_1x}{a^2} + \dfrac{y_1y}{b^2} - \dfrac{z_1z}{c^2} = 1$.

13. $x^2 + y^2 = az$, $2 x_1x + 2 y_1y = a(z + z_1)$.

14. Prove that the tangent plane to a sphere is perpendicular to the radius to the point of contact.

★ 512. Directional Derivative

If $u = f(x, y)$, the partial derivatives $\dfrac{\partial u}{\partial x}$ and $\dfrac{\partial u}{\partial y}$ give the rates of change of u in directions parallel to the X- and Y-axes. In many applied problems, it is desirable to know the rate of change of a function of two variables in an arbitrary direction in the XY-plane. This is expressed by the *directional derivative*.

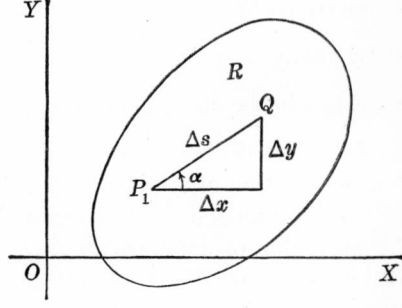

Fig. 208

Let $u = f(x, y)$ be a function defined in a region R of the XY-plane, and let $P_1(x_1, y_1)$ be a point of that region. Choose an arbitrary direction in the XY-plane; denote by α the angle that it makes with the X-axis. Through P_1 draw a line in the α-direction and let $Q(x_1 + \Delta x, y_1 + \Delta y)$ be a neighboring point on that line (Fig. 208). Denote by Δs the distance P_1Q and by Δu the change in u as the point (x, y) moves over the distance Δs from P_1 to Q. That is, $\Delta u = f(x_1 + \Delta x, y_1 + \Delta y) - f(x_1, y_1)$. Then:

*The **directional derivative** of u at P_1 in the α-direction is defined as the limit of the ratio $\Delta u/\Delta s$ when $\Delta s \to 0$, so that Q approaches P_1 along the line from the α-direction.*

Since this directional derivative depends on the direction α, we shall denote it by the new symbol*

$$\mathcal{D}_{(\alpha)}\,u,$$

which is to be read: derivative of u in the direction α.

By the total increment formula, we have

$$\Delta u = \frac{\partial u}{\partial x}\,\Delta x + \frac{\partial u}{\partial y}\,\Delta y + \epsilon_1\,\Delta x + \epsilon_2\,\Delta y,$$

and

$$(a) \qquad \frac{\Delta u}{\Delta s} = \frac{\partial u}{\partial x}\frac{\Delta x}{\Delta s} + \frac{\partial u}{\partial y}\frac{\Delta y}{\Delta s} + \epsilon_1\frac{\Delta x}{\Delta s} + \epsilon_2\frac{\Delta y}{\Delta s}$$

$$= \frac{\partial u}{\partial x}\cos\alpha + \frac{\partial u}{\partial y}\sin\alpha + \epsilon_1\cos\alpha + \epsilon_2\sin\alpha.$$

Since $\epsilon_1,\ \epsilon_2 \to 0$ when $\Delta x,\ \Delta y \to 0$, we have:

If $u = f(x, y)$, the value of the directional derivative of u at P_1 in the direction that makes an angle α with the X-axis is:

$$(18) \qquad \mathcal{D}_{(\alpha)}\,u = \frac{\partial u}{\partial x}\cos\alpha + \frac{\partial u}{\partial y}\sin\alpha,$$

where the partial derivatives are formed at P_1.

By taking $\alpha = 0$ and $\alpha = \frac{1}{2}\pi$, we see that the directional derivatives of u in the directions of the X- and Y-axes are $\dfrac{\partial u}{\partial x}$ and $\dfrac{\partial u}{\partial y}$ respectively. The directional derivative in an arbitrary direction is thus a generalization of the idea of a partial derivative.

The directional derivative is a function of the angle α. There may be one value of α for which $\mathcal{D}_{(\alpha)}u$ has a maximum value. Such a maximum value of the directional derivative of a function u at a given point P_1, for the various values of α, is called the **normal**

---

* See Courant, *Differential and Integral Calculus*, vol. II, page 63.   Most books use either the symbol $\dfrac{du}{ds}$ or the symbol $\dfrac{\partial u}{\partial s}$.

derivative (or the gradient) of u at P_1.   It gives the greatest slope of the surface $z = f(x, y)$ at the point corresponding to P_1 for all possible directions.

EXAMPLE. Find the directional derivative of $u = x^2y + xy^2$ at the point $(1, 1)$ in the direction for which $\alpha = \frac{1}{3}\pi$; also find the direction and value of the normal derivative at $(1, 1)$.

Solution: $\dfrac{\partial u}{\partial x} = 2\,xy + y^2$, $\dfrac{\partial u}{\partial y} = x^2 + 2\,xy$; at $(1, 1)$, $\dfrac{\partial u}{\partial x} = 3$, $\dfrac{\partial u}{\partial y} = 3$.

For $\alpha = \frac{1}{3}\pi$, $\cos \alpha = \frac{1}{2}$, $\sin \alpha = \frac{1}{2}\sqrt{3}$. Therefore, by formula (18), for $\alpha = \frac{1}{3}\pi$,

(b) $$\mathfrak{D}_{(\alpha)}u = 3\cdot\tfrac{1}{2} + 3\cdot\tfrac{1}{2}\sqrt{3} = \tfrac{3}{2}(1 + \sqrt{3}).$$

For a general angle α, at $(1, 1)$,

(c) $$\mathfrak{D}_{(\alpha)}u = 3 \cos \alpha + 3 \sin \alpha.$$

To find the value of α for which this is a maximum, we differentiate this with respect to α and set the result equal to 0:

(d) $$\frac{d}{d\alpha}\,(\mathfrak{D}_{(\alpha)}u) = -3 \sin \alpha + 3 \cos \alpha = 0,$$

whence $\tan \alpha = 1$, and $\alpha = \frac{1}{4}\pi$ or $\alpha = \frac{5}{4}\pi$.   To test these values of α for a maximum directional derivative, we find the second derivative:

(e) $$\frac{d^2}{d\alpha^2}\,(\mathfrak{D}_{(\alpha)}u) = -3 \cos \alpha - 3 \sin \alpha.$$

This is negative when $\alpha = \frac{1}{4}\pi$, which therefore gives the direction of the maximum directional derivative or normal derivative.   For this direction, (c) becomes

(f) $$\mathfrak{D}_{(\alpha)}u = 3\cdot\tfrac{1}{2}\sqrt{2} + 3\cdot\tfrac{1}{2}\sqrt{2} = 3\sqrt{2},$$

which is the value of the required normal derivative.

The directional derivative of a function of three variables in an arbitrary direction in space may be defined in a manner similar to that given for a function of two variables.

★ 513. Exercises

1. Find the directional derivative of the function $u = x^2 - xy + y^2$ at the point $(1, 2)$ in the direction making an angle of $\frac{1}{4}\pi$ with the X-axis.
2. Find the directional derivative of the function $u = e^x \sin y$ at the point $(0, \frac{1}{3}\pi)$ in the direction making an angle of $\frac{1}{6}\pi$ with the X-axis.
3. Find the directional derivative of $u = x^2 + xy + y^2$ at the point $P_1(3, 1)$ in the direction of the normal to the curve $y^2 = x - 2$ at P_1.
4. Find the directional derivative of $u = x^3 + y^3 - 3\,xy$ at the point $P_1(2, 1)$ in the direction of the tangent to the curve $x^2 - 2\,y^2 = 2$ at P_1.

5. The temperature at any point (x, y) of a rectangular plate lying in the XY-plane is given by $T = x \sin 2 y$. Find the rate of change of temperature at the point $(1, \frac{1}{4} \pi)$ in the direction making an angle of $\frac{1}{6} \pi$ with the X-axis.

6. The electric potential V at any point (x, y) in a certain case is given by $V = \ln r$, where $r^2 = x^2 + y^2$. Find the rate of change of the potential V at any point $P(x, y)$: (a) in the direction toward the origin; (b) in the direction perpendicular to the direction toward the origin.

7. Find the direction and the value of the normal derivative of $u = y^2 - 4 x$ at the point $(2, -1)$.

8. Find the direction and the value of the normal derivative of $u = x^2 + 4 y^2 - 2 x$ at the point $(3, 1)$.

9. Find the direction of the maximum rate of change of $u = x^2 - 2 y - 3$ at the point $(1, 2)$, and find the value of this maximum rate.

10. Find the normal derivative of $u = x^2 + y^2$ at the point (x_1, y_1).

11. Find the direction through the point $(2, 1)$ in which the function $u = 4 x^2 + 9 y^2$ has the maximum rate of change. Show that this direction is that of the normal to the curve $4 x^2 + 9 y^2 = 25$ at the point $(2, 1)$. Also find the value of this maximum rate of change.

12. Prove that the maximum value of the directional derivative of a function $u = f(x, y)$ at any point $P_1(x_1, y_1)$ for all directions is in the direction given by $\alpha = \text{Arc tan } (u_y/u_x) \pm \pi$, and that its value is $\sqrt{u_x^2 + u_y^2}$. Thence show that this maximum directional derivative is in the direction of the normal to the curve $u = c$ passing through P_1.

514. Maxima and Minima of Functions of Several Variables

In Chapter VII we discussed maxima and minima of functions of one variable. We now consider very briefly the corresponding subject for functions of two or more independent variables.*

Let $f(x, y)$ be a continuous function, with continuous partial derivatives $\dfrac{\partial f}{\partial x}$ and $\dfrac{\partial f}{\partial y}$. The function may be represented geometrically by a smooth unbroken surface whose equation in rectangular coördinates is $z = f(x, y)$.

*The function $f(x, y)$ is said to have a **maximum value** at a point (a, b) if the value $f(a, b)$ is greater than the values of $f(x, y)$ at all points (x, y) in the neighborhood of the point (a, b).* Similarly we define a **minimum value** by replacing the word "greater" by "less." Both maxima and minima are included under the term *extreme values.*

Using the geometric interpretation of the function, it will be seen that if the function $f(x, y)$ has a maximum value at (a, b), then the

* For a more thorough discussion, see, for example, Fine, *Calculus*, pages 277–279, or Sokolnikoff, *Advanced Calculus*, pages 321–334.

corresponding surface $z = f(x, y)$ will have a *maximum point* at (a, b, c) where $c = f(a, b)$, which is *higher* than all neighboring points on the surface (provided we take the XY-plane horizontal). (Fig. 209.) Similarly, a *minimum point* corresponding to a minimum value of the function will be *lower* than all neighboring points on the surface.

A similar definition may be formulated for a maximum or minimum of a function of three or more variables.

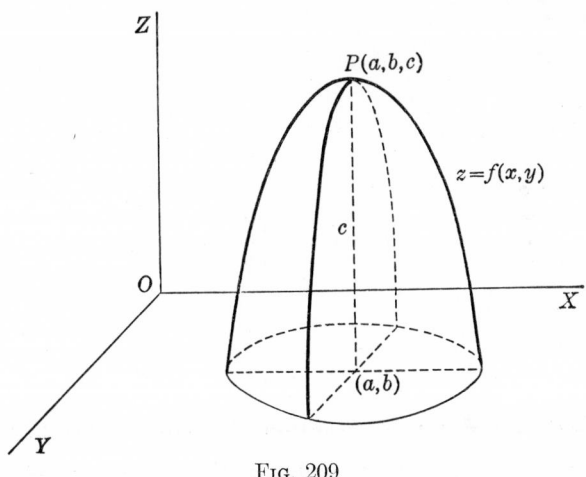

Fig. 209

It follows from the geometric interpretation that at a maximum or minimum point (a, b, c) on the surface $z = f(x, y)$ representing a given function, the curves of intersection of the surface with planes through (a, b, c) parallel to the vertical coördinate planes must have horizontal tangents there. Since their slopes are zero,

$$\frac{\partial f}{\partial x} = 0 \qquad \text{and} \qquad \frac{\partial f}{\partial y} = 0$$

at the extreme point. Hence:

I. *If $f(x, y)$ and its first derivatives are continuous in a region including the point (a, b), a necessary condition that $f(a, b)$ shall be an extreme (maximum or minimum) value of the function $f(x, y)$ is that*

(19) $$\frac{\partial f}{\partial x} = 0, \qquad \frac{\partial f}{\partial y} = 0,$$

where the derivatives are formed at the point (a, b).

Examples show that the equations (19) are *not* a *sufficient* condition for the existence of an extreme value at (a, b).

The conditions $\dfrac{\partial f}{\partial x} = 0$, $\dfrac{\partial f}{\partial y} = 0$ do not enable us to distinguish between maximum values and minimum values; they merely furnish a means of finding *possible* extreme values. In many practical problems, however, the existence and nature of an extreme value is often evident from the problem itself and no test is needed; all that is required is the *location* of the extreme value.

A test for distinguishing maximum values from minimum values may be stated as follows; this statement also gives *sufficient conditions* for the existence of an extreme.

II. *If, at the point* $(a, b,)$,

(a)
$$\frac{\partial f}{\partial x} = 0, \qquad \frac{\partial f}{\partial y} = 0,$$

and if

(b)
$$\Delta = \frac{\partial^2 f}{\partial x^2} \cdot \frac{\partial^2 f}{\partial y^2} - \left(\frac{\partial^2 f}{\partial x \partial y} \right)^2 > 0,$$

then $f(x, y)$ *will have a maximum value or a minimum value* $f(a, b)$ *according as* $\dfrac{\partial^2 f}{\partial x^2} \left(\text{or } \dfrac{\partial^2 f}{\partial y^2} \right)$ *is negative or positive for* $x = a$, $y = b$. *If* (a) *holds, and* $\Delta < 0$, *then* $f(a, b)$ *is neither a maximum nor a minimum; if* $\Delta = 0$, *the test fails to give any information.*

The proof of this theorem is beyond the scope of this book.*

EXAMPLE. Find the shape of a covered rectangular box of given volume with minimum surface area.

Solution: If the dimensions of the box are x, y, z, the volume is $V = xyz = $ constant, and the surface area is $S = 2(xy + yz + zx)$; eliminating z by use of the equation $z = V/xy$, we have the function of two variables:

(c)
$$S = 2 \left(xy + \frac{V}{x} + \frac{V}{y} \right), \ (V \text{ constant}),$$

which is to be made a minimum. We find

(d)
$$\frac{\partial S}{\partial x} = 2 \left(y - \frac{V}{x^2} \right), \quad \frac{\partial S}{\partial y} = 2 \left(x - \frac{V}{y^2} \right);$$

---

* See, for example, Fine, *Calculus*, pages 277–278, or Osgood, *Advanced Calculus*, pages 177–178, or Sokolnikoff, *Advanced Calculus*, pages 322–324.

equating these derivatives to 0, and eliminating V between them, we obtain $x = y = \sqrt[3]{V}$, and from $z = V/xy$, we get $z = \sqrt[3]{V}$, so that $x = y = z$. Therefore, the box of minimum surface area must be a cube.

Necessary conditions for maxima and minima of a function of more than two variables are similar to those for two variables. Thus, for an extreme value of a function $F(x, y, z)$ at (a, b, c), a necessary condition is that the equations

$$\frac{\partial F}{\partial x} = 0, \qquad \frac{\partial F}{\partial y} = 0, \qquad \frac{\partial F}{\partial z} = 0$$

shall be satisfied by $x = a$, $y = b$, $z = c$.

515. Exercises

In Exercises 1–12, examine the given functions for maxima and minima:

1. $z = x^2 + 4y^2 - 4x$.
2. $z = x^2 + 4y^2 - 2x + 8y - 1$.
3. $z = xy$.
4. $z = x^3 + y^2 - 3x$.
5. $z = x^2 + xy + y^2 - 2x - 6y$.
6. $z = x^2 + y^2 + xy + y^3$.
7. $z = x^3 + y^3 - 3xy$.
8. $z = x^3 - 4y^2 + xy^2$.
9. $z = x^2 - y^2$.
10. $z = \sin x + \sin y + \cos(x + y)$.
11. $z = x^3 - 3x - y^2$.
12. $z = x^2 + a^2 - 2ax \cos y$.

13. Divide a number N into three parts such that their product may be the largest possible.
14. Find (by calculus) the shortest distance from the origin to the plane $x + y + z = a$.
15. An open rectangular box has a given volume; what relative dimensions will make the surface area a minimum?
16. An open rectangular box has a given surface area; what relative dimensions will make the volume a maximum?
17. Find the shape of the rectangular parallelopiped of given volume for which the sum of the edges is least.
18. If a covered rectangular box has a fixed surface area, what relative dimensions will it have if the volume is to be a maximum?
19. The base of a rectangular box costs twice as much per square foot as the sides and top; find the most economical relative dimensions for a box of given volume.
20. Show that the largest rectangular parallelopiped that can be inscribed in a sphere is a cube.
21. Find the dimensions and volume of the rectangular parallelopiped of maximum volume which has three faces in the coördinate planes and one vertex in the plane $\dfrac{x}{a} + \dfrac{y}{b} + \dfrac{z}{c} = 1$.
22. Find the dimensions and volume of the rectangular parallelopiped of maximum volume with faces parallel to the coördinate planes, inscribed in the ellipsoid $\dfrac{x^2}{a^2} + \dfrac{y^2}{b^2} + \dfrac{z^2}{c^2} = 1$.

23. Find the equation of the plane through the point (1, 2, 1) which cuts off the least volume from the first octant.

24. A pentagonal frame is composed of a rectangle surmounted by an isosceles triangle. What are the dimensions for maximum area of the pentagon if the perimeter is fixed?

CHAPTER XXVII

Multiple Integrals

516. Double Integrals

In Chapter X we introduced the concept of the definite integral of a function of one variable, as the limit of a sum of a certain type. We shall now extend this notion to the corresponding case of a function of two variables.

In this chapter R will denote a finite plane region including all of its interior points and all points on its boundary, which consists of a finite number of arcs of smooth curves; we call this a *closed region*.

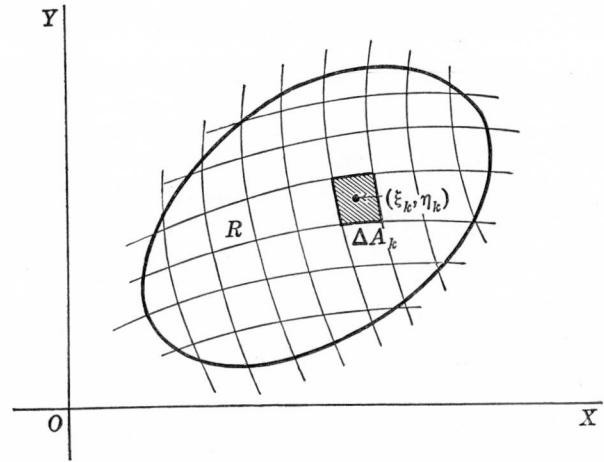

Fig. 210

Let $f(x, y)$ be a single-valued function of the independent variables x and y defined throughout a region R of the XY-plane. Let the region R be divided into n sub-regions ΔA_1, ΔA_2, ΔA_3, $\cdots$, ΔA_n (Fig. 210) by two systems of lines or curves, and let δ be the maximum diameter of any sub-region. Let the system of sub-division be such that $\delta \to 0$ as $n \to \infty$. Let (ξ_k, η_k) be any point within or on the boundary of the k-th sub-region ΔA_k, and form the sum

$$(a) \qquad f(\xi_1, \eta_1)\Delta A_1 + f(\xi_2, \eta_2)\Delta A_2 + \cdots + f(\xi_n, \eta_n)\Delta A_n$$
$$= \sum_{k=1}^{n} f(\xi_k, \eta_k)\Delta A_k,$$

where we use ΔA_k to denote the area of the k-th sub-region as well as the sub-region itself.

If this sum $\sum_{k=1}^{n} f(\xi_k, \eta_k)\Delta A_k$ *approaches a limit as* $\delta \to 0$, *and if this limit is independent of the mode of sub-division and of the choice of* (ξ_k, η_k) *in* ΔA_k, *then this limit is defined as the* **double integral of f(x, y) over the region R,** *and is denoted by the symbol* $\iint_R f(x, y)\, dA$:

$$(1) \qquad \iint_R f(x, y)\, dA = \lim_{\delta \to 0} \sum_{k=1}^{n} f(\xi_k, \eta_k)\Delta A_k.$$

It can be proved* that *the limit* (1) *defining the double integral always exists when the integrand* $f(x, y)$ *is continuous in the closed region* R.

In practice, the usual ways of dividing the region R into sub-regions are: (1) to draw lines parallel to the rectangular axes OX and OY (a rectangular network), so that the sub-regions ΔA_k are rectangles or portions of rectangles (Fig. 211 (a)), or (2) to draw lines from the origin and concentric circles about the origin (a polar network), so that the sub-regions ΔA_k are for the most part "curvilinear rectangles" bounded by straight lines and arcs of circles (Fig. 211 (b)).

The double integral may be given a simple *geometric interpretation*, as will be shown in § 517.

A double integral is *evaluated* by use of *repeated integration*, as will be shown in §§ 520, 524.

In *setting up* numerous important types of problems, geometrical and physical, it will be shown later that the problem is *formulated* as a limit of a sum by a double integral, and the result is *evaluated* by means of a corresponding repeated integral.

---

* See, for example, Franklin, *Treatise on Advanced Calculus*, § 221.

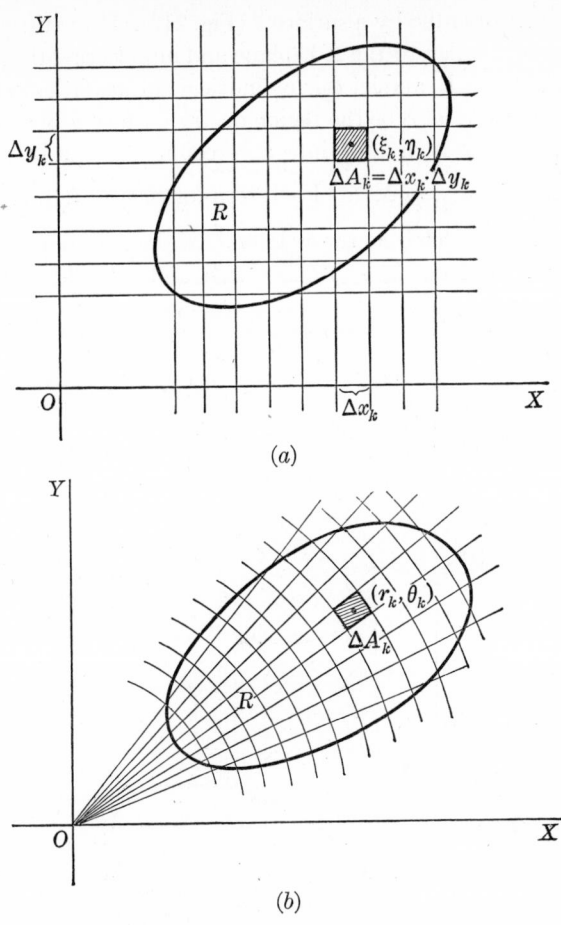

(a)

(b)

Fig. 211

517. Geometric Interpretation of a Double Integral: Volume under a Surface

In Chapter X we saw that the definite integral of a function of one variable, defined as a limit of a sum, could be interpreted geometrically as an *area under a curve*. We shall now show that a double integral, defined as a limit of a sum as in § 516, can be interpreted geometrically in a similar way, as a *volume under a surface*.

Let $f(x, y)$ be a continuous function in a region R of the XY-plane. Let us suppose that $f(x, y)$ is *positive* in the region R. The equation z

$= f(x, y)$ is represented by a surface σ (Fig. 212). Draw the cylindrical surface perpendicular to the XY-plane and intersecting the XY-plane in the boundary of R, and let this cylindrical surface intersect the surface σ in a curve C; let S be the region on the surface σ bounded by C.

Suppose that R is divided into sub-regions ΔA_k as in § 516, and form the sum $\sum_{k=1}^{n} f(\xi_k, \eta_k)\Delta A_k$.   Each term or *element* $f(\xi_k, \eta_k)\Delta A_k$ may evidently be interpreted as the volume of a slender column (cylinder or prism) standing on the sub-region ΔA_k and extending up to some

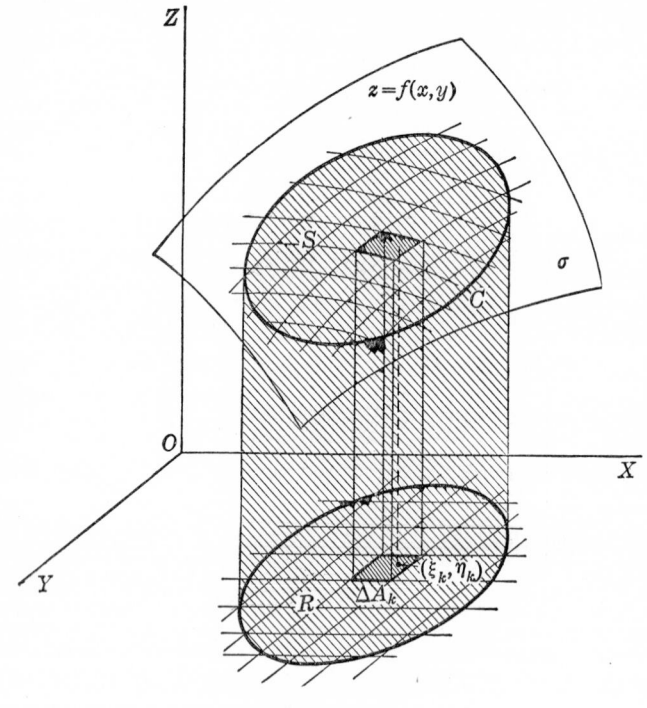

Fig. 212

point in S whose x- and y-coördinates are ξ_k and η_k, so that the height of the column is $f(\xi_k, \eta_k)$.   These columns are cut off at the top by planes parallel to the XY-plane.   It follows from the definition of a double integral (in § 516) that the double integral $\iint_R f(x, y)\ dA$ is represented by the limit of the sum of the volumes of all such columns. It is therefore natural to *define* the **volume** of the solid bounded at the bottom by the region R and at the top by the region S on the surface σ as this limit of the sum of volumes of columns.* This volume may be described briefly as the *volume under the curved surface σ over the region R.*

Hence, *the double integral* $\iint_R f(x, y) \, dA$ *may be interpreted geometrically as the volume under the surface* $z = f(x, y)$ *and over the region R.*

In particular, if $f(x, y) = 1$, the double integral represents the *area* of the region R since, when the height is 1, this area and the volume are equal. Then $A = \iint_R dA$.

518. Iterated Double Integrals

Let $f(x, y)$ be a given continuous function of the independent variables x and y, and let $y_1(x)$ and $y_2(x)$ be two given continuous functions of x. Suppose that we hold x fixed, and let us integrate $f(x, y)$ with respect to y between the limits $y_1(x)$ and $y_2(x)$, to form the definite integral

$$(a) \qquad \int_{y_1(x)}^{y_2(x)} f(x, y) \, dy.$$

The limits of integration $y_1(x)$ and $y_2(x)$ depend on the particular value that has been fixed for x, and are therefore written in functional form. If we now release x from being held constant, this integral is a function of x, say $F(x)$, since y_1 and y_2 are functions of x. Now let a and b be two given constants, and let us integrate $F(x)$ with respect to x between the limits a and b; this result may be written:

$$(b) \qquad \int_a^b F(x) \, dx = \int_a^b \left(\int_{y_1(x)}^{y_2(x)} f(x, y) \, dy \right) dx.$$

This expression:

$$(c) \qquad \int_a^b \left(\int_{y_1(x)}^{y_2(x)} f(x, y) \, dy \right) dx = \int_a^b \int_{y_1(x)}^{y_2(x)} f(x, y) \, dy \, dx$$

is called an **iterated** (*or repeated*) **double integral.**

---

* It can be proved that this definition of volume is consistent with the previous definition of volume in § 185 in cases where the previous definition applies.

It is customary to use the second notation for the iterated integral (c), without the large parentheses. However, we shall retain these parentheses for a time, to emphasize the meaning of the symbols. It is important to note that the *first differential* that appears in the second form indicates the variable of the *first integration* and that the limits of this integration are those placed on the second or inner integral sign.

In a similar way, we may form the *iterated double integral:*

$$(d) \qquad \int_c^d \left(\int_{x_1(y)}^{x_2(y)} f(x, y)\, dx \right) dy = \int_c^d \int_{x_1(y)}^{x_2(y)} f(x, y)\, dx\, dy,$$

in which we first hold y constant and integrate with respect to x, between limits x_1 and x_2 which are given functions of y, and then integrate this resulting function of y with respect to y between given constant limits c and d.

The first integration in each case, which we may call *partial integration*, is analogous to partial differentiation.

If the order of integration is reversed, the corresponding limits are not reversed, for in general they are completely changed.

EXAMPLE 1. Evaluate the iterated integral $\displaystyle \int_0^1 \left(\int_0^x (x^2 + y^2)\, dy \right) dx.$

Solution: $\displaystyle F(x) = \int_{y=0}^{y=x} (x^2 + y^2)\, dy = (x^2 y + \tfrac{1}{3} y^3) \Big|_0^x = \tfrac{4}{3} x^3.$

$\displaystyle \therefore \int_0^1 \left(\int_0^x (x^2 + y^2)\, dy \right) dx = \int_0^1 F(x)\, dx = \tfrac{4}{3} \int_0^1 x^3\, dx = \frac{1}{3}.$

EXAMPLE 2. Evaluate the iterated integral $\displaystyle \int_0^4 \int_{\sqrt{y}}^{y^2} y\, dx\, dy.$

Solution: With y constant,

$$\int_{\sqrt{y}}^{y^2} y\, dx = y \cdot x \Big|_{\sqrt{y}}^{y^2} = y(y^2 - \sqrt{y}) = y^3 - y^{\frac{3}{2}},$$

$$\therefore \int_0^4 \int_{\sqrt{y}}^{y^2} y\, dx\, dy = \int_0^4 (y^3 - y^{\frac{3}{2}})\, dy = (\tfrac{1}{4} y^4 - \tfrac{2}{5} y^{\frac{5}{2}}) \Big|_0^4 = \frac{256}{5}.$$

519. Exercises

Evaluate each of the following iterated double integrals:

1. $\displaystyle \int_0^1 \left(\int_{x^2}^{\sqrt{x}} dy \right) dx.$

2. $\displaystyle \int_0^1 \left(\int_{y^2}^{\sqrt{y}} x\, dx \right) dy.$

3. $\displaystyle \int_{-1}^2 \left(\int_{x^2}^{x+2} dy \right) dx.$

4. $\displaystyle \int_0^1 \left(\int_y^{2y} x\, dx \right) dy.$

5. $\displaystyle\int_1^2\left(\int_x^{x\sqrt{3}} xy\,dy\right)dx.$

6. $\displaystyle\int_0^3\left(\int_y^2 (x^2+y^2)\,dx\right)dy.$

7. $\displaystyle\int_0^1\left(\int_0^x x^2y\,dy\right)dx.$

8. $\displaystyle\int_2^4\left(\int_1^{x^2} \frac{x}{y^2}\,dy\right)dx.$

9. $\displaystyle\int_0^a\int_{a-x}^{\sqrt{a^2-x^2}} y\,dy\,dx.$

10. $\displaystyle\int_a^{2a}\int_y^{\frac{y^2}{a}} (x+y)\,dx\,dy.$

11. $\displaystyle\int_0^1\int_x^{\sqrt{x}} (x^2+y^2)\,dy\,dx.$

12. $\displaystyle\int_0^a\int_{\frac{x^2}{a}}^x \frac{x\,dy\,dx}{x^2+y^2}.$

13. $\displaystyle\int_0^{\frac{\pi}{2}}\left(\int_0^{2a\cos\theta} r\,dr\right)d\theta.$

14. $\displaystyle\int_0^{2\pi}\left(\int_{a\sin\theta}^a r\,dr\right)d\theta.$

15. $\displaystyle\int_0^{2\pi}\left(\int_0^{a(1-\cos\theta)} r\,dr\right)d\theta.$

16. $\displaystyle\int_0^{\frac{\pi}{2}}\left(\int_{a\cos\theta}^a r^4\,dr\right)d\theta.$

17. $\displaystyle\int_0^{2\pi}\int_0^a r^3\,dr\,d\theta.$

18. $\displaystyle\int_{\frac{b}{2}}^b\int_0^{\frac{r}{b}} r\,d\theta\,dr.$

19. $\displaystyle\int_0^{2\pi}\int_0^a r^3\cos^2\theta\,dr\,d\theta.$

20. $\displaystyle\int_0^\pi\int_0^{a(1+\cos\theta)} r^2\sin\theta\,dr\,d\theta.$

520. Evaluation of a Double Integral by an Iterated Integral: Rectangular Coördinates

The *definition* of a double integral as a limit of a sum, as given in § 516, does not give a practicable means of *evaluating* the integral. The evaluation is made by use of an iterated integral as explained below.

Fundamental theorem for double integrals: Let R be a region of the XY-plane as described in § 516. Suppose that any vertical straight line meets the boundary of R in at most two points. The region R therefore has an upper boundary, which is the graph of a function $y = y_2(x)$, and a lower boundary, $y = y_1(x)$. We shall assume that $y_1(x)$ and $y_2(x)$ are continuous from a to b, the extreme values of x in R (Fig. 213 (a)). Then:

If $f(x, y)$ is continuous in the closed region R, the **double integral** *of $f(x, y)$ over R is given by the* **iterated integral** *as follows:*

(2) $$\iint_R f(x, y)\,dA = \int_a^b\left(\int_{y_1(x)}^{y_2(x)} f(x, y)\,dy\right)dx,$$

where the conditions and notation are as described above.

Similarly, *if R has a left-hand boundary $x = x_1(y)$ and a right-hand boundary $x = x_2(y)$, which are continuous from c to d, the extreme*

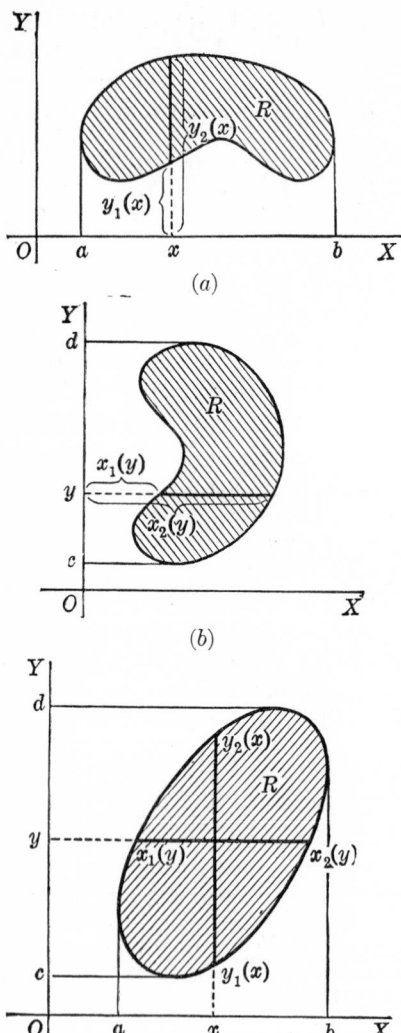

values of y in R (Fig. 213 (b)), *and if f(x, y) is continuous in the closed region R, then*

$$(3) \qquad \iint_R f(x, y)\, dA$$
$$= \int_c^d \left(\int_{x_1(y)}^{x_2(y)} f(x, y)\, dx \right) dy.$$

If R has left-hand and right-hand boundaries as well as upper and lower boundaries of the forms indicated in Fig. 213 *(c), then both iterated integrals in* (2) *and* (3) *are defined and equal to each other.*

An analytic proof of this Fundamental Theorem is given in more advanced books.* The theorem is made plausible by the following geometric interpretation in which the double integral and the iterated integrals are seen to be equal to the same volume and hence to each other. The double integral is defined by

$$(a) \iint_R f(x, y)\, dA$$
$$= \lim_{\delta \to 0} \sum_{k=1}^n f(\xi_k, \eta_k) \Delta A_k.$$

To obtain the sub-regions ΔA_k, let us cover the region R by a rectangular network of lines parallel to the X- and Y-axes (as in Fig. 211

Fɪɢ. 213

---

* See, for example, Fine, *Calculus*, §§ 150–152, or Sokolnikoff, *Advanced Calculus*, § 97, or Franklin, *Treatise on Advanced Calculus*, §§ 223, 224, or Fite, *Advanced Calculus*, §§ 97, 98.

(a)). Except on the boundary, each sub-region is then a rectangle of dimensions Δx_k and Δy_k, and of area $\Delta A_k = \Delta x_k \cdot \Delta y_k$. We visualize the element of integration $f(\xi_k, \eta_k)\Delta A_k$ as the volume of a slender rectangular prism of altitude $f(\xi_k, \eta_k)$ and base $\Delta A_k = \Delta x_k \Delta y_k$ (Fig. 214). The double integral is then represented geometrically by the limit of the sum of all these rectangular prisms over the whole region R, which gives the volume V under the surface $z = f(x, y)$ and over the region R.

Now consider the iterated integral $\int_a^b \left(\int_{y_1}^{y_2} f(x, y)\, dy \right) dx$. We may interpret the first partial integration $\left(\int_{y_1}^{y_2} f(x, y)\, dy \right) dx$ as a limiting summation which combines the prisms into a thin slab parallel to

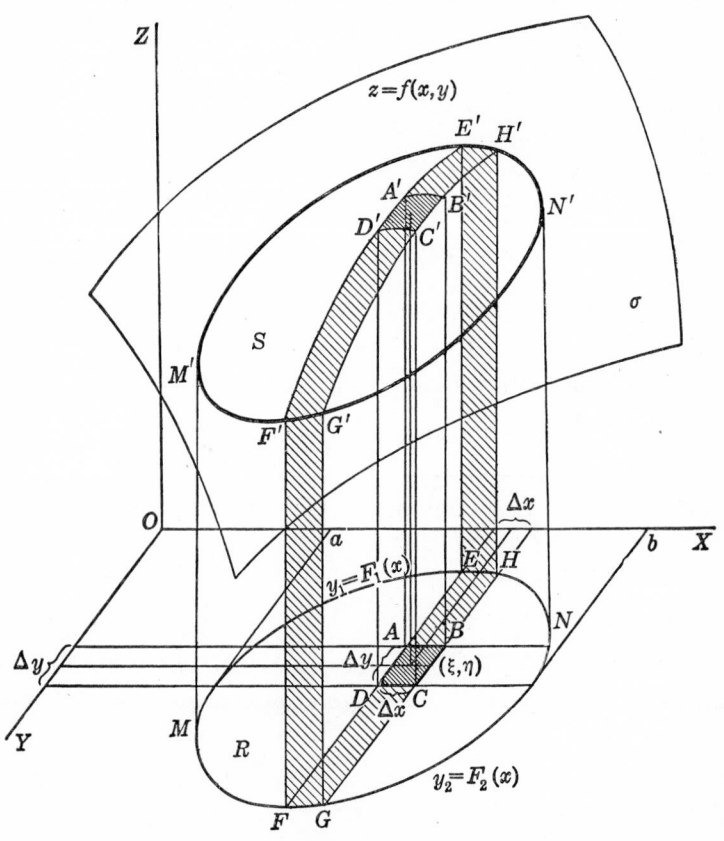

$$\text{FIG. 214}$$

the YZ-plane (see Fig. 214), for a constant value of x. Then the second integration with respect to x may be interpreted as a limiting summation which combines the slabs into the entire volume V. Thus, geometrically, the double integral represents a limiting summation of the elementary prisms into the volume V by a single operation, while the iterated integral represents a limiting summation of the elementary prisms into the volume V by two successive operations.

EXAMPLE 1. Find the limits of the iterated integral for $\iint_R f(x, y)\, dA$ when the region R is bounded by the curve $y = x^2$ and the line $y = x$ (Fig. 215).

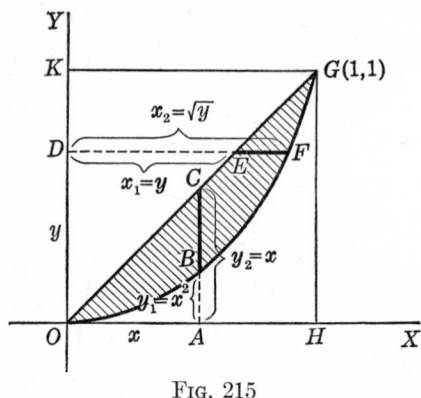

FIG. 215

Solution: In the corresponding iterated integral, if we integrate with respect to y first, y varies from the curve $y = x^2$ to the line $y = x$, so that $y_1 = x^2$ and $y_2 = x$, and since the curve and line intersect at $O(0, 0)$ and $G(1, 1)$, we have $a = 0$ and $b = 1$. Hence,

$$(b) \qquad \iint_R f(x, y)\, dA$$
$$= \int_0^1 \left(\int_{x^2}^x f(x, y)\, dy \right) dx.$$

If we integrate with respect to x first, x varies from the line $y = x$ to the curve $y = x^2$, so that $x_1 = y$ and $x_2 = \sqrt{y}$, and $c = 0$ and $d = 1$. Hence,

$$(c) \qquad \iint_R f(x, y)\, dA = \int_0^1 \left(\int_y^{\sqrt{y}} f(x, y)\, dx \right) dy.$$

In some cases, integration in one order is easier to evaluate than in the other order. If the order of integration is changed, new limits for the iterated integral must be determined.

EXAMPLE 2. Determine the region in the XY-plane over which the iterated integral $\int_0^1 \left(\int_{2x}^{2\sqrt{x}} f(x, y)\, dy \right) dx$ extends, and then reverse the order of integration.

Solution: In the first integration, y varies from $y = 2x$ to $y = 2\sqrt{x}$; these are the straight line and the parabola of Fig. 216, and these curves intersect at $O(0, 0)$ and $(1, 2)$. Since, in the second integration, x varies from 0 to 1, it is evident that the region of integration R is the shaded region in

Fig. 216 between the line and the parabola. To reverse the order of integration, we must integrate first with respect to x, for which x varies from $x = \frac{1}{4} y^2$
to $x = \frac{1}{2} y$, and then integrate with respect to y, for which y varies from 0 to 2. Hence, the given integral is also equal to

$$\int_0^2 \left(\int_{\frac{1}{4}y^2}^{\frac{1}{2}y} f(x, y) \, dx \right) dy.$$

521. Exercises

In Exercises 1–4, write the double integral $\iint_R f(x, y) \, dA$ as an iterated integral, in each order of integration, with the proper limits in each case, for each of the given regions R:

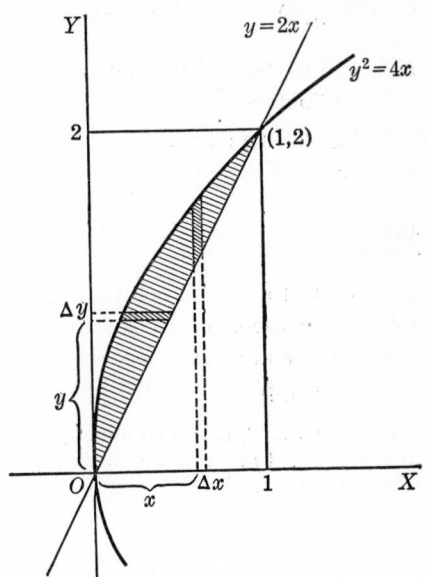

Fig. 216

1. The first quadrant region bounded by $x^2 + y^2 = 4$, $y^2 = 3\,x$, $y = 0$.
2. The region bounded by $y^2 = 4\,x$, $x^2 = 4\,y$.
3. The region bounded by $y^2 = x^3$, $y = x$.
4. The region bounded by $y^2 = 2\,x$, $x^2 + y^2 = 4\,y$.

In Exercises 5–8, determine the region over which each of the given iterated integrals is extended:

5. $\displaystyle \int_0^1 \left(\int_0^y f(x, y) \, dx \right) dy.$

6. $\displaystyle \int_0^2 \left(\int_{x^2}^{2x} f(x, y) \, dy \right) dx.$

7. $\displaystyle \int_0^a \left(\int_0^{\sqrt{a^2 - x^2}} f(x, y) \, dy \right) dx.$

8. $\displaystyle \int_0^2 \left(\int_{\frac{1}{4}y^2}^{\frac{1}{4}(8 - y^2)} f(x, y) \, dx \right) dy.$

In Exercises 9–12, reverse the order of integration in each of the given integrals:

9. $\displaystyle \int_0^1 \int_{y^2}^1 f(x, y) \, dx \, dy.$

10. $\displaystyle \int_0^1 \int_0^{\sqrt{2 - 2x^2}} f(x, y) \, dy \, dx.$

11. $\displaystyle \int_0^1 \int_x^1 f(x, y) \, dy \, dx.$

12. $\displaystyle \int_0^{2\sqrt[3]{2}} \int_{\frac{1}{4}y^2}^{\sqrt{y}} f(x, y) \, dx \, dy.$

Write the double integral $\iint_R f(x, y) \, dA$ as an iterated integral for each of the following functions $f(x, y)$ and for the indicated region R, and then evaluate it:

13. $f(x, y) = x + y$; R is the region bounded by $y = x^2$ and $y^2 = x$.
14. $f(x, y) = x^2 - y^2$; R is the region bounded by $y = x$ and $y = x^2$.
15. $f(x, y) = y^2$; R is the region bounded by $x + y = 2$ and $y = x^2$.
16. $f(x, y) = xy$; R is the region bounded by $y^2 = x + 1$ and $x + y = 1$.

522. Calculation of the Volume under a Surface: Rectangular Coordinates

It has been pointed out already (§ 517) that the volume under a surface $z = f(x, y)$ is *defined* by a double integral

$$(4) \qquad V = \iint_R z \, dA,$$

as a limit of a sum of columns $z \, \Delta A$, and we have seen that a double integral is *evaluated* by an iterated integral. In calculating such volumes, we must therefore set up the double integral for this volume and then apply successive integration.

EXAMPLE 1. Find the volume of the tetrahedron bounded by the plane $x + y + z = 1$ and the coördinate planes. (Fig. 217.)

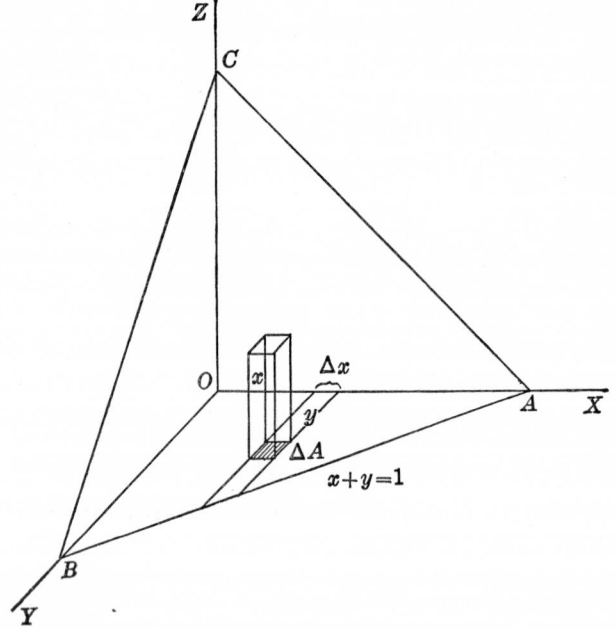

FIG. 217

Solution: The equation of the upper surface of the tetrahedron is

$$z = 1 - x - y,$$

so that the function $z = f(x, y)$ of formula (4) is $z = 1 - x - y$, and the region R is the triangle in the XY-plane bounded by the line $x + y = 1$ or $y = 1 - x$ and the X- and Y-axes. We must then evaluate $V = \iint_R (1 - x - y)\, dA$

Transforming this into an iterated integral, if we integrate first with respect to y, we see that y varies from $y = 0$ to $y = 1 - x$; in the second integration, x varies from 0 to 1. Then

$$V = \int_0^1 \left(\int_0^{1-x} z\, dy \right) dx$$

$$= \int_0^1 \left(\int_0^{1-x} (1 - x - y)\, dy \right) dx = \frac{1}{6}.$$

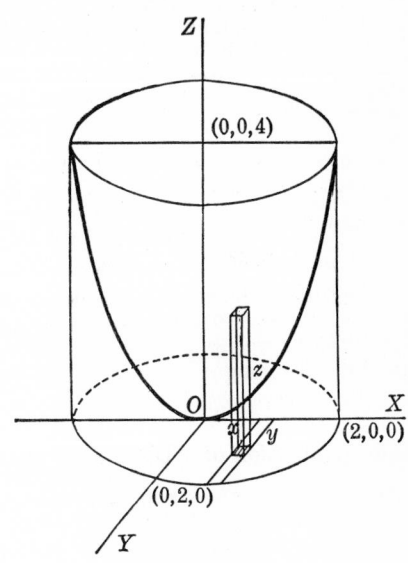

EXAMPLE 2. Find the volume bounded by the surfaces $x^2 + y^2 = z$ and $x^2 + y^2 = 4$ and the XY-plane (Fig. 218).

Solution: The surface $x^2 + y^2 = z$ is a paraboloid passing through the origin and symmetric about the Z-axis, while the surface $x^2 + y^2 = 4$ is a cylinder about the Z-axis, as shown in Fig. 218. The function $z = f(x, y)$ of formula (4) is in this case $z = x^2 + y^2$, and the region R is the interior of the circle $x^2 + y^2 = 4$. By symmetry, the required volume is 4 times the volume in the first octant. Hence,

Fig. 218

$$V = 4 \int_0^2 \left(\int_0^{\sqrt{4-x^2}} (x^2 + y^2)\, dy \right) dx = 8\,\pi.$$

523. Exercises

1. Find the volume of the solid bounded by the cylinder $x^2 + y^2 = 4$, the paraboloid $z = x^2 + y^2 + 2$ and the XY-plane.
2. Find the volume of the solid bounded by the surfaces $x^2 + y^2 = 9$, $z = x + y + 5$ and $z = 0$.
3. Find the volume of the solid bounded by the XY-plane and the surface $az = a^2 - x^2 - y^2$.
4. Find the volume of the solid bounded by the surfaces $z = 4 - x^2 - y^2$, $z = 0$ and $x = 0$.
5. Find the volume in the first octant bounded by the surfaces $x^2 + y^2 = 1$, $z = x$ and $z = x^2$.

6. Find the volume of the elliptic paraboloid $4 x^2 + 9 y^2 = 36 z$ between the planes $z = 0$ and $z = 1$.

7. Find the volume bounded by the cylinder $y^2 = 9 - z$ and the planes $y = x$, $x = 0$ and $z = 0$.

8. Find the volume of the solid bounded by $y^2 + z^2 = 4 x$ and $x = 5$.

9. Find the volume of the solid bounded by the surfaces $x^2 + 3 y^2 = z$, $x^2 + y^2 = 2 x$ and $z = 0$.

10. Find the volume in the first octant bounded by the cylinder $y = 1 - x^2$ and the plane $z = x + y$.

11. Find the volume of one of the two wedges cut from the cylinder $x^2 + y^2 = a^2$ by the planes $z = 0$ and $z = mx$.

12. Find the volume under the paraboloid $z = x^2 + y^2$ over the square bounded by the lines $x = \pm 1$, $y = \pm 1$.

13. Find the volume common to two equal right circular cylinders of radius a, whose axes intersect at right angles.

14. Find the volume of one of the wedges cut from a right circular cylinder 12 inches in diameter by two planes, one of which is perpendicular to the axis of the cylinder, and the other of which is inclined to the former at an angle of $45°$ and meets it in a diameter of the cylinder.

15. Find the volume of the cylindrical column standing on the region common to the two parabolas $y = x^2$ and $y^2 = x$ as base and cut off by the surface $z = 4 + y - x^2$.

16. Find the volume bounded by the paraboloid $z = 1 - x^2 - 4 y^2$ and the XY-plane.

524. Evaluation of a Double Integral in Polar Coördinates

It was shown in § 520 how the double integral $\iint_R f(x, y)\, dA$ can be transformed into an iterated integral when rectangular coördinates are used. Now suppose that the integrand $f(x, y)$ is expressed in polar coördinates r and θ, as $F(r, \theta)$, and suppose that we wish to express the double integral $\iint_R F(r, \theta)\, dA$ in terms of a corresponding iterated integral.

The double integral is defined by

$$(a) \qquad \iint_R F(r, \theta)\, dA = \lim_{\delta \to 0} \sum F(\rho, \phi)\, \Delta A,$$

where (ρ, ϕ) is any point in the typical sub-region ΔA. To obtain the sub-regions ΔA in this case, let us cover the region R by a polar network by drawing circles with center at the origin O and radiating lines through O (Fig. 219); the typical sub-region is then a "curvilinear rectangle," as shown in Fig. 219.

Let the inner and outer radii of a typical sub-region ΔA be r and

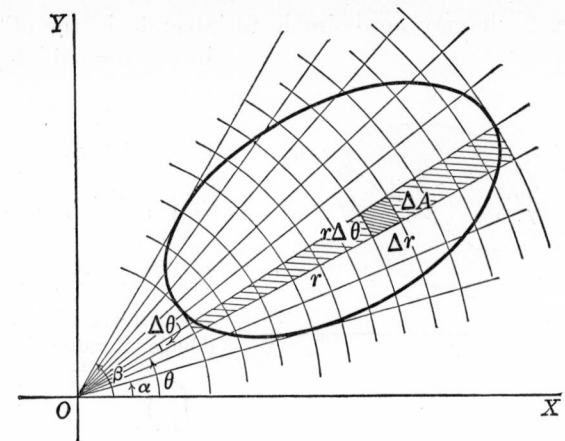

$r + \Delta r$ respectively, and let the angle of ΔA at O be $\Delta\theta$. Then by the formula for the area of a circular sector, we have

$$(b) \qquad \text{area } \Delta A = \tfrac{1}{2}(r + \Delta r)^2 \, \Delta\theta - \tfrac{1}{2}\, r^2 \, \Delta\theta$$
$$= (r + \tfrac{1}{2} \, \Delta r) \, \Delta r \, \Delta\theta.$$

Now since ρ in (a) is the radius vector of *any* point in ΔA, we may choose ρ as $r + \tfrac{1}{2} \, \Delta r$; then area $\Delta A = \rho \, \Delta r \, \Delta\theta$, where $\rho = r + \tfrac{1}{2} \, \Delta r$. Definition (a) then becomes

$$(c) \qquad \iint_R F(r, \theta) \, dA = \lim_{\delta \to 0} \sum F(\rho, \phi) \cdot \rho \, \Delta r \, \Delta\theta.$$

By a method similar to that used in the proof of the theorem of § 520, it may be shown* that

$$(d) \qquad \lim_{\delta \to 0} \sum F(\rho, \phi) \, \rho \, \Delta r \, \Delta\theta = \int_\alpha^\beta \left(\int_{r_1(\theta)}^{r_2(\theta)} F(r, \theta) \, r \, dr \right) d\theta.$$

Hence:

$$(5) \qquad \iint_R F(r, \theta) \, dA = \int_\alpha^\beta \left(\int_{r_1(\theta)}^{r_2(\theta)} F(r, \theta) \, r \, dr \right) d\theta,$$

where the limits r_1, r_2 and α, β are to be chosen so as to cover the region R as shown in Fig. 220 (a).

* See, for example, Sokolnikoff, *Advanced Calculus*, § 46, or Franklin, *Treatise on Advanced Calculus*, § 229, or Osgood, *Advanced Calculus*, pages 81–83, 263–269.

Occasionally it may be desirable to integrate in the other order in the iterated integral, and get

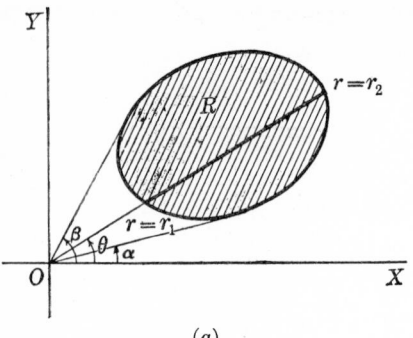

$$(e) \quad \iint_R F(r, \theta) \, dA$$

$$= \int_a^b \left(\int_{\theta_1(r)}^{\theta_2(r)} F(r, \theta) \, r \, d\theta \right) dr$$

(see Fig. 220 (b)).

Example. Evaluate the double iterated integral

$$\int_0^a \int_0^{\sqrt{a^2-x^2}} (x^2 + y^2) \, dy \, dx$$

by changing to polar coördinates.

Solution: The given integral is evidently taken over the portion of the circle $x^2 + y^2 = a^2$ in the first quadrant. In polar coördinates, the equation of this circle is $r = a$ and the integrand is r^2. Therefore,

$$\int_0^a \int_0^{\sqrt{a^2-x^2}} (x^2 + y^2) \, dy \, dx$$

$$= \int_0^{\frac{\pi}{2}} \int_0^a r^2 \cdot r \, dr \, d\theta = \tfrac{1}{8} \pi a^4.$$

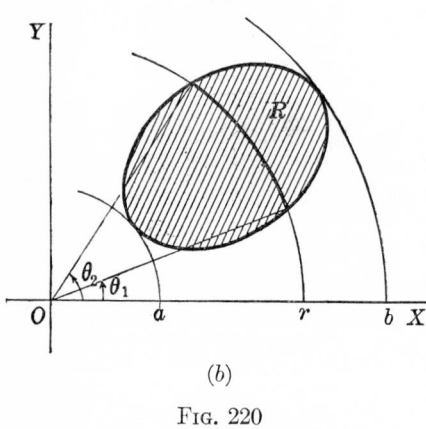

(a)

(b)

Fig. 220

525. Volumes by Double Integrals in Cylindrical Coördinates

It should be recalled that the *cylindrical coördinates* of a point in space consist of the polar coördinates (r, θ) of the projection of the given point on the XY-plane together with the rectangular coördinate z of the given point (Fig. 221). These cylindrical coördinates (r, θ, z) are related to the rectangular coördinates (x, y, z) by the relations $x = r \cos \theta$, $y = r \sin \theta$, $z = z$.

In many cases, volumes may be found conveniently by double integrals, using cylindrical coördinates, especially where there is symmetry about an axis. Let $z = f(r, \theta)$ be the equation in cylindrical coördinates of a surface lying above a region R of the (r, θ)-plane. Let $f(r, \theta)$ be continuous over R. In order to calculate the volume under the surface and directly above R, as in § 517 we have $V = \iint_R z \, dA$.

However, since we are using polar coördinates in the XY-plane, the formula becomes:

$$(a) \qquad V = \iint_R z \, dA$$

$$= \int_\alpha^\beta \int_{r_1(\theta)}^{r_2(\theta)} z \, r \, dr \, d\theta$$

$$= \int_a^b \int_{\theta_1(r)}^{\theta_2(r)} z \, r \, d\theta \, dr,$$

where the limits of integration are determined by the boundary of R in the usual manner.

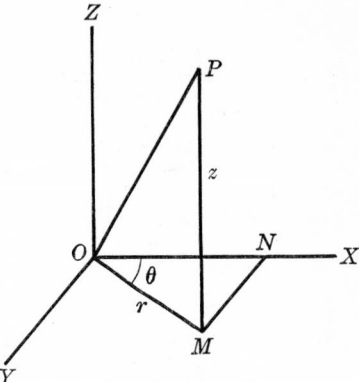

EXAMPLE. Find the volume under the paraboloid $x^2 + y^2 = az$, above the XY-plane and inside the cylinder $x^2 + y^2 = 2\,ax$. (Fig. 222.)

Fig. 221

Solution: The equation of the paraboloid in cylindrical coördinates is $r^2 = az$ or $z = r^2/a$, and the equation of the cylinder is $r = 2\,a \cos \theta$. The required volume is then given by

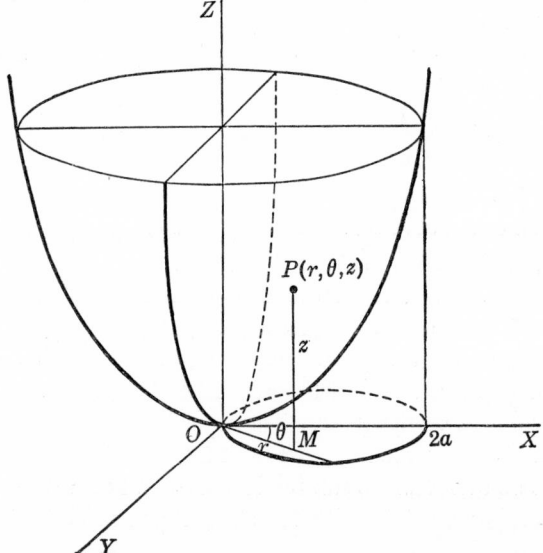

Fig. 222

$$V = 2 \int_0^{\frac{\pi}{2}} \int_0^{2a \cos \theta} z(r \, dr \, d\theta) = 2 \int_0^{\frac{\pi}{2}} \int_0^{2a \cos \theta} \frac{r^2}{a} r \, dr \, d\theta = \tfrac{3}{2} \pi a^3.$$

526. Exercises

In Exercises 1–4, evaluate the given integrals by changing to polar coördinates:

1. $\displaystyle\int_0^a \int_0^{\sqrt{a^2-x^2}} dy \, dx.$ 　　　　　　2. $\displaystyle\int_0^a \int_0^x \sqrt{x^2+y^2} \, dy \, dx.$

3. $\displaystyle\int_0^{2a} \int_0^{\sqrt{2ax-x^2}} (x^2+y^2) \, dy \, dx.$ 　4. $\displaystyle\int_0^a \int_0^{\sqrt{a^2-y^2}} \sqrt{a^2-x^2-y^2} \, dx \, dy.$

5. Reverse the order of integration in: $\displaystyle\int_0^{2\pi} \int_0^a r \, F(r, \theta) \, dr \, d\theta.$

6. Reverse the order of integration in: $\displaystyle\int_0^{\frac{\pi}{4}} \int_0^{a \sec \theta} r \, F(r, \theta) \, dr \, d\theta.$

7. Find the volume bounded above by the sphere $r^2 + z^2 = 8$ and below by the paraboloid $r^2 = 2 z$.

8. Find the volume bounded by the cylinder $r = 2 a \cos \theta$, the XY-plane and the cone $r = z$.

9. Find the volume bounded by the paraboloid $x^2 + y^2 = az$, the XY-plane and the cylinder $x^2 + y^2 = a^2$.

10. Find the volume cut from the cylinder $x^2 + y^2 = 2 ax$ by one nappe of the cone $x^2 + y^2 - z^2 = 0$ below the plane $z = 2 a$.

11. Find the volume cut from the sphere $x^2 + y^2 + z^2 = a^2$ by the cylinder $r = a \cos \theta$.

12. Find the region of integration of: $\displaystyle\int_0^{\frac{\pi}{2}} \int_0^{a \cos \theta} r \, F(r, \theta) \, dr \, d\theta.$

★ 527. Area of a Curved Surface

In § 405, we treated the problem of finding the area of a *surface of revolution*. We now consider the general case of any surface.

Let a given surface σ be represented by the equation $z = f(x, y)$, where the function $f(x, y)$ has continuous first partial derivatives. Suppose that we wish to find the area S of a portion of this surface bounded by one or more curves. Let us project the region S upon the XY-plane, giving a plane region R (Fig. 223). As was done in § 516, let region R be divided into sub-regions ΔA_k, and draw the cylindrical column standing on ΔA_k with its elements parallel to the Z-axis. Let (ξ_k, η_k) be any point of ΔA_k, and let $P_k(\xi_k, \eta_k, \zeta_k)$ be the corresponding point on the given surface σ. Let the tangent plane to the

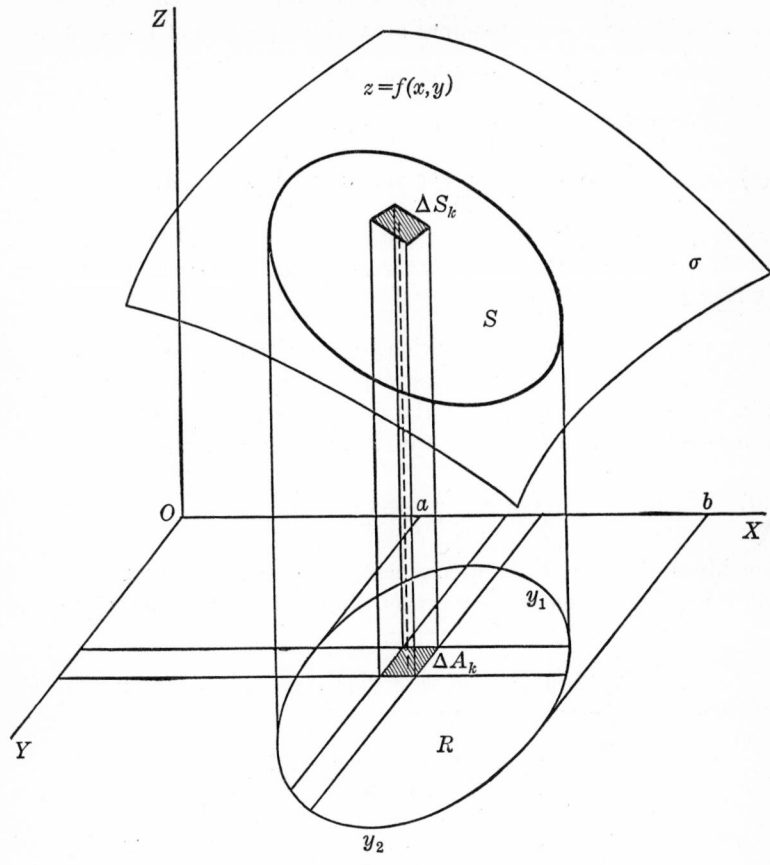

$$z = f(x,y)$$

F<small>IG</small>. 223

surface at the point P_k be drawn. The cylindrical column on ΔA_k will cut from this tangent plane a region of area ΔS_k, say. If γ_k is the acute angle between the tangent plane and the XY-plane, which is also the angle between the Z-axis and the normal to the surface σ at P_k, we have

$$(a) \qquad \Delta A_k = \Delta S_k \cdot \cos \gamma_k{}^* \qquad \text{or} \qquad \Delta S_k = \Delta A_k \cdot \sec \gamma_k,$$

since ΔA_k is the projection of ΔS_k on the XY-plane. We now *define*

---

* If any plane area A is projected upon a plane making an acute angle θ with the plane of A, the projected area is equal to $A \cos \theta$.

$S = \lim\limits_{\delta \to 0} \sum\limits_{k=1}^{n} \Delta S_k$ as the required area of the portion of the surface σ. Then from (a) and the definition of a double integral, we have:

The area S on the surface σ is given by

(6) $$S = \lim\limits_{\delta \to 0} \sum\limits_{k=1}^{n} \sec \gamma_k \, \Delta A_k = \iint_R \sec \gamma \, dA,$$

where γ is the angle between the Z-axis and the normal to the surface σ at the point (x, y, z), and R is the projection of the region S on the XY-plane.

In order to adapt this definition to use with a surface given by an equation $F(x, y, z) = 0$, we must express $\sec \gamma$ in terms of $F(x, y, z)$. Since the direction cosines of the normal to a surface $F(x, y, z) = 0$ are proportional to F_x, F_y, F_z (by § 510), it follows that

(a) $$\cos \gamma = \frac{|F_z|}{\sqrt{F_x{}^2 + F_y{}^2 + F_z{}^2}};$$

the absolute value $|F_z|$ is used since γ is acute and $\cos \gamma$ is therefore positive. The value of $\sec \gamma$ is then obtained by taking the reciprocal of this; substituting this in formula (6) above, we have:

The area S of the portion of the surface $F(x, y, z) = 0$ over the region R of the XY-plane is given by:

(7) $$S = \iint_R \frac{\sqrt{F_x{}^2 + F_y{}^2 + F_z{}^2}}{|F_z|} \, dA.$$

To evaluate this, we convert the double integral into an iterated integral by the method of § 520 or § 524.

If more convenient, we may project the area S upon the YZ-plane or the ZX-plane; the corresponding formula for S will be similar to (7) in an obvious way.

EXAMPLE. Find the area of the surface of the sphere $x^2 + y^2 + z^2 = a^2$ contained within the cylinder $x^2 + y^2 = ax$ and above the XY-plane.

Solution: The region R is that within the circle $x^2 + y^2 = ax$; in polar coördinates, this equation is $r = a \cos \theta$. From the equation of the sphere, $F = x^2 + y^2 + z^2 - a^2$. Then $F_x = 2\,x$, $F_y = 2\,y$, $F_z = 2\,z$, and

$$\sqrt{F_x{}^2 + F_y{}^2 + F_z{}^2} = 2\sqrt{x^2 + y^2 + z^2} = 2\,a,$$

and

$$\sec \gamma = \frac{2\,a}{2\,z} = \frac{a}{\sqrt{a^2 - x^2 - y^2}} = \frac{a}{\sqrt{a^2 - r^2}}.$$

Half the required area is in front of the ZX-plane and half behind it.   The required area is therefore

$$S = 2 \int_0^{\frac{\pi}{2}} \int_0^{a \cos \theta} \frac{a \, r \, dr \, d\theta}{\sqrt{a^2 - r^2}} = (\pi - 2) \, a^2.$$

★ 528. Exercises

1. Find the area of the surface cut from the cone $x^2 + y^2 = z^2$ by a square prism of side 2 and having the Z-axis as its axis. (Use rectangular coördinates.)

2. Find the area of the surface of the cone $x^2 + y^2 = z^2$ within the cylinder $x^2 + y^2 = 2\,x$. (Use rectangular coördinates.)

3. Find the area of that part of the surface of the sphere $x^2 + y^2 + z^2 = 4\,z$ which lies within the paraboloid $x^2 + y^2 = 2\,z$. (Use rectangular coördinates.)

4. Find the area of the portion of the cylinder $y^2 + z^2 = a^2$ lying within the cylinder $x^2 + y^2 = a^2$. (Use rectangular coördinates.)

5. Find the area in the first octant of the surface $z = xy$ which lies within the cylinder $x^2 + y^2 = a^2$. (Change to polar coördinates.)

6. Find the area in the first octant of the surface $z = x^2 - y^2$ which lies within the cylinder $x^2 + y^2 = 4$. (Change to polar coördinates.)

7. Find the area of the portion of the sphere $x^2 + y^2 + z^2 = 4$ which lies outside the paraboloid $x^2 + y^2 + z = 4$. (Change to polar coördinates.)

8. Find the area of the surface of the paraboloid $x^2 + y^2 = 6\,z$ which lies within the sphere $x^2 + y^2 + z^2 = 16$. (Change to polar coördinates.)

529. Centroid of a Plane Area, by Double Integrals

The first moments and the coördinates of the centroid of a plane region were defined in § 201 in terms of definite integrals involving a single integration. They may also be expressed in terms of double integrals, and it will be shown presently that the new definitions are consistent with the old ones. In many problems the expressions by double integrals are more convenient and easier to set up than by the previous method.

Let R be a closed plane region of the XY-plane, as in § 516. Proceeding as in § 516, let R be divided into n sub-regions ΔA_k, let δ be the maximum diameter of any ΔA_k, and let the sub-division be such that $\delta \to 0$ as $n \to \infty$. Let (ξ_k, η_k) be an arbitrary point in ΔA_k, multiply the area of ΔA_k by the distance ξ_k from the Y-axis, and form the sum $\sum_{k=1}^{n} \xi_k \cdot \Delta A_k$ over the region R. The limit of this sum, as $\delta \to 0$, is the double integral $\iint_R x \, dA$. Similarly we form the double integral $\iint_R y \, dA$. Then:

*The **first moments** of a plane region R with respect to the coördinate axes are defined by the double integrals*

$$(8) \qquad M_y = \iint_R x \, dA, \qquad M_x = \iint_R y \, dA.$$

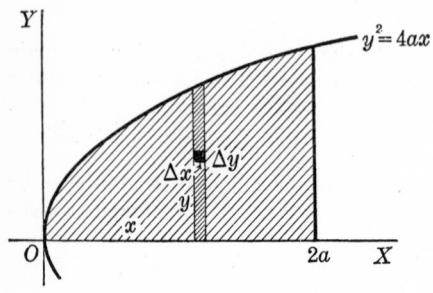

*The **centroid** of the region R is defined as the point $(\bar{x}, \bar{y})$ whose coördinates satisfy the relations*

$$(9) \quad A \, \bar{x} = M_y, \quad A \, \bar{y} = M_x,$$

where A is the area of the region R, given by

$$(10) \qquad A = \iint_R dA.$$

FIG. 224

EXAMPLE 1. Find the centroid of the area bounded by the curve $y^2 = 4 \, ax$, the X-axis and the line $x = 2 \, a$ (Fig. 224).

Solution:

$$M_y = \iint_R x \, dA = \int_0^{2a} \int_0^{2\sqrt{ax}} x \, dy \, dx = 2\sqrt{a} \int_0^{2a} x^{\frac{3}{2}} \, dx = \frac{16\sqrt{2}}{5} a^3,$$

$$M_x = \iint_R y \, dA = \int_0^{2a} \int_0^{2\sqrt{ax}} y \, dy \, dx = 2 \, a \int_0^{2a} x \, dx = 4 \, a^3,$$

$$A = \iint_R dA = \int_0^{2a} \int_0^{2\sqrt{ax}} dy \, dx = 2\sqrt{a} \int_0^{2a} x^{\frac{1}{2}} \, dx = \frac{8\sqrt{2}}{3} a^2;$$

therefore

$$\bar{x} = \frac{16\sqrt{2} \, a^3}{5} \cdot \frac{3}{8\sqrt{2} \, a^2} = \tfrac{6}{5} a, \quad \bar{y} = \frac{4 \, a^3}{1} \cdot \frac{3}{8\sqrt{2} \, a^2} = \tfrac{3}{4}\sqrt{2} \, a.$$

(Compare this solution with that of the same problem in Example 2 of § 201.)

EXAMPLE 2. Find the centroid of the area bounded by the cardioid $r = a(1 - \cos \theta)$.

Solution: Since $x = r \cos \theta$ and $y = r \sin \theta$, we have

$$M_y = \iint_R x \, dA = \iint_R r \cos \theta \, dA = \int_0^{2\pi} \int_0^{a(1-\cos \theta)} r^2 \cos \theta \, dr \, d\theta$$

$$= \tfrac{1}{3} a^3 \int_0^{2\pi} (1 - \cos \theta)^3 \cos \theta \, d\theta = -\tfrac{5}{4}\pi a^3,$$

$$A = \iint_R dA = \int_0^{2\pi} \int_0^{a(1-\cos \theta)} r \, dr \, d\theta = \tfrac{1}{2} a^2 \int_0^{2\pi} (1 - \cos \theta)^2 \, d\theta = \tfrac{3}{2} \pi a^2,$$

$$\therefore \bar{x} = \frac{M_y}{A} = -\frac{5\,\pi a^3}{4}\cdot\frac{2}{3\,\pi a^2} = -\tfrac{5}{6}\,a.$$

Evidently, $\bar{y} = 0$ by symmetry.

We shall now show that the definitions of first moments given above in (8) are consistent with the previous definitions in § 201. In the expression for M_y in (8), let us replace the double integral $\iint_R x\,dA$ by the corresponding iterated integral $\int_a^b \int_{y_1}^{y_2} x\,dy\,dx$, where y_1 and y_2 are the values of y for the boundary of the region R in terms of an arbitrary abscissa x, and a and b are the extreme values of x for R. If we carry out the first integration with respect to y, we get

$$(a) \qquad\qquad M_y = \int_a^b x(y_2 - y_1)\,dx.$$

But $y_2 - y_1$ is the same as $h(x)$ in § 201. Hence, the value of M_y given by (8) is equivalent to that given in § 201. A similar proof can be given for M_x.

Special formulas were stated without proof in § 201 for M_y and M_x for a region bounded by a curve $y = f(x)$, the X-axis and the lines $x = a$ and $x = b$. These formulas may be derived as follows:

$$M_y = \int_a^b \int_0^y x\,dy\,dx = \int_a^b xy\,dx, \qquad M_x = \int_a^b \int_0^y y\,dy\,dx = \int_a^b \tfrac{1}{2}\,y^2\,dx.$$

530. Second Moments of a Plane Area, by Double Integrals

The second moments (or moments of inertia) of a plane area were defined in § 205 by single integration. They may also be defined by means of double integrals, and it will be shown presently that the new definitions are consistent with the previous ones.

Let R be a closed region in the XY-plane, as in § 516, and let us use the same notation as in that article. The second moment I_y with respect to the Y-axis is defined by a limit analogous to that for M_y except that the second power of the distance ξ_k is used instead of the first power. A similar remark applies to the second moment with respect to the X-axis. We then have the following definitions:

*The **second moments** (or moments of inertia) of a plane region R with respect to the coördinate axes are defined by:*

$$(11) \qquad\qquad I_y = \iint_R x^2\,dA, \qquad I_x = \iint_R y^2\,dA.$$

EXAMPLE. Find the second moments of area with respect to the coördinate axes of the region bounded by the curves $y^2 = x$ and $y = x^2$.

$$Solution: \ I_x = \iint_R y^2 \, dA = \int_0^1 \int_{x^2}^{\sqrt{x}} y^2 \, dy \, dx = \tfrac{3}{35},$$

$$I_y = \iint_R x^2 \, dA = \int_0^1 \int_{x^2}^{\sqrt{x}} x^2 \, dy \, dx = \tfrac{3}{35}.$$

That the definitions (11) are consistent with the previous ones in § 205 is shown as follows:

$$I_y = \iint_R x^2 \, dy \, dx = \int_a^b \int_{y_1}^{y_2} x^2 \, dy \, dx = \int_a^b x^2 (y_2 - y_1) \, dx = \int_a^b x^2 \, h(x) \, dx,$$

as in § 205.

Consider the region R bounded by a curve $y = f(x)$, the X-axis and the lines $x = a$ and $x = b$. For this case we have

$$I_x = \iint_R y^2 \, dA = \int_a^b \int_0^y y^2 \, dy \, dx = \int_a^b \tfrac{1}{3} y^3 \, dx.$$

This result proves the formula (a) of § 205.

531. Exercises

Use double integrals in the following problems:

1. Find the centroid of the area bounded by the parabola $y^2 = 4\,ax$, its axis of symmetry and the line $x = b$.
2. Locate the centroid of the area bounded by $y = 4 - x^2$ and $y = 4 - 2\,x$.
3. Find the centroid of the area bounded by $y^2 = x^3$ and $y = x$.
4. Find the centroid of the area outside the parabola $y^2 = 2\,x$ and inside the circle $y^2 = 4\,x - x^2$.
5. Find the centroid of the area bounded by $y^2 = 4\,x$ and $2\,x - y = 4$.
6. Find the centroid of the area bounded by $y = 6\,x - x^2$ and $y = x$.
7. Locate the centroid of the area of the loop in the first-quadrant of the curve $r = a \sin 2\,\theta$.
8. Find the centroid of the area of a semicircle of radius a.
9. Find the centroid of the area inside the circle $r = 2\,a \cos \theta$ and outside the circle $r = a$.
10. Find the centroid of the area of one loop of the lemniscate $r^2 = a^2 \cos 2\,\theta$. [*Hint.* Use $\cos 2\,\theta = 1 - 2 \sin^2 \theta$, and use the substitution $u^2 = 2 \sin^2 \theta$.]
11. Find the second moment with respect to the Y-axis of the area bounded by $y = x^2$ and $y = 2 - x^2$.
12. Find the second moment with respect to the Y-axis of a loop of the curve $y^2 = x^2 \, (2 - x)$.
13. Find the second moments with respect to each of the coördinate axes of the smaller area enclosed by $x^2 + y^2 = a^2$ and $y = a - x$.
14. Find the second moment with respect to each of the coördinate axes of the area in the first quadrant of the circle $x^2 + y^2 = a^2$.

15. Find the second moment with respect to each of the coördinate axes of the area of the ellipse $b^2x^2 + a^2y^2 = a^2b^2$.

16. Find the second moment with respect to the X-axis of the entire area bounded by the hypocycloid $x^{\frac{2}{3}} + y^{\frac{2}{3}} = a^{\frac{2}{3}}$.

17. Find the second moment with respect to the coördinate axes of the area of one loop of the curve $r = a \cos 2\theta$.

18. Find the second moment with respect to the Y-axis of the area bounded by the lemniscate $r^2 = a^2 \cos 2\theta$.

532. Triple Integrals

A *triple integral* of a function of three variables is defined in a manner quite analogous to that used in defining a double integral, by a limit of a sum.

Let $f(x, y, z)$ be a single-valued function of three independent variables defined throughout a closed three-dimensional region B enclosed by one or more surfaces. Let the region V be divided into n sub-regions ΔV_k (Fig. 225) by three systems of planes or surfaces, and let δ be the maximum diameter of any sub-region. Let the system of sub-division be such that $\delta \to 0$ as $n \to \infty$. Let (ξ_k, η_k, ζ_k) be any point in ΔV_k, and form the sum $\sum_{k=1}^{n} f(\xi_k, \eta_k, \zeta_k)\Delta V_k$, where ΔV_k

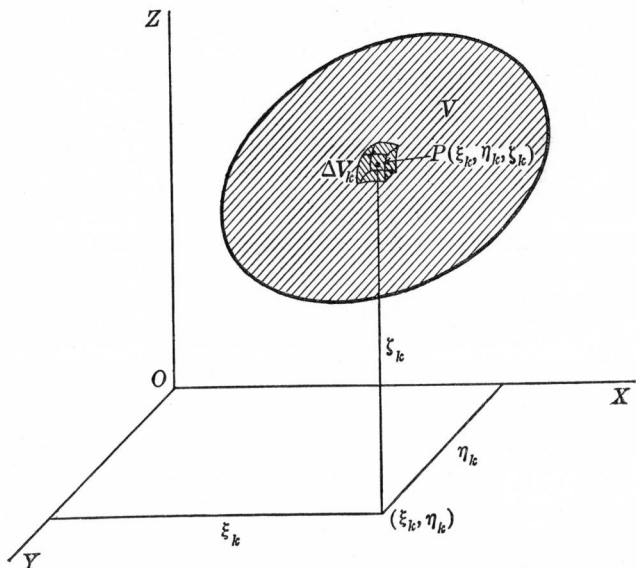

Fig. 225

denotes the volume of the k-th sub-region as well as the sub-region itself.

*If this sum $\sum_{k=1}^{n} f(\xi_k, \eta_k, \zeta_k)\Delta V_k$ approaches a limit as $\delta \to 0$, which is independent of the mode of sub-division and of the choice of (ξ_k, η_k, ζ_k), then this limit is defined as the **triple integral** (or volume integral) of $f(x, y, z)$ over the region V,* and is denoted by the symbol $\iiint_V f(x, y, z)\, dV$:

$$(12) \qquad \iiint_V f(x, y, z)\, dV = \lim_{\delta \to 0} \sum_{k=1}^{n} f(\xi_k, \eta_k, \zeta_k)\Delta V_k.$$

It can be proved that *the limit* (13) *defining the triple integral always exists when the integrand $f(x, y, z)$ is continuous in the closed region V.*

The sub-division of V into sub-regions ΔV_k is usually made by systems of planes parallel to the coördinate planes, corresponding to rectangular coördinates, or by systems of planes, cylindrical surfaces or spherical surfaces, corresponding to cylindrical coördinates or spherical coördinates.

A triple integral is *evaluated* by use of a corresponding iterated integral, as will be shown presently.

533. Iterated Triple Integrals

Just as we defined an iterated double integral by means of successive integrations, so we may define an *iterated* (or repeated) *triple integral:*

$$(a) \qquad \int_a^b \left[\int_{y_1(x)}^{y_2(x)} \left(\int_{z_1(x, y)}^{z_2(x, y)} f(x, y, z)\, dz \right) dy \right] dx,$$

where $f(x, y, z)$ is a given continuous function of the independent variables x, y, z. We first integrate $f(x, y, z)$ with respect to z, holding x and y constant, between the limits z_1 and z_2 which are given functions of x and y; then we integrate this result (which is a function of x and y in general) with respect to y, holding x constant, between limits y_1 and y_2 which are functions of x, and finally we integrate this result with respect to x between constant limits a and b. Such an iterated integral involves two partial integrations.

Other iterated triple integrals of $f(x, y, z)$ may be obtained by changing the order in which the variables x, y, z are used. Thus, we may integrate first with respect to z, then with respect to x and lastly with respect to y; or we may integrate first with respect to x, then with respect to z and lastly with respect to y; etc.

It is customary to omit the parentheses and brackets in the iterated integral, so that (a) is usually written:

(b)
$$\int_a^b \int_{y_1(x)}^{y_2(x)} \int_{z_1(x, y)}^{z_2(x, y)} f(x, y, z)\, dz\, dy\, dx.$$

If the order of integration is changed, new limits of the integrals must be determined.

EXAMPLE. Evaluate the iterated triple integral $\int_0^1 \int_{x^2}^1 \int_0^{1-y} x\, dz\, dy\, dx$.

Solution:
$$\int_{z=0}^{z=1-y} x\, dz = xz \bigg|_{z=0}^{z=1-y} = x(1-y),$$

$$\int_{y=x^2}^{y=1}\left(\int_0^{1-y} x\, dz\right) dy = \int_{y=x^2}^{y=1} x(1-y)\, dy = x(y - \tfrac{1}{2} y^2)\bigg|_{y=x^2}^{y=1}$$

$$= \tfrac{1}{2} x - x^3 + \tfrac{1}{2} x^5,$$

$$\int_{x=0}^{x=1}\left[\int_{x^2}^1\left(\int_0^{1-y} x\, dz\right) dy\right] dx = \int_0^1 (\tfrac{1}{2} x - x^3 + \tfrac{1}{2} x^5)\, dx$$

$$= (\tfrac{1}{4} x^2 - \tfrac{1}{4} x^4 + \tfrac{1}{12} x^6)\bigg|_0^1 = \frac{1}{12}.$$

534. Exercises

Evaluate each of the following iterated triple integrals:

1. $\displaystyle\int_2^4\left[\int_1^x\left(\int_0^x x\, dz\right) dy\right] dx.$

2. $\displaystyle\int_0^1\left[\int_0^{1-x}\left(\int_0^{1-y^2} z\, dz\right) dy\right] dx.$

3. $\displaystyle\int_0^2\left[\int_1^x\left(\int_1^y xz\, dz\right) dy\right] dx.$

4. $\displaystyle\int_0^a\left[\int_0^x\left(\int_0^{x+y} xyz\, dz\right) dy\right] dx.$

5. $\displaystyle\int_0^2\left[\int_{-1}^{x^2}\left(\int_1^y xy\, dz\right) dy\right] dx.$

6. $\displaystyle\int_0^a\left[\int_0^{\sqrt{a^2-z^2}}\left(\int_0^{a-z} z\, dx\right) dy\right] dz.$

7. $\displaystyle\int_0^a\left[\int_0^b\left(\int_0^c (x^2 + y^2 + z^2)\, dz\right) dy\right] dx.$

8. $\displaystyle\int_0^\pi\left[\int_0^{\sin\theta}\left(\int_0^{r\sin\theta} r\cos^2\theta\, dz\right) dr\right] d\theta.$

9. $\displaystyle\int_0^1 \int_0^{\frac{\pi}{3}} \int_0^{r^2\sin^2\theta} r^3\, dz\, d\theta\, dr.$

10. $\displaystyle\int_0^2 \int_0^z \int_0^{y+z} xy\, dx\, dy\, dz.$

11. $\displaystyle\int_0^\pi \int_0^{\frac{\pi}{6}} \int_0^{a\sin\theta} r^2 \cos\theta \sin\phi \, dr \, d\theta \, d\phi$.

12. $\displaystyle\int_0^a \int_0^a \int_0^x \sqrt{x^2 + y^2} \, dy \, dx \, dz$.

535. Evaluation of Triple Integrals by Iterated Integrals: Rectangular Coördinates

In a manner analogous to that used for double integrals, it may be shown* that a triple integral, defined as a limit of a sum, can be evaluated by an iterated integral according to the following theorem:

If $f(x, y, z)$ is continuous in a properly defined region V of space, and if we use rectangular coördinates, then

$$(13) \quad \iiint_V f(x, y, z) \, dV = \int_a^b \left[\int_{y_1(x)}^{y_2(x)} \left(\int_{z_1(x, y)}^{z_2(x, y)} f(x, y, z) \, dz \right) dy \right] dx,$$

and similar iterated integrals for other orders of integration, where the limits z_1, z_2, y_1, y_2, and a, b are chosen with reference to the boundary of V.

The limits of the iterated integral are determined from the boundary of V in a manner so similar to that for double integrals that a formal statement of the process seems unnecessary. The method is illustrated by the following example and by examples in later sections.

EXAMPLE 1. Find the limits of the iterated integral for

$$\iiint_V f(x, y, z) \, dV$$

when the region V is that bounded by the paraboloid $x^2 + 4y^2 = 16 - z$ and the XY-plane, and in the first octant. (Fig. 226.)

Solution: Let us integrate first with respect to z; the integration will extend from the XY-plane to the surface of the paraboloid: $z = 0$ to $z = 16 - x^2 - 4y^2$. Let us next integrate across the quarter ellipse in the XY-plane, with respect to y, from $y = 0$ to $y = \frac{1}{2}\sqrt{16 - x^2}$, since the equation of the ellipse in the XY-plane is $x^2 + 4y^2 = 16$. Finally, we integrate with respect to x from $x = 0$ to $x = 4$. The required iterated integral is then

$$\int_0^4 \int_0^{\frac{1}{2}\sqrt{16 - x^2}} \int_0^{16 - x^2 - 4y^2} f(x, y, z) \, dz \, dy \, dx.$$

---

* See, for example, Sokolnikoff, *Advanced Calculus*, § 45, or Osgood, *Advanced Calculus*, pages 93–100, 270–274, or Franklin, *Treatise on Advanced Calculus*, § 229.

Triple integrals may be used to find volumes of solids, by taking $f(x, y, z) = 1$, but the volumes may usually be found more easily by use of double integrals, as shown in § 522. A more useful application of triple integrals is to such problems as finding centroids and moments of inertia of bodies, and finding masses of bodies of variable density.

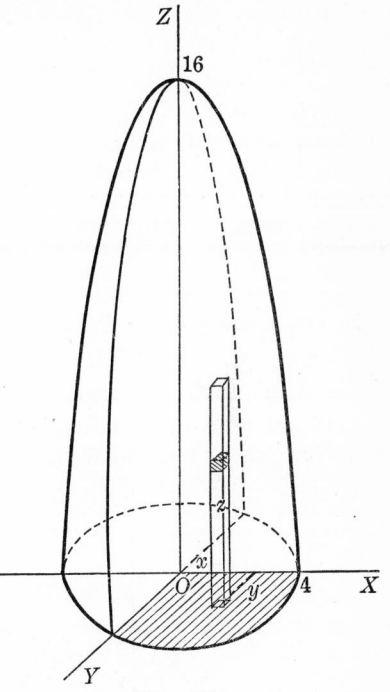

Fig. 226

EXAMPLE 2. Find the mass of the body in the form of a tetrahedron cut from the first octant by the plane

$$x + y + z = 1,$$

if the density varies as the product of the distances from the three coördinate planes.

Solution: Let ΔV be the volume element, and let (x, y, z) be the coördinates of any point in this element. Then the density of the element is $kxyz$ (k constant), the mass of the element is $kxyz\,\Delta V$, and the required mass of the body is given by

$$m = \iiint_V kxyz\,dV = \int_0^1 \int_0^{1-x} \int_0^{1-x-y} kxyz\,dz\,dy\,dx = \tfrac{11}{720}\,k.$$

536. Exercises

In Exercises 1–4, write the triple integral $\iiint_V f(x, y, z)\,dV$ as an iterated integral for each of the given regions V:

1. The volume under the paraboloid $x^2 + y^2 = 4 - z$, within the cylinder $x^2 + y^2 = 1$ and above the XY-plane.
2. The volume above the paraboloid $x^2 + y^2 = z$, under the sphere $x^2 + y^2 + z^2 = 2$ and within the cylinder $x^2 + y^2 = 1$.
3. The volume in the first octant bounded by the sphere $x^2 + y^2 + z^2 = 4$ and the coördinate planes.
4. The volume in the first octant bounded by the cylinder $y = x^2$, and the planes $y + z = 1$, $x = 0$ and $z = 0$.

5. Find the region of integration of: $\int_0^a \int_0^{\sqrt{a^2-y^2}} \int_0^x f(x, y, z)\, dz\, dx\, dy.$

6. Find the region of integration of: $\int_0^1 \int_{x^2}^{\sqrt{x}} \int_0^{4-x^2-y^2} f(x, y, z)\, dz\, dy\, dx.$

7. Find the mass of a right circular cylinder of altitude h and radius of base a, if the density varies as the square of the distance from the axis of the cylinder.

8. Find the mass of a cube of edge a, if the density is proportional to the sum of the distances from three adjacent faces.

9. Find the mass of a cube of edge a, if the density varies as the square of the distance from one corner.

10. Find the mass of a right circular cone of altitude h and radius of base a, if the density varies as the distance from the axis of the cone.

537. Triple Integrals in Cylindrical Coördinates

In many problems in which symmetry about an axis occurs, particularly in problems concerned with cylinders or cones or spheres, the integrations are usually easier when *cylindrical coördinates* are used than when rectangular coördinates are employed.

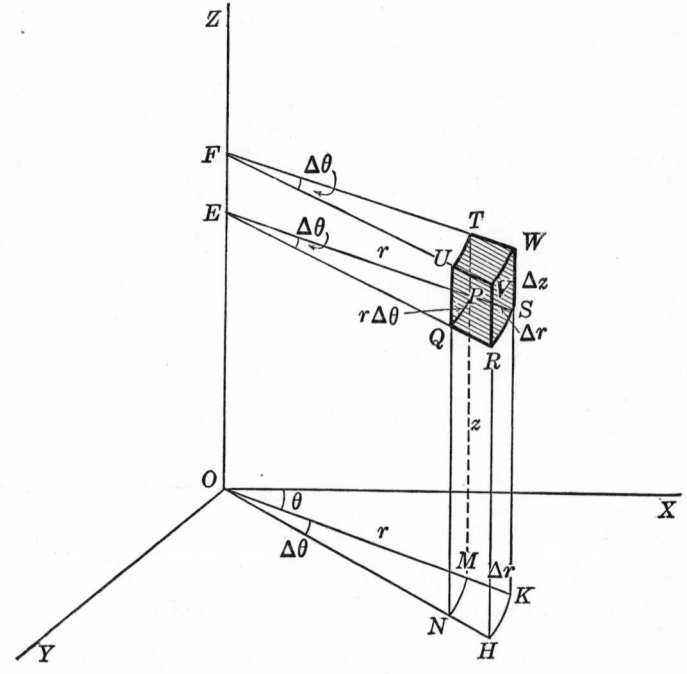

Fig. 227

Let r, θ, z be the cylindrical coördinates of a point. The element of volume for a triple integral in cylindrical coördinates may be obtained as follows. Draw a system of concentric cylinders $r = $ constant, a system of radial planes $\theta = $ constant through the Z-axis, and a system of parallel planes $z = $ constant. These surfaces are mutually orthogonal. A typical element of volume ΔV is shown in Fig. 227; it might be described as a "curvilinear parallelepiped." Its dimensions are $r\Delta\theta$, Δr and Δz, and its volume is approximately $\Delta V = r\Delta\theta \cdot \Delta r \cdot \Delta z$. It can be proved * that for simple regions the corresponding triple integral is

$$(a) \qquad \int_\alpha^\beta \left[\int_{r_1(\theta)}^{r_2(\theta)} \left(\int_{z_1(r,\,\theta)}^{z_2(r,\,\theta)} F(r,\,\theta,\,z)\, r\, dz \right) dr \right] d\theta.$$

The triple integral may also be written in other orders of integration, when convenient.

538. Exercises

Solve the following problems by use of cylindrical coördinates.

1. Find the volume of a paraboloid of revolution of altitude 4 and radius of base 2.
2. Find the volume of a sphere of radius a by use of a triple integral.
3. Find the volume under the surface $z = xy$, above the XY-plane and within the cylinder $x^2 + y^2 = 2\,x$.
4. Find the volume bounded above by the sphere $r^2 + z^2 = 5$ and below by the paraboloid $r^2 = 4\,z$.

539. Center of Mass and Centroid of a Solid, by Triple Integrals

The centroid of a solid of revolution was treated in § 203 by means of single integration. We shall now define the center of mass of a solid body in general; it will be shown presently that the previous definitions are special cases of the new definitions.

Let V be a closed region in space, and let us suppose that this region is occupied by a mass whose density at any point is denoted by $\rho(x, y, z)$ which is assumed to be a continuous function of its variables. Let the region V be divided, as in § 532, into n sub-regions ΔV_k, let δ be the maximum diameter of any ΔV_k, and let the sub-division be such that $\delta \to 0$ when $n \to \infty$. Let (ξ_k, η_k, ζ_k) be an arbitrary point of ΔV_k. If ρ_k is the value of the density function at a suitably chosen point in ΔV_k, the mass of the material in ΔV_k is $\Delta m_k = \rho_k \cdot \Delta V_k$. Now form the product $\xi_k \cdot \Delta m_k = \xi_k \rho_k \Delta V_k$ of the element of mass by

* See, for example, Sokolnikoff, *Advanced Calculus*, § 49.

the distance ξ_k from the YZ-plane, and form the sum $\sum_{k=1}^{n} \xi_k \rho_k \Delta V_k$ of all such products over the region V. The limit of this sum is, by a theorem for triple integrals analogous to Bliss' theorem, the triple integral $\iiint_V x\rho \, dV$. Similarly we form limits of sums by using the distances η_k and ζ_k from the ZX- and XY-planes respectively. Then we have the following definitions:

*The **first moments of mass** with respect to the coördinate planes of a body of density $\rho(x, y, z)$ are defined by:*

$$(14) \quad M_{yz} = \iiint_V \rho x \, dV, \quad M_{zx} = \iiint_V \rho y \, dV, \quad M_{xy} = \iiint_V \rho z \, dV.$$

*The **center of mass** of the body is defined as the point $(\overline{x}, \overline{y}, \overline{z})$ whose coördinates satisfy the relations*

$$(15) \qquad m \, \bar{x} = M_{yz}, \qquad m \, \bar{y} = M_{zx}, \qquad m \, \bar{z} = M_{xy},$$

where the mass m of the body is given by

$$(16) \qquad\qquad m = \iiint_V \rho \, dV.$$

If ρ is constant for the entire body (in which case the body is called a *homogeneous* solid), ρ will cancel out from both members of each equation in (15), and we then obtain the coördinates of the *centroid* of the corresponding geometric solid. But if the density is variable, the center of mass of the body may be different from the centroid of the corresponding solid.

EXAMPLE. Locate the center of mass of a body bounded by the coördinate planes and the plane $x + y + z = 1$, if the density is proportional to the distance from the YZ-plane.

Solution: Since the density is $\rho = kx$ (where k is constant), we have

$$M_{yz} = \int_0^1 \int_0^{1-x} \int_0^{1-x-y} x \cdot kx \cdot dz \, dy \, dx = \tfrac{1}{60} k,$$

$$m = \int_0^1 \int_0^{1-x} \int_0^{1-x-y} kx \cdot dz \, dy \, dx = \tfrac{1}{24} k;$$

therefore, $\overline{x} = \dfrac{k}{60} \cdot \dfrac{24}{k} = \dfrac{2}{5}$. In a similar way, we may calculate the coördinates $\overline{y}$ and $\overline{z}$ of the center of mass.

We shall now show that the formula of § 203 for the first moment of a solid of revolution is a special case of the formulas (14) above. Let the solid of revolution be generated by revolving about the Z-axis the region in the ZX-plane bounded by the curve $x = f(z)$, the Z-axis and the lines $z = a$ and $z = b$ (Fig. 228). If we use cylindrical coordinates, we have, by formula (14),

$$M_{xy} = \iiint_V z \, dV = \int_a^b \int_0^{2\pi} \int_0^x z \cdot r \, dr \, d\theta \, dz$$

$$= \int_a^b \int_0^{2\pi} z \cdot \tfrac{1}{2} x^2 \, d\theta \, dz = \int_a^b z \cdot \tfrac{1}{2} x^2 \cdot 2\pi \, dz = \int_a^b z \cdot \pi x^2 \, dz.$$

This last integral is the expression for M_{xy} by § 203. It can be shown by symmetry that $M_{zx} = 0$ and $M_{yz} = 0$. This shows that the method of § 203 is a special case of the more general definitions given above.

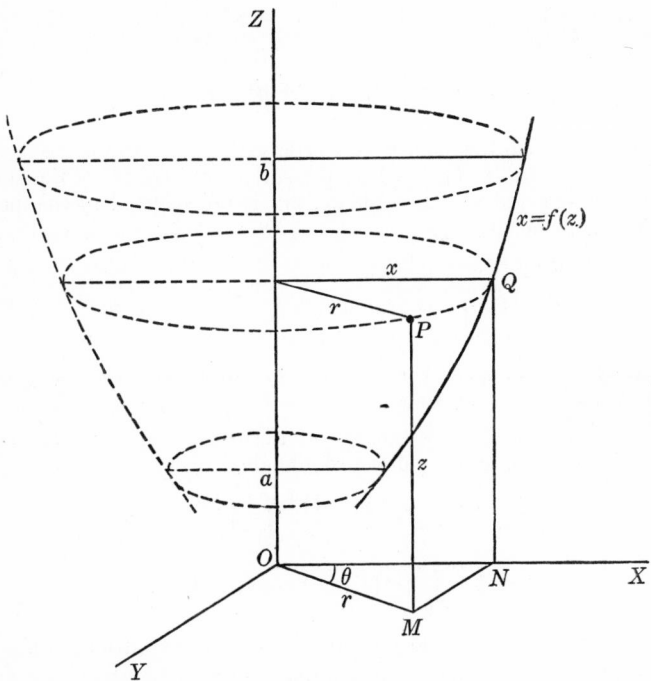

Fig. 228

540. Moments of Inertia or Second Moments of a Solid Body, by Triple Integrals

The second moment or moment of inertia of a solid of revolution was defined in § 207 by the use of a single integration. We shall now define the second moment or moment of inertia of any solid body; and we shall show presently that the previous definition is a special case of this general definition.

We shall use the same notation as in § 532. The square of the distance of the point (ξ_k, η_k, ζ_k) in ΔV_k from the Z-axis is $\xi_k{}^2 + \eta_k{}^2$. We form the sum $\sum_{k=1}^{n} (\xi_k{}^2 + \eta_k{}^2)\rho_k \Delta V_k$ and take the limit when $\delta \to 0$. Similarly we form limits of sums with squares of distances from the Y-axis and the X-axis. Then we have the following definitions:

*The **moments of inertia** or **second moments** with respect to the coördinate axes of a body with density $\rho(x, y, z)$ are defined by:*

$$(17) \qquad I_x = \iiint_V \rho(y^2 + z^2)\, dV, \qquad I_y = \iiint_V \rho(z^2 + x^2)\, dV,$$

$$I_z = \iiint_V \rho(x^2 + y^2)\, dV.$$

EXAMPLE 1. Find the moment of inertia with respect to the Z-axis of the body in the first octant bounded by the surface $z = xy$, the XY-plane and the planes $x = 2$ and $y = 2$, if the density is proportional to the distance from the XY-plane.

Solution: Since $\rho = kz$, we have

$$I_z = \int_0^2 \int_0^2 \int_0^{xy} kz\,(x^2 + y^2)\, dz\, dy\, dx = \tfrac{256}{15}\, k.$$

EXAMPLE 2. Find the second moment with respect to the Z-axis of the solid bounded by the paraboloid $x^2 + y^2 = 4 - z$ and the XY-plane.

Solution: Because of the symmetry of the paraboloid about the Z-axis, it is advantageous to use cylindrical coördinates. Then

$$I_z = \iiint_V (x^2 + y^2)\, dV = \int_0^{2\pi} \int_0^2 \int_0^{4-r^2} r^2(r\, dz\, dr\, d\theta)$$

$$= \int_0^{2\pi} \int_0^2 [r^3\,(4 - r^2)\, dr\, d\theta] = \tfrac{32}{3}\, \pi.$$

Now consider the special case of a solid of revolution in general. Let the solid of revolution be generated by revolving about the Z-axis the region in the ZX-plane bounded by the curve $z = f(x)$, the X-axis and the lines $x = a$ and $x = b$ (Fig. 229). By formula (17) above,

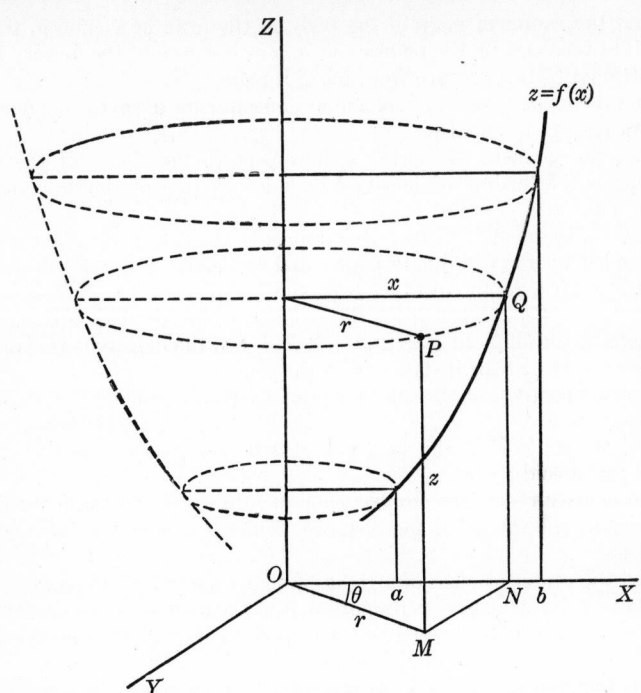

Fig. 229

$I_z = \iiint_V (x^2 + y^2)\, dV.$ Let us express this in cylindrical coördinates. Then

$$I_z = \int_a^b \int_0^{2\pi} \int_0^z r^2\, (r\, dz\, d\theta\, dr) = \int_a^b \int_0^{2\pi} r^3 z\, d\theta\, dr$$

$$= \int_a^b 2\,\pi\, r^3 z\, dr = 2\,\pi \int_a^b x^3 z\, dx.$$

This result is the expression for I_z as given by the definition of § 207.

541. Exercises

1. Find the centroid of the solid bounded by the surface $x^2 + y^2 = 4\,z$ and the plane $z = 2$.

2. Find the centroid of the solid in the first octant bounded by the surface $z = xy$ and the cylinder $x^2 + y^2 = a^2$.

3. Find the center of mass of the body in the first octant bounded by the surface $z = xy$ and the planes $z = 0$, $x = 2$ and $y = 2$, if the density varies as the distance from the XY-plane.

4. Find the center of mass of the body in the form of a cube in the first octant bounded by the planes $x = a$, $y = a$, $z = a$, if the density is proportional to the distance from the XY-plane.

5. Find the moment of inertia of a homogeneous cube of edge a and density δ, with respect to an edge.

6. Find the moment of inertia with respect to the Z-axis of the homogeneous tetrahedron of density δ bounded by the coördinate planes and the plane $x + y + z = 1$.

7. Find the moment of inertia with respect to the Z-axis of the tetrahedron bounded by the coördinate planes and the plane $x + y + z = 1$, if the density varies as the distance from the XY-plane.

8. Set up the triple integral for the moment of inertia with respect to the Z-axis of the ellipsoid $x^2 + 2 y^2 + 3 z^2 = 1$, if the density is proportional to the square of the distance from the center.

9. Find the centroid of the solid bounded by the paraboloid $z = r^2$ and the plane $z = 4$.

10. Find the centroid of the solid bounded by the sphere $r^2 + z^2 = 12$ and the paraboloid $z = r^2$.

11. The density of a right circular cone of altitude h and radius of base a varies as the square of the distance from the axis of the cone; find its mass.

12. Find the center of mass of a right circular cone of altitude h and radius of base a, if the density is proportional to the distance from the base.

13. Find the moment of inertia with respect to its axis of a homogeneous right circular cylinder of altitude h, radius of base a and density δ.

14. Find the moment of inertia with respect to a diameter of a homogeneous sphere of radius a and density δ.

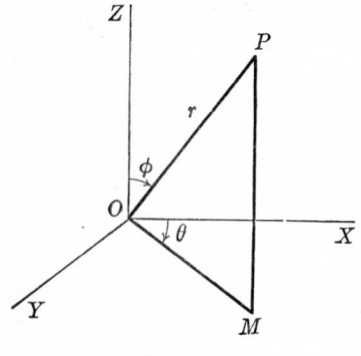

FIG. 230

15. Find the moment of inertia of a paraboloid of revolution of altitude h, radius of base a and density δ, with respect to its axis of symmetry.

16. Find the moment of inertia with respect to the Z-axis of the smaller volume cut from the sphere $x^2 + y^2 + z^2 = 6$ by the paraboloid $x^2 + y^2 = z$, if the density is δ.

★ 542. Triple Integrals in Spherical Coördinates

In certain problems involving triple integrals, the use of *spherical coördinates* greatly simplifies the work.

It should be recalled from § 492 that the spherical coördinates of a point P (Fig. 230) are the numbers r, θ and ϕ, where r is the distance OP from the origin to the given point, θ is the angle XOM (where M is the projection of P on the XY-plane), and ϕ is the angle ZOP between the Z-axis and the line OP.

Let (r, θ, ϕ) be the spherical coördinates of a point. The element of volume for a triple integral in spherical coördinates may be obtained as follows. Draw a system of concentric spheres $r =$ constant, a

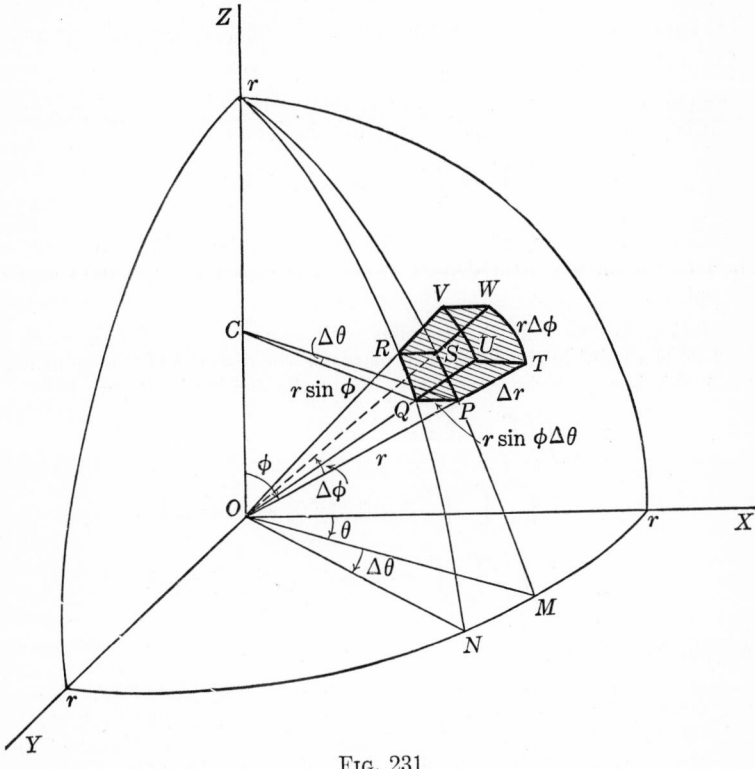

Fig. 231

system of radial planes $\theta =$ constant through the Z-axis, and a system of conical surfaces $\phi =$ constant with vertices at the origin and axes along the Z-axis. These surfaces are mutually orthogonal. A typical element of volume ΔV is shown in Fig. 231. The edges of this "curvilinear parallelopiped" may be found as follows:

$$CP = OP \sin ZOP = r \sin \phi, \qquad PQ = CP \cdot \Delta\theta = r \sin \phi \, \Delta\theta;$$

$$PS = OP \, \Delta\phi = r \, \Delta\phi; \qquad PT = \Delta r.$$

The volume ΔV of this element is approximately

$$PQ \cdot PS \cdot PT = r^2 \sin \phi \, \Delta\theta \, \Delta\phi \, \Delta r.$$

It can be proved* that the corresponding triple iterated integral is:

(18) $$\int_\alpha^\beta \left[\int_{\phi_1(\theta)}^{\phi_2(\theta)} \left(\int_{r_1(\theta,\,\phi)}^{r_2(\theta,\,\phi)} F(r,\,\theta,\,\phi) \, r^2 \sin \phi \, dr \right) d\phi \right] d\theta.$$

The triple integral may also be written in other orders of integration, when convenient.

EXAMPLE 1.   Find the mass of a sphere of radius a if the density at every point is proportional to the distance from the center.

Solution: $m = k \int_0^{2\pi} \int_0^\pi \int_0^a r \cdot r^2 \sin \phi \, dr \, d\phi \, d\theta = k \, \pi a^4.$

EXAMPLE 2.   Find the moment of inertia of a sphere of radius a with respect to a diameter, if the density varies as the distance from the center of the sphere.

Solution: Let us take the moment with respect to the Z-axis; then, if (r, θ, ϕ) is a point in the element of mass dm, the distance of this point from the Z-axis is $r \sin \phi$ (see Fig. 231).   Since the density is $k \, r$, we have

$$\begin{aligned}
I_z &= \iiint_V (r^2 \sin^2 \phi)(kr \, dV) \\
&= k \int_0^{2\pi} \int_0^\pi \int_0^a (r^2 \sin^2 \phi) \, r \, (r^2 \sin \phi \, dr \, d\phi \, d\theta) \\
&= k \int_0^{2\pi} \int_0^\pi \int_0^a r^5 \sin^3 \phi \, dr \, d\phi \, d\theta = \tfrac{4}{9} \, \pi \, ka^6.
\end{aligned}$$

★ 543. Exercises

1. Find the volume of a sphere of radius a, by use of a triple integral.
2. Find the volume cut from a right circular cone, in which an element makes an angle of 30° with the axis, by a sphere of radius 6 inches, if the vertex of the cone is at the center of the sphere.   (Use only one nappe of the cone.)
3. Find the mass of a sphere of radius a if its density is proportional to the square of the distance from the center.
4. Find the mass of a solid inside a sphere of radius $2\,a$, and outside a right circular cylinder of radius a whose axis is a diameter of the sphere, if the density is proportional to the square of the distance from the center of the sphere.
5. Find the center of mass of a solid hemisphere of radius a if the density varies as the distance from the center.

* See, for example, Sokolnikoff, *Advanced Calculus*, § 49.

6. Find the center of mass of a solid hemisphere of radius a, if the density varies as the distance from the axis of symmetry.

7. Find the moment of inertia of the hemisphere of Exercise 6, with respect to its axis of symmetry.

8. Find the moment of inertia of a solid sphere of radius a with respect to a diameter, if the density is proportional to the square of the distance from the center of the sphere.

CHAPTER XXVIII

Differential Equations

---

544. Differential Equations

A **differential equation** *is an equation involving derivatives (or differentials) of one or more unknown functions.*

EXAMPLE. The following are examples of differential equations:

(a) $\dfrac{dy}{dx} = 2\,x;$ (b) $x\,dy - y\,dx = 0;$

(c) $\dfrac{d^2y}{dx^2} + y = 0;$ (d) $\left(\dfrac{dy}{dx}\right)^2 = 4 - y^2;$

(e) $\dfrac{\partial z}{\partial x} + \dfrac{\partial z}{\partial y} = z;$ (f) $\dfrac{\partial^2 u}{\partial x^2} + \dfrac{\partial^2 u}{\partial y^2} = 0.$

Numerous examples of differential equations have been met in previous parts of this book.

If a differential equation involves derivatives of an unknown function with respect to one independent variable, it is called an *ordinary differential equation.* If it involves partial derivatives of an unknown function of two or more independent variables, it is called a *partial differential equation.*

*The **order** of a differential equation is the order of the highest derivative occurring in the equation.*

*When a differential equation is rational and integral with respect to all the derivatives which occur in it, its degree with respect to the derivative of highest order is called the **degree** of the differential equation.*

Thus, equations (a) − (d) of the Example above are ordinary equations, and (e) and (f) are partial differential equations. Equations (a), (b), (d) and (e) are first order equations; equations (c) and (f) are second order equations. Equation (d) is of the second degree, and the remainder are first degree equations.

We shall consider only a few simple but important types of *ordinary differential equations* in this chapter.

545. Solutions of Ordinary Differential Equations

*A **solution** of an ordinary differential equation is a functional relation between the variables involved, not containing derivatives or differentials, which satisfies the differential equation.* Such a solution may be expressed in an explicit function form or in an implicit function form.

EXAMPLE 1. $y = \sin 2x$ is a solution of the differential equation

$$\frac{d^2y}{dx^2} + 4y = 0, \quad \text{since} \quad \frac{dy}{dx} = 2\cos 2x, \quad \frac{d^2y}{dx^2} = -4\sin 2x = -4y.$$

EXAMPLE 2. $x^2 - xy = c$ is a solution of the differential equation

$$x\frac{dy}{dx} = 2x - y, \quad \text{since} \quad \frac{d}{dx}(x^2 - xy - c) = 2x - x\frac{dy}{dx} - y = 0.$$

It is proved in more advanced works that a differential equation of the n-th order may have solutions involving n independent arbitrary constants, but not more than n such constants. On this result is based the following definition:

*The **general solution** of a differential equation of the n-th order is defined as a solution containing n independent arbitrary constants.*

*A **particular solution** of a differential equation is a solution which can be obtained from the general solution by giving particular values to the arbitrary constants of the general solution.*

Some differential equations have **singular solutions,** which cannot be obtained as particular solutions found by assigning values to the constants of the general solution. Singular solutions will not be considered in this book.

EXAMPLE 3. The function $y = Ae^x + Be^{2x}$ is the general solution of the differential equation $y'' - 3y' + 2y = 0$, since

$$y' = Ae^x + 2Be^{2x}, \quad y'' = Ae^x + 4Be^{2x},$$

and therefore

$$y'' - 3y' + 2y = Ae^x + 4Be^{2x} - 3Ae^x - 6Be^{2x} + 2Ae^x + 2Be^{2x} = 0.$$

The given solution contains the two arbitrary constants A and B and the differential equation is of the second order.

Particular solutions of the given differential equation are, for example, $y = e^x, y = e^{2x}, y = 2e^x - e^{2x}$, etc.

For practical applications of differential equations, it is usually a particular solution which is needed. To obtain such a particular solution, it is usually necessary to find first the general solution of the differential equation, and then the arbitrary constants are determined from given data of the problem, usually called *initial conditions*.

A constant of integration may be written in various forms, such as C, $2C$, C^2, $\sqrt{C}$, e^C, $\ln C$, $\sin C$, etc. By proper choice of form of the constant or constants, solutions of differential equations may often be expressed in simple form.

546. Exercises

Show that the following functions are solutions of the corresponding differential equations:

1. $y = \dfrac{x^2}{3} + \dfrac{c}{x}$, $\quad x\dfrac{dy}{dx} + y = x^2$.

2. $y = c_1 e^{kx} + c_2 e^{-kx}$, $\quad \dfrac{d^2y}{dx^2} - k^2 y = 0$.

3. $y = A\cos 2x + B\sin 2x$, $\quad \dfrac{d^2y}{dx^2} + 4y = 0$.

4. $y = e^{-x}(x + c)$, $\quad \dfrac{dy}{dx} + y = e^{-x}$.

5. $y = c_1 x + \dfrac{c_2}{x} + c_3$, $\quad \dfrac{d^3y}{dx^3} + \dfrac{3}{x}\cdot\dfrac{d^2y}{dx^2} = 0$.

6. $4y = \dfrac{1}{3x} + c_1 x^5 + c_2 x$, $\quad x^2 y'' - 5xy' + 5y = \dfrac{1}{x}$.

547. Differential Equations of the First Order and First Degree

A differential equation of the first order and first degree may be written in the derivative form

$$(a) \qquad\qquad \frac{dy}{dx} = f(x, y),$$

or in the differential form

$$(b) \qquad\qquad M\,dx + N\,dy = 0,$$

where M and N are functions of x and y.

It is not possible to solve every differential equation of the first order and first degree by elementary methods. Certain types, of importance in applications, which can be solved by fairly simple means, will be discussed in the next few sections.

548. Differential Equations in Which the Variables Are Separable

If a differential equation $M\,dx + N\,dy = 0$ of the first order and first degree can be put in the form

$$X\,dx + Y\,dy = 0,$$

where X is a function of x only and Y is a function of y only, then the solution of the differential equation may be obtained by direct integration.

In this type of differential equation we say that *the variables are separable.*

EXAMPLE 1. Solve the differential equation $dy/dx = 2\,xy$ for the general solution, and also find the particular solution if $y = 5$ when $x = 0$.

Solution: From $dy = 2\,xy\,dx$, by dividing by y, we obtain

$$\frac{dy}{y} = 2\,x\,dx,$$

in which the variables are separated.   Integrating, we have

$$\ln y = x^2 + \ln C,$$

or

$$\ln y - \ln C = x^2, \quad \ln (y/C) = x^2,$$

$$\therefore \; y/C = e^{x^2} \;\text{ or }\; y = Ce^{x^2}.$$

This is the general solution of the differential equation.

Substituting the initial conditions: $x = 0$, $y = 5$ in the general solution $y = Ce^{x^2}$, we get $5 = C$, so that the required particular solution is $y = 5\,e^{x^2}$.

EXAMPLE 2. Solve the differential equation

$$(xy^2 - x)\,dx + (x^2y + y)\,dy = 0.$$

Solution: Factoring the coefficients of dx and dy, we have

$$x(y^2 - 1)\,dx + y(x^2 + 1)\,dy = 0.$$

Dividing each term by $(x^2 + 1)(y^2 - 1)$, we separate variables and obtain

$$\frac{x\,dx}{x^2 + 1} + \frac{y\,dy}{y^2 - 1} = 0.$$

Integrating, we find

$$\tfrac{1}{2} \ln (x^2 + 1) + \tfrac{1}{2} \ln (y^2 - 1) = k.$$

Putting $k = \tfrac{1}{2} \ln C$, we may write this:

$$\ln [(x^2 + 1)(y^2 - 1)] = \ln C,$$

from which we have

$$(x^2 + 1)(y^2 - 1) = C.$$

This functional relation is the required general solution of the given differential equation.

549. Exercises

In Exercises 1–14, find the general solution of each of the given differential equations:

1. $\dfrac{dy}{dx} = -\dfrac{y}{x}.$

2. $\dfrac{dy}{dx} = 2\,xy^2.$

3. $\dfrac{dy}{dx} = \dfrac{x^2}{y^3}.$

4. $\dfrac{dy}{dx} = \dfrac{y^2 - 1}{\sqrt{1 - x^2}}.$

5. $x\,dy - y\,dx = 0.$

6. $x\,dy + y\,dx = 0.$

7. $(1 + y^2)\,dx + (1 + x^2)\,dy = 0.$

8. $xy\,dx + \sqrt{1 + x^2}\,dy = 0.$

9. $D_x y = \dfrac{xy + y}{x + xy}.$

10. $x^2(y - 1)\,dx + (xy + y)\,dy = 0.$

11. $\dfrac{dy}{dx} = \dfrac{\cos^2 y}{\sin^2 x}.$

12. $x^2\,dy - y\,dx - 4\,dy = 0.$

13. $xy' + y = y^2.$

14. $y' = \dfrac{x(y^2 + 1)}{y(x^2 + 1)}.$

Find the particular solution of each of the following differential equations satisfying the given initial conditions:

15. $\dfrac{dy}{dx} = \dfrac{y}{x},\ y = 3$ when $x = 1.$

16. $\dfrac{dy}{dx} = e^y,\ y = 0$ when $x = 0.$

17. $xy\,dx + \sqrt{1 + x^2}\,dy = 0,\ y = 1$ when $x = 0.$

18. $xy\,dx + (x^2 + 1)\,dy = 0,\ y = 2$ when $x = 1.$

19. $x\,dy + 2\,y\,dx = 0,\ y = 1$ when $x = 2.$

20. $x^2y' + y^2 = 0,\ y = 2$ when $x = 2.$

550. First-Order Equations with Homogeneous Coefficients

A function $f(x, y)$ is called a homogeneous function of degree n if

(a)
$$f(tx, ty) = t^n f(x, y),$$

for all values of t.

EXAMPLE 1. The functions $x^2 + y^2$, $2\,xy$, $x - y$ and x^2/y^2 are homogeneous functions of degrees 2, 2, 1 and 0 respectively.

Suppose that in the differential equation $M\,dx + N\,dy = 0$, the functions M and N are homogeneous functions of x and y of the same degree. If we substitute

(b)
$$y = vx,$$

we obtain a new differential equation in x and v, which can be readily proved to be always of the separable type. Solving this equation for v as a function of x (by the method of § 548), we may replace

v by y/x and obtain a relation between x and y, which will be the required general solution.

EXAMPLE 2. Solve $2\,xy\,dy = (y^2 - x^2)\,dx$.

Solution: This equation has homogeneous coefficients of the second degree, so we put $y = vx$, then $dy = v\,dx + x\,dv$. The equation becomes

$$2\,x \cdot vx(v\,dx + x\,dv) = (v^2x^2 - x^2)\,dx,$$

or

$$(v^2 + 1)\,dx + 2\,xv\,dv = 0.$$

Separating variables, we get

$$\frac{dx}{x} + \frac{2\,v\,dv}{v^2 + 1} = 0.$$

Integrating, we have

$$\ln x + \ln (v^2 + 1) = \ln C,$$
$$\ln [x(v^2 + 1)] = \ln C,$$
$$\therefore x\left[\frac{y^2}{x^2} + 1\right] = C, \quad \text{and} \quad y^2 + x^2 = C\,x.$$

551. Exercises

In Exercises 1–10, find the general solution of each of the given differential equations:

1. $y^2\,dx = (xy - x^2)\,dy$.
2. $y\,dx + (y - x)\,dy = 0$.
3. $(x^2 + y^2)\,dx + 2\,xy\,dy = 0$.
4. $(x^2 + y^2)\,dx + xy\,dy = 0$.
5. $(x + y)\,dx + x\,dy = 0$.
6. $\dfrac{dy}{dx} = \tan\dfrac{y}{x} + \dfrac{y}{x}$.
7. $xy^2\,dy - (x^3 + y^3)\,dx = 0$.
8. $x\,dy = (x\,e^{\frac{y}{x}} + y)\,dx$.
9. $\dfrac{dy}{dx} = \dfrac{x - y}{x + y}$.
10. $x\dfrac{dy}{dx} + 3\,y = 4\,x$.

In Exercises 11–14, find the particular solution of each of the given equations satisfying the given initial conditions:

11. $(x + y)\,dx + (y - 2\,x)\,dy = 0$, $y = 0$ when $x = 1$.
12. $(2\,x + y)\,dx + (x + y)\,dy = 0$, $y = 2$ when $x = 0$.
13. $(x - \sqrt{xy})\,dy = y\,dx$, $y = 1$ when $x = 4$.
14. $\dfrac{dy}{dx} = \dfrac{x^2 + 3\,y^2}{2\,xy}$, $y = 6$ when $x = 2$.

552. Differential Equations Containing Integrable Combinations

When the variables are not separable in a given differential equation, certain *integrable combinations* may occur in the equation, which make it possible to solve the equation.

EXAMPLE 1. Solve $(2x - y) \, dx + (2y - x) \, dy = 0$.

Solution: By regrouping terms, we have

$$(2x \, dx + 2y \, dy) - (y \, dx + x \, dy) = 0$$

or

$$d \, (x^2 + y^2) - d(xy) = 0.$$

Integrating, we get

$$x^2 + y^2 - xy = C.$$

Some of the simpler integrable combinations are the following:

(a) $x \, dy + y \, dx = d(xy);$

(b) $2 x \, dx + 2 y \, dy = d(x^2 + y^2);$

(c) $\dfrac{x \, dy - y \, dx}{x^2} = d \left(\dfrac{y}{x} \right); \qquad \dfrac{y \, dx - x \, dy}{y^2} = d \left(\dfrac{x}{y} \right);$

(d) $\dfrac{x \, dy - y \, dx}{x^2 + y^2} = d \left(\text{Arc tan } \dfrac{y}{x} \right).$

EXAMPLE 2. Solve $x \, dy + \dfrac{x^2}{y} \, dy = y \, dx$.

Solution: $\dfrac{x \, dy - y \, dx}{x^2} + \dfrac{dy}{y} = 0, \quad d \left(\dfrac{y}{x} \right) + d(\ln y) = 0.$

Therefore,

$$\frac{y}{x} + \ln y = \ln C, \text{ or } \frac{y}{x} + \ln \frac{y}{C} = 0.$$

553. Exercises

In Exercises 1–10, find the general solution of each of the given equations:

1. $(x + y) \, dx + x \, dy = 0$.   2. $(y - x) \, dy = y \, dx$.
3. $x \, dy = (x^2 - y) \, dx$.   4. $y \, dx - x \, dy + y^2 \, dx = 0$.

5. $y \, dx - x \, dy + y(x^2 + y^2) \, dy = 0$.   6. $y' = \dfrac{y + y^2}{x}$.

7. $x \, dy - y \, dx - xy^2 \, dx = 0$.   8. $y' = \dfrac{1 - y \cos x}{\sin x}$.

9. $\dfrac{dy}{dx} = \dfrac{x^2 y^2 + y}{x}$.   10. $D_x y = \dfrac{x^2 + y^2 - x}{y}$.

Find the particular solution of each of the following equations satisfying the given initial conditions:

11. $x \, dy = (1 - y) \, dx$, $y = 2$ when $x = 1$.

12. $y' = \dfrac{y^2}{1 - 2xy}$, $y = 1$ when $x = 0$.

13. $x \, dx + y \, dy - \sqrt{x^2 + y^2} \, dx = 0$, $y = 1$ when $x = 0$.
14. $(3 x^2 y - y) \, dx + (3 x^3 + x) \, dy = 0$, $y = 4$ when $x = 2$.

554. Exact Differentials

It should be recalled (from § 501) that the total differential of a function $u = f(x, y)$ is defined by

$$(a) \qquad du = \frac{\partial u}{\partial x}\, dx + \frac{\partial u}{\partial y}\, dy.$$

If P and Q are given functions of x and y, and if there exists a function $u = f(x, y)$ such that $P\, dx + Q\, dy$ is the total differential of u:

$$du = P\, dx + Q\, dy,$$

*then $P\, dx + Q\, dy$ is said to be an **exact differential**.*

EXAMPLE 1. (a) $y\, dx + x\, dy$ is an exact differential, since it is equal to $d(xy)$; (b) $2\, x\, dx + 2\, y\, dy$ is an exact differential since it is equal to $d(x^2 + y^2)$; (c) $\dfrac{x\, dy - y\, dx}{x^2}$ is an exact differential since it is equal to $d\left(\dfrac{y}{x}\right)$.

It is desirable to have a test by which we may determine whether a given differential expression is an exact differential or not. Such a test may be derived as follows:

Let P and Q be given functions of x and y, and suppose that a function $u = f(x, y)$ exists with continuous partial derivatives of the second order such that

$$(b) \qquad du = P\, dx + Q\, dy,$$

so that $P\, dx + Q\, dy$ is an exact differential. By comparing (b) with the definition of a total differential (a), since dx and dy are independent variables, we obtain (see § 506, last part):

$$(c) \qquad \frac{\partial u}{\partial x} = P, \qquad \frac{\partial u}{\partial y} = Q.$$

Differentiating (c) partially with respect to y and x respectively, we have

$$(d) \qquad \frac{\partial P}{\partial y} = \frac{\partial^2 u}{\partial y\, \partial x}, \qquad \frac{\partial Q}{\partial x} = \frac{\partial^2 u}{\partial x\, \partial y}.$$

But since $\dfrac{\partial^2 u}{\partial y\, \partial x} = \dfrac{\partial^2 u}{\partial x\, \partial y}$ (§ 498), we find

$$(e) \qquad \frac{\partial P}{\partial y} = \frac{\partial Q}{\partial x}.$$

This derivation shows that (e) is a *necessary* requirement that $P\, dx + Q\, dy$ be a total differential of a function u.

It may also be shown that equation (e) is a *sufficient condition* that $P\,dx + Q\,dy$ be a total differential (exact differential) of a function u, as follows: Assume that P and Q are functions of x and y such that they satisfy condition (e).   Let M denote the integral $\int P\,dx$, where y is held constant during the integration; then $\dfrac{\partial M}{\partial x} = P$.   Therefore,

$$\frac{\partial^2 M}{\partial y\,\partial x} = \frac{\partial P}{\partial y} = \frac{\partial Q}{\partial x} \qquad \text{(by condition } (e)\text{)}.$$

Then

(f)
$$\frac{\partial Q}{\partial x} = \frac{\partial^2 M}{\partial y\,\partial x} = \frac{\partial^2 M}{\partial x\,\partial y} = \frac{\partial}{\partial x}\left(\frac{\partial M}{\partial y}\right).$$

Integrating this with respect to x we get

$$Q = \frac{\partial M}{\partial y} + F(y),$$

where $F(y)$ is a constant of integration (constant as far as x is concerned).   It follows that

$$P\,dx + Q\,dy = \frac{\partial M}{\partial x}\,dx + \frac{\partial M}{\partial y}\,dy + F(y)\,dy = d[M + \phi(y)],$$

where $\phi(y)$ is such that $F(y)\,dy = d\phi(y)$.   Then we have shown that $P\,dx + Q\,dy$ is the total differential of $u = M + \phi(y)$, a function of x and y, which proves that (e) is a *sufficient* condition for an exact differential.   Hence:

A necessary and sufficient condition that $P\,dx + Q\,dy$ be an exact differential of a function $u = f(x, y)$ is:

(1)
$$\frac{\partial P}{\partial y} = \frac{\partial Q}{\partial x}.$$

In this case,

(2)
$$\frac{\partial u}{\partial x} = P, \qquad \frac{\partial u}{\partial y} = Q.$$

EXAMPLE 2.   The expression $2\,xy^3\,dx + 3\,x^2y^2\,dy$ is an exact differential, since $P = 2\,xy^3$, $Q = 3\,x^2y^2$, $\dfrac{\partial P}{\partial y} = 6\,xy^2 = \dfrac{\partial Q}{\partial x}$.

555. Exact Differential Equations

*When $M\,dx + N\,dy$ is an exact differential, that is, when it is the total differential of some function $u(x, y)$, the differential equation $M\,dx + N\,dy = 0$ is called an **exact differential equation**.*

The equation is then equivalent to $du = 0$, which has the solution $u = C$, where C is a constant.

We have seen in § 554 that the necessary and sufficient condition that an expression $M\, dx + N\, dy$ be an exact differential is that $\frac{\partial M}{\partial y} = \frac{\partial N}{\partial x}$. Hence:

The necessary and sufficient condition that $M\, dx + N\, dy = 0$ be an exact differential equation is that:

$$(3) \qquad \frac{\partial M}{\partial y} = \frac{\partial N}{\partial x}.$$

When $M\, dx + N\, dy = 0$ is an exact differential equation, its solution $u = c$ may be found by the method illustrated by the following example.

EXAMPLE. Solve $(2\,x + 3\,y + 1)\, dx + (3\,x - 2\,y - 2)\, dy = 0$.

Solution: Since $M = 2\,x + 3\,y + 1$ and $N = 3\,x - 2\,y - 2$, we have $\frac{\partial M}{\partial y} = 3$, $\frac{\partial N}{\partial x} = 3$, so that the given equation is exact. Let $u(x, y)$ be the function of which the left-hand side of the equation is the exact (total) differential. By equations (2) of § 554, $\frac{\partial u}{\partial x} = M$, so that in this case,

$$\frac{\partial u}{\partial x} = 2\,x + 3\,y + 1.$$

Integrating with respect to x, holding y fixed, we get

$$u = x^2 + 3\,xy + x + \phi(y),$$

where $\phi(y)$ is the constant of integration, which is constant with reference to x but may be a function of y. From this we find

$$\frac{\partial u}{\partial y} = 3\,x + \phi'(y).$$

But $\frac{\partial u}{\partial y} = N = 3\,x - 2\,y - 2$ by equations (2) of § 554. Comparing these two expressions for $\frac{\partial u}{\partial y}$, we see that

$$\phi'(y) = -2\,y - 2.$$

Then $\phi(y) = -y^2 - 2\,y + C'$, and $u = x^2 + 3\,xy + x - y^2 - 2\,y + C'$. The solution of the differential equation is $u = C_1$, or

$$x^2 + 3\,xy + x - y^2 - 2\,y + C' = C_1.$$

If we put $C_1 - C' = C$, the required solution is

$$x^2 + 3\,xy + x - y^2 - 2\,y = C.$$

A function of one or both independent variables such that, when we multiply the differential equation by it, the equation becomes exact, is called an *integrating factor*.

556. Exercises

In Exercises 1–8, test the given expressions for exact differentials, and for those that are exact find the function of which it is the exact differential:

1. $(x^2 + y^2)\,dx + (2\,xy)\,dy.$ 2. $(2\,x - y)\,dx + (y - x)\,dy.$

3. $x^2y\,dx + xy^2\,dy.$ 4. $\dfrac{y - x}{y^2}\,dy + \dfrac{1}{y}\,dx.$

5. $x^2 \sin y\,dx + x^2 \cos y\,dy.$ 6. $(x^3y + 2\,x)\,dx - (3\,x^2y - 5\,x)\,dy.$

7. $(3\,x^2y + e^x)\,dx + x^3\,dy.$ 8. $e^{-x} \sin y\,dx - e^{-x} \cos y\,dy.$

In Exercises 9–16, determine which of the given differential equations are exact, and solve each equation that is exact:

9. $(2x - y)\,dx + (2y - x)\,dy = 0.$ 10. $(x^2 + y^2)\,dy + 2\,xy\,dx = 0.$

11. $x^3y\,dx + (x + y)\,dy = 0.$ 12. $(2\,x^3 + 3\,x^2y)\,dx - (x^3 + 3\,y^2)\,dy = 0.$

13. $(3\,x^2y - y)\,dx + (3\,x^2 + x)\,dy = 0.$

14. $xe^y\,dx + ye^x\,dy = 0.$

15. $(3\,x^2y + 2\,x)\,dx + (x^3 - 1)\,dy = 0.$

16. $(2\,xy - y^3)\,dx + (x^2 - 3\,xy^2)\,dy = 0.$

In Exercises 17, 18, find the particular solution of each of the given equations satisfying the given initial conditions:

17. $(2\,x + 3\,y)\,dx + (3\,x + 2\,y)\,dy = 0,\ y = 3$ when $x = 0.$

18. $3\,x^2y^2\,dx + 2\,x^3y\,dy = 0,\ y = -2$ when $x = 1.$

Solve each of the following equations in two different ways:

19. $y\,dx + (x + y)\,dy = 0.$ 20. $(x + y)\,dx + (x - y)\,dy = 0.$

21. $(2\,x + y)\,dx + (2\,y + x)\,dy = 0.$ 22. $(2\,x^3 - y)\,dx - x\,dy = 0.$

557. Linear Differential Equations of the First Order

A differential equation which is of the first degree in the function y and its derivatives with respect to the variable x, and whose coefficients are functions of x only, is called a **linear differential equation** *in y.* Thus:

A differential equation of the form

(a) $$\frac{dy}{dx} + Py = Q,$$

where P and Q are functions of x only, is called a **linear differential equation of the first order.**

This type of equation may be solved as follows. As we shall see, the expression $e^{\int P\,dx}$ is an *integrating factor* of equation (a); that is, if both members of (a) are multiplied by $e^{\int P\,dx}$, the equation becomes an *exact* differential equation. After this multiplication, we get

(b)
$$e^{\int P\,dx} \cdot \frac{dy}{dx} + y \cdot e^{\int P\,dx} \cdot P = Q\, e^{\int P\,dx}.$$

Since $\dfrac{d}{dx} \displaystyle\int P\,dx = P$, by differentiation we get

(c)
$$\frac{d}{dx}\left(y \cdot e^{\int P\,dx}\right) = \frac{dy}{dx} \cdot e^{\int P\,dx} + y\, \frac{d}{dx}\left(e^{\int P\,dx}\right)$$

$$= e^{\int P\,dx} \cdot \frac{dy}{dx} + y \cdot e^{\int P\,dx} \cdot P.$$

Therefore, (b) can be written:

(d)
$$\frac{d}{dx}\left(y\, e^{\int P\,dx}\right) = Q\, e^{\int P\,dx}.$$

The solution of equation (a) may now be obtained by integrating (d) with respect to x. This gives the result:

The general solution of the linear equation $\dfrac{dy}{dx} + Py = Q$ is given by:

(4)
$$y\, e^{\int P\,dx} = \int Q\, e^{\int P\,dx}\, dx + C.$$

In the formula (4), the integrating factor $e^{\int P\,dx}$ appears as an exponential; it is frequently possible to simplify it to more convenient form by use of the definition and properties of logarithms. For example,

if $P = \dfrac{2}{x}$, then $\displaystyle\int P\,dx = 2 \ln x = \ln x^2$, and $e^{\int P\,dx} = e^{\ln x^2} = x^2$;

if $P = -\dfrac{1}{x}$, then $\displaystyle\int P\,dx = -\ln x = \ln \dfrac{1}{x}$, and $e^{\int P\,dx} = e^{\ln \frac{1}{x}} = \dfrac{1}{x}$

EXAMPLE. Solve $\dfrac{dy}{dx} + \dfrac{3\,y}{x} = 5\,x$.

Solution: Since $P = \dfrac{3}{x}$, we have $\displaystyle\int P\,dx = 3 \ln x = \ln x^3$, and
$$e^{\int P\,dx} = e^{\ln x^3} = x^3.$$

Then by formula (4),

$$y \cdot x^3 = \int 5\, x \cdot x^3\, dx + C = \int 5\, x^4\, dx + C = x^5 + C.$$

Therefore,

$$y = x^2 + \frac{C}{x^3},$$

which is the general solution of the given equation.

It is to be noted that in evaluating $\int P\, dx$ we can take the constant of integration equal to 0 (as we did in the solution of the Example above), since any other constant, C_1, merely multiplies the equation through by the constant e^{C_1} and has no effect on the result.

558. Exercises

In Exercises 1–16, find the general solution of each of the given equations:

1. $\dfrac{dy}{dx} + y = e^{-x}.$

2. $\dfrac{dy}{dx} - 2\, y = e^x.$

3. $\dfrac{dy}{dx} = x + y.$

4. $\dfrac{dy}{dx} + 2\, y + x = 0.$

5. $\dfrac{dy}{dx} + \dfrac{y}{x} = 2.$

6. $x \dfrac{dy}{dx} + y = \sin x.$

7. $\dfrac{dy}{dx} = 3\, y + xe^{3x}.$

8. $\dfrac{dy}{dx} = \dfrac{e^x - 2\, xy}{x^2}.$

9. $xy' + 2\, y = x^2.$

10. $\dfrac{dy}{dx} - \dfrac{y}{x} = 4\, x^2.$

11. $x\, dy = (x^3 + y)\, dx.$

12. $xy' - 3\, y = x + 1.$

13. $x^2 y' - 2\, xy = 2.$

14. $x\, dy - 2\, y\, dx = x^2\, dx.$

15. $\dfrac{dy}{dx} + 2\, y = 4 \sin 3\, x.$

16. $\dfrac{dy}{dx} = \sin x + y.$

In Exercises 17–20, find the particular solution of each of the given equations satisfying the given initial conditions:

17. $\dfrac{dy}{dx} - \dfrac{y}{x} = 3\, x^3$, $y = 3$ when $x = 1$.

18. $y' = e^{2x} - 3\, y$, $y = 1$ when $x = 0$.

19. $xy' + (1 + x)y = e^{-x}$, $y = 0$ when $x = 1$.

20. $\sin x \dfrac{dy}{dx} + 2\, y \cos x = \sin 2\, x$, $y = 2$ when $x = \frac{1}{6}\, \pi$.

21. Solve the equation: $\dfrac{dx}{dy} = x + y.$ [*Hint.* Treat x as a function of y.]

22. Find the particular solution of the equation $\dfrac{dv}{dt} = g - kv$, which satisfies the conditions: $v = v_0$ when $t = 0$.

23. Solve the equation $\dfrac{dx}{dt} = k(a - x)$ as a linear differential equation, and find the particular solution if $x = 0$ when $t = 0$.

24. Solve the linear differential equation: $D_x y - ay = 0$ (a constant).

559. Applications of First-Order Differential Equations

Solutions of differential equations of the first order find numerous applications in geometrical and physical problems.

An **orthogonal trajectory** of a given system of curves is a curve which cuts each curve of the given system at right angles. To find the equation of an orthogonal trajectory, it follows at once that we must first find the slope dy/dx from the equation of the given system of curves, and then put dy/dx for the orthogonal trajectory equal to the negative reciprocal of the derivative just found, and finally integrate to find y. If the derivative dy/dx found from the equation of the first system contains the parameter of the system, it must be eliminated from the derivative by making use of the equation of the system.

EXAMPLE 1. Find the orthogonal trajectories of the system of circles which pass through the origin and have their centers on the X-axis.

Solution: The equation of the given system of circles (Fig. 232) is

(a) $x^2 + y^2 = 2\,ax,$

where $(a, 0)$ is the center of any circle of the system, and the radius, a, is the parameter of the system. By differentiation,

(b) $x + yy' = a.$

To eliminate the parameter a, we substitute this value of a in (a):

(c) $x^2 + y^2 = 2\,x(x + yy')$

or $y' = \dfrac{y^2 - x^2}{2\,xy}.$

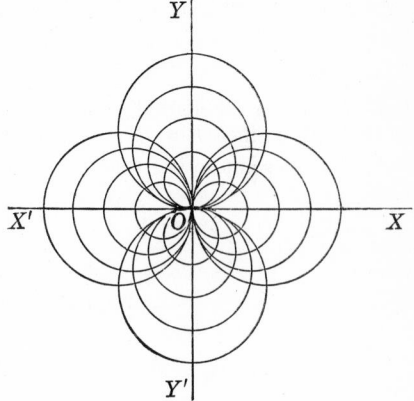

Fig. 232

In the system of orthogonal trajectories, the slope is the negative of the reciprocal of this, so that

(d) $y' = \dfrac{2\,xy}{x^2 - y^2}$ or $(x^2 - y^2)\,dy - 2\,xy\,dx = 0.$

Solving this equation by the method of § 550, we find

(e) $$x^2 + y^2 = 2\,cy$$

for the equation of the orthogonal curves (see Fig. 232). This orthogonal system of curves is the family of circles with centers on the Y-axis and passing through the origin.

Systems of curves which are orthogonal trajectories of a given system of curves occur frequently in many branches of physics. For example, in the theory of electricity and magnetism, lines of force and corresponding equipotential lines form orthogonal systems; and in hydrodynamics and aerodynamics, stream lines and corresponding velocity-equipotential lines form orthogonal systems.

Numerous physical problems require the solution of first-order differential equations. This is illustrated by the following two examples.

EXAMPLE 2. When a simple electric circuit contains resistance R and inductance L in series, and an electromotive force E is impressed on it, the differential equation for the current i at any time t is

(f) $$L\frac{di}{dt} + Ri = E.$$

Solve this equation when: (a) $E = E_0$ (constant), and (b) $E = E_0 \sin \omega t$, where L, R, E_0 and ω are constant.

Solution: In case (a), where $E = E_0$, equation (f) becomes

(g) $$\frac{di}{dt} + \frac{R}{L}\cdot i = \frac{E_0}{L},$$

which is a linear differential equation, which may be solved by the formula (4) of § 557. Since $P = R/L$ (constant), the integrating factor becomes $e^{Rt/L}$, and the solution is given by

$$i\cdot e^{\frac{R}{L}t} = \int \frac{E_0}{L}\, e^{\frac{R}{L}t}\, dt + C = \frac{E_0}{R}\, e^{\frac{R}{L}t} + C,$$

whence

(h) $$i = \frac{E_0}{R} + Ce^{-\frac{R}{L}t}.$$

If $i = 0$ when $t = 0$, we find $C = -E_0/R$, and then

(i) $$i = \frac{E_0}{R}\left(1 - e^{-\frac{R}{L}t}\right).$$

This shows that the current gradually builds up toward the limiting value E_0/R, which is the current that would flow if no inductance were present.

In case (b), where $E = E_0 \sin \omega t$, equation (f) becomes

(j) $$\frac{di}{dt} + \frac{R}{L}\cdot i = \frac{E_0}{L}\sin \omega t,$$

which again is a linear differential equation. By formula (4) of § 557, its solution is given by

$$i \cdot e^{\frac{R}{L}t} = \frac{E_0}{L} \int e^{\frac{R}{L}t} \sin \omega t \, dt + C.$$

Evaluating this integral by the formula (2) of § 369, we get

$$i \cdot e^{\frac{R}{L}t} = \frac{E_0}{L} \cdot \frac{e^{\frac{R}{L}t}}{\frac{R^2}{L^2} + \omega^2} \cdot \left(\frac{R}{L} \sin \omega t - \omega \cos \omega t\right) + C,$$

whence

$$(k) \qquad i = \frac{E_0}{R^2 + L^2 \omega^2} (R \sin \omega t - \omega L \cos \omega t) + C e^{-\frac{Rt}{L}}.$$

By trigonometry, this may also be written:

$$(l) \qquad i = \frac{E_0}{\sqrt{R^2 + L^2 \omega^2}} \sin (\omega t - \phi) + C e^{-\frac{R}{L}t},$$

where $\tan \phi = \omega L/R$.

The term $Ce^{-Rt/L}$ in formula (k) or (l) is called the *transient term*, because it usually becomes negligibly small after a short lapse of time. The first term, called the *permanent term*, varies periodically, with the same period $2\pi/\omega$ as the impressed electromotive force, but lags behind the latter, as is indicated by the term ϕ.

EXAMPLE 3. A tank contains initially 100 gallons of brine holding 150 pounds of dissolved salt in solution. Salt water containing 1 pound of salt per gallon enters the tank at the rate of 2 gallons per minute, and the brine flows out at the same rate. If the mixture is kept uniform by stirring, find the amount of salt in the tank at the end of one hour.

Solution: Let Q be the number of pounds of salt in the tank at the end of t minutes; then dQ/dt is the rate of change of amount of salt at time t. From the incoming solution there is a gain of 2 pounds of salt per minute and from the outgoing solution there is a loss of $0.02\,Q$ pounds of salt per minute. The difference between this gain and this loss is the resultant rate of change of quantity of salt:

$$(m) \qquad \frac{dQ}{dt} = 2 - 0.02\,Q.$$

The initial condition is: $Q = 150$ when $t = 0$.

Separating variables in (m), we have

$$\frac{dQ}{0.02\,Q - 2} = -dt;$$

integrating,

$$(n) \qquad \ln (0.02\,Q - 2) = -0.02\,t + C.$$

Substituting $Q = 150$ and $t = 0$, we find $C = \ln 1 = 0$. Then

$$0.02\,Q - 2 = e^{-0.02\,t},$$

or

(o)
$$Q = 100 + 50\,e^{-0.02\,t}.$$

Now put $t = 60$ (minutes), and we find

$$Q = 100 + 50\,e^{-1.2} = 115.06.$$

The required amount of salt at the end of one hour is then 115.06 pounds.

Equation (m) may also be solved (more briefly, in fact) by the method for linear differential equations in § 557.

It is of interest to note that the compound interest law $\dfrac{dy}{dx} = ky$ is a special case of the linear differential equation of the first order, with separable variables. This differential equation was discussed in § 363, and further applications of first-order differential equations may therefore be found in §§ 363, 364.

560. Exercises

In Exercises 1–4, find the orthogonal trajectories of the given systems of curves; sketch the curves:

1. $x^2 - y^2 = a^2$.
2. $y = ax^2$.
3. $x^2 + cy^2 = 1$.
4. $x = y + ce^y$.

5. Show that the system of confocal parabolas $y^2 = 4\,c(x + c)$ are self-orthogonal, that is, that they are their own orthogonal trajectories.
6. Find the system of curves for which the Y-intercept of the tangent at any point P equals OP.
7. Find the system of curves such that the part of every tangent between the coördinate axes is bisected at the point of tangency.
8. The general equation of the adiabatic change of state of air is: $kp\,dv + v\,dp = 0$ (k constant), where v and p are the volume and pressure respectively. Show that the equation of the adiabatic curve is $p\,v^k = c$.
9. Solve the electrical equation $L\,\dfrac{di}{dt} + Ri = E_0$ (constant) by the method of separation of variables.
10. When an electromotive force E is impressed on a circuit consisting of non-inductive resistance R and capacity C in series, the differential equation $R\,\dfrac{di}{dt} + \dfrac{1}{C}\cdot i = \dfrac{dE}{dt}$ is satisfied. Solve this equation: (a) when $E = E_0$; (b) when $E = E_0 \sin \omega t$, where R, C, E_0 and ω are constant.
11. If cane sugar is dissolved in the presence of acids, it decomposes into other substances at a rate which is approximately proportional to the mass of sugar unchanged. If m is the original mass of sugar and x is the mass that has changed at time t, show that x is given by an expression of the form $x = m(1 - e^{-kt})$.

12. In the study of the distillation of ternary mixtures, the equation $\dfrac{dy}{dx} = \dfrac{ay}{x}$ is used; solve it for y in terms of x.

13. As an airplane runs along the ground to a stop, its speed decreases according to the equation $M\dfrac{dv}{dt} = -F - kv^2$, where M, F and k are constants. If $v = v_0$ at $t = 0$, find v after t seconds.

14. The equation $\dfrac{dv}{dt} = g\cos\alpha - kv$ (g, α, k constants) occurs in the theory of the stability of an airplane; solve it for v in terms of t.

15. The radial stress p in the walls of a hollow cylinder varies with the distance r from the axis according to the equation $r\,dp = 2(a - p)\,dr$ (a constant). Solve this equation for p in terms of r.

16. A tank initially contains 100 gallons of brine with 50 pounds of salt in solution. Brine containing 2 pounds of salt per gallon runs into the tank at the rate of 3 gallons per minute, and the mixture, kept well stirred, runs out at the same rate. How many pounds of salt will the tank contain after 50 minutes?

17. A bullet is fired horizontally into a sand bank in which the retardation or negative acceleration is equal to the square root of the velocity. When will it come to rest if the velocity on entering is 100 feet per second?

18. A body falls from rest in a viscous fluid. Assuming that the retardation is proportional to the velocity, find the proportionality constant if: (a) the body attains a velocity of 10 feet per second in 1 second; (b) the body falls 10 feet in the first second.

561. Second-Order Differential Equations with Dependent Variable Absent

Type I: $y'' = f(x)$.

A differential equation of this form may be solved by two successive integrations with respect to x.

EXAMPLE 1. Solve $\dfrac{d^2y}{dx^2} = \dfrac{1}{x^2}$.

Solution: Integrating with respect to x, we get

$$\frac{dy}{dx} = -\frac{1}{x} + C_1;$$

integrating again with respect to x, we have

$$y = -\ln x + C_1 x + C_2.$$

This method of repeated integration may be applied equally well to the n-th order equation $\dfrac{d^n y}{dx^n} = f(x)$. Many beam problems involve this method.

Type II: $y'' = F(x, y')$.

If we put $\dfrac{dy}{dx} = p$, the equation takes the form $\dfrac{dp}{dx} = F(x, p)$: a differential equation of the first order in p as an unknown function of x. If this equation can be solved by the preceding methods for first-order equations, to express p in terms of x, we may then replace p by $\dfrac{dy}{dx}$, and again we have a first-order equation to solve for y as a function of x.

EXAMPLE 2. Solve $\dfrac{d^2 y}{dx^2} + \dfrac{dy}{dx} = x$.

Solution: If we put $\dfrac{dy}{dx} = p$, the given equation becomes

$$\frac{dp}{dx} + p = x,$$

which is a linear first-order equation, whose solution (by the method of § 557) is

$$p = x - 1 + c_1 e^{-x}.$$

Replacing p by $\dfrac{dy}{dx}$, and integrating directly, we obtain

$$y = \tfrac{1}{2} x^2 - x + c e^{-x} + c' \quad (c = -c_1).$$

562. Exercises

In Exercises 1–10, solve the given equations:

1. $\dfrac{d^2 y}{dx^2} = x$.
2. $\dfrac{d^2 y}{dx^2} = \cos x$.

3. $y'' = x \sin x - x^2$.
4. $xy'' = 1 + x^2$.

5. $x \dfrac{d^2 y}{dx^2} = \dfrac{dy}{dx}$.
6. $xy'' + y' + x = 0$.

7. $(1 + x) \dfrac{d^2 y}{dx^2} + \dfrac{dy}{dx} = 0$.
8. $x^2 y'' + xy' = 1$.

9. $xy'' - y' = x^3$.
10. $\dfrac{d^2 y}{dx^2} - \left(\dfrac{dy}{dx}\right)^2 - 4 = 0$.

11. A beam of length l is fixed in a wall at one end and loaded with a weight W at the free end. If x is the distance measured from the fixed end, the

deflection y from the horizontal is determined by

$$\frac{EI}{W} \frac{d^2y}{dx^2} = l - x,$$

where E, I and W are constants.   Find the deflection y in terms of the distance x.   Also find the maximum deflection.

563. Second-Order Differential Equations with Independent Variable Absent

Type I: $y'' = g(y)$.

Since $\frac{d}{dx}(y'^2) = 2\, y'y''$, we may multiply both sides of the given equation by $2\, y'\, dx$ and obtain

$$d(y'^2) = 2\, y'y''\, dx = 2\, g(y) \cdot y'\, dx = 2\, g(y)\, dy.$$

By integration,

$$y'^2 = \left(\frac{dy}{dx}\right)^2 = 2 \int g(y)\, dy + c_1.$$

After taking the square root, we separate variables and integrate again to obtain y as a function of x.

EXAMPLE 1.   Solve $\frac{d^2y}{dx^2} = -y$.

Solution: $2\, y'y''\, dx = -2\, yy'\, dx$ or $d(y'^2) = -2\, y\, dy$.   Therefore,

$$y'^2 = -y^2 + a^2,$$

where a^2 is the constant of integration.   Then

$$\frac{dy}{dx} = \pm \sqrt{a^2 - y^2}.$$

Separating variables, we get

$$\frac{dy}{\sqrt{a^2 - y^2}} = \pm dx,$$

and integrating again, we have

$$\text{Arc sin}\, \frac{y}{a} = \pm x + c.$$

Hence,

$$y = a \sin(\pm x + c).$$

Type II: $y'' = G(y, y')$.

By the substitution

$$(a) \qquad \frac{dy}{dx} = p, \qquad \frac{d^2y}{dx^2} = \frac{dp}{dx} = \frac{dp}{dy} \cdot \frac{dy}{dx} = p\, \frac{dp}{dy},$$

we may reduce this type of equation to the form

$$(b) \qquad p\frac{dp}{dy} = G(y, p),$$

which is a first-order equation in p as an unknown function of y. If this equation can be solved for p in terms of y, we may then replace p by $\frac{dy}{dx}$, and again we have a first-order equation to solve for y as a function of x.

EXAMPLE 2. Solve $y\frac{d^2y}{dx^2} + \left(\frac{dy}{dx}\right)^2 = 1.$

Solution: If we set $\frac{dy}{dx} = p$, $\frac{d^2y}{dx^2} = p\frac{dp}{dy}$, the given equation becomes

$$yp\frac{dp}{dy} + p^2 = 1.$$

Separating variables and integrating, we get

$$y^2(1 - p^2) = c_1 \text{ or } \frac{dy}{dx} = \frac{\pm\sqrt{y^2 - c_1}}{y}.$$

Separating variables again and integrating, we find

$$y^2 = (\pm x + c_2)^2 + c_1.$$

564. Exercises

In Exercises 1–8, solve the given equations:

1. $\frac{d^2y}{dx^2} + 4y = 0.$

2. $\frac{d^2y}{dx^2} = 4y.$

3. $\frac{d^2y}{dx^2} = -\frac{1}{y^3}.$

4. $\frac{d^2y}{dx^2} = -\frac{1}{y^2}.$

5. $2y\frac{d^2y}{dx^2} = \left(\frac{dy}{dx}\right)^2 + 4.$

6. $y'' = y'^3 + y'.$

7. $yy'' + 2y' = y'^2.$

8. $2yy'' + 2y'^2 = yy'.$

9. Prove that the curve of constant curvature is a circle.

10. Find the equation of the family of curves for which the radius of curvature at any point is proportional to the slope of the curve at that point.

11. Discuss the motion of a particle moving in a medium in which the resistance is proportional to the velocity, if no other force is acting, and if the initial velocity is v_0.

12. A body is projected upward from rest with an initial velocity of 80 feet per second in a medium offering resistance proportional to the square of the velocity, with the proportionality constant 0.005. How far and how long will the body rise?

565. Linear Differential Equations of Higher Order than the First

A differential equation of the form

$$(a) \quad \frac{d^n y}{dx^n} + P_1 \frac{d^{n-1}y}{dx^{n-1}} + P_2 \frac{d^{n-2}y}{dx^{n-2}} + \cdots + P_{n-1} \frac{dy}{dx} + P_n y = Q,$$

*where P_1, P_2, $\cdots$, P_{n-1}, P_n and Q are functions of x only (or constants), is a **linear differential equation of the n-th order.*** It is of the first degree in the function y and its first n derivatives.

For linear differential equations of order higher than the first, there are no elementary methods of solution available in general, except for equations in which the coefficients P_1, P_2, $\cdots$, P_n are all *constant*. We shall therefore consider only the case of constant coefficients.

A linear differential equation *with constant coefficients* may be written in the form

$$(b) \quad \frac{d^n y}{dx^n} + a_1 \frac{d^{n-1}y}{dx^{n-1}} + \cdots + a_{n-1} \frac{dy}{dx} + a_n y = X,$$

where the coefficients a_1, a_2, $\cdots$, a_n are constants and the right-hand member X is a function of x only (or constant).

A convenient form of representation of the equation (b) is obtained by replacing the symbols $\frac{d}{dx}$, $\frac{d^2}{dx^2}$, $\cdots$ by D, D^2, $\cdots$. The symbol D is an *operator* symbol. It indicates that the operation of differentiation is to be applied to the expression following it. In a similar way, D^2 indicates that the operation of differentiation is to be applied twice to the expression following it, etc. Thus,

$$D(x^3 - 5x^2 + x + 1) = 3x^2 - 10x + 1,$$
$$D^2(x^3 - 5x^2 + x + 1) = 6x - 10, \text{ etc.}$$

Equation (b) then becomes, in this notation,

$$(c) \quad D^n y + a_1 D^{n-1} y + \cdots + a_{n-1} D y + a_n y = X,$$

which may naturally be written:

$$(d) \quad (D^n + a_1 D^{n-1} + \cdots + a_{n-1} D + a_n) y = X,$$

where the left-hand member of (d) is *defined* to mean the same as the left-hand member of (c). The expression in the parentheses in (d) looks like a polynomial in a variable D, so we call it a *"polynomial operator"* and denote it by $P(D)$:

(e) $$P(D) = D^n + a_1D^{n-1} + \cdots + a_{n-1}D + a_n.$$

Our differential equation then takes the compact form:

(f) $$P(D)y = X.$$

*A linear differential equation $P(D)y = 0$, in which the right-hand member is 0, is called a **homogeneous equation** (or incomplete equation), and an equation $P(D)y = X$, in which the right-hand member is not 0 but is a function of x, is called a **non-homogeneous equation** (or complete equation).*

We shall now restrict our attention, for the remainder of this chapter, to the solution of *second-order* linear differential equations with constant coefficients, since these occur with greatest frequency in applied problems, and since higher order equations are solved in a similar manner.

566. Linear Differential Equations of the Second Order, with Constant Coefficients

A linear differential equation of the second order with constant coefficients may be written in the form:

(a) $$\frac{d^2y}{dx^2} + p\frac{dy}{dx} + qy = X,$$

where the coefficients p and q are constants and the right-hand member X is a function of x only or 0. In the D-notation, the equation is written:

(b) $$(D^2 + pD + q)y = X.$$

If the equation is indicated by the general form $P(D)y = X$, we have

(c) $$P(D) = D^2 + pD + q.$$

The derivative of a sum of functions is equal to the sum of their derivatives, and the derivative of a constant times a function is equal to the constant times the derivative of the function; the same is evidently true also for the second derivative. It follows readily that the operator $P(D)$ has the following important properties:

(5) $$P(D)(y_1 + y_2) = P(D)y_1 + P(D)y_2,$$

(6) $$P(D)(cy) = c \cdot P(D)y.$$

The two following fundamental theorems underlie the methods of solving linear differential equations with constant coefficients.

I. *If y_1 and y_2 are two linearly independent particular solutions* of the second-order* **homogeneous** *equation $P(D)y = 0$, and if c_1 and c_2 are arbitrary constants, then*

$$(d) \qquad\qquad y = c_1 y_1 + c_2 y_2$$

is the **general** *solution of the differential equation $P(D)y = 0$.*

Proof: By properties (5) and (6) above,

$$(e) \qquad P(D)(c_1 y_1 + c_2 y_2) = P(D)(c_1 y_1) + P(D)(c_2 y_2)$$
$$= c_1 P(D)y_1 + c_2 P(D)y_2.$$

But by hypothesis, $P(D)y_1 = 0$ and $P(D)y_2 = 0$; hence from (e), $P(D)(c_1 y_1 + c_2 y_2) = 0$. Therefore, the function y in (d) satisfies the equation $P(D)y = 0$. Since y_1 and y_2 are linearly independent, the function $y = c_1 y_1 + c_2 y_2$ is the general solution of the given differential equation, since it contains the proper number of arbitrary constants.

II. *If $y = y_p$ is a* **particular** *solution of the* **non-homogeneous** *equation $P(D)y = X$, and if $y = y_c$ is the* **general** *solution of the corresponding homogeneous equation $P(D)y = 0$, then*

$$(f) \qquad\qquad y = y_p + y_c$$

is the **general** *solution of $P(D)y = X$.*

Proof: By property (5) above,

$$(g) \qquad P(D)(y_p + y_c) = P(D)y_p + P(D)y_c.$$

But by hypothesis, $P(D)y_p = X$ and $P(D)y_c = 0$, so that

$$P(D)(y_p + y_c) = X.$$

This shows that $y = y_p + y_c$ is the general solution of the non-homogeneous equation $P(D)y = X$, since it satisfies the equation and since it contains the proper number of arbitrary constants.

The function $y_c = c_1 y_1 + c_2 y_2$ (which is the general solution of the homogeneous equation) is called the **complementary function** of the non-homogeneous equation $P(D)y = X$.

It follows from theorem II that the problem of solving a non-

---

* That is, neither is a constant multiple of the other.

homogeneous linear differential equation reduces to that of finding the general solution of the corresponding homogeneous equation and also finding any particular solution of the given non-homogeneous equation.

567. Solution of Homogeneous Linear Differential Equations of the Second Order, with Constant Coefficients

We now consider methods for the solution of the homogeneous equation

$$(a) \qquad P(D)y = (D^2 + pD + q)y = 0,$$

with real constant coefficients p and q.

It will be seen presently that the *algebraic equation*

$$(b) \qquad P(m) = m^2 + pm + q = 0$$

plays an essential part in the solution of the *differential equation* (a). It is called the **auxiliary equation** (or characteristic equation) for the differential equation $P(D)y = 0$.

It will be found that the form of the general solution of the differential equation depends on the character of the roots of this auxiliary equation.   It is necessary to distinguish between three cases: (1) when the roots are real and unequal, (2) when the roots are real and equal, and (3) when the roots are imaginary.

Case 1.   When the roots of the auxiliary equation are real and distinct, the solution of the differential equation is given by the following theorem:

I. *If the roots m_1 and m_2 of the auxiliary equation $P(m) = 0$ are real and unequal, the general solution of the differential equation $P(D)y = 0$ is*

$$(7) \qquad y = c_1 e^{m_1 x} + c_2 e^{m_2 x},$$

where c_1 and c_2 are arbitrary constants.

Proof: Let m denote either one of the roots m_1, m_2, so that $P(m) = m^2 + pm + q = 0$.   Substitute $y = e^{mx}$ in the given differential equation.   Since

$$D(e^{mx}) = me^{mx} \qquad \text{and} \qquad D^2(e^{mx}) = m^2 e^{mx},$$

we get

$$(c) \quad P(D)y = m^2 e^{mx} + pme^{mx} + qe^{mx} = (m^2 + pm + q)e^{mx} = 0.$$

Hence, $y_1 = e^{m_1 x}$ and $y_2 = e^{m_2 x}$ are solutions of the differential equation. Since m_1 and m_2 are real and unequal, these two solutions y_1 and y_2 are linearly independent because one of them is not a constant multiple of the other. Then, by theorem I of § 566, it follows that $y = c_1 y_1 + c_2 y_2 = c_1 e^{m_1 x} + c_2 e^{m_2 x}$ is the general solution, when c_1 and c_2 are arbitrary constants.

EXAMPLE 1. Solve the differential equation $\dfrac{d^2 y}{dx^2} - \dfrac{dy}{dx} - 6y = 0$.

Solution: In this case, $P(D) = D^2 - D - 6$, and the auxiliary equation is $m^2 - m - 6 = 0$. Since the roots of this equation are $m = 3$, $m = -2$, the general solution of the differential equation is $y = c_1 e^{3x} + c_2 e^{-2x}$.

EXAMPLE 2. Find the particular solution of the differential equation $y'' + y' - 6y = 0$ subject to the initial conditions: $y = 4$ and $y' = 3$ when $x = 0$.

Solution: The roots of the auxiliary equation $m^2 + m - 6 = 0$ are $m = 2$ and $m = -3$, and the general solution of the differential equation is

$$(d) \qquad\qquad y = c_1 e^{2x} + c_2 e^{-3x}.$$

Substituting $x = 0$ and $y = 4$ in this equation, we have $c_1 + c_2 = 4$. Differentiating (d), we have

$$y' = 2 c_1 e^{2x} - 3 c_2 e^{-3x}.$$

Substituting $x = 0$ and $y' = 3$ in this equation, we have $2 c_1 - 3 c_2 = 3$. Solving these two equations for c_1 and c_2, we find $c_1 = 3$, $c_2 = 1$. The required particular solution is therefore $y = 3 e^{2x} + e^{-3x}$.

Case 2. When both roots of the auxiliary equation are equal, the formula (7) of theorem I does not give the *general* solution of the differential equation, because there is then essentially only one arbitrary constant instead of two. The following theorem gives the general solution in this case:

II. *If the roots m_1 and m_2 of the auxiliary equation $P(m) = 0$ are real and equal, each being equal to r, then the general solution of the differential equation $P(D)y = 0$ is:*

(8) $$y = (c_1 + c_2 x)e^{rx},$$

where c_1 and c_2 are arbitrary constants.

Proof: If we take $y_1 = e^{rx}$, it follows from the proof of theorem I that y_1 is a solution of the differential equation.

Now consider the function $y_2 = xe^{rx}$; we find

$$(e) \qquad Dy_2 = e^{rx}(1 + rx), \qquad D^2 y_2 = e^{rx}(2r + r^2 x).$$

Then

(f)
$$P(D)y_2 = (D^2 + pD + q)y_2$$
$$= e^{rx}[(r^2 + pr + q)x + (2r + p)].$$

Since r is a root of $P(m) = 0$, we have $r^2 + pr + q = 0$. By algebra, the condition for equal roots of the quadratic equation $m^2 + pm + q = 0$ is $p^2 - 4q = 0$. The quadratic formula then gives $r = \frac{1}{2}(-p \pm \sqrt{p^2 - 4q}) = -\frac{1}{2}p$, whence $2r + p = 0$. It follows that the right-hand member of (f) is 0, which shows that $y_2 = xe^{rx}$ is a solution of our differential equation. It can be shown that the two functions e^{rx} and xe^{rx} are linearly independent. By theorem I of § 566, since $y_1 = e^{rx}$ and $y_2 = xe^{rx}$ are particular solutions of the differential equation, the general solution is

$$y = c_1 y_1 + c_2 y_2 = c_1 e^{rx} + c_2 x e^{rx} = e^{rx}(c_1 + c_2 x).$$

EXAMPLE 3.   Solve $\dfrac{d^2 y}{dx^2} + 2\dfrac{dy}{dx} + y = 0$.

Solution: The auxiliary equation is $m^2 + 2m + 1 = 0 = (m + 1)^2$, which has the equal roots $m = -1, -1$, so that $r = -1$. Then the general solution of the differential equation is $y = (c_1 + c_2 x)e^{-x}$.

Case 3.   When the roots of the auxiliary equation are imaginary, the formula (7) of theorem I does not give a usable solution of the differential equation, because imaginary exponential functions have not yet been defined and in addition the exponential form would not be convenient for practical computation in this case. The general solution in this case is given by the following theorem:

III. *If the roots m_1 and m_2 of the auxiliary equation $P(m) = 0$ are* **conjugate imaginary numbers:** $m_1 = a + bi$, $m_2 = a - bi$, *then the general solution of the differential equation $P(D)y = 0$ is*

(9) $y = e^{ax}(c_1 \cos bx + c_2 \sin bx),$

where c_1 and c_2 are arbitrary constants.

Proof: Consider first the function $y_1 = e^{ax} \cos bx$. We have

$$Dy_1 = e^{ax}(a \cos bx - b \sin bx),$$
$$D^2 y_1 = e^{ax}(a^2 \cos bx - b^2 \cos bx - 2ab \sin bx);$$

then we find

(g) $P(D)y_1 = e^{ax}[(a^2 - b^2 + pa + q) \cos bx - (2ab + pb) \sin bx].$

But since $a + bi$ is a root of $m^2 + pm + q = 0$, we have

$$(a + bi)^2 + p(a + bi) + q = 0,$$

which reduces to

(h) $$(a^2 - b^2 + pa + q) + i(2\,ab + pb) = 0,$$

where a, b, p and q are real. By algebra, a complex number can be 0 only when the real and the pure imaginary parts are 0 separately, which gives

(i) $$a^2 - b^2 + pa + q = 0, \qquad 2\,ab + pb = 0.$$

These results show that the right-hand member of (g) is equal to 0. Hence, $y_1 = e^{ax} \cos bx$ is a particular solution of $P(D)y = 0$. Similarly, it can be shown that $y_2 = e^{ax} \sin bx$ is a particular solution of the differential equation. These two functions y_1 and y_2 are linearly independent. By theorem I of § 566, it now follows that

$$y = c_1 y_1 + c_2 y_2 = c_1 e^{ax} \cos bx + c_2 e^{ax} \sin bx$$

is the general solution of the differential equation.

EXAMPLE 4. Solve $y'' - 4\,y' + 13\,y = 0$.

Solution: This equation may be written: $(D^2 - 4\,D + 13)y = 0$; the auxiliary equation is $m^2 - 4\,m + 13 = 0$, which has the conjugate imaginary roots $m = 2 \pm 3\,i$. The general solution of the differential equation is therefore $y = e^{2x}(c_1 \cos 3\,x + c_2 \sin 3\,x)$.

EXAMPLE 5. Solve $\dfrac{d^2y}{dx^2} + 16\,y = 0$, subject to the initial conditions:

$y = 0$ and $\dfrac{dy}{dx} = 5$ when $x = 0$.

Solution: The auxiliary equation is $m^2 + 16 = 0$, which has the imaginary roots $m = \pm 4\,i$; the general solution is therefore

(j) $$y = c_1 \cos 4\,x + c_2 \sin 4\,x.$$

Substituting $y = 0$ and $x = 0$ gives $0 = c_1$; (j) then becomes

$$y = c_2 \sin 4\,x.$$

Differentiating this, we have

$$\frac{dy}{dx} = 4\,c_2 \cos 4\,x;$$

substituting $\dfrac{dy}{dx} = 5$ and $x = 0$, we get $5 = 4\,c_2$ or $c_2 = \frac{5}{4}$. The required particular solution is then $y = \frac{5}{4} \sin 4\,x$.

568. Exercises

In Exercises 1–8, find the general solution of each of the given equations:

1. $\dfrac{d^2y}{dx^2} - 5\dfrac{dy}{dx} + 6\,y = 0.$

2. $\dfrac{d^2y}{dx^2} + 5\dfrac{dy}{dx} + 4\,y = 0.$

3. $\dfrac{d^2y}{dx^2} - \dfrac{dy}{dx} - 12\,y = 0.$

4. $\dfrac{d^2y}{dx^2} - \dfrac{dy}{dx} - 2\,y = 0.$

5. $\dfrac{d^2y}{dx^2} - 4\,y = 0.$

6. $(3\,D^2 - 7\,D - 6)y = 0.$

7. $\dfrac{d^2y}{dx^2} - 4\dfrac{dy}{dx} = 0.$

8. $2\,D_x{}^2y + 5\,D_xy - 12\,y = 0.$

In Exercises 9–12, find the particular solution of each of the given equations, subject to the given conditions:

9. $\dfrac{d^2y}{dx^2} - 4\dfrac{dy}{dx} - 5\,y = 0,\ y = 0,\ \dfrac{dy}{dx} = 1$ when $x = 0.$

10. $\dfrac{d^2y}{dx^2} - y = 0,\ y = 0,\ \dfrac{dy}{dx} = 1$ when $x = 0.$

11. $y'' - y' - 2\,y = 0,\ y = -1,\ y' = -5$ when $x = 0.$

12. $y'' - 2\,y' - y = 0,\ y = 3,\ y' = 3 + \sqrt{2}$ when $x = 0.$

In Exercises 13–18, find the general solution of each of the given equations:

13. $\dfrac{d^2y}{dx^2} + 2\dfrac{dy}{dx} + y = 0.$

14. $y'' - 8\,y' + 16\,y = 0.$

15. $4\dfrac{d^2y}{dx^2} - 4\dfrac{dy}{dx} + y = 0.$

16. $9\,D_x{}^2y + 24\,D_xy + 16\,y = 0.$

17. $y'' + 6\,y' + 9\,y = 0.$

18. $\dfrac{d^2s}{dt^2} + 4\dfrac{ds}{dt} + 4\,s = 0.$

In Exercises 19–22, find the particular solution of each of the given equations, subject to the given initial conditions:

19. $\dfrac{d^2y}{dx^2} + 2\dfrac{dy}{dx} + y = 0,\ y = 0,\ \dfrac{dy}{dx} = -1$ when $x = 0.$

20. $y'' - 4\,y' + 4\,y = 0,\ y = 2,\ y' = 3$ when $x = 0.$

21. $y'' + 6\,y' + 9\,y = 0,\ y = -1,\ y' = 4$ when $x = 0.$

22. $9\dfrac{d^2y}{dx^2} + 12\dfrac{dy}{dx} + 4\,y = 0,\ y = 3,\ \dfrac{dy}{dx} = 0$ when $x = 0.$

In Exercises 23–28, find the general solution of each of the given equations:

23. $\dfrac{d^2y}{dx^2} - 2\dfrac{dy}{dx} + 5\,y = 0.$

24. $\dfrac{d^2y}{dx^2} - 4\dfrac{dy}{dx} + 5\,y = 0.$

25. $\dfrac{d^2y}{dx^2} + \dfrac{dy}{dx} + y = 0.$

26. $(4\,D^2 + 1)y = 0.$

27. $D_x{}^2y + 4\,y = 0.$

28. $y'' - y' + 2\,y = 0.$

In Exercises 29–32, find the particular solution of each of the given equations, subject to the given initial conditions·

29. $\dfrac{d^2y}{dx^2} + 2\dfrac{dy}{dx} + 2\,y = 0$, $y = 0$, $\dfrac{dy}{dx} = 3$ when $x = 0$.

30. $\dfrac{d^2y}{dx^2} + 9\,y = 0$, $y = -2$, $\dfrac{dy}{dx} = 3$ when $x = \pi$.

31. $y'' + 2\,y = 0$, $y = 1$, $y' = -1$ when $x = 0$.

32. $y'' + 3\,y' + 4\,y = 0$, $y = 2$, $y' = -3$ when $x = 0$.

33. Solve $(D^2 - 4)y = 0$, and express the general solution in terms of hyperbolic functions.

34. Prove that if $P(m) = 0$ has imaginary roots $a + bi$ and $a - bi$, then $y_2 = e^{ax} \sin bx$ is a solution of $P(D)y = 0$.

569. Solution of Non-Homogeneous Linear Differential Equations, by the Method of Undetermined Coefficients

We shall now consider methods for the solution of the second-order *non-homogeneous* linear equation

$$(a) \qquad P(D)y = (D^2 + pD + q)y = X,$$

with constant coefficients, where X is a function of x.

In the majority of applied problems in which non-homogeneous differential equations occur, the right-hand member X consists of one or more terms of the types: e^{ax}, $\sin ax$, $\cos ax$, or a polynomial in x. For these cases, one of the simplest methods of solution is that called the *method of undetermined coefficients*. This method does not apply to all non-homogeneous linear equations, but it applies to most of the simpler applications.

It should be recalled from theorem II of § 566 that the general solution of a non-homogeneous linear differential equation may be expressed as the sum of the *complementary function* (that is, the general solution of the corresponding homogeneous equation) and a *particular solution* of the given non-homogeneous equation. That is, the general solution of $P(D)y = X$ is $y = y_c + y_p$, where y_c is the general solution of $P(D)y = 0$ and y_p is any particular solution of $P(D)y = X$.

In order to find the particular solution y_p, it must be noted that y_p can contain only types of functions which are contained in X or from which the terms of X can be obtained by differentiation.

The method of undetermined coefficients is based partly on the fact that such functions as e^{ax}, $\sin ax$, $\cos ax$, x^n and linear combinations of them have only a finite number of distinct derivatives.

The general procedure in the *method of undetermined coefficients* is to *assume for y_p a proper expression based on the function X, involving* *certain undetermined coefficients, substitute this in the differential equation, equate coefficients of corresponding types of terms and thereby determine y_p.*

The following general rules may be formulated for the procedure by the method of undetermined coefficients; the reasons for them may be seen in a general way from the preceding remarks.

When	*Assume*
I. $X = a_0x^m + a_1x^{m-1} + \cdots + a_m,$	$y_p = A_0x^m + A_1x^{m-1} + \cdots + A_m,$ *if D is not a factor of $P(D)$;* $y_p = x(A_0x^m + A_1x^{m-1} + \cdots + A_m),$ *if D is a factor of $P(D)$.*
II. $X = ce^{ax},$	$y_p = Ae^{ax},$ *if $D - a$ is not a factor of $P(D)$;* $y_p = xAe^{ax},$ *if $D - a$ is a factor of $P(D)$;* $y_p = x^2Ae^{ax},$ *if $(D - a)^2$ is a factor of $P(D)$.*
III. $X = c \sin ax + b \cos ax,$ *(where c or b may be 0).*	$y_p = A \sin ax + B \cos ax,$ *if $D^2 + a^2$ is not a factor of $P(D)$;* $y_p = x(A \sin ax + B \cos ax),$ *if $D^2 + a^2$ is a factor of $P(D)$.*
IV. $X = a$ *sum of some of the expressions above.*	$y_p = a$ *sum of the corresponding expressions above.*

The constants A, B, A_0, A_1, $\cdots$, A_m are undetermined coefficients.

V. *If $X = e^{ax}p(x)$ (polynomial) or $X = e^{ax} \sin bx$ (or $e^{ax} \cos bx$), the substitution $y = e^{ax} \cdot v$ will reduce the equation to one in v as the unknown function, in which the right-hand member is a polynomial or a sine or cosine term.*

EXAMPLE 1. Solve $\dfrac{d^2y}{dx^2} + \dfrac{dy}{dx} - 2y = 4x^2 - 10x + 1.$

Solution: Solving the homogeneous equation $(D^2 + D - 2)y = 0$, we find for the complementary function

$$y_c = c_1e^x + c_2e^{-2x}.$$

Since D is not a factor of $P(D)$, we put

$$y_p = Ax^2 + Bx + C,$$

then

$$Dy_p = 2Ax + B, \quad D^2y_p = 2A.$$

Substituting these values in the given differential equation, we have

$$2A + 2Ax + B - 2Ax^2 - 2Bx - 2C = 4x^2 - 10x + 1.$$

Equating coefficients of x^2, x and constant terms, we find

$$A = -2, B = 3, C = -1.$$

Hence,

$$y_p = -2\,x^2 + 3\,x - 1,$$

and the required general solution is

$$y = c_1 e^x + c_2 e^{-2x} - 2\,x^2 + 3\,x - 1.$$

EXAMPLE 2. Solve $y'' - 2\,y' - 3\,y = 4\,e^{3x}$.

Solution: In this case, $P(D) = D^2 - 2\,D - 3$; and the auxiliary equation is $m^2 - 2\,m - 3 = 0 = (m - 3)(m + 1)$, which has the roots $m = 3,\ -1$, and the complementary function is therefore

$$y_c = c_1 e^{3x} + c_2 e^{-x}.$$

The exceptional case occurs here, since the right-hand member X contains e^{3x}, with $a = 3$, and $P(D) = (D - 3)(D + 1)$ has $D - 3$ as a factor once. We therefore assume

$$y_p = x A e^{3x};$$

we find

$$Dy_p = x \cdot 3\,A e^{3x} + A e^{3x},$$
$$D^2 y_p = x \cdot 9\,A e^{3x} + 3\,A e^{3x} + 3\,A e^{3x} = 9\,A x e^{3x} + 6\,A e^{3x}.$$

Substituting these in the given differential equation, we get

$$9\,A x e^{3x} + 6\,A e^{3x} - 2(3\,A x e^{3x} + A e^{3x}) - 3\,A x e^{3x} = 4\,e^{3x};$$

the terms involving $x e^{3x}$ cancel, and we have

$$6\,A e^{3x} - 2\,A e^{3x} = 4\,e^{3x},$$

from which we find $A = 1$.   Hence, the general solution is

$$y = c_1 e^{3x} + c_2 e^{-x} + x e^{3x}.$$

EXAMPLE 3. Solve $\dfrac{d^2 y}{dx^2} + 4\,\dfrac{dy}{dx} = 10 \sin 2\,x$.

Solution: The roots of the auxiliary equation $m^2 + 4\,m = 0$ are $m = 0,\ -4$, hence the complementary function is

$$y_c = c_1 + c_2 e^{-4x}.$$

Since $D^2 + 4$ is not a factor of $P(D) = D^2 + 4\,D$, we assume

$$y_p = A \sin 2\,x + B \cos 2\,x.$$

Then

$$Dy_p = 2\,A \cos 2\,x - 2\,B \sin 2\,x,\ D^2 y_p = -4\,A \sin 2\,x - 4\,B \cos 2\,x;$$

substitution of these values in the differential equation gives

$$-4\,A \sin 2\,x - 4\,B \cos 2\,x + 8\,A \cos 2\,x - 8\,B \sin 2\,x = 10 \sin 2\,x.$$

Equating coefficients of $\sin 2\,x$ and $\cos 2\,x$ separately on both sides, we get

$$-4\,A - 8\,B = 10,\ -4\,B + 8\,A = 0.$$

Solution of these simultaneous equations gives $A = -\frac{1}{2},\ B = -1$.   The required general solution is therefore

$$y = c_1 + c_2 e^{-4x} - \tfrac{1}{2} \sin 2\,x - \cos 2\,x.$$

EXAMPLE 4. Solve $\dfrac{d^2y}{dx^2} + 2\,\dfrac{dy}{dx} = 5\,e^{-x}\cos 2\,x$.

Solution: The auxiliary equation $m^2 + 2\,m = 0$ has the roots $m = 0,\ -2$, so that the complementary function is

$$y_c = c_1 + c_2 e^{-2x}.$$

Now put $y = e^{-x}\cdot v$; then

$$Dy = e^{-x}Dv - e^{-x}v,$$

$$D^2y = e^{-x}D^2v - e^{-x}Dv - e^{-x}Dv + e^{-x}v = e^{-x}D^2v - 2\,e^{-x}Dv + e^{-x}v.$$

Substituting these values in the differential equation, we get

$$e^{-x}(D^2v - 2\,Dv + v + 2\,Dv - 2\,v) = 5\,e^{-x}\cos 2\,x,$$

from which, by dividing by e^{-x} on both sides, we obtain the new differential equation

$$D^2v - v = 5\cos 2\,x,$$

to be solved for v. Solving this equation as in Example 3, by putting $v_p = A\sin 2\,x + B\cos 2\,x$, we find $A = 0$ and $B = -1$, so that $v_p = -\cos 2\,x$. Then

$$y_p = -e^{-x}\cos 2\,x.$$

The required general solution of the original differential equation is therefore

$$y = c_1 + c_2 e^{-2x} - e^{-x}\cos 2\,x.$$

570. Exercises

In Exercises 1–8, find the general solution of each of the given equations:

1. $\dfrac{d^2y}{dx^2} - 4\,y = x.$ 2. $(D^2 + 9)y = 3\,x^2.$

3. $\dfrac{d^2y}{dx^2} + \dfrac{dy}{dx} - 6\,y = x^2.$ 4. $(D^2 - 2\,D + 2)y = x^3 - 2\,x.$

5. $y'' - 2\,y' + y = x^2 + x.$ 6. $y'' + 3\,y' = 2 - x^2.$

7. $\dfrac{d^2y}{dx^2} + \dfrac{dy}{dx} = 4\,x.$ 8. $\dfrac{d^2y}{dx^2} - 4\,\dfrac{dy}{dx} = 2\,x - 3.$

In Exercises 9–16, find the general solution of each of the given equations:

9. $(D^2 - 5\,D + 6)y = e^x.$ 10. $y'' + y = 4\,e^{2x}.$

11. $2\,y'' - y' - 6\,y = e^{3x}.$ 12. $y'' + 2\,y' + 2\,y = 3\,e^{-2x}.$

13. $\dfrac{d^2y}{dx^2} + 6\,\dfrac{dy}{dx} + 9\,y = 2\,e^{-x}.$ 14. $\dfrac{d^2y}{dx^2} - 3\,\dfrac{dy}{dx} + 2\,y = 4\,e^x.$

15. $y'' + 4\,y' + 3\,y = e^{-3x}.$ 16. $y'' - y = 5\,e^x.$

In Exercises 17–26, find the general solution of each of the given equations:

17. $\dfrac{d^2y}{dx^2} - \dfrac{dy}{dx} - 2\,y = 2\sin x.$ 18. $y'' - 4\,y' + 4\,y = \cos 4\,x.$

19. $\dfrac{d^2y}{dx^2} + 4\,\dfrac{dy}{dx} = \cos x.$ 20. $(D^2 + 1)y = \sin 3\,x.$

21. $y'' - 2\,y' + y = \sin 2\,x.$ 22. $(D^2 + 2\,D + 5)y = \sin 2\,x.$
23. $y'' + y' = \sin 2\,x + \cos 2\,x.$ 24. $y'' - 5\,y' + 6\,y = 2\sin x + \cos 2\,x.$

25. $\dfrac{d^2y}{dx^2} + 4\,y = 2\cos 2\,x.$ 26. $y'' + y = -3\sin x.$

In Exercises 27–34, find the general solution of each of the given equations

27. $\dfrac{d^2y}{dx^2} + 4\,y = x + 2\,e^{-x}.$ 28. $y'' + 2\,y' + y = x^2 + 2\,x + e^x.$

29. $\dfrac{d^2y}{dx^2} + 9\,y = \sin x + e^{2x}.$ 30. $\dfrac{d^2u}{dz^2} + u = 3\,e^z - \sin 2\,z.$

31. $z'' - z' - 6\,z = e^{2x} + e^{4x}.$ 32. $y'' + 4\,y = \sin x + 2\cos 2\,x.$
33. $y'' + y' = e^x + 3\,x.$ 34. $y'' - 3\,y' - 4\,y = \sin x - e^{-x}.$

In Exercises 35–38, find the particular solution of each of the given equations which satisfies the given conditions:

35. $y'' - 5\,y' + 6\,y = 2\,e^x,\ y = 1,\ y' = 0$ when $x = 0.$
36. $D^2y - 4\,y = 4\sin x,\ y = 4,\ D_xy = 0$ when $x = 0.$
37. $s'' + 4\,s = 8\,t,\ s = 0,\ s' = 4$ when $t = 0.$

38. $\dfrac{d^2y}{dx^2} - 3\,\dfrac{dy}{dx} = 6,\ y = 1,\ \dfrac{dy}{dx} = 1$ when $x = 0.$

Solve each of the following equations:

39. $\dfrac{d^2y}{dx^2} + \dfrac{dy}{dx} - 6\,y = x^2e^x.$ 40. $y'' + 2\,y' = xe^x.$

41. $y'' - 9\,y = e^{3x}\cos x.$ 42. $\dfrac{d^2y}{dx^2} + y = e^x\sin 2\,x.$

571. Applications of Linear Differential Equations

Simple harmonic motion: Simple harmonic motion is frequently defined as *motion in a straight line in which the acceleration is proportional to the displacement from a fixed point on the line and oppositely directed.* With this definition, the differential equation of motion can evidently be written:

(a)
$$\frac{d^2x}{dt^2} = -k^2x \qquad (k \text{ constant}),$$

where x is the displacement and t is the time. This equation is a simple case of a homogeneous linear differential equation, whose solution is

(b)
$$x = A\cos kt + B\sin kt.$$

By a trigonometric transformation, this may be written in the form

(c)
$$x = a\cos(kt - \alpha),$$

where $a = \pm\sqrt{A^2 + B^2},\ \cos \alpha = A/a,\ \sin \alpha = B/a.$

Damped vibrations: Suppose that a particle of mass m which is free to move in a straight line is acted on by a force which is proportional to its displacement x from some central position and acts toward that position, and that there is also a resistance proportional to the velocity. The central force may be represented by $-a^2x$ and the resistance by $-b^2v = -b^2\dfrac{dx}{dt}$. Since the total force acting on a body is equal to its mass times its acceleration, we can write

$$m\frac{d^2x}{dt^2} = -a^2x - b^2\frac{dx}{dt},$$

or

(d) $$\frac{d^2x}{dt^2} + 2\,\mu\frac{dx}{dt} + k^2x = 0,$$

where $2\,\mu = b^2/m$ and $k^2 = a^2/m$ are positive constants indicative of the resistance and of the strength of the central force respectively. When there is no resistance and $\mu = 0$, the equation is the equation of simple harmonic equation. This differential equation (d) is a second-order *homogeneous* linear equation with constant coefficients. The auxiliary equation is $m^2 + 2\,\mu m + k^2 = 0$, whose roots are

(e) $$m = -\mu \pm \sqrt{\mu^2 - k^2}.$$

Evidently, the nature of the roots and the character of the motion depend on the discriminant $\mu^2 - k^2$ and therefore on the relative values of μ and k.

(1) Suppose that $\mu < k$, so that the resistance is relatively small. Put $k^2 - \mu^2 = \gamma^2$. The roots (e) are now imaginary numbers: $m = -\mu \pm \gamma i$. By § 567, the general solution of the differential equation (d) is:

(f) $$x = e^{-\mu t}\left(c_1 \cos \gamma t + c_2 \sin \gamma t\right) = Ce^{-\mu t}\cos\left(\gamma t - \delta\right),$$

where c_1 and c_2, or C and δ are arbitrary constants. The corresponding motion is oscillatory. Its amplitude is $Ce^{-\mu t}$, which decreases and approaches zero as $t \to \infty$. The factor $e^{-\mu t}$ is sometimes called the *damping factor*; it indicates the manner in which the resistance damps out the oscillation. The time required for a complete oscillation is $2\,\pi/\gamma = 2\,\pi/\sqrt{k^2 - \mu^2}$, which is large when μ is large. The resistance therefore has two effects on the motion: it tends to damp it out and it lengthens the time of an oscillation. The motion is represented graphically in Fig. 233. It is called *damped vibration*, and it is of importance in engineering.

(2) Suppose next that $\mu > k$, so that the resistance is relatively large. Let $\mu^2 - k^2 = \lambda^2 > 0$. The roots (e) are now both real and unequal: $m = -\mu \pm \lambda$. By § 567, the solution of the differential equation (d) is:

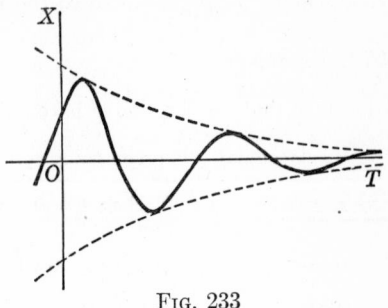

(g) $\quad x = c_1 e^{(-\mu+\lambda)t} + c_2 e^{(-\mu-\lambda)t}$.

Since $0 < \lambda < \mu$, both exponents in (g) are negative, and $x \to 0$ as $t \to \infty$. The motion is non-oscillatory and damped.

Fig. 233

(3) If $\mu = k$, then $m = -\mu$, and we have

(h) $\qquad x = e^{-\mu t}(c_1 + c_2 t)$.

Evidently $x \to 0$ as $t \to \infty$. The motion is non-oscillatory and damped.

Forced vibrations: Suppose that a particle which is free to move in a straight line is acted on by a force which is proportional to its displacement from a fixed point on the line and acts toward that point, and that it is also acted on by an impressed periodic force proportional to $\cos pt$.* The equation of motion is then of the form:

(i) $\qquad \dfrac{d^2x}{dt^2} + k^2 x = a \cos pt$,

where k, a and p are given constants. This differential equation is a *non-homogeneous* linear equation with constant coefficients. By the method of § 569, we find for the general solution:

(j) $\qquad x = A \cos (kt - \alpha) + \dfrac{a}{k^2 - p^2} \cos pt$,

where A and α are arbitrary constants. The corresponding motion is compounded of two simple harmonic motions, of different amplitudes and different periods, in general. It is oscillatory.

---

* An example is that of a tuning fork which, besides its own natural vibrations, is subjected to the attraction of an external electro-magnet with a force proportional to $\cos pt$.

A special case of some interest is that in which k and p are nearly equal; then the amplitude $a/(k^2 - p^2)$ of the second term is very large, and the resulting vibrations may be dangerously great.* The case when $k = p$ gives rise to the phenomenon of *resonance*.

572. Exercises

1. Show that for the simple harmonic motion defined by $\dfrac{d^2x}{dt^2} = -k^2x$, the displacement x is given by $x = a \cos kt$ when the initial conditions are: $x = a$ and $\dfrac{dx}{dt} = 0$ when $t = 0$; and that $x = a \sin kt$ when the initial conditions are: $x = a$, $\dfrac{dx}{dt} = 0$ when $t = \dfrac{\pi}{2\,k}$.

2. A weight attached to a spring moves up and down, so that the equation of motion is

$$\frac{d^2s}{dt^2} + 16\,s = 0,$$

where s is the amount the spring is stretched at time t. If $s = 1$ and $\dfrac{ds}{dt} = 0$ when $t = 0$, find s in terms of t.

3. The motion of a simple pendulum of length l (in a vacuum) is determined by the differential equation

$$\frac{d^2\theta}{dt^2} = -\frac{g}{l} \sin \theta.$$

If the pendulum swings through a small angle, we may replace $\sin \theta$ by θ, for an approximation (§ 261). Solve the differential equation under this assumption, if $\theta = \alpha$ and $\dfrac{d\theta}{dt} = 0$ when $t = 0$.

4. When an electric condenser discharges through a negligible resistance, the current I follows the law

$$\frac{d^2I}{dt^2} = -a^2I,$$

where a is constant. Express the current in terms of the time. When $a = 1000$, what is the frequency (number of alternations per second)?

5. The differential equation

$$EI \frac{d^2y}{dx^2} = -Py,$$

(E, I and P constant) occurs in the theory of struts. Find y in terms of x, if $y = 0$ when $x = 0$, and $y = Y$ when $x = \frac{1}{2} L$.

---

* Bodies of troops crossing bridges are sometimes ordered to break step, so that their rhythm may not too nearly equal the natural period of vibration of the bridge.

6. The current of electricity flowing in a certain circuit satisfies the differential equation

$$L \frac{d^2I}{dt^2} + R \frac{dI}{dt} = 0,$$

where R and L are constants. Find I in terms of t, if $I = a$ and $\frac{dI}{dt} = b$ when $t = 0$.

7. A weight hung on a spring moves under the action of its weight which is 16 pounds, the force exerted by the spring $8\ s$, and air resistance $0.06\ v$, where $v = \frac{ds}{dt}$. The equation of motion is

$$\frac{16}{g} \cdot \frac{d^2s}{dt^2} = -0.06 \frac{ds}{dt} - 8\ s.$$

Find s in terms of t, if the initial conditions are: $s = \frac{1}{2}$, $\frac{ds}{dt} = 0$ when $t = 0$.

(Use $g = 32$.) Show that $s \to 0$ when $t \to \infty$.

8. When a galvanometer is damped, the equation of motion is

$$\frac{d^2\theta}{dt^2} + 2\ k \frac{d\theta}{dt} + \omega^2(\theta - \alpha) = 0,$$

where θ is the deflection of the needle, and k, ω^2 and α are constants. Find the position of the needle at any time.

9. In the case of a stretched elastic string, which has one end fixed and a heavy particle of mass m attached to the other end, the equation of motion is

$$ms'' = - \frac{mg}{e}\ (s - L),$$

where L is the natural length of the string, and e is its elongation due to the weight mg. Find s and $\frac{ds}{dt}$, determining the constants so that $s = s_0$ and $\frac{ds}{dt} = 0$ when $t = 0$.

10. The motion of the piston of an indicator is given by the equation

$$M \frac{d^2x}{dt^2} + \frac{a}{sM} \cdot x = \frac{pa}{m},$$

where M, a, s, m and p are constant. Find x in terms of t.

11. The current of electricity flowing in a certain circuit satisfies the equation

$$2 \frac{d^2I}{dt^2} + 10 \frac{dI}{dt} + 5000\ I = 220.$$

If $I = 0$ and $\frac{dI}{dt} = 0$ when $t = 0$, find I in terms of t.

12. In certain beam problems, the following equation occurs:

$$EI \frac{d^2y}{dx^2} = -M_1 - Sy + V_1 x,$$

where E, I, M_1, S and V_1 are constant. Solve the equation with the initial conditions: $y = 0$ when $x = 0$ and also when $x = l$.

13. The electric current I in a certain circuit is represented by the equation

$$L \frac{d^2I}{dt^2} + \frac{1}{C} \cdot I = E_0 \sin \omega t,$$

where L, C, E and ω are positive constants. If $I = 0$ and $\frac{dI}{dt} = 0$ when $t = 0$, find I in terms of t.

14. If a mass m is suspended from a coiled spring, the spring constant of which is k, and if impulses are applied to the mass along the axis of the spring according to the law $F = P \sin \dfrac{2\pi t}{T}$, then the equation of motion is

$$m \frac{d^2y}{dt^2} + ky = P \sin \frac{2\pi t}{T}.$$

Solve this equation.

Appendix

I. FORMULAS FOR REFERENCE

A. Formulas from Algebra

1. A factor formula:
$$a^n - b^n = (a - b)(a^{n-1} + a^{n-2}b + \cdots + ab^{n-2} + b^{n-1}).$$

2. Binomial formula:
$$(a + x)^n = a^n + na^{n-1}x + \frac{n(n-1)}{2!} a^{n-2}x^2 + \cdots + x^n.$$

   Factorial n: $\quad n! = 1 \cdot 2 \cdot 3 \cdots n; \quad 0! = 1.$

3. Quadratic equations:

   (a) Roots of $ax^2 + bx + c = 0$ are:
   $$x = \frac{-b \pm \sqrt{b^2 - 4ac}}{2a}.$$

   (b) Roots of $ax^2 + bx + c = 0$ (when a, b, c are real) are:
   (1) real and unequal if $b^2 - 4ac > 0$;
   (2) real and equal if $b^2 - 4ac = 0$;
   (3) imaginary if $b^2 - 4ac < 0$.

   (c) Sum of roots of $ax^2 + bx + c = 0$ is $-b/a$; product of roots is c/a.

4. Logarithms:

   (a) If $b^L = N$, then $L = \log_b N$; therefore, $b^{\log_b N} = N$.
   (b) $\log_b 1 = 0$, $\log_b b = 1$.
   (c) Laws of logarithms:

   (1) $\log_b (MN) = \log_b M + \log_b N$;
   (2) $\log_b (M/N) = \log_b M - \log_b N$,
   $\quad \log_b (1/N) = -\log_b N = \operatorname{colog}_b N$;
   (3) $\log_b (M^n) = n \log_b M$;
   (4) $\log_b \sqrt[n]{M} = \dfrac{1}{n} \log_b M.$

   (d) Change of base: $\log_a N = \log_b N \cdot \log_a b = \log_b N / \log_b a$,
   $\quad \log_a b = 1/\log_b a.$

i

B. Formulas from Geometry (Mensuration)

Let r or R denote radius, h altitude, b length of base, B area of base, s slant height, θ central angle in radian measure.

1. Circle: circumference $= 2\pi r$, area $= \pi r^2$.
2. Circular arc: length $= r\theta$.
3. Circular sector: area $= \frac{1}{2}r^2\theta$.
4. Circular segment: area $= \frac{1}{2}r^2(\theta - \sin\theta)$.
5. Triangle: area $= \frac{1}{2}bh$.
6. Trapezoid: area $= \frac{1}{2}h(b_1 + b_2)$.
7. Sphere: volume $= \frac{4}{3}\pi r^3$, area of surface $= 4\pi r^2$.
8. Right circular cylinder: volume $= \pi r^2 h$, lateral surface area $= 2\pi rh$.
9. Right circular cone: volume $= \frac{1}{3}\pi r^2 h$, lateral surface area $= \pi rs$.
10. Frustum of cone: volume $= \frac{1}{3}\pi h(R^2 + r^2 + Rr)$, lateral surface area $= \pi s(R + r)$.
11. Prism: volume $= Bh$.
12. Pyramid: volume $= \frac{1}{3}Bh$.

C. Formulas from Trigonometry

1. Radian measure of angles:

(a) The *radian measure* or *circular measure* of an angle whose vertex is at the center of a circle is the ratio of the intercepted arc to the radius: $\theta = \text{arc}/r$.

A *radian*, the unit angle in circular measure, is an angle which, when placed with its vertex at the center of a circle, intercepts an arc equal in length to the radius.

(b) Relation between degree measure and radian measure:

π radians $= 180°$;

1 radian $= (180/\pi)°$, $= 57.296°$ (approximately),

$1° = (\pi/180)$ radian, $= 0.01745$ radian (approximately).

(c) arc = radius $\times$ circular measure of angle $= r\theta$.
(d) area of circular sector $= \frac{1}{2}r^2\theta$.

2. Definitions of the trigonometric functions (Fig. 234):

$$\sin\theta = y/r, \qquad \cos\theta = x/r, \qquad \tan\theta = y/x,$$
$$\csc\theta = r/y, \qquad \sec\theta = r/x, \qquad \cot\theta = x/y.$$

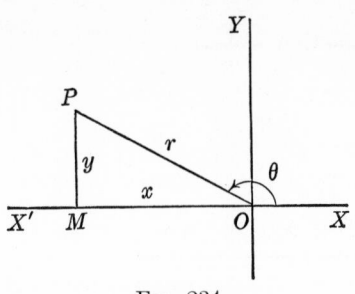

F<small>IG</small>. 234

3. Rule of signs:

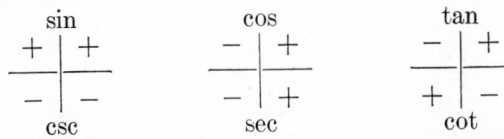

4. Functions of special angles:

Angle Function	0°	30°	45°	60°	90°	180°	270°
sin	0	$\frac{1}{2}$	$\frac{1}{2}\sqrt{2}$	$\frac{1}{2}\sqrt{3}$	1	0	-1
cos	1	$\frac{1}{2}\sqrt{3}$	$\frac{1}{2}\sqrt{2}$	$\frac{1}{2}$	0	-1	0
tan	0	$\frac{1}{3}\sqrt{3}$	1	$\sqrt{3}$	undefined	0	undefined

5. Reciprocal relations of the functions:

$$\csc \theta = 1/\sin \theta, \qquad \sec \theta = 1/\cos \theta, \qquad \cot \theta = 1/\tan \theta,$$
$$\sin \theta = 1/\csc \theta, \qquad \cos \theta = 1/\sec \theta, \qquad \tan \theta = 1/\cot \theta.$$

6. Quotient relations of the functions:

$$\tan \theta = \sin \theta/\cos \theta, \qquad \cot \theta = \cos \theta/\sin \theta.$$

7. Square relations of the functions:

$$\sin^2 \theta + \cos^2 \theta = 1, \qquad \tan^2 \theta + 1 = \sec^2 \theta, \qquad \cot^2 \theta + 1 = \csc^2 \theta.$$

APPENDIX

8. Reduction formulas:

Function / Angle	sin	cos	tan
$-\theta$	$-\sin\theta$	$\cos\theta$	$-\tan\theta$
$90° - \theta$	$\cos\theta$	$\sin\theta$	$\cot\theta$
$90° + \theta$	$\cos\theta$	$-\sin\theta$	$-\cot\theta$
$180° - \theta$	$\sin\theta$	$-\cos\theta$	$-\tan\theta$
$180° + \theta$	$-\sin\theta$	$-\cos\theta$	$\tan\theta$
$270° - \theta$	$-\cos\theta$	$-\sin\theta$	$\cot\theta$
$270° + \theta$	$-\cos\theta$	$\sin\theta$	$-\cot\theta$
$360° - \theta$	$-\sin\theta$	$\cos\theta$	$-\tan\theta$

9. Functions of a sum or difference:

(a) $\sin(x+y) = \sin x \cos y + \cos x \sin y$;

(b) $\sin(x-y) = \sin x \cos y - \cos x \sin y$;

(c) $\cos(x+y) = \cos x \cos y - \sin x \sin y$;

(d) $\cos(x-y) = \cos x \cos y + \sin x \sin y$;

(e) $\tan(x+y) = \dfrac{\tan x + \tan y}{1 - \tan x \tan y}$;

(f) $\tan(x-y) = \dfrac{\tan x - \tan y}{1 + \tan x \tan y}$.

10. Sum or difference of functions into products:

(a) $\sin x + \sin y = 2 \sin \tfrac{1}{2}(x+y) \cos \tfrac{1}{2}(x-y)$;

(b) $\sin x - \sin y = 2 \cos \tfrac{1}{2}(x+y) \sin \tfrac{1}{2}(x-y)$;

(c) $\cos x + \cos y = 2 \cos \tfrac{1}{2}(x+y) \cos \tfrac{1}{2}(x-y)$;

(d) $\cos x - \cos y = -2 \sin \tfrac{1}{2}(x+y) \sin \tfrac{1}{2}(x-y)$.

11. Products of functions into sums or differences:

(a) $2 \sin x \cos y = \sin(x+y) + \sin(x-y)$;

(b) $2 \cos x \sin y = \sin(x+y) - \sin(x-y)$;

(c) $2 \cos x \cos y = \cos(x+y) + \cos(x-y)$;

(d) $2 \sin x \sin y = -\cos(x+y) + \cos(x-y)$.

12. Functions of double and half angles:

(a) $\sin 2x = 2 \sin x \cos x$;

(b) $\cos 2x = \cos^2 x - \sin^2 x, = 2 \cos^2 x - 1, = 1 - 2 \sin^2 x$;

(c) $\tan 2x = \dfrac{2 \tan x}{1 - \tan^2 x}$;

(d) $\sin \frac{1}{2} x = \pm \sqrt{\dfrac{1 - \cos x}{2}}$ or $2 \sin^2 \theta = 1 - \cos 2\theta$;

(e) $\cos \frac{1}{2} x = \pm \sqrt{\dfrac{1 + \cos x}{2}}$ or $2 \cos^2 \theta = 1 + \cos 2\theta$;

(f) $\tan \frac{1}{2} x = \pm \sqrt{\dfrac{1 - \cos x}{1 + \cos x}} = \dfrac{\sin x}{1 + \cos x} = \dfrac{1 - \cos x}{\sin x}$.

13. An important transformation:

(a) $a \cos x + b \sin x = \sqrt{a^2 + b^2} \cos (x - \alpha)$,

where $\cos \alpha = \dfrac{a}{\sqrt{a^2 + b^2}}$, $\sin \alpha = \dfrac{b}{\sqrt{a^2 + b^2}}$.

(b) $a \cos x + b \sin x = \sqrt{a^2 + b^2} \sin (x + \beta)$,

where $\sin \beta = \dfrac{a}{\sqrt{a^2 + b^2}}$, $\cos \beta = \dfrac{b}{\sqrt{a^2 + b^2}}$.

14. Plane triangle formulas:

(a) Law of sines: $a/\sin A = b/\sin B = c/\sin C$;

(b) Law of cosines: $c^2 = a^2 + b^2 - 2ab \cos C$, etc.;

(c) Area of triangle: $\Delta = \frac{1}{2} ab \sin C$, etc.,

$$\Delta = \sqrt{s(s - a)(s - b)(s - c)}, \qquad s = \tfrac{1}{2}(a + b + c).$$

II. DIFFERENTIATION FORMULAS

1. $D_x(c) = 0.$
2. $D_x(x) = 1.$
3. $D_x(cu) = c \cdot D_x u.$
4. $D_x(u + v + w) = D_x u + D_x v + D_x w.$
5. $D_x(u^n) = nu^{n-1} \cdot D_x u.$
6. $D_x(u \cdot v) = u\, D_x v + v\, D_x u.$
7. $D_x\left(\dfrac{u}{v}\right) = \dfrac{v\, D_x u - u\, D_x v}{v^2}.$
8. $D_x\left(\dfrac{1}{v}\right) = -\dfrac{1}{v^2} \cdot D_x v.$
9. $D_x y = D_u y \cdot D_x u.$
10. $D_x y = \dfrac{1}{D_y x}.$
11. $D_x y = \dfrac{D_t y}{D_t x}.$
12. $D_x \sin u = \cos u \cdot D_x u.$
13. $D_x \cos u = -\sin u \cdot D_x u.$
14. $D_x \tan u = \sec^2 u \cdot D_x u.$
15. $D_x \cot u = -\csc^2 u \cdot D_x u.$
16. $D_x \sec u = \sec u \tan u \cdot D_x u.$
17. $D_x \csc u = -\csc u \cot u \cdot D_x u.$
18. $D_x (\text{Arc } \sin u) = \dfrac{1}{\sqrt{1 - u^2}} \cdot D_x u.$
19. $D_x (\text{Arc } \tan u) = \dfrac{1}{1 + u^2} \cdot D_x u.$
20. $D_x (\text{Arc } \cos u) = -\dfrac{1}{\sqrt{1 - u^2}} \cdot D_x u.$
21. $D_x (\text{Arc } \cot u) = -\dfrac{1}{1 + u^2} \cdot D_x u.$
22. $D_x (\ln u) = \dfrac{1}{u} \cdot D_x u.$
23. $D_x(e^u) = e^u \cdot D_x u.$
24. $D_x(a^u) = a^u \ln a \cdot D_x u.$
25. $D_x(\sinh u) = \cosh u \cdot D_x u.$
26. $D_x(\cosh u) = \sinh u \cdot D_x u.$

27. $D_x(\tanh u) = \text{sech}^2 u \cdot D_x u.$

28. $D_x(\coth u) = -\text{csch}^2 u \cdot D_x u.$

29. $D_x(\text{sech } u) = -\text{sech } u \tanh u \cdot D_x u.$

30. $D_x(\text{csch } u) = -\text{csch } u \coth u \cdot D_x u.$

31. $D_x(\sinh^{-1} u) = \dfrac{1}{\sqrt{1 + u^2}} \cdot D_x u.$

32. $D_x(\text{Cosh}^{-1} u) = \dfrac{1}{\sqrt{u^2 - 1}} \cdot D_x u \qquad (u > 1).$

33. $D_x(\tanh^{-1} u) = \dfrac{1}{1 - u^2} \cdot D_x u \qquad (u^2 < 1).$

34. $D_x(\coth^{-1} u) = -\dfrac{1}{u^2 - 1} \cdot D_x u \qquad (u^2 > 1).$

III. A BRIEF TABLE OF INTEGRALS

Some Fundamental Forms

1. $\int du = u + C.$

2. $\int c\, du = c \int du.$

3. $\int (f + g + \cdots)\, du = \int f\, du + \int g\, du + \cdots$

4. $\int u\, dv = uv - \int v\, du.$

5. $\int u^n\, du = \dfrac{u^{n+1}}{n + 1} + C \qquad (n \neq -1).$

6. $\int \dfrac{du}{u} = \ln u + C.$

Rational Forms Involving $a + bu$

7. $\int \dfrac{u\, du}{a + bu} = \dfrac{1}{b^2} [a + bu - a \ln (a + bu)] + C.$

8. $\int \dfrac{u^2\, du}{a + bu} = \dfrac{1}{b^3} [\tfrac{1}{2}(a + bu)^2 - 2\, a(a + bu) + a^2 \ln (a + bu)] + C.$

9. $\int \dfrac{u\, du}{(a + bu)^2} = \dfrac{1}{b^2} \left[\dfrac{a}{a + bu} + \ln (a + bu) \right] + C.$

10. $\int \dfrac{u^2\, du}{(a + bu)^2} = \dfrac{1}{b^3} \left[a + bu - \dfrac{a^2}{a + bu} - 2\, a \ln (a + bu) \right] + C$

11. $\int \dfrac{du}{u(a + bu)} = -\dfrac{1}{a} \ln \dfrac{a + bu}{u} + C.$

12. $\int \dfrac{du}{u^2(a + bu)} = -\dfrac{1}{au} + \dfrac{b}{a^2} \ln \dfrac{a + bu}{u} + C.$

13. $\int \dfrac{du}{u(a + bu)^2} = \dfrac{1}{a(a + bu)} - \dfrac{1}{a^2} \ln \dfrac{a + bu}{u} + C.$

Forms Involving $\sqrt{a + bu}$

14. $\int u\sqrt{a + bu}\, du = \dfrac{2(3\, bu - 2\, a)}{15\, b^2} (a + bu)^{\frac{3}{2}} + C.$

15. $\displaystyle\int u^2\sqrt{a+bu}\,du = \frac{2(15\,b^2u^2 - 12\,abu + 8\,a^2)}{105\,b^3}\,(a+bu)^{\frac{3}{2}} + C.$

16. $\displaystyle\int \frac{u\,du}{\sqrt{a+bu}} = \frac{2(bu - 2\,a)}{3\,b^2}\,\sqrt{a+bu} + C.$

17. $\displaystyle\int \frac{u^2\,du}{\sqrt{a+bu}} = \frac{2(3\,b^2u^2 - 4\,abu + 8\,a^2)}{15\,b^3}\,\sqrt{a+bu} + C.$

18a. $\displaystyle\int \frac{du}{u\sqrt{a+bu}} = \frac{1}{\sqrt{a}}\ln\frac{\sqrt{a+bu} - \sqrt{a}}{\sqrt{a+bu} + \sqrt{a}} + C \qquad (a > 0).$

18b. $\displaystyle\int \frac{du}{u\sqrt{a+bu}} = \frac{2}{\sqrt{-a}}\,\text{Arc}\,\tan\sqrt{\frac{a+bu}{-a}} + C \qquad (a < 0).$

19. $\displaystyle\int \frac{du}{u^2\sqrt{a+bu}} = -\frac{\sqrt{a+bu}}{au} - \frac{b}{2\,a}\int \frac{du}{u\sqrt{a+bu}}.$

20. $\displaystyle\int \frac{\sqrt{a+bu}}{u}\,du = 2\sqrt{a+bu} + a\int \frac{du}{u\sqrt{a+bu}}.$

21. $\displaystyle\int \frac{\sqrt{a+bu}}{u^2}\,du = -\frac{\sqrt{a+bu}}{u} + \frac{b}{2}\int \frac{du}{u\sqrt{a+bu}}.$

Forms Involving $a^2 \pm u^2$ and $u^2 - a^2$

22. $\displaystyle\int \frac{du}{a^2 + u^2} = \frac{1}{a}\,\text{Arc}\,\tan\frac{u}{a} + C, \quad \text{if } a > 0.$

23. $\displaystyle\int \frac{du}{a^2 - u^2} = \frac{1}{2\,a}\ln\frac{a+u}{a-u} + C = \frac{1}{a}\,\tanh^{-1}\frac{u}{a} + C, \quad \text{if } u^2 < a^2.$

24. $\displaystyle\int \frac{du}{u^2 - a^2} = \frac{1}{2\,a}\ln\frac{u-a}{u+a} + C = -\frac{1}{a}\,\coth^{-1}\frac{u}{a} + C, \quad \text{if } u^2 > a^2.$

Forms Involving $\sqrt{a^2 - u^2}$

25. $\displaystyle\int \frac{du}{\sqrt{a^2 - u^2}} = \text{Arc}\,\sin\frac{u}{a} + C, \quad \text{if } u^2 < a^2,\, a > 0.$

26. $\displaystyle\int \sqrt{a^2 - u^2}\,du = \frac{u}{2}\,\sqrt{a^2 - u^2} + \frac{a^2}{2}\,\text{Arc}\,\sin\frac{u}{a} + C.$

27. $\displaystyle\int u^2\sqrt{a^2 - u^2}\,du$

$$= -\frac{u}{4}\,(a^2 - u^2)^{\frac{3}{2}} + \frac{a^2}{8}\,u\sqrt{a^2 - u^2} + \frac{a^4}{8}\,\text{Arc}\,\sin\frac{u}{a} + C.$$

28. $\int \dfrac{\sqrt{a^2 - u^2}}{u}\,du = \sqrt{a^2 - u^2} - a\ln\left(\dfrac{a + \sqrt{a^2 - u^2}}{u}\right) + C.$

29. $\int \dfrac{\sqrt{a^2 - u^2}}{u^2}\,du = -\dfrac{\sqrt{a^2 - u^2}}{u} - \text{Arc}\sin\dfrac{u}{a} + C.$

30. $\int \dfrac{u^2\,du}{\sqrt{a^2 - u^2}} = -\dfrac{u}{2}\sqrt{a^2 - u^2} + \dfrac{a^2}{2}\,\text{Arc}\sin\dfrac{u}{a} + C.$

31. $\int \dfrac{du}{u\sqrt{a^2 - u^2}} = -\dfrac{1}{a}\ln\left(\dfrac{a + \sqrt{a^2 - u^2}}{u}\right) + C.$

32. $\int \dfrac{du}{u^2\sqrt{a^2 - u^2}} = -\dfrac{\sqrt{a^2 - u^2}}{a^2 u} + C.$

33. $\int (a^2 - u^2)^{\frac{3}{2}}\,du$
$$= -\dfrac{u}{8}(2u^2 - 5a^2)\sqrt{a^2 - u^2} + \dfrac{3a^4}{8}\,\text{Arc}\sin\dfrac{u}{a} + C.$$

34. $\int \dfrac{du}{(a^2 - u^2)^{\frac{3}{2}}} = \dfrac{u}{a^2\sqrt{a^2 - u^2}} + C.$

Forms Involving $\sqrt{a^2 + u^2}$

35. $\int \dfrac{du}{\sqrt{a^2 + u^2}} = \ln(u + \sqrt{a^2 + u^2}) + C = \sinh^{-1}\dfrac{u}{a} + C.$

36. $\int \sqrt{a^2 + u^2}\,du = \dfrac{u}{2}\sqrt{a^2 + u^2} + \dfrac{a^2}{2}\ln(u + \sqrt{a^2 + u^2}) + C.$
$$= \dfrac{u}{2}\sqrt{a^2 + u^2} + \dfrac{a^2}{2}\sinh^{-1}\dfrac{u}{a} + C.$$

37. $\int u^2\sqrt{a^2 + u^2}\,du$
$$= \dfrac{u}{8}(2u^2 + a^2)\sqrt{a^2 + u^2} - \dfrac{a^4}{8}\ln(u + \sqrt{a^2 + u^2}) + C$$
$$= \dfrac{u}{8}(2u^2 + a^2)\sqrt{a^2 + u^2} - \dfrac{a^4}{8}\sinh^{-1}\dfrac{u}{a} + C.$$

38. $\int \dfrac{\sqrt{a^2 + u^2}}{u}\,du = \sqrt{a^2 + u^2} - a\ln\left(\dfrac{a + \sqrt{a^2 + u^2}}{u}\right) + C.$

39. $\int \dfrac{\sqrt{a^2 + u^2}}{u^2}\,du = -\dfrac{\sqrt{a^2 + u^2}}{u} + \ln(u + \sqrt{a^2 + u^2}) + C.$
$$= -\dfrac{\sqrt{a^2 + u^2}}{u} + \sinh^{-1}\dfrac{u}{a} + C.$$

40. $\displaystyle\int \frac{u^2\, du}{\sqrt{a^2 + u^2}} = \frac{u}{2}\sqrt{a^2 + u^2} - \frac{a^2}{2}\ln\left(u + \sqrt{a^2 + u^2}\right) + C$

$$= \frac{u}{2}\sqrt{a^2 + u^2} - \frac{a^2}{2}\sinh^{-1}\frac{u}{a} + C.$$

41. $\displaystyle\int \frac{du}{u\sqrt{a^2 + u^2}} = -\frac{1}{a}\ln\left(\frac{\sqrt{a^2 + u^2} + a}{u}\right) + C.$

42. $\displaystyle\int \frac{du}{u^2\sqrt{a^2 + u^2}} = -\frac{\sqrt{a^2 + u^2}}{a^2 u} + C.$

43. $\displaystyle\int (a^2 + u^2)^{\frac{3}{2}}\, du$

$$= \frac{u}{8}(2\,u^2 + 5\,a^2)\sqrt{a^2 + u^2} + \frac{3\,a^4}{8}\ln\left(u + \sqrt{a^2 + u^2}\right) + C$$

$$= \frac{u}{8}(2\,u^2 + 5\,a^2)\sqrt{a^2 + u^2} + \frac{3\,a^4}{8}\sinh^{-1}\frac{u}{a} + C.$$

44. $\displaystyle\int \frac{du}{(a^2 + u^2)^{\frac{3}{2}}} = \frac{u}{a^2\sqrt{a^2 + u^2}} + C.$

Forms Involving $\sqrt{u^2 - a^2}$

45. $\displaystyle\int \frac{du}{\sqrt{u^2 - a^2}} = \ln\left(u + \sqrt{u^2 - a^2}\right) + C = \cosh^{-1}\frac{u}{a} + C.$

46. $\displaystyle\int \sqrt{u^2 - a^2}\, du = \frac{u}{2}\sqrt{u^2 - a^2} - \frac{a^2}{2}\ln\left(u + \sqrt{u^2 - a^2}\right) + C$

$$= \frac{u}{2}\sqrt{u^2 - a^2} - \frac{a^2}{2}\cosh^{-1}\frac{u}{a} + C.$$

47. $\displaystyle\int u^2\sqrt{u^2 - a^2}\, du$

$$= \frac{u}{8}(2\,u^2 - a^2)\sqrt{u^2 - a^2} - \frac{a^4}{8}\ln\left(u + \sqrt{u^2 - a^2}\right) + C$$

$$= \frac{u}{8}(2\,u^2 - a^2)\sqrt{u^2 - a^2} - \frac{a^4}{8}\cosh^{-1}\frac{u}{a} + C.$$

48. $\displaystyle\int \frac{\sqrt{u^2 - a^2}}{u}\, du = \sqrt{u^2 - a^2} - a\operatorname{Arc\,cos}\frac{a}{u} + C$

$$= \sqrt{u^2 - a^2} - a\operatorname{Arc\,sec}\frac{u}{a} + C.$$

49. $\displaystyle\int \frac{\sqrt{u^2 - a^2}}{u^2}\, du = -\frac{\sqrt{u^2 - a^2}}{u} + \ln\left(u + \sqrt{u^2 - a^2}\right) + C$

$$= -\frac{\sqrt{u^2 - a^2}}{u} + \cosh^{-1}\frac{u}{a} + C.$$

50. $\displaystyle\int \frac{u^2\,du}{\sqrt{u^2 - a^2}} = \frac{u}{2}\sqrt{u^2 - a^2} + \frac{a^2}{2}\ln\left(u + \sqrt{u^2 - a^2}\right) + C$

$$= \frac{u}{2}\sqrt{u^2 - a^2} + \frac{a^2}{2}\operatorname{Cosh}^{-1}\frac{u}{a} + C.$$

51. $\displaystyle\int \frac{du}{u\sqrt{u^2 - a^2}} = \frac{1}{a}\operatorname{Arc\,cos}\frac{a}{u} + C = \frac{1}{a}\operatorname{Arc\,sec}\frac{u}{a} + C.$

52. $\displaystyle\int \frac{du}{u^2\sqrt{u^2 - a^2}} = \frac{\sqrt{u^2 - a^2}}{a^2 u} + C.$

53. $\displaystyle\int \left(u^2 - a^2\right)^{\frac{3}{2}}\,du$

$$= \frac{u}{8}\left(2\,u^2 - 5\,a^2\right)\sqrt{u^2 - a^2} + \frac{3\,a^4}{8}\ln\left(u + \sqrt{u^2 - a^2}\right) + C$$

$$= \frac{u}{8}\left(2\,u^2 - 5\,a^2\right)\sqrt{u^2 - a^2} + \frac{3\,a^4}{8}\operatorname{Cosh}^{-1}\frac{u}{a} + C.$$

54. $\displaystyle\int \frac{du}{\left(u^2 - a^2\right)^{\frac{3}{2}}} = -\frac{u}{a^2\sqrt{u^2 - a^2}} + C.$

Forms Involving $\sqrt{2\,au - u^2}$

55. $\displaystyle\int \sqrt{2\,au - u^2}\,du$

$$= \frac{u - a}{2}\sqrt{2\,au - u^2} + \frac{a^2}{2}\operatorname{Arc\,cos}\left(1 - \frac{u}{a}\right) + C.$$

56. $\displaystyle\int u\sqrt{2\,au - u^2}\,du$

$$= \frac{2\,u^2 - au - 3\,a^2}{6}\sqrt{2\,au - u^2} + \frac{a^3}{2}\operatorname{Arc\,cos}\left(1 - \frac{u}{a}\right) + C.$$

57. $\displaystyle\int \frac{\sqrt{2\,au - u^2}}{u}\,du = \sqrt{2\,au - u^2} + a\operatorname{Arc\,cos}\left(1 - \frac{u}{a}\right) + C.$

58. $\displaystyle\int \frac{\sqrt{2\,au - u^2}}{u^2}\,du = -\frac{2\sqrt{2\,au - u^2}}{u} - \operatorname{Arc\,cos}\left(1 - \frac{u}{a}\right) + C.$

59. $\displaystyle\int \frac{du}{\sqrt{2\,au - u^2}} = 2\operatorname{Arc\,sin}\sqrt{\frac{u}{2\,a}} + C = \operatorname{Arc\,cos}\left(1 - \frac{u}{a}\right) + C.$

60. $\displaystyle\int \frac{u\,du}{\sqrt{2\,au - u^2}} = -\sqrt{2\,au - u^2} + a\operatorname{Arc\,cos}\left(1 - \frac{u}{a}\right) + C.$

61. $\displaystyle\int \frac{u^2 \, du}{\sqrt{2\,au - u^2}}$

$$= -\frac{(u + 3\,a)}{2}\sqrt{2\,au - u^2} + \frac{3\,a^2}{2}\operatorname{Arc\,cos}\left(1 - \frac{u}{a}\right) + C.$$

62. $\displaystyle\int \frac{du}{u\sqrt{2\,au - u^2}} = -\frac{\sqrt{2\,au - u^2}}{au} + C.$

63. $\displaystyle\int \frac{du}{(2\,au - u^2)^{\frac{3}{2}}} = \frac{u - a}{a^2\sqrt{2\,au - u^2}} + C.$

Trigonometric Forms

64. $\displaystyle\int \sin u \, du = -\cos u + C.$

65. $\displaystyle\int \cos u \, du = \sin u + C.$

66. $\displaystyle\int \tan u \, du = -\ln \cos u + C = \ln \sec u + C.$

67. $\displaystyle\int \cot u \, du = \ln \sin u + C = -\ln \csc u + C.$

68. $\displaystyle\int \sec u \, du = \ln (\sec u + \tan u) + C = \ln \tan \left(\frac{u}{2} + \frac{\pi}{4}\right) + C.$

69. $\displaystyle\int \csc u \, du = -\ln (\csc u + \cot u) + C = \ln \tan \frac{u}{2} + C.$

70. $\displaystyle\int \sec^2 u \, du = \tan u + C.$

71. $\displaystyle\int \csc^2 u \, du = -\cot u + C.$

72. $\displaystyle\int \sec u \tan u \, du = \sec u + C.$

73. $\displaystyle\int \csc u \cot u \, du = -\csc u + C.$

74. $\displaystyle\int \sin^2 u \, du = \tfrac{1}{2}(u - \sin u \cos u) + C = \tfrac{1}{2} u - \tfrac{1}{4}\sin 2\,u + C.$

75. $\displaystyle\int \cos^2 u \, du = \tfrac{1}{2}(u + \sin u \cos u) + C = \tfrac{1}{2} u + \tfrac{1}{4}\sin 2\,u + C.$

76. $\displaystyle\int \tan^2 u \, du = \tan u - u + C.$

77. $\int \sec^3 u \, du = \frac{1}{2} \sec u \tan u + \frac{1}{2} \ln (\sec u + \tan u) + C.$

78. $\int \sin mu \sin nu \, du = \dfrac{\sin (m - n)u}{2(m - n)} - \dfrac{\sin (m + n)u}{2(m + n)} + C.$

79. $\int \sin mu \cos nu \, du = -\dfrac{\cos (m - n)u}{2(m - n)} - \dfrac{\cos (m + n)u}{2(m + n)} + C.$

80. $\int \cos mu \cos nu \, du = \dfrac{\sin (m - n)u}{2(m - n)} + \dfrac{\sin (m + n)u}{2(m + n)} + C.$

81. $\int u \sin u \, du = \sin u - u \cos u + C.$

82. $\int u \cos u \, du = \cos u + u \sin u + C.$

83. $\int u^2 \sin u \, du = (2 - u^2) \cos u + 2 u \sin u + C.$

84. $\int u^2 \cos u \, du = (u^2 - 2) \sin u + 2 u \cos u + C.$

85a. $\int \sin^m u \cos^n u \, du$

$$= -\frac{\sin^{m-1} u \cos^{n+1} u}{m + n} + \frac{m - 1}{m + n} \int \sin^{m-2} u \cos^n u \, du.$$

85b. $\int \sin^m u \cos^n u \, du$

$$= \frac{\sin^{m+1} u \cos^{n-1} u}{m + n} + \frac{n - 1}{m + n} \int \sin^m u \cos^{n-2} u \, du.$$

86a. $\int \dfrac{du}{a + b \cos u} = \dfrac{2}{\sqrt{a^2 - b^2}} \operatorname{Arc} \tan \left(\dfrac{\sqrt{a^2 - b^2} \tan \dfrac{u}{2}}{a + b} \right) + C,$

$$\text{if} \quad a^2 > b^2.$$

86b. $\int \dfrac{du}{a + b \cos u} = \dfrac{1}{\sqrt{b^2 - a^2}} \ln \left(\dfrac{a + b + \sqrt{b^2 - a^2} \tan \dfrac{u}{2}}{a + b - \sqrt{b^2 - a^2} \tan \dfrac{u}{2}} \right) + C,$

$$\text{if} \quad b^2 > a^2.$$

87a. $\int \dfrac{du}{a + b \sin u} = \dfrac{2}{\sqrt{a^2 - b^2}} \operatorname{Arc} \tan \left(\dfrac{a \tan \dfrac{u}{2} + b}{\sqrt{a^2 - b^2}} \right) + C,$

$$\text{if} \quad a^2 > b^2.$$

$87b.$ $\displaystyle\int \frac{du}{a + b \sin u} = \frac{1}{\sqrt{b^2 - a^2}} \ln \left(\frac{a \tan \dfrac{u}{2} + b - \sqrt{b^2 - a^2}}{a \tan \dfrac{u}{2} + b + \sqrt{b^2 - a^2}} \right) + C,$

$$\text{if} \quad b^2 > a^2.$$

Inverse Trigonometric Forms

88. $\displaystyle\int \text{Arc} \sin u \, du = u \, \text{Arc} \sin u + \sqrt{1 - u^2} + C.$

89. $\displaystyle\int \text{Arc} \cos u \, du = u \, \text{Arc} \cos u - \sqrt{1 - u^2} + C.$

90. $\displaystyle\int \text{Arc} \tan u \, du = u \, \text{Arc} \tan u - \tfrac{1}{2} \ln (1 + u^2) + C.$

Exponential and Logarithmic Forms

91. $\displaystyle\int e^u \, du = e^u + C.$

92. $\displaystyle\int a^u \, du = \frac{a^u}{\ln a} + C.$

93. $\displaystyle\int u \, e^u \, du = e^u(u - 1) + C.$

94. $\displaystyle\int u^n e^u \, du = u^n e^u - n \int u^{n-1} e^u \, du.$

95. $\displaystyle\int \frac{e^u}{u^n} \, du = - \frac{e^u}{(n-1)u^{n-1}} + \frac{1}{n-1} \int \frac{e^u \, du}{u^{n-1}}.$

96. $\displaystyle\int \ln u \, du = u \ln u - u + C.$

97. $\displaystyle\int u^n \ln u \, du = u^{n+1} \left[\frac{\ln u}{n+1} - \frac{1}{(n+1)^2} \right] + C.$

98. $\displaystyle\int \frac{du}{u \ln u} = \ln (\ln u) + C.$

99. $\displaystyle\int e^{au} \sin nu \, du = \frac{e^{au}(a \sin nu - n \cos nu)}{a^2 + n^2} + C.$

100. $\displaystyle\int e^{au} \cos nu \, du = \frac{e^{au}(a \cos nu + n \sin nu)}{a^2 + n^2} + C.$

Hyperbolic Forms

101. $\displaystyle\int \sinh u \, du = \cosh u + C.$

102. $\displaystyle\int \cosh u \, du = \sinh u + C.$

103. $\displaystyle\int \tanh u \, du = \ln \cosh u + C.$

104. $\displaystyle\int \coth u \, du = \ln \sinh u + C.$

105. $\displaystyle\int \operatorname{sech} u \, du = \operatorname{Arc\,tan} (\sinh u) + C = \operatorname{gd} u + C.$

106. $\displaystyle\int \operatorname{csch} u \, du = \ln \tanh \tfrac{1}{2} u + C.$

107. $\displaystyle\int \operatorname{sech}^2 u \, du = \tanh u + C.$

108. $\displaystyle\int \operatorname{csch}^2 u \, du = -\coth u + C.$

109. $\displaystyle\int \operatorname{sech} u \tanh u \, du = -\operatorname{sech} u + C.$

110. $\displaystyle\int \operatorname{csch} u \coth u \, du = -\operatorname{csch} u + C.$

111. $\displaystyle\int \sinh^2 u \, du = \tfrac{1}{4} \sinh 2u - \tfrac{1}{2} u + C.$

112. $\displaystyle\int \cosh^2 u \, du = \tfrac{1}{4} \sinh 2u + \tfrac{1}{2} u + C.$

113. $\displaystyle\int u \sinh u \, du = u \cosh u - \sinh u + C.$

114. $\displaystyle\int u \cosh u \, du = u \sinh u - \cosh u + C.$

115. $\displaystyle\int e^{au} \sinh nu \, du = \frac{e^{au}(a \sinh nu - n \cosh nu)}{a^2 - n^2} + C.$

116. $\displaystyle\int e^{au} \cosh nu \, du = \frac{e^{au}(a \cosh nu - n \sinh nu)}{a^2 - n^2} + C.$

Wallis' Formulas

117. $\displaystyle\int_0^{\frac{\pi}{2}} \sin^n u \, du = \int_0^{\frac{\pi}{2}} \cos^n u \, du$

$$= \begin{cases} \dfrac{(n-1)(n-3) \cdots 4\cdot 2}{n(n-2) \cdots 5\cdot 3\cdot 1,} \text{ , if } n \text{ is an odd integer} > 1; \\[3mm] \dfrac{(n-1)(n-3) \cdots 3\cdot 1}{n(n-2) \cdots 4\cdot 2} \cdot \dfrac{\pi}{2}, \text{ if } n \text{ is a positive even integer.} \end{cases}$$

118. $\displaystyle\int_0^{\frac{\pi}{2}} \sin^m u \cos^n u \, du$

$$= \begin{cases} \dfrac{(n-1)(n-3) \cdots 4\cdot 2}{(m+n)(m+n-2) \cdots (m+5)(m+3)(m+1)}, \\ \qquad \text{if } n \text{ is an odd integer} > 1; \\[3mm] \dfrac{(m-1)(m-3) \cdots 4\cdot 2}{(n+m)(n+m-2) \cdots (n+5)(n+3)(n+1)}, \\ \qquad \text{if } m \text{ is an odd integer} > 1; \\[3mm] \dfrac{(m-1)(m-3) \cdots 3\cdot 1 \cdot (n-1)(n-3) \cdots 3\cdot 1}{(m+n)(m+n-2) \cdots 4\cdot 2} \cdot \dfrac{\pi}{2}, \\ \qquad \text{if } m \text{ and } n \text{ are both positive even integers.} \end{cases}$$

IV. NUMERICAL TABLES

A. Powers and Roots

B. Trigonometric Functions, Degree Measure

C. Trigonometric Functions, Radian Measure

D. Natural Logarithms

E. Exponential and Hyperbolic Functions

APPENDIX

A. Powers and Roots

No.	Square	Square Root	Cube	Cube Root	No.	Square	Square Root	Cube	Cube Root
1	1	1.000	1	1.000	51	2,601	7.141	132,651	3.708
2	4	1.414	8	1.260	52	2,704	7.211	140,608	3.733
3	9	1.732	27	1.442	53	2,809	7.280	148,877	3.756
4	16	2.000	64	1.587	54	2,916	7.348	157,464	3.780
5	25	2.236	125	1.710	55	3,025	7.416	166,375	3.803
6	36	2.449	216	1.817	56	3,136	7.483	175,616	3.826
7	49	2.646	343	1.913	57	3,249	7.550	185,193	3.849
8	64	2.828	512	2.000	58	3,364	7.616	195,112	3.871
9	81	3.000	729	2.080	59	3,481	7.681	205,379	3.893
10	100	3.162	1,000	2.154	60	3,600	7.746	216,000	3.915
11	121	3.317	1,331	2.224	61	3,721	7.810	226,981	3.936
12	144	3.464	1,728	2.289	62	3,844	7.874	238,328	3.958
13	169	3.606	2,197	2.351	63	3,969	7.937	250,047	3.979
14	196	3.742	2,744	2.410	64	4,096	8.000	262,144	4.000
15	225	3.873	3,375	2.466	65	4,225	8.062	274,625	4.021
16	256	4.000	4,096	2.520	66	4,356	8.124	287,496	4.041
17	289	4.123	4,913	2.571	67	4,489	8.185	300,763	4.062
18	324	4.243	5,832	2.621	68	4,624	8.246	314,432	4.082
19	361	4.359	6,859	2.668	69	4,761	8.307	328,509	4.102
20	400	4.472	8,000	2.714	70	4,900	8.367	343,000	4.121
21	441	4.583	9,261	2.759	71	5,041	8.426	357,911	4.141
22	484	4.690	10,648	2.802	72	5,184	8.485	373,248	4.160
23	529	4.796	12,167	2.844	73	5,329	8.544	389,017	4.179
24	576	4.899	13,824	2.884	74	5,476	8.602	405,224	4.198
25	625	5.000	15,625	2.924	75	5,625	8.660	421,875	4.217
26	676	5.099	17,576	2.962	76	5,776	8.718	438,976	4.236
27	729	5.196	19,683	3.000	77	5,929	8.775	456,533	4.254
28	784	5.291	21,952	3.037	78	6,084	8.832	474,552	4.273
29	841	5.385	24,389	3.072	79	6,241	8.888	493,039	4.291
30	900	5.477	27,000	3.107	80	6,400	8.944	512,000	4.309
31	961	5.568	29,791	3.141	81	6,561	9.000	531,441	4.327
32	1,024	5.657	32,768	3.175	82	6,724	9.055	551,368	4.344
33	1,089	5.745	35,937	3.208	83	6,889	9.110	571,787	4.362
34	1,156	5.831	39,304	3.240	84	7,056	9.165	592,704	4.380
35	1,225	5.916	42,875	3.271	85	7,225	9.220	614,125	4.397
36	1,296	6.000	46,656	3.302	86	7,396	9.274	636,056	4.414
37	1,369	6.083	50,653	3.332	87	7,569	9.327	658,503	4.431
38	1,444	6.164	54,872	3.362	88	7,744	9.381	681,472	4.448
39	1,521	6.245	59,319	3.391	89	7,921	9.434	704,969	4.465
40	1,600	6.325	64,000	3.420	90	8,100	9.487	729,000	4.481
41	1,681	6.403	68,921	3.448	91	8,281	9.539	753,571	4.498
42	1,764	6.481	74,088	3.476	92	8,464	9.592	778,688	4.514
43	1,849	6.557	79,507	3.503	93	8,649	9.644	804,357	4.531
44	1,936	6.633	85,184	3.530	94	8,836	9.695	830,584	4.547
45	2,025	6.708	91,125	3.557	95	9,025	9.747	857,375	4.563
46	2,116	6.782	97,336	3.583	96	9,216	9.798	884,736	4.579
47	2,209	6.856	103,823	3.609	97	9,409	9.849	912,673	4.595
48	2,304	6.928	110,592	3.634	98	9,604	9.899	941,192	4.610
49	2,401	7.000	117,649	3.659	99	9,801	9.950	970,299	4.626
50	2,500	7.071	125,000	3.684	100	10,000	10.000	1,000,000	4.642

B. Trigonometric Functions, Degree Measure

Angle	Sin	Tan	Cot	Cos	
0.0°	.0000	.0000	——	1.0000	**90.0°**
0.5°	.0087	.0087	114.59	1.0000	89.5°
1.0°	.0175	.0175	57.290	.9998	89.0°
1.5°	.0262	.0262	38.188	.9997	88.5°
2.0°	.0349	.0349	28.636	.9994	88.0°
2.5°	.0436	.0437	22.904	.9990	**87.5°**
3.0°	.0523	.0524	19.081	.9986	87.0°
3.5°	.0610	.0612	16.350	.9981	86.5°
4.0°	.0698	.0699	14.301	.9976	86.0°
4.5°	.0785	.0787	12.706	.9969	85.5°
5.0°	.0872	.0875	11.430	.9962	**85.0°**
5.5°	.0958	.0963	10.385	.9954	84.5°
6.0°	.1045	.1051	9.5144	.9945	84.0°
6.5°	.1132	.1139	8.7769	.9936	83.5°
7.0°	.1219	.1228	8.1443	.9925	83.0°
7.5°	.1305	.1317	7.5958	.9914	**82.5°**
8.0°	.1392	.1405	7.1154	.9903	82.0°
8.5°	.1478	.1495	6.6912	.9890	81.5°
9.0°	.1564	.1584	6.3138	.9877	81.0°
9.5°	.1650	.1673	5.9758	.9863	80.5°
10.0°	.1736	.1763	5.6713	.9848	**80.0°**
10.5°	.1822	.1853	5.3955	.9833	79.5°
11.0°	.1908	.1944	5.1446	.9816	79.0°
11.5°	.1994	.2035	4.9152	.9799	78.5°
12.0°	.2079	.2126	4.7046	.9781	78.0°
12.5°	.2164	.2217	4.5107	.9763	**77.5°**
13.0°	.2250	.2309	4.3315	.9744	77.0°
13.5°	.2334	.2401	4.1653	.9724	76.5°
14.0°	.2419	.2493	4.0108	.9703	76.0°
14.5°	.2504	.2586	3.8667	.9681	75.5°
15.0°	.2588	.2679	3.7321	.9659	**75.0°**
15.5°	.2672	.2773	3.6059	.9636	74.5°
16.0°	.2756	.2867	3.4874	.9613	74.0°
16.5°	.2840	.2962	3.3759	.9588	73.5°
17.0°	.2924	.3057	3.2709	.9563	73.0°
17.5°	.3007	.3153	3.1716	.9537	**72.5°**
18.0°	.3090	.3249	3.0777	.9511	72.0°
18.5°	.3173	.3346	2.9887	.9483	71.5°
19.0°	.3256	.3443	2.9042	.9455	71.0°
19.5°	.3338	.3541	2.8239	.9426	70.5°
20.0°	.3420	.3640	2.7475	.9397	**70.0°**
20.5°	.3502	.3739	2.6746	.9367	69.5°
21.0°	.3584	.3839	2.6051	.9336	69.0°
21.5°	.3665	.3939	2.5386	.9304	68.5°
22.0°	.3746	.4040	2.4751	.9272	68.0°
22.5°	.3827	.4142	2.4142	.9239	**67.5°**
	Cos	Cot	Tan	Sin	Angle

Angle	Sin	Tan	Cot	Cos	
22.5°	.3827	.4142	2.4142	.9239	**67.5°**
23.0°	.3907	.4245	2.3559	.9205	67.0°
23.5°	.3987	.4348	2.2998	.9171	66.5°
24.0°	.4067	.4452	2.2460	.9135	66.0°
24.5°	.4147	.4557	2.1943	.9100	65.5°
25.0°	.4226	.4663	2.1445	.9063	**65.0°**
25.5°	.4305	.4770	2.0965	.9026	64.5°
26.0°	.4384	.4877	2.0503	.8988	64.0°
26.5°	.4462	.4986	2.0057	.8949	63.5°
27.0°	.4540	.5095	1.9626	.8910	63.0°
27.5°	.4617	.5206	1.9210	.8870	**62.5°**
28.0°	.4695	.5317	1.8807	.8829	62.0°
28.5°	.4772	.5430	1.8418	.8788	61.5°
29.0°	.4848	.5543	1.8040	.8746	61.0°
29.5°	.4924	.5658	1.7675	.8704	60.5°
30.0°	.5000	.5774	1.7321	.8660	**60.0°**
30.5°	.5075	.5890	1.6977	.8616	59.5°
31.0°	.5150	.6009	1.6643	.8572	59.0°
31.5°	.5225	.6128	1.6319	.8526	58.5°
32.0°	.5299	.6249	1.6003	.8480	58.0°
32.5°	.5373	.6371	1.5697	.8434	**57.5°**
33.0°	.5446	.6494	1.5399	.8387	57.0°
33.5°	.5519	.6619	1.5108	.8339	56.5°
34.0°	.5592	.6745	1.4826	.8290	56.0°
34.5°	.5664	.6873	1.4550	.8241	55.5°
35.0°	.5736	.7002	1.4281	.8192	**55.0°**
35.5°	.5807	.7133	1.4019	.8141	54.5°
36.0°	.5878	.7265	1.3764	.8090	54.0°
36.5°	.5948	.7400	1.3514	.8039	53.5°
37.0°	.6018	.7536	1.3270	.7986	53.0°
37.5°	.6088	.7673	1.3032	.7934	**52.5°**
38.0°	.6157	.7813	1.2799	.7880	52.0°
38.5°	.6225	.7954	1.2572	.7826	51.5°
39.0°	.6293	.8098	1.2349	.7771	51.0°
39.5°	.6361	.8243	1.2131	.7716	50.5°
40.0°	.6428	.8391	1.1918	.7660	**50.0°**
40.5°	.6494	.8541	1.1708	.7604	49.5°
41.0°	.6561	.8693	1.1504	.7547	49.0°
41.5°	.6626	.8847	1.1303	.7490	48.5°
42.0°	.6691	.9004	1.1106	.7431	48.0°
42.5°	.6756	.9163	1.0913	.7373	**47.5°**
43.0°	.6820	.9325	1.0724	.7314	47.0°
43.5°	.6884	.9490	1.0538	.7254	46.5°
44.0°	.6947	.9657	1.0355	.7193	46.0°
44.5°	.7009	.9827	1.0176	.7133	45.5°
45.0°	.7071	1.0000	1.0000	.7071	**45.0°**
	Cos	Cot	Tan	Sin	Angle

APPENDIX

C. Trigonometric Functions, Radian Measure

Radians	sin	cos	tan	Radians	sin	cos	tan
0.00	0.0000	1.0000	0.0000	**0.40**	0.3894	0.9211	0.4228
.01	.0100	1.0000	.0100	.41	.3986	.9171	.4346
.02	.0200	0.9998	.0200	.42	.4078	.9131	.4466
.03	.0300	.9996	.0300	.43	.4169	.9090	.4586
.04	.0400	.9992	.0400	.44	.4259	.9048	.4708
.05	.0500	.9988	.0500	.45	.4350	.9004	.4831
.06	.0600	.9982	.0601	.46	.4439	.8961	.4954
.07	.0699	.9976	.0701	.47	.4529	.8916	.5080
.08	.0799	.9968	.0802	.48	.4618	.8870	.5206
.09	.0899	.9960	.0902	.49	.4706	.8823	.5334
.10	.0998	.9950	.1003	.50	.4794	.8776	.5463
.11	.1098	.9940	.1104	.51	.4882	.8727	.5594
.12	.1197	.9928	.1206	.52	.4969	.8678	.5726
.13	.1296	.9916	.1307	.53	.5055	.8628	.5859
.14	.1395	.9902	.1409	.54	.5141	.8577	.5994
.15	.1494	.9888	.1511	.55	.5227	.8525	.6131
.16	.1593	.9872	.1614	.56	.5312	.8473	.6269
.17	.1692	.9856	.1717	.57	.5396	.8419	.6410
.18	.1790	.9838	.1820	.58	.5480	.8365	.6552
.19	.1889	.9820	.1923	.59	.5564	.8309	.6696
.20	.1987	.9801	.2027	.60	.5646	.8253	.6841
.21	.2085	.9780	.2131	.61	.5729	.8196	.6989
.22	.2182	.9759	.2236	.62	.5810	.8139	.7139
.23	.2280	.9737	.2341	.63	.5891	.8080	.7291
.24	.2377	.9713	.2447	.64	.5972	.8021	.7445
.25	.2474	.9689	.2553	.65	.6052	.7961	.7602
.26	.2571	.9664	.2660	.66	.6131	.7900	.7761
.27	.2667	.9638	.2768	.67	.6210	.7838	.7923
.28	.2764	.9611	.2876	.68	.6288	.7776	.8087
.29	.2860	.9582	.2984	.69	.6365	.7712	.8253
.30	.2955	.9553	.3093	.70	.6442	.7648	.8423
.31	.3051	.9523	.3203	.71	.6518	.7584	.8595
.32	.3146	.9492	.3314	.72	.6594	.7518	.8771
.33	.3240	.9460	.3425	.73	.6669	.7452	.8949
.34	.3335	.9428	.3537	.74	.6743	.7385	.9131
.35	.3429	.9394	.3650	.75	.6816	.7317	.9316
.36	.3523	.9359	.3764	.76	.6889	.7248	.9505
.37	.3616	.9323	.3879	.77	.6961	.7179	.9697
.38	.3709	.9287	.3994	.78	.7033	.7109	.9893
.39	.3802	.9249	.4111	.79	.7104	.7038	1.009

Trigonometric Functions, Radian Measure (Continued)

Radians	sin	cos	tan	Radians	sin	cos	tan
0.80	0.7174	0.6967	1.030	1.20	0.9320	0.3624	2.572
.81	.7243	.6895	1.050	1.21	.9356	.3530	2.650
.82	.7311	.6822	1.072	1.22	.9391	.3436	2.733
.83	.7379	.6749	1.093	1.23	.9425	.3342	2.820
.84	.7446	.6675	1.116	1.24	.9458	.3248	2.912
.85	.7513	.6600	1.138	1.25	.9490	.3153	3.010
.86	.7578	.6524	1.162	1.26	.9521	.3058	3.113
.87	.7643	.6448	1.185	1.27	.9551	.2963	3.224
.88	.7707	.6372	1.210	1.28	.9580	.2867	3.341
.89	.7771	.6294	1.235	1.29	.9608	.2771	3.467
.90	.7833	.6216	1.260	1.30	.9636	.2675	3.602
.91	.7895	.6137	1.286	1.31	.9662	.2579	3.747
.92	.7956	.6058	1.313	1.32	.9687	.2482	3.903
.93	.8016	.5978	1.341	1.33	.9711	.2385	4.072
.94	.8076	.5898	1.369	1.34	.9735	.2288	4.256
.95	.8134	.5817	1.398	1.35	.9757	.2190	4.455
.96	.8192	.5735	1.428	1.36	.9779	.2092	4.673
.97	.8249	.5653	1.459	1.37	.9799	.1994	4.913
.98	.8305	.5570	1.491	1.38	.9819	.1896	5.177
.99	.8360	.5487	1.524	1.39	.9837	.1798	5.471
1.00	.8415	.5403	1.557	1.40	.9854	.1700	5.798
1.01	.8468	.5319	1.592	1.41	.9871	.1601	6.165
1.02	.8521	.5234	1.628	1.42	.9887	.1502	6.581
1.03	.8573	.5148	1.665	1.43	.9901	.1403	7.055
1.04	.8624	.5062	1.704	1.44	.9915	.1304	7.602
1.05	.8674	.4976	1.743	1.45	.9927	.1205	8.238
1.06	.8724	.4889	1.784	1.46	.9939	.1106	8.989
1.07	.8772	.4801	1.827	1.47	.9949	.1006	9.887
1.08	.8820	.4713	1.871	1.48	.9959	.0907	10.98
1.09	.8866	.4625	1.917	1.49	.9967	.0807	12.35
1.10	.8912	.4536	1.965	1.50	.9975	.0707	14.10
1.11	.8957	.4447	2.014	1.51	.9982	.0608	16.43
1.12	.9001	.4357	2.066	1.52	.9987	.0508	19.67
1.13	.9044	.4267	2.120	1.53	.9992	.0408	24.50
1.14	.9086	.4176	2.176	1.54	.9995	.0308	32.46
1.15	.9128	.4085	2.234	1.55	.9998	.0208	48.08
1.16	.9168	.3993	2.296	1.56	.9999	.0108	92.62
1.17	.9208	.3902	2.360	1.57	1.0000	.0008	1256.
1.18	.9246	.3809	2.427				
1.19	.9284	.3717	2.498				

APPENDIX

D. Natural Logarithms

	.00	.01	.02	.03	.04	.05	.06	.07	.08	.09
1.0	0.0000	0.0100	0.0198	0.0296	0.0392	0.0488	0.0583	0.0677	0.0770	0.0862
1.1	0.0953	0.1044	0.1133	0.1222	0.1310	0.1398	0.1484	0.1570	0.1655	0.1740
1.2	0.1823	0.1906	0.1989	0.2070	0.2151	0.2231	0.2311	0.2390	0.2469	0.2546
1.3	0.2624	0.2700	0.2776	0.2852	0.2927	0.3001	0.3075	0.3148	0.3221	0.3293
1.4	0.3365	0.3436	0.3507	0.3577	0.3646	0.3716	0.3784	0.3853	0.3920	0.3988
1.5	0.4055	0.4121	0.4187	0.4253	0.4318	0.4383	0.4447	0.4511	0.4574	0.4637
1.6	0.4700	0.4762	0.4824	0.4886	0.4947	0.5008	0.5068	0.5128	0.5188	0.5247
1.7	0.5306	0.5365	0.5423	0.5481	0.5539	0.5596	0.5653	0.5710	0.5766	0.5822
1.8	0.5878	0.5933	0.5988	0.6043	0.6098	0.6152	0.6206	0.6259	0.6313	0.6366
1.9	0.6419	0.6471	0.6523	0.6575	0.6627	0.6678	0.6729	0.6780	0.6831	0.6881
2.0	0.6931	0.6981	0.7031	0.7080	0.7130	0.7178	0.7227	0.7275	0.7324	0.7372
2.1	0.7419	0.7467	0.7514	0.7561	0.7608	0.7655	0.7701	0.7747	0.7793	0.7839
2.2	0.7885	0.7930	0.7975	0.8020	0.8065	0.8109	0.8154	0.8198	0.8242	0.8286
2.3	0.8329	0.8372	0.8416	0.8459	0.8502	0.8544	0.8587	0.8629	0.8671	0.8713
2.4	0.8755	0.8796	0.8838	0.8879	0.8920	0.8961	0.9002	0.9042	0.9083	0.9123
2.5	0.9163	0.9203	0.9243	0.9282	0.9322	0.9361	0.9400	0.9439	0.9478	0.9517
2.6	0.9555	0.9594	0.9632	0.9670	0.9708	0.9746	0.9783	0.9821	0.9858	0.9895
2.7	0.9933	0.9969	1.0006	1.0043	1.0080	1.0116	1.0152	1.0188	1.0225	1.0260
2.8	1.0296	1.0332	1.0367	1.0403	1.0438	1.0473	1.0508	1.0543	1.0578	1.0613
2.9	1.0647	1.0682	1.0716	1.0750	1.0784	1.0818	1.0852	1.0886	1.0919	1.0953
3.0	1.0986	1.1019	1.1053	1.1086	1.1119	1.1151	1.1184	1.1217	1.1249	1.1282
3.1	1.1314	1.1346	1.1378	1.1410	1.1442	1.1474	1.1506	1.1537	1.1569	1.1600
3.2	1.1632	1.1663	1.1694	1.1725	1.1756	1.1787	1.1817	1.1848	1.1878	1.1909
3.3	1.1939	1.1970	1.2000	1.2030	1.2060	1.2090	1.2119	1.2149	1.2179	1.2208
3.4	1.2238	1.2267	1.2296	1.2326	1.2355	1.2384	1.2413	1.2442	1.2470	1.2499
3.5	1.2528	1.2556	1.2585	1.2613	1.2641	1.2669	1.2698	1.2726	1.2754	1.2782
3.6	1.2809	1.2837	1.2865	1.2892	1.2920	1.2947	1.2975	1.3002	1.3029	1.3056
3.7	1.3083	1.3110	1.3137	1.3164	1.3191	1.3218	1.3244	1.3271	1.3297	1.3324
3.8	1.3350	1.3376	1.3403	1.3429	1.3455	1.3481	1.3507	1.3533	1.3558	1.3584
3.9	1.3610	1.3635	1.3661	1.3686	1.3712	1.3737	1.3762	1.3788	1.3813	1.3838
4.0	1.3863	1.3888	1.3913	1.3938	1.3962	1.3987	1.4012	1.4036	1.4061	1.4085
4.1	1.4110	1.4134	1.4159	1.4183	1.4207	1.4231	1.4255	1.4279	1.4303	1.4327
4.2	1.4351	1.4375	1.4398	1.4422	1.4446	1.4469	1.4493	1.4516	1.4540	1.4563
4.3	1.4586	1.4609	1.4633	1.4656	1.4679	1.4702	1.4725	1.4748	1.4770	1.4793
4.4	1.4816	1.4839	1.4861	1.4884	1.4907	1.4929	1.4952	1.4974	1.4996	1.5019
4.5	1.5041	1.5063	1.5085	1.5107	1.5129	1.5151	1.5173	1.5195	1.5217	1.5239
4.6	1.5261	1.5282	1.5304	1.5326	1.5347	1.5369	1.5390	1.5412	1.5433	1.5454
4.7	1.5476	1.5497	1.5518	1.5539	1.5560	1.5581	1.5602	1.5623	1.5644	1.5665
4.8	1.5686	1.5707	1.5728	1.5748	1.5769	1.5790	1.5810	1.5831	1.5851	1.5872
4.9	1.5892	1.5913	1.5933	1.5953	1.5974	1.5994	1.6014	1.6034	1.6054	1.6074
5.0	1.6094	1.6114	1.6134	1.6154	1.6174	1.6194	1.6214	1.6233	1.6253	1.6273
5.1	1.6292	1.6312	1.6332	1.6351	1.6371	1.6390	1.6409	1.6429	1.6448	1.6467
5.2	1.6487	1.6506	1.6525	1.6544	1.6563	1.6582	1.6601	1.6620	1.6639	1.6658
5.3	1.6677	1.6696	1.6715	1.6734	1.6752	1.6771	1.6790	1.6808	1.6827	1.6845
5.4	1.6864	1.6882	1.6901	1.6919	1.6938	1.6956	1.6974	1.6993	1.7011	1.7029

$$\ln (N \cdot 10^m) = \ln N + m \ln 10, \qquad \ln 10 = 2.3026$$

Natural Logarithms (Continued)

	.00	.01	.02	.03	.04	.05	.06	.07	.08	.09
5.5	1.7047	1.7066	1.7084	1.7102	1.7120	1.7138	1.7156	1.7174	1.7192	1.7210
5.6	1.7228	1.7246	1.7263	1.7281	1.7299	1.7317	1.7334	1.7352	1.7370	1.7387
5.7	1.7405	1.7422	1.7440	1.7457	1.7475	1.7492	1.7509	1.7527	1.7544	1.7561
5.8	1.7579	1.7596	1.7613	1.7630	1.7647	1.7664	1.7682	1.7699	1.7716	1.7733
5.9	1.7750	1.7766	1.7783	1.7800	1.7817	1.7834	1.7851	1.7867	1.7884	1.7901
6.0	1.7918	1.7934	1.7951	1.7967	1.7984	1.8001	1.8017	1.8034	1.8050	1.8066
6.1	1.8083	1.8099	1.8116	1.8132	1.8148	1.8165	1.8181	1.8197	1.8213	1.8229
6.2	1.8245	1.8262	1.8278	1.8294	1.8310	1.8326	1.8342	1.8358	1.8374	1.8390
6.3	1.8406	1.8421	1.8437	1.8453	1.8469	1.8485	1.8500	1.8516	1.8532	1.8547
6.4	1.8563	1.8579	1.8594	1.8610	1.8625	1.8641	1.8656	1.8672	1.8687	1.8703
6.5	1.8718	1.8733	1.8749	1.8764	1.8779	1.8795	1.8810	1.8825	1.8840	1.8856
6.6	1.8871	1.8886	1.8901	1.8916	1.8931	1.8946	1.8961	1.8976	1.8991	1.9006
6.7	1.9021	1.9036	1.9051	1.9066	1.9081	1.9095	1.9110	1.9125	1.9140	1.9155
6.8	1.9169	1.9184	1.9199	1.9213	1.9228	1.9242	1.9257	1.9272	1.9286	1.9301
6.9	1.9315	1.9330	1.9344	1.9359	1.9373	1.9387	1.9402	1.9416	1.9430	1.9445
7.0	1.9459	1.9473	1.9488	1.9502	1.9516	1.9530	1.9544	1.9559	1.9573	1.9587
7.1	1.9601	1.9615	1.9629	1.9643	1.9657	1.9671	1.9685	1.9699	1.9713	1.9727
7.2	1.9741	1.9755	1.9769	1.9782	1.9796	1.9810	1.9824	1.9838	1.9851	1.9865
7.3	1.9879	1.9892	1.9906	1.9920	1.9933	1.9947	1.9961	1.9974	1.9988	2.0001
7.4	2.0015	2.0028	2.0042	2.0055	2.0069	2.0082	2.0096	2.0109	2.0122	2.0136
7.5	2.0149	2.0162	2.0176	2.0189	2.0202	2.0215	2.0229	2.0242	2.0255	2.0268
7.6	2.0282	2.0295	2.0308	2.0321	2.0334	2.0347	2.0360	2.0373	2.0386	2.0399
7.7	2.0412	2.0425	2.0438	2.0451	2.0464	2.0477	2.0490	2.0503	2.0516	2.0528
7.8	2.0541	2.0554	2.0567	2.0580	2.0592	2.0605	2.0618	2.0631	2.0643	2.0656
7.9	2.0669	2.0681	2.0694	2.0707	2.0719	2.0732	2.0744	2.0757	2.0769	2.0782
8.0	2.0794	2.0807	2.0819	2.0832	2.0844	2.0857	2.0869	2.0882	2.0894	2.0906
8.1	2.0919	2.0931	2.0943	2.0956	2.0968	2.0980	2.0992	2.1005	2.1017	2.1029
8.2	2.1041	2.1054	2.1066	2.1078	2.1090	2.1102	2.1114	2.1126	2.1138	2.1150
8.3	2.1163	2.1175	2.1187	2.1199	2.1211	2.1223	2.1235	2.1247	2.1258	2.1270
8.4	2.1282	2.1294	2.1306	2.1318	2.1330	2.1342	2.1353	2.1365	2.1377	2.1389
8.5	2.1401	2.1412	2.1424	2.1436	2.1448	2.1459	2.1471	2.1483	2.1494	2.1506
8.6	2.1518	2.1529	2.1541	2.1552	2.1564	2.1576	2.1587	2.1599	2.1610	2.1622
8.7	2.1633	2.1645	2.1656	2.1668	2.1679	2.1691	2.1702	2.1713	2.1725	2.1736
8.8	2.1748	2.1759	2.1770	2.1782	2.1793	2.1804	2.1815	2.1827	2.1838	2.1849
8.9	2.1861	2.1872	2.1883	2.1894	2.1905	2.1917	2.1928	2.1939	2.1950	2.1961
9.0	2.1972	2.1983	2.1994	2.2006	2.2017	2.2028	2.2039	2.2050	2.2061	2.2072
9.1	2.2083	2.2094	2.2105	2.2116	2.2127	2.2138	2.2148	2.2159	2.2170	2.2181
9.2	2.2192	2.2203	2.2214	2.2225	2.2235	2.2246	2.2257	2.2268	2.2279	2.2289
9.3	2.2300	2.2311	2.2322	2.2332	2.2343	2.2354	2.2364	2.2375	2.2386	2.2396
9.4	2.2407	2.2418	2.2428	2.2439	2.2450	2.2460	2.2471	2.2481	2.2492	2.2502
9.5	2.2513	2.2523	2.2534	2.2544	2.2555	2.2565	2.2576	2.2586	2.2597	2.2607
9.6	2.2618	2.2628	2.2638	2.2649	2.2659	2.2670	2.2680	2.2690	2.2701	2.2711
9.7	2.2721	2.2732	2.2742	2.2752	2.2762	2.2773	2.2783	2.2793	2.2803	2.2814
9.8	2.2824	2.2834	2.2844	2.2854	2.2865	2.2875	2.2885	2.2895	2.2905	2.2915
9.9	2.2925	2.2935	2.2946	2.2956	2.2966	2.2976	2.2986	2.2996	2.3006	2.3016

E. Exponential and Hyperbolic Functions

x	e^x	e^{-x}	sinh x	cosh x	tanh x
0.00	1.0000	1.0000	0.0000	1.0000	0.0000
.01	1.0101	0.9900	.0100	1.0001	.0100
.02	1.0202	.9802	.0200	1.0002	.0200
.03	1.0305	.9704	.0300	1.0005	.0300
.04	1.0408	.9608	.0400	1.0008	.0400
.05	1.0513	.9512	.0500	1.0013	.0500
.06	1.0618	.9418	.0600	1.0018	.0599
.07	1.0725	.9324	.0701	1.0025	.0699
.08	1.0833	.9231	.0801	1.0032	.0798
.09	1.0942	.9139	.0901	1.0041	.0898
.10	1.1052	.9048	.1002	1.0050	.0997
.11	1.1163	.8958	.1102	1.0061	.1096
.12	1.1275	.8869	.1203	1.0072	.1194
.13	1.1388	.8781	.1304	1.0085	.1293
.14	1.1503	.8694	.1405	1.0098	.1391
.15	1.1618	.8607	.1506	1.0113	.1489
.16	1.1735	.8521	.1607	1.0128	.1586
.17	1.1853	.8437	.1708	1.0145	.1684
.18	1.1972	.8353	.1810	1.0162	.1781
.19	1.2092	.8270	.1911	1.0181	.1877
.20	1.2214	.8187	.2013	1.0201	.1974
.21	1.2337	.8106	.2115	1.0221	.2070
.22	1.2461	.8025	.2218	1.0243	.2165
.23	1.2586	.7945	.2320	1.0266	.2260
.24	1.2712	.7866	.2423	1.0289	.2355
.25	1.2840	.7788	.2526	1.0314	.2449
.26	1.2969	.7711	.2629	1.0340	.2543
.27	1.3100	.7634	.2733	1.0367	.2636
.28	1.3231	.7558	.2837	1.0395	.2729
.29	1.3364	.7483	.2941	1.0423	.2821
.30	1.3499	.7408	.3045	1.0453	.2913
.31	1.3634	.7334	.3150	1.0484	.3004
.32	1.3771	.7261	.3255	1.0516	.3095
.33	1.3910	.7189	.3360	1.0549	.3185
.34	1.4049	.7118	.3466	1.0584	.3275
.35	1.4191	.7047	.3572	1.0619	.3364
.36	1.4333	.6977	.3678	1.0655	.3452
.37	1.4477	.6907	.3785	1.0692	.3540
.38	1.4623	.6839	.3892	1.0731	.3627
.39	1.4770	.6771	.4000	1.0770	.3714
.40	1.4918	.6703	.4108	1.0811	.3799
.41	1.5068	.6637	.4216	1.0852	.3885
.42	1.5220	.6570	.4325	1.0895	.3969
.43	1.5373	.6505	.4434	1.0939	.4053
.44	1.5527	.6440	.4543	1.0984	.4136

Exponential and Hyperbolic Functions (Continued)

x	e^x	e^{-x}	$\sinh x$	$\cosh x$	$\tanh x$
0.45	1.5683	0.6376	0.4653	1.1030	0.4219
.46	1.5841	.6313	.4764	1.1077	.4301
.47	1.6000	.6250	.4875	1.1125	.4382
.48	1.6161	.6188	.4986	1.1174	.4462
.49	1.6323	.6126	.5098	1.1225	.4542
.50	1.6487	.6065	.5211	1.1276	.4621
.51	1.6653	.6005	.5324	1.1329	.4699
.52	1.6820	.5945	.5438	1.1383	.4777
.53	1.6989	.5886	.5552	1.1438	.4854
.54	1.7160	.5827	.5666	1.1494	.4930
.55	1.7333	.5769	.5782	1.1551	.5005
.56	1.7507	.5712	.5897	1.1609	.5080
.57	1.7683	.5655	.6014	1.1669	.5154
.58	1.7860	.5599	.6131	1.1730	.5227
.59	1.8040	.5543	.6248	1.1792	.5299
.60	1.8221	.5488	.6367	1.1855	.5370
.61	1.8404	.5434	.6485	1.1919	.5441
.62	1.8589	.5379	.6605	1.1984	.5511
.63	1.8776	.5326	.6725	1.2051	.5581
.64	1.8965	.5273	.6846	1.2119	.5649
.65	1.9155	.5220	.6967	1.2188	.5717
.66	1.9348	.5169	.7090	1.2258	.5784
.67	1.9542	.5117	.7213	1.2330	.5850
.68	1.9739	.5066	.7336	1.2402	.5915
.69	1.9937	.5016	.7461	1.2476	.5980
.70	2.0138	.4966	.7586	1.2552	.6044
.71	2.0340	.4916	.7712	1.2628	.6107
.72	2.0544	.4868	.7838	1.2706	.6169
.73	2.0751	.4819	.7966	1.2785	.6231
.74	2.0959	.4771	.8094	1.2865	.6291
.75	2.1170	.4724	.8223	1.2947	.6351
.76	2.1383	.4677	.8353	1.3030	.6411
.77	2.1598	.4630	.8484	1.3114	.6469
.78	2.1815	.4584	.8615	1.3199	.6527
.79	2.2034	.4538	.8748	1.3286	.6584
.80	2.2255	.4493	.8881	1.3374	.6640
.81	2.2479	.4449	.9015	1.3464	.6696
.82	2.2705	.4404	.9150	1.3555	.6751
.83	2.2933	.4360	.9286	1.3647	.6805
.84	2.3164	.4317	.9423	1.3740	.6858
.85	2.3396	.4274	.9561	1.3835	.6911
.86	2.3632	.4232	.9700	1.3932	.6963
.87	2.3869	.4190	.9840	1.4029	.7014
.88	2.4109	.4148	.9981	1.4128	.7064
.89	2.4351	.4107	1.0122	1.4229	.7114

APPENDIX

Exponential and Hyperbolic Functions (Continued)

x	e^x	e^{-x}	$\sinh x$	$\cosh x$	$\tanh x$
0.90	2.4596	0.4066	1.0265	1.4331	0.7163
.91	2.4843	.4025	1.0409	1.4434	.7211
.92	2.5093	.3985	1.0554	1.4539	.7259
.93	2.5345	.3946	1.0700	1.4645	.7306
.94	2.5600	.3906	1.0847	1.4753	.7352
.95	2.5857	.3867	1.0995	1.4862	.7398
.96	2.6117	.3829	1.1144	1.4973	.7443
.97	2.6379	.3791	1.1294	1.5085	.7487
.98	2.6645	.3753	1.1446	1.5199	.7531
.99	2.6912	.3716	1.1598	1.5314	.7574
1.00	2.7183	.3679	1.1752	1.5431	.7616
1.05	2.8577	.3499	1.2539	1.6038	.7818
1.10	3.0042	.3329	1.3356	1.6685	.8005
1.15	3.1582	.3166	1.4208	1.7374	.8178
1.20	3.3201	.3012	1.5085	1.8107	.8337
1.25	3.4903	.2865	1.6019	1.8884	.8483
1.30	3.6693	.2725	1.6984	1.9709	.8617
1.35	3.8574	.2592	1.7991	2.0583	.8741
1.40	4.0552	.2466	1.9043	2.1509	.8854
1.45	4.2631	.2346	2.0143	2.2488	.8957
1.50	4.4817	.2231	2.1293	2.3524	.9051
1.55	4.7115	.2122	2.2496	2.4619	.9138
1.60	4.9530	.2019	2.3756	2.5775	.9217
1.65	5.2070	.1920	2.5075	2.6995	.9289
1.70	5.4739	.1827	2.6456	2.8283	.9354
1.75	5.7546	.1738	2.7904	2.9642	.9414
1.80	6.0496	.1653	2.9422	3.1075	.9468
1.85	6.3598	.1572	3.1013	3.2585	.9517
1.90	6.6859	.1496	3.2682	3.4177	.9562
1.95	7.0287	.1423	3.4432	3.5855	.9603
2.00	7.3891	.1353	3.6269	3.7622	.9640
2.05	7.7679	.1287	3.8196	3.9483	.9674
2.10	8.1662	.1225	4.0219	4.1443	.9705
2.15	8.5849	.1165	4.2342	4.3507	.9732
2.20	9.0250	.1108	4.4571	4.5679	.9757
2.25	9.4877	.1054	4.6912	4.7966	.9780
2.30	9.9742	.1003	4.9370	5.0372	.9801
2.35	10.486	.0954	5.1951	5.2905	.9820
2.40	11.023	.0907	5.4662	5.5569	.9837
2.45	11.588	.0863	5.7510	5.8373	.9852
2.50	12.182	.0821	6.0502	6.1323	.9866
2.55	12.807	.0781	6.3645	6.4426	.9879
2.60	13.464	.0743	6.6947	6.7690	.9890
2.65	14.154	.0707	7.0417	7.1123	.9901
2.70	14.880	.0672	7.4063	7.4735	.9910

Exponential and Hyperbolic Functions (Continued)

x	e^x	e^{-x}	$\sinh x$	$\cosh x$	$\tanh x$
2.75	15.643	0.0639	7.7894	7.8533	0.9919
2.80	16.445	.0608	8.1919	8.2527	.9926
2.85	17.288	.0578	8.6150	8.6728	.9933
2.90	18.174	.0550	9.0596	9.1146	.9940
2.95	19.106	.0523	9.5268	9.5791	.9945
3.00	20.086	.0498	10.018	10.068	.9951
3.05	21.115	.0474	10.534	10.581	.9955
3.10	22.198	.0450	11.076	11.122	.9959
3.15	23.336	.0429	11.647	11.689	.9963
3.20	24.533	.0408	12.246	12.287	.9967
3.25	25.790	.0388	12.876	12.915	.9970
3.30	27.113	.0369	13.538	13.575	.9973
3.35	28.503	.0351	14.234	14.269	.9975
3.40	29.964	.0334	14.965	14.999	.9978
3.45	31.500	.0317	15.734	15.766	.9980
3.50	33.115	.0302	16.543	16.573	.9982
3.55	34.813	.0287	17.392	17.421	.9983
3.60	36.598	.0273	18.286	18.313	.9985
3.65	38.475	.0260	19.224	19.250	.9986
3.70	40.447	.0247	20.211	20.236	.9988
3.75	42.521	.0235	21.249	21.272	.9989
3.80	44.701	.0224	22.339	22.362	.9990
3.85	46.993	.0213	23.486	23.507	.9991
3.90	49.402	.0202	24.691	24.711	.9992
3.95	51.935	.0193	25.958	25.977	.9993
4.00	54.598	.0183	27.290	27.308	.9993
4.10	60.340	.0166	30.162	30.178	.9995
4.20	66.686	.0150	33.336	33.351	.9996
4.30	73.700	.0136	36.843	36.857	.9996
4.40	81.451	.0123	40.719	40.732	.9997
4.50	90.017	.0111	45.003	45.014	.9998
4.60	99.484	.0101	49.737	49.747	.9998
4.70	109.95	.0091	54.969	54.978	.9998
4.80	121.51	.0082	60.751	60.759	.9999
4.90	134.29	.0074	67.141	67.149	.9999
5.00	148.41	.0067	74.203	74.210	.9999
5.20	181.27	.0055	90.633	90.639	.9999
5.40	221.41	.0045	110.70	110.71	1.0000
5.60	270.43	.0037	135.21	135.22	1.0000
5.80	330.30	.0030	165.15	165.15	1.0000
6.00	403.43	.0025	201.71	201.72	1.0000
7.00	1096.6	.0009	548.32	548.32	1.0000
8.00	2981.0	.0003	1490.5	1490.5	1.0000
9.00	8103.1	.0001	4051.5	4051.5	1.0000
10.00	22026.	.00005	11013.	11013.	1.0000

Answers to Odd-Numbered Exercises

§ 6, page 10

3. $(-2, 2)$. **5.** (a) On line parallel to Y-axis, 2 units to left; (b) on line parallel to X-axis, 6 units above. **7.** On bisector of first and third quadrants. **9.** $(3, -2)$. **11.** $(1, 4)$ or $(1, -12)$. **13.** $(1, 4)$, or $(3, -2)$, or $(7, 10)$. **15.** (a) 5; (b) $\sqrt{41}$.

§ 8, page 12

1. (a) 4, 3; (b) 7, -7; (c) 3, 4; (d) 4, 9.

§ 10, page 15

3. (a) 5; (b) 13; (c) $\sqrt{53}$. **5.** 5.39. **7.** $\sqrt{41}$, $\sqrt{73}$, $\sqrt{74}$, $\sqrt{82}$; $\sqrt{80}$, $\sqrt{185}$. **13.** $\sqrt{208}$, 4. **17.** $(x+1)^2 + (y-2)^2 = 16$; on circle of radius 4 with center at $(-1, 2)$.

§ 12, page 16

3. (a) $(3, 2)$; (b) $(\frac{1}{2}, -1)$. **5.** $(3, 7)$. **7.** $\frac{1}{2}\sqrt{346}$; $\sqrt{73}$; $\frac{1}{2}\sqrt{105}$. **13.** $(5, -3)$.

§ 17, page 24

3. (a) 1; (b) $-\sqrt{3}$; (c) 0.700; (d) -0.466. **5.** (a) $30°$; (b) $120°$; (c) $63°$; (d) $141°$. **7.** (a) 1; (b) $-\frac{1}{3}$; (c) $\frac{7}{6}$. **13.** $(6, 6)$, $(-2, 0)$.

§ 19, page 26

1. -2. **3.** $-\frac{7}{9}$.

§ 23, page 30

1. (a) $143°$; (b) $98°$; (c) $70.5°$. **3.** $\frac{35}{12}$. **5.** $A = 81°$, $B = 42°$, $C = 57°$. **7.** $A = 51.5°$, $B = 38.5°$. **9.** 5.

§ 31, page 38

1. (a) $x = 3$; (b) $y = -4$. **3.** (a) $2x - y - 5 = 0$; (b) $3x + 2y - 2 = 0$; (c) $3x + y - 4 = 0$; (d) $x + y + 3 = 0$. **5.** (a) $y = 3x + 2$; (b) $y = -\frac{1}{2}x + 5$; (c) $y = -4x - 4$; (d) $y = -x + \frac{3}{2}$. **7.** $y = -\frac{2}{3}x + 4$. **9.** $5x - 2y + 25 = 0$. **11.** $2x - y + 6 = 0$. **15.** $3x + 2y - 3 = 0$.

§ 34, page 40

1. (a) $4x + 3y - 10 = 0$; (b) $3x - y - 7 = 0$. **3.** $4x - 5y + 13 = 0$, $9x - 2y - 17 = 0$, $5x + 3y + 7 = 0$. **5.** $9x - 2y + 8 = 0$. **7.** -8. **9.** (a) $3x + 4y - 12 = 0$; (b) $4x - 3y - 12 = 0$.

§ 37, page 43

1. (a) $y = \frac{1}{2}x - 2$; (b) $y = -x + 8$; (c) $y = -\frac{1}{2}x + 3$; (d) $y = \frac{5}{2}x - \frac{7}{2}$. **3.** (a) $m = 2, a = -3, b = 6$; (b) $m = -1, a = 4, b = 4$; (c) $m = -\frac{3}{4}, a = 8, b = 6$; (d) $m = -\frac{5}{7}, a = -\frac{8}{5}, b = -\frac{8}{7}$. **7.** $3x - 5y + 9 = 0$.

9. $3x + 2y = 0$. **11.** (b) and (e) are parallel, (c) and (b), (c) and (e), and (a) and (d) are perpendicular. **13.** $2x - 3y - 12 = 0$. **15.** $(\frac{6}{5}, \frac{17}{25})$.
17. $2x - y - 7 = 0$. **21.** Arc tan $\frac{19}{9}$.

§ 39, page 47

1. (a) 5; (b) $\frac{5}{13}\sqrt{13}$. **3.** $\frac{5}{2}$. **5.** 3. **7.** 11. **9.** $15x + 8y + 34 = 0$ or $15x + 8y - 102 = 0$.

§ 41, page 49

1. (a) System of parallel lines with slope 3; (b) system of lines through point $(0, -2)$; (c) system of lines parallel to Y-axis; (d) system of lines through point $(3, 2)$; (e) system of lines through point $(3, 0)$; (f) system of lines through origin; (g) system of lines through point $(-4, -3)$; (h) system of lines through point $(0, -2)$. **3.** (a) $y = -2x + b$; (b) $y = mx - 4$; (c) $y - 3 = m(x - 4)$; (d) $x + y - a = 0$. **5.** $y = 3x - 11$. **7.** $k = -12$. **9.** (a) $8x - 3y = 0$; (b) $5x + 6y - 18 = 0$; (c) $14x - 7y + 4 = 0$; (d) $7x - 6 = 0$.

§ 46, page 59

1. (a) X-intercept 2, no Y-intercept; (b) X-intercepts ± 3, Y-intercepts ± 2; (c) X-intercepts ± 2, no Y-intercept; (d) X-intercepts 1, -2, Y-intercept -2. **3.** No. **5.** (a) Symmetric with respect to X-axis; (b) symmetric with respect to both axes and origin; (c) symmetric with respect to Y-axis; (d) symmetric with respect to origin. **9.** (a) Unlimited extent horizontally, unlimited extent below X-axis but not above; (b) extends horizontally only between -5 and 5, vertically only between -5 and 5; (c) extends horizontally only between -6 and 6, vertically only between -3 and 3; (d) unlimited extent vertically, unlimited extent horizontally to right of $x = 2$ and to left of $x = -2$, but does not extend between -2 and 2. **11.** (a) Asymptotic to X- and Y-axes; (b) vertical asymptote $x = 2$, horizontal asymptote $y = 0$; (c) vertical asymptote $x = -3$, horizontal asymptote $y = 2$; (d) horizontal asymptote $y = 0$; (e) vertical asymptotes $x = 5$ and $x = -5$, horizontal asymptote $y = 1$; (f) vertical asymptotes $x = 2$ and $x = -3$, horizontal asymptote $y = -1$.

§ 52, page 65

5. (a) $(2, 0)$; (b) $(0, 0)$, $(\frac{1}{2}, 1)$; (c) $(2, 0)$, $(\frac{5}{2}, \frac{3}{2})$; (d) $(3, 4)$, $(3, -4)$, $(-3, 4)$, $(-3, -4)$; (e) $(0, 0)$, $(4, 4)$; (f) $(0, 0)$, $(1, 1)$, $(-1, -1)$. **9.** $5\sqrt{2}$.

§ 54, page 68

1. (a) $x = 5$; (b) $x = -3$. **3.** $4x - 3y - 1 = 0$.
5. $x^2 + y^2 - 6x - 4y - 3 = 0$. **7.** $25x^2 + 16y^2 = 400$.
9. $9x^2 - 16y^2 = 144$. **11.** $3x^2 + 3y^2 + 12x + 8y - 52 = 0$.
13. $x^2 - 3y^2 - 10y + 25 = 0$. **15.** $xy - 6x + 10y + 10 = 0$.
17. $3x^2 + 3y^2 - 14y + 11 = 0$. **19.** $x^2 + y^2 - 6x - 8y - 1 = 0$ or $x^2 + y^2 + 2x + 4y - 21 = 0$.

§ 57, page 72

1. $2, 3, 3, 11, 4t^2 - 4t + 3, h^2 + 2, h^2 + 2h, h^2 + 2ah - 2h$.
5. $0, \log 2 + \log a, \log x - \log y, n \log x$. **7.** (a) $2a + h$; (b) $1 - \dfrac{1}{a(a+h)}$.
9. $\sqrt{x^2 - 1}$.

§ 59, page 73

1. $y = \sqrt{25 - x^2}$.   **3.** $l = 2\sqrt{100 - d^2}$.   **5.** $V = x(12 - 2\,x)^2$.

7. $A = \dfrac{2\,V}{r} + 2\,\pi r^2$.   **9.** $A = \dfrac{hx}{b}\,(b - x)$ or $A = \dfrac{bx}{h}\,(h - x)$.

11. $A = 4\,r^2 \sin \frac{1}{2}\alpha \cos \frac{1}{2}\alpha = 2\,r^2 \sin \alpha$.   **13.** $V = \frac{1}{3}\,\pi(20\,h^2 - h^3)$.

15. $V = 2\,\pi r^2 \sqrt{a^2 - r^2}$, $S = 2\,\pi r^2 + 4\,\pi r\sqrt{a^2 - r^2}$.   **17.** $400 + 40\,x - 8\,x^2$.

§ 61, page 75

1. $A = \frac{1}{2}\,bh$.   **3.** $V = \frac{2}{3}\,\pi r^3 + \pi r^2 h$, $S = 3\,\pi r^2 + 2\,\pi rh$.   **5.** $1,\ 7,\ a^2 - ab + b^2,$
$m^2 - m + 1,\ 4\,u^2 - 4\,uv + 4\,v^2,\ x^2$.

§ 65, page 78

1. (a) $\Delta y = 0.41$;   (b) $\Delta y = (2\,x - 2)\Delta x + (\Delta x)^2$.   **3.** $\Delta y / \Delta x = 4,\ 3.1,\ 3.01,$
$3.001,\ 3.0001,\ 3.00001$.   **5.** $\Delta y = (1 + 2\,x)\Delta x + (\Delta x)^2$; $\Delta y / \Delta x = 1 + 2\,x + \Delta x$.

7. $\Delta y = (3\,x^2 - 1)\Delta x + 3\,x(\Delta x)^2 + (\Delta x)^3$; $\Delta y / \Delta x = 3\,x^2 - 1 + 3\,x(\Delta x) + (\Delta x)^2$.

9. $\Delta y = \dfrac{-2(\Delta x)}{(x + 1)(x + \Delta x + 1)}$; $\dfrac{\Delta y}{\Delta x} = -\dfrac{2}{(x + 1)(x + \Delta x + 1)}$.

11. $\Delta y = 4\,x^3(\Delta x) + 6\,x^2(\Delta x)^2 + 4\,x(\Delta x)^3 + (\Delta x)^4$;
$\Delta y / \Delta x = 4\,x^3 + 6\,x^2(\Delta x) + 4\,x(\Delta x)^2 + (\Delta x)^3$.

§ 69, page 82

1. 10.   **3.** 2.   **5.** 0.   **7.** 0.   **9.** $f(x) \to +\infty$.   **11.** $f(x) \to +\infty$.

§ 71, page 83

1. 2.   **3.** $\frac{5}{2}$.   **5.** -1.   **7.** $\frac{9}{4}$.   **9.** 3.   **11.** 0.   **13.** 0.   **15.** 1.   **17.** $y \to +\infty$.
19. $f(x) \to -\infty$.

§ 73, page 85

1. 6.   **3.** $\frac{1}{2}$.   **5.** 12.   **7.** 0.   **9.** (a) 2;   (b) $3\,x^2$.

§ 75, page 88

1. $x = 1$.   **3.** $x = \pm 1$.   **5.** $x = 1,\ -3$.   **7.** $x = 1,\ 6$.   **9.** (a) $x = 0,\ 2$;
(b) $x = \pm 2$.

§ 78, page 92

1. $2\,x - 4$.   **3.** $3\,x^2 - 2$.   **5.** $\dfrac{1}{(x + 1)^2}$.   **7.** $-\dfrac{2}{(z - 1)^2}$.   **9.** 5.   **11.** $\frac{33}{4}$.
13. (a) $2\,x$;   (b) $3\,x^2$;   (c) $4\,x^3$;   (d) $5\,x^4$; $8\,x^7$; $n\,x^{n-1}$.

§ 81, page 96

1. 0; $2(1 - x_1)$.   **3.** At $x = 0$, $m = 2$; at $x = 1$, $m = -1$; at $x = 2$, $m = 2$.
5. 3; $2\,t_1 - 1$.

§ 84, page 97

3. $D_h p = -kp$.   **5.** -2.

§ 92, page 103

1. $20\,x^4$.   **3.** $4 - 2\,x$.   **5.** $12\,x^3 - 6\,x^2$.   **7.** $x^2 - x - 1$.   **9.** $3\,t^2 - 8\,t$.
11. $3 + z^2$.   **13.** 4.   **15.** 23.   **17.** $40\,x - 15\,x^2$.   **19.** $2\,z + 1$.   **21.** (a) 5;   (b) 1.
23. (a) $2\,t - 4$;   (b) $64 - 32\,t$.   **25.** 1.8;   5.4.

§ 95, page 106

1. $3x^2 + 2x + 2$. **3.** $3r^2 - 6r + 1$. **5.** $a^2 - 3x^2$. **7.** $3x^2 - 12x + 1!$.

9. $-\dfrac{2}{(x-1)^2}$. **11.** $\dfrac{1 - 2t - t^2}{(t^2 + 1)^2}$. **13.** $\dfrac{2z^2 - 2}{(1 + z + z^2)^2}$. **15.** $3 + \dfrac{1}{(r+1)^2}$.

17. -4. **19.** 4. **21.** 12. **23.** $\dfrac{2}{(t+1)^2}$.

§ 98, page 107

1. $(a)\ -\dfrac{2v}{x^2};\ (b)\ \dfrac{2}{z^2(1+x)^2}$. **3.** -0.0000036.

§ 100, page 109

1. $(a)\ \frac{1}{3}x^{-\frac{2}{3}};\ (b)\ \frac{5}{2}x^{\frac{3}{2}};\ (c)\ \frac{4}{3}x^{\frac{1}{3}};\ (d)\ \frac{5}{2}x^{\frac{3}{2}};\ (e)\ -2x^{-3};\ (f)\ -5x^{-6};\ (g)\ -\frac{1}{2}x^{-\frac{3}{2}};$
$(h)\ 1.4\,x^{0.4}$. **3.** $-\dfrac{2}{x^2} + \dfrac{6}{x^3}$. **5.** $3 + \dfrac{4}{x^3}$. **7.** $\dfrac{1}{2\sqrt{x}} - \dfrac{1}{2x\sqrt{x}}$. **9.** $\frac{3}{2}\sqrt{t} + \dfrac{1}{2\sqrt{t}}$.

11. $10x(x^2 + 1)^4$. **13.** $-\dfrac{6x}{(x^2 + 4)}$. **15.** $\dfrac{z}{\sqrt{z^2 + 9}}$. **17.** $-\dfrac{t}{(t^2 - 1)^{\frac{3}{2}}}$.

19. 6250. **21.** $\frac{5}{3}$. **23.** $\dfrac{2 - x}{2(1 - x)^{\frac{3}{2}}}$. **25.** $\dfrac{1 - 3x}{2\sqrt{1 - x}}$. **27.** $\dfrac{2x(2x^4 + 1)}{\sqrt{x^4 + 1}}$.

29. $\dfrac{3t^2(1 - t^2)}{(1 + t^2)^4}$. **31.** $\dfrac{1}{(1 + x^2)^{\frac{3}{2}}}$. **33.** $-\dfrac{a^3}{z^2\sqrt{a^2 - z^2}}$. **35.** $-\frac{1}{3}\sqrt{3}$. **37.** $\dfrac{19}{2\sqrt{w}}$.

§ 103, page 112

1. 2. **3.** $-\dfrac{y}{x}$. **5.** $\dfrac{x}{y}$. **7.** $-\dfrac{2y}{2x + y}$. **9.** $\dfrac{2x - y}{x + 6y}$. **11.** $-\dfrac{y^{\frac{1}{2}}}{x^{\frac{1}{2}}}$.

13. $\dfrac{2x - y^2}{2xy + 1}$. **15.** -2. **17.** $-\frac{2}{9}$. **19.** $-\frac{3}{4}$. **21.** 2.

§ 106, page 114

1. $x = \dfrac{y - b}{a}$. **3.** $x = \pm\sqrt{a^2 - y^2},\ y \geqq 0$. **5.** $-\dfrac{1}{2x}$. **7.** $\frac{1}{2}(x + 1)^2$.

§ 108, page 115

1. $2x - 3,\ 2,\ 0$. **3.** $3x^2 + 4x - 5,\ 6x + 4,\ 6,\ 0$. **5.** $4x^3 - 9x^2 + 6$,
$12x^2 - 18x,\ 24x - 18,\ 24,\ 0$. **7.** $5t^4 - 6t^2 + 1,\ 20t^3 - 12t,\ 60t^2 - 12,\ 120t$,
$120,\ 0$. **9.** $\dfrac{3}{4x^2\sqrt{x}}$. **11.** $\dfrac{2}{x^3}$. **13.** $\dfrac{a^2}{(x^2 + a^2)^{\frac{3}{2}}}$. **15.** $\dfrac{3(2z^2 - a^2)}{\sqrt{a^2 - z^2}}$.

17. $(-1)^n\,\dfrac{n!}{x^{n+1}}$. **19.** $(-1)^{n+1}\dfrac{1 \cdot 3 \cdot 5 \cdots (2n - 3)}{2^n}\,x^{-\frac{2n-1}{2}}$. **21.** $(-1)^{n+1}\dfrac{n!}{z^{n+1}}$.

23. $(-1)^n\dfrac{1 \cdot 3 \cdot 5 \cdots (2n - 1)}{2^n}\,(1 + t)^{-\frac{2n+1}{2}}$.

25. $(a)\ n(n - 1)(n - 2) \cdots (n - p + 1)x^{n-p}(p < n);\ (b)\ n!;\ (c)\ 0$.

§ 110, page 117

1. $-\dfrac{a^2}{y^3}$. **3.** $\dfrac{2y}{x^2}$. **5.** $\dfrac{6}{(x - 2y)^3}$. **7.** $\dfrac{3x}{4y}$. **9.** $-\frac{3}{8},\ -\frac{25}{128}$. **11.** $17,\ -32$.

13. $-\dfrac{3a^2x}{y^5}$.

§ 111, page 117

1. $na(ax + b)^{n-1}$.   **3.** $\dfrac{2 - 3x}{2\sqrt{1 - x}}$.   **5.** $\dfrac{x^2 + 2x}{(x + 1)^2}$.   **7.** $\dfrac{1}{(a^2 - r^2)^{\frac{3}{2}}}$.   **9.** $3x\sqrt{x^2 + 4}$.

11. $-6x^{-3} - 2x^{-2}$.   **13.** $-\dfrac{2z}{(z^2 + 1)^2}$.   **15.** $\dfrac{x(x^2 - 2)}{(x^2 - 1)^{\frac{3}{2}}}$.   **17.** $\dfrac{1}{a^2p^2\sqrt{p^2 - 1}}$.

19. $x(5x^2 + 2a^2)\sqrt{a^2 + x^2}$.   **21.** $\dfrac{1}{2\sqrt{x + 2}}$.   **23.** $\dfrac{9}{(y^2 + 9)^{\frac{3}{2}}}$.   **25.** $-\dfrac{x}{\sqrt{1 - x^2}}$.

27. $\dfrac{1 - 2z}{(1 - z + z^2)^2}$.   **29.** $-\dfrac{3x^2}{2\sqrt{1 - x^3}}$.   **31.** $\frac{3}{2}\sqrt{1 + u}$.   **33.** $-\dfrac{2x}{(x - 1)^3}$.

35. $1 - \sqrt{\dfrac{a}{x}}$.

§ 113, page 121

1. $2x - y - 6 = 0, x + 2y - 3 = 0$.   **3.** $9x + y - 5 = 0, x - 9y - 37 = 0$.
5. $x + 16y - 12 = 0,\ 32x - 2y - 127 = 0$.   **7.** $\sqrt{2}x - y + \sqrt{2} = 0$,
$x + \sqrt{2}y - 5 = 0$.   **9.** $3x - 4y - 40 = 0, 4x + 3y - 20 = 0$.
11. $x + 2y - 2 = 0, 2x - y + 1 = 0$.   **17.** $90°$.   **19.** Arc tan $(7/24)$.
21. $x - y - 1 = 0, 27x - 27y + 5 = 0$.   **23.** $90°$, Arc tan $(3/4)$.

§ 115, page 123

1. Double root $x = 2$.   **3.** Double root $x = -1$.   **5.** Double root $x = -\frac{3}{2}$.
7. Double roots $x = 1, x = -2$.

§ 117, page 124

1. $2t - 4, 2$.   **3.** $t^2 - t + 1, 2t - 1$.   **5.** $\dfrac{2}{(t + 1)^2}$, $-\dfrac{4}{(t + 1)^3}$.   **7.** $\dfrac{3t + 2}{2\sqrt{1 + t}}$,

$\dfrac{3t + 4}{4(1 + t)^{\frac{3}{2}}}$.   **9.** $a = -6$ when $t = 1$; $a = 6$ when $t = 3$.

§ 118, page 124

1. (a) 48 radians per second, -32 radians per second per second;   (b) 112 radians per second.   **5.** -8.

§ 120, page 127

1. $1/(8\pi)$ feet per second.   **3.** $(10 - 2\pi)$ cubic feet per minute.   **5.** 0.64 inches per minute.   **7.** 480 feet per minute.   **9.** 3.2 square inches per hour.   **11.** $1/(400\pi)$ feet per minute, 0.2 square feet per minute.   **13.** $\frac{5\cdot1}{1\cdot3}\sqrt{13}$ miles per hour.   **15.** 50 feet per second.   **17.** $\frac{1\cdot6}{7}\sqrt{7}$ feet per second.   **19.** $\frac{2\cdot5\cdot0}{2\cdot7}$ feet per second.   **21.** $\frac{4\cdot5}{4\cdot1}$ feet per second.

§ 122, page 129

1. (a) Falling; (b) rising.   **3.** Increasing for $x > 4$, decreasing for $x < 4$.   **5.** Increasing for $x > 2, x < -2$, decreasing for $-2 < x < 2$.   **11.** Moving to left for $t < 3$, to right for $t > 3$.   **13.** Moving to left for $t < -1$, to right for $-1 < t < 0$, to left for $0 < t < 1$, to right for $t > 1$.

§ 127, page 135

1. Maximum at $x = 1$, minimum at $x = 3$.   **3.** Maximum at $x = -1$, minimum at $x = \frac{5}{3}$.   **5.** Maximum at $x = -2$, minimum at $x = 2$.   **7.** Minimum at $x = 3$.

9. Maximum at $x = 1$, minimum at $x = -1$.   **11.** Maximum at $x = 4$, minimum at $x = 0$.   **13.** No maximum or minimum.   **15.** Maximum at $x = \frac{1}{2}$, minimum at $x = -\frac{1}{2}$.   **17.** Minimum slope at $x = \frac{8}{3}$.   **19.** 73°30′.   **23.** 18, 18.   **25.** \$20.

§ 129, page 137

1. Concave upward for $x > \frac{2}{3}$, downward for $x < \frac{2}{3}$.   **3.** Concave upward for all values of x.   **5.** Concave upward for $x > \frac{1}{3}\sqrt{3}$ and $x < -\frac{1}{3}\sqrt{3}$, downward for $-\frac{1}{3}\sqrt{3} < x < \frac{1}{3}\sqrt{3}$.   **7.** Concave upward for $x > 3$ and $x < -1$, downward for $-1 < x < 3$.   **9.** Concave upward for $x > 3$ and $-3 < x < 0$, downward for $0 < x < 3$ and $x < -3$.

§ 131, page 139

1. Maximum at $x = -1$, minimum at $x = 1$.   **3.** Maximum at $x = -1$, minimum at $x = 2$.   **5.** Minimum at $x = 0$.   **7.** Maximum at $x = \frac{1}{3}\sqrt{6}$ and $x = -\frac{1}{3}\sqrt{6}$, minimum at $x = 0$.   **9.** Maximum at $x = 1$.   **11.** Maximum at $x = -1$, minimum at $x = 1$.   **15.** $\frac{1}{2}$.   **17.** $\frac{1}{6}\sqrt{3}\, l$.

§ 133, page 141

1. 200 cubic inches.   **3.** Radius 5, altitude 5.   **5.** $22\sqrt{5}$ yards, $11\sqrt{5}$ yards.   **7.** In 2 weeks.   **9.** $6\frac{1}{4}$ inches.   **11.** It should land $1\frac{1}{4}$ miles from the point on shore nearest to the first vessel.   **13.** Each side $4\sqrt{2}$.   **15.** $\frac{2}{3}\, a\sqrt{3}$.   **17.** Altitude 5 times the radius of base.   **19.** Base $5\frac{1}{3}$ inches, slant height $5\frac{1}{3}$ inches.

§ 135, page 144

1. Base = twice the altitude.   **5.** Altitude = diameter.   **7.** Side of base = twice the altitude.   **9.** Altitude = $\frac{3}{2}$ radius of base.   **11.** Radius of base = $\frac{2}{3}$ radius of base of cone, altitude = $\frac{1}{3}$ altitude of cone.   **13.** Width = twice height of rectangle.   **15.** Side of base = twice altitude.   **17.** $\frac{2}{3}\, a\sqrt{3}$.   **19.** Altitude = $\sqrt{2} \times$ radius of base.   **21.** Width $\frac{4}{3}\sqrt{3}$, depth $2\sqrt{6}$.   **23.** Altitude = $\sqrt{2} \times$ radius of base.

§ 138, page 148

1. Maximum at $x = 0$, minima at $x = \pm\sqrt{3}$, points of inflection at $x = \pm 1$.   **3.** Minimum at $x = \frac{3}{2}$, points of inflection at $x = 1$ and $x = 0$.   **5.** Maximum at $x = -1$, minimum at $x = 3$, point of inflection at $x = 1$.   **7.** Maximum at $x = 0$, minima at $x = \pm 1$, points of inflection at $x = \pm\frac{1}{3}\sqrt{3}$.   **9.** Maximum at $x = 0$, points of inflection at $x = \pm\frac{2}{3}\sqrt{3}$.   **11.** No maximum or minimum; point of inflection at $x = 0$.   **15.** $\frac{1}{16}\, kl^4$; $x = \frac{1}{6}(3 \pm \sqrt{3})l$.

§ 143, page 154

1. $(3\,x^2 + 3)\, dx$.   **3.** $\dfrac{2\, dx}{(x+1)^2}$.   **5.** $\dfrac{x\, dx}{\sqrt{1+x^2}}$.   **7.** $\dfrac{3\,x+1}{2\sqrt{x}}\, dx$.   **9.** $\dfrac{dx}{x^2\sqrt{x^2-1}}$.

13. $(\Delta x)^2$.   **15.** $dA = 2\,s(\Delta s)$.

§ 146, page 156

1. $\Delta y = 4.01$, $dy = 4$.   **3.** $0.18\,\pi$.   **5.** 0.013824.   **7.** $\frac{1}{4}$ inch.

13. 0.16 square inch.   **15.** $\dfrac{\sqrt{64.4}\, dh}{2\sqrt{h}}$.

§ 148, page 158

1. $\frac{4}{y}\,dx$. **3.** $\frac{1-x}{y}\,dx$. **5.** $\frac{y-2\,x}{4\,y-x}$, $-\frac{14}{(4\,y-x)^3}$. **7.** $-\frac{b^2x}{a^2y}$, $-\frac{b^4}{a^2y^3}$.

9. $-\frac{2\,xy+y^2}{x^2+2\,xy}$, $\frac{6(x^2+xy+y^2)}{(x^2+2\,xy)^3}$. **11.** $-\frac{y^{\frac{1}{2}}}{x^{\frac{1}{2}}}$, $\frac{a^{\frac{1}{2}}}{2\,x^{\frac{3}{2}}}$.

§ 152, page 163

1. 1.154. **3.** 1.625. **5.** 3.135. **7.** 1.157. **9.** 1.2599. **11.** 1.05.

§ 156, page 167

1. $\frac{1}{6}\,x^6+C$. **3.** $-\frac{1}{3\,y^3}+C$. **5.** $\frac{3}{5}\,v^{\frac{5}{3}}+C$. **7.** $-\frac{2}{\sqrt{x}}+C$. **9.** $\frac{3}{4}\,t^{\frac{4}{3}}+C$.

11. $\frac{5}{4}z^{\frac{4}{5}}+C$. **13.** $2\,x^3+3\,x^2-2\,x+C$. **15.** $y^2+\frac{3}{y}+C$.

17. $\frac{3}{2}\,y^{\frac{4}{3}}-\frac{2}{3}\,y^{\frac{3}{2}}+C$. **19.** $2\sqrt{u}+\frac{2}{3}\,u^{\frac{3}{2}}+C$. **21.** $y=\frac{2}{5}\,x^{\frac{5}{2}}+C$.

23. $s=\frac{1}{6}\,t^6-\frac{1}{2}\,t^4+\frac{1}{2}\,t^2+C$. **25.** $u=\frac{1}{3}\,x^3-4\,x-\frac{4}{x}+C$.

27. $z=-\frac{2}{\sqrt{v}}+4\sqrt{v}+\frac{2}{3}\,v^{\frac{3}{2}}+C$. **29.** $\frac{k}{1-\gamma}\,v^{1-\gamma}+C$.

§ 158, page 170

1. $\frac{1}{3}(x^2+1)^3+C$. **3.** $\frac{2}{3}(x-2)^{\frac{3}{2}}+C$. **5.** $-2\sqrt{1-x}+C$.

7. $\frac{1}{3}(y^2-4)^{\frac{3}{2}}+C$. **9.** $\sqrt{z^2+1}+C$. **11.** $\frac{2}{3}(v^3+a^3)^{\frac{3}{2}}+C$.

13. $\sqrt{t^2+2\,t}+C$. **15.** $\frac{1}{10}(1+\sqrt{x})^{10}+C$. **17.** $y=\frac{1}{3}(x^2-1)^{\frac{3}{2}}+C$.

19. $u=-\frac{1}{4(y^2+1)^2}+C$. **21.** $f(t)=\sqrt{t^2-9}+C$.

23. $y=\frac{1}{6}(1+4\,x)^{\frac{3}{2}}+C$. **25.** $\frac{1}{6}(1+x^2)^3+C$ or $\frac{1}{2}\,x^2+\frac{1}{2}\,x^4+\frac{1}{6}\,x^6+C'$.

§ 160, page 171

1. $\frac{2}{15}(3\,x^2-4\,x+8)\sqrt{x+1}+C$. **3.** $\frac{2}{3}(z-6)\sqrt{z+3}+C$.

5. $(x-3)\sqrt{2\,x+3}+C$. **7.** $\frac{2}{105}(15\,x^2-12\,x+8)(1+x)^{\frac{3}{2}}+C$.

9. $-\frac{3}{7}(x+6)(8-x)^{\frac{4}{3}}+C$. **11.** $\frac{3}{40}(5\,x+12)(x-4)^{\frac{5}{3}}+C$.

§ 162, page 172

1. $y=x^3-x^2+x+4$. **3.** $y=\frac{1}{3}(2\,x-1)^{\frac{3}{2}}-1$. **5.** 80.

§ 164, page 174

1. $y=x^2-x+1$. **3.** $y=0.004\,x^2+24$. **5.** $y^2=2\,x^3+4$.

7. $y=4\,x^{\frac{5}{2}}-79\,x+188$.

§ 166, page 176

1. $s=5\,t^2+3$. **3.** $s=2\,t^3+16\,t+30$. **5.** 225 feet, $3\frac{3}{4}$ seconds. **7.** 5 seconds. **9.** 400 feet. **11.** $R=R_0(0.00428\,T+1)$; 5.10286.

§ 168, page 180

1. $\frac{1}{2}\,b^2$.

§ 174, page 187

1. 26. **3.** $-\frac{15}{2}$. **5.** $\frac{125}{6}$. **7.** $\frac{4}{3}\sqrt{2}$. **9.** $\frac{63}{4}$. **11.** 0. **13.** $\frac{20}{3}$.

15. $\dfrac{1}{a} - \dfrac{1}{a\sqrt{2}}$ if $a > 0$. **17.** 2.544. **19.** 0.457. **21.** 1.464. **23.** 54.902.

25. $\dfrac{wL^4}{8\,EI}$. **27.** $\dfrac{\sqrt{2}\,A}{a\sqrt{g}}\,(\sqrt{h} - \sqrt{H})$.

§ 176, page 189

1. $\frac{20}{3}$. **3.** $\frac{2}{3}$. **5.** 2.410. **7.** 44.540. **9.** 6. **11.** $\frac{28}{3}$.

§ 182, page 196

1. $\frac{4}{3}$. **3.** $\frac{1}{4}$. **5.** 16. **7.** $\frac{8}{3}$. **9.** $\frac{9}{2}$. **11.** $\frac{8}{3}$. **13.** $\frac{13}{3}$. **15.** $\frac{9}{2}$. **17.** $\frac{256}{15}$.

§ 184, page 198

1. $\frac{1}{4}$. **3.** $\frac{2}{3}$. **5.** $\frac{9}{2}$. **7.** $\frac{1}{12}$. **9.** $\frac{16}{3}\sqrt{2}$. **11.** $\frac{32}{3}$. **13.** $\frac{7}{6}$.

§ 187, page 202

1. $\frac{16}{15}\pi$. **3.** 32π. **5.** 4π. **7.** $\frac{4}{3}\pi a^3$. **9.** $2\pi ah^2$. **11.** $\frac{4}{3}\pi a^3$. **13.** $\frac{1}{3}\pi r^2 h$.
15. $V = \frac{1}{3}\pi t^2(3R - t)$. **17.** $\frac{1}{2}\pi a^3$. **19.** $\frac{106}{15}\pi$.

§ 189, page 206

1. $\frac{512}{3}\pi$. **3.** $\frac{3}{10}\pi$. **5.** 8π. **7.** $2\sqrt{3}\,\pi a^3$.

§ 191, page 208

1. $\frac{8}{3}\pi$. **3.** $\frac{4}{3}\pi a^3$. **5.** $\frac{7}{8}\pi a^2 h$. **7.** $\frac{64}{3}\pi(\sqrt{2} - 1)$.

§ 193, page 210

1. $0.486\,\pi$. **3.** $\frac{1}{3}a^2 h$. **5.** $2\pi p^3$.

§ 196, page 213

1. $\frac{14}{3}$. **3.** $\frac{8}{27}(10\sqrt{10} - 1)$. **5.** $4\sqrt{3}$. **7.** $ds = \sqrt{1 + 4x^2}\,dx$. **9.** $ds = \dfrac{a}{y}\,dx$.

§ 198, page 215

1. $\frac{1375}{144} \approx 9.55$ foot-pounds. **3.** No. **5.** $28{,}125\,\pi \approx 88{,}357.5$ foot-pounds.

7. $150{,}000\,\pi \approx 471{,}240$ foot-pounds. **9.** $\dfrac{76{,}000}{3}\,\pi \approx 79{,}587$ foot-pounds.

11. 295.37. **13.** $m/2\,a$. **15.** 568.75 foot-pounds.

§ 200, page 218

1. 500 pounds. **5.** $2000\sqrt{2} \approx 2{,}828.4$ pounds. **7.** $\frac{3375}{16} \approx 210.94$ pounds.
9. 2560 pounds.

§ 202, page 223

1. $\bar{x} = \frac{12}{5}, \bar{y} = 0$. **3.** $\bar{x} = 0, \bar{y} = \dfrac{4a}{3\pi}$. **5.** $\bar{x} = \dfrac{4a}{3\pi}, \bar{y} = \dfrac{4b}{3\pi}$.

7. $\bar{x} = \frac{6}{5}, \bar{y} = \frac{3}{2}$. **9.** $\bar{x} = \bar{y} = \dfrac{4}{3(\pi - 2)}$. **11.** $\bar{x} = \frac{2}{5}, \bar{y} = 0$.

§ 204, page 225

1. $\bar{x} = \frac{3}{4}h, \bar{y} = 0$. **3.** $\bar{x} = \frac{4}{3}a, \bar{y} = 0$. **5.** $\bar{x} = \frac{3}{8}a, \bar{y} = 0$. **7.** $\bar{x} = \frac{9}{7}, \bar{y} = 0$.
9. $\bar{x} = 0, \bar{y} = \frac{5}{6}a$. **11.** $\bar{x} = 1, \bar{y} = \frac{1}{5}$.

§ 206, page 227

1. $128, 2\sqrt{2}$. **3.** $\frac{512}{5}, \frac{4}{5}\sqrt{15}$. **5.** $\frac{16}{105}, \frac{2}{35}\sqrt{70}$. **7.** $\frac{256}{5}, \frac{2}{5}\sqrt{30}$. **9.** $\frac{64}{5}, \frac{2}{5}\sqrt{30}$.

11. $\frac{8192}{105}, \frac{8}{35}\sqrt{70}$. **13.** $\frac{512}{3}, \frac{4}{3}\sqrt{6}$.

§ 208, page 230

1. $\frac{1}{6}\pi, \frac{1}{3}\sqrt{3}$. **3.** $\frac{8192}{3}\pi, \frac{8}{3}\sqrt{3}$. **5.** $\frac{64}{35}\pi, \frac{2}{7}\sqrt{7}$. **7.** $\frac{1}{15}\pi, \frac{1}{3}\sqrt{10}$.

§ 211, page 233

1. (a) $x^2 + y^2 = 25$; (b) $(x - 4)^2 + (y - 2)^2 = 36$;
(c) $(x - 5)^2 + (y + 2)^2 = 16$; (d) $(x + 6)^2 + (y + 3)^2 = 1$.
3. $x^2 + y^2 = 13$. **5.** $x^2 + (y - 5)^2 = 25$ or $x^2 + (y + 5)^2 = 25$.
7. $(x + 1)^2 + (y - 1)^2 = 13$. **9.** (a) $(x - 4)^2 + (y + 5)^2 = 36$, center $(4, -5)$,
radius 6; (b) $(x + 8)^2 + (y + 15)^2 = 289$, center $(-8, -15)$, radius 17;
(c) $(x - 3)^2 + y^2 = 16$, center $(3, 0)$, radius 4; (d) $(x + \frac{2}{3})^2 + (y - \frac{5}{3})^2 = \frac{50}{9}$,
center $(-\frac{2}{3}, \frac{5}{3})$, radius $\frac{5}{3}\sqrt{2}$. **11.** (a) Point circle: $(1, -1)$; (b) no locus.
13. X-intercepts 1, 3, Y-intercepts $3 \pm \sqrt{6}$. **15.** $(1, 0), (2, 1)$.
17. (a) $4x - 3y + 25 = 0$; (b) $x - 4y + 6 = 0$. **19.** $(-3, -4)$.
21. At $(8,0)$, $\phi = $ Arc tan $\frac{1}{2}$; at $(0, -4)$, $\phi = 26.5°$.

§ 213, page 235

1. (a) $x^2 + y^2 - 2x + 6y + 5 = 0$; (b) $x^2 + y^2 - 2x - 4y - 20 = 0$;
(c) $x^2 + y^2 - 6x + 8y = 0$. **3.** (a) $(x - 4)^2 + (y + 3)^2 = 34$;
(b) $2x^2 + 2y^2 - 17x - y - 30 = 0$; (c) $x^2 + y^2 - 8x + 2y - 33 = 0$
or $x^2 + y^2 + 4x - 14y + 3 = 0$; (d) $x^2 + y^2 + 2x - 6y - 3 = 0$.
5. (a) $x^2 + y^2 + 2x - 8y + 1 = 0$; (b) $x^2 + y^2 - 10x - 10y + 25 = 0$;
(c) $x^2 + y^2 + 5x + 6y + 12 = 0$; (d) $x^2 + y^2 - 3x - 7y - 18 = 0$.
7. $x^2 + y^2 - 2x - 10y + 1 = 0$ or $x^2 + y^2 - 34x - 170y + 289 = 0$.

§ 215, page 236

1. (a) Concentric circles with centers at $(3, 2)$; (b) circles of radius 3 with centers
on line $y = 2$; (c) circles through origin with centers on line $y = 2$; (d) circles
in first and third quadrants tangent to both coordinate axes.
3. (a) $(x + 2)^2 + (y - 3)^2 = r^2$; (b) $x^2 + y^2 - 2hx - 4hy = 0$.
5. $x^2 + y^2 - 2ky - 9 = 0$.

§ 217, page 238

7. $x^2 + y^2 = 25$. **9.** $4x^2 + 4y^2 + 15x - 24y + 52 = 0$.

§ 221, page 241

1. (a) $F(1, 0)$, directrix $x = -1$, latus rectum 4; (b) $F(-3, 0)$, directrix $x = 3$,
latus rectum 12; (c) $F(0, 2)$, directrix $y = -2$, latus rectum 8; (d) $F(0, -4)$,
directrix $y = 4$, latus rectum 16; (e) $F(\frac{3}{16}, 0)$, directrix $x = -\frac{3}{16}$, latus rectum $\frac{3}{4}$;
(f) $F(0, -\frac{5}{16})$, directrix $y = \frac{5}{16}$, latus rectum $\frac{5}{4}$. **3.** (a) $y^2 = 16x$;
(b) $y^2 = -24x$; (c) $y^2 = 32x$; (d) $x^2 = -20y$; (e) $y^2 = 9x$; (f) $x^2 = -12y$.
9. Parabola $y^2 = \frac{1}{2}px$. **11.** (a) $y^2 - 12x - 4y + 16 = 0$;
(b) $y^2 - 24x + 4y + 148 = 0$; (c) $x^2 - 32y - 64 = 0$;
(d) $x^2 + 4x - 12y - 8 = 0$. **13.** Parabola $y^2 = 2ax$. **15.** $x + 2y + 6 = 0$.
19. At $(0, 0)$, $\phi = 90°$; at $(2p, 2p)$, $\phi = $ Arc tan $\frac{3}{4}$.

§ 225, page 245

1. $hy^2 = r^2 x$. **3.** Focus $\frac{2}{3}$ inch from vertex. **7.** $\frac{128}{15}\pi a^3$. **9.** $\frac{32000}{3}$ foot-pounds.

§ 229, page 250

1. (a) Semi-axes 3, 2; vertices $(3, 0)$, $(-3, 0)$; foci $(\sqrt{5}, 0)$, $(-\sqrt{5}, 0)$, $e = \frac{1}{3}\sqrt{5}$;
(b) semi-axes 4, 3; vertices $(4, 0)$, $(-4, 0)$; foci $(\sqrt{7}, 0)$, $(-\sqrt{7}, 0)$, $e = \frac{1}{4}\sqrt{7}$;
(c) semi-axes 5, 3; vertices $(0, 5)$, $(0, -5)$; foci $(0, 4)$, $(0, -4)$; $e = \frac{4}{5}$;
(d) semi-axes 1, $\frac{2}{3}$; vertices $(0, 1)$, $(0, -1)$; foci $(0, \frac{1}{3}\sqrt{5})$, $(0, -\frac{1}{3}\sqrt{5})$; $e = \frac{1}{3}\sqrt{5}$.
3. (a) $\dfrac{x^2}{25} + \dfrac{y^2}{16} = 1$; (b) $\dfrac{x^2}{29} + \dfrac{y^2}{4} = 1$; (c) $\dfrac{x^2}{9} + \dfrac{y^2}{36} = 1$; (d) $\dfrac{x^2}{36} + \dfrac{y^2}{20} = 1$.
5. (a) $\dfrac{x^2}{25} + \dfrac{y^2}{16} = 1$; (b) $\dfrac{x^2}{9} + \dfrac{y^2}{6} = 1$; (c) $\dfrac{y^2}{16} + \dfrac{9\,x^2}{128} = 1$; (d) $\dfrac{x^2}{9} + \dfrac{5\,y^2}{9} = 1$;
(e) $\dfrac{x^2}{45} + \dfrac{y^2}{81} = 1$. **7.** (a) $\dfrac{x^2}{20} + \dfrac{y^2}{5} = 1$; (b) $12\,x^2 + 5\,y^2 = 128$.
11. $3\,x^2 + 4\,y^2 - 48 = 0$. **13.** Tangent: $2\,x + y - 4 = 0$;
normal: $x - 2\,y + 3 = 0$. **15.** $\phi = $ Arc tan $\frac{65}{72}$.

§ 232, page 252

1. Greatest distance 93,533,333 miles, least distance 90,466,667 miles.
3. 2.572 feet, 4.546 feet, 12 feet.

§ 237, page 259

1. (a) Semi-axes 3, 2; vertices $(3, 0)$, $(-3, 0)$; foci $(\sqrt{13}, 0)$, $(-\sqrt{13}, 0)$;
$e = \frac{1}{3}\sqrt{13}$, (b) semi-axes 4, 3; vertices $(4, 0)$, $(-4, 0)$; foci $(5, 0)$, $(-5, 0)$;
$e = \frac{5}{4}$; (c) semi-axes 2, 4; vertices $(2, 0)$, $(-2, 0)$; foci $(2\sqrt{5}, 0)$, $(-2\sqrt{5}, 0)$;
$e = \sqrt{5}$; (d) semi-axes 1, 3; vertices $(0, 1)$, $(0, -1)$; foci $(0, \sqrt{10})$, $(0, -\sqrt{10})$;
$e = \sqrt{10}$. **3.** (a) $\dfrac{x^2}{9} - \dfrac{y^2}{16} = 1$; (b) $\dfrac{x^2}{36} - \dfrac{y^2}{36} = 1$;
(c) $\dfrac{x^2}{144} - \dfrac{y^2}{25} = 1$; (d) $\dfrac{y^2}{48} - \dfrac{x^2}{16} = 1$. **5.** (a) $\dfrac{x^2}{16} - \dfrac{y^2}{20} = 1$; (b) $\dfrac{x^2}{9} - \dfrac{16\,y^2}{81} = 1$;
(c) $\dfrac{y^2}{64} - \dfrac{x^2}{36} = 1$. **7.** (a) $40\,x^2 - 27\,y^2 = 117$; (b) $x^2 - 3\,y^2 = 6$.
11. $9\,x^2 - 16\,y^2 + 18\,x + 128\,y - 391 = 0$. **13.** $4\,x^2 - 5\,y^2 = 20$.
15. (a) $4\,x + 5\,y = 0$, $4\,x - 5\,y = 0$; (b) $x + 3\,y = 0$, $x - 3\,y = 0$.
17. $F(10, 0)$, $F'(-10, 0)$, $e = \frac{5}{4}$. **19.** (a) $9\,y^2 - 16\,x^2 = 144$, $4\,x + 3\,y = 0$,
$4\,x - 3\,y = 0$; (b) $9\,x^2 - y^2 = 9$, $3\,x + y = 0$, $3\,x - y = 0$.
23. $8\,x + 3\,y \pm 7 = 0$.

§ 243, page 265

1. (a) Foci $(\sqrt{5}, 0)$, $(-\sqrt{5}, 0)$, directrices $x = \frac{9}{5}\sqrt{5}$, $x = \frac{9}{5}\sqrt{5}$;
(b) foci $(0, \sqrt{3})$, $(0, -\sqrt{3})$, directrices $y = \frac{4}{3}\sqrt{3}$, $y = -\frac{4}{3}\sqrt{3}$.
3. $3\,x^2 + 4\,y^2 = 12$. **5.** (a) Foci $(\sqrt{41}, 0)$, $(-\sqrt{41}, 0)$, directrices $x = \frac{25}{41}\sqrt{41}$,
$x = -\frac{25}{41}\sqrt{41}$; (b) foci $(2\sqrt{5}, 0)$, $(-2\sqrt{5}, 0)$, directrices $x = \frac{2}{5}\sqrt{5}$, $x = -\frac{2}{5}\sqrt{5}$.
7. $\dfrac{x^2}{100} - \dfrac{y^2}{300} = 1$.

ANSWERS

§ 245, page 267

1. (a) $x'^2 + 9y'^2 - 9 = 0$; (b) $y'^2 - 4x' = 0$; (c) $4x'^2 - y'^2 + 24 = 0$;
(d) $x'^2 - y'^2 - 4 = 0$. **3.** (a) New origin $(2, -3)$, new equation $x'^2 = 4y'$;
(b) new origin $(-1, 4)$, new equation $9x'^2 + 16y'^2 = 144$.

§ 247, page 269

1. (a) $(y - 3)^2 = 16(x - 1)$; (b) $(x + 2)^2 = 20(y - 1)$;
(c) $(y - 2)^2 = -16(x + 1)$. **3.** (a) $V(1, 2)$, $F(\frac{5}{2}, 2)$, directrix $x = -\frac{1}{2}$,
axis $y = 2$; (b) $V(-3, 4)$, $F(-3, 6)$, directrix $y = 2$, axis $x = -3$;
(c) $V(-1, 2)$, $F(-1, \frac{19}{12})$, directrix $y = \frac{29}{12}$, axis $x = -1$; (d) $V(1, -2)$,
$F(\frac{4}{3}, -2)$, directrix $x = \frac{2}{3}$, axis $y = -2$. **5.** $y = 2x^2 - 3x - 1$.

7. (a) $\dfrac{(x - 2)^2}{25} + \dfrac{(y - 1)^2}{9} = 1$; (b) $\dfrac{(x - 1)^2}{25} + \dfrac{(y - 3)^2}{16} = 1$;

(c) $\dfrac{(x - 1)^2}{25} + \dfrac{(y + 2)^2}{21} = 1$; (d) $\dfrac{(x - 4)^2}{20} + \dfrac{(y - 2)^2}{36} = 1$;

(e) $\dfrac{(x - 2)^2}{16} + \dfrac{(y - 1)^2}{12} = 1$; (f) $\dfrac{(x - 2)^2}{64} + \dfrac{(y + 3)^2}{48} = 1$.

9. (a) Center $(1, -2)$, vertices $(6, -2)$, $(-4, -2)$, foci $(4, -2)$, $(-2, -2)$;
(b) center $(-\frac{9}{2}, 2)$, vertices $(-\frac{9}{2}, \frac{19}{2})$, $(-\frac{9}{2}, -\frac{11}{2})$, foci $(-\frac{9}{2}, 8)$, $(-\frac{9}{2}, -4)$;
(c) center $(-4, -1)$, vertices $(0, -1)$, $(-8, -1)$, foci $(-4 + 2\sqrt{3}, -1)$,
$(-4 - 2\sqrt{3}, -1)$; (d) center $(-\frac{1}{2}, \frac{3}{2})$, vertices $(-\frac{1}{2} + \frac{3}{2}\sqrt{2}, \frac{3}{2})$, $(-\frac{1}{2} - \frac{3}{2}\sqrt{2}, \frac{3}{2})$,
foci $(1, \frac{3}{2})$, $(-2, \frac{3}{2})$. **11.** (a) $\dfrac{(x + 1)^2}{9} - \dfrac{(y - 3)^2}{4} = 1$;

(b) $\dfrac{(x - 1)^2}{9} - \dfrac{(y - 4)^2}{16} = 1$; (c) $\dfrac{(x + 2)^2}{16} - \dfrac{(y + 3)^2}{9} = 1$;

(d) $\dfrac{(y - 1)^2}{9} - \dfrac{(x - 2)^2}{27} = 1$; (e) $\dfrac{(x - 2)^2}{16} - \dfrac{(y - 5)^2}{9} = 1$;

(f) $\dfrac{(x - 3)^2}{36} - \dfrac{(y - 2)^2}{9} = 1$. **13.** (a) Center $(1, 3)$, vertices $(5, 3)$, $(-3, 3)$,
foci $(6, 3)$, $(-4, 3)$, asymptotes $3x - 4y + 9 = 0$, $3x + 4y - 15 = 0$;
(b) center $(-2, 4)$, vertices $(0, 4)$, $(-4, 4)$, foci $(-2 + \sqrt{5}, 4)$, $(-2 - \sqrt{5}, 4)$,
asymptotes $x - 2y + 10 = 0$, $x + 2y - 6 = 0$; (c) center $(\frac{3}{2}, \frac{1}{2})$, vertices
$(\frac{3}{2} + 3\sqrt{2}, \frac{1}{2})$, $(\frac{3}{2} - 3\sqrt{2}, \frac{1}{2})$, foci $(\frac{3}{2} + 2\sqrt{17}, \frac{1}{2})$, $(\frac{3}{2} - 2\sqrt{17}, \frac{1}{2})$, asymptotes
$5x - 3y - 6 = 0$, $5x + 3y - 9 = 0$; (d) center $(1, -4)$, vertices $(1, -2)$,
$(1, -6)$, foci $(1, -1)$, $(1, -7)$, asymptotes $2x - \sqrt{5}y - 2 - 4\sqrt{5} = 0$,
$2x + \sqrt{5}y - 2 + 4\sqrt{5} = 0$.

§ 251, page 277

1. (a) $4x'^2 + 9y'^2 = 36$; (b) $3x'^2 - y'^2 = 16$. **3.** (a) $4x'^2 - y'^2 = 4$;
(b) $16x'^2 + 9y'^2 = 144$. **5.** (a) $4x'^2 + y'^2 = 16$; (b) $y'^2 = 4x'$.

§ 255, page 280

1. (a) 0; (b) 1; (c) 1; (d) −1. **3.** −1. **5.** $\frac{1}{4}\pi^2$. **7.** $2/\pi$. **9.** 1. **11.** 0.
13. $|\cot x| \to +\infty$. **15.** $x = 0$, $\pm\pi$, $\pm 2\pi$, $\pm 3\pi$, $\cdots$
17. $x = 0$, $\pm 2\pi$, $\pm 4\pi$, $\pm 6\pi$, $\cdots$

§ 262, page 288

1. 2. **3.** 1. **5.** 0. **7.** $\frac{1}{2}$. **9.** $\frac{1}{2}$. **11.** $\frac{1}{2}$.

§ 265, page 290

1. $2 \cos 2x$. **3.** $3 \sin^2 x \cos x$. **5.** $x \cos x + \sin x$. **7.** $-\dfrac{\cos x}{2\sqrt{1 - \sin x}}$.

9. $\dfrac{x \cos x - \sin x}{x^2}$. **11.** $\dfrac{2 x \sin x - x^2 \cos x}{\sin^2 x}$. **13.** $-2 \sin(2x - 3)$.

15. $-\sin x$. **17.** $2 \cos x - 3 \sin x$. **19.** $t \cos t + \sin t - 2 \sin 2t$. **21.** $0, \sqrt{3}$.
23. $\cos x, -\sin x, -\cos x, \sin x, \cos x$.

§ 267, page 292

1. $2 \sec^2 2x$. **3.** $-3 \csc^2(x - 1)$. **5.** $\sec 2x \tan 2x$.

7. $-4 \csc(4x - 3) \cot(4x - 3)$. **9.** $\tfrac{1}{2} t \sec^2(t^2)$. **11.** $\dfrac{1}{2\sqrt{z}} \sec \sqrt{z} \tan \sqrt{z}$.

13. $x \sec^2 x + \tan x$. **15.** $2 \sec^2 x \tan x$. **17.** $2 \sec 2t (\tan 2t - \sec 2t)$.

19. $6 \tan^2 2t \sec^2 2t$. **21.** $-\cot^2 z$. **23.** $\dfrac{x \sec^2 x - 2 \tan x}{x^3}$.

27. $4 \cos 4x \, dx$. **29.** $(-x \sin x + \cos x) \, dx$.

§ 269, page 293

1. Arc tan $2\sqrt{2} \approx 70° 32'$, ≈ 1.23 radian. **5.** Maximum points at $x = \tfrac{1}{4}\pi$, $\tfrac{9}{4}\pi$, $\tfrac{17}{4}\pi$, $\cdots$, $-\tfrac{7}{4}\pi$, $-\tfrac{15}{4}\pi$, $\cdots$; minimum points at $x = \tfrac{5}{4}\pi$, $\tfrac{13}{4}\pi$, $\cdots$, $-\tfrac{3}{4}\pi$, $-\tfrac{11}{4}\pi$, $\cdots$; points of inflection at $x = \tfrac{3}{4}\pi$, $\tfrac{7}{4}\pi$, $\tfrac{11}{4}\pi$, $\cdots$, $-\tfrac{1}{4}\pi$, $-\tfrac{5}{4}\pi$, $\cdots$; concave upward between $\tfrac{3}{4}\pi$ and $\tfrac{7}{4}\pi$, etc., concave downward between $-\tfrac{1}{4}\pi$ and $\tfrac{3}{4}\pi$, etc. **7.** Maximum points at $x = 1.11$, 7.39, $\cdots$, -5.17, $\cdots$; minimum points at $x = 4.25$, 10.53, $\cdots$, -2.03, $\cdots$; points of inflection at $x = 2.68$, 5.82, $\cdots$, -0.46, $\cdots$; concave upward between 2.68 and 5.82, etc., concave downward between -0.46 and 2.68, etc. **9.** $v = 4$, $a = 0$.

11. $\tfrac{4}{45}\sqrt{3}\,\pi$ square inches per minute. **13.** $2\tfrac{2}{5}$ feet per second. **15.** $\tfrac{1}{9}\pi$.
17. Sides equal. **19.** Altitude $= \tfrac{4}{3}$ radius of sphere. **21.** 25.40 feet.

§ 271, page 297

1. (a) $\tfrac{1}{3}\pi$; (b) $-\tfrac{1}{6}\pi$; (c) $-\tfrac{1}{2}\pi$; (d) $\tfrac{1}{4}\pi$; (e) $\tfrac{2}{3}\pi$; (f) $\tfrac{1}{3}\pi$; (g) $-\tfrac{1}{4}\pi$; (h) $\tfrac{2}{3}\pi$; (i) $\tfrac{1}{4}\pi$; (j) $-\tfrac{1}{4}\pi$. **3.** $x = \tfrac{1}{3}$ arc sin y. **5.** $x = \tfrac{1}{2} \sin \tfrac{1}{2} y$. **7.** $x = \tfrac{1}{2}$ arc sin $2y$.

§ 273, page 299

1. $\dfrac{2}{\sqrt{1 - 4x^2}}$. **3.** $\dfrac{1}{x^2 - 2x + 2}$. **5.** $\dfrac{z}{1 + z^2}$ + Arc tan z. **7.** $\dfrac{1}{2\sqrt{x(1 - x)}}$.

9. $-\dfrac{1}{\sqrt{(2 - x)^2(3 - 4x + x^2)}}$. **11.** $-\dfrac{2x}{4 + x^2}$ + Arc cot $\tfrac{1}{2} x$.

13. $\dfrac{1}{z(1 + z^2)} - \dfrac{1}{z^2}$ Arc tan z. **15.** $-\dfrac{t^2}{2\sqrt{t^2(t - 1)}} + 2t$ Arc csc $\sqrt{t}$.

17. $\dfrac{2x^2}{\sqrt{a^2 - x^2}}$. **19.** $2x$ Arc tan x. **21.** $\dfrac{x}{(4 - x^2)^{\frac{3}{2}}}$.

§ 275, page 301

1. 2.112 radians per minute (increasing). **3.** 12 feet. **5.** 2.112 radians per minute (decreasing). **7.** $2\sqrt{26} - 4$.

ANSWERS

§ 278, page 303

1. (a) Defined for all finite values of x; (b) defined and real for $x > 1$. **3.** $y = \dfrac{x^4}{b^4}$.

5. $x = \frac{1}{2}\log_{10} y$. **7.** $x = \frac{1}{3}(10^y)$. **9.** 0. **11.** 11.

§ 280, page 305

1. (a) x^2; (b) $\dfrac{1}{x}$; (c) $\dfrac{1}{x^3}$; (d) $x\,e^x$. **3.** (a) $e^{x\ln 10}$; (b) $e^{-2x\ln 10}$. **5.** $x = \ln\dfrac{3 \pm \sqrt{5}}{2}$.

7. (a) 1.9199; (b) 3.5439; (c) 6.2266; (d) 8.1860 − 10; (e) 6.8275 − 10.
9. (a) 4.66; (b) 67.0; (c) 313; (d) 0.558. **11.** (a) 1.2712; (b) 4.2631;
(c) 0.6376; (d) 0.3329.

§ 282, page 307

1. $\dfrac{2}{x}$. **3.** $-\dfrac{1}{x}$. **5.** $\dfrac{x}{x^2 - 1}$. **7.** $-\tan x$. **9.** $\dfrac{1}{z\ln z}$. **11.** $\dfrac{1 - \ln x}{x^2}$.

13. $\dfrac{1}{\sqrt{x^2 + 4}}$. **15.** $\sec x$. **17.** $-\dfrac{y^2 + 1}{y(y^2 - 1)}$. **19.** $-\dfrac{2z}{1 - z^4}$.

21. $\operatorname{Arc\,tan}\dfrac{x}{a}$. **23.** $\dfrac{\sqrt{a^2 + x^2}}{x}$. **25.** (a) 12.3172; (b) −0.0443.

§ 284, page 309

1. $\dfrac{(8 - 6x - 8x^2)(2x + 1)}{(x^2 + 2)^4}$. **3.** $-\dfrac{1}{(x + 1)^{\frac{1}{2}}(x - 1)^{\frac{3}{2}}}$.

5. $-\dfrac{x + 2}{3\sqrt{1 - x}(x + 1)^{\frac{7}{6}}}$. **7.** $\dfrac{1 + x^2}{x^2(1 - x^2)^{\frac{3}{2}}}$. **9.** $x^x(1 + \ln x)$.

§ 286, page 310

1. Minimum point at $x = 1/e$; no point of inflection. **3.** Maximum points at $x = 2n\pi$ $(n = 0, \pm 1, \pm 2, \cdots)$; no points of inflection. **5.** Minimum point at $x = 0$; points of inflection at $x = \pm 1$. **9.** $(bT - a)T^{b-2}e^{\frac{a}{T}+c}$.

§ 288, page 311

1. $\frac{1}{2}e^{\frac{1}{2}x}$. **3.** $-2^{-x}\ln 2$. **5.** $e^x - e^{-x}$. **7.** $\dfrac{1}{x^2}e^{-\frac{1}{x}}$. **9.** $e^x(x + 1)$. **11.** $-2x\,e^{-x^2}$.

13. $e^{\tan x}\sec^2 x$. **15.** $e^x(\cos x - \sin x)$. **17.** $\dfrac{x - 1}{x^2}e^x$. **19.** $e^x\left(\ln x + \dfrac{1}{x}\right)$.

21. $\dfrac{e^x}{1 + e^{2x}}$. **23.** 1. **25.** $\dfrac{1 - y}{x + e^{-y}}$. **29.** $Ak\,e^{kx} - Bk\,e^{-kx}$.

§ 290, page 313

15. $a(k - x)$.

§ 294, page 316

3. (a) 0.5211; (b) 1.8107; (c) 0.6640; (d) 1.1030.

§ 296, page 317

1. $2\sinh 2x$. **3.** $-\operatorname{sech}^2(1 - x)$. **5.** $\sinh 2x$. **7.** $3x\cosh 3x + \sinh 3x$.
9. $\operatorname{sech} z(\operatorname{sech} z + \tanh z)$. **11.** $2\coth 2u$. **13.** $e^{-t}(2\sinh 2t - \cosh 2t)$.
15. $\operatorname{sech} u$.

§ 298, page 318

1. (a) 0; (b) 0; (c) 0; (d) 0. **5.** (a) 0.75; (b) 1.20; (c) 0.55.

§ 300, page 319

1. $\dfrac{2}{\sqrt{1 + 4\,x^2}}$. **3.** $\dfrac{x}{\sqrt{1 + x^2}} + \sinh^{-1} x$. **5.** $\dfrac{e^x}{\sqrt{e^{2x} - 1}}$. **7.** $\dfrac{1}{x^2 - 2\,x}$. **9.** $\frac{1}{2}\sec x$.

§ 302, page 320

1. 0.619. **3.** 0.371. **5.** 0.824. **7.** 0.159. **9.** 0.505. **11.** 1.293. **13.** 0.426. **15.** 0.589. **17.** 1.020. **19.** 0.860.

§ 303, page 320

1. $2\,x\cos 2\,x + \sin 2\,x$. **3.** $\dfrac{z}{\sqrt{1 - z^2}} + \operatorname{Arc}\sin z$. **5.** $\dfrac{2\,y}{y^2 + 1}$. **7.** $e^{-x}(1 - x)$.

9. $-\dfrac{1}{x^2}\operatorname{sech}^2 \dfrac{1}{x}$. **11.** $2\cot 2\,x$. **13.** $e^{-y}(\cos y - \sin y)$. **15.** $\dfrac{\cosh x}{2\sqrt{\sinh x}}$.

17. $2\sqrt{2\,x - x^2}$. **19.** $\dfrac{\cos z}{2\sqrt{1 + \sin z}}$. **21.** $2\,a\,e^{ax}\sin ax$. **23.** $2\coth x$.

25. $\dfrac{(x^2 - 4)^2}{(x^2 + 4)^2}$. **27.** $9\cosh^2 3\,y \sinh 3\,y$. **29.** $\dfrac{z^2}{\sqrt{1 - z^2}} + 2\,z\operatorname{Arc}\sin z$.

31. $\dfrac{\sin t}{2\sqrt{1 - \cos t}}$. **33.** $\tan z$. **35.** $2\sin x\sin 3\,x$. **37.** $-\dfrac{\sqrt{a^2 - x^2}}{x^2}$.

39. $\dfrac{y\sin 2\,y - \sin^2 y}{y^2}$. **41.** $6(\cos 3\,x - \sin 2\,x)$. **43.** $\dfrac{1}{\sqrt{2\,ax - x^2}}$.

45. $\dfrac{1}{2\sqrt{z(z + a)}}$. **47.** $\tan^2 x$. **49.** $(\sin x)^x\,[x\cot x + \ln\sin x]$.

51. $-\dfrac{2\,x}{\sqrt{x^2 - 4}} + 2\,x\operatorname{Arc}\sin\dfrac{2}{x}$. **53.** $2\sec^2 x\,(\tan x + 1)$. **55.** $\dfrac{\sqrt{a^2 - x^2}}{x^2}$.

57. $\dfrac{e^x}{\sqrt{1 - e^{2x}}}$. **59.** $ak\cos(kt + \alpha)$.

§ 305, page 325

3. (a) $(4, 405°), (-4, 225°), (-4, -135°)$; (b) $(3, 300°), (-3, 120°), (-3, -240°)$; (c) $(5, -90°), (-5, 90°), (-5, -270°)$; (d) $(4, \frac{1}{6}\pi), (-4, -\frac{5}{6}\pi), (-4, \frac{19}{6}\pi)$. **7.** On circle of radius 4 with center at pole; on bisector of first and third quadrants. **11.** $\sqrt{13}$.

§ 311, page 332

1. $A(5\sqrt{2}, 5\sqrt{2}), B(-\frac{3}{2}\sqrt{3}, \frac{3}{2}), C(\frac{5}{2}\sqrt{2}, -\frac{5}{2}\sqrt{2}), D(0, -5), E(2, -2\sqrt{3})$. **3.** $A(2\sqrt{3}, 30°), B(2\sqrt{2}, 135°), C(\sqrt{41}, -51.5°), D(3, 180°), E(4, 90°)$. **5.** (a) $x^2 + y^2 = a^2$; (b) $x = 4$; (c) $x^2 + y^2 - 2\,ay = 0$; (d) $(x^2 + y^2)^3 = 4\,a^2x^2y^2$; (e) $(x^2 + y^2)^2 = a^2(x^2 - y^2)$; (f) $x^2 + y^2 = 2\,x + 3\,y$. **7.** (a) $r\cos\theta = 2$; (b) $r = a$; (c) $r = 2\,a\cos\theta$; (d) $2\,r\cos\theta + r\sin\theta = 4$; (e) $r\cos^3\theta = \sin^2\theta$; (f) $r^2 = a^2\cos 2\,\theta$.

§ 314, page 336

3. (a) $r\cos\theta = 3$; (b) $r\sin\theta = 5$; (c) $\theta = \frac{1}{3}\pi$. **5.** (a) Center $(4, 0)$, radius 4;

(b) center $(\frac{5}{2}, \frac{3}{2}\pi)$, radius $\frac{5}{2}$; (c) center at origin, radius 3. **7.** (a) $r = 10\cos\theta$;

(b) $r = 12\sin\theta$; (c) $r = 5$. **13.** (a) Parabola; (b) ellipse; (c) hyperbola;

(d) parabola. **15.** (a) $r = \dfrac{8}{1 - \cos\theta}$; (b) $r = \dfrac{18}{4 - 3\cos\theta}$; (c) $r = \dfrac{8}{1 - 2\sin\theta}$.

§ 316, page 338

3. $r = a\sec\theta \pm b$. **5.** $r^2 = 2\,a^2\cos 2\,\theta$.

§ 318, page 340

1. $(2, \frac{1}{6}\pi)$, $(2, \frac{5}{6}\pi)$. **3.** $(10, 0.93)$, $(10, -0.93)$. **5.** $(0, 0)$, $(\frac{1}{2}\sqrt{2}\,a, \frac{3}{4}\pi)$.

7. $(\frac{1}{2}, \frac{1}{6}\pi)$, $(\frac{1}{2}, \frac{5}{6}\pi)$, $(1, \frac{1}{2}\pi)$, $(0, 0)$. **9.** $(\sqrt{2}\,a, \frac{1}{6}\pi)$, $(\sqrt{2}\,a, \frac{5}{6}\pi)$, $(\sqrt{2}\,a, \frac{7}{6}\pi)$,

$(\sqrt{2}\,a, \frac{11}{6}\pi)$. **11.** $(2, 1)$, $(-2, -1)$. **13.** $(1, \frac{1}{2}\pi)$, $(1, \frac{3}{2}\pi)$. **15.** $(0, 0)$, $(1, \frac{1}{2}\pi)$

§ 320, page 340

1. $-\frac{1}{3}\sqrt{3}$. **3.** -1. **5.** $\tan 3\,\theta_1$. **7.** Arc tan $\frac{4}{3}$ and $\frac{1}{4}\pi$.

§ 322, page 343

1. Center (x_1, y_1), radius a. **5.** (a) $y^2 = x^3$; (b) $x^2 + y^2 = 1$; (c) $y^2 = 2\,px$;

(d) $x^{\frac{2}{3}} + y^{\frac{2}{3}} = a^{\frac{2}{3}}$. **7.** $x = \dfrac{2}{1 + m^2}$, $y = \dfrac{2\,m}{1 + m^2}$. **9.** (a) $x = \dfrac{a(b^2 - a^2 m^2)}{b^2 + a^2 m^2}$,

$y = \dfrac{2\,ab^2 m}{b^2 + a^2 m^2}$; (b) $x = \dfrac{2}{1 - t}$, $y = \dfrac{2\,t}{1 - t}$; (c) $x = \dfrac{3\,at}{1 + t^3}$, $y = \dfrac{3\,at^2}{1 + t^3}$.

§ 329, page 348

1. (a) $4\,t$; (b) $\dfrac{1}{t}$; (c) $-\dfrac{1}{4\,t^3}$; (d) $\dfrac{1 - t^2}{2\,t}$. **3.** $\frac{5}{6}$. **5.** Tangent $3\,x + y - 4 = 0$,

normal $x - 3\,y - 28 = 0$. **7.** $\frac{3}{2}t$. **9.** $-\cot\theta$. **11.** Tangent $y = x - \frac{1}{2}a\pi + 2\,a$

normal $y = -x + \frac{1}{2}a\pi$. **13.** $\dfrac{t^2 - 1}{2\,t}$.

§ 331, page 349

1. (a) $\frac{3}{2}t$, $\dfrac{3}{4\,t}$; (b) $-\dfrac{t}{\sqrt{1 - t^2}}$, $-\dfrac{1}{2(1 - t^2)^{\frac{3}{2}}}$; (c) $-\dfrac{1}{4\,t^5}$, $\dfrac{5}{16\,t^9}$;

(d) $\dfrac{t(2 - t^3)}{1 - 2\,t^3}$, $\dfrac{2(1 + t^3)^4}{3(1 - 2\,t^3)^3}$.

§ 333, page 350

1. $\frac{26}{3}$. **3.** $\frac{8}{3}$. **5.** $\frac{8}{27}(10\sqrt{10} - 1)$.

§ 336, page 355

1. $v = 2\sqrt{5}$, $\alpha = 26°34'$; $v = 2\sqrt{t^2 + 1}$, $\cot\alpha = t$; $y^2 = 4\,x$. **3.** $v = \frac{5}{2}\sqrt{2}$,

$\alpha = 143°08'$; $9\,x^2 + 16\,y^2 = 144$. **5.** $v = 3\sqrt{5}$, $\alpha = 333°26'$. **7.** $v_x = 4\sqrt{2}$,

$v_y = -4\sqrt{2}$; $\alpha = 315°$.

§ 338, page 357

1. $v_x = 2$, $v_y = 4$, $v = 2\sqrt{5}$, $a_x = 0$, $a_y = 2$, $a = 2$; $\alpha = 63°26'$, $\phi = 90°$;

$x^2 = 4\,y$. **3.** $v_x = -2$, $v_y = 0$, $v = 2$, $a_x = 0$, $a_y = 4$, $a = 4$; $\alpha = \pi$, $\phi = \frac{1}{2}\pi$;

$x^2 + y^2 = 1$. **5.** $a = 4\sqrt{3}\,\pi^2$, $\phi = \frac{1}{6}\pi$. **9.** $v_y = \frac{32}{5}\sqrt{5}$, $v = \frac{4}{5}\sqrt{545}$, $a_x = 0$,

$a_y = \frac{1728}{25}\sqrt{5}$. $a = \frac{1728}{25}\sqrt{5}$.

§ 341, page 360

1. $\frac{2}{25}\sqrt{5}$. **3.** $\sqrt{2}$. **5.** $\frac{2}{27}$. **7.** $\frac{30}{169}\sqrt{13}$. **9.** $\frac{6}{169}\sqrt{13}$. **11.** $\dfrac{\sqrt{7}}{49\,a}$.

13. $\dfrac{2\,a^2}{(x_1{}^2 + y_1{}^2)^{\frac{3}{2}}}$. **15.** 1. **17.** $\frac{1}{4}\sqrt{2}$. **19.** $\frac{4}{25}\sqrt{5}$. **21.** $\cos x_1$.

23. $\dfrac{3\,t_1{}^4}{2(t_1{}^6 + 1)^{\frac{3}{2}}}$. **25.** $\dfrac{1}{4\,a}$. **27.** $\frac{2}{9}\sqrt{3}$. **29.** e. **31.** Where $y'' = 0$.

§ 343, page 362

1. $\frac{5}{3}\sqrt{10}$. **3.** 1. **5.** $3\sqrt{2}$. **7.** $\frac{5}{8}\sqrt{5}\,a$. **9.** $\dfrac{1}{a^4 b^4}(a^4 y_1{}^2 + b^4 x_1{}^2)^{\frac{3}{2}}$. **11.** 6.

15. $\frac{3}{2}\sqrt{3}$.

§ 345, page 364

1. $(-4, \frac{7}{2})$. **3.** $(\frac{1}{2}\pi, 0)$. **5.** $(4, 4)$. **7.** $\alpha = x_1 + 3\,x_1^{\frac{1}{3}} y_1^{\frac{1}{3}}$, $\beta = y_1 + 3\,x_1^{\frac{2}{3}} y_1^{\frac{1}{3}}$.

§ 348, page 366

1. $\frac{1}{3}\sin^3 x + C$. **3.** $\frac{1}{4}\tan^4 x + C$. **5.** $-\csc y + C$. **7.** $\frac{1}{3}\sec^3 t + C$.
9. $\frac{1}{3}(\ln x)^3 + C$. **11.** $\frac{2}{3}(1 + e^x)^{\frac{3}{2}} + C$. **13.** $2\sqrt{1 + \tan y} + C$.
15. $\frac{1}{3}\sinh^3 x + C$.

§ 350, page 367

1. $\frac{1}{2}\ln|2\,x + 3| + C$. **3.** $\ln|x^2 + x| + C$. **5.** $-\frac{1}{2}\ln|a^2 - x^2| + C$.

7. $-\dfrac{1}{x} + \ln|x| + C$. **9.** $2\ln 3 - 2$. **11.** $4 - 2\ln 2$. **13.** $2\ln|2\,e^x - 1| + C$.

15. $\frac{1}{2}\ln|2\sin\theta - 1| + C$. **17.** $\ln|\tan\phi + 1| + C$. **19.** $\frac{2}{3}\ln|1 + x\sqrt{x}| + C$.
21. $\frac{1}{2}\ln(4 + \sin^2 t) + C$. **23.** $\ln|\ln v| + C$.

§ 352, page 368

1. $\frac{1}{2}e^{2x+3} + C$. **3.** $e^x - e^{-x} + C$. **5.** $-2\,e^{-x} + C$. **7.** $\dfrac{2^x}{\ln 2} + C$.

9. $-\frac{1}{2}\cdot\dfrac{10^{-x^2}}{\ln 10} + C$. **11.** $2\,(1 - e^{-\frac{5}{2}})$. **13.** $e - 1$. **15.** $-e^{\frac{1}{x}} + C$. **17.** $\frac{1}{2}x^2 + C$.
19. $\ln|e^x - 1| + C$.

§ 354, page 370

1. $\frac{1}{2}\sin(2\,x + 1) + C$. **3.** $\dfrac{1}{2\,m}\tan 2\,mx + C$. **5.** $-\frac{1}{2}\cos(x^2) + C$.

7. $-\frac{1}{2}\ln|\cos 2\,y| + C$. **9.** $\sec y + C$. **11.** $\frac{1}{3}\tan 3\,z - z + C$. **13.** $\sqrt{2}$.
15. $2\sqrt{3} - 2 - \frac{1}{3}\pi$. **17.** $2\ln|\sec v| + \tan v + C$. **19.** $-\frac{1}{3}\cot^3\theta + C$.

§ 356, page 371

1. $\frac{1}{3}$ Arc $\tan\frac{1}{3}x + C$. **3.** $\frac{1}{12}$ Arc $\tan\frac{3}{4}x + C$. **5.** Arc $\sin\frac{1}{4}x + C$.

7. $\frac{1}{3}$ Arc $\sin\frac{3}{5}y + C$. **9.** $\dfrac{1}{\sqrt{30}}$ Arc $\tan\dfrac{6\,t}{\sqrt{30}} + C$. **11.** $\frac{1}{2}$ Arc $\sin(\frac{2}{3}\sqrt{3}\,z) + C$.

13. $\frac{1}{12}\pi$. **15.** 2 Arc $\tan\sqrt{y} + C$. **17.** $\frac{1}{2}$ Arc $\tan\frac{1}{2}$. **19.** $t + C$.

§ 358, page 373

1. $2 \cosh \frac{1}{2} x + C.$ **3.** $\frac{1}{2} \tanh 2 v + C.$ **5.** $-\frac{1}{2} \operatorname{sech} 2 w + C.$
7. $\frac{1}{2} \ln \cosh (2 x - 1) + C.$

§ 361, page 375

1. $\frac{1}{4} \ln \left| \dfrac{x - 2}{x + 2} \right| + C,$ or $-\frac{1}{2} \coth^{-1} \frac{1}{2} x + C.$ **3.** $\ln \left| x + \sqrt{x^2 - 4} \right| + C,$ or

$\operatorname{Cosh}^{-1} \frac{1}{2} x + C.$ **5.** $\ln (z + \sqrt{z^2 + 9}) + C,$ or $\sinh^{-1} \frac{1}{3} z + C.$

7. $\frac{1}{24} \ln \left| \dfrac{3 v - 4}{3 v + 4} \right| + C,$ or $-\frac{1}{12} \coth^{-1} \frac{3}{4} v + C.$ **9.** $\frac{1}{3} \ln \left(\dfrac{12 + 4\sqrt{5}}{9 + \sqrt{17}} \right),$ or

$\frac{1}{3} (\operatorname{Cosh}^{-1} \frac{3}{2} - \operatorname{Cosh}^{-1} \frac{9}{8}).$ **11.** $\frac{1}{3} \ln [\frac{1}{8}(9 + \sqrt{97})],$ or $\frac{1}{3} (\sinh^{-1} \frac{9}{4} - \sinh^{-1} \frac{3}{4}).$

13. $\frac{1}{4} \ln \dfrac{1.64}{0.36},$ or $\frac{1}{2} \tanh^{-1} 0.64.$ **15.** $\frac{1}{2} \ln (y^2 + \sqrt{y^4 - 1}) + C,$

or $\frac{1}{2} \operatorname{Cosh}^{-1} (y^2) + C.$ **17.** $\frac{1}{12} \ln \left| \dfrac{3 + 2 \tan \theta}{3 - 2 \tan \theta} \right| + C,$ or $\frac{1}{6} \tanh^{-1} (\frac{2}{3} \tan \theta) + C.$

19. $\ln (e^w + \sqrt{e^{2w} + 1}) + C,$ or $\sinh^{-1} (e^w) + C.$

§ 362, page 375

1. $\frac{1}{3} x^3 + \frac{1}{2} a x^2 + a^2 x + C.$ **3.** $-\sqrt{4 - x^2} + C.$ **5.** $\frac{1}{2} \ln (a^2 + x^2) + C.$

7. $\cos (1 - x) + C.$ **9.** $-\frac{1}{9} \cos^3 3 x + C.$ **11.** $\frac{2}{15} (3 y - 2)(1 + y)^{\frac{3}{2}} + C.$

13. $\frac{1}{3}.$ **15.** $\frac{4}{3} \sqrt{3}.$ **17.** $\frac{2}{105}(x - 2)^{\frac{3}{2}}(15 x^2 + 24 x + 32) + C.$

19. $-2\sqrt{1 - e^t} + C.$ **21.** $\dfrac{\sin^{n+1} \theta}{n + 1} + C.$

23. $2\sqrt{x + 2} - \ln |x + 3| - 2 \operatorname{Arc} \tan \sqrt{x + 2} + C.$ **25.** $\frac{1}{12} a^6.$

27. $\frac{1}{3} e^{3x+4} + C.$ **29.** $\frac{1}{3}(x^2 + 2 x)^{\frac{3}{2}} + C.$

31. $2\sqrt{z + 2} + \frac{3}{2}\sqrt{2} \ln \dfrac{\sqrt{z + 2} - \sqrt{2}}{\sqrt{z + 2} + \sqrt{2}} + C,$ or

$2\sqrt{z + 2} - 3\sqrt{2} \coth^{-1} \dfrac{\sqrt{z + 2}}{\sqrt{2}} + C$ if $z > 0;$

$2\sqrt{z + 2} + \frac{3}{2}\sqrt{2} \ln \dfrac{2 + \sqrt{z + 2}}{2 - \sqrt{z + 2}} + C,$ or

$2\sqrt{z + 2} - 3\sqrt{2} \tanh^{-1} \dfrac{\sqrt{z + 2}}{\sqrt{2}} + C,$ if $-2 < z < 0.$

33. $\ln |a x^2 + b x + c| + C.$ **35.** $\dfrac{1}{2(4 - t^2)} + C.$ **37.** $-\dfrac{1}{3^y \ln 3} + C.$

39. $-2 \ln |\cot \phi + 4| + C.$ **41.** $\frac{1}{2} \ln |x^2 + 6x - 5| + C.$ **43.** $\frac{1}{2} \operatorname{Arc} \tan 2.$

45. $\frac{1}{3}\sqrt{3} \ln \dfrac{\sqrt{y + 2} - \sqrt{3}}{\sqrt{y + 2} + \sqrt{3}} + C,$ or $-\frac{2}{3}\sqrt{3} \coth^{-1} \dfrac{\sqrt{y + 2}}{\sqrt{3}} + C,$ if $y > 1;$

$\frac{1}{3}\sqrt{3} \ln \dfrac{\sqrt{3} + \sqrt{y + 2}}{\sqrt{3} - \sqrt{y + 2}} + C,$ or $-\frac{2}{3}\sqrt{3} \tanh^{-1} \dfrac{\sqrt{y + 2}}{\sqrt{3}} + C,$ if $-2 < y < 1.$

47. $\dfrac{n}{2 \pi} \sin \dfrac{2 \pi t}{n} + C.$ **49.** $\dfrac{2}{105 a^3} (15 a^2 x^2 - 12 a b x + 8 b^2)(a x + b)^{\frac{3}{2}} + C.$

§ 364, page 378

1. $N = N_0 e^{kt}$. **3.** $P = P_0 e^{kt}$. **5.** 32.385 million. **7.** $T \approx 36.3°$, $t = 426$ seconds.
9. 3649.4. **11.** $x = s - c_1 e^{-kt}$. **13.** $i = 15\,e^{-60t}$. **15.** \$200.

§ 366, page 381

1. $16{,}384\,\sqrt{3}$ feet; 32 seconds; 4096 feet. **7.** 200 feet.

§ 368, page 383

1. $-x\,e^{-x} - e^{-x} + C$. **3.** $x \sin x + \cos x + C$. **5.** $y \tan y + \ln|\cos y| + C$.
7. $x \operatorname{Arc\,sin} x + \sqrt{1-x^2} + C$. **9.** $x \ln|x| - x + C$.
11. $\frac{1}{2} x^2 \operatorname{Arc\,tan} x + \frac{1}{2}\operatorname{Arc\,tan} x - \frac{1}{2} x + C$. **13.** $2(e^2 - 1)$. **15.** $\pi - 2$.
17. $\frac{t^{n+1}}{n+1}\left(\ln|t| - \frac{1}{n+1}\right) + C$. **19.** $y \cosh y - \sinh y + C$.

§ 371, page 385

1. $\frac{1}{2} e^x (\sin x - \cos x) + C$. **3.** $\frac{1}{10} e^{-x} (3 \sin 3x - \cos 3x) + C$.
5. $\frac{1}{13} e^{-3x} (2 \sin 2x - 3 \cos 2x) + C$.

§ 373, page 387

1. $\frac{1}{2} \operatorname{Arc\,tan} \dfrac{x+1}{2} + C$. **3.** $\operatorname{Arc\,sin} \dfrac{x-1}{2} + C$. **5.** $\operatorname{Arc\,sin} \dfrac{x-a}{a} + C$.

7. $\dfrac{2}{\sqrt{3}} \operatorname{Arc\,tan} \dfrac{2t-1}{\sqrt{3}} + C$. **9.** $\dfrac{1}{\sqrt{5}} \ln \dfrac{2s+3-\sqrt{5}}{2s+3+\sqrt{5}} + C$,

or $-\dfrac{2}{\sqrt{5}}\coth^{-1}\dfrac{2s+3}{\sqrt{5}} + C$, if $(2s+3)^2 > 5$;

$\dfrac{1}{\sqrt{5}} \ln \dfrac{\sqrt{5}-2s-3}{\sqrt{5}+2s+3} + C$, or $-\dfrac{2}{\sqrt{5}} \tanh^{-1}\dfrac{2s+3}{\sqrt{5}} + C$, if $(2s+3)^2 < 5$.

11. $\ln(x+2+\sqrt{x^2+4x+5}) + C$, or $\sinh^{-1}(x+2) + C$.
13. $\frac{1}{2}\ln(x^2+1) + \operatorname{Arc\,tan} x + C$. **15.** $\operatorname{Arc\,sin}\frac{1}{2}y - 2\sqrt{4-y^2} + C$.
17. $-\sqrt{8+6x-x^2} - \operatorname{Arc\,sin}\dfrac{x-3}{\sqrt{17}} + C$. **19.** $\ln 1.28 + \frac{11}{4}\operatorname{Arc\,tan}\frac{3}{4} - \frac{11}{16}\pi$.

21. $\dfrac{p}{2\,b^2}\ln(a^2+b^2 x^2) + \dfrac{q}{ab}\operatorname{Arc\,tan}\dfrac{bx}{a} + C$. **23.** $6 - 3\sqrt{3} + \frac{2}{3}\pi$.

§ 375, page 389

1. $-\cos x + \frac{1}{3}\cos^3 x + C$. **3.** $\frac{1}{2}\sin^2 x + C$, or $-\frac{1}{2}\cos^2 x + C'$, or
$-\frac{1}{4}\cos 2x + C''$. **5.** $\frac{1}{4}\sin^4 v - \frac{1}{6}\sin^6 v + C$. **7.** $\frac{1}{5}\sin^5 y - \frac{1}{7}\sin^7 y + C$.
9. $-\frac{2}{21}\sqrt{\cos x}\,(7\cos x - 3\cos^3 x) + C$. **11.** 1. **13.** $\frac{1}{2}x - \frac{1}{4}\sin 2x + C$.
15. $\frac{3}{8}y + \frac{1}{4}\sin 2y + \frac{1}{32}\sin 4y + C$. **17.** $\frac{1}{96}\pi + \frac{1}{64}\sqrt{3}$.
19. $\frac{1}{16}x - \frac{1}{48}\sin^3 2x - \frac{1}{64}\sin 4x + C$. **21.** $-\frac{1}{8}(\cos 4x + 2\cos 2x) + C$.
23. $\frac{1}{12}(\sin 6x + 3\sin 2x) + C$. **25.** $\frac{1}{10}(5\sin y - \sin 5y) + C$.
27. $\frac{1}{30}(3\sin 5y + 5\sin 3y) + C$. **29.** $\frac{1}{3}\tan^3 x - \tan x + x + C$.
31. $-\frac{1}{4}\cot^2 2y - \frac{1}{2}\ln|\sin 2y| + C$. **33.** $2 - \frac{1}{2}\pi$.
35. $-\frac{1}{18}\cot^6 3x + \frac{1}{12}\cot^4 3x - \frac{1}{6}\cot^2 3x - \frac{1}{3}\ln|\sin 3x| + C$.
37. $\frac{1}{5}\tan^5 x + \frac{1}{3}\tan^3 x + C$. **39.** $-\frac{1}{7}\csc^7 z + \frac{1}{5}\csc^5 z + C$.
41. $\frac{4}{135}(27\sqrt{2} - 8\sqrt{3})$. **43.** $\frac{1}{14}\sec^7 2\theta - \frac{1}{5}\sec^5 2\theta + \frac{1}{6}\sec^3 2\theta + C$.
45. $\frac{1}{5}\tan^5 x + \frac{2}{3}\tan^3 x + \tan x + C$. **47.** $-2\cot\frac{1}{2}v - \frac{2}{3}\cot^3\frac{1}{2}v + C$.

49. $-\frac{1}{3} \csc^3 x + \csc x + C.$ **51.** $-\cot x + \tan x + C.$

53. $\frac{2}{21}\sqrt{\tan y}\,(3\tan^3 y + 7\tan y) + C.$ **55.** $\tan\theta - \cot\theta + C.$

57. $\tan x + \sec x + C.$

§ 376, page 391

1. $\frac{1}{3}\cosh^3 x - \cosh x + C.$ **3.** $\frac{1}{2}x + \frac{1}{4}\sinh 2x + C.$ **5.** $z - \tanh z + C.$

7. $\frac{1}{2}\ln\cosh 2t - \frac{1}{4}\tanh^2 2t + C.$ **9.** $\tanh x - \frac{1}{3}\tanh^3 x + C.$

§ 378, page 393

1. $-\dfrac{1}{x}\sqrt{a^2 - x^2} - \operatorname{Arc}\sin\dfrac{x}{a} + C.$

3. $\frac{1}{2}x\sqrt{a^2 + x^2} + \frac{1}{2}a^2\ln(x + \sqrt{a^2 + x^2}) + C.$ **5.** $\frac{1}{2}\operatorname{Arc}\sec\frac{1}{2}y + C.$

7. $\dfrac{x}{a^2\sqrt{a^2 - x^2}} + C.$

9. $\frac{1}{4}x(a^2 + x^2)^{\frac{3}{2}} + \frac{3}{8}a^2 x\sqrt{a^2 + x^2} + \frac{3}{8}a^4\ln(x + \sqrt{a^2 + x^2}) + C.$

11. $\frac{1}{2}t\sqrt{t^2 - 9} + \frac{9}{2}\ln|t + \sqrt{t^2 - 9}| + C.$

13. $\ln(x + \sqrt{x^2 + a^2}) - \dfrac{1}{x}\sqrt{x^2 + a^2} + C.$

15. $\frac{3}{8}a^4\operatorname{Arc}\sin\dfrac{y}{a} + \frac{1}{8}y(5a^2 - 2y^2)\sqrt{a^2 - y^2} + C.$ **17.** $\dfrac{4\sqrt{6} - 7\sqrt{2}}{175}.$

19. $\sqrt{2}.$ **21.** $\dfrac{x - a}{a^2\sqrt{2ax - x^2}} + C.$ **23.** $\operatorname{Arc}\sin(y - 1) - \sqrt{2y - y^2} + C.$

25. $\operatorname{Arc}\sin\dfrac{y - 1}{2} - \sqrt{3 + 2y - y^2} + C.$

27. $-\frac{1}{54}\left(\dfrac{3x}{x^2 - 9} + \frac{1}{2}\ln\left|\dfrac{x - 3}{x + 3}\right|\right) + C.$ **29.** $\frac{3}{8}\operatorname{Arc}\tan x + \dfrac{x(5 + 3x^2)}{8(1 + x^2)^2} + C.$

§ 381, page 396

1. $\ln\left|\dfrac{c(x + 1)^2}{x + 2}\right|.$ **3.** $\frac{1}{12}\ln\left|\dfrac{cx^3(x + 4)}{(x + 1)^4}\right|.$ **5.** $x + \frac{3}{2}\ln\left|\dfrac{x - 3}{x + 3}\right| + C.$

7. $\dfrac{1}{2a^2}\ln\left|\dfrac{cy^2}{a^2 - y^2}\right|.$ **9.** $\frac{1}{60}\ln\left|\dfrac{c(x + 2)^3(x - 3)^2}{(x - 2)^3(x + 3)^2}\right|.$ **11.** $\frac{1}{14}(21\ln 7 - 16\ln 4).$

13. $x = \dfrac{ac\,e^{akt}}{1 + c\,e^{akt}}.$

§ 383, page 398

1. $\ln\left|\dfrac{x + 1}{x}\right| - \dfrac{1}{x} + C.$ **3.** $\frac{1}{9}\ln\left|\dfrac{x}{x + 3}\right| + \frac{1}{3}\cdot\dfrac{1}{x + 3} + C.$

5. $x - 1 + \dfrac{10}{x - 1} - \ln|x - 1| + C.$ **7.** $\frac{1}{2}\cdot\dfrac{1}{1 - x^2} + C.$

9. $x + 2 - \dfrac{5}{x + 2} - 4\ln|x + 2| + C.$ **11.** $\frac{1}{4}\ln 32 + \frac{3}{8}.$

§ 385, page 400

1. $\frac{1}{8}\ln\dfrac{x^2}{x^2 + 4} + \frac{1}{2}\operatorname{Arc}\tan\frac{1}{2} + C.$ **3.** $\frac{1}{8}\ln\dfrac{t^2 + 1}{t^2 + 5} + C.$

5. $\ln|x^3 + x^2 + x| - \dfrac{4}{\sqrt{3}}\operatorname{Arc}\tan\dfrac{2x + 1}{\sqrt{3}} + C.$

7. $\frac{1}{6} \ln \left| \dfrac{(y + 1)^2}{y^2 - y + 1} \right| + \dfrac{1}{\sqrt{3}} \operatorname{Arc} \tan \dfrac{2y - 1}{\sqrt{3}} + C.$

9. $\frac{1}{4} \ln \dfrac{x^4}{(x^2 + 1)(x + 1)^2} - \frac{1}{2} \operatorname{Arc} \tan x + C.$

11. $\frac{1}{36} \ln |(x^2 + 9)^{11}(x^2 - 9)^7| + C.$

§ 387, page 401

1. $3 \ln (x^2 + 1) - \dfrac{3x^2}{x^2 + 1} + C.$ **3.** $\frac{1}{2} \cdot \dfrac{y}{1 - y^2} + \frac{1}{4} \ln \left| \dfrac{1 + y}{1 - y} \right| + C.$

5. $\frac{1}{2} \ln \dfrac{x^2}{x^2 + 1} + \dfrac{1}{2(x^2 + 1)} + C.$ **7.** $-\dfrac{1}{z} - \frac{3}{2} \operatorname{Arc} \tan z - \dfrac{z}{2(1 + z^2)} + C.$

§ 389, page 402

1. $\dfrac{2}{\sqrt{3}} \operatorname{Arc} \tan \left(\dfrac{1}{\sqrt{3}} \tan \frac{1}{2} x \right) + C.$ **3.** $\dfrac{1}{2\sqrt{3}} \ln \left| \dfrac{\tan x + 2 - \sqrt{3}}{\tan x + 2 + \sqrt{3}} \right| + C.$

5. $\frac{1}{5} \ln \left| \dfrac{2 \tan \frac{1}{2} x + 1}{2 \tan \frac{1}{2} x - 4} \right| + C.$ **7.** $\frac{1}{2} \ln |\tan \frac{1}{2} y| - \frac{1}{4} \tan^2 \frac{1}{2} y + C.$

§ 392, page 405

1. $\frac{1}{16} (4x^2 - 12x - 27) + \frac{9}{8} \ln |2x + 3| + C.$ **3.** $\frac{1}{5} (3x + 1)(2x - 1)^{\frac{3}{2}} + C.$

5. $-\dfrac{x}{9\sqrt{x^2 - 9}} + C.$ **7.** $-\frac{1}{2} \ln \left| \dfrac{\sqrt{x^2 + 4} + 2}{x} \right| + C.$

9. $\frac{1}{5} \sin x \cos^4 x + \frac{4}{15} \sin x \cos^2 x + \frac{8}{15} \sin x + C.$

11. $\frac{1}{8} e^{2x}(4x^3 - 6x^2 + 6x - 3) + C.$ **13.** $\frac{1}{2}\pi - 1.$ **15.** $0.242.$

17. $\frac{2}{105}(15x^2 - 24x + 32)(x + 2)^{\frac{3}{2}} + C.$

19. $\frac{1}{4} x(x^2 + 10)\sqrt{x^2 + 4} + 6 \ln (x + \sqrt{x^2 + 4}) + C,$ or

$\frac{1}{4} x(x^2 + 10)\sqrt{x^2 + 4} + 6 \sinh^{-1} \dfrac{x}{2} + C.$

21. $\frac{1}{2}(x - 4)\sqrt{8x - x^2} + 8 \operatorname{Arc} \cos \left(1 - \dfrac{x}{4} \right) + C.$

23. $-\dfrac{\sqrt{16 - x^2}}{x} - \operatorname{Arc} \sin \dfrac{x}{4} + C.$ **25.** $\frac{1}{2}\sqrt{3} - \frac{1}{3}\sqrt{5}.$

27. $\frac{1}{15} \cos x\,(3 \sin^4 x - \sin^2 x - 2) + C.$ **29.** $\pi - 2.$

31. $\frac{1}{27}(9x^2 - 2) \sin 3x + \frac{2}{9} x \cos 3x + C.$

§ 394, page 406

1. $\frac{1}{5} x^5 - \frac{2}{3} x^3 + C.$ **3.** $\frac{1}{4} \operatorname{Arc} \tan \dfrac{x + 2}{4} + C.$ **5.** $\frac{1}{2} \tan 2\theta + C.$

7. $2\sqrt{x} - 2 \operatorname{Arc} \tan \sqrt{x} + C.$ **9.** $\frac{1}{2} \ln (t^2 + 9) + C.$ **11.** $-\cot \theta - \theta + C.$

13. $-e^{\cos x} + C.$ **15.** $\frac{1}{4} (\sin 2x - 2x \cos 2x) + C.$

17. $\frac{1}{5} z^5 + \frac{8}{3} z^3 + 16z + C.$ **19.** $-\frac{2}{315}(128 + 96t + 60t^2 + 35t^3)(2 - t)^{\frac{3}{2}} + C.$

21. $\frac{1}{3} \sin^3 x - \frac{1}{5} \sin^5 x + C.$ **23.** $\sqrt{2y + 1} + C.$

25. $2 \ln |e^t - 2| + e^t + C.$ **27.** $\frac{1}{2} \ln \cosh 2v + C.$

29. $\sin x + \cos x + \ln |\csc x - \cot x| + C.$ **31.** $\frac{1}{8} \ln \left| \dfrac{x^2 - 2}{x^2 + 2} \right| + C.$

33. $\ln |\ln x| + C.$ **35.** $\ln |\cos (\frac{1}{4}\pi - \theta)| + C.$ **37.** $\dfrac{a^x b^x}{\ln (ab)} + C.$

39. $a \operatorname{Arc} \sin \frac{x}{a} - \sqrt{a^2 - x^2} + C.$ **41.** $\frac{1}{3} x^3 + \frac{1}{2} x^2 - x - \ln |x - 1| + C.$

43. $\frac{27}{5} y^4 (y - 2)^4 + C.$ **45.** $-\frac{3}{2} x^2 - 3 x - 3 \ln |x - 1| + C.$

47. $\frac{1}{3} \sin 3 x - \frac{1}{9} \sin^3 3 x + C.$ **49.** $-x - \ln \left| \frac{x - 2}{x + 2} \right| + C.$

51. $\frac{1}{3} x^3 \operatorname{Arc} \sin x + \frac{1}{9} (2 + x^2)\sqrt{1 - x^2} + C.$

53. $6\sqrt{t + 1} + 2 \ln \dfrac{\sqrt{t + 1} - 1}{\sqrt{t + 1} + 1} + C,$ if $t > 0$;

$6\sqrt{t + 1} + 2 \ln \dfrac{1 - \sqrt{1 + t}}{1 + \sqrt{1 + t}} + C,$ if $-1 < t < 0.$

55. $\frac{1}{4} x^2 + \frac{1}{4} x \sin 2 x + \frac{1}{8} \cos 2 x + C.$ **57.** $\dfrac{1}{a} \ln \left| \dfrac{x}{x + a} \right| + C.$

59. $-\frac{1}{2} w^2 - \frac{1}{2} \ln |w^2 - 1| + C.$

§396, page 410

1. 8. **3.** $a^2 \ln 2.$ **5.** Arc tan 2. **7.** $\frac{1}{2} \ln 65.$ **9.** $a^2[2\sqrt{3} + \ln (2 - \sqrt{3})].$
11. $\frac{135}{2} - 72 \ln 2.$ **13.** $\frac{2}{3} + 5 \operatorname{Arc} \sin \frac{2}{5}\sqrt{5}.$ **15.** $\sinh 1.$ **17.** $3 \pi a^2.$

§ 398, page 412

1. $\frac{1}{16} (\pi + 2) a^2.$ **3.** $\frac{1}{8} (e^{2\pi} - 1).$ **5.** $\frac{3}{2} \pi.$ **7.** $\frac{9}{2} \pi.$ **9.** $\frac{1}{8} \pi a^2.$
11. $\frac{4}{3} \pi + \sqrt{3} - 4 \ln (2 + \sqrt{3}).$ **13.** $\frac{1}{2} a^2.$ **15.** $(\frac{1}{3} \pi + \frac{1}{2}\sqrt{3})a^2.$ **17.** $1 - \frac{1}{4} \pi.$
19. $-\frac{7}{3} \pi + \frac{17}{2}\sqrt{3}.$ **21.** $\frac{32}{3} \pi + 4\sqrt{3}.$ **23.** $\pi.$

§ 400, page 415

1. $\frac{1}{2} \pi(e^6 - e^2).$ **3.** $2 \pi^2 - 3\sqrt{3} \pi.$ **5.** $\pi \left(1 - \dfrac{1}{e} \right).$ **7.** (a) $\frac{4}{3} \pi ab^2;$
(b) $\frac{4}{3} \pi a^2 b.$ **9.** $5 \pi^2 a^3.$ **11.** $2 \pi^2 a^3.$

§ 402, page 416

1. $\frac{1}{2} \ln 3.$ **3.** $\sqrt{2} + \ln (1 + \sqrt{2}).$ **5.** $2 + 12 \ln \frac{5}{3}.$
7. $\sqrt{1 + e^2} + \frac{1}{2} \ln \dfrac{\sqrt{1 + e^2} - 1}{\sqrt{1 + e^2} + 1} - \sqrt{2} - \frac{1}{2} \ln (3 - 2\sqrt{2}).$ **9.** $\sinh 1.$
11. $\frac{3}{2} \pi.$ **13.** $a[\sqrt{2} + \ln (1 + \sqrt{2})].$ **15.** $a[\sqrt{2} + \ln (1 + \sqrt{2})].$

§ 404, page 417

1. $8 a.$ **3.** $\frac{1}{2} a[\alpha\sqrt{1 + \alpha^2} + \ln (\alpha + \sqrt{1 + \alpha^2})].$
5. $2 a(\sqrt{7} - 2) + a\sqrt{3} \ln [\frac{1}{2}(7 + 4\sqrt{3})(5 - \sqrt{21})].$

§ 406, page 420

1. $4 \pi a^2.$ **3.** $49 \pi.$ **5.** $\frac{1}{27} \pi(10\sqrt{10} - 1).$ **7.** $\frac{13}{3} \pi.$ **9.** $\frac{1}{27} \pi(730\sqrt{730} - 1).$
11. $\pi[2\sqrt{2} + \ln (3 + 2\sqrt{2})].$
13. $\pi[e\sqrt{1 + e^2} - \sqrt{2} + \ln (e + \sqrt{1 + e^2}) - \ln (1 + \sqrt{2})].$ **15.** $3 \pi.$
17. $4 \pi^2 ab.$ **19.** $\frac{8}{3} \pi a^2(2\sqrt{2} - 1).$ **21.** $\frac{6}{5} \pi a^2.$ **23.** $\frac{32}{5} \pi a^2.$

§ 409, page 424

1. $\bar{x} = \frac{1}{2} \pi - 1, \bar{y} = \frac{1}{8} \pi.$ **3.** $\bar{x} = \bar{y} = \frac{1}{2} a.$ **5.** $\bar{x} = \pi a, \bar{y} = \frac{5}{6} a.$

7. $\bar{x} = a,\ \bar{y} = \dfrac{4\,a}{3\,\pi}.$ **9.** $\bar{x} = \frac{1}{2}\,\pi.$ **11.** $\bar{x} = 0,\ \bar{y} = \dfrac{2\,a}{\pi}.$

13. $\bar{x} = \bar{y} = \frac{2}{5}\,a.$ **15.** $\bar{x} = \dfrac{a\sin\alpha}{\alpha},\ \bar{y} = 0.$ **17.** $\bar{x} = \frac{1}{2}\,a.$

19. $\bar{x} = \frac{1}{2}(a + b).$ **21.** (a) $I_y = e - 2$; (b) $I_x = \frac{1}{6}(e^3 - 1).$

23. $\frac{8}{3}\ln 2 - \frac{7}{9}.$ **25.** $2\,\pi^2 a^2 b.$ **27.** $\bar{y} = \dfrac{2\,a}{\pi}.$

§ 412, page 428

1. 2.750, exact $2.66\frac{2}{3}$. **3.** 0.789, exact 0.75. **5.** 1.308, exact $\ln 11 - \ln 3 \approx 1.299$.
7. 8.411, exact 9. **9.** 4.857. **11.** 1.845. **13.** 2.422. **15.** 16,787.5 cubic yards.
17. 2500 foot-pounds.

§ 415, page 433

1. $333\frac{1}{3}$, exact $333\frac{1}{3}$. **3.** 2.210, exact $\ln 9 \approx 2.197$.
5. 34.107, exact $16\,\pi - 32\,\text{Arc}\sin\frac{1}{4} - \sqrt{60} \approx 34.431$. **7.** 2.001, exact 2.
9. 1.111. **11.** 10.753. **13.** By trapezoidal rule, 0.5622; by Simpson's rule,
0.5620; exact $\frac{1}{2}(\ln 40 - \ln 13) \approx 0.5620$. **15.** By trapezoidal rule, 18.8397;
by Simpson's rule, 18.8372; exact value ≈ 18.8324. **17.** 5.526. **19.** 15.73.
21. 9069.6 foot-pounds.

§ 418, page 438

1. Convergent, 2. **3.** Divergent. **5.** Convergent, $2\sqrt{a}$. **7.** Divergent.
9. Convergent, 0. **11.** Divergent. **13.** Divergent. **15.** Convergent, $\frac{1}{4}\,\pi a^2$.
17. Convergent, π. **19.** Convergent, $\frac{1}{2}\,\pi$. **21.** 4.

§ 420, page 441

1. Convergent, 1. **3.** Divergent. **5.** Divergent. **7.** Convergent, $\frac{1}{2}$.
9. Convergent, $\frac{1}{4}$. **11.** Convergent, $\frac{1}{2}$. **13.** Convergent, $\frac{1}{4}\,\pi$. **15.** Divergent.
17. Convergent, $\dfrac{\pi}{a}$. **19.** Divergent. **21.** Convergent, $\dfrac{1}{2\,a}\ln 3$.

23. Convergent, $1 - \frac{1}{4}\,\pi$. **25.** $4\,\pi a^2$. **27.** $\dfrac{\pi NI}{5\,r}\left(1 - \dfrac{x}{\sqrt{r^2 + x^2}}\right)$.

§ 424, page 447

1. 5. **3.** $-\frac{12}{5}$. **5.** $\frac{1}{2}$. **7.** 2. **9.** 0. **11.** 0. **13.** 1. **15.** $\frac{1}{4}$. **17.** $-\frac{1}{6}$. **19.** $\frac{2}{5}$.
21. 2. **23.** 2. **25.** $\dfrac{\ln 2}{\ln 3}$. **27.** 0. **29.** 1. **31.** $\frac{1}{3}$. **33.** -2. **35.** 1. **37.** 1.
39. 0. **41.** Function $\to +\infty$ from right; function $\to -\infty$ from left.

§ 426, page 448

1. 0. **3.** 1. **5.** 0. **7.** 0. **9.** 2. **11.** 0. **13.** 0. **15.** 0. **17.** 0. **19.** 0.

§ 429, page 451

1. 1. **3.** 1. **5.** 0. **7.** 0. **9.** 1. **11.** 0. **13.** 0. **15.** $2/\pi$. **17.** 0. **19.** 0. **21.** $\frac{1}{2}$.
23. $\frac{1}{2}$. **25.** 1. **27.** 1. **29.** e. **31.** 1. **33.** 1. **35.** 1. **37.** 0. **39.** (a) 1; (b) $-\frac{1}{4}$.

§ 432, page 455

1. $\frac{1}{2}, \frac{2}{5}, \frac{3}{10}, \frac{4}{17}, \frac{5}{26}, \cdots$ **3.** $\dfrac{1}{2\cdot 3}, -\dfrac{2}{3\cdot 4}, \dfrac{3}{4\cdot 5}, -\dfrac{4}{5\cdot 6}, \dfrac{5}{6\cdot 7}, \cdots$

ANSWERS

5. $\dfrac{1}{2\,n-1}\cdot$ **7.** $(-1)^{n+1}\cdot\dfrac{1}{n^2+1}\cdot$ **9.** Converges to 1. **11.** Diverges.

13. Converges to 0. **15.** Diverges. **17.** Converges to 1. **19.** Diverges.
21. Diverges. **23.** Converges to 1. **25.** $\tfrac{2}{3}$. **27.** 2. **29.** 0. **31.** 2.

§ 434, page 457

1. $\tfrac{2}{2}+\tfrac{4}{5}+\tfrac{6}{10}+\tfrac{8}{17}+\tfrac{10}{26}+\cdots$ **3.** $1+\dfrac{2}{2!}+\dfrac{4}{3!}+\dfrac{8}{4!}+\dfrac{16}{5!}+\cdots$

5. $\tfrac{1}{2}-\tfrac{2}{4}+\tfrac{3}{8}-\tfrac{4}{16}+\tfrac{5}{32}-\cdots$ **7.** $x+\dfrac{x^2}{\sqrt{2}}+\dfrac{x^3}{\sqrt{3}}+\dfrac{x^4}{\sqrt{4}}+\dfrac{x^5}{\sqrt{5}}+\cdots$

9. $\dfrac{1}{n^2}\cdot$ **11.** $(-1)^{n+1}\dfrac{1}{n!}\cdot$ **13.** $\dfrac{1}{n(n+2)}\cdot$ **15.** $(-1)^{n+1}\dfrac{x^n}{n}\cdot$ **17.** $s_1=1$,
$s_2=\tfrac{3}{2}$, $s_3=\tfrac{11}{6}$, $s_4=\tfrac{25}{12}$. **19.** $s_1=1$, $s_2=\tfrac{1}{2}$, $s_3=\tfrac{3}{4}$, $s_4=\tfrac{5}{8}$.

§ 441, page 464

1. Convergent. **3.** Divergent. **5.** Convergent.

§ 443, page 467

1. Convergent. **3.** Divergent. **5.** Divergent. **7.** Convergent. **9.** Convergent.
11. Divergent. **13.** Convergent. **15.** Convergent. **17.** Convergent. **19.** Convergent.

§ 445, page 470

1. Convergent. **3.** Convergent. **5.** Convergent. **7.** Divergent. **9.** Convergent.
11. Convergent. **13.** Divergent. **15.** Convergent. **17.** Divergent. **19.** Convergent.

§ 447, page 473

1. Convergent. **3.** Divergent. **5.** Convergent. **7.** Convergent.

9. $E_{20}<\dfrac{1}{21^2}\approx0.0023$. **11.** $E_{10}<\dfrac{1}{22\cdot11^2}\approx0.00038$.

13. $E_6<\tfrac{1}{13}(\tfrac{1}{5})^{13}\approx6.3\times10^{-11}$. **15.** $s_6\approx0.632$. **17.** $s_4\approx0.322$.

§ 449, page 476

1. Absolutely convergent. **3.** Conditionally convergent. **5.** Absolutely convergent. **7.** Absolutely convergent.

§ 451, page 479

1. $-1\le x\le1$. **3.** $-3<x<3$. **5.** All values of x. **7.** Convergent for $x=0$, divergent for $x\ne0$. **9.** Convergent for all values of x. **11.** $-1<x\le1$.
13. Convergent for all values of x. **15.** $0<x<2$. **17.** Convergent for all values of x.

§ 453, page 483

1. $e^{-x}=1-x+\dfrac{x^2}{2!}-\dfrac{x^3}{3!}+\dfrac{x^4}{4!}-\cdots$

3. $\ln(1+x)=x-\dfrac{x^2}{2}+\dfrac{x^3}{3}-\dfrac{x^4}{4}+\cdots$

5. $\cos x=1-\dfrac{x^2}{2!}+\dfrac{x^4}{4!}-\dfrac{x^6}{6!}+\cdots$

7. $\sqrt{1+x}=1+\tfrac{1}{2}x-\tfrac{1}{8}x^2+\tfrac{1}{16}x^3-\cdots$

9. $e^x = e\left[1 + (x - 1) + \dfrac{1}{2!}(x - 1)^2 + \dfrac{1}{3!}(x - 1)^3 + \cdots\right].$

11. $\sin x = \tfrac{1}{2}\sqrt{2}\left[1 + (x - \tfrac{1}{4}\pi) - \dfrac{1}{2!}(x - \tfrac{1}{4}\pi)^2 - \dfrac{1}{3!}(x - \tfrac{1}{4}\pi)^3 + \cdots\right].$

13. $\ln x = (x - 1) - \tfrac{1}{2}(x - 1)^2 + \tfrac{1}{3}(x - 1)^3 - \tfrac{1}{4}(x - 1)^4 + \cdots$

15. $\dfrac{1}{x} = \tfrac{1}{2} - \tfrac{1}{4}(x - 2) + \tfrac{1}{8}(x - 2)^2 - \tfrac{1}{16}(x - 2)^3 + \cdots$

17. $\tan x = x + \tfrac{1}{3}x^3 + \tfrac{2}{15}x^5 + \cdots$

19. $\text{Arc } \tan x = x - \tfrac{1}{3}x^3 + \tfrac{1}{5}x^5 - \cdots$

21. $\ln \cos x = -\tfrac{1}{2}x^2 - \tfrac{1}{12}x^4 - \tfrac{1}{45}x^6 - \cdots$

23. $e^x \cos x = 1 + x - \tfrac{1}{3}x^3 + \cdots$

§ 458, page 491

1. 0.81873. **3.** 0.19867. **5.** 0.04879. **7.** 1.00995. **9.** 1.00500.
11. 8.1662. **13.** 0.8829. **15.** 0.6820. **17.** 1.8107.

§ 460, page 493

1. $\cos^2 x = 1 - x^2 + \tfrac{1}{3}x^4 - \tfrac{2}{45}x^6 + \cdots$
3. $e^x \cos x = 1 + x - \tfrac{1}{3}x^3 - \tfrac{1}{6}x^4 + \cdots$
7. 0.9461. **9.** 1.8090. **11.** 0.0976. **13.** 0.4613. **15.** 0.4921.

§ 464, page 498

3. $(2, 4, 0)$ on XY-plane, $(0, 4, -3)$ on YZ-plane, $(2, 0, -3)$ on ZX-plane.
5. (a) In XY-plane; (b) in plane parallel to ZX-plane, 2 units in front; (c) in line in ZX-plane parallel to Y-axis through point $(2, 0, 3)$; (d) in plane perpendicular to XY-plane bisecting first and third quadrants in XY-plane. **7.** (a) $z = 0$; (b) $x = 0$; (c) $y = 0$. **9.** (a) 5; (b) $\sqrt{13}$.

§ 466, page 499

1. (a) 5; (b) 9; (c) $2\sqrt{6}$; (d) $\sqrt{42}$.
7. $(x - 3)^2 + (y - 1)^2 + (z + 2)^2 = 16$, sphere.
9. Distance from Y-axis $\sqrt{x^2 + z^2}$; distance from X-axis $\sqrt{y^2 + z^2}$.

§ 469, page 503

1. (a) $\pm\tfrac{2}{3}, \mp\tfrac{2}{3}, \mp\tfrac{1}{3}$; (b) $\pm\dfrac{2}{\sqrt{17}}, \pm\dfrac{2}{\sqrt{17}}, \pm\dfrac{3}{\sqrt{17}}.$ **3.** 1, 0, 0; 0, 1, 0; 0, 0, 1.

5. $\gamma = 60°$. **7.** (a) $\pm\tfrac{2}{7}, \mp\tfrac{3}{7}, \pm\tfrac{6}{7}$; (b) $\pm\dfrac{1}{\sqrt{14}}, \mp\dfrac{2}{\sqrt{14}}, \pm\dfrac{3}{\sqrt{14}}.$

§ 471, page 506

1. (a) 83°; (b) 75.5°.

§ 475, page 512

1. (a) Intercepts 8, 12, 6, traces $3x + 2y = 24$, $3x + 4z = 24$, $y + 2z = 12$;
(b) intercepts $a = 3$, $b = 2$, no Z-intercept, trace in XY-plane: $2x + 3y = 6$.

3. (a) $\tfrac{2}{3}x - \tfrac{1}{3}y - \tfrac{2}{3}z = 2$; (b) $\dfrac{3x - 2y + z + 3}{-\sqrt{14}} = 0.$ **5.** $4x - 3y = 12$.

7. $2x - y + 4z - 21 = 0.$ **9.** $17x - 2y + 7z - 35 = 0.$
11. $3x - y + 2z - 1 = 0.$ **15.** $13x - 7y - 11z - 42 = 0.$

17. $3x + z - 4 = 0$.   **19.** $x - 23y - 14z + 46 = 0$.

21. $2x + 3y + 6z - 49 = 0$.   **25.** $x + y + z = 5$.   **27.** $\dfrac{4}{\sqrt{66}}$.

§ 478, page 517

1. $(a)\ \dfrac{x-2}{1} = \dfrac{y-1}{-2} = \dfrac{z-3}{3}$; $(b)\ \dfrac{x-1}{6} = \dfrac{y+5}{-3} = \dfrac{z-6}{-1}$.

3. $\dfrac{x-4}{2} = \dfrac{y-1}{-3} = \dfrac{z+3}{-1}$.   **5.** $\dfrac{x-3}{1} = \dfrac{y-1}{-3} = \dfrac{z+2}{5}$ or

$\dfrac{x-4}{1} = \dfrac{y+2}{-3} = \dfrac{z-3}{5}$.   **11.** $(a)\ \dfrac{x-1}{1} = \dfrac{y}{-3} = \dfrac{z+2}{-7}$;

$(b)\ \dfrac{x-\frac{20}{3}}{11} = \dfrac{y-6}{9} = \dfrac{z}{-3}$.   **15.** $\dfrac{x-3}{1} = \dfrac{y+1}{-6} = \dfrac{z+2}{22}$.

19. $\dfrac{x-3}{3} = \dfrac{y+2}{1} = \dfrac{z-1}{-3}$.   **21.** In XY-plane $(-1, -2, 0)$, in YZ-plane

$(0, -\frac{1}{2}, -\frac{1}{2})$, in ZX-plane $(\frac{1}{3}, 0, -\frac{2}{3})$.   **25.** Lines intersect at $(-\frac{7}{5}, 0, \frac{8}{5})$.

27. $x - 2y + z + 8 = 0$.

§ 481, page 521

1. $(x-4)^2 + (y-1)^2 + (z+2)^2 = 9$.   **3.** (a) Center $(2, -1, 3)$, radius 4;

(b) center $(-3, \frac{5}{2}, \frac{1}{2})$, radius $\frac{1}{2}\sqrt{70}$.   **5.** $(x-2)^2 + (y+1)^2 + (z+2)^2 = 14$.

9. $y^2 + z^2 = 25$.   **11.** $6x + 2y + 3z - 61 = 0$.

§ 483, page 523

1. $(a)\ x^2 + y^2 + z^2 = 4$; $(b)\ x^2 + y^2 = 4z$;

$(c)\ 4x^2 + 4z^2 - 9y^2 + 36y - 36 = 0$.

5. $4a^2(x^2 + z^2) = (x^2 + y^2 + z^2 + a^2 - b^2)^2$.

§ 487, page 530

5. $y^2 + z^2 = \dfrac{r^2 x}{h}$.   **7.** $\frac{1}{2}\pi r^2 h$.   **9.** $\dfrac{64\pi}{3}(\sqrt{2} - 1)$.   **11.** $\frac{1}{4}\pi$.

13. $\frac{8}{3}\pi a^2(2\sqrt{2} - 1)$.   **15.** $\dfrac{4\pi a^5}{15}(64 - 33\sqrt{3})$.

§ 491, page 533

1. $(a)\ (\frac{3}{2}\sqrt{2}, \frac{3}{2}\sqrt{2}, 5)$; $(b)\ (0, 2, 3)$.   **3.** $(a)\ (5, \text{Arc tan } \frac{4}{3}, 5)$; $(b)\ (3\sqrt{2}, \frac{1}{4}\pi, -4)$.

5. $(a)\ r = 4$; $(b)\ r^2 = 4z$; $(c)\ 4r^2 - 9z^2 = 36$; $(d)\ r \cos\theta = 2$.

7. $(a)\ x^2 + y^2 + 4z^2 = 16$; $(b)\ x^2 + y^2 - z^2 = 0$; $(c)\ x^2 + y^2 - 4x = 0$;

$(d)\ x^2 + y^2 - 4z = 0$.   **11.** $(a)\ r^2 + z^2 = a^2$; $(b)\ r = a$; $(c)\ \theta = \frac{1}{4}\pi$.

§ 493, page 535

1. $(a)\ (0, 1, \sqrt{3})$; $(b)\ (\frac{3}{4}, \frac{3}{4}\sqrt{3}, -\frac{3}{2}\sqrt{3})$.   **3.** $(a)\ (\sqrt{6}, \frac{1}{4}\pi, \frac{1}{4}\pi)$;

$(b)\ (5, \text{Arc tan } \frac{4}{3}, \frac{1}{2}\pi)$.   **7.** $(a)\ \rho = 4$; $(b)\ \phi = \text{Arc sin } \frac{2}{5}\sqrt{5}$;

$(c)\ \rho \sin^2\phi - 4\cos\phi = 0$; $(d)\ \rho \sin\phi = \pm 3$.   **9.** $(a)\ x^2 + y^2 + z^2 = 36$;

$(b)\ x^2 + y^2 + z^2 = 4z$; $(c)\ x^2 + y^2 + z^2 = ay$.   **11.** $(a)\ \rho = a$; $(b)\ \rho \sin\phi = a$;

$(c)\ \theta = \frac{1}{4}\pi$.   **15.** $\cos\theta \sin\phi,\ \sin\theta \sin\phi,\ \cos\phi$.

§ 497, page 540

1. $2xy + y^2,\ x^2 + 2xy$.   **3.** $4x(x^2 + y^2),\ 4y(x^2 + y^2)$.   **5.** $e^x \sin y,\ e^x \cos y$.

7. $\dfrac{x}{x^2 + y^2},\ \dfrac{y}{x^2 + y^2}$.   **9.** $\dfrac{1}{y} - \dfrac{y}{x^2},\ -\dfrac{x}{y^2} + \dfrac{1}{x}$.   **11.** $-\dfrac{x}{(x^2 + y^2)^{\frac{3}{2}}},\ -\dfrac{y}{(x^2 + y^2)^{\frac{3}{2}}}$.

13. $-\dfrac{y}{x^2 + y^2}$, $\dfrac{x}{x^2 + y^2}$.   **15.** $y + z, z + x, x + y$.   **17.** $y \sin z - yz \cos x$,

$x \sin z - z \sin x$, $xy \cos z - y \sin x$.   **19.** $\dfrac{1}{z}, \dfrac{1}{z}, -\dfrac{x+y}{z^2}$.   **21.** $\frac{2}{3}\sqrt{3}, \frac{1}{3}\sqrt{3}$.

23. 4, 8.   **25.** (a) $\cos\theta$, $\sin\theta$, $-r\sin\theta$, $r\cos\theta$; (b) $\sec\theta$, $\tan\theta$, $r\sec\theta\tan\theta$, $r\sec^2\theta$.

§ 499, page 542

1. $u_{xx} = 2y$, $u_{xy} = 2x + 2y$, $u_{yy} = 2x$.   **3.** $u_{xx} = 0$, $u_{xy} = \cos y$, $u_{yy} = -x\sin y$.

5. $u_{xx} = cy^2 e^{xy}$, $u_{xy} = cxy\,e^{xy} + c\,e^{xy}$, $u_{yy} = cx^2 e^{xy}$.   **7.** $u_{xx} = \dfrac{y(2x^2 - y^2)}{x^2(x^2 - y^2)^{\frac{3}{2}}}$,

$u_{xy} = -\dfrac{x}{(x^2 - y^2)^{\frac{3}{2}}}$, $u_{yy} = \dfrac{y}{(x^2 - y^2)^{\frac{3}{2}}}$.   **9.** $u_{xx} = 0$, $u_{yy} = 0$, $u_{zz} = 0$, $u_{xy} = 1$,

$u_{yz} = 1$, $u_{zx} = 1$.   **11.** $F_{xx} = e^x \sin y$, $F_{yy} = -e^x \sin y + e^y \sin z$,

$F_{zz} = -e^y \sin z$, $F_{xy} = e^x \cos y$, $F_{yz} = e^y \cos z$, $F_{zx} = 0$.

§ 503, page 547

1. $(2xy + y^2)\,dx + (x^2 + 2xy)\,dy$.   **3.** $2x\,dx + 4y\,dy$.

5. $\sqrt{1 - y^2}\,dx - \dfrac{xy}{\sqrt{1 - y^2}}\,dy$.   **7.** $(y + z)\,dx + (z + x)\,dy + (x + y)\,dz$.

9. $du = 2x\,dx - 2y\,dy + 2z\,dz$.   **11.** $zy\,e^{xy}\,dx + zx\,e^{xy}\,dy + e^{xy}\,dz$.   **13.** Maximum error $r\theta\,|dr| + \frac{1}{2}r^2\,|d\theta|$.   **15.** Maximum error $\approx 1\frac{1}{2}$ square feet;

$\dfrac{dA}{A} = \dfrac{dx}{x} + \dfrac{dy}{y} = \dfrac{3}{160}$.   **17.** Maximum error $= \frac{45}{4}\sqrt{3} + \frac{625}{36}\pi \approx 74.03$ square feet.

§ 505, page 550

1. $(4x + 3y)\sec^2 t + (3x + 8y)\sin 2t$.   **3.** $-\dfrac{2ax}{x^2 - y^2}\sin t - \dfrac{2ay}{x^2 - y^2}\cos t$.

5. $[y\cos(xy) - \sin y]\,e^t + [x\cos(xy) - x\cos y](t\,e^t + e^t)$.

7. $\dfrac{2}{y} + \dfrac{x}{y^2 t^2} - \dfrac{1}{zt^2} - \dfrac{2yt}{z^2}$.

9. $(2xy + z^2)e^t + (x^2 + 2yz)(t\,e^t + e^t) + (y^2 + 2zx)(t^2 e^t + 2t\,e^t)$.

11. $4x + y$.   **13.** $2x - 2y\sec^2 x$.   **15.** $\dfrac{2}{x^2 + y^2} \cdot \dfrac{x^3 - y}{x^2}$.

17. $y + z + (z + x)e^x - (x + y)e^{-x}$.

§ 507, page 553

1. $u_r = (2x - y)s + 2(2y - x)r$, $u_s = (2x - y)r + 2(2y - x)s$.

3. $u_r = ye^{xy} \cdot \dfrac{r}{\sqrt{r^2 + s^2}} - xe^{xy} \cdot \dfrac{s}{r^2 + s^2}$, $u_s = ye^{xy} \cdot \dfrac{s}{\sqrt{r^2 + s^2}} + xe^{xy} \cdot \dfrac{r}{r^2 + s^2}$.

5. (a) $\dfrac{\partial u}{\partial r} = \dfrac{\partial u}{\partial x}\dfrac{\partial x}{\partial r} + \dfrac{\partial u}{\partial y}\dfrac{\partial y}{\partial r}$, $\dfrac{\partial u}{\partial s} = \dfrac{\partial u}{\partial x}\dfrac{\partial x}{\partial s} + \dfrac{\partial u}{\partial y}\dfrac{\partial y}{\partial s}$, $\dfrac{\partial u}{\partial t} = \dfrac{\partial u}{\partial x}\dfrac{\partial x}{\partial t} + \dfrac{\partial u}{\partial y}\dfrac{\partial y}{\partial t}$;

(b) $\dfrac{\partial u}{\partial r} = \dfrac{du}{dx}\dfrac{\partial x}{\partial r}$, $\dfrac{\partial u}{\partial s} = \dfrac{du}{dx}\dfrac{\partial x}{\partial s}$.   **7.** $\dfrac{\partial u}{\partial r} = y - z + xs + zs$,

$\dfrac{\partial u}{\partial s} = 2y - z - x + xr + zr$.

§ 509, page 555

1. $\dfrac{x^2 - ay}{ax - y^2}$.   **3.** $-\dfrac{2x^3 + xy^2}{x^2 y + 2y^3}$.   **5.** $-\dfrac{\sin y + y\cos x}{x\cos y + \sin x}$.   **7.** $-\dfrac{e^x \sin y - e^y \cos x}{e^x \cos y - e^y \sin x}$.

9. $-\tan y$. **11.** $z_x = -\dfrac{x}{z}$, $z_y = -\dfrac{y}{z}$. **13.** $z_x = \dfrac{y+z}{y-x}$, $z_y = \dfrac{x-z}{y-x}$.

15. $z_x = -\dfrac{z}{2z+x}$, $z_y = \dfrac{2y}{2z+x}$. **17.** $z_x = -\dfrac{xy^2+xz^2}{y^2z+x^2z}$, $z_y = -\dfrac{x^2y+yz^2}{y^2z+x^2z}$.

§ 511, page 559

1. $2x - 8y + 6z = 24$, $\dfrac{x-1}{2} = \dfrac{y+2}{-8} = \dfrac{z-1}{6}$.

3. $3x - 2y - 2z = 1$, $\dfrac{x-3}{3} = \dfrac{y-2}{-2} = \dfrac{z-2}{-2}$.

5. $2x - 2y - z = 0$, $\dfrac{x-1}{2} = \dfrac{y-1}{-2} = \dfrac{z}{-1}$.

7. $x + y - 4z = -1$; $\dfrac{x-3}{1} = \dfrac{y-4}{1} = \dfrac{z-2}{-4}$.

9. $4x + 5y - 2z = 16$; $\dfrac{x-1}{4} = \dfrac{y-2}{5} = \dfrac{z+1}{-2}$.

§ 513, page 561

1. $\frac{3}{2}\sqrt{2}$. **3.** $\pm\frac{3}{5}\sqrt{5}$. **5.** $\frac{1}{2}\sqrt{3}$. **7.** arc tan $\frac{1}{2}$ (third quadrant), $2\sqrt{5}$.
9. $\frac{7}{4}\pi$, $2\sqrt{2}$. **11.** Arc tan $\frac{9}{8}$, $2\sqrt{145}$.

§ 515, page 565

1. Minimum at $x = 2$, $y = 0$. **3.** No maximum or minimum. **5.** Minimum
at $x = -\frac{2}{3}$, $y = \frac{10}{3}$. **7.** Minimum at $x = 1$, $y = 1$. **9.** No maximum or minimum. **11.** Maximum at $x = -1$, $y = 0$. **13.** Each part is $\frac{1}{3}N$. **15.** Base
square, altitude $= \frac{1}{2}$ edge of base. **17.** Cube. **19.** Altitude $= \frac{3}{2}$ edge of square
base. **21.** Dimensions $\frac{1}{3}a$, $\frac{1}{3}b$, $\frac{1}{3}c$; $V = \frac{1}{27}abc$. **23.** $2x + y + 2z = 6$.

§ 519, page 572

1. $\frac{1}{3}$. **3.** $\frac{9}{2}$. **5.** $\frac{15}{4}$. **7.** $\frac{1}{10}$. **9.** $\frac{1}{6}a^3$. **11.** $\frac{3}{35}$. **13.** $\frac{1}{2}\pi a^2$. **15.** $\frac{3}{2}\pi a^2$. **17.** $\frac{1}{2}\pi a^4$.
19. $\frac{1}{4}\pi a^4$.

§ 521, page 577

1. $\displaystyle\int_0^{\sqrt{3}}\left(\int_{\frac{1}{3}y^2}^{\sqrt{4-y^2}} f(x,y)\,dx\right) dy$, or

$$\int_0^1\left(\int_0^{\sqrt{3x}} f(x,y)\,dy\right) dx + \int_1^2\left(\int_0^{\sqrt{4-x^2}} f(x,y)\,dy\right) dx.$$

3. $\displaystyle\int_0^1\left(\int_{x^{\frac{3}{2}}}^{x} f(x,y)\,dy\right) dx$, or $\displaystyle\int_0^1\left(\int_y^{y^{\frac{2}{3}}} f(x,y)\,dx\right) dy$.

5. Region bounded by lines $y = x$, $x = 0$ and $y = 1$.

7. Portion of circle $x^2 + y^2 = a^2$ in first quadrant. **9.** $\displaystyle\int_0^1\left(\int_0^{\sqrt{x}} f(x,y)\,dy\right) dx$.

11. $\displaystyle\int_0^1\left(\int_0^{y} f(x,y)\,dx\right) dy$. **13.** $\displaystyle\int_0^1\int_{x^2}^{\sqrt{x}} (x+y)\,dy\,dx = \frac{3}{10}$.

15. $\displaystyle\int_{-2}^1\int_{x^2}^{2-x} y^2\,dy\,dx = \frac{423}{28}$.

§ 523, page 579

1. 16π. **3.** $\frac{1}{2}\pi a^3$. **5.** $\frac{1}{3} - \frac{1}{16}\pi$. **7.** $\frac{81}{4}$. **9.** 2π. **11.** $\frac{2}{3}ma^3$. **13.** $\frac{16}{3}a^3$.
15. $\frac{587}{420}$.

§ 526, page 584

1. $\frac{1}{4}\pi a^2$. **3.** $\frac{3}{4}\pi a^4$. **5.** $\displaystyle\int_0^a\int_0^{2\pi} r\,F(r,\theta)\,d\theta\,dr$. **7.** $\frac{4}{3}\pi(8\sqrt{2}-7)$. **9.** $\frac{1}{2}\pi a^3$.
11. $\frac{2}{9}(3\pi-4)a^3$.

§ 528, page 587

1. $8\sqrt{2}$. **3.** 8π. **5.** $\frac{1}{6}\pi[(a^2+1)^{\frac{3}{2}}-1]$. **7.** 4π.

§ 531, page 590

1. $\bar{x}=\frac{3}{8}b$, $\bar{y}=\frac{3}{4}\sqrt{ab}$. **3.** $\bar{x}=\frac{10}{21}$, $\bar{y}=\frac{5}{12}$. **5.** $\bar{x}=\frac{8}{5}$, $\bar{y}=1$.

7. $\bar{x}=\bar{y}=\dfrac{128\,a}{105\,\pi}$. **9.** $\bar{x}=\dfrac{8\pi+3\sqrt{3}}{4\pi+6\sqrt{3}}\,a$, $\bar{y}=0$. **11.** $I_y=\frac{8}{15}$.

13. $I_x=I_y=\frac{1}{48}(3\pi-4)a^4$. **15.** $I_x=\frac{1}{4}\pi ab^3$, $I_y=\frac{1}{4}\pi a^3 b$.

17. $I_x=\left(\dfrac{3\pi}{128}-\dfrac{1}{15}\right)a^4$, $I_y=\left(\dfrac{3\pi}{128}+\dfrac{1}{15}\right)a^4$.

§ 534, page 593

1. $\frac{124}{3}$. **3.** $\frac{2}{5}$. **5.** 7. **7.** $\frac{1}{3}abc(a^2+b^2+c^2)$. **9.** $\frac{1}{12}(\frac{1}{3}\pi-\frac{1}{4}\sqrt{3})$. **11.** $\frac{1}{96}a^3$.

§ 536, page 595

1. $\displaystyle\int_{-1}^{1}\int_{-\sqrt{1-x^2}}^{\sqrt{1-x^2}}\int_{0}^{4-x^2-y^2} f(x,y,z)\,dz\,dy\,dx$.

3. $\displaystyle\int_{0}^{2}\int_{0}^{\sqrt{4-x^2}}\int_{0}^{\sqrt{4-x^2-y^2}} f(x,y,z)\,dz\,dy\,dx$.

5. Region within cylinder $x^2+y^2=a^2$ under plane $z=x$ and lying in first octant. **7.** $\frac{1}{2}\pi hka^4$. **9.** ka^5.

§ 538, page 597

1. 8π. **3.** $\frac{2}{3}$.

§ 541, page 601

1. $\bar{x}=\bar{y}=0$, $\bar{z}=\frac{4}{3}$. **3.** $\bar{x}=\bar{y}=\bar{z}=\frac{3}{2}$. **5.** $\frac{2}{3}\delta a^5$. **7.** $\frac{1}{180}k$.
9. $\bar{x}=\bar{y}=0$, $\bar{z}=\frac{8}{3}$. **11.** $\frac{1}{10}\pi kha^4$. **13.** $\frac{1}{2}\pi\delta ha^4$. **15.** $\frac{1}{6}\pi\delta ha^4$.

§ 543, page 604

1. $\frac{4}{3}\pi a^3$. **3.** $\frac{4}{5}\pi ka^5$. **5.** $\bar{x}=\bar{y}=0$, $\bar{z}=\frac{2}{5}a$. **7.** $\frac{1}{16}\pi^2 ka^6$.

§ 549, page 610

1. $xy=c$. **3.** $3y^4=4x^3+c$. **5.** $y=cx$. **7.** $x+y=c(1-xy)$.

9. $\ln\dfrac{x}{y}=y-x+c$. **11.** $\cot x+\tan y=c$. **13.** $y-1=cxy$. **15.** $y=3x$.
17. $\sqrt{1+x^2}+\ln|y|=1$. **19.** $x^2y=4$.

§ 551, page 611

1. $y=x\ln|cy|$. **3.** $x^3+3xy^2=c$. **5.** $x^2+2xy=c$. **7.** $y^3=3x^3\ln|x|+cx^3$.
9. $y^2+2xy-x^2=c$.

11. $\ln|y^2-xy+x^2|-2\sqrt{3}\ \text{Arc}\tan\dfrac{2y-x}{\sqrt{3}\,x}=\frac{1}{3}\sqrt{3}\,\pi$.

13. $\dfrac{2}{\sqrt{y}}=\dfrac{-1}{\sqrt{x}}\ln|y|+\dfrac{4}{\sqrt{x}}$.

§ 553, page 612

1. $x^2 + 2xy = c$.   **3.** $3xy = x^3 + c$.   **5.** $y = x \tan \frac{1}{2}(y^2 + c)$.
7. $x^2y + 2x + cy = 0$.   **9.** $x^3y + 3x = cy$.   **11.** $xy = x + 1$.   **13.** $y^2 = 2x + 1$.

§ 556, page 616

1. Exact; $u = \frac{1}{3}x^3 + xy^2 + c$.   **3.** Not exact.   **5.** Not exact.   **7.** Exact;
$u = x^3y + e^x + c$.   **9.** Exact; $x^2 - xy + y^2 = c$.   **11.** Not exact.   **13.** Not exact.   **15.** Exact; $x^3y + x^2 - y = c$.   **17.** $x^2 + 3xy + y^2 = 9$.
19. $2xy + y^2 = c$.   **21.** $x^2 + xy + y^2 = c$.

§ 558, page 618

1. $y = x e^{-x} + c e^{-x}$.   **3.** $y = -x - 1 + c e^x$.   **5.** $y = x + \dfrac{c}{x}$.

7. $y = \frac{1}{2}x^2 e^{3x} + c e^{3x}$.   **9.** $y = \frac{1}{4}x^2 + \dfrac{c}{x^2}$.   **11.** $y = \frac{1}{2}x^3 + cx$.

13. $y = -\dfrac{2}{3x} + cx^2$.   **15.** $y = \frac{4}{13}(2 \sin 3x - 3 \cos 3x) + c e^{-2x}$.

17. $y = x^4 + 2x$.   **19.** $y = e^{-x}\left(1 - \dfrac{1}{x}\right)$.   **21.** $x = -y - 1 + c e^y$.
23. $x = a + c e^{-kt}$; $x = a(1 - e^{-kt})$.

§ 560, page 622

1. $xy = c$.   **3.** $x^2 + y^2 = 2 \ln |cx|$.   **7.** $xy = c$.   **9.** $i = \dfrac{E_0}{R} - c e^{-\frac{Rt}{L}}$.

13. $v = \dfrac{\sqrt{kF}\, v_0 - F \tan\left(\dfrac{\sqrt{kF}}{M}\, t\right)}{\sqrt{kF} + k v_0 \tan\left(\dfrac{\sqrt{kF}}{M}\, t\right)}$.

15. $p = a + \dfrac{c}{r^2}$.   **17.** 20 seconds after entering bank.

§ 562, page 624

1. $y = \frac{1}{6}x^3 + c_1 x + c_2$.   **3.** $y = -2 \cos x - x \sin x - \frac{1}{12}x^4 + c_1 x + c_2$.
5. $y = c_1 x^2 + c_2$.   **7.** $y = c_1 \ln |1 + x| + c_2$.   **9.** $y = \frac{1}{8}x^4 + c_1 x^2 + c_2$.
11. $y = \dfrac{W x^2}{6 EI}(3l - x)$;   maximum $y = \dfrac{W l^3}{3 EI}$.

§ 564, page 626

1. $y = a \sin(2x + b)$.   **3.** $\sqrt{1 + c_1 y^2} = c_1 x + c_2$.   **5.** $2\sqrt{c_1 y - 4} = c_1 x + c_2$.
7. $c_1 y = c_2 e^{c_1 x} - 2$.   **11.** $s = -\dfrac{v_0}{k} e^{-kt} + c$.

§ 568, page 634

1. $y = c_1 e^{2x} + c_2 e^{3x}$.   **3.** $y = c_1 e^{4x} + c_2 e^{-3x}$.   **5.** $y = c_1 e^{2x} + c_2 e^{-2x}$.
7. $y = c_1 + c_2 e^{4x}$.   **9.** $y = \frac{1}{6}(e^{5x} - e^{-x})$.   **11.** $y = -2 e^{2x} + e^{-x}$.
13. $y = (c_1 + c_2 x)e^{-x}$.   **15.** $y = (c_1 + c_2 x)e^{\frac{1}{2}x}$.   **17.** $y = (c_1 + c_2 x)e^{-3x}$.
19. $y = -xe^{-x}$.   **21.** $y = (x - 1)e^{-3x}$.   **23.** $y = e^x(c_1 \cos 2x + c_2 \sin 2x)$.
25. $y = e^{-\frac{1}{2}x}(c_1 \cos \frac{1}{2}\sqrt{3}\, x + c_2 \sin \frac{1}{2}\sqrt{3}\, x)$.   **27.** $y = c_1 \cos 2x + c_2 \sin 2x$.

29. $y = 3 e^{-x} \sin x.$ **31.** $y = \cos \sqrt{2}\, x - \frac{1}{2}\sqrt{2} \sin \sqrt{2}\, x.$
33. $y = c_1 \cosh 2\, x + c_2 \sinh 2\, x.$

§ 570, page 638

1. $y = c_1 e^{2x} + c_2 e^{-2x} - \frac{1}{4}\, x.$ **3.** $y = c_1 e^{2x} + c_2 e^{-3x} - \frac{1}{6}\, x^2 - \frac{1}{18}\, x - \frac{7}{108}.$
5. $y = (c_1 + c_2 x)e^x + x^2 + 5\, x + 8.$ **7.** $y = c_1 + c_2 e^{-x} + 2\, x^2 - 4\, x.$

9. $y = c_1 e^{2x} + c_2 e^{3x} + \frac{1}{2}\, e^x.$ **11.** $y = c_1 e^{2x} + c_2 e^{-\frac{3}{2}x} + \frac{1}{9}\, e^{3x}.$
13. $y = (c_1 + c_2 x)e^{-3x} + \frac{1}{2}\, e^{-x}.$ **15.** $y = c_1 e^{-x} + c_2 e^{-3x} - \frac{1}{2}\, x e^{-3x}.$
17. $y = c_1 e^{2x} + c_2 e^{-x} - \frac{3}{5}\sin x + \frac{1}{5}\cos x.$
19. $y = c_1 + c_2 e^{-4x} - \frac{1}{17}\cos x + \frac{4}{17}\sin x.$
21. $y = (c_1 + c_2 x)e^x - \frac{3}{25}\sin 2\, x + \frac{4}{25}\cos 2\, x.$
23. $y = c_1 + c_2 e^{-x} - \frac{1}{10}\sin 2\, x - \frac{3}{10}\cos 2\, x.$
25. $y = c_1 \cos 2\, x + c_2 \sin 2\, x + \frac{1}{2}\, x \sin 2\, x.$
27. $y = c_1 \cos 2\, x + c_2 \sin 2\, x + \frac{1}{4}\, x + \frac{2}{5}\, e^{-x}.$
29. $y = c_1 \cos 3\, x + c_2 \sin 3\, x + \frac{1}{8}\sin x + \frac{1}{13}\, e^{2x}.$
31. $z = c_1 e^{3x} + c_2 e^{-2x} - \frac{1}{4}\, e^{2x} + \frac{1}{6}\, e^{4x}.$
33. $y = c_1 + c_2 e^{-x} + \frac{1}{2}\, e^x + \frac{3}{2}\, x^2 - 3\, x.$ **35.** $y = e^{2x} - e^{3x} + e^x.$
37. $s = \sin 2\, t + 2\, t.$ **39.** $y = c_1 e^{2x} + c_2 e^{-3x} - \frac{1}{32}(8\, x^2 + 12\, x + 13)e^x.$
41. $y = c_1 e^{3x} + c_2 e^{-3x} + \frac{1}{37}\, e^{3x}(6 \sin x - \cos x).$

§ 572, page 642

3. $\theta = \alpha \cos \left(\sqrt{\dfrac{g}{l}}\, t \right).$ **5.** $y = Y \sin \left(\sqrt{\dfrac{P}{EI}}\, x \right) \Big/ \sin \left(\dfrac{1}{2} \sqrt{\dfrac{P}{EI}} \cdot L \right).$

7. $s = e^{-0.06t}\, (0.5 \cos 4\, t + 0.0075 \sin 4\, t).$

9. $s = (s_0 - L) \cos \left(\sqrt{\dfrac{g}{e}}\, t \right) + L,\ \dfrac{ds}{dt} = -(s_0 - L) \sqrt{\dfrac{g}{e}} \sin \left(\sqrt{\dfrac{g}{e}}\, t \right).$

11. $I = -e^{-2.5t}\, (0.044 \cos 49.935\, t + 0.0022 \sin 49.935\, t) + 0.044.$

13. $I = -\dfrac{E_0 C}{1 - \omega^2 LC} \left(\omega \sqrt{LC} \sin \dfrac{t}{\sqrt{LC}} - \sin \omega t \right).$

Index